INSTRUCTOR'S SOLUTIONS MANUAL

ENGINEERING MECHANICS THIRD EDITION
STATICS

BEDFORD   FOWLER

Prentice Hall

Upper Saddle River, NJ 07458

Executive Editor: Eric Svendsen
Associate Editor: Dee Bernhard
Executive Managing Editor: Vince O'Brien
Managing Editor: David A. George
Production Editor: Barbara A. Till
Supplement Cover Manager: Paul Gourhan
Supplement Cover Designer: PM Workshop Inc.
Manufacturing Buyer: Ilene Kahn

© 2002, 1999, 1995 by Prentice Hall
Prentice-Hall, Inc.
Upper Saddle River, NJ 07458

Printed in the United States of America

10 9 8 7 6 5 4 3 2 1

ISBN 0-13-061575-7

Pearson Education Ltd., *London*
Pearson Education Australia Pty. Ltd., *Sydney*
Pearson Education Singapore, Pte. Ltd.
Pearson Education North Asia Ltd., *Hong Kong*
Pearson Education Canada, Inc., *Toronto*
Pearson Educacíon de Mexico, S.A. de C.V.
Pearson Education—Japan, *Tokyo*
Pearson Education Malaysia, Pte. Ltd.
Pearson Education, *Upper Saddle River, New Jersey*

Contents

Assignments for
Anthony Bedford & Wallace Fowler
Engineering Mechanics: Statics, Third Edition

Week 1

Reading: **Chapter 1**; **Chapter 2**, Sections 2.1–2.3
Problems: 1.2, 1.3, 1.6, 1.12, 1.19, 1.24, 1.28;
2.2, 2.4, 2.7, 2.8, 2.11, 2.14, 2.22, 2.26, 2.29, 2.33, 2.40, 2.44, 2.54, 2.60, 2.64

Week 2

Reading: **Chapter 2**, Sections 2.4–2.7
Problems: 2.72, 2.75, 2.80, 2.81, 2.85, 2.88, 2.90, 2.92, 2.96, 2.102, 2.104, 2.107, 2.109, 2.112, 2.116, 2.122, 2.132, 2.137, 2.138, 2.139, 2.144

Week 3

Reading: **Chapter 3**
Problems: 3.2, 3.3, 3.6, 3.8, 3.12, 3.16, 3.22, 3.23, 3.27, 3.32, 3.37, 3.44, 3.47, 3.54, 3.64, 3.68, 3.70, 3.75, 3.80

Week 4

Reading: **Chapter 4**, Sections 4.1–4.4
Problems: 4.4, 4.6, 4.10, 4.16, 4.24, 4.28, 4.31, 4.38, 4.40, 4.54, 4.59, 4.60, 4.66, 4.78, 4.83, 4.88, 4.92, 4.102, 4.108, 4.110, 4.116, 4.120, 4.122, 4.124

Week 5

Reading: **Chapter 4**, Sections 4.5 and 4.6; **Chapter 5**, Sections 5.1 and 5.2
Problems: 4.128, 4.130, 4.134, 4.136, 4.138, 4.140, 4.144, 4.151, 4.160;
5.2, 5.4, 5.12, 5.14, 5.24, 5.48, 5.57, 5.58, 5.62

Week 6

Reading: **Chapter 5**, Sections 5.4 and 5.5
Problems: 5.78, 5.86, 5.88, 5.92, 5.98, 5.106, 5.108, 5.113, 5.114, 5.116, 5.122, 5.124, 5.126, 5.129, 5.132

Week 7

Reading: **Chapter 6**, Sections 6.1–6.4
Problems: 6.2, 6.6, 6.7, 6.8, 6.10, 6.22, 6.29, 6.30, 6.34, 6.42, 6.51, 6.58, 6.62, 6.64

Week 8

Reading: **Chapter 6**, Section 6.5
Problems: 6.70, 6.71, 6.73, 6.74, 6.78, 6.80, 6.86, 6.90, 6.94, 6.98, 6.100, 6.105, 6.107, 6.108, 6.113

Week 9

Reading: **Chapter 7**, Sections 7.1–7.3
Problems: 7.2, 7.6, 7.8, 7.10, 7.14, 7.27, 7.30, 7.33, 7.39, 7.40, 7.46, 7.48, 7.52, 7.54, 7.56, 7.58

Week 10

Reading: **Chapter 7**, Section 7.4, 7.6–7.8
Problems: 7.60, 7.66, 7.72, 7.74, 7.76, 7.82, 7.84, 7.100, 7.102, 7.104, 7.108, 7.110, 7.111, 7.112

Week 11

Reading: **Chapter 8,** Sections 8.1, 8.2, 8.4, and 8.5
Problems: 8.4, 8.5, 8.9, 8.10, 8.11, 8.18, 8.26, 8.27, 8.28, 8.32, 8.47, 8.48, 8.49, 8.58, 8.59, 8.100, 8.102, 8.104, 8.106, 8.112, 8.113

Week 12

Reading: **Chapter 9**
Problems: 9.4, 9.5, 9.8, 9.10, 9.14, 9.15, 9.20, 9.24, 9.26, 9.30, 9.36, 9.44, 9.46, 9.56, 9.60, 9.66, 9.70, 9.80, 9.84, 9.90, 9.125, 9.126, 9.128, 9.132

Week 13

Reading: **Chapter 10,** Sections 10.1–10.3
Problems: 10.2, 10.4, 10.6, 10.8, 10.14, 10.16, 10.22, 10.24, 10.26, 10.28, 10.41, 10.44, 10.46, 10.47, 10.48

Week 14

Reading: **Chapter 10,** Sections 10.4, 10.5, 10.7, and 10.8
Problems: 10.50, 10.52, 10.54, 10.59, 10.62, 10.82, 10.84, 10.89, 10.90, 10.93, 10.95, 10.96, 10.100, 10.102

Problem 1.1 Express the fractions $\frac{1}{3}$ and $\frac{2}{3}$ to three significant digits.

Solution:

$1/3 = 0.3333.. = 0.333$

$2/3 = 0.6666.. = 0.667$

Problem 1.2 What is the value of e (the base of the natural logarithms) to five significant digits?

Solution: The value of e is 2.718281828.... Record the first five digits, and round the last digit to the nearest integer. The result is $e = 2.7183$ to five significant digits.

Problem 1.3 A machinist drills a circular hole in a panel with radius $r = 5$ mm. Determine the circumference C and area A of the hole to four significant digits.

Solution:

$C = 2\pi r = 10\pi = 31.42$ mm

$A = \pi r^2 = 25\pi = 78.54$ mm^2

Problem 1.4 The opening in a soccer goal is 24 ft wide and 8 ft high. Use these values to determine its dimensions in meters to three significant digits.

Solution: The conversion between feet and meters, found inside the front cover of the textbook, is 1 m = 3.281 ft. The goal width,

$$w = 24 \text{ ft} \left(\frac{1 \text{ m}}{3.281 \text{ ft}} \right) = 7.3148 \text{ m} = 7.31 \text{ m}.$$

The goal height is given by

$$h = 8 \text{ ft} \left(\frac{1 \text{ m}}{3.281 \text{ ft}} \right) = 2.438 \text{ m} = 2.44 \text{ m}.$$

Problem 1.5 The central span of the Golden Gate Bridge is 1280 m long. What is its length in miles to three significant digits?

Solution:

$$(1280 \text{ m}) \left(\frac{39.37 \text{ in}}{1 \text{ m}} \right) \left(\frac{1 \text{ ft}}{12 \text{ in}} \right) \left(\frac{1 \text{ mi}}{5280 \text{ ft}} \right)$$

$$= 0.7953.. \text{ mi} = 0.795 \text{ mi}$$

Problem 1.6 Suppose that you have just purchased a Ferrari F355 coupe and you want to know whether you can use your set of SAE (U.S. Customary Units) wrenches to work on it. You have wrenches with widths $w = 1/4$ in., $1/2$ in., $3/4$ in., and 1 in., and the car has nuts with dimensions $n = 5$ mm, 10 mm, 15 mm, 20 mm, and 25 mm. Defining a wrench to fit if w is no more than 2% larger than n, which of your wrenches can you use?

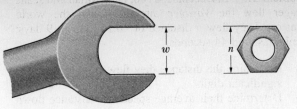

Solution: Convert the metric size n to inches, and compute the percentage difference between the metric sized nut and the SAE wrench. The results are:

$$5 \text{ mm} \left(\frac{1 \text{ inch}}{25.4 \text{ mm}} \right) = 0.19685.. \text{ in}, \quad \left(\frac{0.19685 - 0.25}{0.19685} \right) 100$$

$$= -27.0\%$$

$$10 \text{ mm} \left(\frac{1 \text{ inch}}{25.4 \text{ mm}} \right) = 0.3937.. \text{ in}, \quad \left(\frac{0.3937 - 0.5}{0.3937} \right) 100 = -27.0\%$$

$$15 \text{ mm} \left(\frac{1 \text{ inch}}{25.4 \text{ mm}} \right) = 0.5905.. \text{ in}, \quad \left(\frac{0.5905 - 0.5}{0.5905} \right) 100 = +15.3\%$$

$$20 \text{ mm} \left(\frac{1 \text{ inch}}{25.4 \text{ mm}} \right) = 0.7874.. \text{ in}, \quad \left(\frac{0.7874 - 0.75}{0.7874} \right) 100 = +4.7\%$$

$$25 \text{ mm} \left(\frac{1 \text{ inch}}{25.4 \text{ mm}} \right) = 0.9843.. \text{ in}, \quad \left(\frac{0.9843 - 1.0}{0.9843} \right) 100 = -1.6\%$$

A negative percentage implies that the metric nut is smaller than the SAE wrench; a positive percentage means that the nut is larger then the wrench. Thus within the definition of the 2% fit, the 1 in. wrench will fit the 25 mm nut. **The other wrenches cannot be used.**

Problem 1.7 The orbital velocity of the International Space Station is 7690 m/s. Determine its velocity in km/hr and in mi/hr to three significant digits.

Solution:

$$\left(7690 \, \frac{\text{m}}{\text{s}} \right) \left(\frac{1 \text{ km}}{1000 \text{ m}} \right) \left(\frac{3600 \text{ s}}{1 \text{ hr}} \right) = 27,684 = 27,700 \, \frac{\text{km}}{\text{hr}}$$

$$\left(7690 \, \frac{\text{m}}{\text{s}} \right) \left(\frac{39.37 \text{ in}}{1 \text{ m}} \right) \left(\frac{1 \text{ ft}}{12 \text{ in}} \right) \left(\frac{1 \text{ mi}}{5280 \text{ ft}} \right) \left(\frac{3600 \text{ s}}{1 \text{ hr}} \right)$$

$$= 17,202.. = 17,200 \text{ mi/hr}$$

Problem 1.8 High-speed "bullet trains" began running between Tokyo and Osaka, Japan, in 1964. If a bullet train travels at 240 km/hr, what is its velocity in mi/hr to three significant digits?

Solution: Convert the units using Table 1.2. The results are:

$$240 \left(\frac{\text{km}}{\text{hr}} \right) \left(\frac{1 \text{ mile}}{5280 \text{ ft}} \right) \left(\frac{1 \text{ ft}}{0.3048 \text{ m}} \right) \left(\frac{1000 \text{ m}}{1 \text{ km}} \right)$$

$$= 149.12908 \ldots \left(\frac{\text{mile}}{\text{hr}} \right) = 149 \left(\frac{\text{mile}}{\text{hr}} \right)$$

Problem 1.9 In December 1986, Dick Rutan and Jeana Yeager flew the *Voyager* aircraft around the world nonstop. They flew a distance of 40,212 km in 9 days, 3 minutes, and 44 seconds.

(a) Determine the distance they flew in miles to three significant digits.
(b) Determine their average speed (the distance flown divided by the time required) in kilometers per hour, miles per hour, and knots (nautical miles per hour) to three significant digits.

Solution: Convert the units using Table 1.2.

(a) $40{,}212 \text{ km} \left(\dfrac{1000 \text{ m}}{1 \text{ km}}\right) \left(\dfrac{1 \text{ ft}}{0.3048 \text{ m}}\right) \left(\dfrac{1 \text{ mile}}{5280 \text{ ft}}\right)$

$\qquad = 24{,}987 \text{ mi} = 25{,}000 \text{ mi}$

(b) The time of flight is

$\qquad 9 \text{ days } 3 \text{ min } 44 \text{ sec} = \left((9)(24) + \left(\dfrac{3}{60}\right) + \left(\dfrac{44}{3600}\right) \right) \text{ hours}$

$\qquad\qquad\qquad = 216.062 \text{ hours}.$

The average speed is

$\left(\dfrac{40{,}212 \text{ km}}{216.062 \text{ hours}}\right) = 186.11 \ \dfrac{\text{km}}{\text{hr}}$. Converting,

$\left(186.11 \ \dfrac{\text{km}}{\text{hr}}\right) \left(\dfrac{1 \text{ mile}}{1.609 \text{ km}}\right) = 115.7 \ \dfrac{\text{mi}}{\text{hr}} = 116 \ \dfrac{\text{mi}}{\text{hr}}$, or

$\left(186.11 \ \dfrac{\text{km}}{\text{hr}}\right) \left(\dfrac{1 \text{ nautical mile}}{1.852 \text{ km}}\right) = 100.49 \text{ knots}$

$\qquad = 100 \text{ knots to three significant digits.}$

Problem 1.10 Engineers who study shock waves sometimes express velocity in millimeters per microsecond (mm/μs). Suppose the velocity of a wavefront is measured and determined to be 5 mm/μs. Determine its velocity: (a) in m/s; (b) in mi/s.

Solution: Convert units using Tables 1.1 and 1.2. The results:

(a) $5 \left(\dfrac{\text{mm}}{\mu\text{s}}\right) \left(\dfrac{1 \text{ m}}{1000 \text{ mm}}\right) \left(\dfrac{10^6 \ \mu\text{s}}{1 \text{ s}}\right) = 5000 \left(\dfrac{\text{m}}{\text{s}}\right).$

Next, use this result to get (b):

(b) $5000 \left(\dfrac{\text{m}}{\text{s}}\right) \left(\dfrac{1 \text{ ft}}{0.3048 \text{ m}}\right) \left(\dfrac{1 \text{ mi}}{5280 \text{ ft}}\right) = 3.10685\ldots \left(\dfrac{\text{mi}}{\text{s}}\right)$

$\qquad\qquad\qquad\qquad = 3.11 \left(\dfrac{\text{mi}}{\text{s}}\right)$

Problem 1.11 The kinetic energy of a particle of mass m is defined to be $\frac{1}{2} mv^2$, where v is the magnitude of the particle's velocity. If the value of the kinetic energy of a particle at a given time is 200 when m is in kilograms and v is in meters per second, what is the value when m is in slugs and v is in feet per second?

Solution:

$$\left(200 \ \frac{\text{kg-m}^2}{\text{s}^2} \right) \left(\frac{0.0685 \ \text{slug}}{1 \ \text{kg}} \right) \left(\frac{1 \ \text{ft}}{0.3048 \ \text{m}} \right)^2$$

$$= 147.46 = 147 \ \frac{\text{slug-ft}^2}{\text{s}^2}$$

Problem 1.12 The acceleration due to gravity at sea level in SI units is $g = 9.81 \ \text{m/s}^2$. By converting units, use this value to determine the acceleration due to gravity at sea level in U.S. Customary units.

Solution: Use Table 1.2. The result is:

$$g = 9.81 \left(\frac{\text{m}}{\text{s}^2} \right) \left(\frac{1 \ \text{ft}}{0.3048 \ \text{m}} \right) = 32.185 \ldots \left(\frac{\text{ft}}{\text{s}^2} \right) = 32.2 \left(\frac{\text{ft}}{\text{s}^2} \right)$$

Problem 1.13 A *furlong per fortnight* is a facetious unit of velocity, perhaps made up by a student as a satirical comment on the bewildering variety of units engineers must deal with. A furlong is 660 ft (1/8 mile). A fortnight is 2 weeks (14 days). If you walk to class at 2 m/s, what is your speed in furlongs per fortnight to three significant digits?

Solution: Convert the units using the given conversions. Record the first three digits on the left, and add zeros as required by the number of tens in the exponent. The result is:

$$\left(5 \ \frac{\text{ft}}{\text{s}} \right) \left(\frac{1 \ \text{furlong}}{660 \ \text{ft}} \right) \left(\frac{3600 \ \text{s}}{1 \ \text{hr}} \right) \left(\frac{24 \ \text{hr}}{1 \ \text{day}} \right) \left(\frac{14 \ \text{day}}{1 \ \text{fortnight}} \right)$$

$$= \left(9160 \ \frac{\text{furlongs}}{\text{fortnight}} \right)$$

Problem 1.14 The cross-sectional area of a beam is 480 in². What is its cross-section in m²?

Solution: Convert units using Table 1.2. The result:

$$480 \ \text{in}^2 \left(\frac{1 \ \text{ft}}{12 \ \text{in}} \right)^2 \left(\frac{0.3048 \ \text{m}}{1 \ \text{ft}} \right)^2 = 0.30967 \ldots \text{m}^2 = 0.310 \ \text{m}^2$$

Problem 1.15 At sea level, the weight density (weight per unit volume) of water is approximately 62.4 lb/ft³. 1 lb = 4.448 N, 1 ft = 0.3048 m, and $g = 9.81 \ \text{m/s}^2$. Using only this information, determine the mass density for water in kg/m³.

Solution: Get wt. density in N/m³ first.

$$\left(62.4 \ \frac{\text{lb}}{\text{ft}^3} \right) \left(\frac{4.448 \ \text{N}}{1 \ \text{lb}} \right) \left(\frac{1 \ \text{ft}}{0.3048 \ \text{m}} \right)^3 = 9801.77 \ \frac{\text{N}}{\text{m}^3}$$

(carry extra significant figures till end — then round)

weight = mass $\cdot$ g

$$\text{mass} = \frac{\text{weight}}{g}$$

$$\left(9801.77 \ \frac{\text{N}}{\text{m}^3} \right) \left(\frac{\text{s}^2}{9.81 \ \text{m}} \right) = 999 \left(\frac{\text{N-s}^2}{\text{m}} \right) \left(\frac{1}{\text{m}^3} \right)$$

$$= 999 \ \text{kg/m}^3$$

Problem 1.16 A pressure transducer measures a value of 300 lb/in^2. Determine the value of the pressure in pascals. A pascal (Pa) is one newton per meter squared.

Solution: Convert the units using Table 1.2 and the definition of the Pascal unit. The result:

$$300 \left(\frac{lb}{in^2} \right) \left(\frac{4.448 \text{ N}}{1 \text{ lb}} \right) \left(\frac{12 \text{ in}}{1 \text{ ft}} \right)^2 \left(\frac{1 \text{ ft}}{0.3048 \text{ m}} \right)^2$$

$$= 2.0683 \ldots (10^6) \left(\frac{N}{m^2} \right) = 2.07(10^6) \text{ Pa}$$

Problem 1.17 A horsepower is 550 ft-lb/s. A watt is 1 N-m/s. Determine the number of watts generated by (a) the Wright brothers' 1903 airplane, which had a 12-horsepower engine; (b) a modern passenger jet with a power of 100,000 horsepower at cruising speed.

Solution: Convert units using inside front cover of textbook derive the conversion between horsepower and watts. The result

(a) $12 \text{ hp} \left(\dfrac{746 \text{ watt}}{1 \text{ hp}} \right) = 8950 \text{ watt}$

(b) $10^5 \text{ hp} \left(\dfrac{746 \text{ watt}}{1 \text{ hp}} \right) = 7.46(10^7) \text{ watt}$

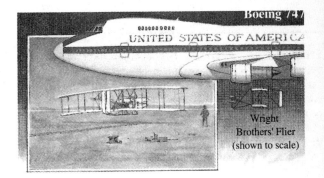

Boeing 747

Wright
Brothers' Flier
(shown to scale)

Problem 1.18 In SI units, the universal gravitational constant $G = 6.67 \times 10^{-11}$ N-m^2/kg^2. Determine the value of G in U.S. Customary units.

Solution: Convert units using Table 1.2. The result:

$$6.67(10^{-11}) \left(\frac{N\text{-}m^2}{kg^2} \right) \left(\frac{1 \text{ lb}}{4.448 \text{ N}} \right) \left(\frac{1 \text{ ft}}{0.3048 \text{ m}} \right)^2 \left(\frac{14.59 \text{ kg}}{1 \text{ slug}} \right)^2$$

$$= 3.43590 \ldots (10^{-8}) \left(\frac{lb\text{-}ft^2}{slug^2} \right) = 3.44(10^{-8}) \left(\frac{lb\text{-}ft^2}{slug^2} \right)$$

Problem 1.19 If the earth is modeled as a homogenous sphere, the velocity of a satellite in a circular orbit is

$$v = \sqrt{\frac{gR_E^2}{r}},$$

where R_E is the radius of the earth and r is the radius of the orbit.

(a) If g is in m/s^2 and R_E and r are in meters, what are the units of v?
(b) If $R_E = 6370$ km and $r = 6670$ km, what is the value of v to three significant digits?
(c) For the orbit described in Part (b), what is the value of v in mi/s to three significant digits?

Solution: For (a), substitute the units into the expression and reduce:

(a) $\sqrt{\dfrac{g\left(\frac{m}{s^2}\right)(R_E m)^2}{(rm)}} = \sqrt{\dfrac{gR_E^2}{r}\left(\dfrac{m^3}{ms^2}\right)} = v\left(\dfrac{m}{s}\right)$

Hence, the units are m/s

For (b), substitute the numerical values into the expression, using $g = 9.81 \left(\frac{m}{s^2}\right)$.

$$v = \sqrt{\dfrac{\left(9.81\frac{m}{s^2}\right)\left((6370 \text{ km})\left(10^3\frac{m}{km}\right)\right)^2}{(6670 \text{ km})\left(10^3\frac{m}{km}\right)}}$$

$$= \sqrt{59.679\ldots(10^6)}\left(\dfrac{m}{s}\right) = 7.7252\ldots(10^3)\left(\dfrac{m}{s}\right)$$

(b) $v = 7730 \left(\dfrac{m}{s}\right)$

For (c), convert units using Table 1.2. The result:

(c) $v = 7730 \left(\dfrac{m}{s}\right)\left(\dfrac{1 \text{ ft}}{0.3048 \text{ m}}\right)\left(\dfrac{1 \text{ mile}}{5280 \text{ ft}}\right)$

$$= 4.803\ldots\left(\dfrac{\text{mile}}{s}\right) = 4.80\left(\dfrac{\text{mile}}{s}\right)$$

Problem 1.20 In the equation

$$T = \tfrac{1}{2}I\omega^2,$$

the term I is in kg-m^2 and ω is in s^{-1}.

(a) What are the SI units of T?
(b) If the value of T is 100 when I is in kg-m^2 and ω is in s^{-1},

what is the value of T when it is expressed in U.S. Customary base units?

Solution: For (a), substitute the units into the expression for T:

(a) $T = \left(\dfrac{1}{2}\right)(I \text{ kg-m}^2)(\omega s^{-1})^2 = \dfrac{\text{kg-m}^2}{s^2}$

For (b), convert units using Table 1.2. The result:

(b) $100 \left(\dfrac{\text{kg-m}^2}{s^2}\right)\left(\dfrac{1 \text{ slug}}{14.59 \text{ kg}}\right)\left(\dfrac{1 \text{ ft}}{0.3048 \text{ m}}\right)^2$

$$= 73.7759\ldots\left(\dfrac{\text{slug-ft}^2}{s^2}\right) = 73.8\left(\dfrac{\text{slug-ft}^2}{s^2}\right)$$

Problem 1.21 The aerodynamic drag force D exerted on a moving object by a gas is given by the expression

$$D = C_\mathrm{D}S\tfrac{1}{2}\rho v^2,$$

where the drag coefficient C_D is dimensionless, S is reference area, ρ is the mass per unit volume of the gas, and v is the velocity of the object relative to the gas.

(a) Suppose that the value of D is 800 when S, ρ, and v are expressed in SI base units. By converting units, determine the value of D when S, ρ, and v are expressed in U.S. Customary units.

(b) The drag force D is in newtons when the expression is evaluated in SI base units and is in pounds when the expression is evaluated in U.S. Customary base units. Using your result from part (a), determine the conversion factor from newtons to pounds.

Solution: For (a), we just carry out the conversion unit by unit.

We get:

(a) $\displaystyle 800(\mathrm{m}^2)\left(\frac{\mathrm{kg}}{\mathrm{m}^3}\right)\left(\frac{\mathrm{m}}{\mathrm{s}}\right)^2 = 800\left(\frac{\mathrm{kg\ m}}{\mathrm{s}^2}\right)$

$\displaystyle = 800\left(\frac{0.0685\ \mathrm{slug}}{1\ \mathrm{kg}}\right)\left(\frac{3.281\ \mathrm{ft}}{1\ \mathrm{m}}\right)\left(\frac{1}{\mathrm{s}^2}\right)$

$\displaystyle = 180\left(\frac{\mathrm{slug\ ft}}{\mathrm{s}^2}\right)$

(b) From (a), 800 N = 180 lb. Hence, 1 N = 0.225 lb.

Problem 1.22 The pressure p at a depth h below the surface of a stationary liquid is given by

$$p = p_\mathrm{s} + \gamma h,$$

where p_s is pressure at the surface and γ is a constant.

(a) If p is in newtons per meter squared and h is in meters, what are the units of γ?

(b) For a particular liquid, the value of γ is 9810 when p is in newtons per meter squared and h is in meters. What is the value for γ when p is in pounds per foot squared and h is in feet?

Solution:

The units of γh are the same as the units of P. Thus, in units

$$\left(\frac{\mathrm{N}}{\mathrm{m}^2}\right) = \gamma(\mathrm{m})$$

units of $\gamma \sim \mathrm{N/m}^3$

We must convert $9810\ \dfrac{\mathrm{N}}{\mathrm{m}^3}$ to $\dfrac{\mathrm{lb}}{\mathrm{ft}^3}$

$$\left(9810\ \frac{\mathrm{N}}{\mathrm{m}^3}\right)\left(\frac{1\ \mathrm{lb}}{4.448\ \mathrm{N}}\right)\left(\frac{0.3048\ \mathrm{m}}{1\ \mathrm{ft}}\right)^3 = 62.4\ \mathrm{lb/ft}^3$$

Problem 1.23 The acceleration due to gravity is 1.62 m/s^2 on the surface of the moon and 9.81 m/s^2 on the surface of the earth. A female astronaut's mass is 57 kg. What is the maximum allowable mass of her spacesuit and equipment if the engineers don't want the total weight on the moon of the woman, her spacesuit and equipment to exceed 180 N?

Solution: Find the mass which weighs 180 N on the moon.

$$m = \frac{w}{g} = \frac{180\ \mathrm{N\text{-}s}^2}{1.62\ \mathrm{m}} = 111.1\ \mathrm{kg}$$

This is the total allowable mass. Thus, the suit & equipment can have mass of

$$m_{\mathrm{S/E}} = 111.1\ \mathrm{kg} - 57\ \mathrm{kg} = 54.1\ \mathrm{kg}$$

Problem 1.24 A person has a mass of 50 kg.

(a) The acceleration due to gravity at sea level is $g = 9.81$ m/s^2. What is the person's weight at sea level?
(b) The acceleration due to gravity on the moon is $g = 1.62$ m/s^2. What would the person weigh on the moon?

Solution: Use Eq (1.6).

(a) $W_e = 50$ kg $\left(9.81 \ \dfrac{\text{m}}{\text{s}^2}\right) = 490.5$ N $= 491$ N, and

(b) $W_{\text{moon}} = 50$ kg $\left(1.62 \ \dfrac{\text{m}}{\text{s}^2}\right) = 81$ N.

Problem 1.25 The acceleration due to gravity at sea level is $g = 9.81$ m/s^2. The radius of the earth is 6370 km. The universal gravitation constant is $G = 6.67 \times 10^{-11}$ N-m^2/kg^2. Use this information to determine the mass of the earth.

Solution: Use Eq (1.3) $a = \dfrac{Gm_E}{R^2}$. Solve for the mass,

$$m_E = \frac{gR^2}{G} = \frac{(9.81 \text{ m/s}^2)(6370 \text{ km})^2 \left(10^3 \ \dfrac{\text{m}}{\text{km}}\right)^2}{6.67(10^{-11}) \left(\dfrac{\text{N-m}^2}{\text{kg}^2}\right)}$$

$$= 5.9679\ldots(10^{24}) \text{ kg} = 5.97(10^{24}) \text{ kg}$$

Problem 1.26 A person weighs 180 lb at sea level. The radius of the earth is 3960 mi. What force is exerted on the person by the gravitational attraction of the earth if he is in a space station in orbit 200 mi above the surface of the earth?

Solution: Use Eq (1.5).

$$W = mg \left(\frac{R_E}{r}\right)^2 = \left(\frac{W_E}{g}\right) g \left(\frac{R_E}{R_E + H}\right)^2 = W_E \left(\frac{3960}{3960 + 200}\right)^2$$

$$= (180)(0.90616) = 163 \text{ lb}$$

Problem 1.27 The acceleration due to gravity on the surface of the moon is 1.62 m/s^2. The radius of the moon is $R_M = 1738$ km.

Determine the acceleration due to gravity of the moon at a point 1738 km above its surface.

Strategy: Write an equation equivalent to Eq. (1.4) for the acceleration due to gravity of the moon.

Solution: Use Eq (1.4), rewritten to apply to the Moon... $a = g_M \left(\dfrac{R_M}{r}\right)^2$

$$a = (1.62 \text{ m/s}^2) \left(\frac{R_M}{R_M + R_M}\right)^2 = (1.62 \text{ m/s}^2) \left(\frac{1}{2}\right)^2 = 0.405 \text{ m/s}^2$$

Problem 1.28 If an object is near the surface of the earth, the variation of its weight with distance from the center of the earth can often be neglected. The acceleration due to gravity at sea level is $g = 9.81$ m/s². The radius of the earth is 6370 km. The weight of an object at sea level is mg, where m is its mass. At what height above the earth does the weight decrease to 0.99 mg?

Solution: Use a variation of Eq (1.5).

$$W = mg\left(\frac{R_E}{R_E + h}\right)^2 = 0.99 \text{ mg}$$

Solve for the radial height,

$$h = R_E\left(\frac{1}{\sqrt{0.99}} - 1\right) = (6370)(1.0050378 - 1.0)$$

$$= 32.09\ldots\text{km} = 32,100 \text{ m} = 32.1 \text{ km}$$

Problem 1.29 The centers of two oranges are 1 m apart. The mass of each orange is 0.2 kg. What gravitational force do they exert on each other? (The universal gravitational constant is $G = 6.67 \times 10^{-11}$ N-m²/kg².)

Solution: Use Eq (1.1) $F = \dfrac{Gm_1 m_2}{r^2}$. Substitute:

$$F = \frac{(6.67)(10^{-11})(0.2)(0.2)}{1^2} = 2.668(10^{-12}) \text{ N}$$

Problem 1.30 At a point between the earth and the moon, the magnitude of the earth's gravitational acceleration equals the magnitude of the moon's gravitational acceleration. What is the distance from the center of the earth to that point to three significant digits? The distance from the center of the earth to the center of the moon is 383,000 km, and the radius of the earth is 6370 km. The radius of the moon is 1738 km, and the acceleration of gravity at its surface is 1.62 m/s².

Solution: Let r_{Ep} be the distance from the Earth to the point where the gravitational accelerations are the same and let r_{Mp} be the distance from the Moon to that point. Then, $r_{Ep} + r_{Mp} = r_{EM} = 383,000$ km. The fact that the gravitational attractions by the Earth and the Moon at this point are equal leads to the equation

$$g_E\left(\frac{R_E}{r_{Ep}}\right)^2 = g_M\left(\frac{R_M}{r_{Mp}}\right)^2,$$

where $r_{EM} = 383,000$ km. Substituting the correct numerical values leads to the equation

$$9.81\left(\frac{\text{m}}{\text{s}^2}\right)\left(\frac{6370 \text{ km}}{r_{Ep}}\right)^2 = 1.62\left(\frac{\text{m}}{\text{s}^2}\right)\left(\frac{1738 \text{ km}}{r_{EM} - r_{Ep}}\right)^2,$$

where r_{Ep} is the only unknown. Solving, we get $r_{Ep} = 344,770$ km = 345,000 km.

Problem 2.1 The magnitudes $|\mathbf{F}_A| = 60$ N and $|\mathbf{F}_B| = 80$ N. The angle $\alpha = 45°$. Graphically determine the magnitude of the sum of the forces $\mathbf{F} = \mathbf{F}_A + \mathbf{F}_B$ and the angle between $\mathbf{F}_B$ and $\mathbf{F}$.

Strategy: Construct the parallelogram for determining the sum of the forces, drawing the lengths of $\mathbf{F}_A$ and $\mathbf{F}_B$ proportional to their magnitudes and accurately measuring the angle α, as we did in Example 2.1. Then you can measure the magnitude of their sum and the angle between their sum and $\mathbf{F}_B$.

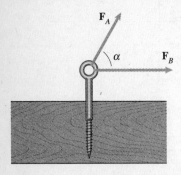

Solution: The graphical construction is shown:

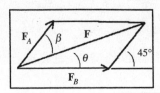

The angle β is graphically determined to be about $26°$ and the angle θ is about $\theta = 19°$. The magnitude of the sum $|\mathbf{F}| = |\mathbf{F}_A + \mathbf{F}_B|$ is about $|\mathbf{F}| = 130$ N. (These values check with a determination using trigonometry, $\beta = 25.9°$, $\boxed{\theta = 19.1°,}$ and $\boxed{|\mathbf{F}| = 129.6 \text{ N}}$.)

Problem 2.2 The magnitudes $|\mathbf{F}_A| = 40$ N and $|\mathbf{F}_A + \mathbf{F}_B| = 80$ N. The angle $\alpha = 60°$. Graphically determine the magnitude of $\mathbf{F}_B$.

Solution: Measuring, $\mathbf{F}_B \cong 52$ N

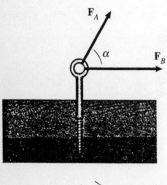

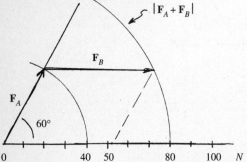

Problem 2.3 The magnitudes $|\mathbf{F}_A| = 100$ lb and $|\mathbf{F}_B| = 140$ lb. The angle $\alpha = 40°$. Use trigonometry to determine the magnitude of the sum of the forces $\mathbf{F} = \mathbf{F}_A + \mathbf{F}_B$ and the angle between $\mathbf{F}_B$ and $\mathbf{F}$.

Strategy: Use the laws of sines and cosines to analyze the triangles formed by the parallelogram rule for the sum of the forces as we did in Example 2.1. The laws of sines and cosines are given in Section A.2 of Appendix A.

Solution: The construction is shown. Use the cosine law to determine the magnitude $|\mathbf{F}|$.

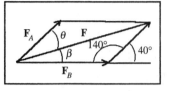

$$|\mathbf{F}|^2 = |\mathbf{F}_A|^2 + |\mathbf{F}_B|^2 - 2|\mathbf{F}_A||\mathbf{F}_B|\cos 140°$$

$$|\mathbf{F}|^2 = (100)^2 + (140)^2 - 2\,(100)\,(140)\cos 140°$$

or $\quad \boxed{|\mathbf{F}| = \sqrt{5.1049\ldots(10^4)} = 225.94\ldots = 225.9 \text{ lb}}$

Use the law of sines to determine the angle θ., i.e., $\dfrac{|\mathbf{F}|}{\sin 140°} = \dfrac{|\mathbf{F}_B|}{\sin \theta}$.
From which we get $\sin\theta = \dfrac{|\mathbf{F}_B|}{|\mathbf{F}|}\sin 140° = 0.398$, and $\theta = 23.47°$. The angle between $\mathbf{F}_B$ and $\mathbf{F}$ is

Thus $\quad \boxed{\beta = 40 - 23.47 = 16.53°}$

Problem 2.4 The magnitudes $|\mathbf{F}_A| = 40$ N and $|\mathbf{F}_A + \mathbf{F}_B| = 80$ N. The angle $\alpha = 60°$. Use trigonometry to determine the magnitude of $\mathbf{F}_B$.

Solution: Draw the force triangle.

From the law of sines

$$\frac{|\mathbf{F}_A + \mathbf{F}_B|}{\sin 120°} = \frac{|\mathbf{F}_A|}{\sin \theta}$$

$$\sin\theta = \frac{|\mathbf{F}_A|}{|\mathbf{F}_A + \mathbf{F}_B|}\sin 120°$$

$$\sin\theta = \left(\frac{40}{80}\right)(0.866)$$

$$\theta = 25.66°$$

$$\theta + \gamma + 120° = 180° \Rightarrow \gamma = 34.34°$$

From the law of sines,

$$\frac{|\mathbf{F}_B|}{\sin \gamma} = \frac{|\mathbf{F}_A + \mathbf{F}_B|}{\sin 120°}$$

$$|\mathbf{F}_B| = \left(\frac{\sin \gamma}{\sin 120°}\right)(80 \text{ N})$$

$$|\mathbf{F}_B| = 52.1 \text{ N}$$

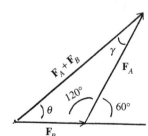

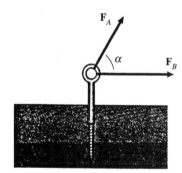

Problem 2.5 The magnitudes $|\mathbf{F}_A| = 100$ lb and $|\mathbf{F}_B| = 140$ lb. If α can have any value, what are the minimum and maximum possible values of the magnitude of the sum of the forces $\mathbf{F} = \mathbf{F}_A + \mathbf{F}_B$, and what are the corresponding values of α?

Solution: A graphical construction shows that the magnitude is a minimum when the two force vectors are opposed, and a maximum when both act in the same direction. The corresponding values are

$$|\mathbf{F}|_{max} = |\mathbf{F}_A + \mathbf{F}_B| = |100 + 140| = 240 \text{ lb, and } \alpha = 0°.$$

$$|\mathbf{F}|_{min} = |\mathbf{F}_A + \mathbf{F}_B| = |100 - 140| = 40 \text{ lb, and } \alpha = 180°.$$

Problem 2.6 The angle $\theta = 30°$. What is the magnitude of the vector $\mathbf{r}_{AC}$?

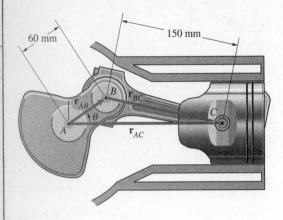

Solution:

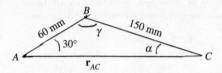

From the law of sines

$$\frac{BC}{\sin 30°} = \frac{AB}{\sin \alpha} = \frac{AC}{\sin \gamma}$$

We know BC and AB. Thus

$$\frac{150}{\sin 30°} = \frac{60}{\sin \alpha} \Rightarrow \alpha = 11.54°$$

Also $30° + \alpha + \gamma = 180° \Rightarrow \gamma = 138.46°$

Now, from the law of sines

$$\frac{150}{\sin 30°} = \frac{AC}{\sin 138.46°}$$

$$AC = |\mathbf{r}_{AC}| = 199 \text{ mm}$$

Problem 2.7 The vectors $\mathbf{F}_A$ and $\mathbf{F}_B$ represent the forces exerted on the pulley by the belt. Their magnitudes are $|\mathbf{F}_A| = 80$ N and $|\mathbf{F}_B| = 60$ N. What is the magnitude $|\mathbf{F}_A + \mathbf{F}_B|$ of the total force the belt exerts on the pulley?

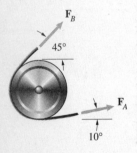

Solution:

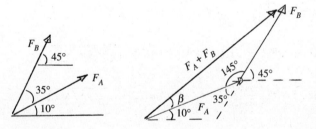

Law of cosines

$$|F_A + F_B| = (80)^2 + (60)^2 - 2(80)(60)\cos 145°$$

$$|F_A + F_B| = 133.66 \approx 134 \text{ N}$$

Law of sines

$$\frac{|F_B|}{\sin \beta} = \frac{|F_A + F_B|}{\sin 145} \Rightarrow \frac{60}{\sin \beta} = \frac{133.66}{\sin 145} \quad \beta = 14.92°$$

$$\therefore |F_A + F_B| = 134 \text{ N}$$

Problem 2.8 The magnitude of the vertical force **F** is 80 N. If you resolve it into components **F**$_{AB}$ and **F**$_{AC}$ that are parallel to the bars AB and AC, what are the magnitudes of the components?

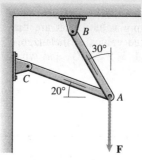

Solution: **F** is made up of components in the two known directions. Since we also know the direction of **F**, we can draw a force triangle (**F**$_{AB}$ + **F**$_{AC}$ = **F**).

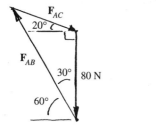

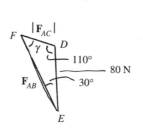

Thus, we have a triangle DEF as shown below

$$\gamma + 110° + 30° = 180°$$

$$\gamma = 40°$$

From the law of sines,

$$\frac{80}{\sin 40°} = \frac{|\mathbf{F}_{AC}|}{\sin 30°} = \frac{|\mathbf{F}_{AB}|}{\sin 110°}$$

$$\boxed{|\mathbf{F}_{AB}| = 117 \text{ N} \quad |\mathbf{F}_{AC}| = 62.2 \text{ N}}$$

Problem 2.9 The rocket engine exerts an upward force of 4 MN (meganewtons) magnitude on the test stand. If you resolve the force into vector components parallel to the bars AB and CD, what are the magnitudes of the components?

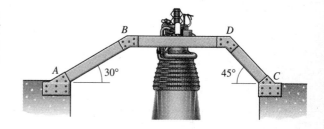

Solution: The vector diagram construction is shown. From the law of sines, $\frac{|\mathbf{F}_{AB}|}{\sin 45°} = \frac{|\mathbf{F}|}{\sin 75°}$, from which

$$|\mathbf{F}_{AB}| = |\mathbf{F}| \left(\frac{\sin 45°}{\sin 75°} \right) = (4)(0.732) = 2.928 \ldots \boxed{= 2.93 \text{ MN}}$$

$$|\mathbf{F}_{BC}| = |\mathbf{F}| \left(\frac{\sin 60}{\sin 75} \right) = (4)(0.8966) = 3.586 \ldots \boxed{= 3.59 \text{ MN}}$$

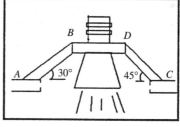

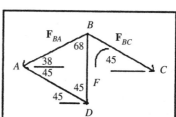

Problem 2.10 If **F** is resolved into components parallel to the bars *AB* and *BC*, the magnitude of the component parallel to bar *AB* is 4 kN. What is the magnitude of **F**?

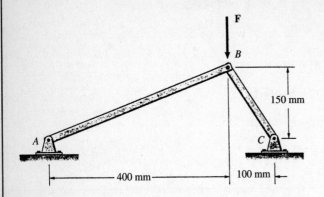

Solution:

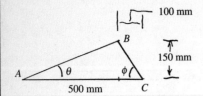

Call the force in *AB* $\mathbf{F}_{AB}$ and the force in $BC \sim \mathbf{F}_{BC}$. Then $\mathbf{F}_{AB} + \mathbf{F}_{BC} = \mathbf{F}$. We know the geometry and that $|\mathbf{F}_{AB}| = 4$ kN. Draw a diagram of the geometry, get the angles, then draw the force triangle.

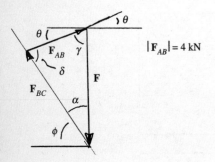

$$\tan\theta = \frac{150}{400} \quad \theta = 20.6°$$

$$\tan\phi = \frac{150}{100} \quad \phi = 56.3°$$

$$\gamma + \theta = 90° \quad \gamma = 69.4°$$

$$\alpha + \phi = 90° \quad \alpha = 33.7°$$

$$\delta + \alpha + \gamma = 180° \quad \delta = 76.9°$$

From the law of sines

$$\frac{|\mathbf{F}|}{\sin\delta} = \frac{|\mathbf{F}_{AB}|}{\sin\alpha}$$

$$|\mathbf{F}| = \left[\frac{\sin(76.9°)}{\sin(33.7°)}\right](4) = 7.02 \text{ kN}$$

Problem 2.11 The forces acting on the sailplane are represented by three vectors. The lift **L** and drag **D** are perpendicular, the magnitude of the weight **W** is 3500 N, and **W** + **L** + **D** = **0**. What are the magnitudes of the lift and drag?

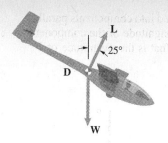

Solution: Draw the force triangle and then use the geometry plus

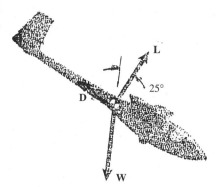

$$\cos 25° = \frac{|\mathbf{L}|}{|\mathbf{W}|}$$

$$\sin 25° = \frac{|\mathbf{D}|}{|\mathbf{W}|}$$

$|\mathbf{W}| = 3500$ N

$|\mathbf{L}| = 3500 \cos 25°$

$|\mathbf{D}| = 3500 \sin 25°$

$|\mathbf{L}| = 3170$ N

$|\mathbf{D}| = 1480$ N

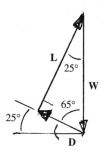

Problem 2.12 The suspended weight exerts a downward 2000-lb force **F** at A. If you resolve **F** into vector components parallel to the wires AB, AC, and AD, the magnitude of the component parallel to AC is 600 lb. What are the magnitudes of the components parallel to AB and AD?

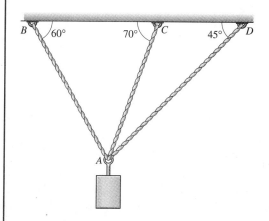

Solution: We resolve the force exerted by the weight into components parallel to the wires:

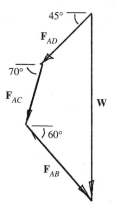

We see that

$$|\mathbf{F}_{AD}| \sin 45° + |\mathbf{F}_{AC}| \sin 70° + |\mathbf{F}_{AB}| \sin 60° = |\mathbf{W}|,$$

$$|\mathbf{F}_{AD}| \cos 45° + |\mathbf{F}_{AC}| \cos 70° - |\mathbf{F}_{AB}| \cos 60° = 0.$$

Setting $|\mathbf{W}| = 2000$ lb and $|\mathbf{F}_{AC}| = 600$ lb and solving, we obtain $\mathbf{F}_{AB} = 1202$ lb, $\mathbf{F}_{AD} = 559$ lb.

Problem 2.13 The wires in Problem 2.12 will safely support the weight if the magnitude of the vector component of **F** parallel to each wire does not exceed 2000 lb. Based on this criterion, how large can the magnitude of **F** be? What are the corresponding magnitudes of the vector components of **F** parallel to the three wires?

Solution: From Problem 2.12 above, we have $F_{AC} = 600$ lb., $F_{AB} = 1202$ lb. The largest force is $F_{AB} = 1202$ lb. We want this value to be 2000 lb and to have all other values scaled accordingly. Hence, we multiply all forces by $k = \dfrac{2000}{1202} = 1.664$. Multiplying all of the forces in Problem 2.12 by this factor, we get

$$\boxed{F_{AB} = 2000 \text{ lb}, \; F_{AC} = 999 \text{ lb}, \; F_{AD} = 931 \text{ lb}, \text{ and } F = 3329 \text{ lb}.}$$

Problem 2.14 Two vectors $\mathbf{r}_A$ and $\mathbf{r}_B$ have magnitudes $|\mathbf{r}_A| = 30$ m and $|\mathbf{r}_B| = 40$ m. Determine the magnitude of their sum $\mathbf{r}_A + \mathbf{r}_B$

(a) if $\mathbf{r}_A$ and $\mathbf{r}_B$ have the same direction.
(b) if $\mathbf{r}_A$ and $\mathbf{r}_B$ are perpendicular.

Solution: The vector constructions are shown.

(a) The magnitude of the sum is the sum of the magnitudes for vectors in the same direction:

$$|\mathbf{r}_A + \mathbf{r}_B| = 30 + 40 = 70 \text{ m}$$

From the cosine law (which reduces to the Pythagorean Theorem for a right triangle)

$$|\mathbf{r}_A + \mathbf{r}_B|^2 = |\mathbf{r}_A^2| + |\mathbf{r}_B^2| = (30)^2 + (40)^2 = 2500 \quad \boxed{|\mathbf{r}_A + \mathbf{r}_B| = 50 \text{ m}}$$

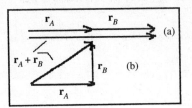

Problem 2.15 A spherical storage tank is supported by cables. The tank is subjected to three forces: the forces $\mathbf{F}_A$ and $\mathbf{F}_B$ exerted by the cables and the weight $\mathbf{W}$. The weight of the tank is $|\mathbf{W}| = 600$ lb. The vector sum of the forces acting on the tank equals zero. Determine the magnitudes of $\mathbf{F}_A$ and $\mathbf{F}_B$ (a) graphically and (b) by using trigonometry.

Solution: The vector construction is shown.

(a) The graphical solution is obtained from the construction by the recognition that since the opposite interior angles of the triangle are equal, the sides (magnitudes of the forces exerted by the cables) are equal. A measurement determines the magnitudes. (b) The trigonometric solution is obtained from the law of sines:

$$\frac{|\mathbf{W}|}{\sin 140°} = \frac{|\mathbf{F}_A|}{\sin 20°} = \frac{|\mathbf{F}_B|}{\sin 20°}$$

Solving:

$$|\mathbf{F}_A| = |\mathbf{F}_B| = |\mathbf{W}| \left(\frac{\sin 20}{\sin 140} \right) = 319.25 \ldots \boxed{= 319.3 \text{ lb}}$$

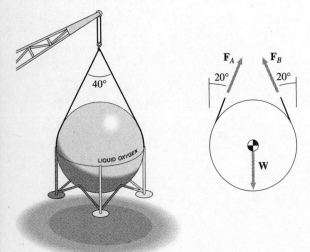

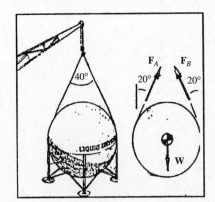

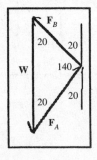

Problem 2.16 The rope ABC exerts the forces $\mathbf{F}_{BA}$ and $\mathbf{F}_{BC}$ on the block at B. Their magnitudes are $|\mathbf{F}_{BA}| = |\mathbf{F}_{BC}| = 800$ N. Determine $|\mathbf{F}_{BA} + \mathbf{F}_{BC}|$ (a) graphically and (b) by using trigonometry.

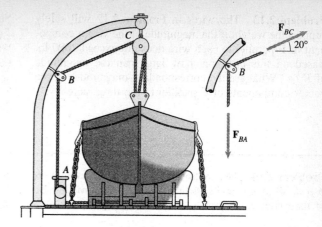

Solution: The vector graphical construction is shown.

(a) The angles are derived from the rule that for equal legs in a triangle the opposite interior angles are equal, and the rule that the sum of the interior angles is 180 deg. Thus from the problem statement the 70° angle is determined; from the equality of angles and the sum of interior angles the other two 55° angles are derived. The magnitude of the sum of the two vectors is then measured from the graph.

(b) The trigonometric solution follows from the law of sines:

$$\frac{|\mathbf{F}_{AB} + \mathbf{F}_{BC}|}{\sin 70°} = \frac{|\mathbf{F}_{AB}|}{\sin 55°} = \frac{|\mathbf{F}_{BC}|}{\sin 55°}.$$

Solve:

$$|\mathbf{F}_{AB} + \mathbf{F}_{BC}| = |\mathbf{F}_{AB}| \left(\frac{\sin 70°}{\sin 55°} \right) = 800(1.1471\ldots)$$

$$= 917.72\ldots \quad \boxed{|\mathbf{F}_A + \mathbf{F}_B| = 917.7 \text{ N}}$$

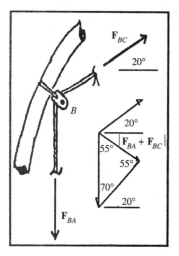

Problem 2.17 Two snowcats tow a housing unit to a new location at McMurdo Base, Antarctica. (The top view is shown. The cables are horizontal.) The sum of the forces $\mathbf{F}_A$ and $\mathbf{F}_B$ exerted on the unit is parallel to the line L, and $|\mathbf{F}_A| = 1000$ lb. Determine $|\mathbf{F}_B|$ and $|\mathbf{F}_A + \mathbf{F}_B|$ (a) graphically and (b) by using trigonometry.

TOP VIEW

Solution: The graphical construction is shown. The sum of the interior angles must be 180°. (a) The magnitudes of $|\mathbf{F}_B|$ and $|\mathbf{F}_A + \mathbf{F}_B|$ are determined from measurements. (b) The trigonometric solution is obtained from the law of sines:

$$\frac{|\mathbf{F}_A + \mathbf{F}_B|}{\sin 100} = \frac{|\mathbf{F}_A|}{\sin 30} = \frac{|\mathbf{F}_B|}{\sin 50}$$

from which $|\mathbf{F}_B| = |\mathbf{F}_A| \left(\dfrac{\sin 50}{\sin 30} \right) = 1000(1.532)$ $\boxed{= 1532 \text{ lb}}$

$|\mathbf{F}_A + \mathbf{F}_B| = |\mathbf{F}_A| \left(\dfrac{\sin 100}{\sin 30} \right) = 1000(1.9696)$ $\boxed{= 1970 \text{ lb}}$

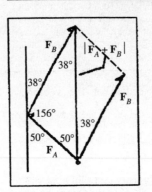

TOP VIEW

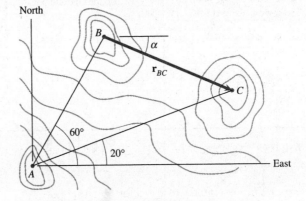

Problem 2.18 A surveyor determines that the horizontal distance from A to B is 400 m and that the horizontal distance from A to C is 600 m. Determine the magnitude of the horizontal vector $\mathbf{r}_{BC}$ from B to C and the angle α (a) graphically and (b) by using trigonometry.

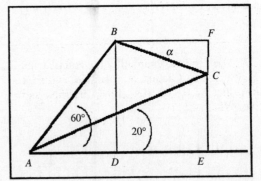

Solution: (a) The graphical solution is obtained by drawing the figure to scale and measuring the unknowns. (b) The trigonometric solution is obtained by breaking the figure into three separate right triangles. The magnitude $|\mathbf{r}_{BC}|$ is obtained by the cosine law:

$$|\mathbf{r}_{BC}|^2 = (400)^2 + (600)^2 - 2(400)(600) \cos 40°$$

or $\boxed{|\mathbf{r}_{BC}| = 390.25 = 390.3 \text{ m}}$

The three right triangles are shown. The distance BD is $BD = (400) \sin 60° = 346.41$ m. The distance CE is $CE = 600 \sin 20° = 205.2$ m. The distance FC is $FC = (346.4 - 205.2) = 141.2$ m.

The angle α is $\sin \alpha = \dfrac{141.2}{390.3} = 0.36177 \ldots$, or $\boxed{\alpha = 21.2°}$

18

Problem 2.19 The vector **r** extends from point A to the midpoint between points B and C. Prove that

$$\mathbf{r} = \tfrac{1}{2}(\mathbf{r}_{AB} + \mathbf{r}_{AC}).$$

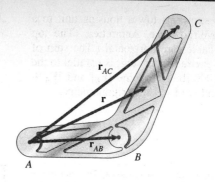

Solution: The proof is straightforward:

$$\mathbf{r} = \mathbf{r}_{AB} + \mathbf{r}_{BM}, \text{ and } \mathbf{r} = \mathbf{r}_{AC} + \mathbf{r}_{CM}.$$

Add the two equations and note that $\mathbf{r}_{BM} + \mathbf{r}_{CM} = 0$, since the two vectors are equal and opposite in direction.

Thus $2\mathbf{r} = \mathbf{r}_{AC} + \mathbf{r}_{AB}$, or $\mathbf{r} = \left(\tfrac{1}{2}\right)(\mathbf{r}_{AC} + \mathbf{r}_{AB})$

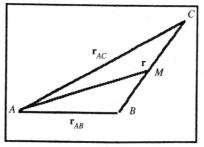

Problem 2.20 By drawing sketches of the vectors, explain why

$$\mathbf{U} + (\mathbf{V} + \mathbf{W}) = (\mathbf{U} + \mathbf{V}) + \mathbf{W}.$$

Solution: Additive associativity for vectors is usually given as an axiom in the theory of vector algebra, and of course axioms are not subject to proof. However we can by sketches show that associativity for vector addition is intuitively reasonable: Given the three vectors to be added, (a) shows the addition first of $\mathbf{V} + \mathbf{W}$, and then the addition of $\mathbf{U}$. The result is the vector $\mathbf{U} + (\mathbf{V} + \mathbf{W})$.

(b) shows the addition of $\mathbf{U} + \mathbf{V}$, and then the addition of $\mathbf{W}$, leading to the result $(\mathbf{U} + \mathbf{V}) + \mathbf{W}$.

The final vector in the two sketches is the same vector, illustrating that associativity of vector addition is intuitively reasonable.

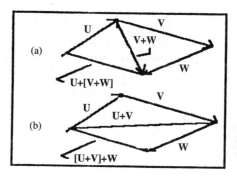

Problem 2.21 A force $\mathbf{F} = 40\,\mathbf{i} - 20\,\mathbf{j}$ (N). What is its magnitude $|\mathbf{F}|$?

Strategy: The magnitude of a vector in terms of its components is given by Eq. (2.8).

Solution: $|\mathbf{F}| = \sqrt{40^2 + 20^2} = 44.7$ N

Problem 2.22 An engineer estimating the components of a force $\mathbf{F} = F_x\,\mathbf{i} + F_y\,\mathbf{j}$ acting on a bridge abutment has determined that $F_x = 130$ MN, $|\mathbf{F}| = 165$ MN, and F_y is negative. What is F_y?

Solution:

$$|\mathbf{F}| = \sqrt{|\mathbf{F}_x|^2 + |\mathbf{F}_y|^2}$$

Thus $|\mathbf{F}_y| = \sqrt{|\mathbf{F}|^2 - |\mathbf{F}_x|^2}$ (mN)

$$|\mathbf{F}_y| = \sqrt{165^2 - 130^2} \text{ (mN)}$$

$$|\mathbf{F}_y| = 101.6 \text{ mN}$$

$$F_y = -102 \text{ mN}$$

Problem 2.23 A support is subjected to a force $\mathbf{F} = F_x\mathbf{i} + 80\mathbf{j}$ (N). If the support will safely support a force of 100 N, what is the allowable range of values of the component F_x?

Solution: Use the definition of magnitude in Eq. (2.8) and reduce algebraically.

$100 \geq \sqrt{(F_x)^2 + (80)^2}$, from which $(100)^2 - (80)^2 \geq (F_x)^2$.

Thus $|F_x| \leq \sqrt{3600}$, or $\boxed{-60 \leq (F_x) \leq +60 \text{ (N)}}$

Problem 2.24 If $\mathbf{F}_A = 600\mathbf{i} - 800\mathbf{j}$ (kip) and $\mathbf{F}_B = 200\mathbf{i} - 200\mathbf{j}$ (kip), what is the magnitude of the force $\mathbf{F} = \mathbf{F}_A - 2\mathbf{F}_B$?

Solution: Take the scalar multiple of $\mathbf{F}_B$, add the components of the two forces as in Eq. (2.9), and use the definition of the magnitude. $\mathbf{F} = (600 - 2(200))\mathbf{i} + (-800 - 2(-200))\mathbf{j} = 200\mathbf{i} - 400\mathbf{j}$

$\boxed{|\mathbf{F}| = \sqrt{(200)^2 + (-400)^2} = 447.2 \text{ kip}}$

Problem 2.25 If $\mathbf{F}_A = \mathbf{i} - 4.5\mathbf{j}$ (kN) and $\mathbf{F}_B = -2\mathbf{i} - 2\mathbf{j}$ (kN), what is the magnitude of the force $\mathbf{F} = 6\mathbf{F}_A + 4\mathbf{F}_B$?

Solution: Take the scalar multiples and add the components.

$\mathbf{F} = (6 + 4(-2))\mathbf{i} + (6(-4.5) + 4(-2))\mathbf{j} = -2\mathbf{i} - 35\mathbf{j}$, and

$|\mathbf{F}| = \sqrt{(-2)^2 + (-35)^2} = 35.1 \text{ kN}$

Problem 2.26 Two perpendicular vectors $\mathbf{U}$ and $\mathbf{V}$ lie in the x-y plane. The vector $\mathbf{U} = 6\mathbf{i} - 8\mathbf{j}$ and $|\mathbf{V}| = 20$. What are the components of $\mathbf{V}$?

Solution: The two possible values of $\mathbf{V}$ are shown in the sketch. The strategy is to (a) determine the unit vector associated with $\mathbf{U}$, (b) express this vector in terms of an angle, (c) add $\pm 90°$ to this angle, (d) determine the two unit vectors perpendicular to $\mathbf{U}$, and (e) calculate the components of the two possible values of $\mathbf{V}$. The unit vector parallel to $\mathbf{U}$ is

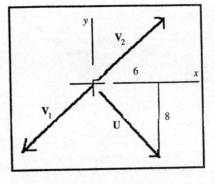

$$\mathbf{e}_U = \frac{6\mathbf{i}}{\sqrt{6^2 + (-8)^2}} - \frac{8\mathbf{j}}{\sqrt{6^2 + (-8)^2}} = 0.6\mathbf{i} - 0.8\mathbf{j}$$

Expressed in terms of an angle,

$\mathbf{e}_U = \mathbf{i}\cos\alpha - \mathbf{j}\sin\alpha = \mathbf{i}\cos(53.1°) - \mathbf{j}\sin(53.1°)$

Add $\pm 90°$ to find the two unit vectors that are perpendicular to this unit vector:

$\mathbf{e}_{p1} = \mathbf{i}\cos(143.1°) - \mathbf{j}\sin(143.1°) = -0.8\mathbf{i} - 0.6\mathbf{j}$

$\mathbf{e}_{p2} = \mathbf{i}\cos(-36.9°) - \mathbf{j}\sin(-36.9°) = 0.8\mathbf{i} + 0.6\mathbf{j}$

Take the scalar multiple of these unit vectors to find the two vectors perpendicular to $\mathbf{U}$.

$\mathbf{V}_1 = |\mathbf{V}|(-0.8\mathbf{i} - 0.6\mathbf{j}) = -16\mathbf{i} - 12\mathbf{j}$.

The components are $V_x = -16$, $V_y = -12$

$\mathbf{V}_2 = |\mathbf{V}|(0.8\mathbf{i} + 0.6\mathbf{j}) = 16\mathbf{i} + 12\mathbf{j}$.

The components are $V_x = 16$, $V_y = 12$

Problem 2.27 A fish exerts a 40-N force on the line that is represented by the vector **F**. Express **F** in terms of components using the coordinate system shown.

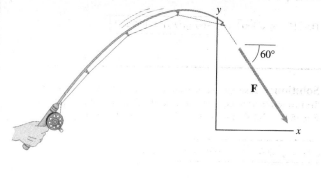

Solution:

$$F_x = |\mathbf{F}| \cos 60° = (40)(0.5) = 20 \ (\text{N})$$

$$F_y = -|\mathbf{F}| \sin 60° = -(40)(0.866) = -34.6 \ (\text{N})$$

$$\mathbf{F} = 20\mathbf{i} - 34.6\mathbf{j} \ (\text{N})$$

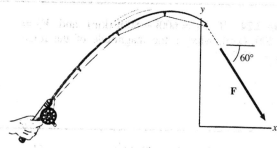

Problem 2.28 A person exerts a 60-lb force **F** to push a crate onto a truck. Express **F** in terms of components.

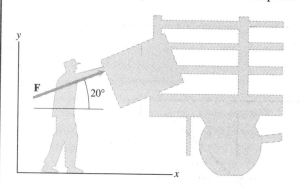

Solution: The strategy is to express the force **F** in terms of the angle. Thus

$$\mathbf{F} = (\mathbf{i}|\mathbf{F}| \cos(20°) + \mathbf{j}|\mathbf{F}| \sin(20°))$$

$$\mathbf{F} = (60)(0.9397\mathbf{i} + 0.342\mathbf{j}) \text{ or } \mathbf{F} = 56.4\mathbf{i} + 20.5\mathbf{j} \ (\text{lb})$$

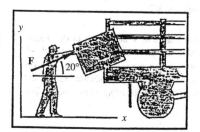

Problem 2.29 The missile's engine exerts a 260-kN force **F**. Express **F** in terms of components using the coordinate system shown.

Solution:

$$F_x = |\mathbf{F}| \cos 40°$$

$$F_x = 199 \ \text{N}$$

$$F_y = |\mathbf{F}| \sin 40°$$

$$F_y = 167 \ \text{N}$$

$$\mathbf{F} = 199\mathbf{i} + 167\mathbf{j} \ (\text{N})$$

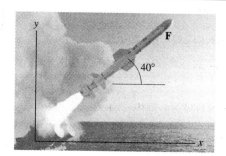

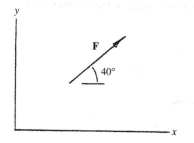

Problem 2.30 The coordinates of two points A and B of a truss are shown. Express the position vector from point A to point B in terms of components.

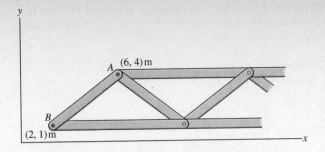

Solution: The strategy is find the distance along each axis by taking the difference between the coordinates.

$$\mathbf{r}_{AB} = (2 - 6)\mathbf{i} + (1 - 4)\mathbf{j} = -4\mathbf{i} - 3\mathbf{j} \text{ (m)}$$

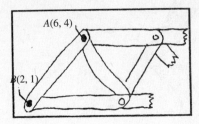

Problem 2.31 The points A, B, ... are the joints of the hexagonal structural element. Let $\mathbf{r}_{AB}$ be the position vector from joint A to joint B, $\mathbf{r}_{AC}$ the position vector from joint A to joint C, and so forth. Determine the components of the vectors $\mathbf{r}_{AC}$ and $\mathbf{r}_{AF}$.

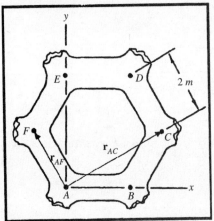

Solution: Use the xy coordinate system shown and find the locations of C and F in those coordinates. The coordinates of the points in this system are the scalar components of the vectors $\mathbf{r}_{AC}$ and $\mathbf{r}_{AF}$. For $\mathbf{r}_{AC}$, we have

$$\mathbf{r}_{AC} = \mathbf{r}_{AB} + \mathbf{r}_{BC} = (x_B - x_A)\mathbf{i} + (y_B - y_A)\mathbf{j}$$

$$+ (x_C - x_B)\mathbf{i} + (y_C - y_B)\mathbf{j}$$

or $\quad \mathbf{r}_{AC} = (2m - 0)\mathbf{i} + (0 - 0)\mathbf{j} + (2m\cos 60° - 0)\mathbf{i}$

$$+ (2m\cos 60° - 0)\mathbf{j},$$

giving

$$\mathbf{r}_{AC} = (2m + 2m\cos 60°)\mathbf{i} + (2m\sin 60°)\mathbf{j}.$$ For $\mathbf{r}_{AF}$, we have

$$\mathbf{r}_{AF} = (x_F - x_A)\mathbf{i} + (y_F - y_A)\mathbf{j}$$

$$= (-2m\cos 60°x_F - 0)\mathbf{i} + (2m\sin 60° - 0)\mathbf{j}.$$

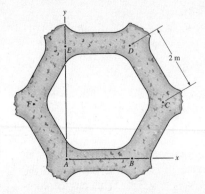

22

Problem 2.32 For the hexagonal structural element in Problem 2.31, determine the components of the vector $\mathbf{r}_{AB} - \mathbf{r}_{BC}$.

Solution: $\mathbf{r}_{AB} - \mathbf{r}_{BC}$.
The angle between BC and the x-axis is 60°.

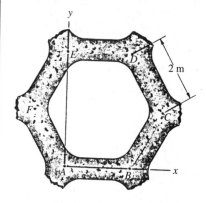

$\mathbf{r}_{BC} = 2\cos(60°)\mathbf{i} + 2(\sin(60°))\mathbf{j}$ (m)

$\mathbf{r}_{BC} = 1\mathbf{i} + 1.73\mathbf{j}$ (m)

$\mathbf{r}_{AB} - \mathbf{r}_{BC} = 2\mathbf{i} - 1\mathbf{i} - 1.73\mathbf{j}$ (m)

$\mathbf{r}_{AB} - \mathbf{r}_{BC} = 1\mathbf{i} - 1.73\mathbf{j}$ (m)

Problem 2.33 The coordinates of point A are (1.8, 3.0) m. The y coordinate of point B is 0.6 m and the magnitude of the vector $\mathbf{r}_{AB}$ is 3.0 m. What are the components of $\mathbf{r}_{AB}$?

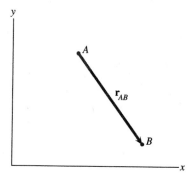

Solution: Let the x-component of point B be x_B. The vector from A to B can be written as

$\mathbf{r}_{AB} = (x_B - x_A)\mathbf{i} + (y_B - y_A)\mathbf{j}$ (m)

or $\mathbf{r}_{AB} = (x_B - 1.8)\mathbf{i} + (0.6 - 3.0)\mathbf{j}$ (m)

$\mathbf{r}_{AB} = (x_B - 1.8)\mathbf{i} - 2.4\mathbf{j}$ (m)

We also know $|\mathbf{r}_{AB}| = 3.0$ m. Thus

$3^2 = (x_B - 1.80)^2 + (-2.4)^2$

Solving, $x_B = 3.60$. Thus

$\mathbf{r}_{AB} = 1.80\mathbf{i} - 2.40\mathbf{j}$ (m)

23

Problem 2.34 (a) Express the position vector from point A of the front-end loader to point B in terms of components.
(b) Express the position vector from point B to point C in terms of components.
(c) Use the results of (a) and (b) to determine the distance from point A to point C.

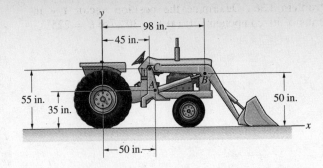

Solution: The coordinates are $A(50, 35)$; $B(98, 50)$; $C(45, 55)$.

(a) The vector from point A to B:

$$\mathbf{r}_{AB} = (98 - 50)\mathbf{i} + (50 - 35)\mathbf{j} = 48\mathbf{i} + 15\mathbf{j} \text{ (in.)}$$

(b) The vector from point B to C is

$$\mathbf{r}_{BC} = (45 - 98)\mathbf{i} + (55 - 50)\mathbf{j} = -53\mathbf{i} + 5\mathbf{j} \text{ (in.).}$$

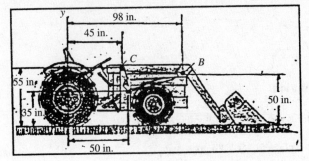

(c) The distance from A to C is the magnitude of the sum of the vectors,

$$\mathbf{r}_{AC} = \mathbf{r}_{AB} + \mathbf{r}_{BC} = (48 - 53)\mathbf{i} + (15 + 5)\mathbf{j} = -5\mathbf{i} + 20\mathbf{j}.$$

The distance from A to C is

$$|\mathbf{r}_{AC}| = \sqrt{(-5)^2 + (20)^2} = 20.62 \text{ in.}$$

Problem 2.35 Consider the front-end loader in Problem 2.34. To raise the bucket, the operator increases the length of the hydraulic cylinder AB. The distance between points B and C remains constant. If the length of the cylinder AB is 65 in., what is the position vector from point A to point B?

Solution: Assume that the two points A and C are fixed. The strategy is to determine the unknown angle θ from the geometry. From Problem 2.34 $|\mathbf{r}_{AC}| = 20.6$ and the angle β is $\tan \beta = \left(\frac{-20}{5}\right) = -4$, $\beta = 76°$. Similarly, $|\mathbf{r}_{CB}| = \sqrt{53^2 + 5^2} = 53.2$. The angle a is found from the cosine law:

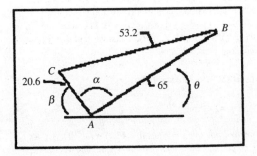

$$\cos \alpha = \frac{(20.6)^2 + (65)^2 - (53.2)^2}{2(20.6)(65)} = 0.6776,$$

$\alpha = 47.3°$. Thus the angle θ is

$$\theta = 180° - 47.34° - 75.96° = 56.69\ldots = 56.7°. \text{ The vector}$$

$$\mathbf{r}_{AB} = 65(\mathbf{i}\cos\theta + \mathbf{j}\sin\theta) = 35.69\ldots\mathbf{i} + 54.32\ldots\mathbf{j}$$

$$= 35.7\mathbf{i} + 54.3\mathbf{j} \text{ (in.)}$$

Problem 2.36 Determine the position vector $\mathbf{r}_{AB}$ in terms of its components if: (a) $\theta = 30°$, (b) $\theta = 225°$.

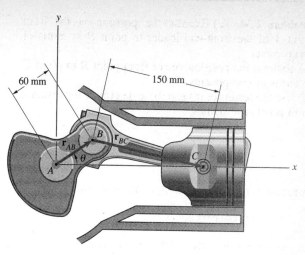

Solution:

(a) $\mathbf{r}_{AB} = (60)\cos(30°)\mathbf{i} + (60)\sin(30°)\mathbf{j}$, or

   $\mathbf{r}_{AB} = 51.96\mathbf{i} + 30\mathbf{j}$ mm. And

(b) $\mathbf{r}_{AB} = (60)\cos(225°)\mathbf{i} + (60)\sin(225°)\mathbf{j}$ or

   $\mathbf{r}_{AB} = -42.4\mathbf{i} - 42.4\mathbf{j}$ mm.

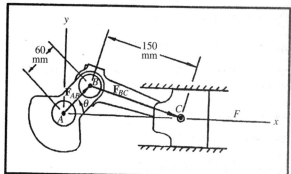

Problem 2.37 In problem 2.36 determine the position vector $\mathbf{r}_{BC}$ in terms of its components if: (a) $\theta = 30°$, (b) $\theta = 225°$.

Solution:

(a) From Problem 2.36, $\mathbf{r}_{AB} = 51.96\mathbf{i} + 30\mathbf{j}$ mm. Thus, the coordinates of point B are (51.96, 30) mm. The vector $\mathbf{r}_{BC}$ is given by $\mathbf{r}_{BC} = (x_C - x_B)\mathbf{i} + (y_C - y_B)\mathbf{j}$, where $y_C = 0$. The magnitude of the vector $\mathbf{r}_{BC}$ is 150 mm. Using these facts, we find that $y_{BC} = -30$ mm, and $x_{BC} = 146.97$ mm.

(b) $\mathbf{r}_{AB} = (60)\cos(225°)\mathbf{i} + (60)\sin(225°)\mathbf{j}$ or

   $\mathbf{r}_{AB} = -42.4\mathbf{i} - 42.4\mathbf{j}$ mm.

   From Problem 2.36, $\mathbf{r}_{AB} = -42.4\mathbf{i} - 42.4\mathbf{j}$ mm. Thus, the coordinates of point B are $(-42.4, -42.4)$ mm. The vector $\mathbf{r}_{BC}$ is given by $\mathbf{r}_{BC} = (x_C - x_B)\mathbf{i} + (y_C - y_B)\mathbf{j}$, where $y_C = 0$. The magnitude of the vector $\mathbf{r}_{BC}$ is 150 mm. Using these facts, we find that $y_{BC} = 42.4$ mm, and $x_{BC} = 143.9$ mm.

Problem 2.38 A surveyor measures the location of point A and determines that $\mathbf{r}_{OA} = 400\mathbf{i} + 800\mathbf{j}$ (m). He wants to determine the location of a point B so that $|\mathbf{r}_{AB}| = 400$ m and $|\mathbf{r}_{OA} + \mathbf{r}_{AB}| = 1200$ m. What are the cartesian coordinates of point B?

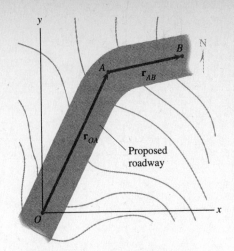

Solution: Two possibilities are: The point B lies west of point A, or point B lies east of point A, as shown. The strategy is to determine the unknown angles α, β, and θ. The magnitude of OA is

$$|\mathbf{r}_{OA}| = \sqrt{(400)^2 + (800)^2} = 894.4.$$

The angle β is determined by

$$\tan \beta = \frac{800}{400} = 2, \quad \beta = 63.4°.$$

The angle α is determined from the cosine law:

$$\cos \alpha = \frac{(894.4)^2 + (1200)^2 - (400)^2}{2(894.4)(1200)} = 0.9689.$$

$\alpha = 14.3°$. The angle θ is $\theta = \beta \pm \alpha = 49.12°, 77.74°$.

The two possible sets of coordinates of point B are

$$\begin{cases} \mathbf{r}_{OB} = 1200(\mathbf{i}\cos 77.7 + \mathbf{j}\sin 77.7) = 254.67\mathbf{i} + 1172.66\mathbf{j} \text{ (m)} \\ \mathbf{r}_{OB} = 1200(\mathbf{i}\cos 49.1 + \mathbf{j}\sin 49.1) = 785.33\mathbf{i} + 907.34\mathbf{j} \text{ (m)} \end{cases}$$

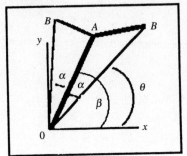

The two possibilities lead to $B(254.7$ m, 1172.7 m$)$ or $B(785.3$ m, 907.3 m$)$

Problem 2.39 Bar AB is 8.5 m long and bar AC is 6 m long. Determine the components of the position vector $\mathbf{r}_{AB}$ from point A to point B.

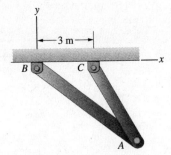

Solution: The key to this solution is to find the coordinates of point A. We know the lengths of all three sides of the triangle. The law of cosines can be used to give us the angle θ.

$$|\mathbf{r}_{AC}|^2 = |\mathbf{r}_{AB}|^2 + |\mathbf{r}_{BC}|^2 - 2|\mathbf{r}_{AB}||\mathbf{r}_{BC}|\cos\theta$$

$$6^2 = 8.5^2 + 3^2 - 2(8.5)(3)\cos\theta$$

$$\cos\theta = 0.887 \quad \theta = 27.5°$$

$$\mathbf{r}_{AB} = |\mathbf{r}_{AB}|\cos\theta\mathbf{i} - |\mathbf{r}_{AB}|\sin\theta\mathbf{j}$$

$$\mathbf{r}_{AB} = (8.5)\cos 27.5°\mathbf{i} - (8.5)\sin 27.5°\mathbf{j} \text{ (m)}$$

$$\mathbf{r}_{AB} = 7.54\mathbf{i} - 3.92\mathbf{j} \text{ m}$$

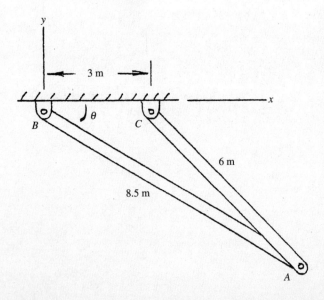

Problem 2.40 For the truss in Problem 2.39, determine the components of a unit vector $\mathbf{e}_{AC}$ that points from point A toward point C.

Strategy: Determine the components of the position vector from point A to point C and divide the position vector by its magnitude.

Solution: From the solution of Problem 2.39, point A is located at $(7.54, -3.92)$. From the diagram, Point C is located at $(3.0, 0)$. The vector from A to C is

$$\mathbf{r}_{AC} = (x_C - x_A)\mathbf{i} + (y_C - y_A)\mathbf{j} \text{ (m)}$$

$$\mathbf{r}_{AC} = (3 - 7.54)\mathbf{i} + (0 - (-3.92))\mathbf{j} \text{ (m)}$$

$$\mathbf{r}_{AC} = -4.54\mathbf{i} + 3.92\mathbf{j} \text{ (m)}$$

and $|\mathbf{r}_{AC}| = 6$ m

Thus $\mathbf{e}_{AC} = \dfrac{\mathbf{r}_{AC}}{|\mathbf{r}_{AC}|} = -\dfrac{4.54}{6}\mathbf{i} + \dfrac{3.92}{6}\mathbf{j}$

$$\mathbf{e}_{AC} = -0.757\mathbf{i} + 0.653\mathbf{j}$$

Problem 2.41 The x and y coordinates of points A, B, and C of the sailboat are shown.

(a) Determine the components of a unit vector that is parallel to the forestay AB and points from A toward B.
(b) Determine the components of a unit vector that is parallel to the backstay BC and points from C toward B.

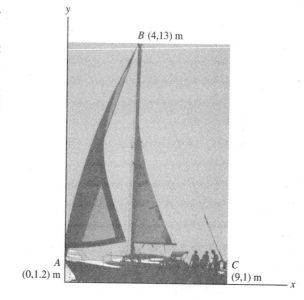

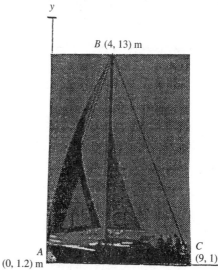

Solution:

$$\mathbf{r}_{AB} = (x_B - x_A)\mathbf{i} + (y_B - y_A)\mathbf{j}$$

$$\mathbf{r}_{CB} = (x_B - x_C)\mathbf{i} + (y_C - y_B)\mathbf{j}$$

Points are: A $(0, 1.2)$, B $(4, 13)$ and C $(9, 1)$

Substituting, we get

$$\mathbf{r}_{AB} = 4\mathbf{i} + 11.8\mathbf{j} \text{ (m)}, \quad |\mathbf{r}_{AB}| = 12.46 \text{ (m)}$$

$$\mathbf{r}_{CB} = -5\mathbf{i} + 12\mathbf{j} \text{ (m)}, \quad |\mathbf{r}_{CB}| = 13 \text{ (m)}$$

The unit vectors are given by

$$\mathbf{e}_{AB} = \frac{\mathbf{r}_{AB}}{|\mathbf{r}_{AB}|} \quad \text{and} \quad \mathbf{e}_{CB} = \frac{\mathbf{r}_{CB}}{|\mathbf{r}_{CB}|}$$

Substituting, we get

$$\mathbf{e}_{AB} = 0.321\mathbf{i} + 0.947\mathbf{j}$$

$$\mathbf{e}_{CB} = -0.385\mathbf{i} + 0.923\mathbf{j}$$

Problem 2.42 Consider the force vector $\mathbf{F} = 3\mathbf{i} - 4\mathbf{j}$ (kN). Determine the components of a unit vector $\mathbf{e}$ that has the same direction as $\mathbf{F}$.

Solution: The magnitude of the force vector is

$$|\mathbf{F}| = \sqrt{3^2 + 4^2} = 5.$$

The unit vector is

$$\mathbf{e} = \frac{\mathbf{F}}{|\mathbf{F}|} = \frac{3}{5}\mathbf{i} - \frac{4}{5}\mathbf{j} = 0.6\mathbf{i} - 0.8\mathbf{j} \quad \text{As a check, the magnitude:}$$

$$|\mathbf{e}| = \sqrt{0a.6^2 + 0.8^2} = 1$$

Problem 2.43 Determine the components of a unit vector that is parallel to the hydraulic actuator BC and points from B toward C.

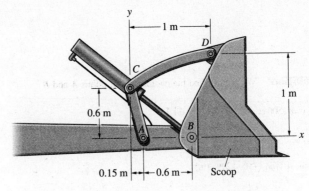

Solution: Point B is at (0.75, 0) and point C is at (0, 0.6). The vector

$$\mathbf{r}_{BC} = (x_C - x_B)\mathbf{i} + (y_C - y_B)\mathbf{j}$$

$$\mathbf{r}_{BC} = (0 - 0.75)\mathbf{i} + (0.6 - 0)\mathbf{j} \text{ (m)}$$

$$\mathbf{r}_{BC} = -0.75\mathbf{i} + 0.6\mathbf{j} \text{ (m)}$$

$$|\mathbf{r}_{BC}| = \sqrt{(0.75)^2 + (0.6)^2} = 0.960 \text{ (m)}$$

$$\mathbf{e}_{BC} = \frac{\mathbf{r}_{BC}}{|\mathbf{r}_{BC}|} = \frac{-0.75}{0.96}\mathbf{i} + \frac{0.6}{0.96}\mathbf{j}$$

$$\mathbf{e}_{BC} = -0.781\mathbf{i} + 0.625\mathbf{j}$$

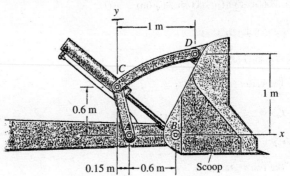

Problem 2.44 The hydraulic actuator BC in Problem 2.43 exerts a 1.2-kN force $\mathbf{F}$ on the joint at C that is parallel to the actuator and points from B toward C. Determine the components of $\mathbf{F}$.

Solution: From the solution to Problem 2.43,

$$\mathbf{e}_{BC} = -0.781\mathbf{i} + 0.625\mathbf{j}$$

The vector $\mathbf{F}$ is given by $\mathbf{F} = |\mathbf{F}|\mathbf{e}_{BC}$

$$\mathbf{F} = (1.2)(-0.781\mathbf{i} + 0.625\mathbf{j}) \text{ (k · N)}$$

$$\mathbf{F} = -937\mathbf{i} + 750\mathbf{j} \text{ (N)}$$

Problem 2.45 A surveyor finds that the length of the line OA is 1500 m and the length of line OB is 2000 m.

(a) Determine the components of the position vector from point A to point B.
(b) Determine the components of a unit vector that points from point A toward point B.

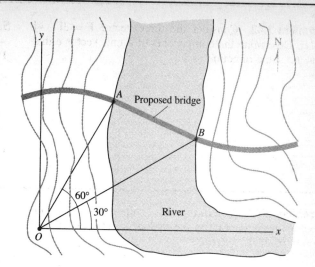

Solution: We need to find the coordinates of points A and B

$$\mathbf{r}_{OA} = 1500 \cos 60° \mathbf{i} + 1500 \sin 60° \mathbf{j}$$

$$\mathbf{r}_{OA} = 750\mathbf{i} + 1299\mathbf{j} \text{ (m)}$$

Point A is at (750, 1299) (m)

$$\mathbf{r}_{OB} = 2000 \cos 30° \mathbf{i} + 2000 \sin 30° \mathbf{j} \text{ (m)}$$

$$\mathbf{r}_{OB} = 1723\mathbf{i} + 1000\mathbf{j} \text{ (m)}$$

Point B is at (1732, 1000) (m)

(a) The vector from A to B is

$$\mathbf{r}_{AB} = (x_B - x_A)\mathbf{i} + (y_B - y_A)\mathbf{j}$$

$$\mathbf{r}_{AB} = 982\mathbf{i} - 299\mathbf{j} \text{ (m)}$$

(b) The unit vector $\mathbf{e}_{AB}$ is

$$\mathbf{e}_{AB} = \frac{\mathbf{r}_{AB}}{|\mathbf{r}_{AB}|} = \frac{982\mathbf{i} - 299\mathbf{j}}{1026.6}$$

$$\mathbf{e}_{AB} = 0.957\mathbf{i} - 0.291\mathbf{j}$$

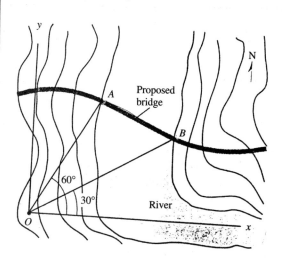

Problem 2.46 The positions at a given time of the Sun (S) and the planets Mercury (M), Venus (V), and Earth (E) are shown. The approximate distance from the Sun to Mercury is 57×10^6 km, the distance from the Sun to Venus is 108×10^6 km, and the distance from the Sun to the Earth is 150×10^6 km. Assume that the Sun and planets lie in the $x - y$ plane. Determine the components of a unit vector that points from the Earth toward Mercury.

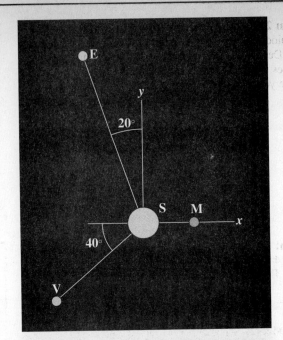

Solution: We need to find $\mathbf{r}_E$ and $\mathbf{r}_M$ in the coordinates shown

$$\mathbf{r}_E = |\mathbf{r}_E|(-\sin 20°\mathbf{i}) + |\mathbf{r}_E|(\cos 20°)\mathbf{j} \text{ (km)}$$

$$\mathbf{r}_M = |\mathbf{r}_M|\cos 0°\mathbf{i} \text{ (km)}$$

$$\mathbf{r}_E = (-51.3 \times 10^6)\mathbf{i} + (141 \times 10^6)\mathbf{j} \text{ (km)}$$

$$\mathbf{r}_M = 57 \times 10^6\mathbf{i} \text{ (km)}$$

$$\mathbf{r}_{EM} = (x_M - x_E)\mathbf{i} + (y_M - y_E)\mathbf{j} \text{ (km)}$$

$$\mathbf{r}_{EM} = (108.3 \times 10^6)\mathbf{i} - (141 \times 10^6\mathbf{j}) \text{ (km)}$$

$$|\mathbf{r}_{EM}| = 177.8 \times 10^6 \text{ (km)}$$

$$\mathbf{e}_{EM} = \frac{\mathbf{r}_{EM}}{|\mathbf{r}_{EM}|} = +0.609\mathbf{i} - 0.793\mathbf{j}$$

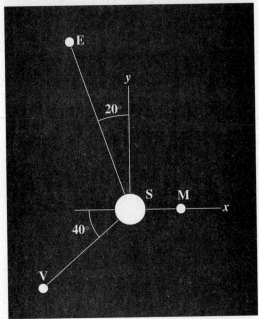

Problem 2.47 For the positions described in Problem 2.46, determine the components of a unit vector that points from Earth toward Venus.

Solution: From the solution to Problem 2.47,

$$\mathbf{r}_E = (-51.3 \times 10^6)\mathbf{i} + (141 \times 10^6)\mathbf{j} \text{ (km)}$$

The position of Venus is

$$\mathbf{r}_V = -|\mathbf{r}_V|\cos 40°\mathbf{i} - |\mathbf{r}_V|\sin 40°\mathbf{j} \text{ (km)}$$

$$\mathbf{r}_V = (-82.7 \times 10^6)\mathbf{i} - (69.4 \times 10^6)\mathbf{j} \text{ (km)}$$

$$\mathbf{r}_{EV} = (x_V - x_E)\mathbf{i} + (y_V - y_E)\mathbf{j} \text{ (km)}$$

$$\mathbf{r}_{EV} = (-31.4 \times 10^6)\mathbf{i} - (210.4 \times 10^6)\mathbf{j} \text{ (km)}$$

$$|\mathbf{r}_{EV}| = 212.7 \times 10^6 \text{ (km)}$$

$$\mathbf{e}_{EV} = \frac{\mathbf{r}_{EV}}{|\mathbf{r}_{EV}|}$$

$$\mathbf{e}_{EV} = -0.148\mathbf{i} - 0.989\mathbf{j}$$

Problem 2.48 The rope ABC exerts forces $\mathbf{F}_{BA}$ and $\mathbf{F}_{BC}$ on the block at B. Their magnitudes are $|\mathbf{F}_{BA}| = |\mathbf{F}_{BC}| = 800$ N. Determine the magnitude of the vector sum of the forces by resolving the forces into components, and compare your answer with that of Problem 2.16.

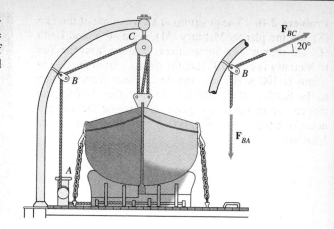

Solution: The strategy is to use the magnitudes and the angles to determine the force vectors, and then to determine the magnitude of their sum. The force vectors are:

$\mathbf{F}_{BA} = 0\mathbf{i} - 800\mathbf{j}$, and

$\mathbf{F}_{BC} = 800(\mathbf{i}\cos 20° + \mathbf{j}\sin 20°) = 751.75\mathbf{i} + 273.6\mathbf{j}$

The sum is given by: $\boxed{\mathbf{F}_{BA} + \mathbf{F}_{BC} = 751.75\mathbf{i} - 526.4\mathbf{j}}$

The magnitude is given by

$|\mathbf{F}_{BA} + \mathbf{F}_{BC}| = \sqrt{(751.75)^2 + (526.4)^2} = 917.7$ N

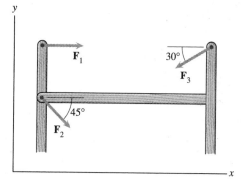

Problem 2.49 The magnitudes of the forces are $|\mathbf{F}_1| = |\mathbf{F}_2| = |\mathbf{F}_3| = 5$ kN. What is the magnitude of the vector sum of the three forces?

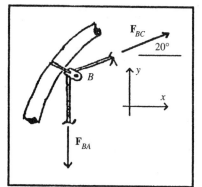

Solution: The strategy is to use the magnitudes and the angles to determine the force vectors, and then to take the magnitude of their sum. The force vectors are:

$\mathbf{F}_1 = 5\mathbf{i} + 0\mathbf{j}$ (kN),

$\mathbf{F}_2 = 5(\mathbf{i}\cos(-45°) + \mathbf{j}\sin(-45°)) = 3.54\mathbf{i} - 3.54\mathbf{j}$

$\mathbf{F}_3 = 5(\mathbf{i}\cos 210° + \mathbf{j}\sin 210°) = -4.33\mathbf{i} - 2.50\mathbf{j}$

The sum is given by $\mathbf{F}_1 + \mathbf{F}_2 + \mathbf{F}_3 = 4.21\mathbf{i} - 6.04\mathbf{j}$ and the magnitude is

$\boxed{|\mathbf{F}_1 + \mathbf{F}_2 + \mathbf{F}_3| = \sqrt{(4.21)^2 + (6.04)^2} = 7.36 \text{ kN}}$

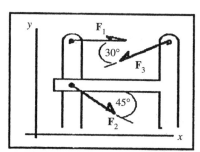

Problem 2.50 Four groups engage in a tug-of-war. The magnitudes of the forces exerted by groups B, C, and D are $|\mathbf{F}_B| = 800$ lb, $|\mathbf{F}_C| = 1000$ lb, $|\mathbf{F}_D| = 900$ lb. If the vector sum of the four forces equals zero, what are the magnitude of $\mathbf{F}_A$ and the angle α?

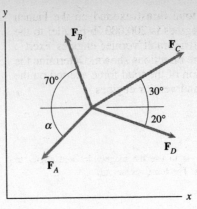

Solution: The strategy is to use the angles and magnitudes to determine the force vector components, to solve for the unknown force $\mathbf{F}_A$ and then take its magnitude. The force vectors are

$$\mathbf{F}_B = 800(\mathbf{i}\cos 110° + \mathbf{j}\sin 110°) = -273.6\mathbf{i} + 751.75\mathbf{j}$$

$$\mathbf{F}_C = 1000(\mathbf{i}\cos 30° + \mathbf{j}\sin 30°) = 866\mathbf{i} + 500\mathbf{j}$$

$$\mathbf{F}_D = 900(\mathbf{i}\cos(-20°) + \mathbf{j}\sin(-20°)) = 845.72\mathbf{i} - 307.8\mathbf{j}$$

$$\mathbf{F}_A = |\mathbf{F}_A|(\mathbf{i}\cos(180 + \alpha) + \mathbf{j}\sin(180 + \alpha))$$

$$= |\mathbf{F}_A|(-\mathbf{i}\cos\alpha - \mathbf{j}\sin\alpha)$$

The sum vanishes:

$$\mathbf{F}_A + \mathbf{F}_B + \mathbf{F}_C + \mathbf{F}_D = \mathbf{i}(1438.1 - |\mathbf{F}_A|\cos\alpha)$$

$$+ \mathbf{j}(944 - |\mathbf{F}_A|\sin\alpha) = 0$$

From which $\mathbf{F}_A = 1438.1\mathbf{i} + 944\mathbf{j}$. The magnitude is

$$\boxed{|\mathbf{F}_A| = \sqrt{(1438)^2 + (944)^2} = 1720 \text{ lb}}$$

The angle is: $\tan\alpha = \dfrac{944}{1438} = 0.6565$, or $\boxed{\alpha = 33.3°}$

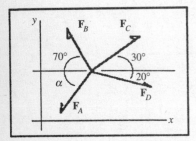

32

Problem 2.51 The total thrust exerted on the launch vehicle by its main engines is 200,000 lb parallel to the y axis. Each of the two small vernier engines exert a thrust of 5000 lb in the directions shown. Determine the magnitude and direction of the total force exerted on the booster by the main and vernier engines.

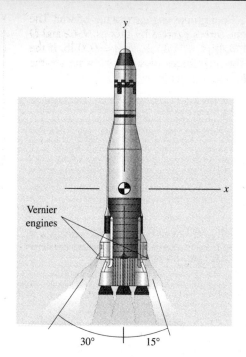

Solution: The strategy is to use the magnitudes and angles to determine the force vectors. The force vectors are:

$\mathbf{F}_{ME} = 0\mathbf{i} - 200\mathbf{j}$ (kip)

$\mathbf{F}_{LV} = 5(\mathbf{i}\cos 240° + \mathbf{j}\sin 240°) = -2.5\mathbf{i} - 4.33\mathbf{j}$ (kip)

$\mathbf{F}_{RV} = 5(\mathbf{i}\cos 285° + \mathbf{j}\sin 285°) = 1.29\mathbf{i} - 4.83\mathbf{j}$ (kip)

The sum of the forces:

$\mathbf{F}_{ME} + \mathbf{F}_{RV} + \mathbf{F}_{LV} = -1.21\mathbf{i} - 209.2\mathbf{j}$ (kip).

The magnitude of the sum is

$|\mathbf{F}_R| = \sqrt{(1.21)^2 + (209.2)^2} = 209.2$ (kip)

The direction relative to the y-axis is

$\tan \alpha = \dfrac{1.21}{209.2} = 0.005784$, or $\alpha = 0.3314°$

measured clockwise from the negative y-axis.

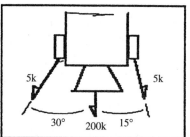

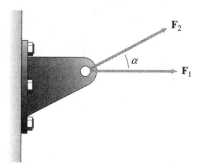

Problem 2.52 The magnitudes of the forces acting on the bracket are $|\mathbf{F}_1| = |\mathbf{F}_2| = 2$ kN. If $|\mathbf{F}_1 + \mathbf{F}_2| = 3.8$ kN, what is the angle α? (Assume $0 \leq \alpha \leq 90°$)

Solution:

Let $|\mathbf{F}_1| = |\mathbf{F}_2| = a = 2$ kn

and $|\mathbf{F}_1 + \mathbf{F}_2| = b$

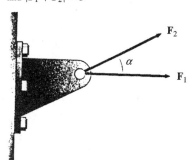

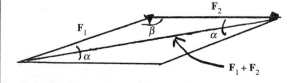

Angle β is given by

$\dfrac{\alpha}{2} + \beta + \dfrac{\alpha}{2} = 180°$

$\beta = 180° - \alpha \quad b = 3.8$ kN

$a = 2$ kN

From the law of cosines

$b^2 = a^2 + a^2 - 2a^2 \cos \beta$

$\beta = 143.6°$

$\alpha = 180° - \beta \quad \alpha = 36.4°$

Problem 2.53 The figure shows three forces acting on a joint of a structure. The magnitude of $\mathbf{F}_c$ is 60 kN, and $\mathbf{F}_A + \mathbf{F}_B + \mathbf{F}_C = 0$. What are the magnitudes of $\mathbf{F}_A$ and $\mathbf{F}_B$?

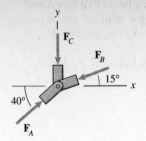

Solution: We need to write each force in terms of its components.

$$\mathbf{F}_A = |\mathbf{F}_A|\cos 40\mathbf{i} + |\mathbf{F}_A|\sin 40\mathbf{j} \ (\text{kN})$$

$$\mathbf{F}_B = |\mathbf{F}_B|\cos 195°\mathbf{i} + |\mathbf{F}_B|\sin 195°\mathbf{j} \ (\text{kN})$$

$$\mathbf{F}_C = |\mathbf{F}_C|\cos 270°\mathbf{i} + |\mathbf{F}_C|\sin 270°\mathbf{j} \ (\text{kN})$$

Thus $\mathbf{F}_C = -60\mathbf{j}$ kN

Since $\mathbf{F}_A + \mathbf{F}_B + \mathbf{F}_C = 0$, their components in each direction must also sum to zero.

$$\begin{cases} F_{Ax} + F_{Bx} + F_{Cx} = 0 \\ F_{Ay} + F_{By} + F_{Cy} = 0 \end{cases}$$

Thus,

$$\begin{cases} |\mathbf{F}_A|\cos 40° + |\mathbf{F}_B|\cos 195° + 0 = 0 \\ |\mathbf{F}_A|\sin 40° + |\mathbf{F}_B|\sin 195° - 60 \ (\text{kN}) = 0 \end{cases}$$

Solving for $|\mathbf{F}_A|$ and $|\mathbf{F}_B|$, we get

$$|\mathbf{F}_A| = 137 \ \text{kN}, \quad |\mathbf{F}_B| = 109 \ \text{kN}$$

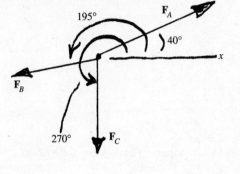

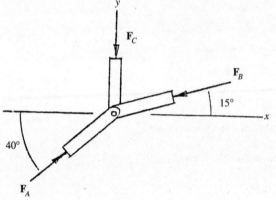

Problem 2.54 Four forces act on a beam. The vector sum of the forces is zero. The magnitudes $|\mathbf{F}_B| = 10$ kN and $|\mathbf{F}_C| = 5$ kN. Determine the magnitudes of $\mathbf{F}_A$ and $\mathbf{F}_D$.

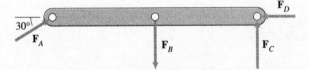

Solution: Use the angles and magnitudes to determine the vectors, and then solve for the unknowns. The vectors are:

$$\mathbf{F}_A = |\mathbf{F}_A|(\mathbf{i}\cos 30° + \mathbf{j}\sin 30°) = 0.866|\mathbf{F}_A|\mathbf{i} + 0.5|\mathbf{F}_A|\mathbf{j}$$

$$\mathbf{F}_B = 0\mathbf{i} - 10\mathbf{j}, \quad \mathbf{F}_C = 0\mathbf{i} + 5\mathbf{j}, \quad \mathbf{F}_D = -|\mathbf{F}_D|\mathbf{i} + 0\mathbf{j}.$$

Take the sum of each component in the x- and y-directions:

$$\sum \mathbf{F}_x = (0.866|\mathbf{F}_A| - |\mathbf{F}_D|)\mathbf{i} = 0$$

and $\sum \mathbf{F}_y = (0.5|\mathbf{F}_A| - (10 - 5))\mathbf{j} = 0.$

From the second equation we get $\boxed{|\mathbf{F}_A| = 10 \ \text{kN}}$. Using this value in the first equation, we get $\boxed{|\mathbf{F}_D| = 8.7 \ \text{kN}}$

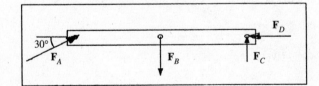

34

Problem 2.55 Six forces act on a beam that forms part of a building's frame. The vector sum of the forces is zero. The magnitudes $|\mathbf{F}_B| = |\mathbf{F}_E| = 20$ kN, $|\mathbf{F}_C| = 16$ kN, and $|\mathbf{F}_D| = 9$ kN. Determine the magnitudes of $\mathbf{F}_A$ and $\mathbf{F}_G$.

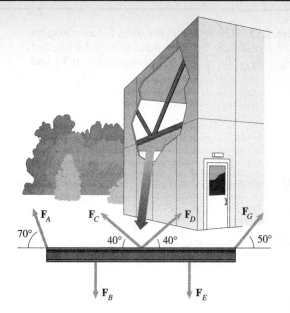

Solution: Write each force in terms of its magnitude and direction as

$$\mathbf{F} = |\mathbf{F}| \cos\theta\,\mathbf{i} + |\mathbf{F}| \sin\theta\,\mathbf{j}$$

where θ is measured counterclockwise from the $+x$-axis.

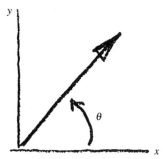

Thus, (all forces in kN)

$$\mathbf{F}_A = |\mathbf{F}_A| \cos 110°\,\mathbf{i} + |\mathbf{F}_A| \sin 110°\,\mathbf{j} \text{ (kN)}$$

$$\mathbf{F}_B = 20 \cos 270°\,\mathbf{i} + 20 \sin 270°\,\mathbf{j} \text{ (kN)}$$

$$\mathbf{F}_C = 16 \cos 140°\,\mathbf{i} + 16 \sin 140°\,\mathbf{j} \text{ (kN)}$$

$$\mathbf{F}_D = 9 \cos 40°\,\mathbf{i} + 9 \sin 40°\,\mathbf{j} \text{ (kN)}$$

$$\mathbf{F}_E = 20 \cos 270°\,\mathbf{i} + 20 \sin 270°\,\mathbf{j} \text{ (kN)}$$

$$\mathbf{F}_G = |\mathbf{F}_G| \cos 50°\,\mathbf{i} + |\mathbf{F}_G| \sin 50°\,\mathbf{j} \text{ (kN)}$$

We know that the x components and y components of the forces must add separately to zero.

Thus

$$\begin{cases} F_{Ax} + F_{Bx} + F_{Cx} + F_{Dx} + F_{Ex} + F_{Gx} = 0 \\ F_{Ay} + F_{By} + F_{Cy} + F_{Dy} + F_{Ey} + F_{Gy} = 0 \end{cases}$$

$$\begin{cases} |\mathbf{F}_A| \cos 110° + 0 - 12.26 + 6.89 + 0 + |\mathbf{F}_G| \cos 50° = 0 \\ |\mathbf{F}_A| \sin 110° - 20 + 10.28 + 5.79 - 20 + |\mathbf{F}_G| \sin 50° = 0 \end{cases}$$

Solving, we get

$$|\mathbf{F}_A| = 13.0 \text{ kN} \quad |\mathbf{F}_G| = 15.3 \text{ kN}$$

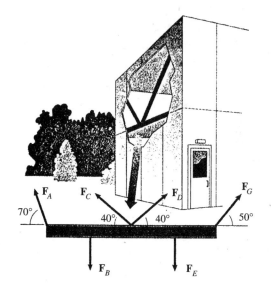

Problem 2.56 The total weight of the man and parasail is $|\mathbf{W}| = 230$ lb. The drag force $\mathbf{D}$ is perpendicular to the lift force $\mathbf{L}$. If the vector sum of the three forces is zero, what are the magnitudes of $\mathbf{L}$ and $\mathbf{D}$?

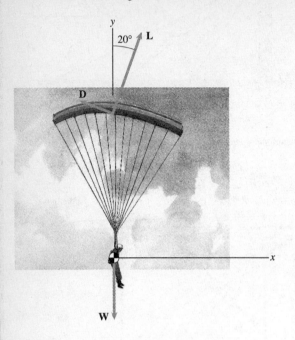

Solution: Three forces in equilibrium form a closed triangle. In this instance it is a right triangle. The law of sines is

$$\frac{|\mathbf{W}|}{\sin 90°} = \frac{|\mathbf{L}|}{\sin 70°} = \frac{|\mathbf{D}|}{\sin 20°}$$

From which:

$$|\mathbf{L}| = |\mathbf{W}|\sin 70° = (230)(0.9397) = 216.1 \text{ lb}$$

$$|\mathbf{D}| = |\mathbf{W}|\sin 20° = (230)(0.3420) = 78.66 \text{ lb}$$

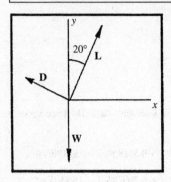

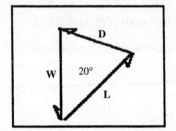

Problem 2.57 Two cables AB and CD extend from the rocket gantry to the ground. Cable AB exerts a force of magnitude 10,000 lb on the gantry, and cable CD exerts a force of magnitude 5000 lb.

(a) Using the coordinate system shown, express each of the two forces exerted on the gantry by the cables in terms of scalar components.

(b) What is the magnitude of the total force exerted on the gantry by the two cables?

Solution: Use the angles and magnitudes to determine the components of the two forces, and then determine the magnitude of their sum. The forces:

(a) $\quad \mathbf{F}_{AB} = 10(\mathbf{i}\cos(-50°) + \mathbf{j}\sin(-50°))$

$\qquad = 6.428\mathbf{i} - 7.660\mathbf{j}$ kip

$\quad \mathbf{F}_{CD} = 5(\mathbf{i}\cos(-60°) + \mathbf{j}\sin(-60°)) = 2.50\mathbf{i} - 4.330\mathbf{j}$ kip

The sum: $\mathbf{F}_{AB} + \mathbf{F}_{CD} = 8.928\mathbf{i} - 11.990\mathbf{j}$,

The magnitude is:

(b) $\quad |\mathbf{F}_{AB} + \mathbf{F}_{CD}| = \sqrt{(8.928)^2 + (11.99)^2} = 14.95$ kip

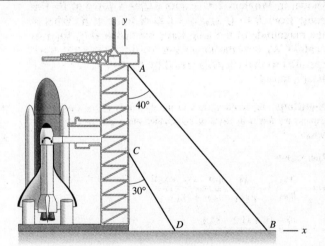

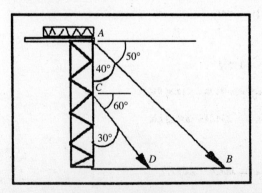

Problem 2.58 The cables A, B, and C help support a pillar that forms part of the supports of a structure. The magnitudes of the forces exerted by the cables are equal: $|\mathbf{F}_A| = |\mathbf{F}_B| = |\mathbf{F}_C|$. The magnitude of the vector sum of the three forces is 200 kN. What is $|\mathbf{F}_A|$?

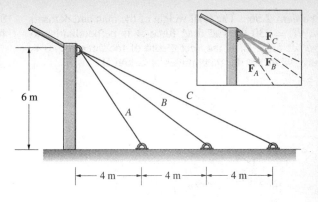

Solution: Use the angles and magnitudes to determine the vector components, take the sum, and solve for the unknown. The angles between each cable and the pillar are:

$$\theta_A = \tan^{-1}\left(\frac{4\text{ m}}{6\text{ m}}\right) = 33.7°,$$

$$\theta_B = \tan^{-1}\left(\frac{8}{6}\right) = 53.1°$$

$$\theta_C = \tan^{-1}\left(\frac{12}{6}\right) = 63.4°.$$

Measure the angles counterclockwise form the x-axis. The force vectors acting along the cables are:

$$\mathbf{F}_A = |\mathbf{F}_A|(\mathbf{i}\cos 303.7° + \mathbf{j}\sin 303.7°) = 0.5548|\mathbf{F}_A|\mathbf{i} - 0.8319|\mathbf{F}_A|\mathbf{j}$$

$$\mathbf{F}_B = |\mathbf{F}_B|(\mathbf{i}\cos 323.1° + \mathbf{j}\sin 323.1°) = 0.7997|\mathbf{F}_B|\mathbf{i} - 0.6004|\mathbf{F}_B|\mathbf{j}$$

$$\mathbf{F}_C = |\mathbf{F}_C|(\mathbf{i}\cos 333.4° + \mathbf{j}\sin 333.4°) = 0.8944|\mathbf{F}_C|\mathbf{i} - 0.4472|\mathbf{F}_C|\mathbf{j}$$

The sum of the forces are, noting that each is equal in magnitude, is

$$\sum \mathbf{F} = (2.2489|\mathbf{F}_A|\mathbf{i} - 1.8795|\mathbf{F}_A|\mathbf{j}).$$

The magnitude of the sum is given by the problem:

$$200 = |\mathbf{F}_A|\sqrt{(2.2489)^2 + (1.8795)^2} = 2.931|\mathbf{F}_A|,$$

from which $|\mathbf{F}_A| = 68.24$ kN

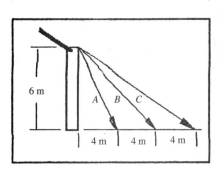

Problem 2.59 The cable from B to A on the sailboat shown in Problem 2.41 exerts a 230-N force at B. The cable from B to C exerts a 660-N force at B. What is the magnitude of the total force exerted at B by the two cables? What is the magnitude of the downward force (parallel to the y axis) exerted by the two cables on the boat's mast?

Solution: Find unit vectors in the directions of the two forces-express the forces in terms of magnitudes times unit vectors-add the forces.

Unit vectors:

$$\mathbf{e}_{BA} = \frac{\mathbf{r}_{BA}}{|\mathbf{r}_{BA}|} = \frac{(x_A - x_B)\mathbf{i} + (y_A - y_B)\mathbf{j}}{\sqrt{(x_A - x_B)^2 + (y_A - y_B)^2}}$$

$$= \frac{(0 - 4)\mathbf{i} + (1.2 - 13)\mathbf{j}}{\sqrt{4^2 + 11.8^2}}$$

$$\mathbf{e}_{BA} = -0.321\mathbf{i} - 0.947\mathbf{j}$$

Similarly,

$$\mathbf{e}_{BC} = 0.385\mathbf{i} - 0.923\mathbf{j}$$

$$\mathbf{F}_{BA} = |\mathbf{F}_{BA}|\mathbf{e}_{BA} = -73.8\mathbf{i} - 217.8\mathbf{j} \text{ kN}$$

$$\mathbf{F}_{BC} = |\mathbf{F}_{BC}|\mathbf{e}_{BC} = 254.1\mathbf{i} - 609.2\mathbf{j} \text{ kN}$$

Adding

$$\mathbf{F} = \mathbf{F}_{BA} + \mathbf{F}_{BC} = 180.3\mathbf{i} - 827\mathbf{j} \text{ kN}$$

$$|\mathbf{F}| = \sqrt{F_x^2 + F_y^2} = 846 \text{ kN (Total force)}$$

$$F_y = -827 \text{ kN (downward force)}$$

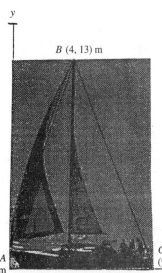

37

Problem 2.60 The structure shown forms part of a truss designed by an architectural engineer to support the roof of an orchestra shell. The members AB, AC, and AD exert forces $\mathbf{F}_{AB}$, $\mathbf{F}_{AC}$, and $\mathbf{F}_{AD}$ on the joint A. The magnitude $|\mathbf{F}_{AB}| = 4$ kN. If the vector sum of the three forces equals zero, what are the magnitudes of $\mathbf{F}_{AC}$ and $\mathbf{F}_{AD}$?

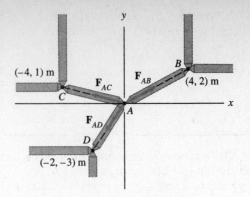

Solution: Determine the unit vectors parallel to each force:

$$\mathbf{e}_{AD} = \frac{-2}{\sqrt{2^2 + 3^2}}\mathbf{i} + \frac{-3}{\sqrt{2^2 + 3^2}}\mathbf{j} = -0.5547\mathbf{i} - 0.8320\mathbf{j}$$

$$\mathbf{e}_{AC} = \frac{-4}{\sqrt{4^2 + 1^2}}\mathbf{i} + \frac{1}{\sqrt{4^2 + 1^2}}\mathbf{j} = -0.9701\mathbf{i} + 0.2425\mathbf{j}$$

$$\mathbf{e}_{AB} = \frac{4}{\sqrt{4^2 + 2^2}}\mathbf{i} + \frac{2}{\sqrt{4^2 + 2^2}}\mathbf{j} = 0.89443\mathbf{i} + 0.4472\mathbf{j}$$

The forces are $\mathbf{F}_{AD} = |\mathbf{F}_{AD}|\mathbf{e}_{AD}$, $\mathbf{F}_{AC} = |\mathbf{F}_{AC}|\mathbf{e}_{AC}$,

$\mathbf{F}_{AB} = |\mathbf{F}_{AB}|\mathbf{e}_{AB} = 3.578\mathbf{i} + 1.789\mathbf{j}$. Since the vector sum of the forces vanishes, the x- and y-components vanish separately:

$$\sum \mathbf{F}_x = (-0.5547|\mathbf{F}_{AD}| - 0.9701|\mathbf{F}_{AC}| + 3.578)\mathbf{i} = 0, \text{ and}$$

$$\sum \mathbf{F}_y = (-0.8320|\mathbf{F}_{AD}| + 0.2425|\mathbf{F}_{AC}| + 1.789)\mathbf{j} = 0$$

These simultaneous equations in two unknowns can be solved by any standard procedure. An HP-28S hand held calculator was used here:

The results: $\boxed{|\mathbf{F}_{AC}| = 2.108 \text{ kN}}$, $\boxed{|\mathbf{F}_{AD}| = 2.764 \text{ kN}}$

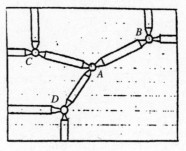

Problem 2.61 The distance $s = 45$ in.

(a) Determine the unit vector $\mathbf{e}_{BA}$ that points from B toward A.
(b) Use the unit vector you obtained in (a) to determine the coordinates of the collar C.

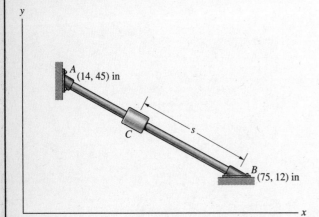

Solution: The unit vector from B to A is the vector from B to A divided by its magnitude. The vector from B to A is given by

$$\mathbf{r}_{BA} = (x_A - x_B)\mathbf{i} + (y_A - y_B)\mathbf{j} \text{ or } \mathbf{r}_{BA} = (14 - 75)\mathbf{i} + (45 - 12)\mathbf{j} \text{ in.}$$

Hence, vector from B to A is given by $\mathbf{r}_{BA} = (-61)\mathbf{i} + (33)\mathbf{j}$ in. The magnitude of the vector from B to A is 69.4 in. and the unit vector from B toward A is $\mathbf{e}_{BA} = -0.880\mathbf{i} + 0.476\mathbf{j}$.

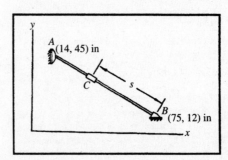

Problem 2.62 In Problem 2.61, determine the x and y coordinates of the collar C as functions of the distance s.

Solution: The coordinates of the point C are given by

$$x_C = x_B + s(-0.880) \text{ and } y_C = y_B + s(0.476).$$

Thus, the coordinates of point C are $x_C = 75 - 0.880s$ in. and $y_C = 12 + 0.476s$ in. Note from the solution of Problem 2.61 above, $0 \le s \le 69.4$ in.

Problem 2.63 The position vector $\mathbf{r}$ goes from point A to a point on the straight line between B and C. Its magnitude is $|\mathbf{r}| = 6$ ft. Express $\mathbf{r}$ in terms of scalar components.

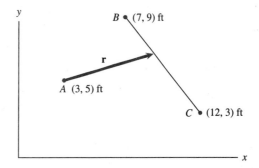

Solution: Determine the perpendicular vector to the line BC from point A, and then use this perpendicular to determine the angular orientation of the vector $\mathbf{r}$. The vectors are

$$\mathbf{r}_{AB} = (7 - 3)\mathbf{i} + (9 - 5)\mathbf{j} = 4\mathbf{i} + 4\mathbf{j}, \quad |\mathbf{r}_{AB}| = 5.6568$$

$$\mathbf{r}_{AC} = (12 - 3)\mathbf{i} + (3 - 5)\mathbf{j} = 9\mathbf{i} - 2\mathbf{j}, \quad |\mathbf{r}_{AC}| = 9.2195$$

$$\mathbf{r}_{BC} = (12 - 7)\mathbf{i} + (3 - 9)\mathbf{j} = 5\mathbf{i} - 6\mathbf{j}, \quad |\mathbf{r}_{BC}| = 7.8102$$

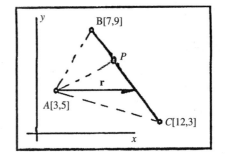

The unit vector parallel to BC is

$$\mathbf{e}_{BC} = \frac{\mathbf{r}_{BC}}{|\mathbf{r}_{BC}|} = 0.6402\mathbf{i} - 0.7682\mathbf{j} = \mathbf{i}\cos 50.19° - \mathbf{j}\sin 50.19°.$$

Add $\pm 90°$ to the angle to find the two possible perpendicular vectors:

$$\mathbf{e}_{AP1} = \mathbf{i}\cos 140.19° - \mathbf{j}\sin 140.19°, \text{ or}$$

$$\mathbf{e}_{AP2} = \mathbf{i}\cos 39.8° + \mathbf{j}\sin 39.8°.$$

Choose the latter, since it points from A to the line.

Given the triangle defined by vertices A, B, C, then the magnitude of the perpendicular corresponds to the altitude when the base is the line BC. The altitude is given by $h = \dfrac{2(\text{area})}{\text{base}}$. From geometry, the area of a triangle with known sides is given by

$$\text{area} = \sqrt{s(s - |\mathbf{r}_{BC}|)(s - |\mathbf{r}_{AC}|)(s - |\mathbf{r}_{AB}|)},$$

where s is the semiperimeter, $s = \frac{1}{2}(|\mathbf{r}_{AC}| + |\mathbf{r}_{AB}| + |\mathbf{r}_{BC}|)$. Substituting values, $s = 11.343$, and area $= 22.0$ and the magnitude of the perpendicular is $|\mathbf{r}_{AP}| = \dfrac{2(22)}{7.8102} = 5.6333$. The angle between the vector $\mathbf{r}$ and the perpendicular $\mathbf{r}_{AP}$ is $\beta = \cos^{-1}\dfrac{5.6333}{6} = 20.1°$. Thus the angle between the vector $\mathbf{r}$ and the x-axis is $\alpha = 39.8 \pm 20.1 = 59.1°$ or $19.7°$. The first angle is ruled out because it causes the vector $\mathbf{r}$ to lie above the vector $\mathbf{r}_{AB}$, which is at a $45°$ angle relative to the x-axis. Thus:

$$\boxed{\mathbf{r} = 6(\mathbf{i}\cos 19.7° + \mathbf{j}\sin 19.7°) = 5.65\mathbf{i} + 2.02\mathbf{j}}$$

Problem 2.64 Let **r** be the position vector from point C to the point that is a distance s meters from point A along the straight line between A and B. Express **r** in terms of scalar components. (Your answer will be in terms of s.)

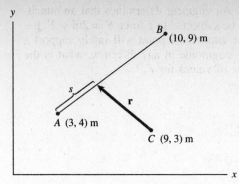

Solution: Determine the ratio of the parts of the line AB and use this value to determine **r**. The vectors are:

$$\mathbf{r}_{AB} = (10-3)\mathbf{i} + (9-4)\mathbf{j} = 7\mathbf{i} + 5\mathbf{j}, \quad |\mathbf{r}_{AB}| = 8.602$$

$$\mathbf{r}_{CA} = (3-9)\mathbf{i} + (4-3) = -6\mathbf{i} + 1\mathbf{j}, \quad |\mathbf{r}_{CA}| = 6.0828$$

$$\mathbf{r}_{CB} = (10-9)\mathbf{i} + (9-3)\mathbf{j} = 1\mathbf{i} + 6\mathbf{j}, \quad |\mathbf{r}_{CB}| = 6.0828$$

The ratio of the magnitudes of the two parts of the line is

$$\frac{|\mathbf{r}_{BP}|}{|\mathbf{r}_{PA}|} = R = \frac{s}{|\mathbf{r}_{BC}| - s}$$

Since the ratio is a scalar, then $\mathbf{r}_{BP} = R\mathbf{r}_{PA}$, from which $(\mathbf{r} - \mathbf{r}_{CA}) = R(\mathbf{r}_{CB} - \mathbf{r})$.

Solve for the vector **r**, $\mathbf{r} = \dfrac{R\mathbf{r}_{CB} + \mathbf{r}_{CA}}{1+R}$. Substitute the values of the vectors, note that $R = \dfrac{s}{8.602 - s}$, and reduce algebraically:

$$\boxed{\mathbf{r} = (0.8138s - 6)\mathbf{i} + (0.5813s + 1)\mathbf{j} \text{ (m)} :}$$

Check: An alternate solution: Find the angle of the line AB:

$$\theta = \tan^{-1}\left(\tfrac{5}{7}\right) = 35.54°.$$

The components of **s**,

$$\mathbf{s} = |\mathbf{s}|(\mathbf{i}\cos\theta + \mathbf{j}\sin\theta) = |\mathbf{s}|(0.8138\mathbf{i} + 0.5812\mathbf{j}).$$

The coordinates of point P $(3 + 0.8138|\mathbf{s}|, 4 + 0.5812|\mathbf{s}|)$. Subtract coordinates of point C to get

$$\boxed{\mathbf{r} = (0.8135|\mathbf{s}| - 6)\mathbf{i} + (0.5812|\mathbf{s}| + 1)\mathbf{j}} \quad check.$$

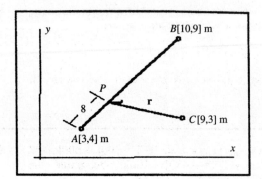

Problem 2.65 A vector $\mathbf{U} = 3\mathbf{i} - 4\mathbf{j} - 12\mathbf{k}$. What is its magnitude?

Strategy: The magnitude of a vector is given in terms of its components by Eq. (2.14).

Solution: Use definition given in Eq. (14). The vector magnitude is

$$\boxed{|\mathbf{U}| = \sqrt{3^2 + (-4)^2 + (-12)^2} = 13}$$

Problem 2.66 A force vector $\mathbf{F} = 20\mathbf{i} + 60\mathbf{j} - 90\mathbf{k}$ (N). Determine its magnitude.

Solution: Use definition given in Eq. (14). The magnitude of the vector is

$$\boxed{|\mathbf{F}| = \sqrt{(20)^2 + (60)^2 + (-90)^2} = 110 \text{ N}}$$

Problem 2.67 An engineer determines that an attachment point will be subjected to a force $\mathbf{F} = 20\mathbf{i} + F_y\mathbf{j} - 45\mathbf{k}$ (kN). If the attachment point will safely support a force of 80-kN magnitude in any direction, what is the acceptable range of values for F_y?

Solution:

$$80^2 \geq F_x^2 + F_y^2 + F_z^2$$

$$80^2 \geq 20^2 + F_y^2 + (45)^2$$

To find limits, use equality.

$$F_{y_{\text{LIMIT}}}^2 = 80^2 - 20^2 - (45)^2$$

$$F_{y_{\text{LIMIT}}}^2 = 3975$$

$$F_{y_{\text{LIMIT}}} = +63.0, -63.0 \ (\text{kN})$$

$$|F_{y_{\text{LIMIT}}}| \leq 63.0 \ \text{kN} - 63.0 \ \text{kN} \leq F_y \leq 63.0 \ \text{kN}$$

Problem 2.68 A vector $\mathbf{U} = U_x\mathbf{i} + U_y\mathbf{j} + U_z\mathbf{k}$. Its magnitude is $|\mathbf{U}| = 30$. Its components are related by the equations $U_y = -2U_x$ and $U_z = 4U_y$. Determine the components.

Solution: Substitute the relations between the components, determine the magnitude, and solve for the unknowns. Thus

$$\mathbf{U} = U_x\mathbf{i} + (-2U_x)\mathbf{j} + (4(-2U_x))\mathbf{k} = U_x(1\mathbf{i} - 2\mathbf{j} - 8\mathbf{k})$$

where U_x can be factored out since it is a scalar. Take the magnitude, noting that the absolute value of $|U_x|$ must be taken:

$$30 = |U_x|\sqrt{1^2 + 2^2 + 8^2} = |U_x|(8.31).$$

Solving, we get $|U_x| = 3.612$, or $U_x = \pm 3.61$. The two possible vectors are

$$\mathbf{U} = +3.61\mathbf{i} + (-2(3.61))\mathbf{j} + (4(-2)(3.61))\mathbf{k}$$

$$\boxed{= 3.61\mathbf{i} - 7.22\mathbf{j} - 28.9\mathbf{k}}$$

$$\mathbf{U} = -3.61\mathbf{i} + (-2(-3.61))\mathbf{j}$$

$$+ 4(-2)(-3.61)\mathbf{k} \boxed{= -3.61\mathbf{i} + 7.22\mathbf{j} + 28.9\mathbf{k}}$$

Problem 2.69 A vector $\mathbf{U} = 100\mathbf{i} + 200\mathbf{j} - 600\mathbf{k}$, and a vector $\mathbf{V} = -200\mathbf{i} + 450\mathbf{j} + 100\mathbf{k}$. Determine the magnitude of the vector $-2\mathbf{U} + 3\mathbf{V}$.

Solution: The resultant is

$$-2\mathbf{U} + 3\mathbf{V} = (-2(100) + 3(-200))\mathbf{i} + (-2(200) + 3(450))\mathbf{j}$$

$$+ (-2(-600) + 3(100))\mathbf{k}$$

$$-2\mathbf{U} + 3\mathbf{V} = -800\mathbf{i} + 950\mathbf{j} + 1500\mathbf{k}$$

The magnitude is:

$$\boxed{|-2\mathbf{U} + 3\mathbf{V}| = \sqrt{(-800)^2 + (950)^2 + (1500)^2} = 1947.4}$$

Problem 2.70 Two vectors $\mathbf{U} = 3\mathbf{i} - 2\mathbf{j} + 6\mathbf{k}$ and $\mathbf{V} = 4\mathbf{i} + 12\mathbf{j} - 3\mathbf{k}$.

(a) Determine the magnitudes of $\mathbf{U}$ and $\mathbf{V}$.
(b) Determine the magnitude of the vector $3\mathbf{U} + 2\mathbf{V}$.

Solution: The magnitudes:

(a) $\boxed{|\mathbf{U}| = \sqrt{3^2 + 2^2 + 6^2} = 7}$ and $\boxed{|\mathbf{V}| = \sqrt{4^2 + 12^2 + 3^2} = 13}$

The resultant vector

$$3\mathbf{U} + 2\mathbf{V} = (9 + 8)\mathbf{i} + (-6 + 24)\mathbf{j} + (18 - 6)\mathbf{k}$$

$$= 17\mathbf{i} + 18\mathbf{j} + 12\mathbf{k}$$

(b) The magnitude $\boxed{|3\mathbf{U} + 2\mathbf{V}| = \sqrt{17^2 + 18^2 + 12^2} = 27.51}$

Problem 2.71   A vector $\mathbf{U} = 40\mathbf{i} - 70\mathbf{j} - 40\mathbf{k}$.

(a) What is its magnitude?
(b) What are the angles θ_x, θ_y, and θ_z between $\mathbf{U}$ and the positive coordinate axes?

Strategy: Since you know the components of $\mathbf{U}$, you can determine the angles θ_x, θ_y, and θ_z from Eqs. (2.15).

Solution: The magnitude:

(a) $|\mathbf{U}| = \sqrt{40^2 + 70^2 + 40^2} = 90$

(b) The direction cosines:

$$\mathbf{U} = 90\left(\frac{40}{90}\mathbf{i} - \frac{70}{90}\mathbf{j} - \frac{40}{90}\mathbf{k}\right)$$

$$= 90(0.4444\mathbf{i} - 0.7777\mathbf{j} - 0.4444\mathbf{k})$$

$$\boxed{\mathbf{U} = 90(\mathbf{i}\cos 63.6° + \mathbf{j}\cos 141.1° + \mathbf{k}\cos 116.4°)}$$

Problem 2.72   A force $\mathbf{F} = 600\mathbf{i} - 700\mathbf{j} + 600\mathbf{k}$ (lb). What are the angles θ_x, θ_y, and θ_z between the vector $\mathbf{F}$ and the positive coordinate axes?

Solution: The magnitude: $\boxed{|\mathbf{F}| = \sqrt{600^2 + 700^2 + 600^2} = 1100}$

The unit vector is:

$$\mathbf{e} = \frac{\mathbf{F}}{|\mathbf{F}|} = \frac{600}{1100}\mathbf{i} - \frac{700}{1100}\mathbf{j} + \frac{600}{1100}\mathbf{k} = 0.5455\mathbf{i} - 0.6364\mathbf{j} + 0.5455\mathbf{k}$$

The angles are

$\boxed{\theta_x = \cos^{-1}(0.5455) = 56.9°}$, $\boxed{\theta_y = \cos^{-1}(-0.6364) = 129.5°}$,

and $\boxed{\theta_z = \cos^{-1}(0.5455) = 56.9°}$

Problem 2.73   The cable exerts a 50-lb force $\mathbf{F}$ on the metal hook at O. The angle between $\mathbf{F}$ and the x axis is $40°$, and the angle between $\mathbf{F}$ and the y axis is $70°$. The z component of $\mathbf{F}$ is positive.

(a) Express $\mathbf{F}$ in terms of components.
(b) What are the direction cosines of $\mathbf{F}$?

Strategy: Since you are given only two of the angles between $\mathbf{F}$ and the coordinate axes, you must first determine the third one. Then you can obtain the components of $\mathbf{F}$ from Eqs. (2.15).

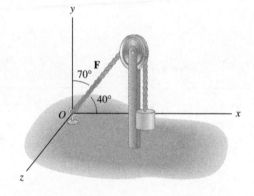

Solution: Use Eqs. (2.15) and (2.16).

The force $\mathbf{F} = 50(\mathbf{i}\cos 40° + \mathbf{j}\cos 70° + \mathbf{k}\cos\theta_z)$. Since

$1^2 = \cos^2 40° + \cos^2 70° + \cos^2\theta_z$, by definition (see Eq. (2.16)) then

$\cos\theta_z = \pm\sqrt{1 - 0.5868 - 0.1170} = \pm 0.5442$.

Thus the components of $\mathbf{F}$ are

(a) $\mathbf{F} = 50(0.7660\mathbf{i} + 0.3420\mathbf{j} + 0.5442\mathbf{k})$,

$\boxed{= 38.3\mathbf{i} + 17.1\mathbf{j} + 27.2\mathbf{k} \text{ (lb)}}$

(b) the direction cosines are

$\boxed{\cos\theta_x = 0.7660, \quad \cos\theta_y = 0.3420, \quad \cos\theta_z = 0.5442}$

Problem 2.74   A unit vector has direction cosines $\cos\theta_x = -0.5$ and $\cos\theta_y = 0.2$. Its z component is positive. Express it in terms of components.

Solution: Use Eq. (2.15) and (2.16). The third direction cosine is

$\cos\theta_z = \pm\sqrt{1 - (0.5)^2 - (0.2)^2} = +0.8426$.

The unit vector is

$\boxed{\mathbf{u} = -0.5\mathbf{i} + 0.2\mathbf{j} + 0.8426\mathbf{k}}$

Problem 2.75 The airplane's engines exert a total thrust force **T** of 200-kN magnitude. The angle between **T** and the x axis is $120°$, and the angle between **T** and the y axis is $130°$. The z component of **T** is positive.

(a) What is the angle between **T** and the z axis?
(b) Express **T** in terms of components.

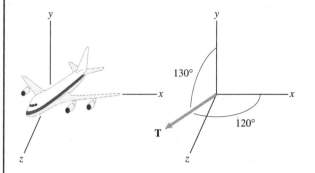

Solution: The x- and y-direction cosines are

$$l = \cos 120° = -0.5, \quad m = \cos 130° = -0.6428$$

from which the z-direction cosine is

$$n = \cos\theta_z = \pm\sqrt{1 - (0.5)^2 - (0.6428)^2} = +0.5804.$$

Thus the angle between **T** and the z-axis is

(a) $\boxed{\theta_z = \cos^{-1}(0.5804) = 54.5°}$, and the thrust is

$$\mathbf{T} = 200(-0.5\mathbf{i} - 0.6428\mathbf{j} + 0.5804\mathbf{k}), \text{ or:}$$

(b) $\boxed{\mathbf{T} = -100\mathbf{i} - 128.6\mathbf{j} + 116.1\mathbf{k} \text{ (kN)}}$

Problem 2.76 The position vector from a point A to a point B is $3\mathbf{i} + 4\mathbf{j} - 4\mathbf{k}$ (ft). The position vector from point A to point C is $-3\mathbf{i} + 13\mathbf{j} - 2\mathbf{k}$. ft

(a) What is the distance from point B to point C?
(b) What are the direction cosines of the position vector from point B to point C?

Solution: The vector from point B to point C is $\mathbf{r}_{BC} = \mathbf{r}_{AC} - \mathbf{r}_{AB}$. Thus

$$\mathbf{r}_{BC} = (-3 - 3)\mathbf{i} + (13 - 4)\mathbf{j} + (-2 - (-4))\mathbf{k} = -6\mathbf{i} + 9\mathbf{j} + 2\mathbf{k}.$$

The distance between points B and C is

(a) $|\mathbf{r}_{BC}| = \sqrt{6^2 + 9^2 + 2^2} = 11$ (ft). The direction cosines are

(b) $\boxed{\begin{aligned} \cos\theta_x &= \frac{-6}{11} = -0.5454, \quad \cos\theta_y = \frac{9}{11} = 0.8182, \\ \cos\theta_z &= \frac{2}{11} = 0.1818 \end{aligned}}$

Problem 2.77 A vector $\mathbf{U} = 3\mathbf{i} - 2\mathbf{j} + 6\mathbf{k}$. Determine the components of the unit vector that has the same direction as **U**.

Solution: By definition, the unit vector is the vector whose components are the direction cosines of **U**. (See discussion following Eq. (2.15)). The magnitude is $|\mathbf{U}| = \sqrt{3^2 + 2^2 + 6^2} = 7$. Thus the unit vector is

$$\boxed{\mathbf{u} = \frac{\mathbf{U}}{|\mathbf{U}|} = \frac{3}{7}\mathbf{i} - \frac{2}{7}\mathbf{j} + \frac{6}{7}\mathbf{k}}$$

Problem 2.78 A force vector $\mathbf{F} = 3\mathbf{i} - 4\mathbf{j} - 2\mathbf{k}$ (N).

(a) What is the magnitude of **F**?
(b) Determine the components of the unit vector that has the same direction as **F**.

Solution: By definition, the unit vector is the vector whose components are the direction cosines of **F**. The magnitude is

(a) $|\mathbf{F}| = \sqrt{3^2 + 4^2 + 2^2} = 5.385$ (N) The unit vector is

(b) $\mathbf{e} = \frac{3}{5.385}\mathbf{i} - \frac{4}{5.385}\mathbf{j} - \frac{2}{5.385}\mathbf{k}$

$$\boxed{= 0.5571\mathbf{i} - 0.7428\mathbf{j} - 0.3714\mathbf{k}}$$

Problem 2.79 A force vector **F** points in the same direction as the unit vector $\mathbf{e} = \frac{2}{7}\mathbf{i} - \frac{6}{7}\mathbf{j} - \frac{3}{7}\mathbf{k}$. The magnitude of **F** is 700 lb. Express **F** in terms of components.

Solution: By definition, $\mathbf{F} = |\mathbf{F}|\mathbf{e}$, where **e** is a unit vector in the direction of **F**. (See discussion following Eq. (2.16).) Thus

$$\boxed{\mathbf{F} = 700\left(\frac{2}{7}\mathbf{i} - \frac{6}{7}\mathbf{j} - \frac{3}{7}\mathbf{k}\right) = 200\mathbf{i} - 600\mathbf{j} - 300\mathbf{k}}$$

Problem 2.80 A force vector **F** points in the same direction as the position vector $\mathbf{r} = 4\mathbf{i} + 4\mathbf{j} - 7\mathbf{k}$ (m). The magnitude of **F** is 90 kN. Express **F** in terms of components.

Solution: By definition, $\mathbf{F} = |\mathbf{F}|\mathbf{e}$, where **e** is a unit vector in the direction of **F**. Find the unit vector from the position vector. The magnitude is $|\mathbf{r}| = \sqrt{4^2 + 4^2 + 7^2} = 9$; the unit vector is $\mathbf{e} = \frac{4}{9}\mathbf{i} + \frac{4}{9}\mathbf{j} - \frac{7}{9}\mathbf{k}$. The components are

$$\mathbf{F} = 90\left(\frac{4}{9}\mathbf{i} + \frac{4}{9}\mathbf{j} - \frac{7}{9}\mathbf{k}\right) = 40\mathbf{i} + 40\mathbf{j} - 70\mathbf{k} \text{ (kN)}$$

Problem 2.81 Astronauts on the space shuttle use radar to determine the magnitudes and direction cosines of the position vectors of two satellites A and B. The vector $\mathbf{r}_A$ from the shuttle to satellite A has magnitude 2 km, and direction cosines $\cos\theta_x = 0.768, \cos\theta_y = 0.384, \cos\theta_z = 0.512$. The vector $\mathbf{r}_B$ from the shuttle to satellite B has magnitude 4 km and direction cosines $\cos\theta_x = 0.743$, $\cos\theta_y = 0.557$, $\cos\theta_z = -0.371$. What is the distance between the satellites?

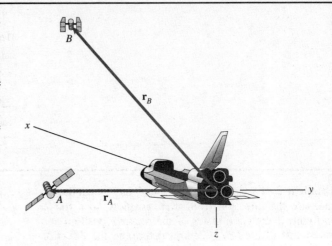

Solution: The two position vectors are:

$\mathbf{r}_A = 2(0.768\mathbf{i} + 0.384\mathbf{j} + 0.512\mathbf{k}) = 1.536\mathbf{i} + 0.768\mathbf{j} + 1.024\mathbf{k}$ (km)

$\mathbf{r}_B = 4(0.743\mathbf{i} + 0.557\mathbf{j} - 0.371\mathbf{k}) = 2.972\mathbf{i} + 2.228\mathbf{j} - 1.484\mathbf{k}$ (km)

The distance is the magnitude of the difference:

$|\mathbf{r}_A - \mathbf{r}_B|$

$= \sqrt{(1.536 - 2.927)^2 + (0.768 - 2.228)^2 + (1.024 - (-1.484))^2}$

$= 3.24$ (km)

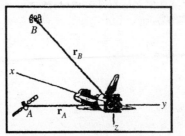

Problem 2.82 Archaeologists measure a pre-Columbian ceremonial structure and obtain the dimensions shown. Determine (a) the magnitude and (b) the direction cosines of the position vector from point A to point B.

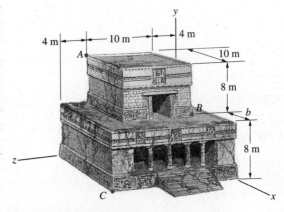

Solution: The coordinates are $A(0, 16, 14)$, and $B(10, 8, 4)$. The vector from A to B is

$\mathbf{r}_{AB} = (10 - 0)\mathbf{i} + (8 - 16)\mathbf{j} + (4 - 14)\mathbf{k} = 10\mathbf{i} - 8\mathbf{j} - 10\mathbf{k}.$

The magnitude is

(a) $|\mathbf{r}_{AB}| = \sqrt{10^2 + 8^2 + 10^2} = 16.2$ m , and

(b) The direction cosines are

$\cos\theta_x = \dfrac{10}{16.2} = 0.6155,$

$\cos\theta_y = \dfrac{-8}{16.2} = -0.4938,$

and $\cos\theta_z = \dfrac{-10}{16.2} = -0.6155$.

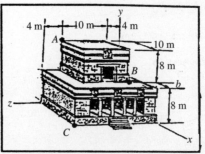

Problem 2.83 Consider the structure described in Problem 2.82. After returning to the United States, an archaeologist discovers that he lost the notes containing the dimension b, but other notes indicate that the distance from point B to point C is 16.4 m. What are the direction cosines of the vector from B to C?

Solution: The coordinates of B and C are $B(10, 8, 4)$ and $C(10 + b, 0, 18)$. The vector from B to C is

$$\mathbf{r}_{BC} = (10 + b - 10)\mathbf{i} + (0 - 8)\mathbf{j} + (18 - 4)\mathbf{k} = b\mathbf{i} - 8\mathbf{j} + 14\mathbf{k}.$$

The magnitude of this vector is known:

$$16.4 = \sqrt{b^2 + 8^2 + 14^2} = \sqrt{b^2 + 260}, \text{ from which}$$

$$b^2 = (16.4)^2 - 260 = 8.96, \text{ or } b = \pm 3 = +3 \text{ m}.$$

The direction cosines are

$$\boxed{\cos\theta_x = \frac{3}{16.4} = 0.1829,} \qquad \boxed{\cos\theta_y = \frac{-8}{16.4} = -0.4878,}$$

$$\boxed{\cos\theta_z = \frac{14}{16.4} = 0.8537}$$

Problem 2.84 Observers at A and B use theodolites to measure the direction from their positions to a rocket in flight. If the coordinates of the rocket's position at a given instant are $(4, 4, 2)$ km, determine the direction cosines of the vectors $\mathbf{r}_{AR}$ and $\mathbf{r}_{BR}$ that the observers would measure at that instant.

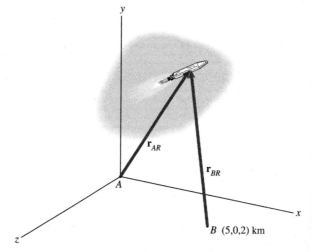

Solution: The vector $\mathbf{r}_{AR}$ is given by

$$\mathbf{r}_{AR} = 4\mathbf{i} + 4\mathbf{j} + 2\mathbf{k} \text{ km}$$

and the magnitude of $\mathbf{r}_{AR}$ is given by

$$|\mathbf{r}_{AR}| = \sqrt{(4)^2 + (4)^2 + (2)^2} \text{ km} = 6 \text{ km}.$$

The unit vector along AR is given by

$$\mathbf{u}_{AR} = \mathbf{r}_{AR}/|\mathbf{r}_{AR}|.$$

Thus, $\mathbf{u}_{AR} = 0.667\mathbf{i} + 0.667\mathbf{j} + 0.333\mathbf{k}$

and the direction cosines are

$$\boxed{\cos\theta_x = 0.667, \cos\theta_y = 0.667, \text{ and } \cos\theta_z = 0.333.}$$

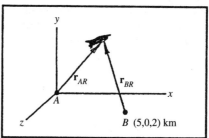

The vector $\mathbf{r}_{BR}$ is given by

$$\mathbf{r}_{BR} = (x_R - x_B)\mathbf{i} + (y_R - y_B)\mathbf{j} + (z_R - z_B)\mathbf{k} \text{ km}$$

$$= (4 - 5)\mathbf{i} + (4 - 0)\mathbf{j} + (2 - 2)\mathbf{k} \text{ km}$$

and the magnitude of $\mathbf{r}_{BR}$ is given by

$$|\mathbf{r}_{BR}| = \sqrt{(1)^2 + (4)^2 + (0)^2} \text{ km} = 4.12 \text{ km}.$$

The unit vector along BR is given by

$$\mathbf{e}_{BR} = \mathbf{r}_{BR}/|\mathbf{r}_{BR}|.$$

Thus, $\mathbf{u}_{BR} = -0.242\mathbf{i} + 0.970\mathbf{j} + 0\mathbf{k}$

and the direction cosines are

$$\boxed{\cos\theta_x = -0.242, \cos\theta_y = 0.970, \text{ and } \cos\theta_z = 0.0.}$$

Problem 2.85 In Problem 2.84, suppose that the coordinates of the rocket's position are unknown. At a given instant, the person at A determines that the direction cosines of $\mathbf{r}_{AR}$ are $\cos\theta_x = 0.535$, $\cos\theta_y = 0.802$, and $\cos\theta_z = 0.267$, and the person at B determines that the direction cosines of $\mathbf{r}_{BR}$ are $\cos\theta_x = -0.576$, $\cos\theta_y = 0.798$, and $\cos\theta_z = -0.177$. What are the coordinates of the rocket's position at that instant.

Solution: The vector from A to B is given by

$$\mathbf{r}_{AB} = (x_B - x_A)\mathbf{i} + (y_B - y_A)\mathbf{j} + (z_B - z_A)\mathbf{k} \text{ or}$$

$$\mathbf{r}_{AB} = (5 - 0)\mathbf{i} + (0 - 0)\mathbf{j} + (2 - 0)\mathbf{k} = 5\mathbf{i} + 2\mathbf{k} \text{ km}.$$

The magnitude of $\mathbf{r}_{AB}$ is given by $|\mathbf{r}_{AB}| = \sqrt{(5)^2 + (2)^2} = 5.39$ km. The unit vector along AB, $\mathbf{u}_{AB}$, is given by

$$\mathbf{u}_{AB} = \mathbf{r}_{AB}/|\mathbf{r}_{AB}| = 0.928\mathbf{i} + 0\mathbf{j} + 0.371\mathbf{k} \text{ km}.$$

The unit vector along the line AR,

$$\mathbf{u}_{AR} = \cos\theta_x\mathbf{i} + \cos\theta_y\mathbf{j} + \cos\theta_z\mathbf{k} = 0.535\mathbf{i} + 0.802\mathbf{j} + 0.267\mathbf{k}.$$

Similarly, the vector along BR, $\mathbf{u}_{BR} = -0.576\mathbf{i} + 0.798 - 0.177\mathbf{k}$. From the diagram in the problem statement, we see that $\mathbf{r}_{AR} = \mathbf{r}_{AB} + \mathbf{r}_{BR}$. Using the unit vectors, the vectors $\mathbf{r}_{AR}$ and $\mathbf{r}_{BR}$ can be written as

$$\mathbf{r}_{AR} = 0.535 r_{AR}\mathbf{i} + 0.802 r_{AR}\mathbf{j} + 0.267 r_{AR}\mathbf{k}, \text{ and}$$

$$\mathbf{r}_{BR} = -0.576 r_{BR}\mathbf{i} + 0.798 r_{BR}\mathbf{j} - 0.177 r_{BR}\mathbf{k}.$$

Substituting into the vector addition $\mathbf{r}_{AR} = \mathbf{r}_{AB} + \mathbf{r}_{BR}$ and equating components, we get, in the x direction, $0.535 r_{AR} = -0.576 r_{BR}$, and in the y direction, $0.802 r_{AR} = 0.798 r_{BR}$. Solving, we get that $r_{AR} = 4.489$ km. Calculating the components, we get

$$\mathbf{r}_{AR} = r_{AR}\mathbf{e}_{AR} = 0.535(4.489)\mathbf{i} + 0.802(4.489)\mathbf{j} + 0.267(4.489)\mathbf{k}.$$

Hence, the coordinates of the rocket, R, are (2.40, 3.60, 1.20) km.

Problem 2.86 The height of Mount Everest was originally measured by a surveyor using the following procedure. He first measured the distance between two points A and B of equal altitude. Suppose that they are 10,000 ft above sea level and are 32,000 ft apart. He then used a theodolite to measure the direction cosines of the vectors from point A to the top of the mountain P and from point B to P. Suppose that for $\mathbf{r}_{AP}$, the direction cosines are $\cos\theta_x = 0.509$, $\cos\theta_y = 0.509$, $\cos\theta_z = 0.694$, and for $\mathbf{r}_{BP}$ they are $\cos\theta_x = -0.605$, $\cos\theta_y = 0.471$, $\cos\theta_z = 0.642$. The z axis of the coordinate system is vertical. What is the height of Mount Everest above sea level?

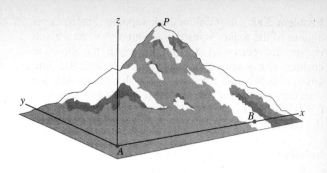

Solution: Construct the two triangles: (a) Triangle ABP, which has one known side, AB, and two known adjacent interior angles θ_A and θ_B (b) Triangle AOP, which is a right triangle with a derived known interior angle θ_{AO}. From triangle ABP, determine the length of AP, and from triangle APO and the derived interior angle, determine the height above the base, OP. The interior angles of the triangle ABP are

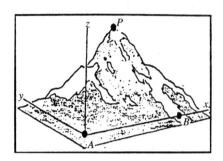

$$\theta_A = \theta_{AX} = \cos^{-1}(0.509) = 59.4°,$$

$$\theta_B = 180 - \theta_{BX} = 180 - \cos^{-1}(-0.605)$$

$$= 180° - 127.2° = 52.77° \text{ and}$$

$$\beta = 180 - 59.4 - 52.77 = 67.83°.$$

From the law of sines:

$$\frac{|\mathbf{r}_{AB}|}{\sin 67.83°} = \frac{|\mathbf{r}_{BP}|}{\sin 59.4°} = \frac{|\mathbf{r}_{AP}|}{\sin 52.77°}.$$

Therefore the length of side AP is

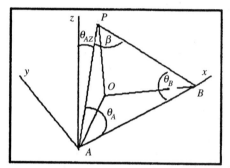

$$|\mathbf{r}_{AP}| = |\mathbf{r}_{AB}|\left(\frac{\sin 52.77}{\sin 67.83}\right) = 32000(0.8598) = 27512.9 \text{ ft}.$$

The interior angle of the triangle APO is $\theta_{AO} = 90 - \theta_{AZ} = 90 - \cos^{-1}(0.694) = 90 - 46.05 = 43.95°$. Therefore the length of the side OP is $h_{OP} = |\mathbf{r}_{AP}|\sin 43.95° = 27512.9(0.6940) = 19093.9$ ft. *Check:* The z-component of $|\mathbf{r}_{AP}|$ is $h_{op} = |\mathbf{r}_{AP}|\sin\theta_{AZ} = 19093.9$ ft. *check.*

The base is 10000 ft above sea level, hence the height of P above sea level is

$$\boxed{P = 19093.9 + 10000 = 29094 \text{ ft}}$$

Problem 2.87 The distance from point O to point A is 20 ft. The straight line AB is parallel to the y axis, and point B is in the x-z plane. Express the vector $\mathbf{r}_{OA}$ in terms of scalar components.

Strategy: You can resolve $\mathbf{r}_{OA}$ into a vector from O to B and a vecotr from B to A. You can then resolve the vector form O to B into vector components parallel to the x and z axes. See Example 2.9.

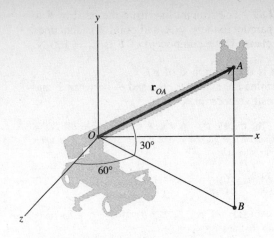

Solution: See Example 2.10. The length BA is, from the right triangle OAB,

$$|\mathbf{r}_{AB}| = |\mathbf{r}_{OA}|\sin 30° = 20(0.5) = 10 \text{ ft.}$$

Similarly, the length OB is

$$|\mathbf{r}_{OB}| = |\mathbf{r}_{OA}|\cos 30° = 20(0.866) = 17.32 \text{ ft}$$

The vector $\mathbf{r}_{OB}$ can be resolved into components along the axes by the right triangles OBP and OBQ and the condition that it lies in the x-z plane.
Hence,

$$\mathbf{r}_{OB} = |\mathbf{r}_{OB}|(\mathbf{i}\cos 30° + \mathbf{j}\cos 90° + \mathbf{k}\cos 60°) \text{ or}$$

$$\mathbf{r}_{OB} = 15\mathbf{i} + 0\mathbf{j} + 8.66\mathbf{k}.$$

The vector $\mathbf{r}_{BA}$ can be resolved into components from the condition that it is parallel to the y-axis. This vector is

$$\mathbf{r}_{BA} = |\mathbf{r}_{BA}|(\mathbf{i}\cos 90° + \mathbf{j}\cos 0° + \mathbf{k}\cos 90°) = 0\mathbf{i} + 10\mathbf{j} + 0\mathbf{k}.$$

The vector $\mathbf{r}_{OA}$ is given by $\mathbf{r}_{OA} = \mathbf{r}_{OB} + \mathbf{r}_{BA}$, from which

$$\boxed{\mathbf{r}_{OA} = 15\mathbf{i} + 10\mathbf{j} + 8.66\mathbf{k} \text{ (ft)}}$$

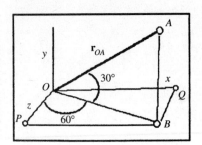

Problem 2.88 The magnitude of $\mathbf{r}$ is 100 in. The straight line from the head of $\mathbf{r}$ to point A is parallel to the x axis, and point A is contained in the y-z plane. Express $\mathbf{r}$ in terms of scalar components.

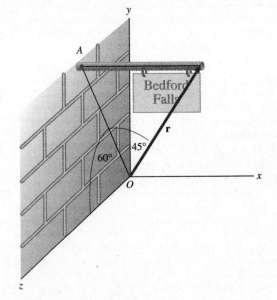

Solution: The vector $\mathbf{r}$ can be expressed as the sum of the two vectors, $\mathbf{r} = \mathbf{r}_{OA} + \mathbf{r}_{AP}$, both of which can be resolved into direction cosine components. The magnitudes can be determined from the law of sines for the triangle OAP.

$$\mathbf{r}_{OA} = |\mathbf{r}_{OA}|(\mathbf{i}\cos 90° + \mathbf{j}\cos 30° + \mathbf{k}\cos 60°)$$

$$\mathbf{r}_{OA} = |\mathbf{r}_{OA}|(0\mathbf{i} + 0.866\mathbf{j} + 0.5\mathbf{k}). \text{ Similarly,}$$

$$\mathbf{r}_{AP} = |\mathbf{r}_{AP}|(\mathbf{i}\cos 0 + \mathbf{j}\cos 90 + \mathbf{k}\cos 90) = |\mathbf{r}_{AP}|(1\mathbf{i} + 0\mathbf{j} + 0\mathbf{k})$$

Since $\mathbf{r}_{AP}$ is parallel to the x-axis, it makes an angle of 90° with the y-z plane, and the triangle OAP is a right triangle. From the law of sines

$$\frac{|\mathbf{r}|}{\sin 90°} = \frac{|\mathbf{r}_{AP}|}{\sin 45°} = \frac{|\mathbf{r}_{OA}|}{\sin 45°},$$

from which $|\mathbf{r}_{AP}| = |\mathbf{r}_{OA}| = 100(0.707) = 70.7$. Substituting these values into the vectors

$$\mathbf{r} = \mathbf{r}_{OA} + \mathbf{r}_{AP} = 70.7(1\mathbf{i} + 0.866\mathbf{j} + 0.5\mathbf{k})$$

$$\boxed{= 70.7\mathbf{i} + 61.2\mathbf{j} + 35.4\mathbf{k} \text{ (in.)}}$$

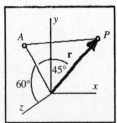

Problem 2.89 The straight line from the head of **F** to point A is parallel to the y axis, and point A is contained in the x-z plane. The x component of **F** is $F_x = 100$ N.

(a) What is the magnitude of **F**?.
(b) Determine the angles θ_x, θ_y, and θ_z between **F** and the positive coordinate axes.

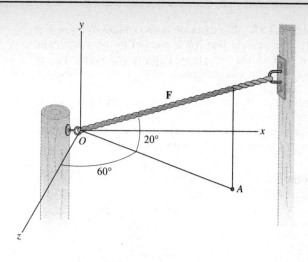

Solution: The triangle OpA is a right triangle, since OA lies in the x-z plane, and Ap is parallel to the y-axis. Thus the magnitudes are given by the sine law:

$$\frac{|\mathbf{r}_{Ap}|}{\sin 20°} = \frac{|\mathbf{F}|}{\sin 90°} = \frac{|\mathbf{r}_{OA}|}{\sin 70°},$$

thus $|\mathbf{r}_{Ap}| = |\mathbf{F}|(0.342)$ and $|\mathbf{r}_{OA}| = |\mathbf{F}|(0.9397)$. The components of the two vectors are from the geometry

$$\mathbf{r}_{OA} = |\mathbf{r}_{OA}|(\mathbf{i}\cos 30° + \mathbf{j}\cos 90° + \mathbf{k}\cos 60°)$$

$$= |\mathbf{r}_{OA}|(0.866\mathbf{i} + 0\mathbf{j} + 0.5\mathbf{k}) \text{ and}$$

$$\mathbf{r}_{Ap} = |\mathbf{r}_{Ap}|(\mathbf{i}\cos 90° + \mathbf{j}\cos 0° + \mathbf{k}\cos 90°) = |\mathbf{r}_{Ap}|(0\mathbf{i} + 1\mathbf{j} + 0\mathbf{k})$$

Noting $\mathbf{F} = \mathbf{r}_{OA} + \mathbf{r}_{Ap}$, then from above

$$\mathbf{F} = |\mathbf{F}|(0.3420)(0\mathbf{i} + 1\mathbf{j} + 0\mathbf{k}) + |\mathbf{F}|(0.9397)(0.866\mathbf{i} + 0\mathbf{j} + 0.5\mathbf{k})$$

$$\mathbf{F} = |\mathbf{F}|(0.8138\mathbf{i} + 0.342\mathbf{j} + 0.4699\mathbf{k})$$

The x-component is given to be 100 N. Thus,

(a) $|\mathbf{F}| = \dfrac{100}{0.8138} = 122.9$ N The angles are given by

(b) $\boxed{\theta_x = \cos^{-1}(0.8138) = 35.5°}$,

$\boxed{\theta_y = \cos^{-1}(0.342) = 70°}$ and $\boxed{\theta_z = \cos^{-1}(0.4699) = 62°}$

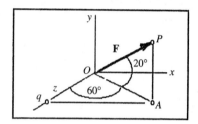

Problem 2.90 The position of a point P on the surface of the earth is specified by the longitude λ, measured from the point G on the equator directly south of Greenwich, England, and the latitude L measured from the equator. Longitude is given as west (W) longitude or east (E) longitude, indicating whether the angle is measured west or east from point G. Latitude is given as north (N) latitude or south (S) latitude, indicating whether the angle is measured north or south from the equator. Suppose that P is at longitude 30° W and latitude 45° N. Let R_E be the radius of the earth. Using the coordinate system shown, determine the components of the position vector of P relative to the center of the earth. (Your answer will be in terms of R_E.)

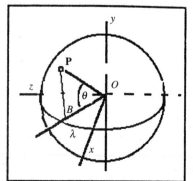

Solution: Drop a vertical line from point P to the equatorial plane. Let the intercept be B (see figure). The vector position of P is the sum of the two vectors: $\mathbf{P} = \mathbf{r}_{OB} + \mathbf{r}_{BP}$. The vector $\mathbf{r}_{OB} = |\mathbf{r}_{OB}|(\mathbf{i}\cos\lambda + 0\mathbf{j} + \mathbf{k}\sin\lambda)$. From geometry, the magnitude is $|\mathbf{r}_{OB}| = R_E\cos\theta$. The vector $\mathbf{r}_{BP} = |\mathbf{r}_{BP}|(0\mathbf{i} + 1\mathbf{j} + 0\mathbf{k})$. From geometry, the magnitude is $|\mathbf{r}_{BP}| = R_E\sin\theta_P$. Substitute: $\mathbf{P} = \mathbf{r}_{OB} + \mathbf{r}_{BP} = R_E(\mathbf{i}\cos\lambda\cos\theta + \mathbf{j}\sin\theta + \mathbf{k}\sin\lambda\cos\theta)$. Substitute from the problem statement: $\lambda = +30°$, $\theta = 45°$. Hence $\boxed{\mathbf{P} = R_E(0.6124\mathbf{i} + 0.707\mathbf{j} + 0.3536\mathbf{k})}$

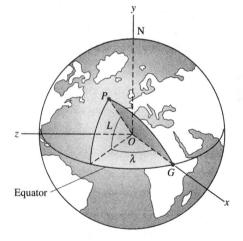

Problem 2.91 An engineer calculates that the magnitude of the axial force in one of the beams of a geodesic dome is $|\mathbf{P}| = 7.65$ kN. The cartesian coordinates of the endpoints A and B of the straight beam are $(-12.4, 22.0, -18.4)$ m and $(-9.2, 24.4, -15.6)$ m, respectively. Express the force $\mathbf{P}$ in terms of scalar components.

Solution: The components of the position vector from B to A are

$$\mathbf{r}_{BA} = (A_x - B_x)\mathbf{i} + (A_y - B_y)\mathbf{j} + (A_z - B_z)\mathbf{k}$$

$$= (-12.4 + 9.2)\mathbf{i} + (22.0 - 24.4)\mathbf{j}$$

$$+ (-18.4 + 15.6)\mathbf{k}$$

$$= -3.2\mathbf{i} - 2.4\mathbf{j} - 2.8\mathbf{k} \ (\text{m}).$$

Dividing this vector by its magnitude, we obtain a unit vector that points from B toward A:

$$\mathbf{e}_{BA} = -0.655\mathbf{i} - 0.492\mathbf{j} - 0.573\mathbf{k}.$$

Therefore

$$\mathbf{P} = |\mathbf{P}|\mathbf{e}_{BA}$$

$$= 7.65\,\mathbf{e}_{BA}$$

$$= -5.01\mathbf{i} - 3.76\mathbf{j} - 4.39\mathbf{k} \ (\text{kN}).$$

Problem 2.92 The cable BC exerts an 8-kN force $\mathbf{F}$ on the bar AB at B.

(a) Determine the components of a unit vector that points from B toward point C.

(b) Express $\mathbf{F}$ in terms of components.

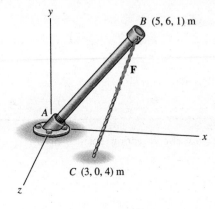

Solution:

(a) $$\mathbf{e}_{BC} = \frac{\mathbf{r}_{BC}}{|\mathbf{r}_{BC}|} = \frac{(x_C - x_B)\mathbf{i} + (y_C - y_B)\mathbf{j} + (z_C - z_B)\mathbf{k}}{\sqrt{(x_C - x_B)^2 + (y_C - y_B)^2 + (z_C - z_B)^2}}$$

$$\mathbf{e}_{BC} = \frac{-2\mathbf{i} - 6\mathbf{j} + 3\mathbf{k}}{\sqrt{2^2 + 6^2 + 3^2}} = -\frac{2}{7}\mathbf{i} - \frac{6}{7}\mathbf{j} + \frac{3}{7}\mathbf{k}$$

$$\mathbf{e}_{BC} = -0.286\mathbf{i} - 0.857\mathbf{j} + 0.429\mathbf{k}$$

(b) $$\mathbf{F} = |\mathbf{F}|\mathbf{e}_{BC} = 8\mathbf{e}_{BC} = -2.29\mathbf{i} - 6.86\mathbf{j} + 3.43\mathbf{k} \ (\text{kN})$$

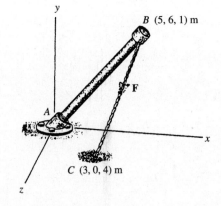

Problem 2.93   A cable extends from point C to point E. It exerts a 50-lb force $\mathbf{T}$ on plate C that is directed along the line from C to E. Express $\mathbf{T}$ in terms of scalar components.

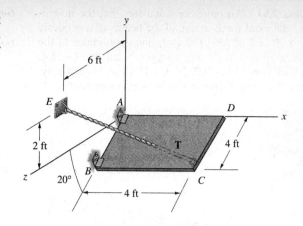

Solution: Find the unit vector $\mathbf{e}_{CE}$ and multiply it times the magnitude of the force to get the vector in component form,

$$\mathbf{e}_{CE} = \frac{\mathbf{r}_{CE}}{|\mathbf{r}_{CE}|} = \frac{(x_E - x_C)\mathbf{i} + (y_E - y_C)\mathbf{j} + (z_E - z_C)\mathbf{k}}{\sqrt{(x_E - x_C)^2 + (y_E - y_C)^2 + (z_E - z_C)^2}}$$

The coordinates of point C are $(4, -4\sin 20°, 4\cos 20°)$ or $(4, -1, 37,$ 3.76) (ft) The coordinates of point E are $(0, 2, 6)$ (ft)

$$\mathbf{e}_{CE} = \frac{(0-4)\mathbf{i} + (2-(-1.37))\mathbf{j} + (6-3.76)\mathbf{k}}{\sqrt{4^2 + 3.37^2 + 2.24^2}}$$

$$\mathbf{e}_{CE} = -0.703\mathbf{i} + 0.592\mathbf{j} + 0.394\mathbf{k}$$

$$\mathbf{T} = 50\mathbf{e}_{CE} \text{ (lb)}$$

$$\mathbf{T} = -35.2\mathbf{i} + 29.6\mathbf{j} + 19.7\mathbf{k} \text{ (lb)}$$

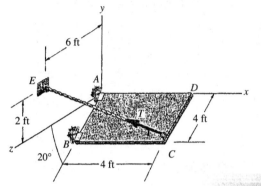

Problem 2.94   What are the direction cosines of the force $\mathbf{T}$ in Problem 2.93?

Solution: From the solution to Problem 2.93,

$$\mathbf{e}_{CE} = -0.703\mathbf{i} + 0.592\mathbf{j} + 0.394\mathbf{k}$$

However

$$\mathbf{e}_{CE} = \cos\theta_x\mathbf{i} + \cos\theta_y\mathbf{j} + \cos\theta_z\mathbf{k}$$

Hence,

$$\cos\theta_x = -0.703$$

$$\cos\theta_y = 0.592$$

$$\cos\theta_z = 0.394$$

Problem 2.95 The cable AB exerts a 200-lb force $\mathbf{F}_{AB}$ at point A that is directed along the line from A to B. Express $\mathbf{F}_{AB}$ in terms of scalar components.

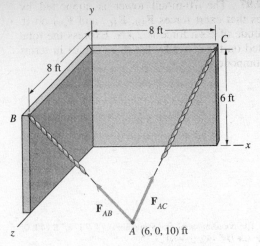

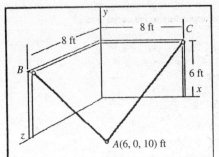

Solution: The coordinates of B are $B(0,6,8)$. The position vector from A to B is

$$\mathbf{r}_{AB} = (0-6)\mathbf{i} + (6-0)\mathbf{j} + (8-10)\mathbf{k} = -6\mathbf{i} + 6\mathbf{j} - 2\mathbf{k}$$

The magnitude is $|\mathbf{r}_{AB}| = \sqrt{6^2 + 6^2 + 2^2} = 8.718$ ft.

The unit vector is

$$\mathbf{u}_{AB} = \frac{-6}{8.718}\mathbf{i} + \frac{6}{8.718}\mathbf{j} - \frac{2}{8.718}\mathbf{k}$$

$\mathbf{F}_{AB} = |\mathbf{F}_{AB}|\mathbf{u}_{AB} = 200(-0.6882\mathbf{i} + 0.6882\mathbf{j} - 0.2294\mathbf{k})$ or

$\mathbf{u}_{AB} = -0.6882\mathbf{i} + 0.6882\mathbf{j} - 0.2294\mathbf{k}$.

The components of the force are

$\mathbf{F}_{AB} = |\mathbf{F}_{AB}|\mathbf{u}_{AB} = 200(-0.6882\mathbf{i} + 0.6882\mathbf{j} - 0.2294\mathbf{k})$ or

$$\boxed{\mathbf{F}_{AB} = -137.6\mathbf{i} + 137.6\mathbf{j} - 45.9\mathbf{k}}$$

Problem 2.96 Consider the cables and wall described in Problem 2.95. Cable AB exerts a 200-lb force $\mathbf{F}_{AB}$ at point A that is directed along the line from A to B. The cable AC exerts a 100-lb force $\mathbf{F}_{AC}$ at point A that is directed along the line from A to C. Determine the magnitude of the total force exerted at point A by the two cables.

Solution: Refer to the figure in Problem 2.81. From Problem 2.81 the force $\mathbf{F}_{AB}$ is

$$\mathbf{F}_{AB} = -137.6\mathbf{i} + 137.6\mathbf{j} - 45.9\mathbf{k}$$

The coordinates of C are $C(8,6,0)$. The position vector from A to C is

$$\mathbf{r}_{AC} = (8-6)\mathbf{i} + (6-0)\mathbf{j} + (0-10)\mathbf{k} = 2\mathbf{i} + 6\mathbf{j} - 10\mathbf{k}.$$

The magnitude is $|\mathbf{r}_{AC}| = \sqrt{2^2 + 6^2 + 10^2} = 11.83$ ft.
The unit vector is

$$\mathbf{u}_{AC} = \frac{2}{11.83}\mathbf{i} + \frac{6}{11.83}\mathbf{j} - \frac{10}{11.83}\mathbf{k} = 0.1691\mathbf{i} + 0.5072\mathbf{j} - 0.8453\mathbf{k}.$$

The force is

$$\mathbf{F}_{AC} = |\mathbf{F}_{AC}|\mathbf{u}_{AC} = 100\mathbf{u}_{AC} = 16.9\mathbf{i} + 50.7\mathbf{j} - 84.5\mathbf{k}.$$

The resultant of the two forces is

$$\mathbf{F}_R = \mathbf{F}_{AB} + \mathbf{F}_{AC} = (-137.6 + 16.9)\mathbf{i} + (137.6 + 50.7)\mathbf{j}$$
$$+ (-84.5 - 45.9)\mathbf{k}.$$

$$\mathbf{F}_R = -120.7\mathbf{i} + 188.3\mathbf{j} - 130.4\mathbf{k}.$$

The magnitude is

$$\boxed{|\mathbf{F}_R| = \sqrt{120.7^2 + 188.3^2 + 130.4^2} = 258.9 \text{ lb}}$$

Problem 2.97 The 70-m-tall tower is supported by three cables that exert forces $\mathbf{F}_{AB}$, $\mathbf{F}_{AC}$, and $\mathbf{F}_{AD}$ on it. The magnitude of each force is 2 kN. Express the total force exerted on the tower by the three cables in terms of scalar components.

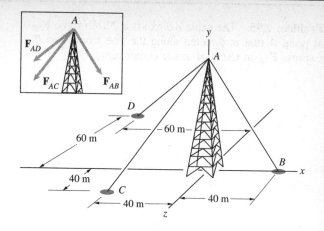

Solution: The coordinates of the points are A (0, 70, 0), B (40, 0, 0), C (−40, 0, 40) D (−60, 0, −60).

The position vectors corresponding to the cables are:

$$\mathbf{r}_{AD} = (-60 - 0)\mathbf{i} + (0 - 70)\mathbf{j} + (-60 - 0)\mathbf{k}$$

$$\mathbf{r}_{AD} = -60\mathbf{i} - 70\mathbf{k} - 60\mathbf{k}$$

$$\mathbf{r}_{AC} = (-40 - 0)\mathbf{i} + (0 - 70)\mathbf{j} + (40 - 0)\mathbf{k}$$

$$\mathbf{r}_{AC} = -40\mathbf{i} - 70\mathbf{j} + 40\mathbf{k}$$

$$\mathbf{r}_{AB} = (40 - 0)\mathbf{i} + (0 - 70)\mathbf{j} + (0 - 0)\mathbf{k}$$

$$\mathbf{r}_{AB} = 40\mathbf{i} - 70\mathbf{j} + 0\mathbf{k}$$

The unit vectors corresponding to these position vectors are:

$$\mathbf{u}_{AD} = \frac{\mathbf{r}_{AD}}{|\mathbf{r}_{AD}|} = \frac{-60}{110}\mathbf{i} - \frac{70}{110}\mathbf{j} - \frac{60}{110}\mathbf{k}$$

$$= -0.5455\mathbf{i} - 0.6364\mathbf{j} - 0.5455\mathbf{k}$$

$$\mathbf{u}_{AC} = \frac{\mathbf{r}_{AC}}{|\mathbf{r}_{AC}|} = -\frac{40}{90}\mathbf{i} - \frac{70}{90}\mathbf{j} + \frac{40}{90}\mathbf{k}$$

$$= -0.4444\mathbf{i} - 0.7778\mathbf{j} + 0.4444\mathbf{k}$$

$$\mathbf{u}_{AB} = \frac{\mathbf{r}_{AB}}{|\mathbf{r}_{AB}|} = \frac{40}{80.6}\mathbf{i} - \frac{70}{80.6}\mathbf{j} + 0\mathbf{k} = 0.4963\mathbf{i} - 0.8685\mathbf{j} + 0\mathbf{k}$$

The forces are:

$$\mathbf{F}_{AB} = |\mathbf{F}_{AB}|\mathbf{u}_{AB} = 0.9926\mathbf{i} - 1.737\mathbf{j} + 0\mathbf{k}$$

$$\mathbf{F}_{AC} = |\mathbf{F}_{AC}|\mathbf{u}_{AC} = -0.8888\mathbf{i} - 1.5556\mathbf{j} + 0.8888$$

$$\mathbf{F}_{AD} = |\mathbf{F}_{AD}|\mathbf{u}_{AD} = -1.0910\mathbf{i} - 1.2728\mathbf{j} - 1.0910\mathbf{k}$$

The resultant force exerted on the tower by the cables is:

$$\boxed{\mathbf{F}_R = \mathbf{F}_{AB} + \mathbf{F}_{AC} + \mathbf{F}_{AD} = -0.9872\mathbf{i} - 4.5654\mathbf{j} - 0.2022\mathbf{k} \text{ kN}}$$

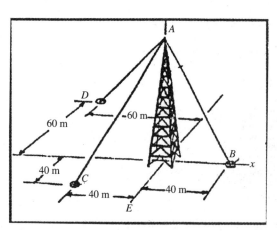

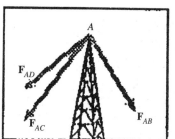

Problem 2.98 Consider the tower described in Problem 2.97. The magnitude of the force $\mathbf{F}_{AB}$ is 2 kN. The x and z components of the vector sum of the forces exerted on the tower by the three cables are zero. What are the magnitudes of $\mathbf{F}_{AC}$ and $\mathbf{F}_{AD}$?

Solution: From the solution of Problem 2.83, the unit vectors are:

$$\mathbf{u}_{AC} = \frac{\mathbf{r}_{AC}}{|\mathbf{r}_{AC}|} = -\frac{40}{90}\mathbf{i} - \frac{70}{90}\mathbf{j} + \frac{40}{90}\mathbf{k}$$

$$= -0.4444\mathbf{i} - 0.7778\mathbf{j} + 0.4444\mathbf{k}$$

$$\mathbf{u}_{AD} = \frac{\mathbf{r}_{AD}}{|\mathbf{r}_{AD}|} = \frac{-60}{110}\mathbf{i} - \frac{70}{110}\mathbf{j} - \frac{60}{110}\mathbf{k}$$

$$= -0.5455\mathbf{i} - 0.6364\mathbf{j} - 0.5455\mathbf{k}$$

From the solution of Problem 2.83 the force $\mathbf{F}_{AB}$ is

$$\mathbf{F}_{AB} = |\mathbf{F}_{AB}|\mathbf{u}_{AB} = 0.9926\mathbf{i} - 1.737\mathbf{j} + 0\mathbf{k}$$

The forces $\mathbf{F}_{AC}$ and $\mathbf{F}_{AD}$ are:

$$\mathbf{F}_{AC} = |\mathbf{F}_{AC}|\mathbf{u}_{AC} = |\mathbf{F}_{AC}|(-0.4444\mathbf{i} - 0.7778\mathbf{j} + 0.4444\mathbf{k})$$

$$\mathbf{F}_{AD} = |\mathbf{F}_{AD}|\mathbf{u}_{AD} = |\mathbf{F}_{AD}|(-0.5455\mathbf{i} - 0.6364\mathbf{j} - 0.5455\mathbf{k})$$

Taking the sum of the forces:

$$\mathbf{F}_R = \mathbf{F}_{AB} + \mathbf{F}_{AC} + \mathbf{F}_{AD} = (0.9926 - 0.4444|\mathbf{F}_{AC}| - 0.5455|\mathbf{F}_{AD}|)\mathbf{i}$$

$$+ (-1.737 - 0.7778|\mathbf{F}_{AC}| - 0.6364|\mathbf{F}_{AD}|)\mathbf{j}$$

$$+ (0.4444|\mathbf{F}_{AC}| - 0.5455|\mathbf{F}_{AD}|)\mathbf{k}$$

The sum of the x- and z-components vanishes, hence the set of simultaneous equations:

$$0.4444|\mathbf{F}_{AC}| + 0.5455|\mathbf{F}_{AD}| = 0.9926 \text{ and}$$

$$0.4444|\mathbf{F}_{AC}| - 0.5455|\mathbf{F}_{AD}| = 0$$

These can be solved by means of standard algorithms, or by the use of commercial packages such as TK Solver Plus ® or Mathcad®. Here a hand held calculator was used to obtain the solution:

$$\boxed{|\mathbf{F}_{AC}| = 1.1168 \text{ kN}} \qquad \boxed{|\mathbf{F}_{AD}| = 0.9098 \text{ kN}}$$

Problem 2.99 Express the position vector from point O to the collar at A in terms of scalar components.

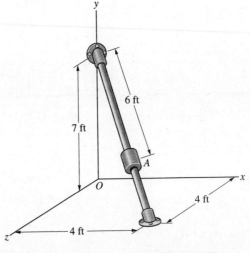

Solution: The vector from O to A can be expressed as the sum of the vectors $\mathbf{r}_{OT}$ from O to the top of the slider bar, and $\mathbf{r}_{TA}$ from the top of the slider bar to A. The coordinates of the top and base of the slider bar are: T (0, 7, 0), B (4, 0, 4). The position vector of the top of the bar is: $\mathbf{r}_{OT} = 0\mathbf{i} + 7\mathbf{j} + 0\mathbf{k}$. The position vector from the top of the bar to the base is:

$$\mathbf{r}_{TB} = (4 - 0)\mathbf{i} + (0 - 7)\mathbf{j} + (4 - 0)\mathbf{k}. \text{ or}$$

$\mathbf{r}_{TB} = 4\mathbf{i} - 7\mathbf{j} + 4\mathbf{k}$. The unit vector pointing from the top of the bar to the base is

$$\mathbf{u}_{TB} = \frac{\mathbf{r}_{TB}}{|\mathbf{r}_{TB}|} = \frac{4}{9}\mathbf{i} - \frac{7}{9}\mathbf{j} + \frac{4}{9}\mathbf{k} = 0.4444\mathbf{i} - 0.7778\mathbf{j} + 0.4444\mathbf{k}.$$

The collar position is

$$\mathbf{r}_{TA} = |\mathbf{r}_{TA}|\mathbf{u}_{TB} = 6(0.4444\mathbf{i} - 0.7778\mathbf{j} + 0.4444\mathbf{k})$$

$$= 2.6667\mathbf{i} - 4.6667\mathbf{j} + 2.6667,$$

measured along the bar. The sum of the two vectors is the position vector of A from origin O:

$$\mathbf{r}_{OA} = (2.6667 + 0)\mathbf{i} + (-4.6667 + 7)\mathbf{j} + (2.6667 + 0)\mathbf{k}$$

$$= 2.67\mathbf{i} + 2.33\mathbf{j} + 2.67\mathbf{k} \text{ ft}$$

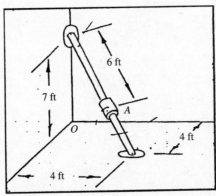

Problem 2.100 The cable AB exerts a 32-lb force $\mathbf{T}$ on the collar at A. Express $\mathbf{T}$ in terms of scalar components.

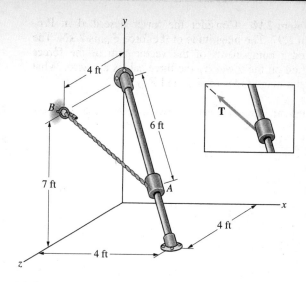

Solution: The coordinates of point B are B (0, 7, 4). The vector position of B is $\mathbf{r}_{OB} = 0\mathbf{i} + 7\mathbf{j} + 4\mathbf{k}$.

The vector from point A to point B is given by

$$\mathbf{r}_{AB} = \mathbf{r}_{OB} - \mathbf{r}_{OA}.$$

From Problem 2.86, $\mathbf{r}_{OA} = 2.67\mathbf{i} + 2.33\mathbf{j} + 2.67\mathbf{k}$. Thus

$$\mathbf{r}_{AB} = (0 - 2.67)\mathbf{i} + (7 - 2.33)\mathbf{j} + (4 - 2.67)\mathbf{j}$$

$$\mathbf{r}_{AB} = -2.67\mathbf{i} + 4.67\mathbf{j} + 1.33\mathbf{k}.$$

The magnitude is

$$|\mathbf{r}_{AB}| = \sqrt{2.67^2 + 4.67^2 + 1.33^2} = 5.54 \text{ ft}.$$

The unit vector pointing from A to B is

$$\mathbf{u}_{AB} = \frac{\mathbf{r}_{AB}}{|\mathbf{r}_{AB}|} = -0.4819\mathbf{i} + 0.8429\mathbf{j} + 0.2401\mathbf{k}$$

The force $\mathbf{T}$ is given by

$$\boxed{\mathbf{T}_{AB} = |\mathbf{T}_{AB}|\mathbf{u}_{AB} = 32\mathbf{u}_{AB} = -15.4\mathbf{i} + 27.0\mathbf{j} + 7.7\mathbf{k} \text{ (lb)}}$$

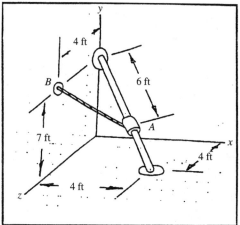

Problem 2.101 The circular bar has a 4-m radius and lies in the x-y plane. Express the position vector from point B to the collar at A in terms of scalar components.

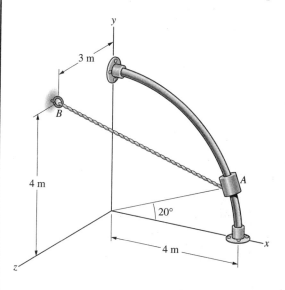

Solution: From the figure, the point B is at (0, 4, 3) m. The coordinates of point A are determined by the radius of the circular bar and the angle shown in the figure. The vector from the origin to A is $\mathbf{r}_{OA} = 4\cos(20°)\mathbf{i} + 4\sin(20°)\mathbf{j}$ m. Thus, the coordinates of point A are (3.76, 1.37, 0) m. The vector from B to A is given by $\mathbf{r}_{BA} = (x_A - x_B)\mathbf{i} + (y_A - y_B)\mathbf{j} + (z_A - z_B)\mathbf{k} = 3.76\mathbf{i} - 2.63\mathbf{j} - 3\mathbf{k}$ m. Finally, the scalar components of the vector from B to A are (3.76, −2.63, −3) m.

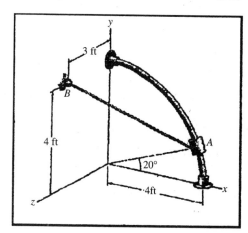

55

Problem 2.102   The cable AB in Problem 2.101 exerts a 60-N force $\mathbf{T}$ on the collar at A that is directed along the line from A toward B. Express $\mathbf{T}$ in terms of scalar components.

Solution: We know $\mathbf{r}_{BA} = 3.76\mathbf{i} - 2.63\mathbf{j} - 3\mathbf{k}$ m from Problem 2.101. The unit vector $\mathbf{u}_{AB} = -\mathbf{r}_{BA}/|\mathbf{r}_{BA}|$. The unit vector is $\mathbf{u}_{AB} = -0.686\mathbf{i} + 0.480\mathbf{j} + 0.547\mathbf{k}$. Hence, the force vector $\mathbf{T}$ is given by

$$\boxed{\mathbf{T} = |\mathbf{T}|(-0.686\mathbf{i} + 0.480\mathbf{j} + 0.547\mathbf{k}) \text{ N} = -41.1\mathbf{i} + 28.8\mathbf{j} + 32.8\mathbf{k} \text{ N}}$$

Problem 2.103   Determine the dot product of the vectors

$$\mathbf{U} = 8\mathbf{i} - 6\mathbf{j} + 4\mathbf{k}$$

and $\mathbf{V} = 3\mathbf{i} + 7\mathbf{j} + 9\mathbf{k}$.

Solution:

$$\mathbf{U} \cdot \mathbf{V} = U_x V_x + U_y V_y + U_z V_z$$

$$= (8)(3) + (-6)(7) + (4)(9)$$

$$\mathbf{U} \cdot \mathbf{V} = 18$$

Problem 2.104   Determine the dot product $\mathbf{U} \cdot \mathbf{V}$ of the vectors $\mathbf{U} = 40\mathbf{i} + 20\mathbf{j} + 60\mathbf{k}$ and $\mathbf{V} = -30\mathbf{i} + 15\mathbf{k}$.

Solution: Use Eq. 2.23.

$$\boxed{\mathbf{U} \cdot \mathbf{V} = (40)(-30) + (20)(0) + (15)(60) = -300}$$

Problem 2.105   What is the dot product of the position vector $\mathbf{r} = -10\mathbf{i} + 25\mathbf{j}$ (m) and the force

$\mathbf{F} = 300\mathbf{i} + 250\mathbf{j} + 300\mathbf{k}$ (N)?

Solution: Use Eq. (2.23).

$$\boxed{\mathbf{F} \cdot \mathbf{r} = (300)(-10) + (250)(25) + (300)(0) = 3250 \text{ N-m}}$$

Problem 2.106   What is the dot product of the position vector $\mathbf{r} = 4\mathbf{i} - 12\mathbf{j} - 3\mathbf{k}$ (ft) and the force $\mathbf{F} = 20\mathbf{i} + 30\mathbf{j} - 10\mathbf{k}$ (lb)?

Solution: Use Eq. (2.23).

$$\boxed{\mathbf{r} \cdot \mathbf{F} = 4(20) + 30(-12) - 10(-3) = -250 \text{ ft lb}}$$

Problem 2.107   Two *perpendicular* vectors are given in terms of their components by

$$\mathbf{U} = U_x\mathbf{i} - 4\mathbf{j} + 6\mathbf{k}$$

and $\mathbf{V} = 3\mathbf{i} + 2\mathbf{j} - 3\mathbf{k}$.

Use the dot product to determine the component U_x.

Solution: When the vectors are perpendicular, $\mathbf{U} \cdot \mathbf{V} \equiv 0$. Thus

$$\mathbf{U} \cdot \mathbf{V} = U_x V_x + U_y V_y + U_z V_z = 0$$

$$= 3U_x + (-4)(2) + (6)(-3) = 0$$

$$3U_x = 26$$

$$U_x = 8.67$$

Problem 2.108 Three vectors

$$U = U_x\mathbf{i} + 3\mathbf{j} + 2\mathbf{k}$$

$$V = -3\mathbf{i} + V_y\mathbf{j} + 3\mathbf{k}$$

$$W = -2\mathbf{i} + 4\mathbf{j} + W_z\mathbf{k}$$

are mutually perpendicular. Use the dot product to determine the components U_x, V_y, and W_z

Solution: For mutually perpendicular vectors, we have three equations, i.e.,

$$\mathbf{U} \cdot \mathbf{V} = 0$$

$$\mathbf{U} \cdot \mathbf{W} = 0$$

$$\mathbf{V} \cdot \mathbf{W} = 0$$

Thus

$$\left.\begin{array}{l} -3U_x + 3V_y + 6 = 0 \\ -2U_x + 12 + 2W_z = 0 \\ +6 + 4V_y + 3W_z = 0 \end{array}\right\} \begin{array}{l} \text{3 Eqns} \\ \text{3 Unknowns} \end{array}$$

Solving, we get

$$\boxed{\begin{array}{ll} U_x & = 2.857 \\ V_y & = 0.857 \\ W_z & = -3.143 \end{array}}$$

Problem 2.109 The magnitudes $|\mathbf{U}| = 10$ and $|\mathbf{V}| = 20$.

(a) Use the definition of the dot product to determine $\mathbf{U} \cdot \mathbf{V}$.

(b) Use Eq. (2.23) to obtain $\mathbf{U} \cdot \mathbf{V}$.

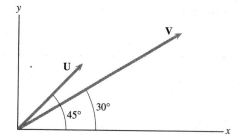

Solution:

(a) The definition of the dot product (Eq. (2.18)) is

$$\mathbf{U} \cdot \mathbf{V} = |\mathbf{U}||\mathbf{V}| \cos\theta. \text{ Thus}$$

$$\mathbf{U} \cdot \mathbf{V} = (10)(20)\cos(45° - 30°) = 193.2$$

(b) The components of $\mathbf{U}$ and $\mathbf{V}$ are

$$\mathbf{U} = 10(\mathbf{i}\cos 45° + \mathbf{j}\sin 45°) = 7.07\mathbf{i} + 7.07\mathbf{j}$$

$$\mathbf{V} = 20(\mathbf{i}\cos 30° + \mathbf{j}\sin 30°) = 17.32\mathbf{i} + 10\mathbf{j}$$

From Eq. (2.23) $\boxed{\mathbf{U} \cdot \mathbf{V} = (7.07)(17.32) + (7.07)(10) = 193.2}$

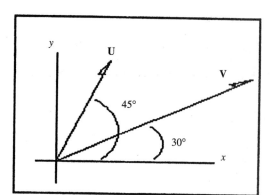

Problem 2.110 By evaluating the dot product $\mathbf{U} \cdot \mathbf{V}$, prove the identity $\cos(\theta_1 - \theta_2) = \cos\theta_1 \cos\theta_2 + \sin\theta_1 \sin\theta_2$.

Strategy: Evaluate the dot product both by using the definition and by using Eq. (2.23).

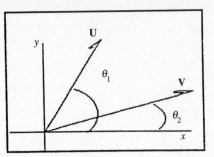

Solution: The strategy is to use the definition Eq. (2.18) and the Eq. (2.23). From Eq. (2.18) and the figure,

$\mathbf{U} \cdot \mathbf{V} = |\mathbf{U}||\mathbf{V}| \cos(\theta_1 - \theta_2)$. From Eq. (2.23) and the figure,

$$\mathbf{U} = |\mathbf{U}|(\mathbf{i}\cos\theta_1 + \mathbf{j}\sin\theta_2), \quad \mathbf{V} = |\mathbf{V}|(\mathbf{i}\cos\theta_2 + \mathbf{j}\sin\theta_2),$$

and the dot product is $\mathbf{U} \cdot \mathbf{V} = |\mathbf{U}||\mathbf{V}|(\cos\theta_1 \cos\theta_2 + \sin\theta_1 \sin\theta_2)$.

Equating the two results:

$$\mathbf{U} \cdot \mathbf{V} = |\mathbf{U}||\mathbf{V}| \cos(\theta_1 - \theta_2) = |\mathbf{U}||\mathbf{V}|(\cos\theta_1 \cos\theta_2 + \sin\theta_1 \sin\theta_2),$$

from which if $|\mathbf{U}| \neq 0$ and $|\mathbf{V}| \neq 0$, it follows that

$$\boxed{\cos(\theta_1 - \theta_2) = \cos\theta_1 \cos\theta_2 + \sin\theta_1 \sin\theta_2}, \quad \text{Q.E.D.}$$

Problem 2.111 Use the dot product to determine the angle between the forestay (cable AB) and the backstay (cable BC) of the sailboat in Problem 2.41.

Solution: The unit vector from B to A is

$$\mathbf{e}_{BA} = \frac{\mathbf{r}_{BA}}{|\mathbf{r}_{BA}|} = -0.321\mathbf{i} - 0.947\mathbf{j}$$

The unit vector from B to C is

$$\mathbf{e}_{BC} = \frac{\mathbf{r}_{BC}}{|\mathbf{r}_{BC}|} = 0.385\mathbf{i} - 0.923\mathbf{j}$$

From the definition of the dot product, $\mathbf{e}_{BA} \cdot \mathbf{e}_{BC} = 1 \cdot 1 \cdot \cos\theta$, where θ is the angle between BA and BC. Thus

$$\cos\theta = (-0.321)(0.385) + (-0.947)(-0.923)$$

$$\cos\theta = 0.750_{496}$$

$$\theta = 41.3°$$

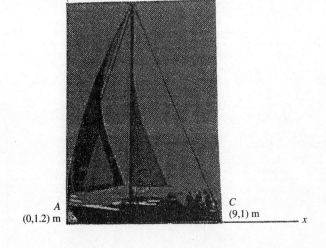

58

Problem 2.112 What is the angle θ between the straight lines AB and AC?

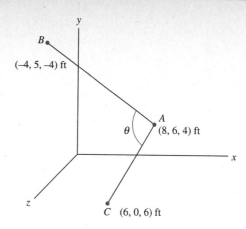

Solution: From the given coordinates, the position vectors are:

$\mathbf{r}_{OB} = -4\mathbf{i} + 5\mathbf{j} - 4\mathbf{k}$, $\mathbf{r}_{OA} = 8\mathbf{i} + 6\mathbf{j} + 4\mathbf{k}$, and

$\mathbf{r}_{OC} = 6\mathbf{i} + 0\mathbf{j} + 6\mathbf{k}$.

The straight lines correspond to the vectors:

$\mathbf{r}_{AB} = \mathbf{r}_{OB} - \mathbf{r}_{OA} = -12\mathbf{i} - \mathbf{j} - 8\mathbf{k}$,

$\mathbf{r}_{AC} = \mathbf{r}_{OC} - \mathbf{r}_{AC} = -2\mathbf{i} - 6\mathbf{j} + 2\mathbf{k}$

The dot product is given by

$\mathbf{r}_{AB} \cdot \mathbf{r}_{AC} = (-2)(-12) + (-1)(-6) + (+2)(-8) = 14$.

The magnitudes of the vectors are:

$|\mathbf{r}_{AC} = \sqrt{2^2 + 6^2 + 2^2}| = 6.6333$, and

$|\mathbf{r}_{AB} = \sqrt{12^2 + 1^2 + 8^2}| = 14.456$.

From the definition of the dot product, the angle is

$\cos\theta = \dfrac{\mathbf{r}_{AC} \cdot \mathbf{r}_{AB}}{|\mathbf{r}_{AC}||\mathbf{r}_{AB}|} = \dfrac{14}{(14.456)(6.633)} = 0.1460$.

Take the principal value: $\boxed{\theta = 81.6°}$

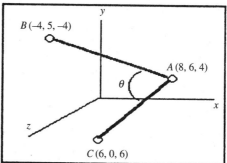

Problem 2.113 The ship O measures the positions of the ship A and the airplane B and obtains the coordinates shown. What is the angle θ between the lines of sight OA and OB?

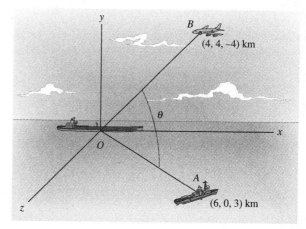

Solution: From the coordinates, the position vectors are:

$\mathbf{r}_{OA} = 6\mathbf{i} + 0\mathbf{j} + 3\mathbf{k}$ and $\mathbf{r}_{OB} = 4\mathbf{i} + 4\mathbf{j} - 4\mathbf{k}$

The dot product: $\mathbf{r}_{OA} \cdot \mathbf{r}_{OB} = (6)(4) + (0)(4) + (3)(-4) = 12$

The magnitudes: $|\mathbf{r}_{OA}| = \sqrt{6^2 + 0^2 + 3^2} = 6.71$ km and

$\qquad\qquad |\mathbf{r}_{OA}| = \sqrt{4^2 + 4^2 + 4^2} = 6.93$ km.

From Eq. (2.24) $\cos\theta = \dfrac{\mathbf{r}_{OA} \cdot \mathbf{r}_{OB}}{|\mathbf{r}_{OA}||\mathbf{r}_{OB}|} = 0.2581$, from which $\theta = \pm75°$.
From the problem and the construction, only the positive angle makes sense, hence $\boxed{\theta = 75°}$

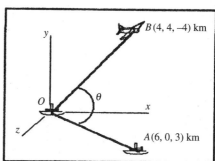

Problem 2.114 Astronauts on the space shuttle use radar to determine the magnitudes and direction cosines of the position vectors of two satellites A and B. The vector $\mathbf{r}_A$ from the shuttle to satellite A has magnitude 2 km and direction cosines $\cos\theta_x = 0.768$, $\cos\theta_y = 0.384$, $\cos\theta_z = 0.512$. The vector $\mathbf{r}_B$ from the shuttle to satellite B has magnitude 4 km and direction cosines $\cos\theta_x = 0.743$, $\cos\theta_y = 0.557$, $\cos\theta_z = -0.371$. What is the angle θ between the vectors $\mathbf{r}_A$ and $\mathbf{r}_B$?

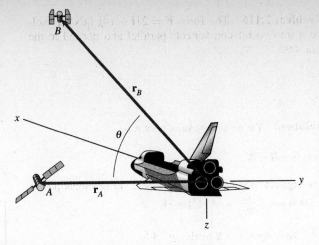

Solution: The direction cosines of the vectors along $\mathbf{r}_A$ and $\mathbf{r}_B$ are the components of the unit vectors in these directions (i.e., $\mathbf{u}_A = \cos\theta_x \mathbf{i} + \cos\theta_y \mathbf{j} + \cos\theta_z \mathbf{k}$, where the direction cosines are those for $\mathbf{r}_A$). Thus, through the definition of the dot product, we can find an expression for the cosine of the angle between $\mathbf{r}_A$ and $\mathbf{r}_B$.

$$\cos\theta = \cos\theta_{x_A}\cos\theta_{x_B} + \cos\theta_{y_A}\cos\theta_{y_B} + \cos\theta_{z_A}\cos\theta_{z_B}.$$

Evaluation of the relation yields

$$\boxed{\cos\theta = 0.594 \Rightarrow \theta = 53.5°}$$

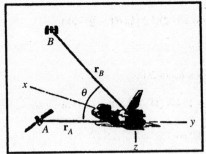

Problem 2.115 The cable BC exerts an 800-N force $\mathbf{F}$ on the bar AB at B. Use Eq. (2.26) to determine the vector component of $\mathbf{F}$ parallel to the bar.

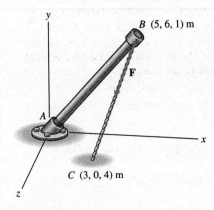

Solution: Eqn. 2.26 is $\mathbf{U}_P = (\mathbf{e} \cdot \mathbf{U})\mathbf{e}$ where $\mathbf{U}$ is the vector for which you want the component parallel to the direction indicated by the unit vector $\mathbf{e}$.

For the problem at hand, we must find two unit vectors. We need $\mathbf{e}_{BC}$ to be able to write the force $\mathbf{F}(\mathbf{F} = |\mathbf{F}|\mathbf{e}_{BC})$ and $\mathbf{e}_{BA} \sim$ the direction parallel to the bar.

$$\mathbf{e}_{BC} = \frac{\mathbf{r}_{BC}}{|\mathbf{r}_{BC}|} = \frac{(x_C - x_B)\mathbf{i} + (y_C - y_B)\mathbf{j} + (z_C - z_B)\mathbf{k}}{\sqrt{(x_C - x_B)^2 + (y_C - y_B)^2 + (z_C - z_B)^2}}$$

$$\mathbf{e}_{BC} = \frac{(3-5)\mathbf{i} + (0-6)\mathbf{j} + (4-1)\mathbf{k}}{\sqrt{2^2 + 6^2 + 3^2}}$$

$$\mathbf{e}_{BC} = -\frac{2}{7}\mathbf{i} - \frac{6}{7}\mathbf{j} + \frac{3}{7}\mathbf{k}$$

Similarly

$$\mathbf{e}_{BA} = \frac{-5\mathbf{i} - 6\mathbf{j} - 1\mathbf{k}}{\sqrt{5^2 + 6^2 + 1^2}}$$

$$\mathbf{e}_{BA} = -0.635\mathbf{i} - 0.762\mathbf{j} - 0.127\mathbf{k}$$

Now $\mathbf{F} = |\mathbf{F}|\mathbf{e}_{BC} = 800\,\mathbf{e}_{BC}$

$$\mathbf{F} = -228.6\mathbf{i} - 685.7\mathbf{j} + 342.9\mathbf{k}\ \text{N}$$

$$\mathbf{F}_P = (\mathbf{F} \cdot \mathbf{e}_{BA})\mathbf{e}_{BA}$$

$$\mathbf{F}_P = (624.1)\mathbf{e}_{BA}$$

$$\mathbf{F}_P = -396.3\mathbf{i} - 475.6\mathbf{j} - 79.3\mathbf{k}\ \text{N}$$

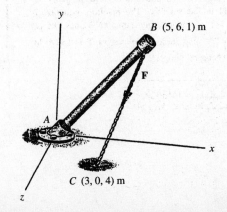

Problem 2.116 The force $\mathbf{F} = 21\mathbf{i} + 14\mathbf{j}$ (kN). Resolve it into vector components parallel and normal to the line OA.

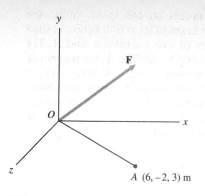

Solution: The position vector of point A is

$$\mathbf{r}_A = 6\mathbf{i} - 2\mathbf{j} + 3\mathbf{k}$$

The magnitude is $|\mathbf{r}_A| = \sqrt{6^2 + 2^2 + 3^2} = 7$. The unit vector parallel to OA is $\mathbf{e}_{OA} = \dfrac{\mathbf{r}_A}{|\mathbf{r}_A|} = \dfrac{6}{7}\mathbf{i} - \dfrac{2}{7}\mathbf{j} + \dfrac{3}{7}\mathbf{k}$

(a) The component of $\mathbf{F}$ parallel to OA is

$$(\mathbf{F} \cdot \mathbf{e}_{OA})\,\mathbf{e}_{OA} = ((3)(6) + (-2)(2))\left(\tfrac{1}{7}\right)(6\mathbf{i} - 2\mathbf{j} + 3\mathbf{k})$$

$$\mathbf{F}_P = 12\mathbf{i} - 4\mathbf{j} + 6\mathbf{k} \text{ (kN)}$$

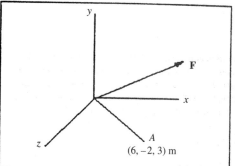

(b) The component of $\mathbf{F}$ normal to OA is

$$\mathbf{F}_N = \mathbf{F} - \mathbf{F}_p = (21 - 12)\mathbf{i} + (14 - (-4))\mathbf{j} + (0 - 6)\mathbf{k}$$

$$= 9\mathbf{i} + 18\mathbf{j} - 6\mathbf{k} \text{ (kN)}$$

Problem 2.117 At the instant shown, the Harrier's thrust vector is $\mathbf{T} = 3800\mathbf{i} + 15{,}300\mathbf{j} - 1800\mathbf{k}$ (lb), and its velocity vector is $\mathbf{v} = 24\mathbf{i} + 6\mathbf{j} - 2\mathbf{k}$ (ft/s). Resolve $\mathbf{T}$ into vector components parallel and normal to $\mathbf{v}$. (These are the components of the airplane's thrust parallel and normal to the direction of its motion.)

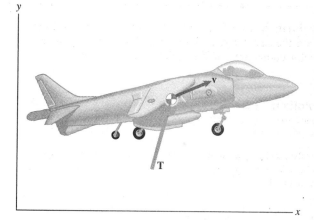

Solution: The magnitude of the velocity vector is given by

$$|\mathbf{v}| = \sqrt{v_x^2 + v_y^2 + v_z^2} = \sqrt{24^2 + 6^2 + (-2)^2}.$$

Thus, $|\mathbf{v}| = 24.8$ ft/s. The components of the unit vector in the direction of the velocity vector are given by

$$e_x = \frac{v_x}{|\mathbf{v}|},\ e_y = \frac{v_y}{|\mathbf{v}|},\ \text{and } e_z = \frac{v_z}{|\mathbf{v}|}.$$

Substituting numerical values, we get $e_x = 0.967$, $e_y = 0.242$, and $e_z = -0.0806$. The dot product of $\mathbf{T}$ and this unit vector gives the component of $\mathbf{T}$ parallel to the velocity. The resulting equation is $T_{\text{parallel}} = T_x e_x + T_y e_y + T_z e_z$. Substituting numerical values, we get $\boxed{T_{\text{parallel}} = 7232.12 \text{ lb.}}$ The magnitude of the vector $\mathbf{T}$ is 15870 lb. Using the Pythagorean Theorem, we get

$$\boxed{T_{\text{normal}} = \sqrt{|T|^2 - (T_{\text{parallel}})^2} = 14130 \text{ lb.}}$$

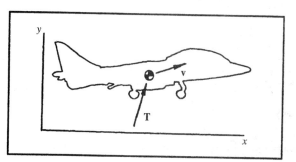

Problem 2.118 Cables extend from A to B and from A to C. The cable AC exerts a 1000-lb force $\mathbf{F}$ at A.

(a) What is the angle between the cables AB and AC?
(b) Determine the vector component of $\mathbf{F}$ parallel to the cable AB.

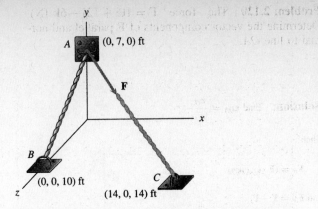

Solution: Use Eq. (2.24) to solve.

(a) From the coordinates of the points, the position vectors are:

$$\mathbf{r}_{AB} = (0-0)\mathbf{i} + (0-7)\mathbf{j} + (10-0)\mathbf{k}$$

$$\mathbf{r}_{AB} = 0\mathbf{i} - 7\mathbf{j} + 10\mathbf{k}$$

$$\mathbf{r}_{AC} = (14-0)\mathbf{i} + (0-7)\mathbf{j} + (14-0)\mathbf{k}$$

$$\mathbf{r}_{AC} = 14\mathbf{i} - 7\mathbf{j} + 14\mathbf{k}$$

The magnitudes are:

$$|\mathbf{r}_{AB}| = \sqrt{7^2 + 10^2} = 12.2 \text{ (ft) and}$$

$$|\mathbf{r}_{AB}| = \sqrt{14^2 + 7^2 + 14^2} = 21.$$

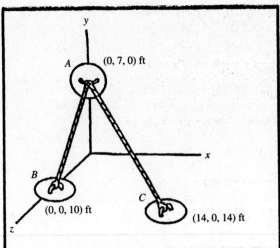

The dot product is given by

$$\mathbf{r}_{AB} \cdot \mathbf{r}_{AC} = (14)(0) + (-7)(-7) + (10)(14) = 189.$$

The angle is given by

$$\cos\theta = \frac{189}{(12.2)(21)} = 0.7377,$$

from which $\theta = \pm 42.5°$. From the construction: $\theta = +42.5°$

(b) The unit vector associated with AB is

$$\mathbf{e}_{AB} = \frac{\mathbf{r}_{AB}}{|\mathbf{r}_{AB}|} = 0\mathbf{i} - 0.5738\mathbf{j} + 0.8197\mathbf{k}.$$

The unit vector associated with AC is

$$\mathbf{e}_{AC} = \frac{\mathbf{r}_{AC}}{|\mathbf{r}_{AC}|} = 0.6667\mathbf{i} - 0.3333\mathbf{j} + 0.6667\mathbf{k}.$$

Thus the force vector along AC is

$$\mathbf{F}_{AC} = |\mathbf{F}|\mathbf{e}_{AC} = 666.7\mathbf{i} - 333.3\mathbf{j} + 666.7\mathbf{k}.$$

The component of this force parallel to AB is

$$(\mathbf{F}_{AC} \cdot \mathbf{e}_{AB})\mathbf{e}_{AB} = (737.5)\mathbf{e}_{AB} = 0\mathbf{i} - 423.2\mathbf{j} + 604.5\mathbf{k} \text{ (lb)}$$

Problem 2.119 Consider the cables AB and AC shown in Problem 2.118. Let $\mathbf{r}_{AB}$ be the position vector from point A to point B. Determine the vector component of $\mathbf{r}_{AB}$ parallel to the cable AC.

Solution: From Problem 2.100, $\mathbf{r}_{AB} = 0\mathbf{i} - 7\mathbf{j} + 10\mathbf{k}$, and $\mathbf{e}_{AC} = 0.6667\mathbf{i} - 0.3333\mathbf{j} + 0.6667\mathbf{k}$. Thus $\mathbf{r}_{AB} \cdot \mathbf{e}_{AC} = 9$, and $(\mathbf{r}_{AB} \cdot \mathbf{e}_{AC})\mathbf{e}_{AC} = 6\mathbf{i} - 3\mathbf{j} + 6\mathbf{k}$

Problem 2.120 The force $\mathbf{F} = 10\mathbf{i} + 12\mathbf{j} - 6\mathbf{k}$ (N). Determine the vector components of $\mathbf{F}$ parallel and normal to line OA.

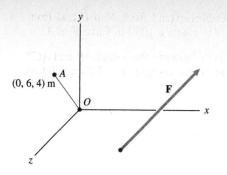

Solution: Find $\mathbf{e}_{OA} = \dfrac{\mathbf{r}_{OA}}{|\mathbf{r}_{OA}|}$

Then

$$\mathbf{F}_P = (\mathbf{F} \cdot \mathbf{e}_{OA})\mathbf{e}_{OA}$$

and $\mathbf{F}_N = \mathbf{F} - \mathbf{F}_P$

$$\mathbf{e}_{OA} = \frac{0\mathbf{i} + 6\mathbf{j} + 4\mathbf{k}}{\sqrt{6^2 + 4^2}} = \frac{6\mathbf{j} + 4\mathbf{k}}{\sqrt{52}}$$

$$\mathbf{e}_{OA} = \frac{6}{7.21}\mathbf{j} + \frac{4}{7.21}\mathbf{k} = 0.832\mathbf{j} + 0.555\mathbf{k}$$

$$\mathbf{F}_P = [(10\mathbf{i} + 12\mathbf{j} - 6\mathbf{k}) \cdot (0.832\mathbf{j} + 0.555\mathbf{k})]\mathbf{e}_{OA}$$

$$\mathbf{F}_P = [6.656]\mathbf{e}_{OA} = 0\mathbf{i} + 5.54\mathbf{j} + 3.69\mathbf{k} \text{ (N)}$$

$$\mathbf{F}_N = \mathbf{F} - \mathbf{F}_P$$

$$\mathbf{F}_N = 10\mathbf{i} + (12 - 5.54)\mathbf{j} + (-6 - 3.69\mathbf{k})$$

$$\mathbf{F}_N = 10\mathbf{i} + 6.46\mathbf{j} - 9.69\mathbf{k} \text{ N}$$

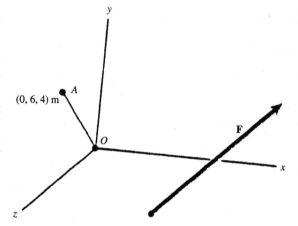

Problem 2.121 The rope AB exerts a 50-N force $\mathbf{T}$ on collar A. Determine the vector component of $\mathbf{T}$ parallel to bar CD.

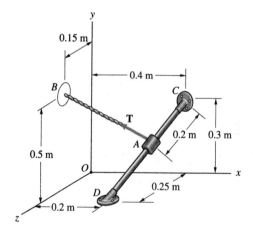

Solution: The vector from C to D is $\mathbf{r}_{CD} = (x_D - x_C)\mathbf{i} + (y_D - y_C)\mathbf{j} + (z_D - z_C)\mathbf{k}$. The magnitude of the vector

$$|\mathbf{r}_{CD}| = \sqrt{(x_D - x_C)^2 + (y_D - y_C)^2 + (z_D - z_C)^2}.$$

The components of the unit vector along CD are given by $u_{CDx} = (x_D - x_C)/|\mathbf{r}_{CD}|$, $u_{CDy} = (y_D - y_C)/|\mathbf{r}_{CD}|$, etc. Numerical values are $|\mathbf{r}_{CD}| = 0.439$ m, $u_{CDx} = -0.456$, $u_{CDy} = -0.684$, and $u_{CDz} = 0.570$. The coordinates of point A are given by $x_A = x_C + |\mathbf{r}_{CA}|e_{CDx}$, $y_A = y_C + |\mathbf{r}_{CA}|u_{CDy}$, etc. The coordinates of point A are (0.309, 0.163, 0.114) m. The vector from A to B and the corresponding unit vector are found in the same manner as from C to D above. The results are $|\mathbf{r}_{AB}| = 0.458$ m, $u_{ABx} = -0.674$, $u_{ABy} = 0.735$, and $u_{ABz} = 0.079$. The force $\mathbf{T}$ is given by $\mathbf{T} = |\mathbf{T}|\mathbf{u}_{AB}$. The result is $\mathbf{T} = -33.7\mathbf{i} + 36.7\mathbf{j} + 3.93\mathbf{k}$ N.

The component of $\mathbf{T}$ parallel to CD is given

$$\boxed{T_{\text{parallel}} = \mathbf{T} \bullet \mathbf{u}_{CD} = -7.52 \text{ N.}}$$

The negative sign means that the component of $\mathbf{T}$ parallel to CD points from D toward C (opposite to the direction of the unit vector from C to D).

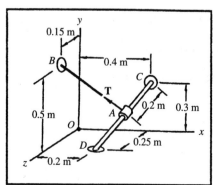

Problem 2.122 In Problem 2.121, determine the vector component of **T** normal to the bar *CD*.

Solution: From the solution of Problem 2.121, $|T| = 50$ N, and the component of **T** parallel to bar *CD* is $T_{parallel} = -7.52$ N. The component of **T** normal to bar *CD* is given by

$$T_{normal} = \sqrt{|T|^2 - (T_{parallel})^2} = 49.4 \text{ N.}$$

Problem 2.123 The disk *A* is at the midpoint of the sloped surface. The string from *A* to *B* exerts a 0.2-lb force **F** on the disk. If you resolve **F** into vector components parallel and normal to the sloped surface, what is the component normal to the surface?

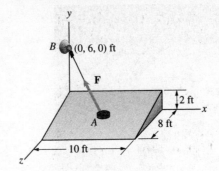

Solution: Consider a line on the sloped surface from *A* perpendicular to the surface. (see the diagram above) By SIMILAR triangles we see that one such vector is $r_N = 8j + 2k$. Let us find the component of **F** parallel to this line.
The unit vector in the direction normal to the surface is

$$e_N = \frac{r_N}{|r_N|} = \frac{8j + 2k}{\sqrt{8^2 + 2^2}} = 0.970j + 0.243k$$

The unit vector e_{AB} can be found by

$$e_{AB} = \frac{(x_B - x_A)i + (y_B - y_A)j + (z_B - z_A)h}{\sqrt{(x_B - x_A)^2 + (y_B - y_A)^2 + (z_B - z_A)^2}}$$

Point *B* is at (0, 6, 0) (ft) and *A* is at (5, 1, 4) (ft).

Substituting, we get

$$e_{AB} = -0.615i + 0.615j - 0.492k$$

Now $F = |F|e_{AB} = (0.2)e_{AB}$

$$F = -0.123i + 0.123j - 0.0984k \text{ (lb)}$$

The component of **F** normal to the surface is the component parallel to the unit vector e_N.

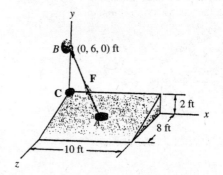

$$F_{NORMAL} = (F \cdot e_N)e_N = (0.955)e_N$$

$$F_{NORMAL} = 0i + 0.0927j + 0.0232k \text{ lb}$$

Problem 2.124 In Problem 2.123, what is the vector component of **F** parallel to the surface?

Solution: From the solution to Problem 2.123,

$$F = -0.123i + 0.123j - 0.0984k \text{ (lb) and}$$

$$F_{NORMAL} = 0i + 0.0927j + 0.0232k \text{ (lb)}$$

The component parallel to the surface and the component normal to the surface add to give **F** ($F = F_{NORMAL} + F_{parallel}$).

Thus

$$F_{parallel} = F - F_{NORMAL}$$

Substituting, we get

$$F_{parallel} = -0.1231i + 0.0304j - 0.1216k \text{ lb}$$

Problem 2.125 An astronaut in a maneuvering unit approaches a space station. At the present instant, the station informs him that his position relative to the origin of the station's coordinate system is $\mathbf{r}_G = 50\mathbf{i} + 80\mathbf{j} + 180\mathbf{k}$ (m) and his velocity is $\mathbf{v} = -2.2\mathbf{j} - 3.6\mathbf{k}$ (m/s). The position of the airlock is $\mathbf{r}_A = -12\mathbf{i} + 20\mathbf{k}$ (m). Determine the angle between his velocity vector and the line from his position to the airlock's position.

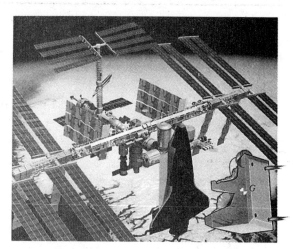

Solution: Points G and A are located at G: (50, 80, 180) m and A: (−12, 0, 20) m. The vector $\mathbf{r}_{GA}$ is $\mathbf{r}_{GA} = (x_A - x_G)\mathbf{i} + (y_A - y_G)\mathbf{j} + (z_A - z_G)\mathbf{k} = (-12 - 50)\mathbf{i} + (0 - 80)\mathbf{j} + (20 - 180)\mathbf{k}$ m. The dot product between $\mathbf{v}$ and $\mathbf{r}_{GA}$ is $\mathbf{v} \bullet \mathbf{r}_{GA} = |v||r_{GA}|\cos\theta = v_x x_{GA} + v_y y_{GA} + v_z z_{GA}$, where θ is the angle between $\mathbf{v}$ and $\mathbf{r}_{GA}$. Substituting in the numerical values, we get $\boxed{\theta = 19.7°.}$

Problem 2.126 In Problem 2.125, determine the vector component of the astronaut's velocity parallel to the line from his position to the airlock's position.

Solution: The dot product $\mathbf{v} \bullet \mathbf{r}_{GA} = v_x x_{GA} + v_y y_{GA} + v_z z_{GA} = 752$ $(m/s)^2$ and the component of $\mathbf{v}$ parallel to GA is $\mathbf{v}_{parallel} = |\mathbf{v}|\cos\theta$ where θ is defined as in Problem 2.125 above.

$$\boxed{\mathbf{v}_{parallel} = (4.22)(0.941) = 3.96 \ m/s}$$

Problem 2.127 Point P is at longitude 30°W and latitude 45°N on the Atlantic Ocean between Nova Scotia and France. (See Problem 2.90.) Point Q is at longitude 60°E and latitude 20°N in the Arabian Sea. Use the dot product to determine the shortest distance along the surface of the earth from P to Q in terms of the radius of the earth R_E.

Strategy: Use the dot product to detrmine the angle between the lines OP and OQ; then use the definition of an angle in radians to determine the distance along the surface of the earth from P to Q.

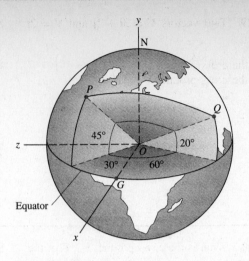

Solution: The distance is the product of the angle and the radius of the sphere, $d = R_E \theta$, where θ is in radian measure. From Eqs. (2.18) and (2.24), the angular separation of P and Q is given by

$$\cos\theta = \left(\frac{\mathbf{P} \cdot \mathbf{Q}}{|\mathbf{P}||\mathbf{Q}|}\right).$$

The strategy is to determine the angle θ in terms of the latitude and longitude of the two points. Drop a vertical line from each point P and Q to b and c on the equatorial plane. The vector position of P is the sum of the two vectors: $\mathbf{P} = \mathbf{r}_{OB} + \mathbf{r}_{BP}$. The vector $\mathbf{r}_{OB} = |\mathbf{r}_{OB}|(\mathbf{i}\cos\lambda_P + 0\mathbf{j} + \mathbf{k}\sin\lambda_P)$. From geometry, the magnitude is $|\mathbf{r}_{OB}| = R_E \cos\theta_P$. The vector $\mathbf{r}_{BP} = |\mathbf{r}_{BP}|(0\mathbf{i} + 1\mathbf{j} + 0\mathbf{k})$. From geometry, the magnitude is $|\mathbf{r}_{BP}| = R_E \sin\theta_P$. Substitute and reduce to obtain:

$$\mathbf{P} = \mathbf{r}_{OB} + \mathbf{r}_{BP} = R_E(\mathbf{i}\cos\lambda_P\cos\theta_P + \mathbf{j}\sin\theta_P + \mathbf{k}\sin\lambda_P\cos\theta_P).$$

A similar argument for the point Q yields

$$\mathbf{Q} = \mathbf{r}_{OC} + \mathbf{r}_{CQ} = R_E(\mathbf{i}\cos\lambda_Q\cos\theta_Q + \mathbf{j}\sin\theta_Q + \mathbf{k}\sin\lambda_Q\cos\theta_Q)$$

Using the identity $\cos^2\beta + \sin^2\beta = 1$, the magnitudes are

$$|\mathbf{P}| = |\mathbf{Q}| = R_E$$

The dot product is

$$\mathbf{P} \cdot \mathbf{Q} = R_E^2(\cos(\lambda_P - \lambda_Q)\cos\theta_P\cos\theta_Q + \sin\theta_P\sin\theta_Q)$$

Substitute:

$$\cos\theta = \frac{\mathbf{P} \cdot \mathbf{Q}}{|\mathbf{P}||\mathbf{Q}|} = \cos(\lambda_P - \lambda_Q)\cos\theta_P\cos\theta_Q + \sin\theta_P\sin\theta_Q$$

Substitute $\lambda_P = +30°$, $\lambda_Q = -60°$, $\theta_p = +45°$, $\theta_Q = +20°$, to obtain $\cos\theta = 0.2418$, or $\theta = 1.326$ radians. Thus the distance is $d = 1.326R_E$

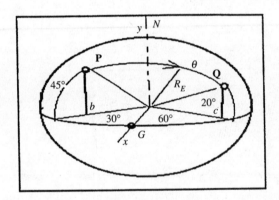

Problem 2.128 Determine the cross product $\mathbf{U} \times \mathbf{V}$ of the vectors $\mathbf{U} = 8\mathbf{i} - 6\mathbf{j} + 4\mathbf{k}$ and $\mathbf{V} = 3\mathbf{i} + 7\mathbf{j} + 9\mathbf{k}$.

Strategy: Sine the vectors are expressed in terms of their components, you can use Eq. (2.34) to determine their cross product.

Solution:

$$\mathbf{U} \times \mathbf{V} = \begin{vmatrix} \mathbf{i} & \mathbf{j} & \mathbf{k} \\ 8 & -6 & 4 \\ 3 & 7 & 9 \end{vmatrix}$$

$$= (-54 - 28)\mathbf{i} + (12 - 72)\mathbf{j} + (56 + 18)\mathbf{k}$$

$$\mathbf{U} \times \mathbf{V} = -82\mathbf{i} - 60\mathbf{j} + 74\mathbf{k}$$

Problem 2.129 Two vectors $\mathbf{U} = 3\mathbf{i} + 2\mathbf{j}$ and $\mathbf{V} = 2\mathbf{i} + 4\mathbf{j}$.

(a) What is the cross product $\mathbf{U} \times \mathbf{V}$?
(b) What is the cross product $\mathbf{V} \times \mathbf{U}$?

Solution: Use Eq. (2.34) and expand into 2 by 2 determinants.

$$\mathbf{U} \times \mathbf{V} = \begin{vmatrix} \mathbf{i} & \mathbf{j} & \mathbf{k} \\ 3 & 2 & 0 \\ 2 & 4 & 0 \end{vmatrix} = \mathbf{i}((2)(0) - (4)(0)) - \mathbf{j}((3)(0) - (2)(0))$$

$$+ \mathbf{k}((3)(4) - (2)(2)) = 8\mathbf{k}$$

$$\mathbf{V} \times \mathbf{U} = \begin{vmatrix} \mathbf{i} & \mathbf{j} & \mathbf{k} \\ 2 & 4 & 0 \\ 3 & 2 & 0 \end{vmatrix} = \mathbf{i}((4)(0) - (2)(0)) - \mathbf{j}((2)(0) - (3)(0))$$

$$+ \mathbf{k}((2)(2) - (3)(4)) = -8\mathbf{k}$$

Problem 2.130 What is the cross product $\mathbf{r} \times \mathbf{F}$ of the position vector $\mathbf{r} = 2\mathbf{i} + 2\mathbf{j} + 2\mathbf{k}$ (m) and the force $\mathbf{F} = 20\mathbf{i} - 40\mathbf{k}$ (N)?

Solution: Use Eq. (2.34) and expand into 2 by 2 determinants.

$$\mathbf{r} \times \mathbf{F} = \begin{vmatrix} \mathbf{i} & \mathbf{j} & \mathbf{k} \\ 2 & 2 & 2 \\ 20 & 0 & -40 \end{vmatrix} = \mathbf{i}((2)(-40) - (0)(2)) - \mathbf{j}((2)(-40)$$

$$- (20)(2)) + \mathbf{k}((2)(0) - (2)(20))$$

$$\mathbf{r} \times \mathbf{F} = -80\mathbf{i} + 120\mathbf{j} - 40\mathbf{k} \text{ (N-m)}$$

Problem 2.131 Determine the cross product $\mathbf{r} \times \mathbf{F}$ of the position vector $\mathbf{r} = 4\mathbf{i} - 12\mathbf{j} + 3\mathbf{k}$ (m) and the force

$\mathbf{F} = 16\mathbf{i} - 22\mathbf{j} - 10\mathbf{k}$ (N).

Solution:

$$\mathbf{r} \times \mathbf{F} = \begin{vmatrix} \mathbf{i} & \mathbf{j} & \mathbf{k} \\ 4 & -12 & 3 \\ 16 & -22 & -10 \end{vmatrix}$$

$$\mathbf{r} \times \mathbf{F} = (120 - (-66))\mathbf{i} + (48 - (-40))\mathbf{j}$$

$$+ (-88 - (-192))\mathbf{k} \text{ (N-m)}$$

$$\mathbf{r} \times \mathbf{F} = 186\mathbf{i} + 88\mathbf{j} + 104\mathbf{k} \text{ (N-m)}$$

Problem 2.132 Consider the vectors $\mathbf{U} = 6\mathbf{i} - 2\mathbf{j} - 3\mathbf{k}$ and $\mathbf{V} = -12\mathbf{i} + 4\mathbf{j} + 6\mathbf{k}$.

(a) Determine the cross product $\mathbf{U} \times \mathbf{V}$.
(b) What can you conclude about $\mathbf{U}$ and $\mathbf{V}$ from the result of (a)?

Solution: For (a) Use Eq. (2.34) and expand into 2 by 2 determinants.

$$\mathbf{U} \times \mathbf{V} = \begin{vmatrix} \mathbf{i} & \mathbf{j} & \mathbf{k} \\ 6 & -2 & -3 \\ -12 & 4 & 6 \end{vmatrix}$$

$$= \mathbf{i}((-2)(6) - (4)(-3)) + \mathbf{j}((6)(6)$$

$$- (-12)(-3)) + \mathbf{k}((6)(4) - (-12)(-2))$$

$$\mathbf{U} \times \mathbf{V} = 0\mathbf{i} + 0\mathbf{j} + 0\mathbf{k}$$

(b) From the definition of the cross product (see Eq. (2.28)) $\mathbf{U} \times \mathbf{V} = |\mathbf{U}||\mathbf{V}| \sin\theta\mathbf{e}$, where θ is the angle between the two vectors, and $\mathbf{e}$ is a unit vector perpendicular to both $\mathbf{U}$ and $\mathbf{V}$. If $\mathbf{U} \times \mathbf{V} = 0$ and if $|\mathbf{U}| \neq 0$ and $|\mathbf{V}| \neq 0$ then since by definition $\mathbf{e} \neq 0$, $\sin\theta$ must be zero: $\sin\theta = 0$, and $\theta = 0°$ or $\theta = 180°$, and *the two vectors are said to be parallel.* (A graphical construction confirms this interpretation.)

Problem 2.133 The cross product of two vectors $\mathbf{U}$ and $\mathbf{V}$ is $\mathbf{U} \times \mathbf{V} = -30\mathbf{i} + 40\mathbf{k}$. The vector $\mathbf{V} = 4\mathbf{i} - 2\mathbf{j} + 3\mathbf{k}$. Determine the components of $\mathbf{U}$.

Solution: We know

$$\mathbf{U} \times \mathbf{V} = \begin{vmatrix} \mathbf{i} & \mathbf{j} & \mathbf{k} \\ U_x & U_y & U_z \\ 4 & -2 & 3 \end{vmatrix}$$

$\mathbf{U} \times \mathbf{V} = (3U_y + 2U_z)\mathbf{i} + (4U_z - 3U_x)\mathbf{j} + (-2U_x - 4U_y)\mathbf{k}$ **(1)**

We also know

$\mathbf{U} \times \mathbf{V} = -30\mathbf{i} + 0\mathbf{j} + 40\mathbf{k}$ **(2)**

Equating components of (1) and (2), we get

$$3U_y + 2U_z = -30$$

$$4U_z - 3U_x = 0$$

$$-2U_x - 4U_y = 40$$

Setting $U_x = 4$ and solving, we get

$$\mathbf{U} = 4\mathbf{i} - 12\mathbf{j} + 3\mathbf{k}$$

Problem 2.134 The magnitudes $|\mathbf{U}| = 10$ and $|\mathbf{V}| = 20$.

(a) Use the definition of the cross product to determine $\mathbf{U} \times \mathbf{V}$.

(b) Use the definition of the cross product to determine $\mathbf{V} \times \mathbf{U}$.

(c) Use Eq. (2.34) to determine $\mathbf{U} \times \mathbf{V}$.

(d) Use Eq. (2.34) to determine $\mathbf{V} \times \mathbf{U}$.

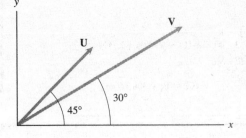

Solution: From Eq. (228) $\mathbf{U} \times \mathbf{V} = |\mathbf{U}||\mathbf{V}| \sin \theta \mathbf{e}$. From the sketch, the positive z-axis is out of the paper. For $\mathbf{U} \times \mathbf{V}$, $\mathbf{e} = -1\mathbf{k}$ (points into the paper); for $\mathbf{V} \times \mathbf{U}$, $\mathbf{e} = +1\mathbf{k}$ (points out of the paper). The angle $\theta = 15°$, hence (a) $\mathbf{U} \times \mathbf{V} = (10)(20)(0.2588)(\mathbf{e}) = 51.8\mathbf{e} = -51.8\mathbf{k}$. Similarly, (b) $\mathbf{V} \times \mathbf{U} = 51.8\mathbf{e} = 51.8\mathbf{k}$ (c) The two vectors are:

$$\mathbf{U} = 10(\mathbf{i} \cos 45° + \mathbf{j} \sin 45) = 7.07\mathbf{i} + 0.707\mathbf{j},$$

$$\mathbf{V} = 20(\mathbf{i} \cos 30° + \mathbf{j} \sin 30°) = 17.32\mathbf{i} + 10\mathbf{j}$$

$$\mathbf{U} \times \mathbf{V} = \begin{vmatrix} \mathbf{i} & \mathbf{j} & \mathbf{k} \\ 7.07 & 7.07 & 0 \\ 17.32 & 10 & 0 \end{vmatrix} = \mathbf{i}(0) - \mathbf{j}(0) + \mathbf{k}(70.7 - 122.45)$$

$$= -\mathbf{k}51.8$$

$$\text{(d) } \mathbf{V} \times \mathbf{U} = \begin{vmatrix} \mathbf{i} & \mathbf{j} & \mathbf{k} \\ 17.32 & 10 & 0 \\ 7.07 & 7.07 & 0 \end{vmatrix} = \mathbf{i}(0) - \mathbf{j}(0) + \mathbf{k}(122.45 - 70.7)$$

$$= 51.8\mathbf{k}$$

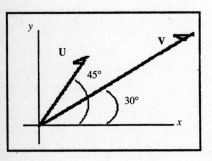

Problem 2.135 The force $\mathbf{F} = 10\mathbf{i} - 4\mathbf{j}$ (N). Determine the cross product $\mathbf{r}_{AB} \times \mathbf{F}$.

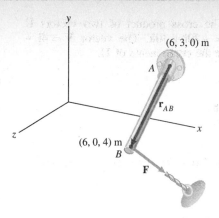

Solution: The position vector is

$$\mathbf{r}_{AB} = (6 - 6)\mathbf{i} + (0 - 3)\mathbf{j} + (4 - 0)\mathbf{k} = 0\mathbf{i} - 3\mathbf{j} + 4\mathbf{k}$$

The cross product:

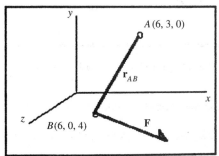

$$\mathbf{r}_{AB} \times \mathbf{F} = \begin{vmatrix} \mathbf{i} & \mathbf{j} & \mathbf{k} \\ 0 & -3 & 4 \\ 10 & -4 & 0 \end{vmatrix} = \mathbf{i}(16) - \mathbf{j}(-40) + \mathbf{k}(30)$$

$$= 16\mathbf{i} + 40\mathbf{j} + 30\mathbf{k} \text{ (N-m)}$$

Problem 2.136 By evaluating the cross product $\mathbf{U} \times \mathbf{V}$, prove the identity $\sin(\theta_1 - \theta_2) = \sin\theta_1 \cos\theta_2 - \cos\theta_1 \sin\theta_2$.

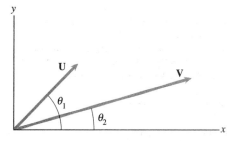

Solution: Assume that both $\mathbf{U}$ and $\mathbf{V}$ lie in the x-y plane. The strategy is to use the definition of the cross product (Eq. 2.28) and the Eq. (2.34), and equate the two. From Eq. (2.28) $\mathbf{U} \times \mathbf{V} = |\mathbf{U}||\mathbf{V}| \sin(\theta_1 - \theta_2)\mathbf{e}$. Since the positive z-axis is out of the paper, and $\mathbf{e}$ points into the paper, then $\mathbf{e} = -\mathbf{k}$. Take the dot product of both sides with $\mathbf{e}$, and note that $\mathbf{k} \cdot \mathbf{k} = 1$. Thus

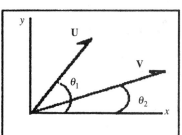

$$\sin(\theta_1 - \theta_2) = -\left(\frac{(\mathbf{U} \times \mathbf{V}) \cdot \mathbf{k}}{|\mathbf{U}||\mathbf{V}|} \right)$$

The vectors are:

$$\mathbf{U} = |\mathbf{U}|(\mathbf{i}\cos\theta_1 + \mathbf{j}\sin\theta_2), \text{ and } \mathbf{V} = |\mathbf{V}|(\mathbf{i}\cos\theta_2 + \mathbf{j}\sin\theta_2).$$

The cross product is

$$\mathbf{U} \times \mathbf{V} = \begin{vmatrix} \mathbf{i} & \mathbf{j} & \mathbf{k} \\ |\mathbf{U}|\cos\theta_1 & |\mathbf{U}|\sin\theta_1 & 0 \\ |\mathbf{V}|\cos\theta_2 & |\mathbf{V}|\sin\theta_2 & 0 \end{vmatrix}$$

$$= \mathbf{i}(0) - \mathbf{j}(0) + \mathbf{k}(|\mathbf{U}||\mathbf{V}|)(\cos\theta_1 \sin\theta_2 - \cos\theta_2 \sin\theta_1)$$

Substitute into the definition to obtain: $\sin(\theta_1 - \theta_2) = \sin\theta_1 \cos\theta_2 - \cos\theta_1 \sin\theta_2$. Q.E.D.

Problem 2.137 Use the cross product to determine the components of a unit vector **e** that is normal to both of the vectors $\mathbf{U} = 8\mathbf{i} - 6\mathbf{j} + 4\mathbf{k}$ and $\mathbf{V} = 3\mathbf{i} + 7\mathbf{j} + 9\mathbf{k}$.

Solution: First, find $\mathbf{U} \times \mathbf{V} = \mathbf{R}$

$$\mathbf{R} = \mathbf{U} \times \mathbf{V} = \begin{vmatrix} \mathbf{i} & \mathbf{j} & \mathbf{k} \\ 8 & -6 & 4 \\ 3 & 7 & 9 \end{vmatrix}$$

$$\mathbf{R} = (-54 - 28)\mathbf{i} + (12 - 72)\mathbf{j} + (56 - (-18))\,\mathbf{k}$$

$$\mathbf{R} = -82\mathbf{i} - 60\mathbf{j} + 74\mathbf{k}$$

$$\mathbf{e}_R = \pm \frac{\mathbf{R}}{|\mathbf{R}|} = \pm \left(\frac{-82\mathbf{i} - 60\mathbf{j} + 74\mathbf{k}}{125.7} \right)$$

$$\mathbf{e}_r = \pm(-0.652\mathbf{i} - 0.477\mathbf{j} + 0.589\mathbf{k})$$

Problem 2.138 (a) What is the cross product $\mathbf{r}_{OA} \times \mathbf{r}_{OB}$? (b) Determine a unit vector **e** that is perpendicular to $\mathbf{r}_{OA}$ and $\mathbf{r}_{OB}$.

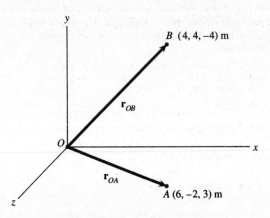

Solution: The two radius vectors are

$$\mathbf{r}_{OB} = 4\mathbf{i} + 4\mathbf{j} - 4\mathbf{k}, \quad \mathbf{r}_{OA} = 6\mathbf{i} - 2\mathbf{j} + 3\mathbf{k}$$

(a) The cross product is

$$\mathbf{r}_{OA} \times \mathbf{r}_{OB} = \begin{vmatrix} \mathbf{i} & \mathbf{j} & \mathbf{k} \\ 6 & -2 & 3 \\ 4 & 4 & -4 \end{vmatrix} = \mathbf{i}(8 - 12) - \mathbf{j}(-24 - 12)$$

$$+ \mathbf{k}(24 + 8)$$

$$= -4\mathbf{i} + 36\mathbf{j} + 32\mathbf{k} \ (\mathrm{m}^2)$$

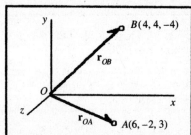

The magnitude is

$$|\mathbf{r}_{OA} \times \mathbf{r}_{OB}| = \sqrt{4^2 + 36^2 + 32^2} = 48.33 \ \mathrm{m}^2$$

(b) The unit vector is

$$\mathbf{e} = \pm \left(\frac{\mathbf{r}_{OA} \times \mathbf{r}_{OB}}{|\mathbf{r}_{OA} \times \mathbf{r}_{OB}|} \right) = \pm(-0.0828\mathbf{i} + 0.7448\mathbf{j} + 0.6621\mathbf{k})$$

(Two vectors.)

Problem 2.139 For the points O, A, and B in Problem 2.138, use the cross product to determine the length of the shortest straight line from point B to the straight line that passes through points O and A.

Solution:

$$\mathbf{r}_{OA} = 6\mathbf{i} - 2\mathbf{j} + 3\mathbf{k} \ (\text{m})$$

$$\mathbf{r}_{OB} = 4\mathbf{i} + 4\mathbf{j} - 4\mathbf{k} \ (\text{m})$$

$$\mathbf{r}_{OA} \times \mathbf{r}_{OB} = \mathbf{C}$$

($\mathbf{C}$ is $\perp$ to both $\mathbf{r}_{OA}$ and $\mathbf{r}_{OB}$)

$$\mathbf{C} = \begin{vmatrix} \mathbf{i} & \mathbf{j} & \mathbf{k} \\ 6 & -2 & 3 \\ 4 & 4 & -4 \end{vmatrix} = \begin{matrix} (+8-12)\mathbf{i} \\ +(12+24)\mathbf{j} \\ +(24+8)\mathbf{k} \end{matrix}$$

$$\mathbf{C} = -4\mathbf{i} + 36\mathbf{j} + 32\mathbf{k}$$

$\mathbf{C}$ is $\perp$ to both $\mathbf{r}_{OA}$ and $\mathbf{r}_{OB}$. Any line $\perp$ to the plane formed by $\mathbf{C}$ and $\mathbf{r}_{OA}$ will be parallel to the line BP on the diagram. $\mathbf{C} \times \mathbf{r}_{OA}$ is such a line. We then need to find the component of $\mathbf{r}_{OB}$ in this direction and compute its magnitude.

$$\mathbf{C} \times \mathbf{r}_{OA} = \begin{vmatrix} \mathbf{i} & \mathbf{j} & \mathbf{k} \\ -4 & +36 & 32 \\ 6 & -2 & 3 \end{vmatrix}$$

$$\mathbf{C} = 172\mathbf{i} + 204\mathbf{j} - 208\mathbf{k}$$

The unit vector in the direction of $\mathbf{C}$ is

$$\mathbf{e}_C = \frac{\mathbf{C}}{|\mathbf{C}|} = 0.508\mathbf{i} + 0.603\mathbf{j} - 0.614\mathbf{k}$$

(The magnitude of $\mathbf{C}$ is 338.3)

We now want to find the length of the projection, P, of line OB in direction $\mathbf{e}_c$.

$$P = \mathbf{r}_{OB} \cdot \mathbf{e}_C$$

$$= (4\mathbf{i} + 4\mathbf{j} - 4\mathbf{k}) \cdot \mathbf{e}_C$$

$$P = 6.90 \ \text{m}$$

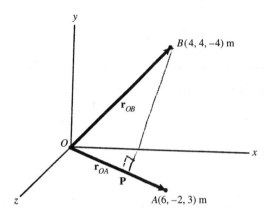

Problem 2.140 The cable BC exerts a 1000-lb force $\mathbf{F}$ on the hook at B. Determine $\mathbf{r}_{AB} \times \mathbf{F}$.

Solution: The coordinates of points A, B, and C are $A\ (16, 0, 12)$, $B\ (4, 6, 0)$, $C\ (4, 0, 8)$. The position vectors are

$$\mathbf{r}_{OA} = 16\mathbf{i} + 0\mathbf{j} + 12\mathbf{k}, \ \mathbf{r}_{OB} = 4\mathbf{i} + 6\mathbf{j} + 0\mathbf{k}, \ \mathbf{r}_{OC} = 4\mathbf{i} + 0\mathbf{j} + 8\mathbf{k}.$$

The force $\mathbf{F}$ acts along the unit vector

$$\mathbf{e}_{BC} = \frac{\mathbf{r}_{BC}}{|\mathbf{r}_{BC}|} = \frac{\mathbf{r}_{OC} - \mathbf{r}_{OB}}{|\mathbf{r}_{OC} - \mathbf{r}_{OB}|} = \frac{\mathbf{r}_{AB}}{|\mathbf{r}_{AB}|}$$

Noting $\mathbf{r}_{OC} - \mathbf{r}_{OB} = (4-4)\mathbf{i} + (0-6)\mathbf{j} + (8-0)\mathbf{k} = 0\mathbf{i} - 6\mathbf{j} + 8\mathbf{k}$

$|\mathbf{r}_{OC} - \mathbf{r}_{OB}| = \sqrt{6^2 + 8^2} = 10$. Thus

$\mathbf{e}_{BC} = 0\mathbf{i} - 0.6\mathbf{j} + 0.8\mathbf{k}$, and $\mathbf{F} = |\mathbf{F}|\mathbf{e}_{BC} = 0\mathbf{i} - 600\mathbf{j} + 800\mathbf{k}$ (lb).

The vector

$$\mathbf{r}_{AB} = (4-16)\mathbf{i} + (6-0)\mathbf{j} + (0-12)\mathbf{k} = -12\mathbf{i} + 6\mathbf{j} - 12\mathbf{k}$$

Thus the cross product is

$$\mathbf{r}_{AB} \times \mathbf{F} = \begin{vmatrix} \mathbf{i} & \mathbf{j} & \mathbf{k} \\ -12 & 6 & -12 \\ 0 & -600 & 800 \end{vmatrix} = -2400\mathbf{i} + 9600\mathbf{j} + 7200\mathbf{k} \ (\text{ft-lb})$$

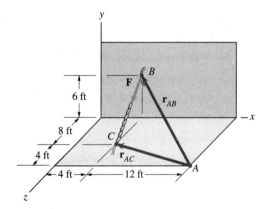

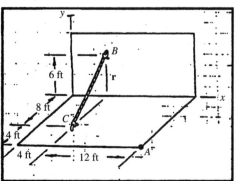

Problem 2.141 The cable BC shown in Problem 2.140 exerts a 300-lb force $\mathbf{F}$ on the hook at B.

(a) Determine $\mathbf{r}_{AB} \times \mathbf{F}$ and $\mathbf{r}_{AC} \times \mathbf{F}$.
(b) Use the definition of the cross product to explain why the result of (a) are equal.

Solution: (a) From Problem 2.140, the unit vector

$\mathbf{e}_{BC} = 0\mathbf{i} - 0.6\mathbf{j} + 0.8\mathbf{k}$, and $\mathbf{r}_{AB} = -12\mathbf{i} + 6\mathbf{j} - 12\mathbf{k}$

Thus $\mathbf{F} = |\mathbf{F}|\mathbf{e}_{BC} = 0\mathbf{i} - 180\mathbf{j} + 240\mathbf{k}$, and the cross product is

$$\mathbf{r}_{AB} \times \mathbf{F} = \begin{vmatrix} \mathbf{i} & \mathbf{j} & \mathbf{k} \\ -12 & 6 & -12 \\ 0 & -180 & 240 \end{vmatrix} = -720\mathbf{i} + 2880\mathbf{j} + 2160\mathbf{k} \text{ (ft-lb)}$$

The vector $\mathbf{r}_{AC} = (4 - 16)\mathbf{i} + 0\mathbf{j} + (8 - 12)\mathbf{k} = -12\mathbf{i} + 0\mathbf{j} - 4\mathbf{k}$.

Thus the cross product is

$$\mathbf{r}_{AC} \times \mathbf{F} = \begin{vmatrix} \mathbf{i} & \mathbf{j} & \mathbf{k} \\ -12 & 0 & -4 \\ 0 & -180 & 240 \end{vmatrix} = -720\mathbf{i} + 2880\mathbf{j} + 2160\mathbf{k} \text{ (ft-lb)}$$

(b) The definition of the cross product is $\mathbf{r} \times \mathbf{F} = |\mathbf{r}||\mathbf{F}| \sin\theta\mathbf{e}$. Since the two cross products above are equal, $|\mathbf{r}_{AB}||\mathbf{F}| \sin\theta_1\mathbf{e} = |\mathbf{r}_{AC}||\mathbf{F}| \sin\theta_2\mathbf{e}$. Note that $\mathbf{r}_{AC} = \mathbf{r}_{AB} + \mathbf{r}_{BC}$ from Problem 2.116, hence $\mathbf{r}_{AC} \times \mathbf{F} = \mathbf{r}_{AB} \times \mathbf{F} + \mathbf{r}_{BC} \times \mathbf{F} = |\mathbf{r}_{AB}||\mathbf{F}| \sin\theta_1\mathbf{e} + |\mathbf{r}_{BC}||\mathbf{F}| \sin 0\mathbf{e} = |\mathbf{r}_{AB}||\mathbf{F}| \sin\theta_1\mathbf{e}$, since $\mathbf{r}_{BC}$ and $\mathbf{F}$ are parallel. Thus the two results are equal.

Problem 2.142 The rope AB exerts a 50-N force $\mathbf{T}$ on the collar at A. Let $\mathbf{r}_{CA}$ be the position vector from point C to point A. Determine the cross product $\mathbf{r}_{CA} \times \mathbf{T}$.

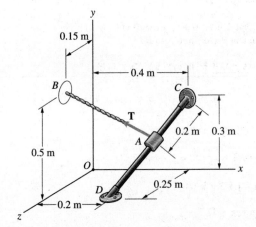

Solution: The vector from C to D is $\mathbf{r}_{CD} = (x_D - x_C)\mathbf{i} + (y_D - y_C)\mathbf{j} + (z_D - z_C)\mathbf{k}$. The magnitude of the vector

$$|\mathbf{r}_{CD}| = \sqrt{(x_D - x_C)^2 + (y_D - y_C)^2 + (z_D - z_C)^2}.$$

The components of the unit vector along CD are given by $u_{CDx} = (x_D - x_C)/|\mathbf{r}_{CD}|$, $u_{CDy} = (y_D - y_C)/|\mathbf{r}_{CD}|$, etc. Numerical values are $|\mathbf{r}_{CD}| = 0.439$ m, $u_{CDx} = -0.456$, $u_{CDy} = -0.684$, and $u_{CDz} = 0.570$. The coordinates of point A are given by $x_A = x_C + |\mathbf{r}_{CA}|u_{CDx}$, $y_A = y_C + |\mathbf{r}_{CA}|u_{CDy}$, etc. The coordinates of point A are (0.309, 0.162, 0.114) m. The vector $\mathbf{r}_{CA}$ is given by $\mathbf{r}_{CA} = (x_A - x_C)\mathbf{i} + (y_A - y_C)\mathbf{j} + (z_A - z_C)\mathbf{k}$. The vector $\mathbf{r}_{CA}$ is $\mathbf{r}_{CA} = (-0.091)\mathbf{i} + (-0.137)\mathbf{j} + (0.114)\mathbf{k}$ m. The vector from A to B and the corresponding unit vector are found in the same manner as from C to D above. The results are $|\mathbf{r}_{AB}| = 0.458$ m, $u_{ABx} = -0.674$, $u_{ABy} = 0.735$, and $u_{ABz} = 0.079$. The force $\mathbf{T}$ is given by $\mathbf{T} = |\mathbf{T}|u_{AB}$. The result is $\mathbf{T} = -33.7\mathbf{i} + 36.7\mathbf{j} + 3.93\mathbf{k}$ N.

The cross product $\mathbf{r}_{CA} \times \mathbf{T}$ can now be calculated.

$$\mathbf{r}_{CA} \times \mathbf{T} = \begin{vmatrix} \mathbf{i} & \mathbf{j} & \mathbf{k} \\ -0.091 & -0.138 & 0.114 \\ -33.7 & 36.7 & 3.93 \end{vmatrix}$$

$$= (-4.65)\mathbf{i} + (-3.53)\mathbf{j} + (-7.98)\mathbf{k} \text{ N-m}$$

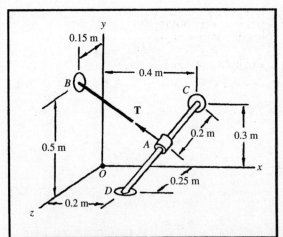

Problem 2.143 In Problem 2.142, let $\mathbf{r}_{CB}$ be the position vector from point C to point B. Determine the cross product $\mathbf{r}_{CB} \times \mathbf{T}$ and compare your answer to the answer to Problem 2.142.

Solution: We need $\mathbf{r}_{CB}$ and $\mathbf{T}$ in component form.

$$\mathbf{r}_{CB} = (x_B - x_C)\mathbf{i} + (y_B - y_C)\mathbf{j} + (z_B - z_C)\mathbf{k}$$

where B is at $(0, 0.5, 0.15)$ (m) and C is at $(0.4, 0.3, 0)$ (m)

$$\mathbf{r}_{CB} = -0.4\mathbf{i} + 0.2\mathbf{j} + 0.15\mathbf{k} \text{ (m)}$$

We now need to find T. From Problem 2.142, its magnitude is 50 N. We need a unit vector $\mathbf{e}_{AB}$ to be able to write $\mathbf{T}$ as $\mathbf{T} = 50\,\mathbf{e}_{AB}$ and then perform the required cross product. We need the coordinates of point A. Let us find $\mathbf{e}_{CA} = \mathbf{e}_{CD}$ and use this plus the known location of C to get the location of A. Point D is located at $(0.2, 0, 0.25)$

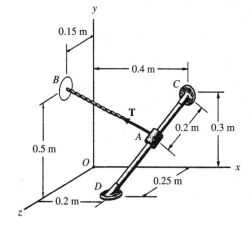

$$\mathbf{e}_{CD} = \mathbf{e}_{CA} = \frac{\mathbf{r}_{CD}}{|\mathbf{r}_{CD}|} = 0$$

$$\mathbf{e}_{CD} = -0.456\mathbf{i} - 0.684\mathbf{j} + 0.570\mathbf{k}$$

From the diagram, $d_{AC} = 0.2$ m

$$x_A = x_C + d_{AC}(e_{CDx})$$

$$y_A = y_C + d_{AC}(e_{CDy})$$

$$z_A = z_C + d_{AC}(e_{CDz})$$

Recall C is at $(0.4, 0.3, 0)$

Substituting, we find A is at $(0.309, 0.163, 0.114)$.
We now need the unit vector from A to B.

$$\mathbf{e}_{AB} = \frac{\mathbf{r}_{AB}}{|\mathbf{r}_{AB}|} = \frac{(x_B - x_A)\mathbf{i} + (y_B - y_A)\mathbf{j} + (z_B - z_A)\mathbf{k}}{|\mathbf{r}_{AB}|}$$

or

$$\mathbf{e}_{AB} = -0.674\mathbf{i} + 0.735\mathbf{j} + 0.078\mathbf{k}$$

We now want $\mathbf{T} = |\mathbf{T}|\mathbf{e}_{AB} = 50\,\mathbf{e}_{AB}$ we get

$$\mathbf{T} = 33.69\mathbf{i} + 36.74\mathbf{j} + 3.93\mathbf{k} \text{ (N)}$$

we can now form $\mathbf{r}_{CB} \times \mathbf{T}$

$$\mathbf{r}_{CB} \times \mathbf{T} = \begin{vmatrix} \mathbf{i} & \mathbf{j} & \mathbf{k} \\ -0.4 & +0.2 & +0.15 \\ 33.69 & 36.74 & 3.93 \end{vmatrix}$$

$$\mathbf{r}_{CB} \times \mathbf{T} = -4.72\mathbf{i} + 6.626\mathbf{j} - 21.434\mathbf{k} \text{ (N-m)}$$

Problem 2.144 The bar AB is 6 m long and is perpendicular to the bars AC and AD. Use the cross product to determine the coordinates x_B, y_B, z_B of point B.

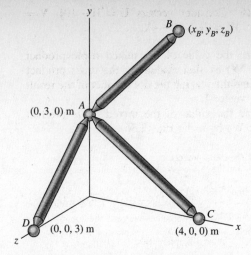

Solution: The strategy is to determine the unit vector perpendicular to both AC and AD, and then determine the coordinates that will agree with the magnitude of AB. The position vectors are:

$\mathbf{r}_{OA} = 0\mathbf{i} + 3\mathbf{j} + 0\mathbf{k}$, $\mathbf{r}_{OD} = 0\mathbf{i} + 0\mathbf{j} + 3\mathbf{k}$, and

$\mathbf{r}_{OC} = 4\mathbf{i} + 0\mathbf{j} + 0\mathbf{k}$. The vectors collinear with the bars are:

$\mathbf{r}_{AD} = (0 - 0)\mathbf{i} + (0 - 3)\mathbf{j} + (3 - 0)\mathbf{k} = 0\mathbf{i} - 3\mathbf{j} + 3\mathbf{k}$, $\mathbf{r}_{AC}$

$= (4 - 0)\mathbf{i} + (0 - 3)\mathbf{j} + (0 - 0)\mathbf{k} = 4\mathbf{i} - 3\mathbf{j} + 0\mathbf{k}$.

The vector collinear with $\mathbf{r}_{AB}$ is

$$\mathbf{R} = \mathbf{r}_{AD} \times \mathbf{r}_{AC} = \begin{vmatrix} \mathbf{i} & \mathbf{j} & \mathbf{k} \\ 0 & -3 & 3 \\ 4 & -3 & 0 \end{vmatrix} = 9\mathbf{i} + 12\mathbf{j} + 12\mathbf{k}$$

The magnitude $|\mathbf{R}| = 19.21$ (m). The unit vector is

$$\mathbf{e}_{AB} = \frac{\mathbf{R}}{|\mathbf{R}|} = 0.4685\mathbf{i} + 0.6247\mathbf{j} + 0.6247\mathbf{k}.$$

Thus the vector collinear with AB is

$\mathbf{r}_{AB} = 6\mathbf{e}_{AB} = +2.811\mathbf{i} + 3.75\mathbf{j} + 3.75\mathbf{k}.$

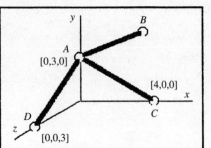

Using the coordinates of point A:

$x_B = 2.81 + 0 = 2.81$ (m)

$y_B = 3.75 + 3 = 6.75$ (m)

$z_B = 3.75 + 0 = 3.75$ (m)

Problem 2.145 Determine the minimum distance from point P to the plane defined by the three points A, B, and C.

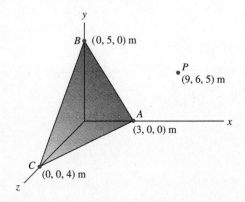

Solution: The strategy is to find the unit vector perpendicular to the plane. The projection of this unit vector on the vector OP: $\mathbf{r}_{OP} \cdot \mathbf{e}$ is the distance from the origin to P along the perpendicular to the plane. The projection on $\mathbf{e}$ of any vector into the plane ($\mathbf{r}_{OA} \cdot \mathbf{e}$, $\mathbf{r}_{OB} \cdot \mathbf{e}$, or $\mathbf{r}_{OC} \cdot \mathbf{e}$) is the distance from the origin to the plane along this same perpendicular. Thus the distance of P from the plane is

$d = \mathbf{r}_{OP} \cdot \mathbf{e} - \mathbf{r}_{OA} \cdot \mathbf{e}.$

The position vectors are: $\mathbf{r}_{OA} = 3\mathbf{i}$, $\mathbf{r}_{OB} = 5\mathbf{j}$, $\mathbf{r}_{OC} = 4\mathbf{k}$ and $\mathbf{r}_{OP} = 9\mathbf{i} + 6\mathbf{j} + 5\mathbf{k}$. The unit vector perpendicular to the plane is found from the cross product of any two vectors lying in the plane. Noting: $\mathbf{r}_{BC} = \mathbf{r}_{OC} - \mathbf{r}_{OB} = -5\mathbf{j} + 4\mathbf{k}$, and $\mathbf{r}_{BA} = \mathbf{r}_{OA} - \mathbf{r}_{OB} = 3\mathbf{i} - 5\mathbf{j}$. The cross product:

$$\mathbf{r}_{BC} \times \mathbf{r}_{BA} = \begin{vmatrix} \mathbf{i} & \mathbf{j} & \mathbf{k} \\ 0 & -5 & 4 \\ 3 & -5 & 0 \end{vmatrix} = 20\mathbf{i} + 12\mathbf{j} + 15\mathbf{k}.$$

The magnitude is $|\mathbf{r}_{BC} \times \mathbf{r}_{BA}| = 27.73$, thus the unit vector is $\mathbf{e} = 0.7212\mathbf{i} + 0.4327\mathbf{j} + 0.5409\mathbf{k}$. The distance of point P from the plane is $d = \mathbf{r}_{OP} \cdot \mathbf{e} - \mathbf{r}_{OA} \cdot \mathbf{e} = 11.792 - 2.164 = 9.63$ m. The second term is the distance of the plane from the origin; the vectors $\mathbf{r}_{OB}$, or $\mathbf{r}_{OC}$ could have been used instead of $\mathbf{r}_{OA}$.

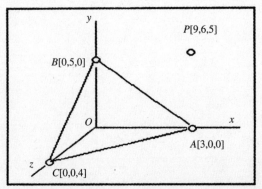

Problem 2.146 Consider vectors $U = 3i - 10j$, $V = -6j + 2k$, and $W = 2i + 6j - 4k$.

(a) Determine the value of the mixed triple product $U \cdot (V \times W)$ by first evaluating the cross product $V \times W$ and then taking the dot product of the result with the vector U.

(b) Determine the value of the mixed triple product $U \cdot (V \times W)$ by using Eq. (2.36).

Solution: (a) The cross product

$$V \times W = \begin{vmatrix} i & j & k \\ 0 & -6 & 2 \\ 2 & 6 & -4 \end{vmatrix} = (+24 - 12)i - (0 - 4)j + (0 + 12)k$$

$$= 12i + 4j + 12k$$

Take the dot product: $U \cdot (V \times W) = (3)(12) + (4)(-10) + 0 = -4$

(b) Eq. (2.36) expresses the mixed triple product as a 3X3 determinant.

$$U \cdot (V \times W) = \begin{vmatrix} 3 & -10 & 0 \\ 0 & -6 & 2 \\ 2 & 6 & -4 \end{vmatrix} = (3)(24 - 12) - (-10)(-4) + (0)$$

$$= 36 - 40 = -4$$

Problem 2.147 For the vectors $U = 6i + 2j - 4k$, $V = 2i + 7j$, and $W = 3i + 2k$, evaluate the following mixed triple products: (a) $U \cdot (V \times W)$; (b) $W \cdot (V \times U)$; (c) $V \cdot (W \times U)$.

Solution: Use Eq. (2.36).

(a) $U \cdot (V \times W) = \begin{vmatrix} 6 & 2 & -4 \\ 2 & 7 & 0 \\ 3 & 0 & 2 \end{vmatrix}$

$$= 6(14) - 2(4) + (-4)(-21) = 160$$

(b) $W \cdot (V \times U) = \begin{vmatrix} 3 & 0 & 2 \\ 2 & 7 & 0 \\ 6 & 2 & -4 \end{vmatrix}$

$$= 3(-28) - (0) + 2(4 - 42) = -160$$

(c) $V \cdot (W \times U) = \begin{vmatrix} 2 & 7 & 0 \\ 3 & 0 & 2 \\ 6 & 2 & -4 \end{vmatrix}$

$$= 2(-4) - 7(-12 - 12) + (0) = 160$$

Problem 2.148 Use the mixed triple product to calculate the volume of the parallelepiped.

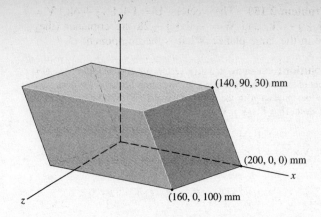

(140, 90, 30) mm

(200, 0, 0) mm

(160, 0, 100) mm

Solution: We are given the coordinates of point D. From the geometry, we need to locate points A and C. The key to doing this is to note that the length of side OD is 200 mm and that side OD is the x axis. Sides OD, AE, and CG are parallel to the x axis and the coordinates of the point pairs (O and D), (A and E), and (C and D) differ only by 200 mm in the x coordinate. Thus, the coordinates of point A are $(-60, 90, 30)$ mm and the coordinates of point C are $(-40, 0, 100)$ mm. Thus, the vectors $\mathbf{r}_{OA}$, $\mathbf{r}_{OD}$, and $\mathbf{r}_{OC}$ are $\mathbf{r}_{OD} = 200\mathbf{i}$ mm, $\mathbf{r}_{OA} = -60\mathbf{i} + 90\mathbf{j} + 30\mathbf{k}$ mm, and $\mathbf{r}_{OC} = -40\mathbf{i} + 0\mathbf{j} + 100\mathbf{k}$ mm. The mixed triple product of the three vectors is the volume of the parallelepiped. The volume is

$$\mathbf{r}_{OA} \cdot (\mathbf{r}_{OC} \times \mathbf{r}_{OD}) = \begin{vmatrix} -60 & 90 & 30 \\ -40 & 0 & 100 \\ 200 & 0 & 0 \end{vmatrix}$$

$$= -60(0) + 90(200)(100) + (30)(0) \text{ mm}^3$$

$$= 1,800,000 \text{ mm}^3$$

A figure to the right shows the parallelepiped with labeled vertices: A, B, E, F, O, D, C, G with y axis up, x axis to the right, z axis forward. Points labeled: (140, 90, 30) mm near E, (200, 0, 0) mm near D, (160, 0, 100) mm near G.

Problem 2.149 By using Eqs. (2.23) and (2.34), show that

$$\mathbf{U} \cdot (\mathbf{V} \times \mathbf{W}) = \begin{vmatrix} U_x & U_y & U_z \\ V_x & V_y & V_z \\ W_x & W_y & W_z \end{vmatrix}$$

Solution: One strategy is to expand the determinant in terms of its components, take the dot product, and then collapse the expansion. Eq. (2.23) is an expansion of the dot product: Eq. (2.23): $\mathbf{U} \cdot \mathbf{V} = U_X V_X + U_Y V_Y + U_Z V_Z$. Eq. (2.34) is the determinant representation of the cross product:

Eq. (2.34) $\mathbf{U} \times V = \begin{vmatrix} \mathbf{i} & \mathbf{j} & \mathbf{k} \\ U_X & U_Y & U_Z \\ V_X & V_Y & V_Z \end{vmatrix}$

For notational convenience, write $\mathbf{P} = (\mathbf{U} \times \mathbf{V})$. Expand the determinant about its first row:

$$\mathbf{P} = \mathbf{i} \begin{vmatrix} U_Y & U_Z \\ V_Y & V_Z \end{vmatrix} - \mathbf{j} \begin{vmatrix} U_X & U_Z \\ V_X & V_Z \end{vmatrix} + \mathbf{k} \begin{vmatrix} U_X & U_Z \\ V_X & V_Z \end{vmatrix}$$

Since the two-by-two determinants are scalars, this can be written in the form: $\mathbf{P} = \mathbf{i}P_X + \mathbf{j}P_Y + \mathbf{k}P_Z$ where the scalars P_X, P_Y, and P_Z are the two-by-two determinants. Apply Eq. (2.23) to the dot product of a vector $\mathbf{Q}$ with $\mathbf{P}$. Thus $\mathbf{Q} \cdot \mathbf{P} = Q_X P_X + Q_Y P_Y + Q_Z P_Z$. Substitute P_X, P_Y, and P_Z into this dot product

$$\mathbf{Q} \cdot \mathbf{P} = Q_X \begin{vmatrix} U_Y & U_Z \\ V_Y & V_Z \end{vmatrix} - Q_Y \begin{vmatrix} U_X & U_Z \\ V_X & V_Z \end{vmatrix} + Q_z \begin{vmatrix} U_X & U_Z \\ V_X & V_Z \end{vmatrix}$$

But this expression can be collapsed into a three-by-three determinant directly, thus:

$$\mathbf{Q} \cdot (\mathbf{U} \times \mathbf{V}) = \begin{vmatrix} Q_X & Q_Y & Q_Z \\ U_X & U_Y & U_Z \\ V_X & V_Y & V_Z \end{vmatrix}.$$ This completes the demonstration.

Problem 2.150 The vectors $\mathbf{U} = \mathbf{i} + U_Y\mathbf{j} + 4\mathbf{k}$, $\mathbf{V} = 2\mathbf{i} + \mathbf{j} - 2\mathbf{k}$, and $\mathbf{W} = -3\mathbf{i} + \mathbf{j} - 2\mathbf{k}$ are coplanar (they lie in the same plane). What is the component U_y?

Solution: Since the non-zero vectors are coplanar, the cross product of any two will produce a vector perpendicular to the plane, and the dot product with the third will vanish, by definition of the dot product. Thus $\mathbf{U} \cdot (\mathbf{V} \times \mathbf{W}) = 0$, for example.

$$\mathbf{U} \cdot (\mathbf{V} \times \mathbf{W}) = \begin{vmatrix} 1 & U_Y & 4 \\ 2 & 1 & -2 \\ -3 & 1 & -2 \end{vmatrix}.$$

$$= 1(-2+2) - (U_Y)(-4-6) + (4)(2+3)$$

$$= +10U_Y + 20 = 0$$

Thus $U_Y = -2$

Problem 2.151 The magnitude of $\mathbf{F}$ is 8 kN. Express $\mathbf{F}$ in terms of scalar components.

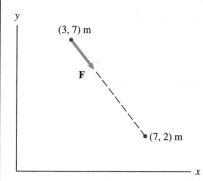

Solution: The unit vector collinear with the force $\mathbf{F}$ is developed as follows: The collinear vector is $\mathbf{r} = (7-3)\mathbf{i} + (2-7)\mathbf{j} = 4\mathbf{i} - 5\mathbf{j}$

The magnitude: $|\mathbf{r}| = \sqrt{4^2 + 5^2} = 6.403$ m. The unit vector is

$$\mathbf{e} = \frac{\mathbf{r}}{|\mathbf{r}|} = 0.6247\mathbf{i} - 0.7809\mathbf{j}.$$ The force vector is

$$\mathbf{F} = |\mathbf{F}|\mathbf{e} = 4.997\mathbf{i} - 6.247\mathbf{j} = 5\mathbf{i} - 6.25\mathbf{j} \text{ (kN)}$$

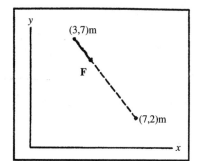

Problem 2.152 The magnitude of the vertical force $\mathbf{W}$ is 600 lb, and the magnitude of the force $\mathbf{B}$ is 1500 lb. Given that $\mathbf{A} + \mathbf{B} + \mathbf{W} = 0$, determine the magnitude of the force $\mathbf{A}$ and the angle α.

Solution: The strategy is to use the condition of force balance to determine the unknowns. The weight vector is $\mathbf{W} = -600\mathbf{j}$. The vector $\mathbf{B}$ is

$$\mathbf{B} = 1500(\mathbf{i}\cos 50° + \mathbf{j}\sin 50°) = 964.2\mathbf{i} + 1149.1\mathbf{j}$$

The vector $\mathbf{A}$ is $\mathbf{A} = |\mathbf{A}|(\mathbf{i}\cos(180 + \alpha) + \mathbf{j}\sin(180 + \alpha))$

$\mathbf{A} = |\mathbf{A}|(-\mathbf{i}\cos\alpha - \mathbf{j}\sin\alpha)$. The forces balance, hence $\mathbf{A} + \mathbf{B} + \mathbf{W} = 0$, or $(964.2 - |\mathbf{A}|\cos\alpha)\mathbf{i} = 0$, and $(1149.1 - 600 - |\mathbf{A}|\sin\alpha)\mathbf{j} = 0$. Thus $|\mathbf{A}|\cos\alpha = 964.2$, and $|\mathbf{A}|\sin\alpha = 549.1$. Take the ratio of the two equations to obtain $\tan\alpha = 0.5695$, or $\alpha = 29.7°$. Substitute this angle to solve: $\boxed{|\mathbf{A}| = 1110 \text{ lb}}$

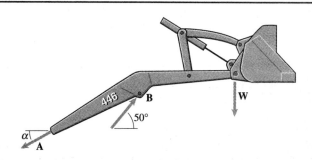

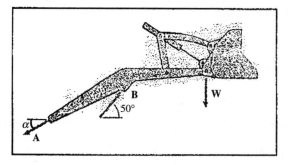

Problem 2.153 The magnitude of the vertical force vector **A** is 200 lb. If $\mathbf{A} + \mathbf{B} + \mathbf{C} = 0$, what are the magnitudes of the force vectors **B** and **C**?

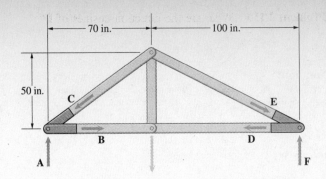

Solution: The strategy is to express the forces in terms of scalar components, and then solve the force balance equations for the unknowns. $\mathbf{C} = |\mathbf{C}|(-\mathbf{i}\cos\alpha - \mathbf{j}\sin\alpha)$, where

$$\tan\alpha = \frac{50}{70} = 0.7143, \text{ or } \alpha = 35.5°.$$

Thus $\mathbf{C} = |\mathbf{C}|(-0.8137\mathbf{i} - 0.5812\mathbf{j})$. Similarly, $\mathbf{B} = +|\mathbf{B}|\mathbf{i}$, and $\mathbf{A} = +200\mathbf{j}$. The force balance equation is $\mathbf{A} + \mathbf{B} + \mathbf{C} = 0$. Substituting, $(-0.8137|\mathbf{C}| + |\mathbf{B}|)\mathbf{i} = 0$, and $(-0.5812|\mathbf{C}| + 200)\mathbf{j} = 0$. Solving, $|\mathbf{C}| = 344.1$ lb, $|\mathbf{B}| = 280$ lb

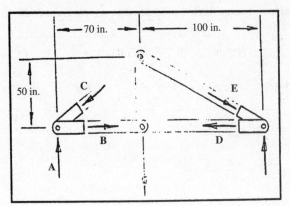

Problem 2.154 The magnitude of the horizontal force vector **D** in Problem 2.153 is 280 lb. If $\mathbf{D} + \mathbf{E} + \mathbf{F} = 0$, what are the magnitudes of the force vectors **E** and **F**?

Refer to the following diagram when solving Problems 2.155 through 2.160.

Solution: The strategy is to express the force vectors in terms of scalar components, and then solve the force balance equation for the unknowns. The force vectors are:

$\mathbf{E} = |\mathbf{E}|(\mathbf{i}\cos\beta - \mathbf{j}\sin\beta)$, where $\tan\beta = \frac{50}{100} = 0.5$, or $\beta = 26.6°$.

Thus

$\mathbf{E} = |\mathbf{E}|(0.8944\mathbf{i} - 0.4472\mathbf{j})$

$\mathbf{D} = -280\mathbf{i}$, and $\mathbf{F} = |\mathbf{F}|\mathbf{j}$.

The force balance equation is $\mathbf{D} + \mathbf{E} + \mathbf{F} = 0$. Substitute and resolve into two equations:

$(0.8944|\mathbf{E}| - 280)\mathbf{i} = 0$, and $(-0.4472|\mathbf{E}| + |\mathbf{F}|)\mathbf{j} = 0$.

Solve: $|\mathbf{E}| = 313.1$ lb, $|\mathbf{F}| = 140$ lb

Problem 2.155   What are the direction cosines of **F**?

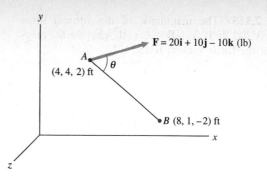

Solution: Use the definition of the direction cosines and the ensuing discussion.

The magnitude of **F**: $|\mathbf{F}| = \sqrt{20^2 + 10^2 + 10^2} = 24.5$.

The direction cosines are $\cos\theta_x = \dfrac{F_x}{|\mathbf{F}|} = \dfrac{20}{24.5} = 0.8165$,

$\cos\theta_y = \dfrac{F_y}{|\mathbf{F}|} = \dfrac{10}{24.5} = 0.4082$

$\cos\theta_z = \dfrac{F_z}{|\mathbf{F}|} = \dfrac{-10}{24.5} = -0.4082$

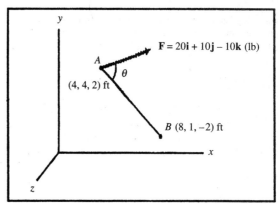

Problem 2.156   Determine the scalar components of a unit vector parallel to line AB that points from A toward B.

Solution: Use the definition of the unit vector, we get

The position vectors are: $\mathbf{r}_A = 4\mathbf{i} + 4\mathbf{j} + 2\mathbf{k}$, $\mathbf{r}_B = 8\mathbf{i} + 1\mathbf{j} - 2\mathbf{k}$. The vector from A to B is $\mathbf{r}_{AB} = (8-4)\mathbf{i} + (1-4)\mathbf{j} + (-2-2)\mathbf{k} = 4\mathbf{i} - 3\mathbf{j} - 4\mathbf{k}$. The magnitude: $|\mathbf{r}_{AB}| = \sqrt{4^2 + 3^2 + 4^2} = 6.4$. The unit vector is

$$\mathbf{e}_{AB} = \frac{\mathbf{r}_{AB}}{|\mathbf{r}_{AB}|} = \frac{4}{6.4}\mathbf{i} - \frac{3}{6.4}\mathbf{j} - \frac{4}{6.4}\mathbf{k} = 0.6247\mathbf{i} - 0.4688\mathbf{j} - 0.6247\mathbf{k}$$

Problem 2.157   What is the angle θ between the line AB and the force **F**?

Solution: Use the definition of the dot product Eq. (2.18), and Eq. (2.24):

$$\cos\theta = \frac{\mathbf{r}_{AB} \cdot \mathbf{F}}{|\mathbf{r}_{AB}||\mathbf{F}|}.$$

From the solution to Problem 2.130, the vector parallel to AB is $\mathbf{r}_{AB} = 4\mathbf{i} - 3\mathbf{j} - 4\mathbf{k}$, with a magnitude $|\mathbf{r}_{AB}| = 6.4$. From Problem 2.129, the force is $\mathbf{F} = 20\mathbf{i} + 10\mathbf{j} - 10\mathbf{k}$, with a magnitude of $|\mathbf{F}| = 24.5$. The dot product is $\mathbf{r}_{AB} \cdot \mathbf{F} = (4)(20) + (-3)(10) + (-4)(-10) = 90$. Substituting, $\cos\theta = \dfrac{90}{(6.4)(24.5)} = 0.574$, $\boxed{\theta = 55^\circ}$

Problem 2.158   Determine the vector component of **F** that is parallel to the line AB.

Solution: Use the definition in Eq. (2.26): $\mathbf{U}_P = (\mathbf{e} \cdot \mathbf{U})\mathbf{e}$, where **e** is parallel to a line L. From Problem 2.130 the unit vector parallel to line AB is $\mathbf{e}_{AB} = 0.6247\mathbf{i} - 0.4688\mathbf{j} - 0.6247\mathbf{k}$. The dot product is

$\mathbf{e} \cdot \mathbf{F} = (0.6247)(20) + (-0.4688)(10) + (-0.6247)(-10) = 14.053$.

The parallel vector is

$(\mathbf{e} \cdot \mathbf{F})\mathbf{e} = (14.053)\mathbf{e} = 8.78\mathbf{i} - 6.59\mathbf{j} - 8.78\mathbf{k}$ (lb)

Problem 2.159 Determine the vector component of **F** that is normal to the line AB.

Solution: Use the Eq. (2.27) and the solution to Problem 2.132.

$$\mathbf{F}_N = \mathbf{F} - \mathbf{F}_P = (20 - 8.78)\mathbf{i} + (10 + 6.59)\mathbf{j} + (-10 + 8.78)\mathbf{k}$$

$$= 11.22\mathbf{i} + 16.59\mathbf{j} - 1.22\mathbf{k} \text{ (lb)}$$

Problem 2.160 Determine the vector $\mathbf{r}_{BA} \times \mathbf{F}$, where $\mathbf{r}_{BA}$ is the position vector from B to A.

Solution: Use the definition in Eq. (2.34). Noting $\mathbf{r}_{BA} = -\mathbf{r}_{AB}$, from Problem 2.157 $\mathbf{r}_{BA} = -4\mathbf{i} + 3\mathbf{j} + 4\mathbf{k}$. The cross product is

$$\mathbf{r}_{BA} \times \mathbf{F} = \begin{vmatrix} \mathbf{i} & \mathbf{j} & \mathbf{k} \\ -4 & 3 & 4 \\ 20 & 10 & -10 \end{vmatrix} = (-30 - 40)\mathbf{i} - (40 - 80)\mathbf{j}$$

$$+ (-40 - 60)$$

$$= -70\mathbf{i} + 40\mathbf{j} - 100\mathbf{k} \text{ (ft-lb)}$$

Problem 2.161 (a) Write the position vector $\mathbf{r}_{AB}$ from point A to point B in terms of scalar components.
(b) The vector **F** has magnitude $|\mathbf{F}| = 200$ N and is parallel to the line from A to B. Write **F** in terms of scalar components.

Solution:

(a) $\mathbf{r}_{AB} = (B_x - A_x)\mathbf{i} + (B_y - A_y)\mathbf{j} + (B_z - A_z)\mathbf{k}$

$$= (8 - 1)\mathbf{i} + (1 - 5)\mathbf{j} + (1 + 1)\mathbf{k}$$

$$= 7\mathbf{i} - 4\mathbf{j} + 2\mathbf{k} \text{ (m)}.$$

(b) By dividing $\mathbf{r}_{AB}$ by its magnitude, we obtain a unit vector parallel to **F**:

$$\mathbf{e}_{AB} = \frac{\mathbf{r}_{AB}}{|\mathbf{r}_{AB}|} = 0.843\mathbf{i} - 0.482\mathbf{j} + 0.241\mathbf{k}.$$

Then

$$\mathbf{F} = 200\mathbf{e}_{AB} = 169\mathbf{i} - 93.3\mathbf{j} + 48.2\mathbf{k} \text{ (N)}.$$

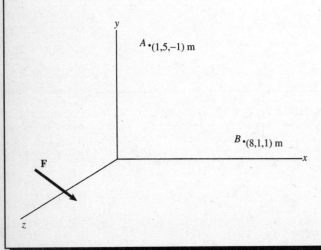

Problem 2.162 The rope exerts a force of magnitude $|\mathbf{F}| = 200$ lb on the top of the pole at B.

(a) Determine the vector $\mathbf{r}_{AB} \times \mathbf{F}$, where $\mathbf{r}_{AB}$ is the position vector from A to B.
(b) Determine the vector $\mathbf{r}_{AC} \times \mathbf{F}$, where $\mathbf{r}_{AC}$ is the position vector from A to C.

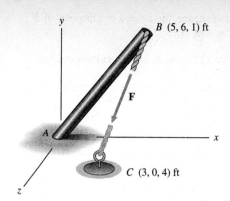

Solution: The strategy is to define the unit vector pointing from B to A, express the force in terms of this unit vector, and take the cross product of the position vectors with this force. The position vectors

$$\mathbf{r}_{AB} = 5\mathbf{i} + 6\mathbf{j} + 1\mathbf{k}, \quad \mathbf{r}_{AC} = 3\mathbf{i} + 0\mathbf{j} + 4\mathbf{k},$$

$$\mathbf{r}_{BC} = (3-5)\mathbf{i} + (0-6)\mathbf{j} + (4-1)\mathbf{k} = -2\mathbf{i} - 6\mathbf{j} + 3\mathbf{k}.$$

The magnitude $|\mathbf{r}_{BC}| = \sqrt{2^2 + 6^2 + 3^2} = 7$. The unit vector is

$$\mathbf{e}_{BC} = \frac{\mathbf{r}_{BC}}{|\mathbf{r}_{BC}|} = -0.2857\mathbf{i} - 0.8571\mathbf{j} + 0.4286\mathbf{k}.$$

The force vector is

$$\mathbf{F} = |\mathbf{F}|\mathbf{e}_{BC} = 200\mathbf{e}_{BC} = -57.14\mathbf{i} - 171.42\mathbf{j} + 85.72\mathbf{k}.$$

The cross products:

$$\mathbf{r}_{AB} \times \mathbf{F} = \begin{vmatrix} \mathbf{i} & \mathbf{j} & \mathbf{k} \\ 5 & 6 & 1 \\ -57.14 & -171.42 & 85.72 \end{vmatrix}$$

$$= 685.74\mathbf{i} - 485.74\mathbf{j} - 514.26\mathbf{k}$$

$$= 685.7\mathbf{i} - 485.7\mathbf{j} - 514.3\mathbf{k} \text{ (ft-lb)}$$

$$\mathbf{r}_{AC} \times \mathbf{F} = \begin{vmatrix} \mathbf{i} & \mathbf{j} & \mathbf{k} \\ 3 & 0 & 4 \\ -57.14 & -171.42 & 85.72 \end{vmatrix}$$

$$= 685.68\mathbf{i} - 485.72\mathbf{j} - 514.26\mathbf{k}$$

$$= 685.7\mathbf{i} - 485.7\mathbf{j} - 514.3\mathbf{k} \text{ (ft-lb)}$$

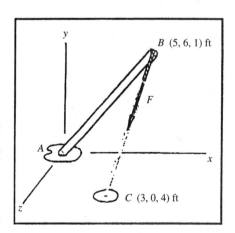

Problem 2.163 The magnitude of $\mathbf{F}_B$ is 400 N and $|\mathbf{F}_A + \mathbf{F}_B| = 900$ N. Determine the components of $\mathbf{F}_A$.

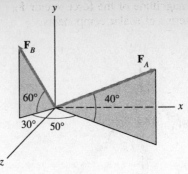

Solution:

$|\mathbf{F}_B| = 400$ N

We need to write each vector in terms of its known or unknown components. From the diagram

$F_{Ax} = (|\mathbf{F}_A| \cos 40°) \cos 40° = 0.587$

$F_{Az} = (|\mathbf{F}_A| \cos 40°) \cos 50° = 0.492$

$F_{Ay} = |\mathbf{F}_A| \sin 40° = 0.642$

$F_{Bx} = -(400 \cos 60°) \cos 60°$

$F_{Bz} = (400 \cos 60°) \cos 30°$

$F_{By} = 400 \sin 60°$

Let $F_A = |\mathbf{F}_A|$ and $F_B = |\mathbf{F}_B| = 400$ N.
The components of the vectors are

$\mathbf{F}_A = F_A \cos 40° \sin 50° \mathbf{i} + F_A \sin 40° \mathbf{j} + F_A \cos 40° \cos 50° \mathbf{k}$

$= F_A(0.587\mathbf{i} + 0.643\mathbf{j} + 0.492\mathbf{k}),$ **(1)**

$\mathbf{F}_B = -F_B \cos 60° \sin 30° \mathbf{i} + F_B \sin 60° \mathbf{j} + F_B \cos 60° \cos 30° \mathbf{k}$

$= -100\mathbf{i} + 346\mathbf{j} + 173\mathbf{k}$ (N).

Setting

$900 \text{ N} = |\mathbf{F}_A + \mathbf{F}_B|$

$= [(0.587F_A - 100)^2 + (0.643F_A + 346)^2$

$+ (0.492F_A + 173)^2]^{1/2}$

and solving, we obtain $F_A = 595$ N. Substituting this result into Eq. (1),

$\mathbf{F}_A = 349\mathbf{i} + 382\mathbf{j} + 293\mathbf{k}$ (N).

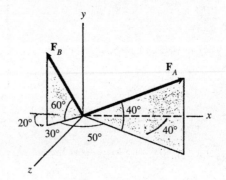

Problem 2.164 Suppose that the forces $\mathbf{F}_A$ and $\mathbf{F}_B$ shown in Problem 2.163 have the same magnitude and $\mathbf{F}_A \cdot \mathbf{F}_B = 600$ N^2. What are $\mathbf{F}_A$ and $\mathbf{F}_B$?

Solution: From Problem 2.163, the forces are:

$\mathbf{F}_A = |\mathbf{F}_A|(\mathbf{i} \cos 40° \sin 50° + \mathbf{j} \sin 40° + \mathbf{k} \cos 40° \cos 50°)$

$= |\mathbf{F}_A|(0.5868\mathbf{i} + 0.6428\mathbf{j} + 0.4924\mathbf{k})$

$\mathbf{F}_B = |\mathbf{F}_B|(-\mathbf{i} \cos 60° \sin 30° + \mathbf{j} \sin 60° + \mathbf{k} \cos 60° \cos 30°)$

$= |\mathbf{F}_B|(-0.25\mathbf{i} + 0.866\mathbf{j} + 0.433\mathbf{k})$

The dot product: $\mathbf{F}_A \cdot \mathbf{F}_B = |\mathbf{F}_A||\mathbf{F}_B|(0.6233) = 600$ N^2, from

$|\mathbf{F}_A| = |\mathbf{F}_B| = \sqrt{\dfrac{600}{0.6233}} = 31.03$ N,

and

$\mathbf{F}_A = 18.21\mathbf{i} + 19.95\mathbf{j} + 15.28\mathbf{k}$ (N)

$\mathbf{F}_B = -7.76\mathbf{i} + 26.87\mathbf{j} + 13.44\mathbf{k}$ (N)

Problem 2.165 The magnitude of the force vector $\mathbf{F}_B$ is 2 kN. Express it in terms of scalar components.

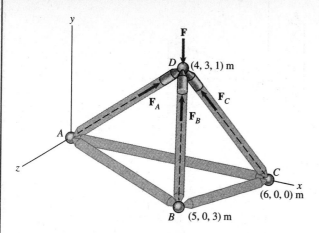

Solution: The strategy is to determine the unit vector collinear with $\mathbf{F}_B$ and then express the force in terms of this unit vector.

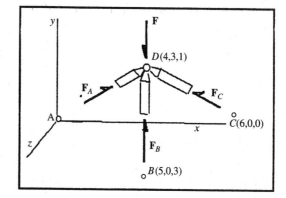

The radius vector collinear with $\mathbf{F}_B$ is

$$\mathbf{r}_{BD} = (4-5)\mathbf{i} + (3-0)\mathbf{j} + (1-3)\mathbf{k} \text{ or } \mathbf{r}_{BD} = -1\mathbf{i} + 3\mathbf{j} - 2\mathbf{k}.$$

The magnitude is

$$|\mathbf{r}_{BD}| = \sqrt{1^2 + 3^2 + 2^2} = 3.74.$$

The unit vector is

$$\mathbf{e}_{BD} = \frac{\mathbf{r}_{BD}}{|\mathbf{r}_{BD}|} = -0.2673\mathbf{i} + 0.8018\mathbf{j} - 0.5345\mathbf{k}$$

The force is

$$\mathbf{F}_B = |\mathbf{F}_B|\mathbf{e}_{BD} = 2\mathbf{e}_{BD} \text{ (kN) } \mathbf{F}_B = -0.5345\mathbf{i} + 1.6036\mathbf{j} - 1.0693\mathbf{k}$$

$$= -0.53\mathbf{i} + 1.60\mathbf{j} - 1.07\mathbf{k} \text{ (kN)}$$

Problem 2.166 The magnitude of the vertical force vector $\mathbf{F}$ in Problem 2.165 is 6 kN. Determine the vector components of $\mathbf{F}$ parallel and normal to the line from B to D.

Solution: The projection of the force $\mathbf{F}$ onto the line from B to D is $\mathbf{F}_P = (\mathbf{F} \cdot \mathbf{e}_{BD})\mathbf{e}_{BD}$. The vertical force has the component $\mathbf{F} = -6\mathbf{j}$ (kN). From Problem 2.139, the unit vector pointing from B to D is $\mathbf{e}_{BD} = -0.2673\mathbf{i} + 0.8018\mathbf{j} - 0.5345\mathbf{k}$. The dot product is $\mathbf{F} \cdot \mathbf{e}_{BD} = -4.813$. Thus the component parallel to the line BD is $\mathbf{F}_P = -4.813\mathbf{e}_{BD} = +1.29\mathbf{i} - 3.86\mathbf{j} + 2.57\mathbf{k}$ (kN). The component perpendicular to the line is: $\mathbf{F}_N = \mathbf{F} - \mathbf{F}_P$. Thus $\mathbf{F}_N = -1.29\mathbf{i} - 2.14\mathbf{j} - 2.57\mathbf{k}$ (kN)

Problem 2.167 The magnitude of the vertical force vector $\mathbf{F}$ in Problem 2.165 is 6 kN. Given that $\mathbf{F} + \mathbf{F}_A + \mathbf{F}_B + \mathbf{F}_C = 0$, what are the magnitudes of $\mathbf{F}_A$, $\mathbf{F}_B$, and $\mathbf{F}_C$?

Solution: The strategy is to expand the forces into scalar components, and then use the force balance equation to solve for the unknowns. The unit vectors are used to expand the forces into scalar components. The position vectors, magnitudes, and unit vectors are:

$$\mathbf{r}_{AD} = 4\mathbf{i} + 3\mathbf{j} + 1\mathbf{k}, \quad |\mathbf{r}_{AD}| = \sqrt{26} = 5.1,$$

$$\mathbf{e}_{AD} = 0.7845\mathbf{i} + 0.5883\mathbf{j} + 0.1961\mathbf{k}.$$

$$\mathbf{r}_{BD} = -1\mathbf{i} + 3\mathbf{j} - 2\mathbf{k}, \quad |\mathbf{r}_{BD}| = \sqrt{14} = 3.74,$$

$$\mathbf{e}_{BD} = -0.2673\mathbf{i} + 0.8018\mathbf{j} - 0.5345\mathbf{k}.$$

$$\mathbf{r}_{CD} = -2\mathbf{i} + 3\mathbf{j} + 1\mathbf{k}, \quad |\mathbf{r}_{CD}| = \sqrt{14} = 3.74,$$

$$\mathbf{e}_{CD} = -0.5345\mathbf{i} + 0.8018\mathbf{j} + 0.2673\mathbf{k}$$

The forces are:

$$\mathbf{F}_A = |\mathbf{F}_A|\mathbf{e}_{AD}, \mathbf{F}_B = |\mathbf{F}_B|\mathbf{e}_{BD}, \mathbf{F}_C = |\mathbf{F}_C|\mathbf{e}_{CD}, \mathbf{F} = -6\mathbf{j} \text{ (kN)}.$$

Substituting into the force balance equation

$$\mathbf{F} + \mathbf{F}_A + \mathbf{F}_B + \mathbf{F}_C = 0,$$

$$(0.7843|\mathbf{F}_A| - 0.2674|\mathbf{F}_B| - 0.5348|\mathbf{F}_C|)\mathbf{i} = 0$$

$$(0.5882|\mathbf{F}_A| + 0.8021|\mathbf{F}_B| + 0.8021|\mathbf{F}_C| - 6)\mathbf{j}$$

$$= 0(0.1961|\mathbf{F}_A| - 0.5348|\mathbf{F}_B| + 0.2674|\mathbf{F}_C|)\mathbf{k} = 0$$

These simple simultaneous equations can be solved a standard method (e.g., Gauss elimination) or, conveniently, by using a commercial package, such as TK Solver®, Mathcad®, or other. An HP-28S hand held calculator was used here: $|\mathbf{F}_A| = 2.83$ (kN), $|\mathbf{F}_B| = 2.49$ (kN), $|\mathbf{F}_C| = 2.91$ (kN)

Problem 2.168 The magnitude of the vertical force $\mathbf{W}$ is 160 N. The direction cosines of the position vector from A to B are $\cos\theta_x = 0.500$, $\cos\theta_y = 0.866$, and $\cos\theta_z = 0$, and the direction cosines of the position vector from B to C are $\cos\theta_x = 0.707$, $\cos\theta_y = 0.619$, and $\cos\theta_z = -0.342$. Point G is the midpoint of the line from B to C. Determine the vector $\mathbf{r}_{AG} \times \mathbf{W}$, where $\mathbf{r}_{AG}$ is the position vector from A to G.

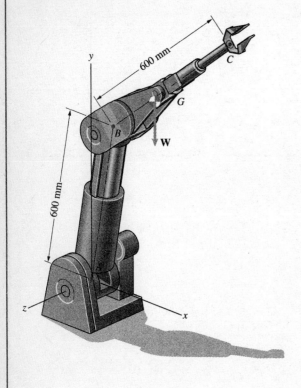

Solution: Express the position vectors in terms of scalar components, calculate $\mathbf{r}_{AG}$, and take the cross product. The position vectors are: $\mathbf{r}_{AB} = 0.6(.5\mathbf{i} + 0.866\mathbf{j} + 0\mathbf{k})\ \mathbf{r}_{AB} = 0.3\mathbf{i} + 0.5196\mathbf{j} + 0\mathbf{k}$,

$$\mathbf{r}_{BG} = 0.3(0.707\mathbf{i} + 0.619\mathbf{j} - 0.342\mathbf{k}),$$

$$\mathbf{r}_{BG} = 0.2121\mathbf{i} + 0.1857\mathbf{j} - 0.1026\mathbf{k}.$$

$$\mathbf{r}_{AG} = \mathbf{r}_{AB} + \mathbf{r}_{BG} = 0.5121\mathbf{i} + 0.7053\mathbf{j} - 0.1026\mathbf{k}.$$

$$\mathbf{W} = -160\mathbf{j}$$

$$\mathbf{r}_{AG} \times \mathbf{W} = \begin{vmatrix} \mathbf{i} & \mathbf{j} & \mathbf{k} \\ 0.5121 & 0.7053 & -0.1026 \\ 0 & -160 & 0 \end{vmatrix}$$

$$= -16.44\mathbf{i} + 0\mathbf{j} - 81.95\mathbf{k} = -16.4\mathbf{i} + 0\mathbf{j} - 82\mathbf{k} \text{ (N m)}$$

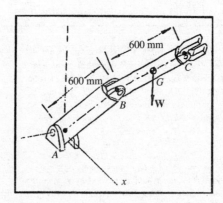

Problem 2.169 The rope CE exerts a 500-N force $\mathbf{T}$ on the door $ABCD$. Determine the vector component of $\mathbf{T}$ in the direction parallel to the line from point A to point B.

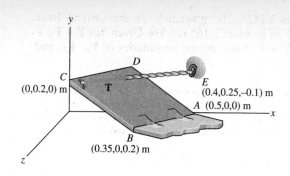

Solution: Two vectors are needed, $\mathbf{r}_{CE}$ and $\mathbf{r}_{AB}$. The end points of these vectors are given in the figure. Thus, $\mathbf{r}_{CE} = (x_E - x_C)\mathbf{i} + (y_E - y_C)\mathbf{j} + (z_E - z_C)\mathbf{k}$ and a similar form holds for $\mathbf{r}_{AB}$. Calculating these vectors, we get

$\mathbf{r}_{CE} = 0.4\mathbf{i} + 0.05\mathbf{j} - 0.1\mathbf{k}$ m and $\mathbf{r}_{AB} = -0.15\mathbf{i} + 0\mathbf{j} + 0.2\mathbf{k}$ m.

The unit vector along CE is $\mathbf{e}_{CE} = 0.963\mathbf{i} + 0.120\mathbf{j} - 0.241\mathbf{k}$ and the force $\mathbf{T}$, is $\mathbf{T} = |\mathbf{T}|\mathbf{e}_{CE}$. Hence, $\mathbf{T} = 500(0.963\mathbf{i} + 0.120\mathbf{j} - 0.241\mathbf{k}) = 482\mathbf{i} + 60.2\mathbf{j} - 120\mathbf{k}$ N. The unit vector along AB is given by $\mathbf{e}_{AB} = -0.6\mathbf{i} + 0\mathbf{j} + 0.8\mathbf{k}$ and the component of $\mathbf{T}$ parallel to AB is given by $\mathbf{T}_{AB} = \mathbf{T} \bullet \mathbf{e}_{AB}$. Thus, $T_{AB} = (482)(-0.6) + (60.2)(0) + (-120)(0.8) = -385.2$ N

Problem 2.170 In Problem 2.169, let $\mathbf{r}_{BC}$ be the position vector from point B to point C. Determine the cross product $\mathbf{r}_{BC} \times \mathbf{T}$.

Solution: The vector from B to C is

$\mathbf{r}_{BC} = (x_C - x_B)\mathbf{i} + (y_C - y_B)\mathbf{j} + (z_C - z_B)\mathbf{k}$

$\quad = -0.35\mathbf{i} + 0.2\mathbf{j} - 0.2\mathbf{k}$ m.

The vector $\mathbf{T}$ is $\mathbf{T} = 482\mathbf{i} + 60.2\mathbf{j} - 120\mathbf{k}$ N. The cross product of these vectors is given by

$$\mathbf{r}_{BC} \times \mathbf{T} = \begin{vmatrix} \mathbf{i} & \mathbf{j} & \mathbf{k} \\ -0.35 & 0.2 & -0.2 \\ 482 & 60.2 & -120 \end{vmatrix} = -12.0\mathbf{i} - 138\mathbf{j} - 117\mathbf{k} \text{ N m}$$

Problem 2.171 In Problem 2.169, let $\mathbf{r}_{BC}$ be the position vector from point B to point C, and let $\mathbf{e}_{AB}$ be a unit vector that points from point A toward point B. Evaluate the mixed triple product

$\mathbf{e}_{AB} \bullet (\mathbf{r}_{BC} \times \mathbf{T})$.

Solution: We have $\mathbf{e}_{AB} = -0.6\mathbf{i} + 0\mathbf{j} + 0.8\mathbf{k}$ and $\mathbf{r}_{BC} \times \mathbf{T} = -12.0\mathbf{i} - 138\mathbf{j} - 117\mathbf{k}$ N m. Thus, the mixed triple product is given by $\mathbf{e}_{AB} \bullet (\mathbf{r}_{BC} \times \mathbf{T}) = (-0.6)(-12.0) + (0)(-138) + (0.8)(-117)$ N m. Hence $\mathbf{e}_{AB} \bullet (\mathbf{r}_{BC} \times \mathbf{T}) = -86.7$ N m

Problem 2.172   A structural engineer determines that the truss in Problem 2.10 will safely support the force $\mathbf{F}$ if the magnitudes of the vector components of $\mathbf{F}$ parallel to the bars do not exceed 20 kN. Based on this criterion, what is the largest safe magnitude of $\mathbf{F}$?

Solution: We resolve the force into its components parallel to the bars:

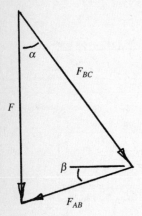

The angles $\alpha = \arctan(100/150) = 33.7°$ and $\beta = \arctan(150/400) = 20.6°$. Note that

$$F_{BC}\cos\alpha + F_{AB}\sin\beta = F,$$

$$F_{BC}\sin\alpha - F_{AB}\cos\beta = 0.$$

F_{BC} is clearly the largest component, so we set $F_{BC} = 20$ kN and solve for F_{AB} and F, obtaining

$$F_{AB} = 11.8 \text{ kN}, \quad F = 20.8 \text{ kN}.$$

Problem 2.173   Consider the sling supporting the storage tank in Problem 2.15. The tension in the supporting cable is $|\mathbf{F}_A| = |\mathbf{F}_B|$. Suppose that you want a factor of safety of 1.5, which means the cable can support 1.5 times the tension to which it is expected to be subjected.

(a)   What minimum tension must the cable used be able to support?

(b)   Suppose that design constraints require you to increase the 40° angle. If the cable used will support a tension of 800 lb, what is the maximum acceptable value of the angle?

Solution: The free-body diagram of the tank is

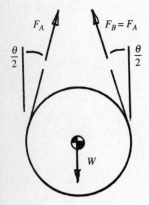

(a)   we see that

$$2F_A \cos\frac{\theta}{2} - W = 0,$$

so the cable tension is

$$F_A = \frac{W}{2\cos(\theta/2)}$$

$$= \frac{600}{2\cos 20°}$$

$$= 319 \text{ lb}.$$

For a factor of safety of 1.5, the minimum tension is $(1.5)(319) = 479$ lb.

(b)   For a factor of safety of 1.5, the actual cable tension should not exceed $800/1.5 = 533$ lb. Setting

$$533 = \frac{600}{2\cos(\theta/2)},$$

we obtain $\theta = 112°$.

Problem 2.174 By moving the block at B, the designer of the system supporting the lifeboat in Problem 2.16 can increase the 20° angle between the vector $\mathbf{F}_{BC}$ and the horizontal, thereby decreasing the total force $|\mathbf{F}_{BA} + \mathbf{F}_{BC}|$ exerted on the block. (Assume that the support at A is also moved so that the vector $\mathbf{F}_{BA}$ remains vertical.) If the designer does not want the block to be subjected to a force greater than 740 N, what is the minimum acceptable value of the angle?

Solution: The forces exerted on the block by the rope are

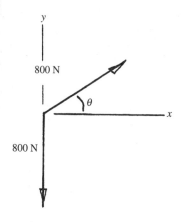

Their sum is

$$\mathbf{F} = 800\cos\theta\,\mathbf{i} + (800\sin\theta - 800)\mathbf{j} \ (\text{N}).$$

The magnitude of the sum is

$$|\mathbf{F}| = \sqrt{(800\cos\theta)^2 + (800\sin\theta - 800)^2}$$

$$= 800\sqrt{2(1 - \sin\theta)}.$$

setting $|\mathbf{F}| = 740$ N and solving for θ, we obtain $\theta = 34.9°$.

Problem 2.175 Suppose that the bracket in Problem 2.52 is to be subjected to forces $|\mathbf{F}_1| = |\mathbf{F}_2| = 3$ kN, and it will safely support a total force of 4-kN magnitude in any direction. What is the acceptable range of the angle α?

Solution:

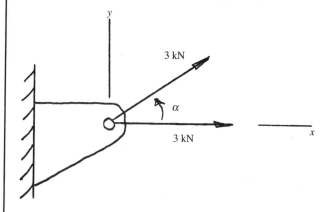

The total force on the bracket is

$$\mathbf{F} = (3 + 3\cos\alpha)\mathbf{i} + 3\sin\alpha\,\mathbf{j} \ (\text{kN}).$$

Its magnitude is

$$|\mathbf{F}| = \sqrt{(3 + 3\cos\alpha)^2 + (3\sin\alpha)^2}$$

$$= 3\sqrt{2(1 + \cos\alpha)} \ \text{kN}. \qquad (1)$$

We plot the magnitude as a function of α:

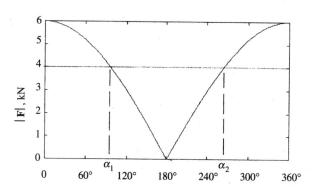

Setting $|\mathbf{F}| = 4$ kN and solving Eq. (1) for α, we obtain $\alpha_1 = 96.4°$. The angle $\alpha_2 = 360° - \alpha_1 = 263.6°$. The acceptable range is

$$96.4° \leq \alpha \leq 263.6°.$$

Problem 3.1 The figure shows the external forces acting on an object in equilibrium. The forces $F_1 = 32$ N and $F_3 = 50$ N. Determine F_2 and the angle α.

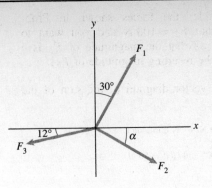

Solution: Write the forces in component form.

$\mathbf{F}_1 = 32 \sin 30° \mathbf{i} + 32 \cos 30° \mathbf{j}$

$\mathbf{F}_1 = 16\mathbf{i} + 27.7\mathbf{j}$ N

$\mathbf{F}_2 = -50 \cos 12° \mathbf{i} - 50 \sin 12° \mathbf{j}$

$\mathbf{F}_2 = -48.9\mathbf{i} - 10.4\mathbf{j}$ (N)

$\mathbf{F}_2 = F_2 \cos \alpha \mathbf{i} - F_2 \sin \alpha \mathbf{j}$

Sum components in x and y directions

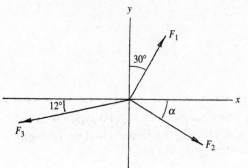

$\begin{cases} \sum F_x = 16 - 48.9 + F_2 \cos \alpha = 0 \\ \sum F_y = 27.7 - 10.4 - F_2 \sin \alpha = 0 \end{cases}$

Solving, we get
$\boxed{\begin{array}{l} F_z = 37.2 \text{ N} \\ \alpha = 27.73° \end{array}}$

Problem 3.2 The force $F_1 = 100$ N and the angle $\alpha = 60°$. The weight of the ring is negligible. Determine the forces F_2 and F_3.

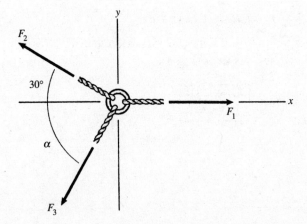

Solution: Write the forces in component form.

$\mathbf{F}_1 = F_1\mathbf{i} + 0\mathbf{j}$

$\mathbf{F}_2 = -F_2 \cos 30° \mathbf{i} + F_2 \sin 30° \mathbf{j}$

$\mathbf{F}_3 = -F_3 \cos \alpha \mathbf{i} - F_3 \sin \alpha \mathbf{j}$

We know $\sum \mathbf{F} = 0$, thus $\sum F_x = 0$ and $\sum F_y = 0$. Writing the equilibrium equations, we have

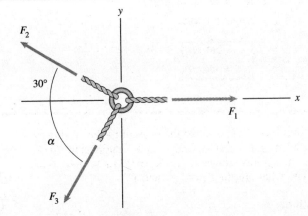

$\begin{cases} \sum F_x = F_1 - F_2 \cos 30° - F_3 \cos \alpha = 0 \\ \sum F_y = F_2 \sin 30° - F_3 \sin \alpha = 0 \end{cases}$

$F_1 = 100$ N, $\alpha = 60°$

Solving, we get

$F_2 = 86.6$ N, $F_3 = 50$ N

Problem 3.3 Consider the forces shown in Problem 3.2. Suppose that $F_2 = 100$ N and you want to choose the angle α so that the magnitude of F_3 is a minimum. What is the resulting magnitude of F_3?

Strategy: Draw a vector diagram of the sum of the three forces.

Solution: $|F_2| = 100$ N, F_1 is horizontal, and $\sum F = 0$.

From the diagram, $\alpha = 90°$ and $|F_3| = 50$ N

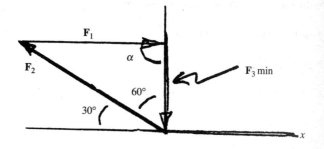

Problem 3.4 The beam is in equilibrium. If $A_x = 77$ kN, $B = 400$ kN, and the beam's weight is negligible, what are the forces A_y and C?

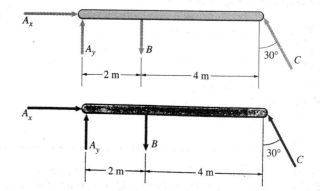

Solution:

$$\begin{cases} \xrightarrow{+} \sum F_x = A_x - C \sin 30° = 0 \\ +\uparrow \sum F_y = A_y - B + C \cos 30° = 0 \\ \qquad A_x = 77 \text{ kN}, \quad B = 400 \text{ kN} \end{cases}$$

Solving, we get

$A_y = 267$ kN
$C = 154$ kN

Problem 3.5 Suppose that the mass of the beam shown in Problem 3.4 is 20 kg and it is in equilibrium. The force A_y points upward. If $A_y = 258$ kN and $B = 240$ kN, what are the forces A_x and C?

Solution:

$$\begin{cases} \xrightarrow{+} \sum F_x = 0 = A_x - C \sin 30° = 0 \\ +\uparrow \sum F_y = 0 = A_y - B - (20)(9.81) + C \cos 30° = 0 \\ \qquad A_y = 258 \text{ kN}, \quad B = 240 \text{ kN} \end{cases}$$

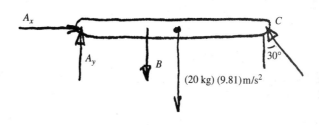

Solving, we get

$A_x = 103$ kN
$C = 206$ kN

Problem 3.6 A zoologist estimates that the jaw of a predator, *Martes*, is subjected to a force P as large as 800 N. What forces T and M must be exerted by the temporalis and masseter muscles to support this value of P?

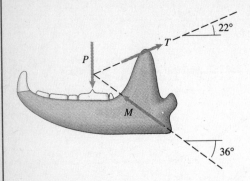

Solution: Resolve the forces into scalar components, and solve the equilibrium equations...Express the forces in terms of horizontal and vertical unit vectors:

$$T = |T|(i \cos 22° + j \sin 22°) = |T|(0.927i + 0.375j)$$

$$P = 800(i \cos 270° + j \sin 270°) = 0i - 800j$$

$$M = |M|(i \cos 144° + j \sin 144°) = |M|(-0.809i + 0.588j)$$

Apply the equilibrium conditions,

$$\sum F = 0 = T + M + P = 0$$

Collect like terms: $\sum F_x = (0.927|T| - 0.809|M|)i = 0$

$$\sum F_y = (0.375|T| - 0.588|M| - 800)j = 0$$

Solve the first equation, $|T| = \left(\dfrac{0.809}{0.927}\right)|M| = 0.873|M|$

Substitute this value into the second equation, reduce algebraically, and solve: $\boxed{|M| = 874 \text{ N}, \ |T| = 763.3 \text{ N}}$

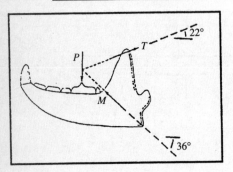

Problem 3.7 The two springs are identical, with un-stretched lengths 250 mm and spring constants $k = 1200$ N/m.

(a) Draw the free-body diagram of block A.
(b) Draw the free-body diagram of block B.
(c) What are the masses of the two blocks?

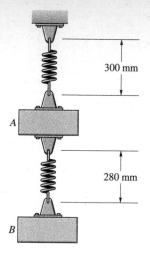

300 mm

280 mm

A

B

Solution: The tension in the upper spring acts on block A in the positive Y direction, Solve the spring force-deflection equation for the tension in the upper spring. Apply the equilibrium conditions to block A. Repeat the steps for block B.

$$\mathbf{T}_{UA} = 0\mathbf{i} + \left(1200 \ \frac{\text{N}}{\text{m}}\right)(0.3 \text{ m} - 0.25 \text{ m})\mathbf{j} = 0\mathbf{i} + 60\mathbf{j} \text{ N}$$

Similarly, the tension in the lower spring acts on block A in the negative Y direction

$$\mathbf{T}_{LA} = 0\mathbf{i} - \left(1200 \ \frac{\text{N}}{\text{m}}\right)(0.28 \text{ m} - 0.25 \text{ m})\mathbf{j} = 0\mathbf{i} - 36\mathbf{j} \text{ N}$$

The weight is $\mathbf{W}_A = 0\mathbf{i} - |\mathbf{W}_A|\mathbf{j}$

The equilibrium conditions are

$$\sum \mathbf{F} = \sum \mathbf{F}_x + \sum \mathbf{F}_y = 0, \quad \sum \mathbf{F} = \mathbf{W}_A + \mathbf{T}_{UA} + \mathbf{T}_{LA} = 0$$

Collect and combine like terms in $\mathbf{i}, \mathbf{j}$

$$\sum \mathbf{F}_y = (-|\mathbf{W}_A| + 60 - 36)\mathbf{j} = 0$$

Solve $|\mathbf{W}_A| = (60 - 36) = 24$ N

The mass of A is

$$m_A = \frac{|\mathbf{W}_L|}{|\mathbf{g}|} = \frac{24 \text{ N}}{9.81 \text{ m/s}^2} = 2.45 \text{ kg}$$

The free body diagram for block B is shown.

The tension in the lower spring $\mathbf{T}_{LB} = 0\mathbf{i} + 36\mathbf{j}$

The weight: $\mathbf{W}_B = 0\mathbf{i} - |\mathbf{W}_B|\mathbf{j}$
Apply the equilibrium conditions to block B.

$$\sum \mathbf{F} = \mathbf{W}_B + \mathbf{T}_{LB} = 0$$

Collect and combine like terms in $\mathbf{i}, \mathbf{j}$:

$$\sum \mathbf{F}_y = (-|\mathbf{W}_B| + 36)\mathbf{j} = 0$$

Solve: $|\mathbf{W}_B| = 36$ N

The mass of B is given by $m_B = \dfrac{|\mathbf{W}_B|}{|\mathbf{g}|} = \dfrac{36 \text{ N}}{9.81 \text{ m/s}^2} = 3.67$ kg

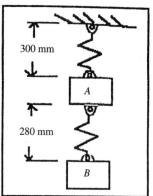

300 mm

A

280 mm

B

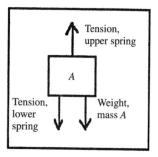

Tension, upper spring

A

Tension, lower spring

Weight, mass A

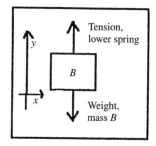

Tension, lower spring

y

B

x

Weight, mass B

Problem 3.8 The two springs in Problem 3.7 are identical, with unstretched lengths 250 mm and spring constants k. The sum of the masses of blocks A and B is 10 kg. Determine the value of k and the masses of the two blocks.

Solution: All of the forces are in the vertical direction so we will use scalar equations. First, consider the upper spring supporting both masses (10 kg total mass). The equation of equilibrium for block the entire assembly supported by the upper spring is A is $T_{UA} - (m_A + m_B)g = 0$, where $T_{UA} = k(\ell_U - 0.25)$ N. The equation of equilibrium for block B is $T_{UB} - m_B g = 0$, where $T_{UB} = k(\ell_L - 0.25)$ N. The equation of equilibrium for block A alone is $T_{UA} + T_{LA} - m_A g = 0$ where $T_{LA} = -T_{UB}$. Using $g = 9.81$ m/s², and solving simultaneously, we get $\boxed{k = 1962 \text{ N/m}, \ m_A = 4 \text{ kg, and } m_B = 6 \text{ kg}}$.

Problem 3.9 The 200-kg horizontal steel bar is suspended by the three springs. The stretch of each spring is 0.1 m. The constant of spring B is $k_B = 8000$ N/m. Determine the constants $k_A = k_C$ of springs A and C.

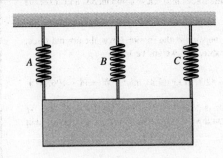

Solution:

$\delta = 0.1$ m

$K_A = K_C$

$+\uparrow \sum F_y = K_A\delta + K_B\delta + K_C\delta - (200)(9.81) = 0$

$2K_A(0.1) + (8000)(0.1) = 1962$ N

Solving

$K_A = 5810$ N/m $= K_C$

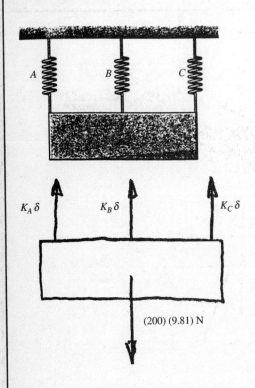

$K_A\delta \qquad K_B\delta \qquad K_C\delta$

$(200)(9.81)$ N

Problem 3.10 The mass of the crane is 20 Mg (mega-grams), and the tension in its cable is 1 kN. The crane's cable is attached to a caisson whose mass is 400 kg. Determine the magnitudes of the normal and friction forces exerted on the crane by the level ground.

Strategy: Draw the free-body diagram of the crane and the part of its cable within the dashed line.

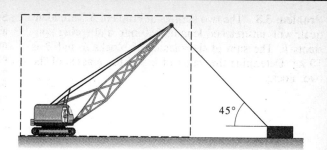

Solution: Resolve the forces into scalar components, and solve the equilibrium equations.

The external forces are the weight, the friction force, the normal force, and the tension in the cable. The weight vector is

$$\mathbf{W} = 0\mathbf{i} - m_c|\mathbf{g}|\mathbf{j} = 0\mathbf{i} - (20000 \text{ kg})(9.81 \text{ m/s}^2)\mathbf{j} \quad \mathbf{W} = 0\mathbf{i} - 196,200\mathbf{j}$$

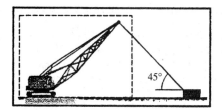

The normal force vector is $\mathbf{N} = (0\mathbf{i} + \mathbf{N}_y + \mathbf{j})$. The friction force by definition acts at right angles to the normal force, in a direction that holds the crane in place.

$$\mathbf{F}_x = -|\mathbf{F}_x|\mathbf{i} + 0\mathbf{j}$$

The angle between the tension vector and the positive x axis is $-45° = 315°$, hence the tension vector projection is

$$\mathbf{T} = |\mathbf{T}|(\mathbf{i}\cos 315° + \mathbf{j}\sin 315°) = 707\mathbf{i} - 707\mathbf{j} \text{ N}$$

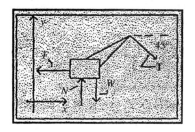

The equilibrium conditions are,

$$\sum \mathbf{F}_x = (-|\mathbf{F}_x| + 707)\mathbf{i} = 0, \quad \sum \mathbf{F}_y = (|\mathbf{N}_y| - 707 - 196200)\mathbf{j} = 0$$

Solve:

$$|\mathbf{F}_x| = 707 \text{ N} \quad |\mathbf{N}_y| = 196200 + 707 = 196,907 \text{ N}.$$

Thus the friction force is directed toward the left, and the normal force acts upward.

Problem 3.11 What is the tension in the horizontal cable AB in Example 3.1 if the 20° angle is increased to 25°?

Solution:

$$m = 1440 \text{ kg}$$

$$mg = (1440)9.81$$

$$\sum F_x = T - N\sin 25° = 0$$

$$\sum F_y = N\cos 25° - mg = 0$$

or $\begin{cases} T - N\sin 25° = 0 \\ N\cos 25° - 14.126 \text{ kN} = 0 \end{cases}$

Solving, we get

$$T = 6.59 \text{ kN}, \quad N = 15.59 \text{ kN}$$

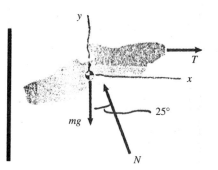

Problem 3.12 The 2400-lb car will remain in equilibrium on the sloping road only if the friction force exerted on the car by the road is not greater than 0.6 times the normal force. What is the largest angle α for which the car will remain in equilibrium?

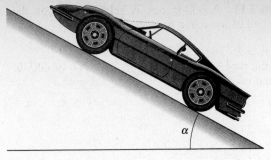

Solution:

$$\sum F_x = W \sin \alpha - f = 0,$$

$$\sum F_y = N - W \cos \alpha = 0.$$

Set $f = 0.6$ N and write the equilibrium equations as

$W \sin \alpha = 0.6$ N,   (1)

$W \cos \alpha = $ N.   (2)

Divide Eq. (1) by Eq. (2):

$$\frac{\sin \alpha}{\cos \alpha} = \tan \alpha = 0.6.$$

Solving, $\alpha = 31.0°$

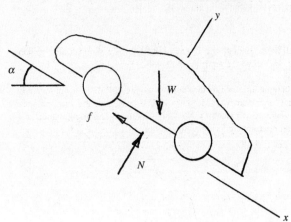

Problem 3.13 The crate is in equilibrium on the smooth surface. (Remember that "smooth" means that friction is negligible). The spring constant is $k = 2500$ N/m and the stretch of the spring is 0.055 m. What is the mass of the crate?

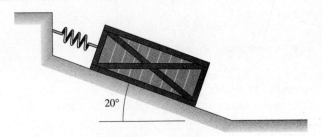

Solution:

$K = 2500$ N/m

$\delta = 0.055$ m

$$\searrow + \sum F_x = -K\delta + m(9.81)\sin 20° = 0$$

$$\nearrow + \sum F_y = \text{N} - m(9.81)\cos 20° = 0$$

$$\begin{cases} -(2500)(0.055) + 3.355 \ m = 0 \\ N - 9.218 \ m = 0 \end{cases}$$

Solving, $m = 41.0$ kg, $N = 378$ (N)

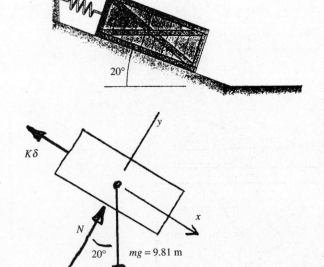

Problem 3.14 A 600-lb box is held in place on the smooth bed of the dump truck by the rope AB.

(a) If $\alpha = 25°$, what is the tension in the rope?
(b) If the rope will safely support a tension of 400 lb, what is the maximum allowable value of α?

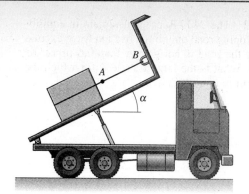

Solution: Isolate the box. Resolve the forces into scalar components, and solve the equilibrium equations.

The external forces are the weight, the tension in the rope, and the normal force exerted by the surface. The angle between the x axis and the weight vector is $-(90 - \alpha)$ (or $270 + \alpha$). The weight vector is

$$\mathbf{W} = |\mathbf{W}|(\mathbf{i}\sin\alpha - \mathbf{j}\cos\alpha) = (600)(\mathbf{i}\sin\alpha - \mathbf{j}\cos\alpha)$$

The projections of the rope tension and the normal force are

$$\mathbf{T} = -|T_x|\mathbf{i} + 0\mathbf{j} \quad \mathbf{N} = 0\mathbf{i} + |N_y|\mathbf{j}$$

The equilibrium conditions are

$$\sum \mathbf{F} = \mathbf{W} + \mathbf{N} + \mathbf{T} = 0$$

Substitute, and collect like terms

$$\sum \mathbf{F}_x = (600\sin\alpha - |\mathbf{T}_x|)\mathbf{i} = 0$$

$$\sum \mathbf{F}_y = (-600\cos\alpha + |\mathbf{N}_y|)\mathbf{j} = 0$$

Solve for the unknown tension when

$$\alpha = 25° |\mathbf{T}_x| = 600\sin\alpha = 253.6 \text{ lb.}$$

For a tension of 400 lb, $(600\sin\alpha - 400) = 0$. Solve for the unknown angle

$$\sin\alpha = \frac{400}{600} = 0.667 \text{ or } \alpha = 41.84°$$

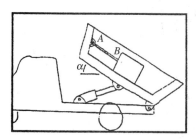

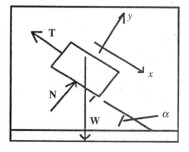

Problem 3.15 Three forces act on the free-body diagram of a joint of a structure. If the structure is in equilibrium and $F_A = 4.20$ kN, what are F_B and F_C?

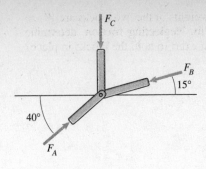

Solution:

$$\begin{cases} \sum F_x = F_A \cos 40° - F_B \cos 15° = 0 \\ \sum F_y = F_A \sin 40° - F_B \sin 15° - F_C = 0 \\ F_A = 4.20 \text{ kN} \end{cases}$$

Substitute in the value for F_A and solve the resulting two equations in two unknowns. We get

$F_B = 3.33$ kN, $F_C = 1.84$ kN

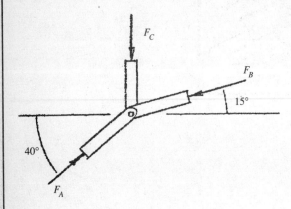

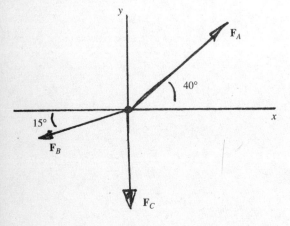

Problem 3.16 The weights of the two blocks are $W_1 = 200$ lb and $W_2 = 50$ lb. Neglecting friction, determine the force the man must exert to hold the blocks in place?

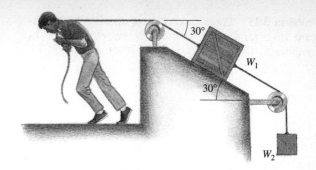

Solution: Isolate block W_2 and apply equilibrium conditions. Repeat for block W_1.

For W_2: The weight vector: $\mathbf{W}_2 = 0\mathbf{i} - 50\mathbf{j}$

The rope tension: $\mathbf{T}_2 = 0\mathbf{i} + |\mathbf{T}_2|\mathbf{j}$

The equilibrium conditions are

$$\sum \mathbf{F}_x = 0, \quad \sum \mathbf{F}_y = (-50 + |\mathbf{T}_2|)\mathbf{j} = 0, \text{ or } |\mathbf{T}_2| = 50$$

For W_1: The magnitude of the rope tension $|\mathbf{T}_2|$ is unchanged by passage over the frictionless lower pulley, hence,

$$\mathbf{T}_2 = |\mathbf{T}_2|\mathbf{i} + 0\mathbf{j} = 50\mathbf{i} + 0\mathbf{j}.$$

The rope tension $\mathbf{T}_1$: $\mathbf{T}_1 = -|\mathbf{T}_1|\mathbf{i} + 0\mathbf{j}$. The normal force is $\mathbf{N} = 0\mathbf{i} + |\mathbf{N}|\mathbf{j}$. The angle between the x axis and the weight vector is $-(90 - \alpha)$ (or $270 + \alpha$). The projection of the weight vector is

$$\mathbf{W} = |\mathbf{W}|(\mathbf{i}\sin\alpha - \mathbf{j}\cos\alpha) = 100\mathbf{i} - 173.2\mathbf{j}.$$

The equilibrium conditions are

$$\sum \mathbf{F} = \mathbf{T}_1 + \mathbf{T}_2 + \mathbf{N} + \mathbf{W}_1 = 0$$

Substitute and collect like terms,

$$\sum \mathbf{F}_x = (-|\mathbf{T}_1| + 50 + 100)\mathbf{i} = 0,$$

$$\sum \mathbf{F}_y = (|\mathbf{N}| - 173.2)\mathbf{j} = 0$$

Solve: $|\mathbf{T}_1| = 150$ lb. Since the frictionless pulley does not change the magnitude of the rope tension, then the tension at the man's hands is $|\mathbf{T}_1| = 150$ lb.

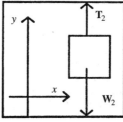

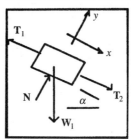

Problem 3.17   The two springs have the same unstretched length, and the inclined surface is smooth. Show that the magnitudes of the forces exerted by the two springs are

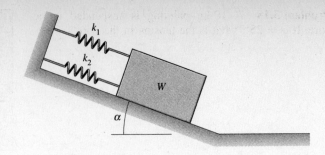

$$F_1 = \frac{W \sin \alpha}{\left(1 + \dfrac{k_2}{k_1}\right)}, \quad F_2 = \frac{W \sin \alpha}{\left(1 + \dfrac{k_1}{k_2}\right)}$$

Solution: Isolate the block. Apply the linear spring force-deflection relations to find the ratios of the spring forces. The spring forces are,

$$\mathbf{F}_1 = -|\mathbf{F}_1|\mathbf{i} + 0\mathbf{j}, \quad \mathbf{F}_2 = -|\mathbf{F}_2|\mathbf{i} + 0\mathbf{j}.$$

The normal force is, $\mathbf{N} = 0\mathbf{i} + |\mathbf{N}|\mathbf{j}$. The angle between the x axis and the weight vector is $-(90 - \alpha)$ (or $270 + \alpha$). The weight vector is

$$\mathbf{W} = |\mathbf{W}|(\mathbf{i} \sin \alpha - \mathbf{j} \cos \alpha).$$

The equilibrium conditions are

$$\sum \mathbf{F} = \mathbf{W} + \mathbf{N} + \mathbf{F}_1 + \mathbf{F}_2 = 0.$$

Substitute and collect like terms,

$$\sum \mathbf{F}_x = (|\mathbf{W}| \sin \alpha - |\mathbf{F}_1| - |\mathbf{F}_2|)\mathbf{i} = 0,$$

$$\sum \mathbf{F}_y = (|\mathbf{N}| - W \cos \alpha)\mathbf{j} = 0.$$

For equal extensions, $\Delta L_1 = \Delta L_2 = \Delta L$, the forces are $|\mathbf{F}_1| = k_1 \Delta L$, and $|\mathbf{F}_2| = k_2 \Delta L$.

The ratio is, $\dfrac{|\mathbf{F}_1|}{|\mathbf{F}_2|} = \left(\dfrac{k_1}{k_2}\right)$.

Substitute to eliminate the unknowns $|\mathbf{F}_2|$, and $|\mathbf{F}_1|$. Solve,

$$|\mathbf{F}_2| = \frac{|\mathbf{W}| \sin \alpha}{\left(1 + \dfrac{k_1}{k_2}\right)}, \quad |\mathbf{F}_1| = \frac{|\mathbf{W}| \sin \alpha}{\left(1 + \dfrac{k_2}{k_1}\right)}$$

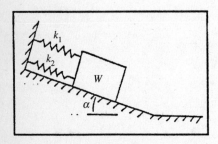

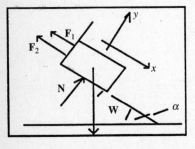

Problem 3.18 A 10-kg painting is suspended by a wire. If $\alpha = 25°$, what is the tension in the wire?

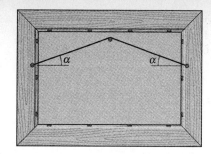

Solution: Isolate support pin fixed to the wall or other support. The angle of the right hand wire with the positive x axis is $-\alpha$, hence the tension is

$$\mathbf{F}_2 = |\mathbf{F}_2|(\mathbf{i}\cos\alpha - \mathbf{j}\sin\alpha)$$

The angle of the left hand wire is $(180° + \alpha)$ hence

$$\mathbf{F}_1 = |\mathbf{F}_1|(-\mathbf{i}\cos\alpha - \mathbf{j}\sin\alpha).$$

The weight is $\mathbf{W} = 0\mathbf{i} + |\mathbf{W}|\mathbf{j}$

The equilibrium conditions are

$$\sum \mathbf{F} = \mathbf{W} + \mathbf{F}_1 + \mathbf{F}_2 = 0$$

Substitute the vector forces, and collect like terms,

$$\sum \mathbf{F}_x = (|\mathbf{F}_2|\cos\alpha - |\mathbf{F}_1|\cos\alpha)\mathbf{i} = 0,$$

$$\sum \mathbf{F}_y = (|\mathbf{W}| - |\mathbf{F}_2|\sin\alpha - |\mathbf{F}_1|\sin\alpha)\mathbf{j} = 0.$$

Thus $|\mathbf{F}_1| = |\mathbf{F}_2|$, and

$$|\mathbf{F}_1| = |\mathbf{F}_2| = \frac{1}{2}\left(\frac{|\mathbf{W}|}{\sin\alpha}\right).$$

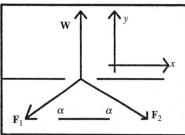

With $\alpha = 25°$ and $|\mathbf{W}| = (10 \text{ kg})\left(9.81\ \frac{\text{m}}{\text{s}^2}\right) = 98.1$ N

$$|\mathbf{F}_1| = |\mathbf{F}_2| = \left(\frac{1}{2}\right)\left(\frac{98.1}{0.423}\right) = 116.06 \text{ N}$$

Problem 3.19 If the wire supporting the suspended painting in Problem 3.18 breaks when the tension exceeds 150 N and you want a 100 percent safety factor (that is, you want the wire to be able to support twice the actual weight of the painting), what is the smallest value of α you can use?

Solution: From Problem 3.18

$$|\mathbf{F}_1| = |\mathbf{F}_2| = \frac{1}{2}\left(\frac{\mathbf{W}}{\sin\alpha}\right)$$

and $|\mathbf{W}| = (10 \text{ kg})\left(9.81\ \frac{\text{m}}{\text{s}^2}\right) = 98.1$ N.

Thus

$$\sin\alpha = \left(\frac{1}{2}\right)\left(\frac{98.1}{|\mathbf{F}|}\right) \quad \text{For a tension } |\mathbf{F}| = \frac{150}{2} = 75,$$

$$\sin\alpha = \left(\frac{1}{2}\right)\left(\frac{98.1}{75}\right) = 0.654 \text{ or } \alpha = 40.8°$$

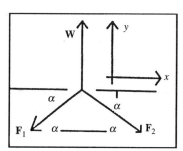

Problem 3.20 Assume that the 150-lb climber is in equilibrium. What are the tensions in the rope on the left and right sides?

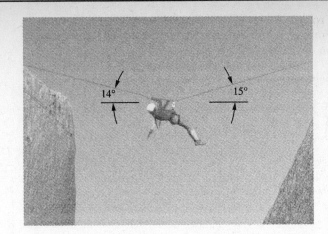

Solution:

$$\begin{cases} \sum F_x = T_R \cos(15°) - T_L \cos(14°) = 0 \\ \sum F_y = T_R \sin(15°) + T_L \sin(14°) - 150 = 0 \end{cases}$$

Solving, we get $T_L = 299$ lb, $T_R = 300$ lb

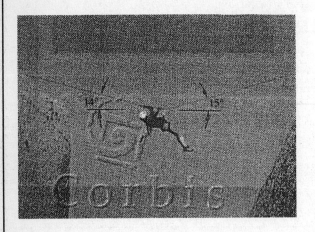

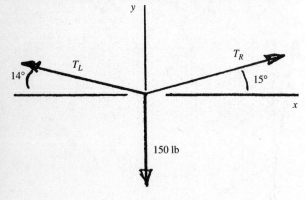

Problem 3.21 If the mass of the climber shown in Problem 3.20 is 80 kg, what are the tensions in the rope on the left and right sides?

Solution:

$$\begin{cases} \sum F_x = T_R \cos(15°) - T_R \cos(14°) = 0 \\ \sum F_y = T_R \sin(15°) + T_R \sin(14°) - mg = 0 \end{cases}$$

Solving, we get

$$T_L = 1.56 \text{ kN}, \quad T_R = 1.57 \text{ kN}$$

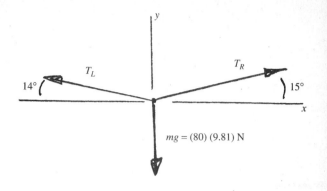

Problem 3.22 A construction worker holds a 180-kg crate in the position shown. What force must she exert on the cable?

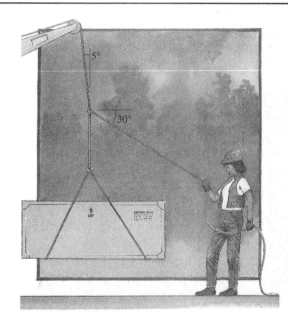

Solution: *Eqns. of Equilibrium:*

$$\begin{cases} \sum F_x = T_2 \cos 30° - T_1 \sin 5° = 0 \\ \sum F_y = T_1 \cos 5° - T_2 \sin 30° - mg = 0 \\ \quad mg = (180)(9.81) \text{ N} \end{cases}$$

Solving, we get

$$T_1 = 1867 \text{ N} \quad T_2 = 188 \text{ N}$$

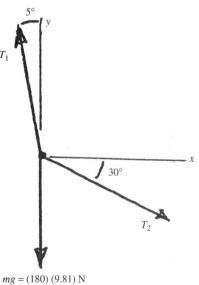

Problem 3.23 A construction worker on the moon (acceleration due to gravity 1.62 m/s^2) holds the same crate described in Problem 3.22 in the position shown. What force must she exert on the cable?

Solution *Eqns. of Equilibrium*

$$\begin{cases} \sum F_x = T_2 \cos 30° - T_1 \sin 5° = 0 \\ \sum F_y = T_1 \cos 5° - T_2 \sin 30° - mg = 0 \\ \quad mg = (180)(1.62) \text{ N} \end{cases}$$

Solving, we get

$$T_1 = 308 \text{ N} \quad T_2 = 31.0 \text{ N}$$

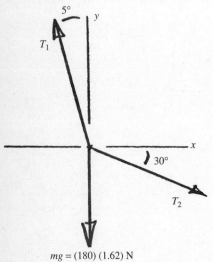

5°

T_1

y

x

30°

T_2

$mg = (180)(1.62)$ N

Problem 3.24 A student on his summer job needs to pull a crate across the floor. Pulling as shown in Fig. a, he can exert a tension of 60 lb. He finds that the crate doesn't move, so he tries the arrangement in Fig. b, exerting a vertical force of 60 lb on the rope. What is the magnitude of the horizontal force he exerts on the crate in each case?

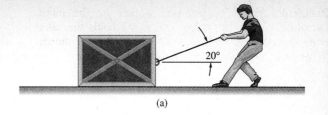

(a)

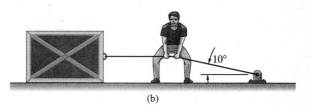

(b)

Solution:

(a) The force diagram for part (a) is as shown. The horizontal component of the 60 lb is

$$F_{\text{horiz}} = (60)\cos(20°) = 56.4 \text{ lb}.$$

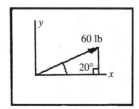

(a)

(b) The free body diagram for the point where the student's hands grasp the rope is shown to the right. The equations of equilibrium are

$$\sum F_x = F_{\text{floor}}\cos(10°) - F_{\text{box}} = 0,$$

and $\sum F_y = 60 \text{ lb} - F_{\text{floor}}\sin(10°) = 0.$

Solving these two equations simultaneously, we find that

$F_{\text{floor}} = 345.5 \text{ lb},$ and $\boxed{F_{\text{box}} = 340.3 \text{ lb}}.$

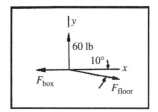

(b)

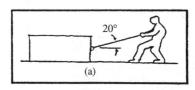

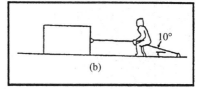

Note: We should keep this problem in mind when we try to exert a large force on an object. Here, the floor did most of the pulling and the arrangement amplified the student's effort by a factor of almost six. Note that the angles are critical in this Problem. Small changes can make big differences.

Problem 3.25 The 140-kg traffic light is suspended above the street by two cables. What is the tension in the cables?

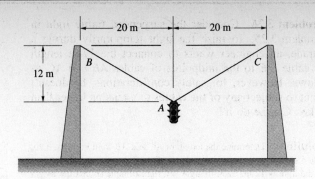

Solution: Isolate the traffic light. From symmetry, the angles α formed by the suspension cables are equal.

$$\tan \alpha = \left(\frac{12 \text{ m}}{20 \text{ m}}\right) = 0.6, \quad \alpha = 30.964° \cong 31°$$

The angle formed by cable **C** and the +x axis is α. The tension is

$$\mathbf{C} = |\mathbf{C}|(\mathbf{i} \cos \alpha + \mathbf{j} \sin \alpha).$$

The angle formed by cable B and the +x axis is $(180° - \alpha)$. The tension is

$$\mathbf{B} = |\mathbf{B}|(\mathbf{i} \cos(180 - \alpha) + \mathbf{j} \sin(180 - \alpha)).$$

The weight is $\mathbf{W} = 0\mathbf{i} - \mathbf{j}|\mathbf{W}|$. The equilibrium conditions are

$$\sum \mathbf{F} = \mathbf{W} + \mathbf{B} + \mathbf{C} = 0.$$

Substitute, and collect like terms. From the first equation, $|\mathbf{B}| = |\mathbf{C}|$. Substitute this into the second equation

$$|\mathbf{B}| = |\mathbf{C}| = \left(\frac{1}{2}\right)\left(\frac{|\mathbf{W}|}{\sin \alpha}\right).$$

For values of

$$|\mathbf{W}| = (140 \text{ kg})\left(9.81 \; \frac{\text{m}}{\text{s}^2}\right) = 1373.4 \text{ N}$$

and $\alpha = 30.96 \cong 31°$,

$$|\mathbf{B}| = |\mathbf{C}| = \left(\frac{1}{2}\right)\left(\frac{1373.4}{\sin \alpha}\right) = 1334.7 \text{ N}.$$

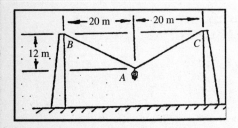

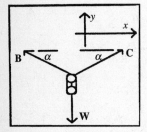

Problem 3.26 Consider the suspended traffic light in Problem 3.25. To raise the light temporarily during a parade, an engineer wants to connect the 17-m length of cable DE to the midpoints of cables AB and AC as shown. However, for safety considerations, he doesn't want to subject any of the cables to a tension larger than 4 kN. Can he do it?

Solution: Determine the length of AC and AB from Problem 3.26: The distance between support poles is 40 m. The vertical drop distance of the light is 12 m. Each triangle is a right triangle so that the length of the cables is

$$D_{AC} = D_{AB} = \sqrt{(20)^2 + (12)^2} = 23.32 \text{ m}.$$

Since the cable DE is attached to the midpoint of the cables AC and AB, AD and AE are each half of this distance, or 11.66 m. The cable DE is given to be 17 m. From this, the angle α is found:

$$\cos \alpha = \left(\frac{8.5 \text{ m}}{11.66 \text{ m}}\right) = 0.729 \quad \alpha = 43.2°.$$

Isolate the traffic light as shown. The angle formed by cable AD and the positive x axis is $(180° - \alpha)$. The tension is: $\mathbf{T}_{AD} = |\mathbf{T}_{AD}|(\mathbf{i}\cos(180 - \alpha) + \mathbf{j}\sin(180 - \alpha))$.

The angle formed by cable AE and the positive x axis is α, hence the tension is $\mathbf{T}_{AE} = |\mathbf{T}_{AE}|(\mathbf{i}\cos\alpha + \mathbf{j}\sin\alpha)$.

The weight is $\mathbf{W} = 0\mathbf{i} - \mathbf{j}|\mathbf{W}|$. The equilibrium conditions are

$$\sum \mathbf{F} = \mathbf{W} + \mathbf{T}_{AD} + \mathbf{T}_{AE} = 0.$$

Substitute and collect like terms

$$\sum \mathbf{F}_x = (-|\mathbf{T}_{AD}|\cos\alpha + |\mathbf{T}_{AE}|\cos\alpha)\mathbf{i} = 0,$$

$$\sum \mathbf{F}_y = (|\mathbf{T}_{AD}|\sin\alpha + |\mathbf{T}_{AE}|\sin\alpha - |\mathbf{W}|)\mathbf{j} = 0.$$

Solve, $|\mathbf{T}_{AD}| = |\mathbf{T}_{AE}|..$, $|\mathbf{T}_{AD}| = |\mathbf{T}_{AE}| = \left(\frac{1}{2}\right)\left(\frac{|\mathbf{W}|}{\sin\alpha}\right)$.

For $|\mathbf{W}| = (140 \text{ kg})\left(9.81 \dfrac{\text{m}}{\text{s}^2}\right) = 1373.4 \text{ N}$

and $\alpha = 43.2°$, $|\mathbf{T}_{AD}| = |\mathbf{T}_{AE}| = \left(\dfrac{1}{2}\right)\left(\dfrac{1373.4}{\sin 43.2}\right) = 1003 \text{ N}.$

Isolate the cable juncture E as shown. The angle θ is found as follows: The cable EC is 11.66 m. The distance between poles 40 m. The cable DE is 17 m, and cable DE is horizontal. Thus EC projects onto the x-axis

$$H_{EC} = \left(\frac{1}{2}\right)(40 - 17) = 11.5 \text{ m}.$$

The ratio is the cosine of the angle,

$$\cos\theta = \left(\frac{11.5}{11.66}\right) = 0.9863, \quad \text{or} \quad \theta = 9.5°.$$

From the law of sines:

$$\frac{|\mathbf{T}_{AD}|}{\sin\theta} = \frac{|\mathbf{T}_{CE}|}{\sin(180 - \alpha)}$$

from which $|\mathbf{T}_{CE}| = 4159.6 \text{ N}.$

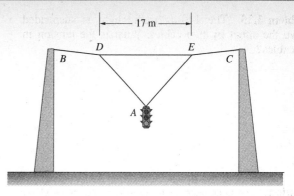

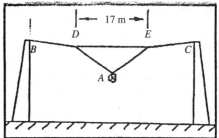

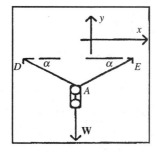

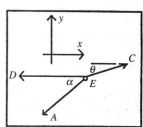

Thus the tension in the cable CE exceeds the allowable limit of 4 kN.

Check: Use components: The angle between AE and the positive x axis is $(180° + \alpha)$. The tension in AE is

$$\mathbf{T}_{AE} = |\mathbf{T}_{AE}|(\mathbf{i}\cos(180 + \alpha) + \mathbf{j}\sin(180 + \alpha))$$

$$\mathbf{T}_{AE} = |\mathbf{T}_{AE}|(-\mathbf{i}\cos\alpha - \mathbf{j}\sin\alpha).$$

The tension in ED is: $\mathbf{T}_{ED} = -|\mathbf{T}_{ED}|\mathbf{i} + 0\mathbf{j}$.

The angle between CE and the positive x axis is θ.

The tension in CE is: $\mathbf{T}_{CE} = |\mathbf{T}_{CE}|(\mathbf{i}\cos\theta + \mathbf{j}\sin\theta)$. The equilibrium conditions are

$$\sum \mathbf{F} = \mathbf{T}_{AE} + \mathbf{T}_{ED} + \mathbf{T}_{CE} = 0.$$

Substitute and collect like terms:

$$\sum \mathbf{F}_x = (-|\mathbf{T}_{AE}|\cos\alpha - |\mathbf{T}_{ED}| + |\mathbf{T}_{CE}|\cos\theta)\mathbf{i} = 0,$$

$$\sum \mathbf{F}_y = (-|\mathbf{T}_{AE}|\sin\alpha + |\mathbf{T}_{CE}|\sin\theta)\mathbf{j} = 0.$$

From the second equation, $|\mathbf{T}_{CE}| = \left(\dfrac{\sin\alpha}{\sin\theta}\right)|\mathbf{T}_{AE}|.$

For $\alpha = 43.2°$, $\theta = 9.5°$, and $|\mathbf{T}_{AE}| = 1003.2 \text{ N}$,

$$|\mathbf{T}_{CE}| = \left(\frac{0.6845}{0.1651}\right)(1003.2) = 4159.6 \text{ N} \quad check.$$

Problem 3.27 The mass of the suspended crate is 5 kg. What are the tensions in the cables AB and AC?

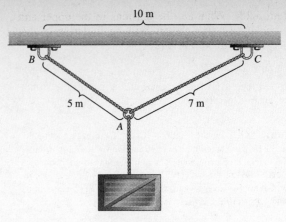

Solution: Find the interior angles in the figure, then apply the equilibrium conditions to the isolated crate. Given the triangle shown, with known sides A, B, and C, find the unknown interior angles α, β, and γ using the. law of cosines

$$B^2 = A^2 + C^2 - 2AC \cos \beta$$

Solve: $\cos \beta = \dfrac{A^2 + C^2 - B^2}{2AC}$. Similarly,

$$\cos \gamma = \dfrac{A^2 + B^2 - C^2}{2AB}.$$

For $A = 10$, $B = 7$, $C = 5$, $\gamma = 27.66°$ and $\beta = 40.54°$. The third angle is

$$\alpha = (180 - 27.66 - 40.64) = 111.8°$$

Isolate the cable juncture at A. The angle between the positive x axis and the tension $\mathbf{T}_{AC}$ is γ. The tension is

$$\mathbf{T}_{AC} = |\mathbf{T}_{AC}|(\mathbf{i} \cos \gamma + \mathbf{j} \sin \gamma).$$

The angle between the positive x axis and the tension $\mathbf{T}_{AB}$ is $(180° - \beta)$,

$$\mathbf{T}_{AB} = |\mathbf{T}_{AB}|(\mathbf{i} \cos(180° - \beta) + \mathbf{j} \sin(180° - \beta))$$

$$\mathbf{T}_{AB} = |\mathbf{T}_{AB}|(-\mathbf{i} \cos \beta + \mathbf{j} \sin \beta).$$

The weight is $\mathbf{W} = 0\mathbf{i} - |\mathbf{W}|\mathbf{j}$.

The equilibrium conditions are

$$\sum \mathbf{F} = \mathbf{W} + \mathbf{T}_{AB} + \mathbf{T}_{AC} = 0.$$

Substitute and collect like terms,

$$\sum \mathbf{F}_x = (|\mathbf{T}_{AC}| \cos \gamma - |\mathbf{T}_{AB}| \cos \beta)\mathbf{i} = 0$$

$$\sum \mathbf{F}_y = (|\mathbf{T}_{AC}| \sin \gamma + |\mathbf{T}_{AB}| \sin \beta - |\mathbf{W}|) = 0$$

Solve: $|\mathbf{T}_{AC}| = \left(\dfrac{\cos \beta}{\cos \gamma}\right)|\mathbf{T}_{AB}|$,

$$|\mathbf{T}_{AB}| = \left(\dfrac{|\mathbf{W}| \cos \gamma}{\sin(\beta + \gamma)}\right),$$

$$|\mathbf{T}_{AC}| = \left(\dfrac{|\mathbf{W}| \cos \beta}{\sin(\beta + \gamma)}\right).$$

For $\quad |\mathbf{W}| = (5 \text{ kg}) \left(9.81 \dfrac{\text{m}}{\text{s}^2}\right) = 49.05 \text{ N}$,

and $\quad \beta = 40.54°, \quad \gamma = 27.66°$

$$|\mathbf{T}_{AB}| = 46.79 \text{ N},$$

$$|\mathbf{T}_{AC}| = 40.15 \text{ N}$$

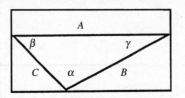

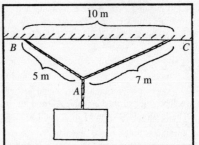

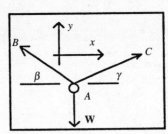

Problem 3.28 What are the tensions in the upper and lower cables? (Your answers will be in terms of W. Neglect the weight of the pulley.)

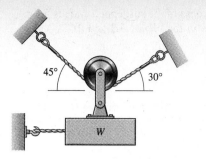

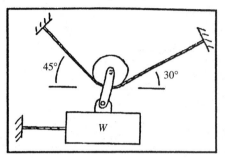

Solution: Isolate the weight. The frictionless pulley changes the direction but not the magnitude of the tension. The angle between the right hand upper cable and the x axis is α, hence

$$\mathbf{T}_{UR} = |\mathbf{T}_U|(\mathbf{i}\cos\alpha + \mathbf{j}\sin\alpha).$$

The angle between the positive x and the left hand upper pulley is $(180° - \beta)$, hence

$$\mathbf{T}_{UL} = |\mathbf{T}_U|(\mathbf{i}\cos(180 - \beta) + \mathbf{j}\sin(180 - \beta))$$

$$= |\mathbf{T}_U|(-\mathbf{i}\cos\beta + \mathbf{j}\sin\beta).$$

The lower cable exerts a force: $\mathbf{T}_L = -|\mathbf{T}_L|\mathbf{i} + 0\mathbf{j}$

The weight: $\mathbf{W} = 0\mathbf{i} - |\mathbf{W}|\mathbf{j}$

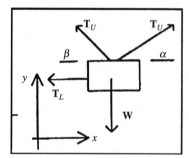

The equilibrium conditions are

$$\sum \mathbf{F} = \mathbf{W} + \mathbf{T}_{UL} + \mathbf{T}_{UR} + \mathbf{T}_L = 0$$

Substitute and collect like terms,

$$\sum \mathbf{F}_x = (-|\mathbf{T}_U|\cos\beta + |\mathbf{T}_U|\cos\alpha - |\mathbf{T}_L|)\mathbf{i} = 0$$

$$\sum \mathbf{F}_y = (|\mathbf{T}_U|\sin\alpha + |\mathbf{T}_U|\sin\beta - |\mathbf{W}|)\mathbf{j} = 0.$$

Solve: $\quad |\mathbf{T}_U| = \left(\dfrac{|\mathbf{W}|}{(\sin\alpha + \sin\beta)}\right),$

$$|\mathbf{T}_L| = |\mathbf{T}_U|(\cos\alpha - \cos\beta).$$

From which $\quad |\mathbf{T}_L| = |\mathbf{W}|\left(\dfrac{\cos\alpha - \cos\beta}{\sin\alpha + \sin\beta}\right).$

For $\quad \alpha = 30°$ and $\beta = 45°$

$\quad |\mathbf{T}_U| = 0.828|\mathbf{W}|,$

$\quad |\mathbf{T}_L| = 0.132|\mathbf{W}|$

Problem 3.29 Two tow trucks lift a motorcycle out of a ravine following an accident. If the 100-kg motorcycle is in equilibrium in the position shown, what are the tensions in cables AB and AC?

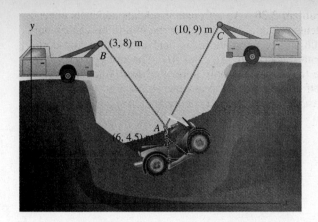

Solution: We need to find unit vectors $\mathbf{e}_{AB}$ and $\mathbf{e}_{AC}$. Then write $\mathbf{T}_{AB} = T_{AB}\mathbf{e}_{AB}$ and $\mathbf{T}_{AC} = T_{AC}\mathbf{e}_{AC}$. Finally, write and solve the equations of equilibrium.

For the ring at A.

From the known locations of points A, B, and C,

$$\mathbf{e}_{AB} = \frac{\mathbf{r}_{AB}}{|\mathbf{r}_{AB}|} \quad \mathbf{e}_{AC} = \frac{\mathbf{r}_{AC}}{|\mathbf{r}_{AC}|}$$

$$\mathbf{r}_{AB} = -3\mathbf{i} + 3.5\mathbf{j} \text{ m} \quad |\mathbf{r}_{AB}| = 4.61 \text{ m}$$

$$\mathbf{r}_{AC} = 4\mathbf{i} + 4.5\mathbf{j} \text{ m} \quad |\mathbf{r}_{AC}| = 6.02 \text{ m}$$

$$\mathbf{e}_{AB} = -0.651\mathbf{i} + 0.759\mathbf{j}$$

$$\mathbf{e}_{AC} = 0.664\mathbf{i} + 0.747\mathbf{j}$$

$$\mathbf{T}_{AB} = -0.651T_{AB}\mathbf{i} + 0.759T_{AB}\mathbf{j}$$

$$\mathbf{T}_{AC} = 0.664T_{AC}\mathbf{i} + 0.747T_{AC}\mathbf{j}$$

$$\mathbf{W} = -mg\mathbf{j} = -(100)(9.81)\mathbf{j} \text{ N}$$

For equilibrium,

$$\mathbf{T}_{AB} + \mathbf{T}_{AC} + \mathbf{W} = 0$$

In component form, we have

$$\begin{cases} \sum F_x = -0.651T_{AB} + 0.664T_{AC} = 0 \\ \sum F_y = +0.759T_{AB} + 0.747T_{AC} - 981 = 0 \end{cases}$$

Solving, we get

$$T_{AB} = 658 \text{ N}, \ T_{AC} = 645 \text{ N}$$

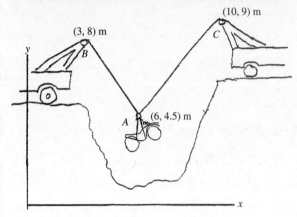

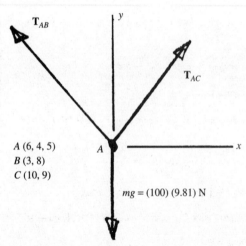

$A\ (6, 4, 5)$
$B\ (3, 8)$
$C\ (10, 9)$

$mg = (100)\ (9.81)$ N

Problem 3.30 An astronaut candidate conducts experiments on an airbearing platform. While he carries out calibrations, the platform is held in place by the horizontal tethers AB, AC, and AD. The forces exerted by the tethers are the only horizontal forces acting on the platform. If the tension in tether AC is 2 N, what are the tensions in the other two tethers?

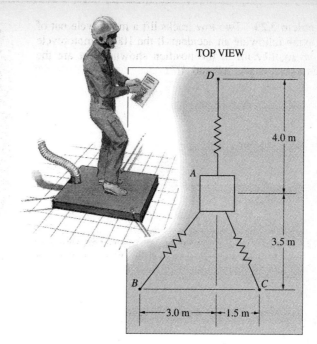

TOP VIEW

Solution: Isolate the platform. The angles α and β are

$$\tan \alpha = \left(\frac{1.5}{3.5}\right) = 0.429, \quad \alpha = 23.2°.$$

Also, $\tan \beta = \left(\frac{3.0}{3.5}\right) = 0.857, \quad \beta = 40.6°.$

The angle between the tether AB and the positive x axis is $(180° - \beta)$, hence

$$\mathbf{T}_{AB} = |\mathbf{T}_{AB}|(\mathbf{i}\cos(180° - \beta) + \mathbf{j}\sin(180° - \beta))$$

$$\mathbf{T}_{AB} = |\mathbf{T}_{AB}|(-\mathbf{i}\cos \beta + \mathbf{j}\sin \beta).$$

The angle between the tether AC and the positive x axis is $(180° + \alpha)$. The tension is

$$\mathbf{T}_{AC} = |\mathbf{T}_{AC}|(\mathbf{i}\cos(180° + \alpha) + \mathbf{j}\sin(180° + \alpha))$$

$$= |\mathbf{T}_{AC}|(-\mathbf{i}\cos \alpha - \mathbf{j}\sin \alpha).$$

The tether AD is aligned with the positive x axis, $\mathbf{T}_{AD} = |\mathbf{T}_{AD}|\mathbf{i} + 0\mathbf{j}$.

The equilibrium condition:

$$\sum \mathbf{F} = \mathbf{T}_{AD} + \mathbf{T}_{AB} + \mathbf{T}_{AC} = 0.$$

Substitute and collect like terms,

$$\sum \mathbf{F}_x = (-|\mathbf{T}_{AB}|\cos \beta - |\mathbf{T}_{AC}|\cos \alpha + |\mathbf{T}_{AD}|)\mathbf{i} = 0,$$

$$\sum \mathbf{F}_y = (|\mathbf{T}_{AB}|\sin \beta - |\mathbf{T}_{AC}|\sin \alpha)\mathbf{j} = 0.$$

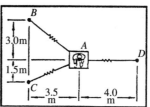

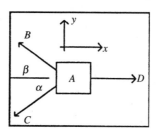

Solve: $|\mathbf{T}_{AB}| = \left(\frac{\sin \alpha}{\sin \beta}\right)|\mathbf{T}_{AC}|,$

$$|\mathbf{T}_{AD}| = \left(\frac{|\mathbf{T}_{AC}|\sin(\alpha + \beta)}{\sin \beta}\right).$$

For $|\mathbf{T}_{AC}| = 2$ N, $\alpha = 23.2°$ and $\beta = 40.6°$,

$$|\mathbf{T}_{AB}| = 1.21 \text{ N}, \quad |\mathbf{T}_{AD}| = 2.76 \text{ N}$$

Problem 3.31 The forces exerted on the shoes and back of the 72-kg climber by the walls of the "chimney" are perpendicular to the walls exerting them. The tension in the rope is 640 N. What is the magnitude of the force exerted on his back?

Solution: Draw a free body diagram of the climber-treating all forces as if they act at a point. Write the forces in components and then apply the conditions for particle equilibrium.

$$\begin{cases} \sum F_x = F_{\text{FEET}} \cos 4° - F_{\text{BACK}} \cos 3° - T_{\text{ROPE}} \sin 10° = 0 \\ \sum F_y = F_{\text{FEET}} \sin 4° + F_{\text{BACK}} \sin 3° + T_{\text{ROPE}} \cos 10° - mg = 0 \\ \quad mg = (72)9.81 \text{ N}, \ T_{\text{ROPE}} = 640 \text{ N} \end{cases}$$

Solving, we get

$$F_{\text{BACK}} = 559 \text{ N}, \ F_{\text{FEET}} = 671 \text{ N}$$

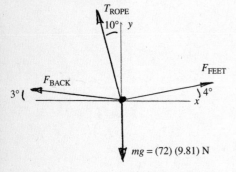

Problem 3.32 The slider A is in equilibrium and the bar is smooth. What is the mass of the slider?

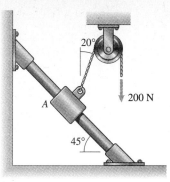

Solution: The pulley does not change the tension in the rope that passes over it. There is no friction between the slider and the bar.

Eqns. of Equilibrium:

$$\begin{cases} \sum F_x = T \sin 20° + N \cos 45° = 0 \quad (T = 200 \text{ N}) \\ \sum F_y = N \sin 45° + T \cos 20° - mg = 0 \quad g = 9.81 \text{ m/s}^2 \end{cases}$$

Substituting for T and g, we have two eqns in two unknowns (N and m).

Solving, we get $N = -96.7$ N, $m = 12.2$ kg.

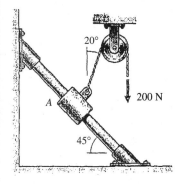

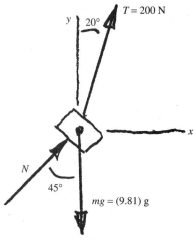

$T = 200$ N

$mg = (9.81)$ g

Problem 3.33 The unstretched length of the spring AB is 660 mm, and the spring constant $k = 1000$ N/m. What is the mass of the suspended object?

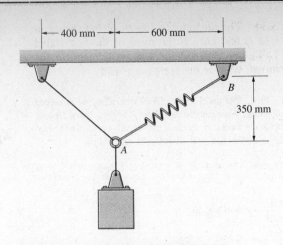

Solution: Use the linear spring force-extension relation to find the magnitude of the tension in spring AB. Isolate juncture A. The forces are the weight and the tensions in the cables. The angles are

$$\tan \alpha = \left(\frac{350}{600}\right) = 0.5833, \quad \alpha = 30.26°.$$

$$\tan \beta = \left(\frac{350}{400}\right) = 0.875, \quad \beta = 41.2°.$$

The angle between the x axis and the spring is α. The tension is

$$\mathbf{T}_{AB} = |\mathbf{T}_{AB}|(\mathbf{i}\cos\alpha + \mathbf{j}\sin\alpha).$$

The angle between the x axis and AC is $(180 - \beta)$. The tension is

$$\mathbf{T}_{AC} = |\mathbf{T}_{AC}|(\mathbf{i}\cos(180 - \beta) + \mathbf{j}\sin(180 - \beta))$$

$$\mathbf{T}_{AC} = |\mathbf{T}_{AC}|(-\mathbf{i}\cos\beta + \mathbf{j}\sin\beta).$$

The weight is: $\mathbf{W} = 0\mathbf{i} - |\mathbf{W}|\mathbf{j}.$

The equilibrium conditions: $\sum \mathbf{F} = \mathbf{W} + \mathbf{T}_{AB} + \mathbf{T}_{AC} = 0.$

Substitute and collect like terms

$$\sum F_x = (|\mathbf{T}_{AB}|\cos\alpha - |\mathbf{T}_{AC}|\cos\beta)\mathbf{i} = 0,$$

$$\sum F_y = (|\mathbf{T}_{AC}|\sin\alpha + |\mathbf{T}_{AB}|\sin\beta - |\mathbf{W}|)\mathbf{j} = 0.$$

Solve: $|\mathbf{T}_{AC}| = \left(\frac{\cos\alpha}{\cos\beta}\right)|\mathbf{T}_{AB}|$ and $|\mathbf{W}| = \left(\frac{\sin(\alpha + \beta)}{\cos\beta}\right)|\mathbf{T}_{AB}|.$

The tension $|\mathbf{T}_{AB}|$ is found from the linear spring force-deflection relation. The spring extension is

$$\Delta L = \sqrt{(350)^2 + (600)^2} - 660 = 694.62 - 660 = 34.62 \text{ mm}$$

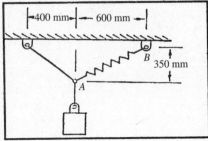

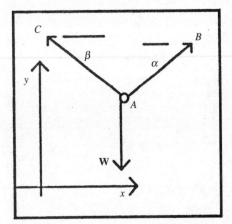

The tension is $|\mathbf{T}_{AB}| = k\Delta L = (1000)(0.03462) = 34.6$ N.

For $\alpha = 30.26°$ and $\beta = 41.2°$; the weight is

$$|\mathbf{W}| = \left(\frac{0.948}{0.752}\right)(34.6) = 43.62 \text{ N};$$

The mass is $\boxed{m = \left(\frac{|\mathbf{W}|}{|\mathbf{g}|}\right) = \left(\frac{43.62}{9.81}\right) = 4.447 \text{ kg}}$

Problem 3.34 The unstretched length of the spring in Problem 3.33 is 660 mm. If the mass of the suspended object is 10 kg and the system is in equilibrium in the position shown, what is the spring constant?

Solution: First, find the distance AB to determine the stretched length of the spring. Write unit vectors from A toward B and from A toward C. Write the forces, in terms of these unit vectors. Then write the equations of equilibrium and solve for the unknowns.

From the diagram, A is at $(0,0)$, B is at $(0.6, 0.35)$ m, and C is at $(-0.4, 0.35)$ m.

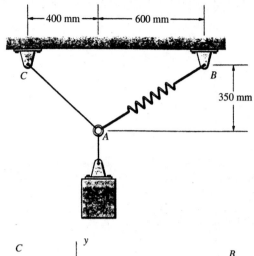

$$\begin{cases} \mathbf{e}_{AB} = \dfrac{\mathbf{r}_{AB}}{|\mathbf{r}_{AB}|} = 0.864\mathbf{i} + 0.504\mathbf{j} \\ \mathbf{e}_{AC} = \dfrac{\mathbf{r}_{AC}}{|\mathbf{r}_{AC}|} = -0.753\mathbf{i} + 0.659\mathbf{j} \end{cases}$$

$$\begin{cases} \mathbf{T}_{AB} = 0.864 T_{AB}\mathbf{i} + 0.504 T_{AB}\mathbf{j} \\ \mathbf{T}_{AC} = -0.753 T_{AC}\mathbf{i} + 0.659 T_{AC}\mathbf{j} \\ \mathbf{W} = 0\mathbf{i} - 98.1\mathbf{j} \text{ (N)} \end{cases}$$

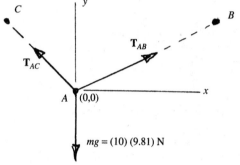

From our calculations

$|\mathbf{r}_{AB}| = 0.695$ m

••• the stretched length of the spring.

Thus, the stretch in the spring is given by

$\delta = |\mathbf{r}_{AB}| - \ell_{\text{unstretched}}$

$\delta = 0.6946 - 0.6600 = 0.0346$ (m)

We know that

$T_{AB} = K\delta = 0.0346$

The equilibrium equations are

$$\begin{cases} \sum F_x = 0.864 T_{AB} - 0.753 T_{AC} = 0 \\ \sum F_y = 0.504 T_{AB} + 0.659 T_{AC} - 98.1 = 0 \end{cases}$$

Solving, we get

$T_{AB} = 77.88$ N $T_{AC} = 89.38$ N

Finally solving for K, we get

$K = 2250$ N/m

Problem 3.35 The collar A slides on the smooth vertical bar. The masses $m_A = 20$ kg and $m_B = 10$ kg. When $h = 0.1$ m, the spring is unstretched. When the system is in equilibrium, $h = 0.3$ m. Determine the spring constant k.

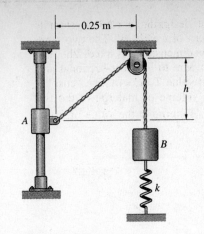

Solution: The triangles formed by the rope segments and the horizontal line level with A can be used to determine the lengths L_u and L_s. The equations are

$$L_u = \sqrt{(0.25)^2 + (0.1)^2} \text{ and } L_s = \sqrt{(0.25)^2 + (0.3)^2}.$$

The stretch in the spring when in equilibrium is given by $\delta = L_s - L_u$. Carrying out the calculations, we get $L_u = 0.269$ m, $L_s = 0.391$ m, and $\delta = 0.121$ m. The angle, θ, between the rope at A and the horizontal when the system is in equilibrium is given by $\tan \theta = 0.3/0.25$, or $\theta = 50.2°$. From the free body diagram for mass A, we get two equilibrium equations. They are

$$\sum F_x = -N_A + T \cos \theta = 0$$

and $\sum F_y = T \sin \theta - m_A g = 0.$

We have two equations in two unknowns and can solve. We get $N_A = 163.5$ N and $T = 255.4$ N. Now we go to the free body diagram for B, where the equation of equilibrium is $T - m_B g - k\delta = 0$. This equation has only one unknown. Solving, we get $\boxed{k = 1297 \text{ N/m}}$

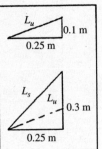

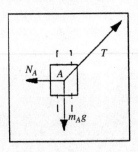

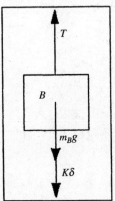

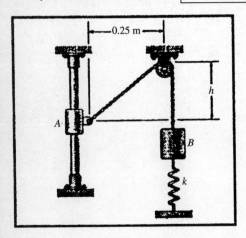

Problem 3.36 You are designing a cable system to support a suspended object of weight W. The two wires must be identical, and the dimension b is fixed. The ratio of the tension T in each wire to its cross-sectional area A must equal a specified value $T/A = \sigma$. The "cost" of your design is the total volume of material in the two wires, $V = 2A\sqrt{b^2 + h^2}$. Determine the value of h that minimizes the cost.

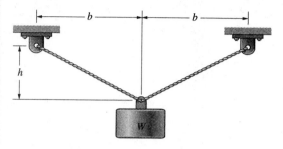

Solution: From the equation

$$\sum F_y = 2T \sin\theta - W = 0,$$

we obtain $T = \dfrac{W}{2\sin\theta} = \dfrac{W\sqrt{b^2 + h^2}}{2h}$.

Since $T/A = \sigma$, $A = \dfrac{T}{\sigma} = \dfrac{W\sqrt{b^2 + h^2}}{2\sigma h}$

and the "cost" is $V = 2A\sqrt{b^2 + h^2} = \dfrac{W(b^2 + h^2)}{\sigma h}$.

To determine the value of h that minimizes V, we set

$$\frac{dV}{dh} = \frac{W}{\sigma}\left[-\frac{(b^2 + h^2)}{h^2} + 2 \right] = 0$$

and solve for h, obtaining $h = b$.

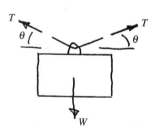

Problem 3.37 The system of cables suspends a 1000-lb bank of lights above a movie set. Determine the tensions in cables AB, CD, and CE.

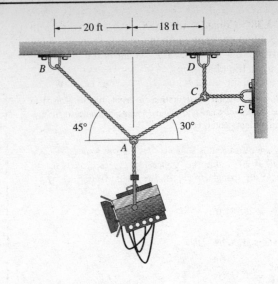

Solution: Isolate juncture A, and solve the equilibrium equations. Repeat for the cable juncture C.

The angle between the cable AC and the positive x axis is α. The tension in AC is $\mathbf{T}_{AC} = |\mathbf{T}_{AC}|(\mathbf{i}\cos\alpha + \mathbf{j}\sin\alpha)$

The angle between the x axis and AB is $(180° - \beta)$. The tension is

$\mathbf{T}_{AB} = |\mathbf{T}_{AB}|(\mathbf{i}\cos(180 - \beta) + \mathbf{j}\sin(180 - \beta))$

$\mathbf{T}_{AB} = (-\mathbf{i}\cos\beta + \mathbf{j}\sin\beta)$.

The weight is $\mathbf{W} = 0\mathbf{i} - |\mathbf{W}|\mathbf{j}$.

The equilibrium conditions are

$$\sum \mathbf{F} = 0 = \mathbf{W} + \mathbf{T}_{AB} + \mathbf{T}_{AC} = 0.$$

Substitute and collect like terms,

$$\sum \mathbf{F}_x = (|\mathbf{T}_{AC}|\cos\alpha - |\mathbf{T}_{AB}|\cos\beta)\mathbf{i} = 0$$

$$\sum \mathbf{F}_y = (|\mathbf{T}_{AB}|\sin\beta + |\mathbf{T}_{AC}|\sin\alpha - |\mathbf{W}|)\mathbf{j} = 0.$$

Solving, we get

$$|\mathbf{T}_{AB}| = \left(\frac{\cos\alpha}{\cos\beta}\right)|\mathbf{T}_{AC}| \quad \text{and} \quad |\mathbf{T}_{AC}| = \left(\frac{|\mathbf{W}|\cos\beta}{\sin(\alpha + \beta)}\right),$$

$|\mathbf{W}| = 1000$ lb, and $\alpha = 30°$, $\beta = 45°$

$$|\mathbf{T}_{AC}| = (1000)\left(\frac{0.7071}{0.9659}\right) = 732.05 \text{ lb}$$

$$|\mathbf{T}_{AB}| = (732)\left(\frac{0.866}{0.7071}\right) = 896.5 \text{ lb}$$

Isolate juncture C. The angle between the positive x axis and the cable CA is $(180° - \alpha)$. The tension is

$$\mathbf{T}_{CA} = |\mathbf{T}_{CA}|(\mathbf{i}\cos(180° + \alpha) + \mathbf{j}\sin(180° + \alpha)),$$

or $\mathbf{T}_{CA} = |\mathbf{T}_{CA}|(-\mathbf{i}\cos\alpha - \mathbf{j}\sin\alpha)$.

The tension in the cable CE is

$$\mathbf{T}_{CE} = \mathbf{i}|\mathbf{T}_{CE}| + 0\mathbf{j}.$$

The tension in the cable CD is $\mathbf{T}_{CD} = 0\mathbf{i} + \mathbf{j}|\mathbf{T}_{CD}|$.

The equilibrium conditions are

$$\sum \mathbf{F} = 0 = \mathbf{T}_{CA} + \mathbf{T}_{CE} + \mathbf{T}_{CD} = 0$$

Substitute t and collect like terms,

$$\sum \mathbf{F}_x = (|\mathbf{T}_{CE}| - |\mathbf{T}_{CA}|\cos\alpha)\mathbf{i} = 0,$$

$$\sum \mathbf{F}_y = (|\mathbf{T}_{CD}| - |\mathbf{T}_{CA}|\sin\alpha)\mathbf{j} = 0.$$

Solve: $|\mathbf{T}_{CE}| = |\mathbf{T}_{CA}|\cos\alpha$,

$|\mathbf{T}_{CD}| = |\mathbf{T}_{CA}|\sin\alpha$;

for $|\mathbf{T}_{CA}| = 732$ lb and $\alpha = 30°$,

$|\mathbf{T}_{AB}| = 896.6$ lb,

$|\mathbf{T}_{CE}| = 634$ lb,

$|\mathbf{T}_{CD}| = 366$ lb

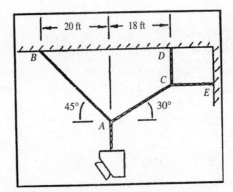

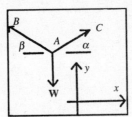

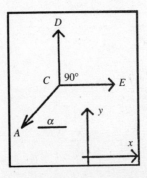

116

Problem 3.38 Consider the 1000-lb bank of lights in Problem 3.37. A technician changes the position of the lights by removing the cable CE. What is the tension in cable AB after the change?

Solution: The original configuration in Problem 3.35 is used to solve for the dimensions and the angles. Isolate the juncture A, and solve the equilibrium conditions.

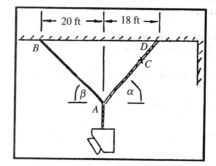

The lengths are calculated as follows: The vertical interior distance in the triangle is 20 ft, since the angle is 45 deg. and the base and altitude of a 45 deg triangle are equal. The length AB is given by

$$\overline{AB} = \frac{20 \text{ ft}}{\cos 45°} = 28.284 \text{ ft.}$$

The length AC is given by

$$\overline{AC} = \frac{18 \text{ ft}}{\cos 30°} = 20.785 \text{ ft.}$$

The altitude of the triangle for which AC is the hypotenuse is $18 \tan 30° = 10.392$ ft. The distance CD is given by $20 - 10.392 = 9.608$ ft.

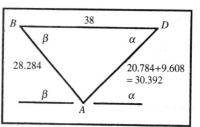

The distance AD is given by

$$AD = AC + CD = 20.784 + 9.608 = 30.392$$

The new angles are given by the cosine law

$$AB^2 = 38^2 + AD^2 - 2(38)(AD) \cos \alpha.$$

Reduce and solve:

$$\cos \alpha = \left(\frac{38^2 + (30.392)^2 - (28.284)^2}{2(38)(30.392)} \right) = 0.6787, \quad \alpha = 47.23°.$$

$$\cos \beta = \left(\frac{(28.284)^2 + (38)^2 - (30.392)^2}{2(28.284)(38)} \right) = 0.6142, \quad \beta = 52.1°.$$

Isolate the juncture A. The angle between the cable AD and the positive x axis is α. The tension is:

$$\mathbf{T}_{AD} = |\mathbf{T}_{AD}|(\mathbf{i} \cos \alpha + \mathbf{j} \sin \alpha).$$

The angle between x and the cable AB is $(180° - \beta)$. The tension is

$$\mathbf{T}_{AB} = |\mathbf{T}_{AB}|(-\mathbf{i} \cos \beta + \mathbf{j} \sin \beta).$$

The weight is $\mathbf{W} = 0\mathbf{i} - |\mathbf{W}|\mathbf{j}$

The equilibrium conditions are

$$\sum \mathbf{F} = 0 = \mathbf{W} + \mathbf{T}_{AB} + \mathbf{T}_{AD} = 0.$$

Substitute and collect like terms,

$$\sum \mathbf{F}_x = (|\mathbf{T}_{AD}| \cos \alpha - |\mathbf{T}_{AB}| \cos \beta)\mathbf{i} = 0,$$

$$\sum \mathbf{F}_y = (|\mathbf{T}_{AB}| \sin \beta + |\mathbf{T}_{AD}| \sin \alpha - |\mathbf{W}|)\mathbf{j} = 0.$$

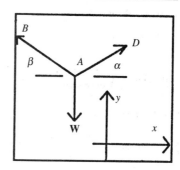

Solve: $|\mathbf{T}_{AB}| = \left(\frac{\cos \alpha}{\cos \beta} \right) |\mathbf{T}_{AD}|,$

and $|\mathbf{T}_{AD}| = \left(\frac{|\mathbf{W}| \cos \beta}{\sin(\alpha + \beta)} \right).$

For $|\mathbf{W}| = 1000$ lb, and $\alpha = 51.2°$, $\beta = 47.2°$

$$|\mathbf{T}_{AD}| = (1000) \left(\frac{0.6142}{0.989} \right) = 621.03 \text{ lb,}$$

$$|\mathbf{T}_{AB}| = (622.3) \left(\frac{0.6787}{0.6142} \right) = 687.9 \text{ lb}$$

Problem 3.39 While working on another exhibit, a curator at the Smithsonian Institution pulls the suspended *Voyager* aircraft to one side by attaching three horizontal cables as shown. The mass of the aircraft is 1250 kg. Determine the tensions in the cable segments AB, BC, and CD.

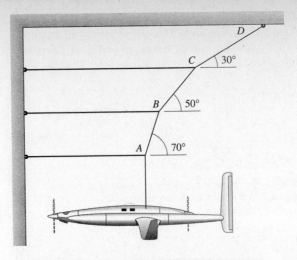

Solution: Isolate each cable juncture, beginning with A and solve the equilibrium equations at each juncture. The angle between the cable AB and the positive x axis is $\alpha = 70°$; the tension in cable AB is $\mathbf{T}_{AB} = |\mathbf{T}_{AB}|(\mathbf{i}\cos\alpha + \mathbf{j}\sin\alpha)$. The weight is $\mathbf{W} = 0\mathbf{i} - |\mathbf{W}|\mathbf{j}$. The tension in cable AT is $\mathbf{T} = -|\mathbf{T}|\mathbf{i} + 0\mathbf{j}$. The equilibrium conditions are

$$\sum \mathbf{F} = \mathbf{W} + \mathbf{T} + \mathbf{T}_{AB} = 0.$$

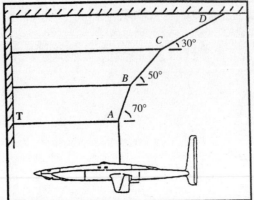

Substitute and collect like terms

$$\sum \mathbf{F}_x(|\mathbf{T}_{AB}|\cos\alpha - |\mathbf{T}|)\mathbf{i} = 0,$$

$$\sum \mathbf{F}_y = (|\mathbf{T}_{AB}|\sin\alpha - |\mathbf{W}|)\mathbf{j} = 0.$$

Solve: the tension in cable AB is $|\mathbf{T}_{AB}| = \left(\dfrac{|\mathbf{W}|}{\sin\alpha}\right)$.

For $|\mathbf{W}| = (1250 \text{ kg})\left(9.81 \dfrac{\text{m}}{\text{s}^2}\right) = 12262.5$ N and $\alpha = 70°$

$$|\mathbf{T}_{AB}| = \left(\frac{12262.5}{0.94}\right) = 13049.5 \text{ N}$$

Isolate juncture B. The angles are $\alpha = 50°$, $\beta = 70°$, and the tension cable BC is $\mathbf{T}_{BC} = |\mathbf{T}_{BC}|(\mathbf{i}\cos\alpha + \mathbf{j}\sin\alpha)$. The angle between the cable BA and the positive x axis is $(180 + \beta)$; the tension is

$$\mathbf{T}_{BA} = |\mathbf{T}_{BA}|(\mathbf{i}\cos(180+\beta) + \mathbf{j}\sin(180+\beta))$$

$$= |\mathbf{T}_{BA}|(-\mathbf{i}\cos\beta - \mathbf{j}\sin\beta)$$

The tension in the left horizontal cable is $\mathbf{T} = -|\mathbf{T}|\mathbf{i} + 0\mathbf{j}$. The equilibrium conditions are

$$\sum \mathbf{F} = \mathbf{T}_{BA} + \mathbf{T}_{BC} + \mathbf{T} = 0.$$

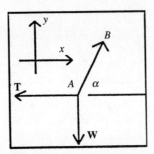

Substitute and collect like terms

$$\sum \mathbf{F}_x = (|\mathbf{T}_{BC}|\cos\alpha - |\mathbf{T}_{BA}|\cos\beta - |\mathbf{T}|)\mathbf{i} = 0$$

$$\sum \mathbf{F}_y = (|\mathbf{T}_{BC}|\sin\alpha - |\mathbf{T}_{BA}|\sin\beta)\mathbf{j} = 0.$$

Solve: $|\mathbf{T}_{BC}| = \left(\dfrac{\sin\beta}{\sin\alpha}\right)|\mathbf{T}_{BA}|$.

For $|\mathbf{T}_{BA}| = 13049.5$ N, and $\alpha = 50°$, $\beta = 70°$,

$$|\mathbf{T}_{BC}| = (13049.5)\left(\frac{0.9397}{0.7660}\right) = 16007.6 \text{ N}$$

Isolate the cable juncture C. The angles are $\alpha = 30°$, $\beta = 50°$. By symmetry with the cable juncture B above, the tension in cable CD is

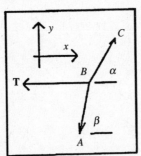

$$|\mathbf{T}_{CD}| = \left(\frac{\sin\beta}{\sin\alpha}\right)|\mathbf{T}_{CB}|.$$

Substitute: $|\mathbf{T}_{CD}| = (16007.6)\left(\dfrac{0.7660}{0.5}\right) = 24525.0$ N.

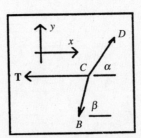

This completes the problem solution.

Problem 3.40 A truck dealer wants to suspend a 4-Mg (megagram) truck as shown for advertising. The distance $b = 15$ m, and the sum of the lengths of the cables AB and BC is 42 m. What are the tensions in the cables?

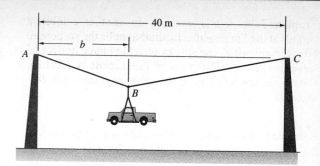

Solution: Determine the dimensions and angles of the cables. Isolate the cable juncture B, and solve the equilibrium conditions. The dimensions of the triangles formed by the cables:

$$b = 15 \text{ m}, \quad L = 25 \text{ m}, \quad AB + BC = S = 42 \text{ m}.$$

Subdivide into two right triangles with a common side of unknown length. Let the unknown length of this common side be d, then by the Pythagorean Theorem $b^2 + d^2 = AB^2$, $L^2 + d^2 = BC^2$.

Subtract the first equation from the second to eliminate the unknown d, $L^2 - b^2 = BC^2 - AB^2$.

Note that $BC^2 - AB^2 = (BC - AB)(BC + AB)$.

Substitute and reduce to the pair of simultaneous equations in the unknowns

$$BC - AB = \left(\frac{L^2 - b^2}{S}\right), \quad BC + AB = S$$

Solve: $BC = \left(\frac{1}{2}\right)\left(\frac{L^2 - b^2}{S} + S\right)$

$$= \left(\frac{1}{2}\right)\left(\frac{25^2 - 15^2}{42} + 42\right) = 25.762 \text{ m}$$

and $AB = S - BC = 42 - 25.762 = 16.238$ m.

The interior angles are found from the cosine law:

$$\cos \alpha = \left(\frac{(L+b)^2 + BC^2 - AB^2}{2(L+b)(BC)}\right) = 0.9704 \quad \alpha = 13.97°$$

$$\cos \beta = \left(\frac{(L+b)^2 + AB^2 - BC^2}{2(L+b)(AB)}\right) = 0.9238 \quad \beta = 22.52°$$

Isolate cable juncture B. The angle between BC and the positive x axis is α; the tension is

$$\mathbf{T}_{BC} = |\mathbf{T}_{BC}|(\mathbf{i} \cos \alpha + \mathbf{j} \sin \alpha)$$

The angle between BA and the positive x axis is $(180° - \beta)$; the tension is

$$\mathbf{T}_{BA} = |\mathbf{T}_{BA}|(\mathbf{i} \cos(180 - \beta) + \mathbf{j} \sin(180 - \beta))$$

$$= |\mathbf{T}_{BA}|(-\mathbf{i} \cos \beta + \mathbf{j} \sin \beta).$$

The weight is $\mathbf{W} = 0\mathbf{i} - |\mathbf{W}|\mathbf{j}$.

The equilibrium conditions are

$$\sum \mathbf{F} = \mathbf{W} + \mathbf{T}_{BA} + \mathbf{T}_{BC} = 0.$$

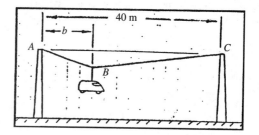

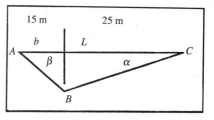

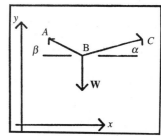

Substitute and collect like terms

$$\sum \mathbf{F}_x = (|\mathbf{T}_{BC}| \cos \alpha - |\mathbf{T}_{BA}| \cos \beta)\mathbf{i} = 0,$$

$$\sum \mathbf{F}_y = (|\mathbf{T}_{BC}| \sin \alpha + |\mathbf{T}_{BA}| \sin \beta - |\mathbf{W}|)\mathbf{j} = 0$$

Solve: $|\mathbf{T}_{BC}| = \left(\frac{\cos \beta}{\cos \alpha}\right)|\mathbf{T}_{BA}|,$

and $|\mathbf{T}_{BA}| = \left(\frac{|\mathbf{W}| \cos \alpha}{\sin(\alpha + \beta)}\right).$

For $|\mathbf{W}| = (4000)(9.81) = 39240$ N,

and $\alpha = 13.97°$, $\beta = 22.52°$,

$|\mathbf{T}_{BA}| = 64033 = 64$ kN,

$|\mathbf{T}_{BC}| = 60953 = 61$ kN

Problem 3.41 The distance $h = 12$ in., and the tension in cable AD is 200 lb. What are the tensions in cables AB and AC?

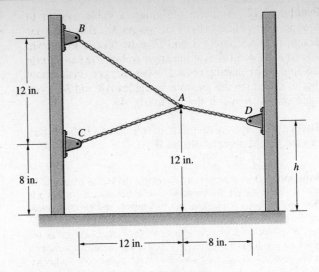

Solution: Isolated the cable juncture. From the sketch, the angles are found from

$$\tan \alpha = \left(\frac{8}{12}\right) = 0.667 \quad \alpha = 33.7°$$

$$\tan \beta = \left(\frac{4}{12}\right) = 0.333 \quad \beta = 18.4°$$

The angle between the cable AB and the positive x axis is $(180° - \alpha)$, the tension in AB is:

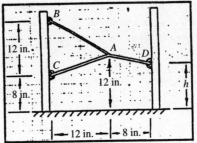

$$\mathbf{T}_{AB} = |\mathbf{T}_{AB}|(\mathbf{i}\cos(180 - \alpha) + \mathbf{j}\sin(180 - \alpha))$$

$$\mathbf{T}_{AB} = |\mathbf{T}_{AB}|(-\mathbf{i}\cos\alpha + \mathbf{j}\sin\alpha).$$

The angle between AC and the positive x axis is $(180 + \beta)$. The tension is

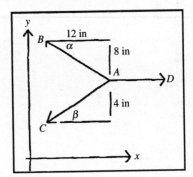

$$\mathbf{T}_{AC} = |\mathbf{T}_{AC}|(\mathbf{i}\cos(180 + \beta) + \mathbf{j}\sin(180 + \beta))$$

$$\mathbf{T}_{AC} = |\mathbf{T}_{AC}|(-\mathbf{i}\cos\beta - \mathbf{j}\sin\beta).$$

The tension in the cable AD is

$$\mathbf{T}_{AD} = |\mathbf{T}_{AD}|\mathbf{i} + 0\mathbf{j}.$$

The equilibrium conditions are

$$\sum \mathbf{F} = \mathbf{T}_{AC} + \mathbf{T}_{AB} + \mathbf{T}_{AD} = 0.$$

Substitute and collect like terms,

$$\sum \mathbf{F}_x = (-|\mathbf{T}_{AB}|\cos\alpha - |\mathbf{T}_{AC}|\cos\beta + |\mathbf{T}_{AD}|)\mathbf{i} = 0$$

$$\sum \mathbf{F}_y = (|\mathbf{T}_{AB}|\sin\alpha - |\mathbf{T}_{AC}|\sin\beta)\mathbf{j} = 0.$$

Solve: $|\mathbf{T}_{AB}| = \left(\dfrac{\sin\beta}{\sin\alpha}\right)|\mathbf{T}_{AC}|,$

and $|\mathbf{T}_{AC}| = \left(\dfrac{\sin\alpha}{\sin(\alpha + \beta)}\right)|\mathbf{T}_{AD}|.$

For $|\mathbf{T}_{AD}| = 200$ lb, $\alpha = 33.7°$, $\beta = 18.4°$

$|\mathbf{T}_{AC}| = 140.6$ lb, $|\mathbf{T}_{AB}| = 80.1$ lb

Problem 3.42 You are designing a cable system to support a suspended object of weight W. Because your design requires points A and B to be placed as shown, you have no control over the angle α, but you can choose the angle β by placing point C wherever you wish. Show that to minimize the tensions in cables AB and BC, you must choose $\beta = \alpha$ if the angle $\alpha \geq 45°$.

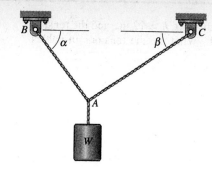

Strategy: Draw a diagram of the sum of the forces exerted by the three cables at A.

Solution: Draw the free body diagram of the knot at point A. Then draw the force triangle involving the three forces. Remember that α is fixed and the force W has both fixed magnitude and direction. From the force triangle, we see that the force T_{AC} can be smaller than T_{AB} for a large range of values for β. By inspection, we see that the minimum simultaneous values for T_{AC} and T_{AB} occur when the two forces are equal. This occurs when $\alpha = \beta$. Note: this does not happen when $\alpha < 45°$.

In this case, we solved the problem without writing the equations of equilibrium. For reference, these equations are:

$$\sum F_x = -T_{AB} \cos \alpha + T_{AC} \cos \beta = 0$$

and $\sum F_y = T_{AB} \sin \alpha + T_{AC} \sin \beta - W = 0.$

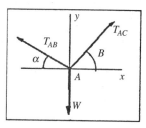

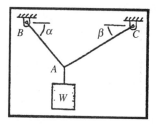

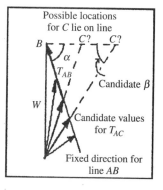

Problem 3.43 In Problem 3.42, suppose that you have no control over the angle α and you want to design the cable system so that the tension in cable AC is minimum. What is the required angle β?

Solution: From Problem 3.32 above, the angle required to minimize the tension in cable AC, for large values of α is $\beta = \alpha$. However, for small values of $\propto$, the situation is different. In this situation, the force triangle is as shown in the figure. It is obvious from the figure that the minimum value for tension in cable AC is obtained when the T_{AC} is perpendicular to T_{AB}.

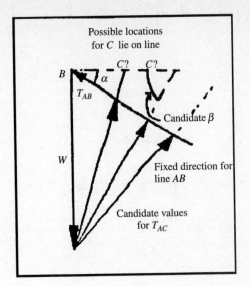

Problem 3.44 The masses of the boxes on the left and right are 25 kg and 40 kg, respectively. The surfaces are smooth and the boxes are in equilibrium. Determine the tension in the cable and the angle α.

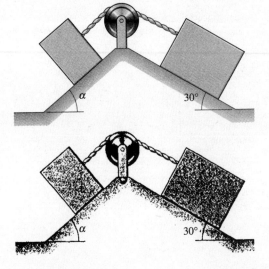

Solution: We now need to write the equilibrium equations for each box.

For the left box,

$$\begin{cases} \sum F_x = T - m_L g \sin \alpha = 0 \\ \sum F_y = N_L - m_L g \cos \alpha = 0 \end{cases}$$

For the right box,

$$\begin{cases} \sum F_{x'} = -T + m_R g \sin 30° = 0 \\ \sum F_{y'} = N_R - m_R g \cos 30° = 0 \end{cases}$$

We have four equations in the four unknowns T, N_L, N_R, and α. ($m_L = 25$ kg, $m_R = 40$ kg). Solving, we get

$N_L = 147$ N, $N_R = 340$ N $\quad T = 196.2$ N, $\alpha = 53.1°$

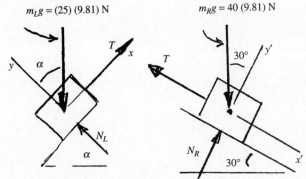

Problem 3.45 Consider the system shown in Problem 3.44. The angle $\alpha = 45°$, the surfaces are smooth, and the boxes are in equilibrium. Determine the ratio of the mass of the right box to the mass of the left box.

Solution: Use the free body diagrams of Problem 3.44. The equations of equilibrium are the same as for Problem 3.44.

$$\begin{cases} T - m_L g \sin \alpha = 0 \\ N_L - m_L g \cos \alpha = 0 \\ -T + m_R g \sin 30° = 0 \\ N_R - m_R g \cos 30° = 0 \end{cases}$$

where $g = 9.81 \ m/s^2$, $m_L = 1$, $\alpha = 45°$.

Solving, we get $m_R = 1.41$.

$$\therefore \ m_{R/m_L} = 1.41/1 = 1.41$$

Problem 3.46 The 3000-lb car and the 4600-lb tow truck are stationary. The muddy surface on which the car rests exerts a negligible friction force on the car. What is the tension in the tow cable?

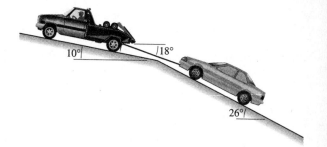

Solution: From the geometry, the angle between the cable and the x axis is 8°. From the free body diagram, the equations of equilibrium are

$$\sum F_x = -T \cos(8°) + 3000 \sin(26°) = 0$$

and $\sum F_y = N - 3000 \cos(26°) = 0$.

The first equation can be solved for the tension in the cable. The tension is $T = 3000 \sin(26°)/\cos(8°) = 1328$ lb.

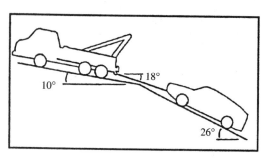

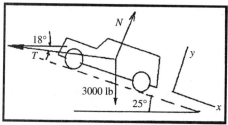

Problem 3.47 The hydraulic cylinder is subjected to three forces. An 8-kN force is exerted on the cylinder at B that is parallel to the cylinder and points from B toward C. The link AC exerts a force at C that is parallel to the line from A to C. The link CD exerts a force at C that is parallel to the line from C to D.

(a) Draw the free-body diagram of the cylinder. (The cylinder's weight is negligible).
(b) Determine the magnitudes of the forces exerted by the links AC and CD.

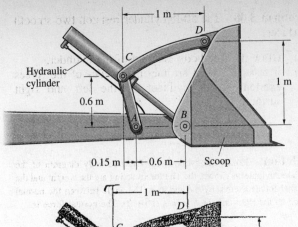

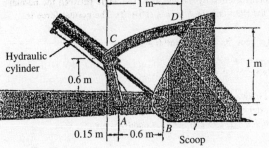

Solution: From the figure, if C is at the origin, then points A, B, and D are located at

$A(0.15, -0.6)$

$B(0.75, -0.6)$

$D(1.00, 0.4)$

and forces $\mathbf{F}_{CA}$, $\mathbf{F}_{BC}$, and $\mathbf{F}_{CD}$ are parallel to CA, BC, and CD, respectively.

We need to write unit vectors in the three force directions and express the forces in terms of magnitudes and unit vectors. The unit vectors are given by

$$\mathbf{e}_{CA} = \frac{\mathbf{r}_{CA}}{|\mathbf{r}_{CA}|} = 0.243\mathbf{i} - 0.970\mathbf{j}$$

$$\mathbf{e}_{CB} = \frac{\mathbf{r}_{CB}}{|\mathbf{r}_{CB}|} = 0.781\mathbf{i} - 0.625\mathbf{j}$$

$$\mathbf{e}_{CD} = \frac{\mathbf{r}_{CD}}{|\mathbf{r}_{CD}|} = 0.928\mathbf{i} + 0.371\mathbf{j}$$

Now we write the forces in terms of magnitudes and unit vectors. We can write $\mathbf{F}_{BC}$ as $\mathbf{F}_{CB} = -8\mathbf{e}_{CB}$ kN or as $\mathbf{F}_{CB} = 8(-\mathbf{e}_{CB})$ kN (because we were told it was directed from B toward C and had a magnitude of 8 kN. Either way, we must end up with

$\mathbf{F}_{CB} = -6.25\mathbf{i} + 5.00\mathbf{j}$ kN

Similarly,

$\mathbf{F}_{CA} = 0.243F_{CA}\mathbf{i} - 0.970F_{CA}\mathbf{j}$

$\mathbf{F}_{CD} = 0.928F_{CD}\mathbf{i} + 0.371F_{CD}\mathbf{j}$

For equilibrium, $\mathbf{F}_{CA} + \mathbf{F}_{CB} + \mathbf{F}_{CD} = 0$

In component form, this gives

$$\begin{cases} \sum F_x = 0.243F_{CA} + 0.928F_{CD} - 6.25 \text{ (kN)} = 0 \\ \sum F_y = -0.970F_{CA} + 0.371F_{CD} + 5.00 \text{ (kN)} = 0 \end{cases}$$

Solving, we get

$F_{CA} = 7.02$ kN, $F_{CD} = 4.89$ kN

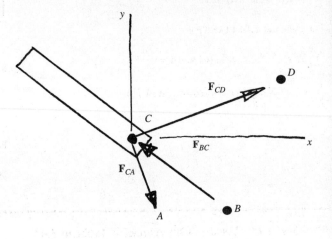

Problem 3.48 The 50-lb cylinder rests on two smooth surfaces.

(a) Draw the free-body diagram of the cylinder.
(b) If $\alpha = 30°$, what are the magnitudes of the forces exerted on the cylinder by the left and right surfaces?

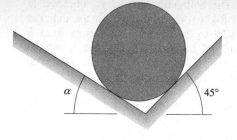

Solution: Isolate the cylinder. (a) The free body diagram of the isolated cylinder is shown. (b) The forces acting are the weight and the normal forces exerted by the surfaces. The angle between the normal force on the right and the x axis is $(90 + \beta)$. The normal force is

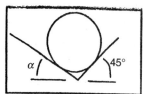

$$\mathbf{N}_R = |\mathbf{N}_R|(\mathbf{i}\cos(90 + \beta) + \mathbf{j}\sin(90 + \beta))$$

$$\mathbf{N}_R = |\mathbf{N}_R|(-\mathbf{i}\sin\beta + \mathbf{j}\cos\beta).$$

The angle between the positive x axis and the left hand force is normal $(90 - \alpha)$; the normal force is $\mathbf{N}_L = |\mathbf{N}_L|(\mathbf{i}\sin\alpha + \mathbf{j}\cos\alpha)$. The weight is $\mathbf{W} = 0\mathbf{i} - |\mathbf{W}|\mathbf{j}$. The equilibrium conditions are

$$\sum \mathbf{F} = \mathbf{W} + \mathbf{N}_R + \mathbf{N}_L = 0.$$

Substitute and collect like terms,

$$\sum \mathbf{F}_x = (-|\mathbf{N}_R|\sin\beta + |\mathbf{N}_L|\sin\alpha)\mathbf{i} = 0,$$

$$\sum \mathbf{F}_y = (|\mathbf{N}_R|\cos\beta + |\mathbf{N}_L|\cos\alpha - |\mathbf{W}|)\mathbf{j} = 0.$$

Solve: $|\mathbf{N}_R| = \left(\dfrac{\sin\alpha}{\sin\beta}\right)|\mathbf{N}_L|,$

and $|\mathbf{N}_L| = \left(\dfrac{|\mathbf{W}|\sin\beta}{\sin(\alpha + \beta)}\right).$

For $|\mathbf{W}| = 50$ lb, and $\alpha = 30°$, $\beta = 45°$, the normal forces are

$|\mathbf{N}_L| = 36.6$ lb, $|\mathbf{N}_R| = 25.9$ lb

Problem 3.49 For the 50-lb cylinder in Problem 3.48, obtain an equation for the force exerted on the cylinder by the left surface in terms of the angle α in two ways: (a) using a coordinate system with the y axis vertical, (b) using a coordinate system with the y axis parallel to the right surface.

Solution: The solution for Part (a) is given in Problem 3.48 (See free body diagram).

$$|\mathbf{N}_R| = \left(\frac{\sin\alpha}{\sin\beta}\right)|\mathbf{N}_L| \quad |\mathbf{N}_L| = \left(\frac{|\mathbf{W}|\sin\beta}{\sin(\alpha + \beta)}\right).$$

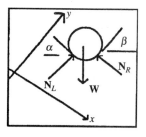

Part (b): The isolated cylinder with the coordinate system is shown. The angle between the right hand normal force and the positive x axis is 180°. The normal force: $\mathbf{N}_R = -|\mathbf{N}_R|\mathbf{i} + 0\mathbf{j}$. The angle between the left hand normal force and the positive x is $180 - (\alpha + \beta)$. The normal force is $\mathbf{N}_L = |\mathbf{N}_L|(-\mathbf{i}\cos(\alpha + \beta) + \mathbf{j}\sin(\alpha + \beta))$.

The angle between the weight vector and the positive x axis is $-\beta$. The weight vector is $\mathbf{W} = |\mathbf{W}|(\mathbf{i}\cos\beta - \mathbf{j}\sin\beta)$. The equilibrium conditions are

$$\sum \mathbf{F} = \mathbf{W} + \mathbf{N}_R + \mathbf{N}_L = 0.$$

Substitute and collect like terms,

$$\sum \mathbf{F}_x = (-|\mathbf{N}_R| - |\mathbf{N}_L|\cos(\alpha + \beta) + |\mathbf{W}|\cos\beta)\mathbf{i} = 0,$$

$$\sum \mathbf{F}_y = (|\mathbf{N}_L|\sin(\alpha + \beta) - |\mathbf{W}|\sin\beta)\mathbf{j} = 0.$$

Solve: $|\mathbf{N}_L| = \left(\dfrac{|\mathbf{W}|\sin\beta}{\sin(\alpha + \beta)}\right)$

Problem 3.50 The 50-kg sphere is at rest on the smooth horizontal surface. The horizontal force $F = 500$ N. What is the normal force exerted on the sphere by the surface?

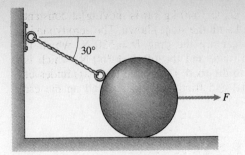

Solution: Isolate the sphere and solve the equilibrium equations. The angle between the cable and the positive x is $(180 - \alpha)$. The tension:

$$\mathbf{T} = |\mathbf{T}|(-\mathbf{i}\cos\alpha + \mathbf{j}\sin\alpha).$$

The other forces are

$$\mathbf{F} = |\mathbf{F}|\mathbf{i} + 0\mathbf{j}, \quad \mathbf{N} = 0\mathbf{i} + |\mathbf{N}|\mathbf{j}, \quad \mathbf{W} = 0\mathbf{i} - |W|\mathbf{j}.$$

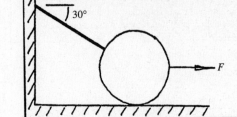

The equilibrium conditions are

$$\sum \mathbf{F} = \mathbf{T} + \mathbf{F} + \mathbf{N} + \mathbf{W} = 0.$$

Substitute and collect like terms,

$$\sum \mathbf{F}_x = (-|\mathbf{T}|\cos\alpha + |\mathbf{F}|)\mathbf{i} = 0,$$

$$\sum \mathbf{F}_y = (|\mathbf{N}| - |\mathbf{W}| + |\mathbf{T}|\sin\alpha)\mathbf{j} = 0.$$

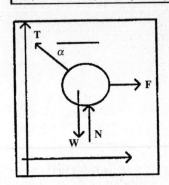

Solve: $|\mathbf{T}| = \left(\dfrac{|\mathbf{F}|}{\cos\alpha}\right)$, and $|\mathbf{N}| = |\mathbf{W}| - |\mathbf{F}|\tan\alpha$.

For $|\mathbf{W}| = (50)(9.81) = 490.5$ N, $|\mathbf{F}| = 500$ N, and $\alpha = 30°$

$$|\mathbf{N}| = 490.5 - (500)(0.577) = 201.8 \text{ N}$$

Problem 3.51 Consider the stationary sphere in Problem 3.50.

(a) Draw a graph of the normal force exerted on the sphere by the surface as a function of the force F from $F = 0$ to $F = 1$ kN.

(b) In the result of (a), notice that the normal force decreases to zero and becomes negative as F increases. What does that mean?

Solution: From the solution of Problem 3.50,

$$|\mathbf{N}| = |\mathbf{W}| - |\mathbf{F}|\tan\alpha.$$

(a) The commercial package **TK Solver Plus** was used to produce the graph of the normal force vs. the applied force, for $|\mathbf{W}| = (50)(9.81) = 490.5$ N and $\alpha = 30°$, as shown.

(b) The normal force becomes negative when the cylinder is lifted from the surface (it would take a negative force to keep it in contact with the surface).

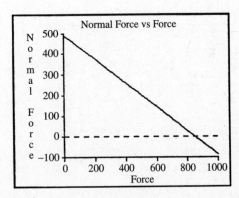

Problem 3.52 The 1440-kg car is moving at constant speed on a road with the slope shown. The aerodynamic forces on the car are the drag $D = 530$ N, which is parallel to the road, and the lift $L = 360$ N, which is perpendicular to the road. Determine the magnitudes of the total normal and friction forces exerted on the car by the road.

Solution: From the free body diagram, the equations of equilibrium are

$$\sum F_x = f - D - W \sin 15° = 0$$

$$\sum F_y = L + N - W \cos 15° = 0$$

$$W = mg = (1440)(9.81) \text{ N}$$

$$L = 360 \text{ N}, \ D = 530 \text{ N}$$

$$m = 1440 \text{ kg}, \ g = 9.81 \text{ m/s}^2$$

Solving, we get

$$f = 4.19 \text{ kN}, \ N = 13.29 \text{ kN}$$

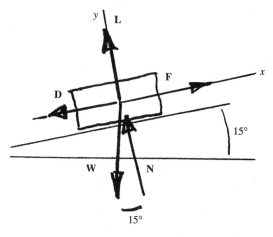

Problem 3.53 The device shown is towed beneath a ship to measure water temperature and salinity. The mass of the device is 130 kg. The angle $\alpha = 20°$. The motion of the water relative to the device causes a horizontal drag force D. The hydrostatic pressure distribution in the water exerts a vertical "buoyancy" force B. The magnitude of the buoyancy force is equal to the product of the volume of the device, $V = 0.075$ m^3, and the weight density of the water, $\gamma = 9500$ N/m^3. Determine the drag force D and the tension in the cable.

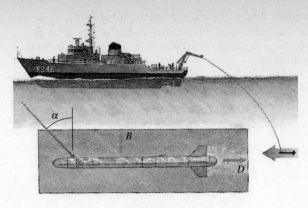

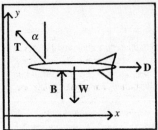

Solution: Calculate the magnitude of the buoyancy force. Draw a free body diagram of the device. The drag, buoyancy and drag forces are

$$\mathbf{D} = |\mathbf{D}|\mathbf{i} + 0\mathbf{j}, \quad \mathbf{B} = 0\mathbf{i} + |\mathbf{B}|\mathbf{j}, \quad \mathbf{W} = 0\mathbf{i} - \mathbf{j}|\mathbf{W}|.$$

The angle between the tow cable and the positive x axis is $(90° + \alpha)$; the cable tension is

$$\mathbf{T} = |\mathbf{T}|(\mathbf{i}\cos(90 + \alpha) + \mathbf{j}\sin(90 + \alpha))$$

$$\mathbf{T} = |\mathbf{T}|(-\mathbf{i}\sin\alpha + \mathbf{j}\cos\alpha).$$

The equilibrium conditions are

$$\sum \mathbf{F} = \mathbf{W} + \mathbf{B} + \mathbf{T} + \mathbf{D} = 0.$$

Substitute and collect terms

$$\sum \mathbf{F}_x = (|\mathbf{D}| - |\mathbf{T}|\sin\alpha)\mathbf{i} = 0$$

$$\sum \mathbf{F}_y = (|\mathbf{T}|\cos\alpha + |\mathbf{B}| - |\mathbf{W}|)\mathbf{j} = 0.$$

The magnitude of the buoyancy force is

$$B = \rho V = (970)(0.15) = 145.5 \text{ N}.$$

Solve: $|\mathbf{D}| = |\mathbf{T}|\sin\alpha$, and $|\mathbf{T}| = \left(\dfrac{|\mathbf{W}| - |\mathbf{B}|}{\cos\alpha}\right).$

For $|\mathbf{W}| = (130)(9.81) = 1275.3$ N, and $\alpha = 20°$, the tension in the cable and the drag are $|\mathbf{T}| = 1202$ N, $|\mathbf{D}| = 411.2$ N

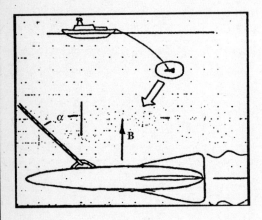

Problem 3.54 The mass of each pulley of the system is m and the mass of the suspended object A is m_A. Determine the force T necessary for the system to be in equilibrium.

Solution: Draw free body diagrams of each pulley and the object A. Each pulley and the object A must be in equilibrium. The weights of the pulleys and object A are $W = mg$ and $W_A = m_A g$. The equilibrium equations for the lower pulley, middle pulley, and upper pulley are, respectively, $A - 2T - W = 0$, $B - 2A - W = 0$, and $C - 2B - W = 0$. The equilibrium equation for the weight is $T + A + B - W_A = 0$. Solving the first equation for A in terms of T and W, substituting for A in the second equation and solving for B in terms of T and W, we get $A = 2T + W$ and $B = 4T + 3W$. Substituting for A and B in the equilibrium equation for the weight, we get $7T = W_A - 4W = m_A g - 4mg$. Thus, the tension, T, in terms of masses and g is $T = \left(\dfrac{g}{7}\right)(m_A - 4m)$.

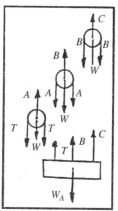

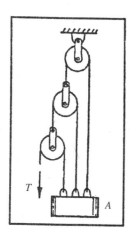

Problem 3.55 The mass of each pulley of the system is m and the mass of the suspended object A is m_A. Determine the force T necessary for the system to be in equilibrium.

Solution: Draw free body diagrams of each pulley and the object A. Each pulley and the object A must be in equilibrium. The weights of the pulleys and object A are $W = mg$ and $W_A = m_Ag$. The equilibrium equations for the weight A, the lower pulley, second pulley, third pulley, and the top pulley are, respectively, $B - W_A = 0$, $2C - B - W = 0$, $2D - C - W = 0$, $2T - D - W = 0$, and $F_S - 2T - W = 0$. Begin with the first equation and solve for B, substitute for B in the second equation and solve for C, substitute for C in the third equation and solve for D, and substitute for D in the fourth equation and solve for T, to get T in terms of W and W_A. The result is

$$B = W_A, \quad C = \frac{W_A}{2} + \frac{W}{2},$$

$$D = \frac{W_A}{4} + \frac{3W}{4}, \text{ and } T = \frac{W_A}{8} + \frac{7W}{8},$$

or in terms of the masses,

$$T = \frac{g}{8}(m_A + 7m).$$

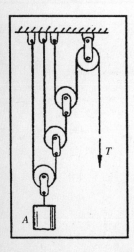

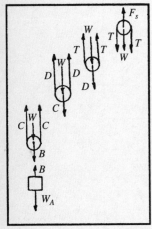

Problem 3.56 The system is in equilibrium. What are the coordinates of A?

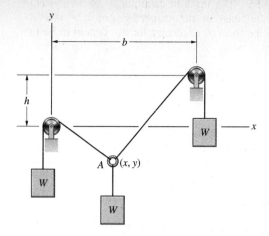

Solution: Determine from geometry the coordinates x, y. Isolate the cable juncture A. Since the frictionless pulleys do not change the magnitude of cable tension, and since each cable is loaded with the same weight, arbitrarily set this weight to unity, $|\mathbf{W}| = 1$. The angle between the cable AB and the positive x axis is α; the tension in AB is

$$|\mathbf{T}_{AB}| = \mathbf{i}\cos\alpha + \mathbf{j}\sin\alpha.$$

The angle between AC and the positive x axis is $(180° - \beta)$; the tension is

$$\mathbf{T}_{AC} = |\mathbf{T}_{AC}|(-\mathbf{i}\cos\beta + \mathbf{j}\sin\beta).$$

The weight is $|\mathbf{W}| = 0\mathbf{i} - \mathbf{j}1$. The equilibrium conditions are

$$\sum \mathbf{F} = \mathbf{T}_{AB} + \mathbf{T}_{AC} + \mathbf{W} = 0.$$

Substitute and collect like terms,

$$\sum \mathbf{F}_x = (\cos\alpha - \cos\beta)\mathbf{i} = 0,$$

$$\sum \mathbf{F}_y = (\sin\alpha + \sin\beta - 1)\mathbf{j} = 0.$$

From the first equation $\cos\alpha = \cos\beta$. On the realistic assumption that both angles are in the same quadrant, then $\alpha = \beta$. From the second equation $\sin\alpha = \left(\frac{1}{2}\right)$ or $\alpha = 30°$. With the angles known, geometry can be used to determine the coordinates x, y. The origin of the x, y coordinate system is at the pulley B, so that the coordinate x of the point A is positive. Define the positive distance ε as shown, so that

$$\left(\frac{\varepsilon}{x}\right) = \tan\alpha.$$

Similarly, $\left(\dfrac{h+\varepsilon}{b-x}\right) = \tan\alpha.$

Reduce to obtain

$$x = b - h\cot\alpha - \varepsilon\cot\alpha.$$

Substitute into the first equation to obtain

$$x = \left(\frac{1}{2}\right)(b - h\cot\alpha).$$

Multiply this equation by $\tan\alpha$ and use $\varepsilon = x\tan\alpha$ to obtain

$$\varepsilon = \left(\frac{\tan\alpha}{2}\right)(b - h\cot\alpha).$$

The sign of the coordinate y is determined as follows: Since the coordinate x is positive, the condition $(b - h\cot\alpha) > 0$ is required; with this inequality satisfied (as it must be, or the problem is invalid), ε is also positive, as required. But the angle α is in the first quadrant, so that the point A is below the pulley B. Thus $y = -\varepsilon$ and the coordinates of the point A are:

$$x = \left(\frac{1}{2}\right)(b - h\cot\alpha), \quad y = -\frac{1}{2}(b\tan\alpha - h), \quad \alpha = 30°$$

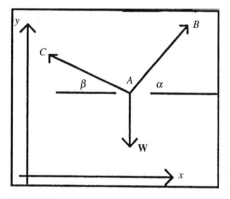

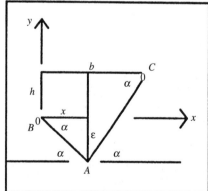

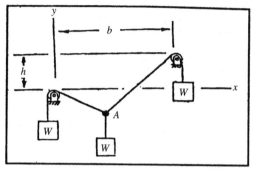

Problem 3.57 The light fixture of weight W is suspended from a circular arch by a large number N of equally spaced cables. The tension T in each cable is the same. Show that

$$T = \left(\frac{\pi W}{2\,N} \right).$$

Strategy: Consider an element of the arch defined by an angle $d\theta$ measured from the point where the cables join:

Since the total angle described by the arch is π radians, the number of cables attached to the element is $(N/pi)d\theta$. You can use this result to write the equilibrium equations for the part of the cable system where the cables join.

Solution: The angle between any cable and the positive x axis is $k\delta\theta$, where $k = 0, 1, 2, 3 \ldots K$, where $K = \left(\frac{\pi}{\delta\theta} \right)$ is the number of intervals, one less than the number of cables. The tension in the kth cable is $\mathbf{T}_k = |\mathbf{T}_k|(\mathbf{i} \cos k\delta\theta + \mathbf{j} \sin k\delta\theta)$. The weight is $\mathbf{W} = 0\mathbf{i} - |\mathbf{W}|\mathbf{j}$. The equilibrium conditions are

$$\sum \mathbf{F} = \mathbf{W} + \sum_{k=0}^{K} \mathbf{T}_k = 0$$

where N is the number of cables.

Substitute and collect like terms:

$$\sum \mathbf{F}_x = \sum_{k=0}^{K} (|\mathbf{T}_k| \cos k\delta\theta)\mathbf{i} = 0$$

$$\sum \mathbf{F}_y = \left(\sum_{k=0}^{K} (|\mathbf{T}_k| \sin k\delta\theta) - |\mathbf{W}| \right) \mathbf{j} = 0$$

Since the tension in each cable is the same, $|\mathbf{T}_k| = |\mathbf{T}|$, the tension can be removed from the sum, and the second equation solved for the tension:

$$|\mathbf{T}| = \left(\frac{|\mathbf{W}|}{\displaystyle\sum_{k=0}^{K} \sin k\delta\theta} \right).$$

The trigonometric sum can be found in handbooks[1]:

$$\sum_{k=0}^{K} \sin k\delta\theta = \left(\frac{\sin \left(\frac{1}{2}(N+1)\delta\theta \right) \sin \left(\frac{1}{2}N\delta\theta \right)}{\sin \left(\frac{1}{2}\delta\theta \right)} \right).$$

The angle is divided into K intervals over the arc, $K = \frac{\pi}{\delta\theta}$.

Substitute into the sum to obtain

$$\sum_{k=0}^{K} \sin k\delta\theta = \left(\frac{\cos \left(\frac{1}{2}\delta\theta \right)}{\sin \left(\frac{1}{2}\delta\theta \right)} \right).$$

Substitute into the solution for the tension

$$|\mathbf{T}| = \left(\frac{|\mathbf{W}|}{\displaystyle\sum_{k=0}^{K} \sin k\delta\theta} \right) = \left(\frac{|\mathbf{W}| \sin \left(\frac{1}{2}\delta\theta \right)}{\cos \left(\frac{1}{2}\delta\theta \right)} \right) = |\mathbf{W}| \tan \left(\frac{1}{2}\delta\theta \right).$$

If $\delta\theta = \frac{\pi}{K} \cong \frac{\pi}{N} \ll 1$, $\tan \left(\frac{\delta\theta}{2} \right) \cong \frac{\delta\theta}{2}$, therefore:

$$|\mathbf{T}| = \frac{|\mathbf{W}|\pi}{2\,N}$$

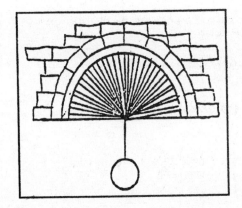

Problem 3.58 The solution to Problem 3.57 is an "asymptotic" result whose accuracy increases as N increases. Determine the exact tension T_{exact} for $N = 3$, 5, 9, and 17, and confirm the numbers in the following table. (For example, for $N = 3$, the cables are attached at $\theta = 0$, $\theta = 90°$, and $\theta = 180°$).

N	3	5	9	17
$\dfrac{T_{\text{exact}}}{\pi W / 2N}$	1.91	1.32	1.14	1.07

Solution: From Problem 3.57, the tension is

$$|\mathbf{T}| = \left(\frac{|\mathbf{W}|}{\displaystyle\sum_{k=01}^{K} \sin k\delta\theta} \right)$$

where the denominator is

$$\sum_{k=0}^{K} \sin(k\delta\theta) = \left(\frac{\sin\left(\frac{1}{2}(K+1)\delta\theta\right)\sin\left(\frac{1}{2}K\delta\theta\right)}{\sin\left(\frac{1}{2}\delta\theta\right)} \right)$$

where N is the number of cables. The angle is divided into K segments over the interval, thus

$$K = \frac{\pi}{\delta\theta} \quad \text{and} \quad N = \left(\frac{\pi}{\delta\theta}\right) + 1,$$

since the number of cables is one more than the number of intervals Substitute this into the sum to obtain

$$\sum_{k=0}^{K} \sin(k\delta\theta) = \left(\frac{\cos\left(\frac{1}{2}\delta\theta\right)}{\sin\left(\frac{1}{2}\delta\theta\right)} \right).$$

Substitute this into the expression for the tension:

$$|\mathbf{T}| = \left(\frac{|\mathbf{W}|}{\displaystyle\sum_{k=0}^{N} \sin k\delta\theta} \right) = \left(\frac{|\mathbf{W}|\sin\left(\frac{1}{2}\delta\theta\right)}{\cos\left(\frac{1}{2}\delta\theta\right)} \right) = |\mathbf{W}|\tan\left(\frac{1}{2}\delta\theta\right).$$

Since $\delta\theta = \dfrac{\pi}{N-1}$,

the exact solution for the tension in a cable is given by

$$|\mathbf{T}| = |\mathbf{W}|\tan\left(\frac{\pi}{2(N-1)}\right)$$

where $N - 1$ is the number of intervals in an arc of π radians. If the angle increment $\delta\theta$ is sufficiently small,

$$\tan\left(\frac{\delta\theta}{2}\right) \cong \frac{\delta\theta}{2}, \quad \text{and} \quad |\mathbf{T}| = \frac{|\mathbf{W}|\pi}{2(N-1)} \cong \frac{|\mathbf{W}|\pi}{2N}$$

is the asymptotic solution. The asymptotic solution, the exact solution, and the ratio of the exact solution to the asymptotic solution for the two configurations are given in the table below for 3, 5, 9, and 17 cables for the two configurations.

N	$\dfrac{\pi}{2N}$	$\tan\left(\dfrac{\pi}{2(N-1)}\right)$	Ratio
3	0.5235	1	1.909
5	0.3142	0.4142	1.318
7	0.2244	0.2679	1.194
9	0.1745	0.1989	1.140
17	0.0924	0.0985	1.066

Problem 3.59 The system in Fig. a provides lateral support for a load resting on the smooth bed of a truck. The spring constant $k = 100$ lb/ft, and the unstretched length of each spring is 2 ft. When the load is subjected to an effective lateral load F (Fig. b), the distance from the original position of the load to its equilibrium position is $\delta = 1$ ft. What is F?

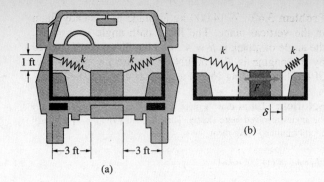

(a)

(b)

Solution: After the load shift, the extension of the left spring is

$$\sqrt{(3+\delta)^2 + 1^2} - 2 = 2.123 \text{ ft.}$$

The right spring extension is $\sqrt{(3-\delta)^2 + 1^2} - 2 = 0.236$.

The magnitude of the force on the left spring is

$$|\mathbf{T}_L| = k\Delta L = (100)(2.123) = 212.3 \text{ lb.}$$

The magnitude of the force on right spring is

$$|\mathbf{T}_R| = k\Delta L = (100)(0.236) = 23.6 \text{ lb.}$$

The angle for the new position of the box for the left spring,

$$\tan \beta = \frac{1}{3+\delta} = 0.25, \quad \beta = 14°.$$

The angle for the right spring in the new position is

$$\tan \alpha = \frac{1}{3-\delta} = 0.5, \quad \alpha = 26.6°.$$

The angle between the right spring force and the positive x axis is α; the spring force is

$$\mathbf{T}_R = |\mathbf{T}_R|(\mathbf{i}\cos\alpha + \mathbf{j}\sin\alpha).$$

The angle between the left spring force and the positive x axis is $(180 - \beta)$; the left spring force is

$$\mathbf{T}_L = |\mathbf{T}_L|(\mathbf{i}\cos(180-\beta) + \mathbf{j}\sin(180-\beta)) = |\mathbf{T}_L|(-\mathbf{i}\cos\beta + \mathbf{j}\sin\beta).$$

The lateral load $\mathbf{F} = |\mathbf{F}|\mathbf{i} + 0\mathbf{j}$.

The weight is $\mathbf{W} = 0\mathbf{i} - |\mathbf{W}|\mathbf{j}$. The normal force is $\mathbf{N} = 0\mathbf{i} + |\mathbf{N}|\mathbf{j}$. The equilibrium conditions are

$$\sum \mathbf{F} = \mathbf{T}_L + \mathbf{T}_R + \mathbf{W} + \mathbf{N} + \mathbf{F} = 0.$$

Substitute and collect like terms:

$$\sum \mathbf{F}_x = (|\mathbf{T}_R|\cos\alpha - |\mathbf{T}_L|\cos\beta + |\mathbf{F}|)\mathbf{i} = 0,$$

$$\sum \mathbf{F}_y = (|\mathbf{T}_R|\sin\alpha + |\mathbf{T}_L|\sin\beta - |\mathbf{W}| + |\mathbf{N}|)\mathbf{j} = 0.$$

Solve for the lateral load,

$$|\mathbf{F}| = |\mathbf{T}_L|\cos\beta - |\mathbf{T}_R|\cos\alpha.$$

For $|\mathbf{T}_L| = 212.3$ lb,

$$|\mathbf{T}_R| = 23.6 \text{ lb,}$$

$$\alpha = 26.6°, \quad \beta = 14°,$$

the lateral load is $|\mathbf{F}| = 184.9$ lb

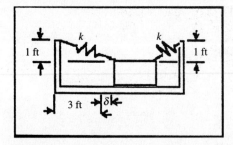

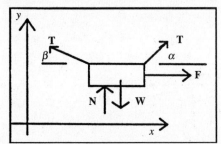

Problem 3.60 A 14,000-kg airplane is in steady flight in the vertical plane. The flight path angle is $\gamma = 10°$, the angle of attack is $\alpha = 4°$, and the thrust force exerted by the engine is $T = 60$ kN. What are the magnitudes of the lift and drag forces acting on the airplane?

Solution: Let us draw a more detailed free body diagram to see the angles involved more clearly. Then we will write the equations of equilibrium and solve them.

$W = mg = (14,000)(9.81)$ N

The equilibrium equations are

$$\begin{cases} \sum F_x = T\cos\alpha - D - W\sin\gamma = 0 \\ \sum F_y = T\sin\alpha + L - W\cos\gamma = 0 \end{cases}$$

$T = 60$ kN $= 60000$ N

Solving, we get

$D = 36.0$ kN, $L = 131.1$ kN

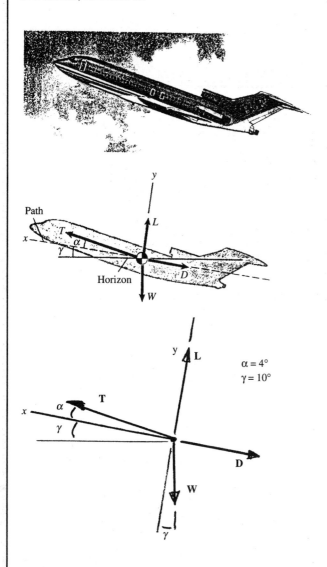

135

Problem 3.61 An airplane is in steady flight, the angle of attack $\alpha = 0$, the thrust-to-drag ratio $T/D = 2$, and the lift-to-drag ratio $L/D = 4$. What is the flight path angle γ?

Solution: Use the same strategy as in Problem 3.52. The angle between the thrust vector and the positive x axis is α,

$$\mathbf{T} = |\mathbf{T}|(\mathbf{i}\cos\alpha + \mathbf{j}\sin\alpha)$$

The lift vector: $\mathbf{L} = 0\mathbf{i} + |\mathbf{L}|\mathbf{j}$

The drag: $\mathbf{D} = -|\mathbf{D}|\mathbf{i} + 0\mathbf{j}$. The angle between the weight vector and the positive x axis is $(270 - \gamma)$;

$$\mathbf{W} = |\mathbf{W}|(-\mathbf{i}\sin\gamma - \mathbf{j}\cos\gamma).$$

The equilibrium conditions are

$$\sum \mathbf{F} = \mathbf{T} + \mathbf{L} + \mathbf{D} + \mathbf{W} = 0.$$

Substitute and collect like terms

$$\sum \mathbf{F}_x = (|\mathbf{T}|\cos\alpha - |\mathbf{D}| - |\mathbf{W}|\sin\gamma)\mathbf{i} = 0,$$

and $\sum \mathbf{F}_y = (|\mathbf{T}|\sin\alpha + |\mathbf{L}| - |\mathbf{W}|\cos\gamma)\mathbf{j} = 0$

Solve the equations for the terms in γ:

$$|\mathbf{W}|\sin\gamma = |\mathbf{T}|\cos\alpha - |\mathbf{D}|,$$

and $|\mathbf{W}|\cos\gamma = |\mathbf{T}|\sin\alpha + |\mathbf{L}|.$

Take the ratio of the two equations

$$\tan\gamma = \left(\frac{|\mathbf{T}|\cos\alpha - |\mathbf{D}|}{|\mathbf{T}|\sin\alpha + |\mathbf{L}|}\right).$$

Divide top and bottom on the right by $|\mathbf{D}|$.

For $\alpha = 0$, $\dfrac{|\mathbf{T}|}{|\mathbf{D}|} = 2$, $\dfrac{|\mathbf{L}|}{|\mathbf{D}|} = 4$, $\tan\gamma = \left(\dfrac{2-1}{4}\right) = \dfrac{1}{4}$ or $\gamma = 14°$

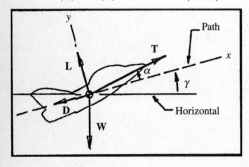

Problem 3.62 An airplane glides in steady flight ($T = 0$), and its lift-to-drag ratio is $L/D = 4$.

(a) What is the flight path angle γ?
(b) If the airplane glides from an altitude of 1000 m to zero altitude, what horizontal distance does it travel?

Solution: Use the same strategy as in Problem 3.52. The angle between the thrust vector and the positive x axis is α:

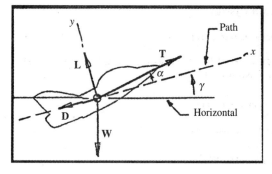

$$\mathbf{T} = |\mathbf{T}|(\mathbf{i}\cos\alpha + \mathbf{j}\sin\alpha).$$

The lift vector: $\mathbf{L} = 0\mathbf{i} + |\mathbf{L}|\mathbf{j}$.

The drag: $\mathbf{D} = -|\mathbf{D}|\mathbf{i} + 0\mathbf{j}$. The angle between the weight vector and the positive $\mathbf{x}$ axis is $(270 - \gamma)$:

$$\mathbf{W} = |\mathbf{W}|(-\mathbf{i}\sin\gamma - \mathbf{j}\cos\gamma).$$

The equilibrium conditions are

$$\sum \mathbf{F} = \mathbf{T} + \mathbf{L} + \mathbf{D} + \mathbf{W} = 0.$$

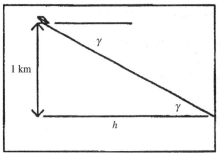

Substitute and collect like terms:

$$\sum \mathbf{F}_x = (|\mathbf{T}|\cos\alpha - |\mathbf{D}| - |\mathbf{W}|\sin\gamma)\mathbf{i} = 0$$

$$\sum \mathbf{F}_y = (|\mathbf{T}|\sin\alpha + |\mathbf{L}| - |\mathbf{W}|\cos\gamma)\mathbf{j} = 0$$

Solve the equations for the terms in γ,

$$|\mathbf{W}|\sin\gamma = |\mathbf{T}|\cos\alpha - |\mathbf{D}|,$$

and $|\mathbf{W}|\cos\gamma = |\mathbf{T}|\sin\alpha + |\mathbf{L}|$

Part (a): Take the ratio of the two equilibrium equations:

$$\tan\gamma = \left(\frac{|\mathbf{T}|\cos\alpha - |\mathbf{D}|}{|\mathbf{T}|\sin\alpha + |\mathbf{L}|} \right).$$

Divide top and bottom on the right by $|\mathbf{D}|$.

For $\alpha = 0$, $|\mathbf{T}| = 0$, $\dfrac{|\mathbf{L}|}{|\mathbf{D}|} = 4$, $\tan\gamma = \left(\dfrac{-1}{4} \right)$ $\gamma = -14°$

Part (b): The flight path angle is a negative angle measured from the horizontal, hence from the equality of opposite interior angles the angle γ is also the positive elevation angle of the airplane measured at the point of landing.

$$\tan\gamma = \frac{1}{h}, \quad h = \frac{1}{\tan\gamma} = \frac{1}{\left(\dfrac{1}{4}\right)} = 4 \text{ km}$$

Problem 3.63 If the coordinates of point A in Example 3.5 are changed to $(0, -2, 0)$ m, what are the tensions in cables AB, AC, and AD?

Solution: We need to write unit vectors $\mathbf{e}_{AB}$, $\mathbf{e}_{AC}$, and $\mathbf{e}_{AD}$.

$$\begin{cases} \mathbf{e}_{AB} = 0.816\mathbf{i} + 0.408\mathbf{j} + 0.408\mathbf{k} \\ \mathbf{e}_{AC} = -0.577\mathbf{i} + 0.577\mathbf{j} - 0.577\mathbf{k} \\ \mathbf{e}_{AD} = -0.640\mathbf{i} + 0.426\mathbf{j} + 0.640\mathbf{k} \end{cases}$$

We now need to write the four forces acting at point A.

$$\begin{cases} \mathbf{T}_{AB} = 0.816T_{AB}\mathbf{i} + 0.408T_{AB}\mathbf{j} + 0.408T_{AB}\mathbf{k} \\ \mathbf{T}_{AC} = -0.577T_{AC}\mathbf{i} + 0.577T_{AC}\mathbf{j} - 0.577T_{AC}\mathbf{k} \\ \mathbf{T}_{AD} = -0.640T_{AD}\mathbf{i} + 0.426T_{AD}\mathbf{j} + 0.640T_{AD}\mathbf{k} \\ \mathbf{W} = -981\mathbf{j} \text{ (N)} \end{cases}$$

Equilibrium: $\mathbf{T}_{AB} + \mathbf{T}_{AC} + \mathbf{T}_{AD} + \mathbf{W} = 0$

$$\begin{cases} \sum F_x = 0.816T_{AB} - 0.577T_{AC} - 0.640T_{AD} = 0 \\ \sum F_y = 0.408T_{AB} + 0.577T_{AC} + 0.426T_{AD} - 981 = 0 \\ \sum F_z = +0.408T_{AB} - 0.577T_{AC} + 0.640T_{AD} = 0 \end{cases}$$

Solving, we get

$$\boxed{\begin{aligned} T_{AB} &= 848 \text{ N} \\ T_{AC} &= 900 \text{ N} \\ T_{AD} &= 271 \text{ N} \end{aligned}}$$

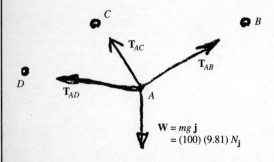

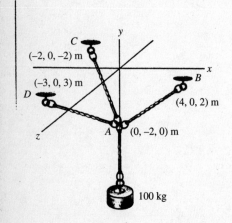

138

Problem 3.64 The force $\mathbf{F} = 5\mathbf{i}$ (kN) acts on point A where the cables AB, AC, and AD are joined. What are the tensions in the three cables?

Strategy: Isolate part of the cable system near point A. See Example 3.5.

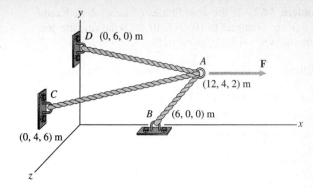

Solution: Isolate the cable juncture A. Get the unit vectors parallel to the cables using the coordinates of the end points. Express the tensions in terms of these unit vectors, and solve the equilibrium conditions. The coordinates of points A, B, C, D are:

$$A(12, 4, 2), \quad B(6, 0, 0), \quad C(0, 4, 6), \quad D(0, 6, 0).$$

The unit vector $\mathbf{e}_{AB}$ is, by definition,

$$\mathbf{e}_{AB} = \frac{\mathbf{r}_B - \mathbf{r}_A}{|\mathbf{r}_B - \mathbf{r}_A|} = \frac{(6-12)\mathbf{i} + (0-4)\mathbf{j} + (0-2)\mathbf{k}}{\sqrt{(6-12)^2 + (4)^2 + (2)^2}}$$

$$= \frac{-6}{7.483}\mathbf{i} - \frac{4}{7.483}\mathbf{j} - \frac{2}{7.483}\mathbf{k}$$

$$\mathbf{e}_{AB} = 0.8018\mathbf{i} - 0.5345\mathbf{j} - 0.267\mathbf{k}.$$

Similarly, the other unit vectors are

$$\mathbf{e}_{AB} = -0.9487\mathbf{i} + 0\mathbf{j} + 0.3163\mathbf{k},$$

$$\mathbf{e}_{AD} = -0.9733\mathbf{i} + 0.1622\mathbf{j} - 0.1622\mathbf{k}.$$

The tensions in the cables are expressed in terms of the unit vectors,

$$\mathbf{T}_{AB} = |\mathbf{T}_{AB}|\mathbf{e}_{AB}, \quad \mathbf{T}_{AC} = |\mathbf{T}_{AC}|\mathbf{e}_{AC}, \quad \mathbf{T}_{AD} = |\mathbf{T}_{AD}|\mathbf{e}_{AD}.$$

The external force acting on the juncture is, $\mathbf{F} = 5\mathbf{i} + 0\mathbf{j} + 0\mathbf{k}$. The equilibrium conditions are

$$\sum \mathbf{F} = 0 = \mathbf{T}_{AB} + \mathbf{T}_{AC} + \mathbf{T}_{AD} + \mathbf{F} = 0.$$

Substitute and collect like terms,

$$\sum F_x = (-0.8018|\mathbf{T}_{AB}| - 0.9487|\mathbf{T}_{AC}| - 0.9733|\mathbf{T}_{AD}| + 5)\mathbf{i} = 0$$

$$\sum F_y = (-0.5345|\mathbf{T}_{AB}| + 0|\mathbf{T}_{AC}| - 0.1622|\mathbf{T}_{AD}|)\mathbf{j} = 0$$

$$\sum F_z = (-0.2673|\mathbf{T}_{AB}| - 0.3163|\mathbf{T}_{AC}| - 0.1622|\mathbf{T}_{AD}|)\mathbf{k} = 0.$$

A hand held calculator was used to solve these simultaneous equations. The results are:

$$|\mathbf{T}_{AB}| = 0.7795 \text{ kN}, \quad |\mathbf{T}_{AC}| = 1.9765 \text{ kN}, \quad |\mathbf{T}_{AD}| = 2.5688 \text{ kN}.$$

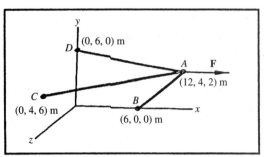

Problem 3.65 The cables in Problem 3.64 will safely support a tension of 25 kN. Based on this criterion, what is the largest safe magnitude of the force $\mathbf{F} = F\mathbf{i}$?

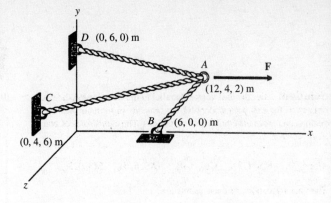

Solution: This problem offers a new challenge. We need to be able to solve the problem with one of the forces $\mathbf{F}_{AB}$, $\mathbf{F}_{AC}$, or $\mathbf{F}_{AD}$ equal to 25 kN and the other two forces must be smaller. Note that in all of our earlier work, forces have appeared linearly in our equations of equilibrium. This means that if we increase $\mathbf{F}$ by some factor, all other forces increase by the same factor.

Plan of Attack: Assume $\mathbf{F}$ has a value of 1 kN and solve for all forces. Find the largest force in the three cables and scale it up to 25 kN — increasing all forces by the same scale factor.

We must write our forces in terms of unit vectors.

$$\mathbf{e}_{AB} = \frac{\mathbf{r}_{AB}}{|\mathbf{r}_{AB}|}, \quad \mathbf{e}_{AC} = \frac{\mathbf{r}_{AC}}{|\mathbf{r}_{AC}|}, \quad \mathbf{e}_{AD} = \frac{\mathbf{r}_{AD}}{|\mathbf{r}_{AD}|}$$

where the points A, B, C, and D are

A: $(12, 4, 2)$ m, B: $(6, 0, 0)$ m

C: $(0, 4, 6)$ m, D: $(0, 6, 0)$ m

The unit vectors are

$$\begin{cases} \mathbf{e}_{AB} = -0.802\mathbf{i} - 0.535\mathbf{j} - 0.267\mathbf{k} \\ \mathbf{e}_{AC} = -0.949\mathbf{i} + 0\mathbf{j} + 0.316\mathbf{k} \\ \mathbf{e}_{AD} = -0.973\mathbf{i} + 0.162\mathbf{j} - 0.162\mathbf{k} \end{cases}$$

The forces are

$$\begin{cases} \mathbf{T}_{AB} = -0.802T_{AB}\mathbf{i} - 0.535T_{AB}\mathbf{j} - 0.267T_{AB}\mathbf{k} \\ \mathbf{T}_{AC} = -0.949T_{AC}\mathbf{i} + 0\mathbf{j} + 0.316T_{AC}\mathbf{k} \\ \mathbf{T}_{AD} = -0.973T_{AD}\mathbf{i} + 0.162T_{AD}\mathbf{j} - 0.162T_{AD}\mathbf{k} \\ \mathbf{F} = F\mathbf{i} \end{cases}$$

Summing forces in the three coord. directions, we get

$$\begin{cases} \sum F_x = -0.802T_{AB} - 0.949T_{AC} - 0.973T_{AD} + F = 0 \\ \sum F_y = -0.535T_{AB} + 0.162T_{AD} = 0 \\ \sum F_z = -0.267T_{AB} + 0.316T_{AC} - 0.162T_{AD} = 0 \end{cases}$$

We set $F = 1$ and solve the three eqns in 3 unknowns.

Solving, we get

$$F_{AB} = 0.155 \text{ kN}, \quad F_{AC} = 0.395 \text{ kN}$$

and $F_{AD} = 0.513$ for $F = 1$ kN

Scaling, we want $F_{AD} \to 25$ kN we get $\mathbf{F} = 48.7$ kN$\mathbf{i}$. When $|\mathbf{F}_{AD}| = 25$ kN

Problem 3.66 To support the tent, the tension in the rope AB must be 40 lb. What are the tensions in the ropes AC, AD, and AE?

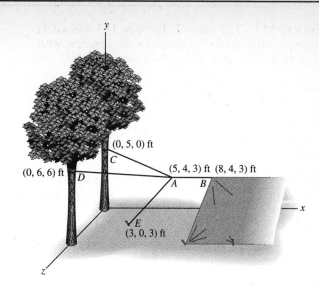

Solution: Get the unit vectors parallel to the cables using the coordinates of the end points. Express the tensions in terms of these unit vectors, and solve the equilibrium conditions. The coordinates of points A, B, C, D, E are:

$A(5, 4, 3)$, $B(8, 4, 3)$, $C(0, 5, 0)$, $D(0, 6, 6)$, $E(3, 0, 3)$.

The vector locations of these points are,

$$\mathbf{r}_A = 5\mathbf{i} + 4\mathbf{j} + 3\mathbf{k}, \quad \mathbf{r}_B = 8\mathbf{i} + 4\mathbf{j} + 3\mathbf{k},$$

$$\mathbf{r}_C = 0\mathbf{i} + 5\mathbf{j} + 0\mathbf{k}, \quad \mathbf{r}_D = 0\mathbf{i} + 6\mathbf{j} + 6\mathbf{k},$$

$$\mathbf{r}_E = 3\mathbf{i} + 0\mathbf{j} + 3\mathbf{k}.$$

The unit vector parallel to the tension acting between the points A, B in the direction of B is by definition

$$\mathbf{e}_{AB} = \frac{\mathbf{r}_B - \mathbf{r}_A}{|\mathbf{r}_B - \mathbf{r}_A|}.$$

Perform this operation for each unit vector. We get

$$\mathbf{e}_{AB} = 1\mathbf{i} + 0\mathbf{j} + 0\mathbf{k}$$

$$\mathbf{e}_{AC} = -0.8452\mathbf{i} + 0.1690\mathbf{j} - 0.5071\mathbf{k}$$

$$\mathbf{e}_{AD} = -0.8111\mathbf{i} + 0.3244\mathbf{j} + 0.4867\mathbf{k}$$

$$\mathbf{e}_{AE} = -0.4472\mathbf{i} - 0.8944\mathbf{j} + 0\mathbf{k}$$

The tensions in the cables are,

$$\mathbf{T}_{AB} = |T_{AB}|\mathbf{e}_{AB} = 40\mathbf{e}_{AB}, \quad \mathbf{T}_{AC} = |T_{AC}|\mathbf{e}_{AC},$$

$$\mathbf{T}_{AD} = |T_{AD}|\mathbf{e}_{AD}, \quad \mathbf{T}_{AE} = |T_{AE}|\mathbf{e}_{AE}.$$

The equilibrium conditions are

$$\sum \mathbf{F} = 0 = \mathbf{T}_{AB} + \mathbf{T}_{AC} + \mathbf{T}_{AD} + \mathbf{T}_{AE} = 0.$$

Substitute the tensions,

$$\sum \mathbf{F}_x = (40 - 0.8452|T_{AC}| - 0.8111|T_{AD}| - 0.4472|T_{AE}|)\mathbf{i} = 0$$

$$\sum \mathbf{F}_y = (+0.1690|T_{AC}| - 0.3244|T_{AD}| - 0.8944|T_{AE}|)\mathbf{j} = 0$$

$$\sum \mathbf{F}_z = (-0.5071|T_{AC}| - 0.4867|T_{AD}|)\mathbf{k} = 0.$$

This set of simultaneous equations in the unknown forces may be solved using any of several standard algorithms.: The results are:

$$|T_{AE}| = 11.7 \text{ lb}, \quad |T_{AC}| = 20.6 \text{ lb}, \quad |T_{AD}| = 21.4 \text{ lb}.$$

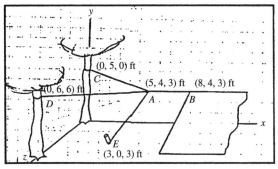

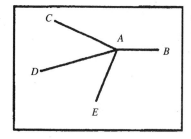

Problem 3.67 The bulldozer exerts a force $\mathbf{F} = 2\mathbf{i}$ (kip) at A. What are the tensions in cables AB, AC, and AD?

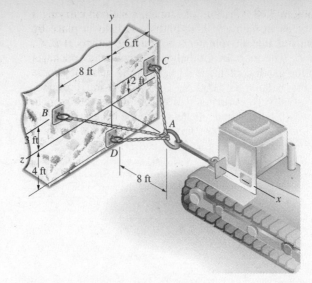

Solution: Isolate the cable juncture. Express the tensions in terms of unit vectors. Solve the equilibrium equations. The coordinates of points A, B, C, D are:

$A(8, 0, 0)$, $B(0, 3, 8)$, $C(0, 2, -6)$, $D(0, -4, 0)$.

The radius vectors for these points are

$\mathbf{r}_A = 8\mathbf{i} + 0\mathbf{j} + 0\mathbf{k}$, $\mathbf{r}_B = 0\mathbf{i} + 3\mathbf{j} + 8\mathbf{k}$,

$\mathbf{r}_C = 0\mathbf{i} + 2\mathbf{j} + 6\mathbf{k}$, $\mathbf{r}_D = 0\mathbf{i} + 4\mathbf{j} + 0\mathbf{k}$.

By definition, the unit vector parallel to the tension in cable AB is

$$\mathbf{e}_{AB} = \frac{\mathbf{r}_B - \mathbf{r}_A}{|\mathbf{r}_B - \mathbf{r}_A|}.$$

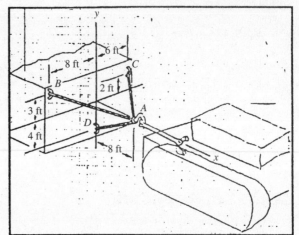

Carrying out the operations for each of the cables, the results are:

$\mathbf{e}_{AB} = -0.6835\mathbf{i} + 0.2563\mathbf{j} - 0.6835\mathbf{k}$,

$\mathbf{e}_{AC} = -0.7845\mathbf{i} + 0.1961\mathbf{j} - 0.5883\mathbf{k}$,

$\mathbf{e}_{AD} = -0.8944\mathbf{i} + 0.4472\mathbf{j} + 0\mathbf{k}$.

The tensions in the cables are expressed in terms of the unit vectors,

$\mathbf{T}_{AB} = |\mathbf{T}_{AB}|\mathbf{e}_{AB}$, $\mathbf{T}_{AC} = |\mathbf{T}_{AC}|\mathbf{e}_{AC}$, $\mathbf{T}_{AD} = |\mathbf{T}_{AD}|\mathbf{e}_{AD}$.

The external force acting on the juncture is $\mathbf{F} = 2000\mathbf{i} + 0\mathbf{j} + 0\mathbf{k}$. The equilibrium conditions are

$$\sum \mathbf{F} = 0 = \mathbf{T}_{AB} + \mathbf{T}_{AC} + \mathbf{T}_{AD} + \mathbf{F} = 0.$$

Substitute the vectors into the equilibrium conditions:

$$\sum \mathbf{F}_x = (-0.6835|\mathbf{T}_{AB}| - 0.7845|\mathbf{T}_{AC}| - 0.8944|\mathbf{T}_{AD}| + 2000)\mathbf{i} = 0$$

$$\sum \mathbf{F}_y = (0.2563|\mathbf{T}_{AB}| + 0.1961|\mathbf{T}_{AC}| - 0.4472|\mathbf{T}_{AD}|)\mathbf{j} = 0$$

$$\sum \mathbf{F}_z = (0.6835|\mathbf{T}_{AB}| - 0.5883|\mathbf{T}_{AC}| + 0|\mathbf{T}_{AD}|)\mathbf{k} = 0$$

The commercial program **TK Solver Plus** was used to solve these equations. The results are

$|\mathbf{T}_{AB}| = 780.31$ lb , $|\mathbf{T}_{AC}| = 906.9$ lb , $|\mathbf{T}_{AD}| = 844.74$ lb .

Problem 3.68 Prior to its launch, a balloon carrying a set of experiments to high altitude is held in place by groups of student volunteers holding the tethers at B, C, and D. The mass of the balloon, experiments package, and the gas it contains is 90 kg, and the buoyancy force on the balloon is 1000 N. The supervising professor conservatively estimates that each student can exert at least a 40-N tension on the tether for the necessary length of time. Based on this estimate, what minimum numbers of students are needed at B, C, and D?

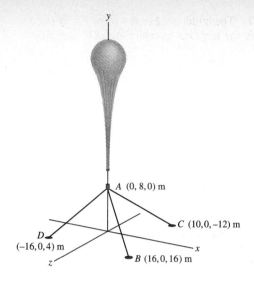

Solution:

$$\sum F_y = 1000 - (90)(9.81) - T = 0$$

$$T = 117.1 \text{ N}$$

$A(0, 8, 0)$

$B(16, 0, 16)$

$C(10, 0, -12)$

$D(-16, 0, 4)$

We need to write unit vectors $\mathbf{e}_{AB}$, $\mathbf{e}_{AC}$, and $\mathbf{e}_{AD}$.

$$\mathbf{e}_{AB} = 0.667\mathbf{i} - 0.333\mathbf{j} + 0.667\mathbf{k}$$

$$\mathbf{e}_{AC} = 0.570\mathbf{i} - 0.456\mathbf{j} - 0.684\mathbf{k}$$

$$\mathbf{e}_{AD} = -0.873\mathbf{i} - 0.436\mathbf{j} + 0.218\mathbf{k}$$

We now write the forces in terms of magnitudes and unit vectors

$$\begin{cases} \mathbf{F}_{AB} = 0.667F_{AB}\mathbf{i} - 0.333F_{AB}\mathbf{j} + 0.667F_{AB}\mathbf{k} \\ \mathbf{F}_{AC} = 0.570F_{AC}\mathbf{i} - 0.456F_{AC}\mathbf{j} - 0.684F_{AC}\mathbf{k} \\ \mathbf{F}_{AD} = -0.873F_{AD}\mathbf{i} - 0.436F_{AC}\mathbf{j} + 0.218F_{AC}\mathbf{k} \\ \mathbf{T} = 117.1\mathbf{j} \text{ (N)} \end{cases}$$

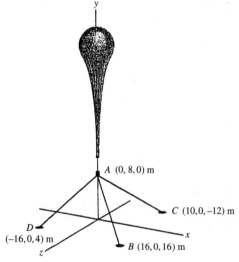

The equations of equilibrium are

$$\sum F_x = 0.667F_{AB} + 0.570F_{AC} - 0.873F_{AD} = 0$$

$$\sum F_y = -0.333F_{AB} - 0.456F_{AC} - 0.436F_{AC} + 117.1 = 0$$

$$\sum F_z = 0.667F_{AB} - 0.684F_{AC} + 0.218F_{AC} = 0$$

Solving, we get

$$F_{AB} = 64.8 \text{ N} \sim 2 \text{ students}$$

$$F_{AC} = 99.8 \text{ N} \sim 3 \text{ students}$$

$$F_{AD} = 114.6 \text{ N} \sim 3 \text{ students}$$

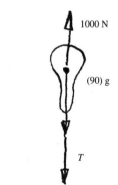

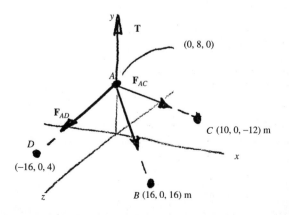

Problem 3.69 The 20-kg mass is suspended by cables attached to three vertical 2-m posts. Point A is at $(0, 1.2, 0)$ m. Determine the tensions in cables AB, AC, and AD.

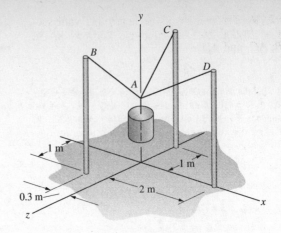

Solution: Points A, B, C, and D are located at

$A(0, 1.2, 0)$, $B(-0.3, 2, 1)$,

$C(0, 2, -1)$, $D(2, 2, 0)$

Write the unit vectors $\mathbf{e}_{AB}$, $\mathbf{e}_{AC}$, $\mathbf{e}_{AD}$

$\mathbf{e}_{AB} = -0.228\mathbf{i} + 0.608\mathbf{j} + 0.760\mathbf{k}$

$\mathbf{e}_{AC} = 0\mathbf{i} + 0.625\mathbf{j} - 0.781\mathbf{k}$

$\mathbf{e}_{AD} = 0.928\mathbf{i} + 0.371\mathbf{j} + 0\mathbf{k}$

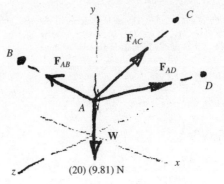

The forces are

$\mathbf{F}_{AB} = -0.228F_{AB}\mathbf{i} + 0.608F_{AB}\mathbf{j} + 0.760F_{AB}\mathbf{k}$

$\mathbf{F}_{AC} = 0F_{AC}\mathbf{i} + 0.625F_{AC}\mathbf{j} - 0.781F_{AC}\mathbf{k}$

$\mathbf{F}_{AD} = 0.928F_{AD}\mathbf{i} + 0.371F_{AD}\mathbf{j} + 0\mathbf{k}$

$\mathbf{W} = -(20)(9.81)\mathbf{j}$

The equations of equilibrium are

$$\begin{cases} \sum F_x = -0.228F_{AB} + 0 + 0.928F_{AD} = 0 \\ \sum F_y = 0.608F_{AB} + 0.625F_{AC} + 0.371F_{AD} - 20(9.81) = 0 \\ \sum F_z = 0.760F_{AB} - 0.781F_{AC} + 0 = 0 \end{cases}$$

We have 3 eqns in 3 unknowns solving, we get

$$\boxed{\begin{aligned} F_{AB} &= 150.0 \text{ N} \\ F_{AC} &= 146.1 \text{ N} \\ F_{AD} &= 36.9 \text{ N} \end{aligned}}$$

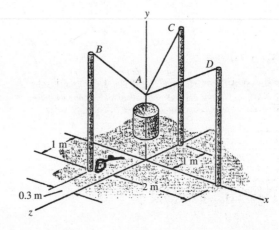

144

Problem 3.70 The weight of the horizontal wall section is $W = 20,000$ lb. Determine the tensions in the cables AB, AC, and AD.

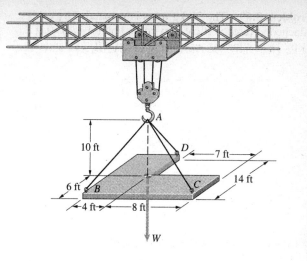

Solution: Set the coordinate origin at A with axes as shown. The upward force, T, at point A will be equal to the weight, W, since the cable at A supports the entire wall. The upward force at A is $\mathbf{T} = W$ $\mathbf{k}$. From the figure, the coordinates of the points in feet are

$A(4, 6, 10)$, $B(0, 0, 0)$, $C(12, 0, 0)$,   and $D(4, 14, 0)$.

The three unit vectors are of the form

$$\mathbf{e}_{AI} = \frac{((x_I x_A)\mathbf{i} + (y_I y_A)\mathbf{j} + (z_I - Z_A)\mathbf{k})}{\sqrt{(x_I x_A)^2 + (y_I y_A)^2 + (z_I - Z_A)^2}},$$

where I takes on the values B, C, and D. The denominators of the unit vectors are the distances AB, AC, and AD, respectively. Substitution of the coordinates of the points yields the following unit vectors:

$\mathbf{e}_{AB} = -0.324\mathbf{i} - 0.487\mathbf{j} - 0.811\mathbf{k}$,

$\mathbf{e}_{AC} = 0.566\mathbf{i} - 0.424\mathbf{j} - 0.707\mathbf{k}$,

and $\mathbf{e}_{AD} = 0\mathbf{i} + 0.625\mathbf{j} - 0.781\mathbf{k}$.

The forces are

$\mathbf{T}_{AB} = T_{AB}\mathbf{e}_{AB}$, $\mathbf{T}_{AC} = T_{AC}\mathbf{e}_{AC}$,   and $\mathbf{T}_{AD} = T_{AD}\mathbf{e}_{AD}$.

The equilibrium equation for the knot at point A is

$\mathbf{T} + \mathbf{T}_{AB} + \mathbf{T}_{AC} + \mathbf{T}_{AD} = 0$.

From the vector equilibrium equation, write the scalar equilibrium equations in the x, y, and z directions. We get three linear equations in three unknowns. Solving these equations simultaneously, we get

$\boxed{T_{AB} = 9393 \text{ lb}, \ T_{AC} = 5387 \text{ lb}, \ \text{and} \ T_{AD} = 10{,}977 \text{ lb}}$

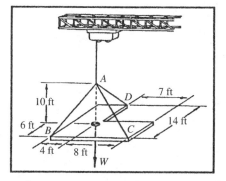

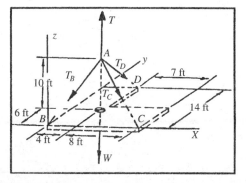

145

Problem 3.71 In Problem 3.70, each cable will safely support a tension of 40,000 lb. Based on this criterion, what is the largest safe value of the weight W?

Solution: There are two possible solutions to this problem, depending on how we interpret the problem. One solution considers the cable extending upward from A as one of the cables subject to the 40,000 lb limit and the other does not.

(a) Assume that the cable upward from A is subject to the limit. From the solution to Problem 3.70, we see that the largest tension in the cables is the tension in the cable extending upward from A. If we double the weight, we increase the tension in this cable to 40,000 lb. For this case, $\boxed{W_{MAX} = 40{,}000 \text{ lb.}}$

(b) Assume that the cable upward from A is not subject to the limit. From the solution to Problem 3.70, the largest force in the three supporting cables is $T_{AD} = 10977$ lb. The scale factor must increase this force to 40,000 lb. The scale factor, f, is given by

$$f = 40{,}000/10{,}977 = 3.644.$$

The maximum allowable weight is

$$\boxed{W_{MAX} = 20{,}000f = (20{,}000)(3.644) = 72{,}880 \text{ lb.}}$$

Problem 3.72 The 680-kg load suspended from the helicopter is in equilibrium. The aerodynamic drag force on the load is horizontal. The y axis is vertical, and cable OA lies in the x-y plane. Determine the magnitude of the drag force and the tension in cable OA.

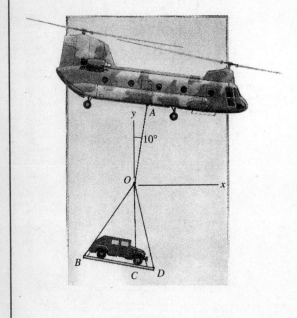

Solution:

$$\sum F_x = T_{OA} \sin 10° - D = 0,$$

$$\sum F_y = T_{OA} \cos 10° - (680)(9.81) = 0.$$

Solving, we obtain $D = 1176$ N, $T_{OA} = 6774$ N.

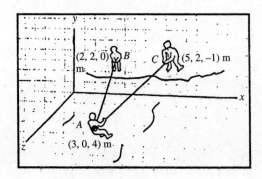

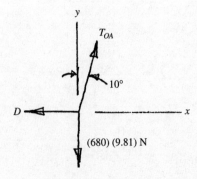

146

Problem 3.73 In Problem 3.72, the coordinates of the three cable attachment points B, C, and D are $(-3.3, -4.5, 0)$ m, $(1.1, -5.3, 1)$ m, and $(1.6, -5.4, -1)$ m, respectively. What are the tensions in cables OB, OC, and OD?

Solution: The position vectors from O to pts B, C, and D are

$$\mathbf{r}_{OB} = -3.3\mathbf{i} - 4.5\mathbf{j} \text{ (m),}$$

$$\mathbf{r}_{OC} = 1.1\mathbf{i} - 5.3\mathbf{j} + \mathbf{k} \text{ (m),}$$

$$\mathbf{r}_{OD} = 1.6\mathbf{i} - 5.4\mathbf{j} - \mathbf{k} \text{ (m).}$$

Dividing by the magnitudes, we obtain the unit vectors

$$\mathbf{e}_{OB} = -0.591\mathbf{i} - 0.806\mathbf{j},$$

$$\mathbf{e}_{OC} = 0.200\mathbf{i} - 0.963\mathbf{j} + 0.182\mathbf{k},$$

$$\mathbf{e}_{OD} = 0.280\mathbf{i} - 0.944\mathbf{j} - 0.175\mathbf{k}.$$

Using these unit vectors, we obtain the equilibrium equations

$$\sum F_x = T_{OA} \sin 10° - 0.591 T_{OB} + 0.200 T_{OC} + 0.280 T_{OD} = 0,$$

$$\sum F_y = T_{OA} \cos 10° - 0.806 T_{OB} - 0.963 T_{OC} - 0.944 T_{OD} = 0,$$

$$\sum F_z = 0.182 T_{OC} - 0.175 T_{OD} = 0.$$

From the solution of Problem 3.72, $T_{OA} = 6774$ N. Solving these equations, we obtain

$$T_{OB} = 3.60 \text{ kN,} \quad T_{OC} = 1.94 \text{ kN,} \quad T_{OD} = 2.02 \text{ kN.}$$

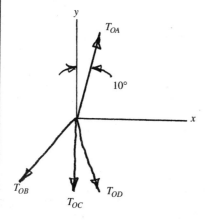

Problem 3.74 The small sphere A weighs 20 lb, and its coordinates are $(4, 0, 6)$ ft. It is supported by two smooth flat plates labeled 1 and 2 and the cable AB. The unit vector $e_1 = \frac{4}{9}i + \frac{7}{9}j + \frac{4}{9}k$ is perpendicular to plate 1, and the unit vector $e_2 = -\frac{9}{11}i + \frac{2}{11}j + \frac{6}{11}k$ is perpendicular to plate 2. What is the tension in the cable?

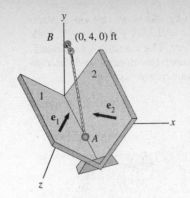

Solution: A and B are located at A $(4, 0, 6)$, B $(0, 4, 0)$ feet.

The vector locations of the points A and B are:

$$r_A = 4i + 0j + 6k, \quad r_B = 0i + 4j + 0k.$$

The unit vector parallel to the tension acting from A toward B is

$$e_{AB} = \frac{r_B - r_A}{|r_B - r_A|}.$$

The weight is $W = 0i - |W|j0k = 0i - 20j + 0k$.

The unit vectors are

$$e_{AB} = -0.4851i + 0.4851j - 0.7276k$$

$$e_1 = 0.4444i + 0.7778j + 0.4444k$$

$$e_2 = -0.8182i + 0.1818j + 0.5455k$$

where the values of the last two were given by the problem statement. The forces are expressed in terms of the unit vectors,

$$T_{AB} = |T_{AB}|e_{AB}, \quad N_1 = |N_1|e_1, \quad N_2 = |N_2|e_2.$$

The equilibrium conditions are

$$\sum F = 0 = T_{AB} + N_1 + N_2 + W = 0$$

Substitute the force vectors and collect like terms,

$$\sum F_x = (-0.4851|T_{AB}| + 0.4444|N_1| - 0.8182|N_2|)i = 0$$

$$\sum F_y = (0.4851|T_{AB}| + 0.7778|N_1| - 0.1818|N_2| - 20)j = 0$$

$$\sum F_z = (-0.7276|T_{AB}| + 0.4444|N_1| - 0.5455|N_2|)k = 0$$

An electronic calculator was used to solve these equations. The solution is:

$$\boxed{|T_{AB}| = 12.34 \text{ lb}}, \quad \boxed{|N_1| = 17.51 \text{ lb}}, \quad \boxed{|N_2| = 2.19 \text{ lb}}.$$

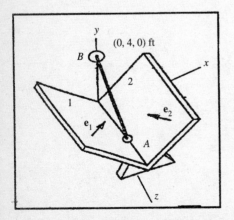

Problem 3.75 The 1350-kg car is at rest on a plane surface. The unit vector $\mathbf{e}_n = 0.231\mathbf{i} + 0.923\mathbf{j} + 0.308\mathbf{k}$ is perpendicular to the surface. The y axis points upward. Determine the magnitudes of the normal and friction forces the car's wheels exert on the surface.

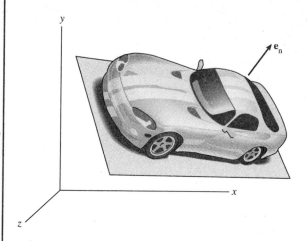

Solution: The weight force is

$$\mathbf{W} = -mg\mathbf{j} = -(1350)(9.81)\mathbf{j} = -13240\mathbf{j} \text{ N}.$$

The component of $\mathbf{W}$ normal to the surface is

$$F_N = \mathbf{W} \cdot \mathbf{e} = W_x\mathbf{e}_x + W_y\mathbf{e}_y + W_z\mathbf{e}_z = W_y\mathbf{e}_y$$

$$= (-13240)(0.923) = -12220 \text{ N}.$$

The component of $\mathbf{W}$ tangent to the surface (the friction force) can be calculated from

$$F_T = \sqrt{W^2 - F_N^2} = \sqrt{(13240)^2 - (12220)^2} = 5096 \text{ N}.$$

Thus, $F_N = 12220$ N and $F_T = 5096$ N.

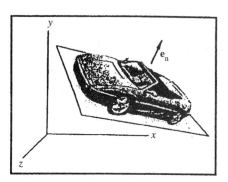

Problem 3.76 The system shown anchors a stanchion of a cable-suspended roof. If the tension in cable AB is 900 kN, what are the tensions in cables EF and EG?

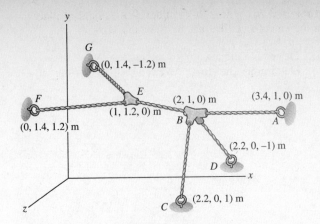

Solution: From the figure, the coordinates of the points (in meters) are

$A(3.4, 1, 0)$, $B(1.8, 1, 0)$, $C(2, 0, 1)$, $D(2, 0, -1)$,

$E(0.9, 1.2, 0)$, $F(0, 1.4, 1.2)$, and $G(0, 1.4, -1.2)$.

The unit vectors are of the form

$$e_{IK} = \frac{((x_I - x_K)\mathbf{i} + (y_I - y_K)\mathbf{j} + (z_I - z_K)\mathbf{k})}{\sqrt{(x_I - x_K)^2 + (y_I - y_K)^2 + (z_I - z_K)^2}},$$

where IK takes on the values BA, BC, BD, BE, EF, and EG.

We need to find unit vectors e_{BA}, e_{BC}, e_{BD}, e_{BE}, e_{EF}, and e_{EG}.

Substitution of the coordinates of the points yields the following six unit vectors:

$e_{BA} = 1\mathbf{i} + 0\mathbf{j} + 0\mathbf{k}$,

$e_{BC} = 0.140\mathbf{i} - 0.707\mathbf{j} + 0.707\mathbf{k}$,

$e_{BD} = 0.140\mathbf{i} - 0.707\mathbf{j} - 0.707\mathbf{k}$,

$e_{BE} = -0.981\mathbf{i} + 0.196\mathbf{j} + 0\mathbf{k}$,

$e_{EF} = -0.635\mathbf{i} + 0.127\mathbf{j} + 0.762\mathbf{k}$,

and $e_{EG} = -0.635\mathbf{i} + 0.127\mathbf{j} - 0.762\mathbf{k}$.

The forces are of the form $\mathbf{T}_{IK} = T_{IK}e_{IK}$ where IK takes on the same values as above. The known force magnitude $|\mathbf{T}_{BA}| = 900$ kN. Thus,

$\mathbf{T}_{BA} = T_{BA}e_{BA} = 900(1\mathbf{i} + 0\mathbf{j} + 0\mathbf{k})$ kN $= 900\mathbf{i}$ kN.

The vector equation of equilibrium at point B (see the first free body diagram) is

$\mathbf{T}_{BA} + \mathbf{T}_{BC} + \mathbf{T}_{BD} + \mathbf{T}_{BE} = 0$.

Use the unit vectors as $\mathbf{T}_{BA}$ above to write this equation in component form, and then solve the resulting linear equations for the three scalar unknowns T_{BC}, T_{BD}, and T_{BE}.

The result is

$\mathbf{T}_{BC} = 127.3$ kN, $\mathbf{T}_{BD} = 127.3$ kN, and $\mathbf{T}_{BE} = 917.8$ kN.

Once we know $\mathbf{T}_{BE}$, we can use the second free body diagram and the equilibrium equation at point E to solve for the tensions $\mathbf{T}_{EF}$ and $\mathbf{T}_{EG}$. The vector equilibrium equation at point E (see the second free body diagram) is $-\mathbf{T}_{BE} + \mathbf{T}_{EF} + \mathbf{T}_{EG} = 0$. Using the unit vectors as above and solving for $\mathbf{T}_{EF}$ and $\mathbf{T}_{EG}$, we get $\mathbf{T}_{EF} = \mathbf{T}_{EG} = 708.7$ kN.

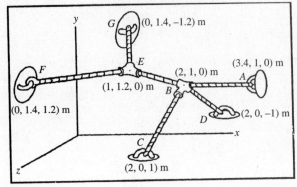

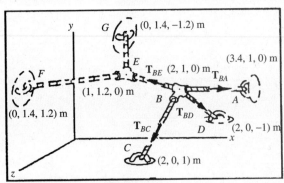

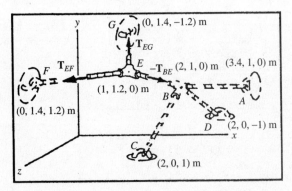

Problem 3.77 The cables of the system in Problem 3.76 will each safely support a tension of 1500 kN. Based on this criterion, what is the largest safe value of the tension in cable AB?

Solution: The largest load found in the solution of Problem 3.76 is $T_{BE} = 917.8$ kN. The scale factor, scaling this force up to 1500 kN is $f = (1500/917.8) = 1.634$. The largest safe value for the load in cable AB is $T_{AB\,max} = T_{BA}f = (900)(1.634) = 1471$ kN.

Problem 3.78 The 200-kg slider at A is held in place on the smooth vertical bar by the cable AB.

(a) Determine the tension in the cable.
(b) Determine the force exerted on the slider by the bar.

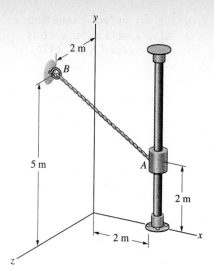

Solution: The coordinates of the points A, B are $A(2, 2, 0)$, $B(0, 5, 2)$. The vector positions

$$\mathbf{r}_A = 2\mathbf{i} + 2\mathbf{j} + 0\mathbf{k}, \quad \mathbf{r}_B = 0\mathbf{i} + 5\mathbf{j} + 2\mathbf{k}$$

The equilibrium conditions are:

$$\sum \mathbf{F} = \mathbf{T} + \mathbf{N} + \mathbf{W} = 0.$$

Eliminate the slider bar normal force as follows: The bar is parallel to the y axis, hence the unit vector parallel to the bar is $\mathbf{e}_B = 0\mathbf{i} + 1\mathbf{j} + 0\mathbf{k}$. The dot product of the unit vector and the normal force vanishes: $\mathbf{e}_B \cdot \mathbf{N} = 0$. Take the dot product of $\mathbf{e}_B$ with the equilibrium conditions: $\mathbf{e}_B \cdot \mathbf{N} = 0$.

$$\sum \mathbf{e}_B \cdot \mathbf{F} = \mathbf{e}_B \cdot \mathbf{T} + \mathbf{e}_B \cdot \mathbf{W} = 0.$$

The weight is

$$\mathbf{e}_B \cdot \mathbf{W} = 1\mathbf{j} \cdot (-\mathbf{j}|\mathbf{W}|) = -|\mathbf{W}| = -(200)(9.81) = -1962 \text{ N}.$$

The unit vector parallel to the cable is by definition,

$$\mathbf{e}_{AB} = \frac{\mathbf{r}_B - \mathbf{r}_A}{|\mathbf{r}_B - \mathbf{r}_A|}.$$

Substitute the vectors and carry out the operation:

$$\mathbf{e}_{AB} = -0.4851\mathbf{i} + 0.7278\mathbf{j} + 0.4851\mathbf{k}.$$

(a) The tension in the cable is $\mathbf{T} = |\mathbf{T}|\mathbf{e}_{AB}$. Substitute into the modified equilibrium condition

$$\sum \mathbf{e}_B \mathbf{F} = (0.7276|\mathbf{T}| - 1962) = 0.$$

Solve: $|\mathbf{T}| = 2696.5$ N from which the tension vector is

$$\mathbf{T} = |\mathbf{T}|\mathbf{e}_{AB} = -1308\mathbf{i} + 1962\mathbf{j} + 1308\mathbf{k}.$$

(b) The equilibrium conditions are

$$\sum \mathbf{F} = 0 = \mathbf{T} + \mathbf{N} + \mathbf{W} = -1308\mathbf{i} + 1308\mathbf{k} + \mathbf{N} = 0.$$

Solve for the normal force: $\mathbf{N} = 1308\mathbf{i} - 1308\mathbf{k}$. The magnitude is $|\mathbf{N}| = 1850$ N.

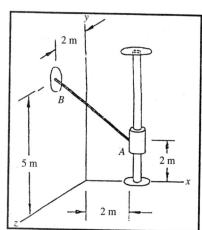

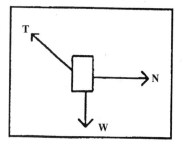

Note: For this specific configuration, the problem can be solved without eliminating the slider bar normal force, since it does not appear in the y-component of the equilibrium equation (the slider bar is parallel to the y-axis). However, in the general case, the slider bar will not be parallel to an axis, and the unknown normal force will be projected onto all components of the equilibrium equations (see Problem 3.79 below). In this general situation, it will be necessary to eliminate the slider bar normal force by some procedure equivalent to that used above. *End Note.*

Problem 3.79 The 100-lb slider at A is held in place on the smooth circular bar by the cable AB. The circular bar is contained in the x-y plane.

(a) Determine the tension in the cable.
(b) Determine the normal force exerted on the slider by the bar.

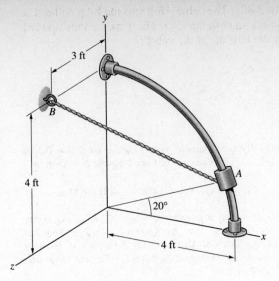

Solution: Strategy: Develop the unit vectors (i) parallel to the cable and (ii) parallel to the slider bar. Apply the equilibrium conditions. Eliminate the slider bar normal force by taking the dot product of the slider bar unit vector with the equilibrium conditions. Solve for the force parallel to the cable. Substitute this force into the equilibrium condition to find the slider bar normal force.

Assume that the circular bar is a quarter circle, so that the slider is located on a radius vector (4 ft). With this assumption the coordinates of the points A, B are

$A(4 \cos \alpha, 4 \sin \alpha, 0) = A(3.76, 1.37, 0), B(0, 4, 3)$.

The vector positions are

$\mathbf{r}_A = 3.76\mathbf{i} + 1.37\mathbf{j} + 0\mathbf{k}, \quad \mathbf{r}_B = 0\mathbf{i} + 4\mathbf{j} + 3\mathbf{k}$

The equilibrium conditions are: $\sum \mathbf{F} = \mathbf{T} + \mathbf{N} + \mathbf{W} = 0$.

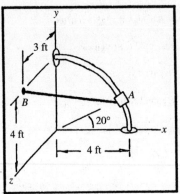

The normal force is to be eliminated from the equilibrium equations. The bar is normal to the radius vector at point A. Hence the unit vector parallel to the bar is $|\mathbf{T}| = 137.1$ lb.

The dot product with the normal force is zero, $\mathbf{e}_B\mathbf{N} = 0$. Take the dot product of the unit vector and the equilibrium condition:

$$\sum \mathbf{e}_B\mathbf{F} = \mathbf{e}_B\mathbf{T} + \mathbf{e}_B\mathbf{W} = 0.$$

The weight is

$\mathbf{e}_B\mathbf{W} = \mathbf{e}_B(-\mathbf{j}|\mathbf{W}|) = -0.9397|\mathbf{W}| = -(0.9397)(100) = -94$ lb.

The unit vector parallel to the cable is by definition,

$$\mathbf{e}_{AB} = \frac{\mathbf{r}_B - \mathbf{r}_A}{|\mathbf{r}_B - \mathbf{r}_A|}.$$

Substitute the vectors and carry out the operation

$\mathbf{e}_{AB} = -0.6856\mathbf{i} + 0.4801\mathbf{j} + 0.5472\mathbf{k}$.

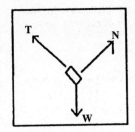

(a) The tension in the cable is $\mathbf{T} = |\mathbf{T}|\mathbf{e}_{AB}$. Substitute into the modified equilibrium condition

$$\sum \mathbf{e}_B\mathbf{F} = (0.6854|\mathbf{T}| - 94) = 0.$$

Solve: $|\mathbf{T}| = 137.1$ lb, from which the tension vector is

$\mathbf{T} = |\mathbf{T}|\mathbf{e}_{AB} = -94\mathbf{i} + 65.8\mathbf{j} + 75\mathbf{k}$

(b) Substitute $\mathbf{T}$ into the original equilibrium conditions,

$$\sum \mathbf{F} = 0 = \mathbf{T} + \mathbf{N} + \mathbf{W} = -94\mathbf{i} + 65.8\mathbf{j}$$

$$+ 75\mathbf{k} + \mathbf{N} - 100\mathbf{j} = 0.$$

Solve for the normal force exerted by the bar on the slider

$\mathbf{N} = 94\mathbf{i} + 34.2\mathbf{j} - 75\mathbf{k}$ (lb)

Problem 3.80 The cable AB keeps the 8-kg collar A in place on the smooth bar CD. The y axis points upward. What is the tension in the cable?

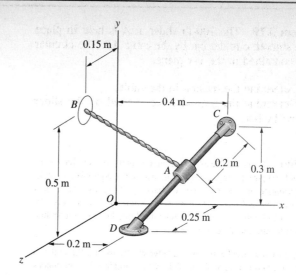

Solution: The coordinates of points C and D are C (0.4, 0.3, 0), and D (0.2, 0, 0.25). The unit vector from C toward D is given by

$$\mathbf{e}_{CD} = e_{CDx}\mathbf{i} + e_{CDy}\mathbf{j} + e_{CDz}\mathbf{k} = -0.456\mathbf{i} - 0.684\mathbf{j} + 0.570\mathbf{k}.$$

The location of point A is given by $x_A = x_C + d_{CA}e_{CDx}$, with similar equations for y_A and z_A. From the figure, $d_{CA} = 0.2$ m. From this, we find the coordinates of A are A (0.309, 0.162, 0.114). From the figure, the coordinates of B are B (0, 0.5, 0.15). The unit vector from A toward B is then given by

$$\mathbf{e}_{AB} = e_{ABx}\mathbf{i} + e_{ABy}\mathbf{j} + e_{ABz}\mathbf{k} = -0.674\mathbf{i} + 0.735\mathbf{j} + 0.079\mathbf{k}.$$

The tension force in the cable can now be written as

$$\mathbf{T}_{AB} = -0.674 T_{AB}\mathbf{i} + 0.735 T_{AB}\mathbf{j} + 0.079 T_{AB}\mathbf{k}.$$

From the free body diagram, the equilibrium equations are:

$$F_{Nx} + T_{AB}e_{ABx} = 0, \quad F_{Ny} + T_{AB}e_{ABy} - mg = 0,$$

and $F_{Nz} + T_{AB}e_{ABz} = 0$.

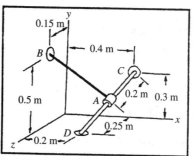

We have three equation in four unknowns. We get another equation from the condition that the bar CD is smooth. This means that the normal force has no component parallel to CD. Mathematically, this can be stated as $\mathbf{F}_N \cdot \mathbf{e}_{CD} = 0$. Expanding this, we get

$$F_{Nx}e_{CDx} + F_{Ny}e_{CDy} + F_{Nz}e_{CDz} = 0.$$

We now have four equations in our four unknowns. Substituting in the numbers and solving, we get

$$T_{AB} = 57.7 \text{ N}, \quad F_{Nx} = 38.9 \text{ N},$$

$$F_{Ny} = 36.1 \text{ N}, \quad \text{and } F_{Nz} = -4.53 \text{ N}.$$

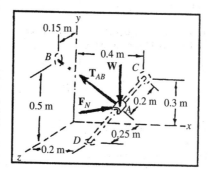

Problem 3.81 In Problem 3.80, determine the magnitude of the normal force exerted on the collar A by the smooth bar.

Solution: The solution to Problem 3.80 above provides the magnitudes of the components of the normal force exerted on the collar at A.

$$|F_N| = \sqrt{(F_{Nx})^2 + (F_{Ny})^2 + (F_{Nz})^2}.$$

Substituting in the values found in Problem 3.81, we get

$$|F_N| = 53.2 \text{ N}.$$

Problem 3.82 The 10-kg collar A and 20-kg collar B are held in place on the smooth bars by the 3-m cable from A to B and the force F acting on A. The force F is parallel to the bar. Determine F.

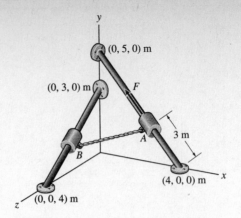

Solution: The geometry is the first part of the Problem. To ease our work, let us name the points C, D, E, and G as shown in the figure. The unit vectors from C to D and from E to G are essential to the location of points A and B. The diagram shown contains two free bodies plus the pertinent geometry. The unit vectors from C to D and from E to G are given by

$$\mathbf{e}_{CD} = e_{rCDx}\mathbf{i} + e_{CDy}\mathbf{j} + e_{CDz}\mathbf{k},$$

and $\mathbf{e}_{EG} = e_{rEGx}\mathbf{i} + e_{EGy}\mathbf{j} + e_{EGz}\mathbf{k}.$

Using the coordinates of points C, D, E, and G from the picture, the unit vectors are

$$\mathbf{e}_{CD} = -0.625\mathbf{i} + 0.781\mathbf{j} + 0\mathbf{k},$$

and $\mathbf{e}_{EG} = 0\mathbf{i} + 0.6\mathbf{j} + 0.8\mathbf{k}.$

The location of point A is given by

$$x_A = x_C + CAe_{CDx}, \quad y_A = y_C + CAe_{CDy},$$

and $z_A = z_C + CAe_{CDz},$

where $CA = 3$ m. From these equations, we find that the location of point A is given by A (2.13, 2.34, 0) m. Once we know the location of point A, we can proceed to find the location of point B. We have two ways to determine the location of B. First, B is 3 m from point A along the line AB (which we do not know). Also, B lies on the line EG. The equations for the location of point B based on line AB are:

$$x_B = x_A + ABe_{ABx}, \quad y_B = y_A + ABe_{ABy},$$

and $z_B = z_A + ABe_{ABz}.$

The equations based on line EG are:

$$x_B = x_E + EBe_{EGx}, \quad y_B = y_E + EBe_{EGy},$$

and $z_B = z_E + EBe_{EGz}.$

We have six new equations in the three coordinates of B and the distance EB. Some of the information in the equations is redundant. However, we can solve for EB (and the coordinates of B). We get that the length EB is 2.56 m and that point B is located at (0, 1.53, 1.96) m. We next write equilibrium equations for bodies A and B. From the free body diagram for A, we get

$$N_{Ax} + T_{AB}e_{ABx} + Fe_{CDx} = 0,$$

$$N_{Ay} + T_{AB}e_{ABy} + Fe_{CDy} - m_Ag = 0,$$

and $N_{Az} + T_{AB}e_{ABz} + Fe_{CDz} = 0.$

From the free body diagram for B, we get

$$N_{Bx} - T_{AB}e_{ABx} = 0,$$

$$N_{by} - T_{AB}e_{ABy} - m_Bg = 0,$$

and $N_{Bz} - T_{AB}e_{ABz} = 0.$

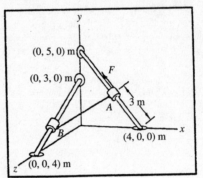

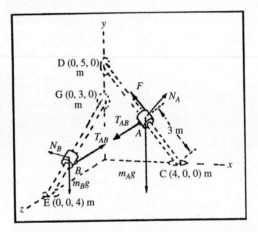

We now have two fewer equation than unknowns. Fortunately, there are two conditions we have not yet invoked. The bars at A and B are smooth. This means that the normal force on each bar can have no component along that bar. This can be expressed by using the dot product of the normal force and the unit vector along the bar. The two conditions are

$$\mathbf{N}_A \cdot \mathbf{e}_{CD} = N_{Ax}e_{CDx} + N_{Ay}e_{CDy} + N_{Az}e_{CDz} = 0$$

for slider A and

$$\mathbf{N}_B \cdot \mathbf{e}_{EG} = N_{Bx}e_{EGx} + N_{By}e_{EGy} + N_{Bz}e_{EGz} = 0.$$

Solving the eight equations in the eight unknowns, we obtain

$$\boxed{F = 36.6 \text{ N}}.$$

Other values obtained in the solution are $EB = 2.56$ m,

$$N_{Ax} = 145 \text{ N}, \quad N_{Ay} = 116 \text{ N}, \quad N_{Az} = -112 \text{ N},$$

$$N_{Bx} = -122 \text{ N}, \quad N_{By} = 150 \text{ N}, \quad \text{and} \quad N_{Bz} = 112 \text{ N}.$$

Problem 3.83 (a) Plot the tensions in cables AB and AC for values of d from $d = 0$ to $d = 1.8$ m.
(b) Each cable will safely support a tension of 1 kN. Use your graph to estimate the acceptable range of values of d.

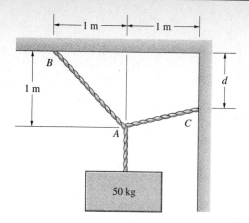

Solution: Isolate the cable juncture A. Find the interior angles α and β. Solve the equilibrium conditions in terms of distance d. Plot the result.

The angle between the positive x axis and the tension $\mathbf{T}_{AC}$ is α.

The tension: $\mathbf{T}_{AC} = |\mathbf{T}_{AC}|(\mathbf{i}\cos\alpha + \mathbf{j}\sin\alpha)$

The angle between the positive x axis and AB is $(180° - \beta)$.

The tension is $\mathbf{T}_{AB} = |\mathbf{T}_{AB}|(-\mathbf{i}\cos\beta + \mathbf{j}\sin\beta)$.

The weight is $\mathbf{W} = 0\mathbf{i} - |\mathbf{W}|\mathbf{j}$. The equilibrium conditions are

$$\sum \mathbf{F} = \mathbf{W} + \mathbf{T}_{AB} + \mathbf{T}_{AC} = 0.$$

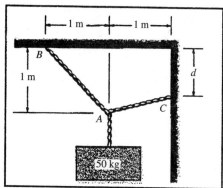

Substitute the vectors and collect like terms,

$$\sum \mathbf{F}_x = (|\mathbf{T}_{AC}|\cos\alpha - |\mathbf{T}_{AB}|\cos\beta)\mathbf{i} = 0$$

$$\sum \mathbf{F}_y = (|\mathbf{T}_{AC}|\sin\alpha + |\mathbf{T}_{AB}|\sin\beta - |\mathbf{W}|).$$

Solve: $|\mathbf{T}_{AC}| = \left(\dfrac{\cos\beta}{\cos\alpha}\right)|\mathbf{T}_{AB}|$,

$$|\mathbf{T}_{AB}| = \left(\frac{|\mathbf{W}|\cos\alpha}{\sin(\beta+\alpha)}\right),$$

and $|\mathbf{T}_{AC}| = \left(\dfrac{|\mathbf{W}|\cos\beta}{\sin(\beta+\alpha)}\right)$.

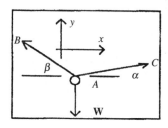

The weight is $|\mathbf{W}| = (50\text{ kg})\left(9.81\ \dfrac{\text{m}}{\text{s}^2}\right) = 490$ N.

The angles α and β are to be determined. Subdivide the cable interior into two right triangles as shown. From geometry,

$$\tan\beta = \frac{1\text{ m}}{1\text{ m}} = 1, \quad \beta = 45°,$$

$$\tan\alpha = \left(\frac{1-d}{1}\right) = (1-d), \quad \alpha = \tan^{-1}(1-d).$$

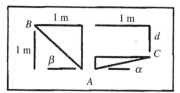

(Note that the argument $(1-d)$ is dimensionless, since it has been divided by 1 m.) The commercial package **TK Solver Plus** was used to produce a graph of the tensions vs. the distance d. From the intersection of the tension line with the 1000 N line, the range of d for safe tension is $0 \leq d \leq 1.31$ m.

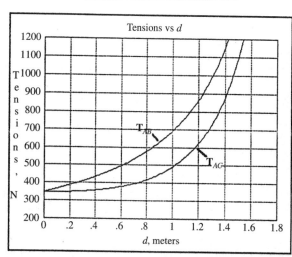

Tensions vs d

Problem 3.84 The suspended traffic light weighs 100 lb. The cables AB, BC, AD, and DE are each 11 ft long. Determine the smallest permissible length of the cable BD if the tensions in the cables must not exceed 1000 lb.

Strategy: Plot the tensions in the cables for a range of lengths of the cable BD.

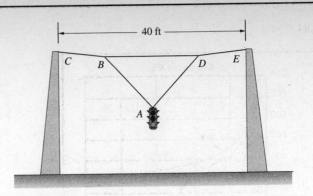

Solution: Isolate the cable juncture A. Find the interior angles α and β. Solve the equilibrium conditions in terms of distance d. Repeat for the cable junctures B and D.

From symmetry, the angles α formed by the suspension cables are equal. The two right triangles formed by the cables ABD have a base length of one half BD. Denote this distance by $d/2$. Note $AD = AB = 11$ ft. The angle α is given by

$$\cos\alpha = \frac{d}{22}, \quad \alpha = \cos^{-1}\left(\frac{d}{22}\right).$$

The angle formed by cable AD and the positive x axis is α. The tension is $\mathbf{T}_{AD} = |\mathbf{T}_{AD}|(\mathbf{i}\cos\alpha + \mathbf{j}\sin\alpha)$.

The angle formed by cable AB and the positive x axis is $(180 - \alpha)$.

The tension is $\mathbf{T}_{AB} = |\mathbf{T}_{AB}|(-\mathbf{i}\cos\alpha + \mathbf{j}\sin\alpha)$.

The weight is $\mathbf{W} = 0\mathbf{i} - \mathbf{j}|\mathbf{W}| = -100\mathbf{j}$.

The equilibrium conditions are $\sum\mathbf{F} = \mathbf{W} + \mathbf{T}_{AD} + \mathbf{T}_{AB} = 0$.

Substitute and collect like terms

$$\sum\mathbf{F}_x = (|\mathbf{T}_{AD}|\cos\alpha - |\mathbf{T}_{AB}|\cos\alpha)\mathbf{i} = 0$$

$$\sum\mathbf{F}_y = (|\mathbf{T}_{AD}|\sin\alpha + |\mathbf{T}_{AB}|\sin\alpha - |\mathbf{W}|)\mathbf{j} = 0.$$

Solve: $|\mathbf{T}_{AD}| = |\mathbf{T}_{AB}| = \left(\dfrac{1}{2}\right)\left(\dfrac{|\mathbf{W}|}{\sin\alpha}\right).$

Isolate the cable juncture D.

Subdivide the upper cable system into two right triangles and a rectangle.

The base of each right triangle is $\left(20 - \dfrac{d}{2}\right)$.

The distance DE is 11 ft, hence $\cos\theta = \dfrac{40 - d}{22}$.

The tension in DE is $\mathbf{T}_{DE} = |\mathbf{T}_{DE}|(\mathbf{i}\cos\theta + \mathbf{j}\sin\theta)$.

The tension in BD is $\mathbf{T}_{BD} = -|\mathbf{T}_{BD}|\mathbf{i} + 0\mathbf{j}$.

The cable AD makes an angle $(180 + \alpha)$ with the positive x axis:

$$\mathbf{T}_{DA} = |\mathbf{T}_{DA}|(-\mathbf{i}\cos\alpha - \mathbf{j}\sin\alpha).$$

The equilibrium conditions are $\sum\mathbf{F} = \mathbf{T}_{DE} + \mathbf{T}_{BD} + \mathbf{T}_{DA} = 0$.

Substitute and collect like terms.

$$\sum\mathbf{F}_x = (-|\mathbf{T}_{DA}|\cos\alpha - |\mathbf{T}_{BD}| + |\mathbf{T}_{DE}|\cos\theta)\mathbf{i} = 0$$

$$\sum\mathbf{F}_y = (-|\mathbf{T}_{DA}|\sin\alpha + |\mathbf{T}_{DE}|\sin\theta)\mathbf{j} = 0.$$

Solve: $|\mathbf{T}_{DE}| = \left(\dfrac{\sin\alpha}{\sin\theta}\right)|\mathbf{T}_{DA}|,$

and $\quad |\mathbf{T}_{BD}| = |\mathbf{T}_{DA}|\left(\dfrac{\sin(\alpha - \theta)}{\sin\theta}\right)$

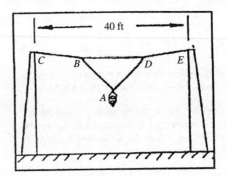

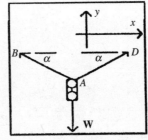

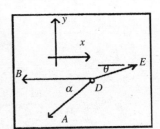

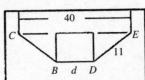

156

3.84 *Contd.*

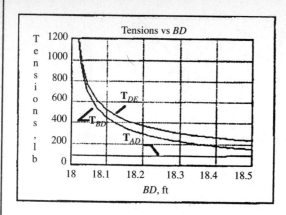

Combine terms, $|\mathbf{T}_{BD}| = \left(\dfrac{1}{2}\right)\left(\dfrac{|\mathbf{W}|\sin(\alpha - \theta)}{\sin\theta\sin\alpha}\right).$

$$|\mathbf{T}_{DE}| = \left(\frac{1}{2}\right)\left(\frac{|\mathbf{W}|}{\sin\theta}\right).$$

$$|\mathbf{T}_{AD}| = \left(\frac{1}{2}\right)\left(\frac{|\mathbf{W}|}{\sin\alpha}\right)$$

For $|\mathbf{W}| = 100$ lb, $\alpha = \cos^{-1}\left(\dfrac{d}{22}\right),$

and $\quad \theta = \cos^{-1}\left(\dfrac{40 - d}{22}\right)$

the commercial package **TK Solver Plus** was used to produce a graph of the tensions vs. the distance d over the interval $18 < d \le 18.5$.

The shortest length of *BD* for the maximum tension not to exceed 1000 lb is $d = 18.028$ ft. From the graph, it is clear that for lengths near 18 ft, a few hundredths of a foot change in length can have tremendous effect on the maximum cable tension.

Problem 3.85 The 2000-lb scoreboard A is suspended above a sports arena by the cables AB and AC. Each cable is 160 ft long. Suppose you want to move the scoreboard out of the way for a tennis match by shortening cable AB while keeping the length of cable AC constant.

(a) Plot the tension in cable AB as a function of its length for values of the length from 142 ft to 160 ft.
(b) Use your graph to estimate how much you can raise the scoreboard relative to its original position if you don't want to subject the cable AB to a tension greater than 6000 lb.

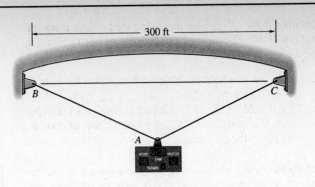

Solution: Isolate the scoreboard. Use the cosine law to find the angles as a function of AB. Solve the equilibrium conditions, and plot the result. The cosine law is:

$$\cos\beta = \frac{d^2 + 300^2 - 160^2}{(2)(300)(d)} = \frac{d^2 + 64400}{600d}$$

$$\cos\alpha = \frac{300^2 + 160^2 - d^2}{2(300)(160)} = \frac{115600 - d^2}{96000}.$$

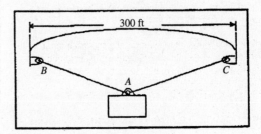

The angle formed by cable AB and the positive x axis is $(180° - \beta)$. The tension is

$$\mathbf{T}_{AB} = |\mathbf{T}_{AB}|(-\mathbf{i}\cos\beta + \mathbf{j}\sin\beta).$$

The angle formed by cable C and the positive x axis is α. The tension is

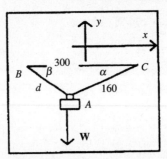

$$\mathbf{T}_{AC} = |\mathbf{T}_{AC}|(\mathbf{i}\cos\alpha + \mathbf{j}\sin\alpha).$$

The weight is $\mathbf{W} = 0\mathbf{i} - \mathbf{j}|\mathbf{W}| = 0\mathbf{i} - 2000\mathbf{j}$.

The equilibrium conditions are

$$\sum \mathbf{F} = \mathbf{W} + \mathbf{T}_{AB} + \mathbf{T}_{AC} = 0.$$

Substitute:

$$\sum \mathbf{F}_x = (-|\mathbf{T}_{AB}|\cos\alpha + |\mathbf{T}_{AC}|\cos\beta)\mathbf{i} = 0$$

$$\sum \mathbf{F}_y = (|\mathbf{T}_{AB}|\sin\alpha + |\mathbf{T}_{AC}|\sin\beta - |\mathbf{W}|)\mathbf{j} = 0.$$

Solve: $|\mathbf{T}_{AB}| = |\mathbf{T}_{AC}|\left(\dfrac{\cos\beta}{\cos\alpha}\right)$,

and $|\mathbf{T}_{AC}| = \left(\dfrac{|\mathbf{W}|\cos\alpha}{\sin(\alpha + \beta)}\right)$

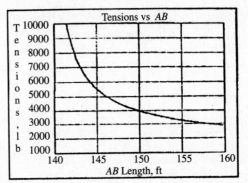

where

$$\alpha = \cos^{-1}\left(\frac{115600 - d^2}{96000}\right), \quad \beta = \cos^{-1}\left(\frac{64400 + d^2}{600d}\right)$$

The commercial package **TK Solver Plus** was used to produce a graph of the tensions vs. the length AB. Both cables have approximately the same tension; the values are so close to one another that the difference cannot be distinguished on the scale in the graph. (The tension in cable AB is slightly higher than the tension in cable AC.)The cable AB is 144.29 ft long at the 6000 lb limit on the tension. At this point the drop of the scoreboard from the ceiling is $144.26\sin\beta = 25.32$ ft, where $\beta = 10.1°$. The original drop was $160\sin\beta = 55.68$ ft, where $\beta = 20.4°$. Thus the scoreboard can be raised $55.68 - 25.32 = 30.36$ ft before the tension limit is exceeded.

Problem 3.86 Consider the suspended 4-Mg truck in Problem 3.40. The sum of the lengths of the cables AB and BC is 42 m.

(a) Plot the tensions in cables AB and BC for values of b from zero to 20 m.
(b) Each cable will safely support a tension of 60 kN. Use the results of (a) to estimate the allowable range of the distance b.

Solution: Isolate the scoreboard. Use the cosine law to find the angles as a functionw of AB. Solve the equilibrium conditions, and plot the result.

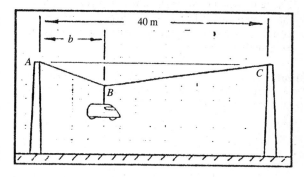

The triangle formed by the cables is shown, where $AC = 40$ m, $AB + BC = S = 42$ m.

The triangle can be subdivided into two right angles with a common side of unknown length. Let the unknown length of this common side be d, then by the Pythagorean Theorem

$$b^2 + d^2 = AB^2 \quad L^2 + d^2 = BC^2$$

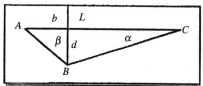

Subtract the first equation from the second to eliminate the unknown d, $L^2 - b^2 = BC^2 - AB^2$. Note that

$$L^2 - b^2 = (L - b)(L + b) = 40(40 - 2b) = 1600 - 80b$$

$$BC^2 - AB^2 = (BC - AB)(BC + AB) = 42(BC - AB).$$

Substitute and reduce to obtain the pair of simultaneous equations in the unknowns $BC - AB = \dfrac{800 - 40b}{21}$, $BC + AB = 42$.

Solve: $BC = \dfrac{841 - 20b}{21}$, $AB = \dfrac{41 + 20b}{21}$.

$$\cos\alpha = \left(\frac{(L+b)^2 + BC^2 - AB^2}{2(L+b)(BC)}\right) = \left(\frac{40^2 + (40^2 - 80b)}{2(40)\left(\dfrac{841 - 20b}{21}\right)}\right)$$

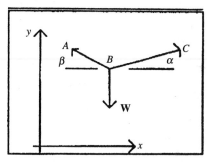

$$= \left(\frac{(21)(40 - b)}{841 - 20b}\right)$$

$$\cos\beta = \left(\frac{(L+b)^2 + AB^2 - BC^2}{2(L+b)(AB)}\right) = \left(\frac{40^2 - (40^2 - 80b)}{2(40)\left(\dfrac{41 + 20b}{21}\right)}\right)$$

$$= \left(\frac{21b}{41 + 20b}\right).$$

The angle between the cable BC and the positive x axis is α, hence the tension $\mathbf{T}_{BC} = |\mathbf{T}_{BC}|(\mathbf{i}\cos\alpha + \mathbf{j}\sin\alpha)$.

The angle between the cable BA and the positive x axis is $(180° - \beta)$, hence the tension is $\mathbf{T}_{BA} = |\mathbf{T}_{BA}|(-\mathbf{i}\cos\beta + \mathbf{j}\sin\beta)$.

The weight is $\mathbf{W} = 0\mathbf{i} - |\mathbf{W}|\mathbf{j}$.

The equilibrium conditions are $\sum \mathbf{F} = \mathbf{W} + \mathbf{T}_{BA} + \mathbf{T}_{BC} = 0$. Substitute and collect like terms

$$\sum \mathbf{F}_x = (|\mathbf{T}_{BC}|\cos\alpha - |\mathbf{T}_{BA}|\cos\beta)\mathbf{i} = 0,$$

$$\sum \mathbf{F}_y = (|\mathbf{T}_{BC}|\sin\alpha + |\mathbf{T}_{BA}|\sin\beta - |\mathbf{W}|)\mathbf{j} = 0$$

Solve: $|\mathbf{T}_{BA}| = \left(\dfrac{|\mathbf{W}|\cos\alpha}{\sin(\alpha + \beta)}\right)$, $|\mathbf{T}_{BC}| = \left(\dfrac{|\mathbf{W}|\cos\beta}{\sin(\alpha + \beta)}\right)$.

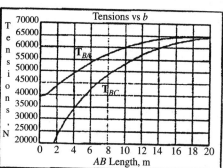

Tensions vs b

For $|\mathbf{W}| = (4000)(9.81) = 39240$ N,

and $\alpha = \cos^{-1}\left(\dfrac{21(40 - b)}{841 - 20b}\right)$, $\beta = \cos^{-1}\left(\dfrac{21b}{41 + 20b}\right)$.

The commercial package **TK Solver Plus** was used to produce a graph of the tension in the two cables as a function of the distance b. The values of b for which the maximum tension is less that 60 kN are $0 \le b \le 10$ m. By symmetry, the distance b may be measured from either the left or right side.

Problem 3.87 The unstretched length of the spring AB is 660 mm. The system is in equilibrium in the position shown when the mass of the suspended object is 10 kg. If the 10-kg object is replaced by a 30-kg object, what is the resulting tension in the spring?

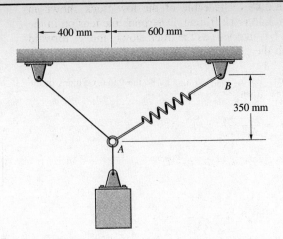

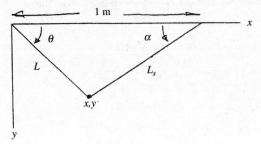

Solution: From the solution of Problem 3.34, the spring constant is $k = 2250$ N/m.

$$\left. \begin{array}{l} L = [(0.4)^2 + (0.35)^2]^{1/2}. \\ x = L\cos\theta, \quad y = L\sin\theta, \\ L_s = [y^2 + (1-x)^2]^{1/2}. \end{array} \right\} \quad (1)$$

The tension in the spring is

$$F_s = k(L_s - 0.66). \quad (2)$$

The angle α is

$$\alpha = \arctan[y/(1-x)] \quad (3)$$

From the fbd,

$$\left. \begin{array}{l} T\sin\theta + F_s\sin\alpha = mg, \\ T\cos\theta = F_s\cos\alpha. \end{array} \right\} \quad (4)$$

Choosing a value of θ, Eqs. (1)-(3) can be solved for F_s and α. Then Eqs. (4) can be solved for the value of m necessary for equilibrium. By plotting m as a function of θ.

We see that $m = 30$ kg at $\theta = 47.4°$. Then from Eqs. (1) and (2) we obtain $F_s = 203$ N.

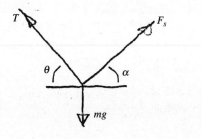

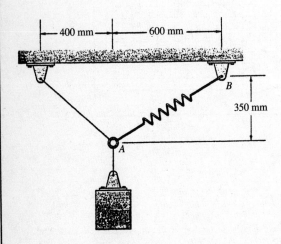

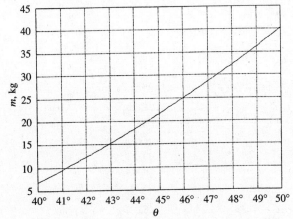

Problem 3.88 The cable of the tow truck shown in Problem 3.46 is 12 ft long. Determine the tension in the cable at 1-ft intervals as the truck slowly moves forward 5 ft from the position shown.

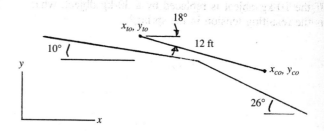

Solution: Let x_{to}, y_{to} and x_{co}, y_{to} be the initial positions of the truck and car. Then

$$\tan 18° = \frac{y_{to} - y_{co}}{x_{co} - x_{to}}$$

and $(x_{co} - x_{to})^2 + (y_{to} - y_{co})^2 = (12)^2$.

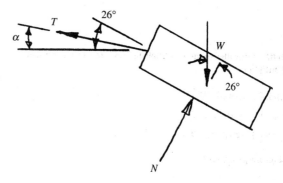

Solving yields

$x_{co} - x_{to} = 11.41$ ft, $y_{to} - y_{co} = 3.71$ ft.

Let d_t be the distance the truck moves forward and d_c the distance the car moves forward. Their new positions are

$$x_t = x_{to} - d_t \cos 10°, \quad y_t = y_{to} + d_t \sin 10°,$$

$$x_c = x_{co} - d_c \cos 26°, \quad y_c = y_{co} + d_c \sin 26°.$$

From these equations,

$$y_t - y_c = y_{to} - y_{co} + d_t \sin 10° - d_c \sin 26°, \quad (1)$$

$$x_c - x_t = x_{co} - x_{to} - d_c \cos 26° + d_T \cos 10°. \quad (2)$$

Also,

$$(x_c - x_t)^2 + (y_t - y_c)^2 = (12)^2 \quad (3)$$

If d_t is specified, Eqs. (1)-(3) can be solved for $x_c - x_t$, $y_t - yx_c$, and d_c. The 18° angle changes into an angle α, where

$$\tan \alpha = \frac{y_t - y_c}{x_c - x_t}. \quad (4)$$

From the free-body diagram of the car,

$T \cos(26° - \alpha) = W \sin 26°$.

T can be determined once α is know from Eq. (3):

d_t, ft	T, lb
0	1328.0
1	1332.7
2	1338.2
3	1344.5
4	1351.7
5	1359.7

Problem 3.89 The system in Problem 3.59 provides lateral support for a load resting on the smooth bed of a truck. When the load is subjected to an effective lateral load F (Fig. b), the distance from the original position of the load to its equilibrium position is δ. The unstretched length of each spring is 1 ft. Suppose that the load is subjected to an effective lateral load of $F = 200$ lb.

(a) Plot the spring constant k for values of δ from 0.5 ft to 3 ft.
(b) Use the results of (a) to estimate the values of k for $\delta = 1$ ft and $\delta = 2$ ft.

Solution: From the solution of Problem 3.59 the lateral load is given by

$$|F| = |T_L| \cos \beta - |T_R| \cos \alpha,$$

where the tension in the left hand spring is

$$|T_L| = k \Delta L_L = k(\sqrt{(3 + \delta)^2 + 1^2} - 1),$$

and the tension in the right hand spring is

$$|T_L| = k \Delta L_L = k(\sqrt{(3 + \delta)^2 + 1^2} - 1).$$

The angles are also given in the solution of Problem 3.59

$$\tan \alpha = \frac{1}{3 - \delta}, \quad \text{and} \quad \tan \beta = \frac{1}{3 + \delta}.$$

For, $|F| = 200$ lb, the equation to be solved for k is

$$f(k) = k(\Delta L_L \cos \beta - \Delta L_R \cos \alpha) - 200 = 0.$$

The commercial package **TK Solver Plus** was used to graph the spring constant vs. the displacement δ, as shown below. The values of k at $\delta = 1$ ft and $\delta = 2$ ft are $k = 104$ lb/ft and $k = 54$ lb/ft, respectively.

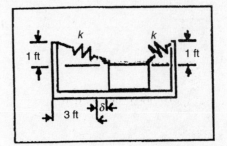

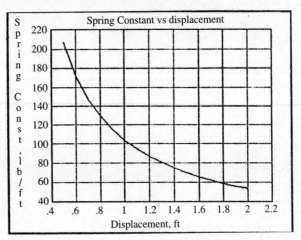

Problem 3.90 Consider the tethered balloon in Problem 3.68. The mass of the balloon, experiments package, and the gas it contains is 90 kg, and the buoyancy force on the balloon is 1000 N. If the tethers AB, AC, and AD will each safely support a tension of 500 N and the coordinates of point A are $(0, h, 0)$, What is the minimum allowable height h?

Solution: See the solution to Problem 3.68. Solve the problem by computer with values of h ranging from 1 to 4 meters. F_{AD} is always the largest force. At $h = 1$ m, $F_{AD} = 827$ N and at $h = 2$ m, $F_{AD} = 416$ N. Now solve for values between 1 and 2 meters.

h (m)	F_{AD} (N)
1.1	752
1.2	689
1.3	637
1.4	591
1.5	552
1.6	518
1.7	488
1.62	511
1.64	505
1.66	499
1.68	493

$$h \cong 1.66 \text{ m}$$

Problem 3.91 The collar A slides on a smooth vertical bar. The masses $m_A = 20$ kg and $m_B = 10$ kg, and the spring constant $k = 360$ N/m. When $h = 0.2$ m, the spring is unstretched. Determine the value of h when the system is in equilibrium.

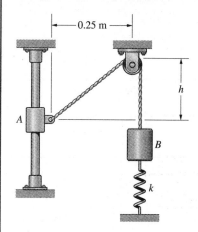

Solution: The diagram of the triangle shows that the amount of stretch in the spring is given by $\delta = c - c_0$.

From the free body diagrams of masses A and B, the equations of equilibrium are:

For A: $\qquad \sum F_x = T \cos \alpha - N = 0$

and $\qquad \sum F_y = T \sin \alpha - m_A g = 0$,

and for B: $\sum F_y = T - k(c - c_0) - m_B g = 0$.

From the geometry, we know that

$$c_0 = \sqrt{h_0^2 + (0.25)^2}, \quad c = \sqrt{h^2 + (0.25)^2},$$

and that $\sin \alpha = \dfrac{h}{c}$.

Substituting in the known values, we get a set of equations which must be solved either by iteration or by graphical methods. Using an iterative solution, we get $\boxed{h = 0.218 \text{ m}}$.

A graphical solution strategy can be easily employed. Once we know a value for h, we can calculate the values of all of the forces in the Problem. The only equation which will not be satisfied is the y-direction equilibrium equation for mass A. We see from the free body diagram for A that the weight of A must be balanced by the vertical component of T for equilibrium. We need only calculate the vertical component of the force T acting on A and compare this to the weight of A. The results of such a comparison are shown here. Note that the sloping line (the vertical component of T) crosses the horizontal line (the weight of A) at $h \approx 0.217$ m. This is very close to our previous result.

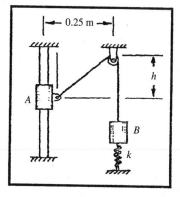

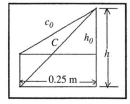

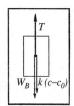

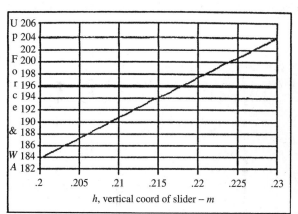

h, vertical coord of slider – m

Problem 3.92 The cable AB keeps the 8-kg collar A in place on the smooth bar CD. The y axis points upward. Determine the distance s from C to the collar A for which the tension in the cable is 150 N.

Solution: From the figure, the coordinates of the points (in meters) are $B(0, 0.5, 0.15)$, $C(0.4, 0.3, 0)$, and $D(0.2, 0, 0.25)$.

The first unit vector is of the form,

$$\mathbf{e}_{IK} = \frac{((x_I - x_K)\mathbf{i} + (y_I - y_K)\mathbf{j} - (z_I - z_K)\mathbf{k})}{\sqrt{(x_I - x_K)^2 + (y_I - y_K)^2 + (z_I - z_K)^2}},$$

where IK takes on the value CD. The coordinates of point A are given by

$$A_x = C_x + se_{CDx}, \quad A_y = C_y + se_{CDy},$$

and $A_z = C_z + se_{CDz}$,

where we do not know the value of s. The equations of equilibrium for this problem are:

$$\sum F_x = T_{AB}e_{ABx} + F_{Nx} = 0,$$

$$\sum F_y = T_{AB}e_{ABy} + F_{Ny} - W = 0,$$

and $\sum F_z = T_{AB}e_{ABz} + F_{Nz} = 0,$

where $T_{AB} = 150$ N.

The weight of the collar is given by

$W = mg$, or $W = (8)(9.81) = 78.48$ N.

The condition that the force $\mathbf{F}_N$ is perpendicular to CD is

$\mathbf{F}_N \cdot \mathbf{e}_{CD} = 0$, or $F_N \cdot \mathbf{e}_{CD} = F_{Nx}e_{CDx} + F_{Ny}e_{CDy} + F_{Nz}e_{CDz} = 0.$

We have three equilibrium equations plus the dot product equation in the four unknowns, s and the three components of $\mathbf{F}_N$. Several methods of solution are open to us. Any iterative algebraic solution method should give the result $s = 0.3046$ m and that

$\mathbf{F}_N = 80.7\mathbf{i} - 47.7\mathbf{j} + 7.29\mathbf{k}$ N.

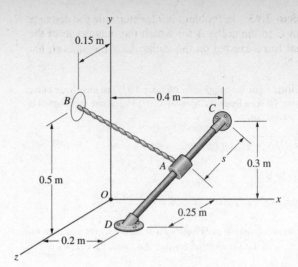

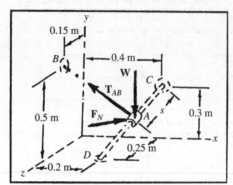

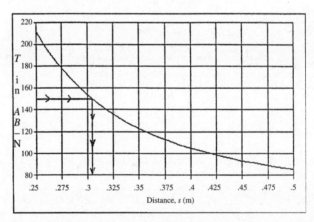

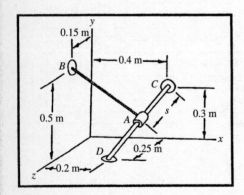

Alternative Solution: The complication in the algebra in the solution is because we do not know the location of point A. We can assume the location of A is known (assume that we know the distance s) and solve for the value of the tension in cable AB which corresponds to that location for A. We can plot the value of the tension versus the distance s and find the value of s at which the tension is 150 N. If we do this, we get the plot shown. From the plot, $s \cong 0.305$ N.

Problem 3.93 In Problem 3.92, determine the distance s from C to the collar A for which the magnitude of the normal force exerted on the collar A by the smooth bar is 50 N.

Solution: Use the solution for Problem 3.92. The magnitude of the tension in AB is no longer to be equal to 150 N. Instead, the magnitude of the normal force

$$|\mathbf{F}_N| = \sqrt{F_{Nx}^2 + F_{Ny}^2 + F_{Nz}^2}$$

must be 50 N.

From the plot, the correct value of s is $\boxed{s \cong 0.395 \text{ m}}$.

An iterative solution of the equations four equations derived in Problem 3.92, with the values from this problem, gives $\boxed{s = 0.396 \text{ m}}$.

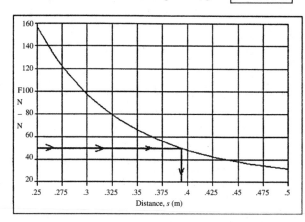

Problem 3.94 The 10-kg collar A and 20-kg collar B slide on the smooth bars. The cable from A to B is 3 m in length. Determine the value of the distance s in the range $1 \leq s \leq 5$ m for which the system is in equilibrium.

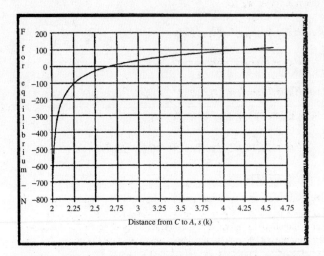

Solution: The geometry is the first part of the Problem. To ease our work, let us name the points C, D, E, and G as shown in the figure. The unit vectors from C to D and from E to G are essential to the location of points A and B. The diagram shown contains two free bodies plus the pertinent geometry. The unit vectors from C to D and from E to G are given by

$$\mathbf{e}_{CD} = er_{CDx}\mathbf{i} + e_{CDy}\mathbf{j} + e_{CDz}\mathbf{k},$$

and $\mathbf{e}_{EG} = er_{EGx}\mathbf{i} + e_{EGy}\mathbf{j} + e_{EGz}\mathbf{k}.$

Using the coordinates of points C, D, E, and G from the picture, the unit vectors are

$$\mathbf{e}_{CD} = -0.625\mathbf{i} + 0.781\mathbf{j} + 0\mathbf{k},$$

and $\mathbf{e}_{EG} = 0\mathbf{i} + 0.6\mathbf{j} + 0.8\mathbf{k}.$

The location of point A is given by

$$x_A = x_C + CA\mathbf{e}_{CDx}, \quad y_A = y_C + CA\mathbf{e}_{CDy},$$

and $z_A = z_C + CA\mathbf{e}_{CDz},$

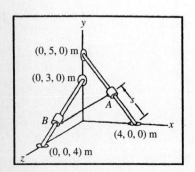

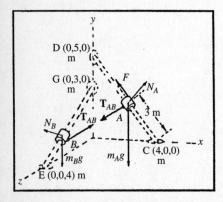

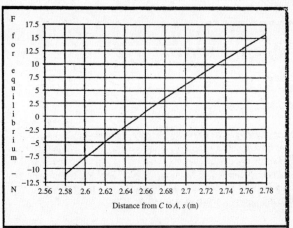

where $CA = s$, the parameter we vary to find $F(s)$.

From these equations, we can find that the location of point A for any value of s. Once we know the location of point A, we can proceed to find the location of point B. We have two ways to determine the location of B. First, B is 3 m from point A along the line AB (which we do not know). Also, B lies on the line EG. The equations for the location of point B based on line AB are:

$$x_B = x_A + AB\mathbf{e}_{ABx}, \quad y_B = y_A + AB\mathbf{e}_{ABy},$$

and $z_B = z_A + AB\mathbf{e}_{ABz}.$

166

The equations for the location of point B based on line EG are:

$$x_B = x_E + EBe_{EGx},$$

$$y_B = y_E + EBe_{EGy},$$

and $z_B = z_E + EBe_{EGz}$.

We have six new equations in the three coordinates of B and the distance EB. Some of the information in the equations is redundant. However, we can solve for EB (and the coordinates of B). We next write equilibrium equations for bodies A and B. From the free body diagram for A, we get

$$N_{Ax} + T_{AB}e_{ABx} + Fe_{CDx} = 0,$$

$$N_{Ay} + T_{AB}e_{ABy} + Fe_{CDy} - m_A g = 0,$$

and $N_{Az} + T_{AB}e_{ABz} + Fe_{CDz} = 0$.

From the free body diagram for B, we get

$$N_{Bx} - T_{AB}e_{ABx} = 0, \quad N_{by} - T_{AB}e_{ABy} - m_B g = 0,$$

and $N_{Bz} - T_{AB}e_{ABz} = 0$.

We now have two fewer equation than unknowns. Fortunately, there are two conditions we have not yet invoked. The bars at A and B are smooth. This means that the normal force on each bar can have no component along that bar. This can be expressed by using the dot product of the normal force and the unit vector along the bar.

The two conditions are

$$\mathbf{N}_A \cdot \mathbf{e}_{CD} = N_{Ax}e_{CDx} + N_{Ay}e_{CDy} + N_{Az}e_{CDz} = 0$$

for slider A and

$$N_B \cdot e_{EG} = N_{Bx}e_{EGx} + N_{By}e_{EGy} + N_{Bz}e_{EGz} = 0.$$

Solving the eight equations in the eight unknowns, we obtain $F(s)$ for any given s. The plot of $F(s)$ vs s, found using **TK Solver Plus** is shown below. We see from the plot that the force F goes to zero somewhere between $s = 2.5$ m and $s = 2.75$ m. We can expand the plot around the zero crossing to obtain a more exact result. The plot right hand plot is such an expansion.

From the second plot, the value $s = 2.65$ m is necessary for the configuration to be in equilibrium.

Problem 3.95 The 100-lb crate is held in place on the smooth surface by the rope AB. Determine the tension in the rope and the magnitude of the normal force exerted on the crate by the surface.

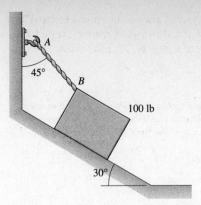

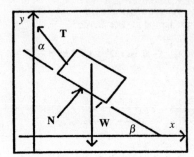

Solution: Isolate the crate, and solve the equilibrium conditions. The weight is $\mathbf{W} = 0\mathbf{i} - 100\mathbf{j}$. The angle between the normal force and the positive x axis is $(90 - 30) = 60°$. The normal force is

$$\mathbf{N} = |\mathbf{N}|(\mathbf{i}\cos 60 + \mathbf{j}\sin 60) = |\mathbf{N}|(0.5\mathbf{i} + 0.866\mathbf{j}).$$

The angle between the string tension and the positive x axis is $(180° - 45°) = 135°$, hence the tension is

$$\mathbf{T} = |\mathbf{T}|(\mathbf{i}\cos 135° + \mathbf{j}\sin 135°) = |\mathbf{T}|(-0.7071\mathbf{i} + 0.7071\mathbf{j}).$$

The equilibrium conditions are $\sum \mathbf{F} = \mathbf{W} + \mathbf{N} + \mathbf{T} = 0$.

Substituting, and collecting like terms

$$\sum \mathbf{F}_x = (0.5|\mathbf{N}| - 0.7071|\mathbf{T}|)\mathbf{i} = 0$$

$$\sum \mathbf{F}_y = (0.866|\mathbf{N}| + 0.7071|\mathbf{T}| - 100)\mathbf{j} = 0$$

Solve: $|\mathbf{T}| = 51.8$ lb, $|\mathbf{N}| = 73.2$ lb

Check: Use a coordinate system with the x axis parallel to the inclined surface. The equilibrium equation for the x-coordinate is

$$\sum F_x |\mathbf{W}| \sin 30° - |\mathbf{T}| \cos 15° = 0$$

from which $|\mathbf{T}| = \left(\dfrac{\sin 30°}{\cos 15°} \right) 100 = 51.76 = 51.8$ lb.

The equilibrium equation for the y-coordinate is

$$\sum F_y = |\mathbf{N}| - \mathbf{W}\cos 30° + |\mathbf{T}|\sin 15° - 0,$$

from which $|\mathbf{N}| = 73.2$ lb. *check.*

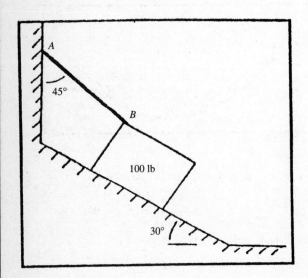

Problem 3.96 The system shown is called Russell's traction. If the sum of the downward forces exerted at A and B by the patient's leg is 32.2 lb, what is the weight W?

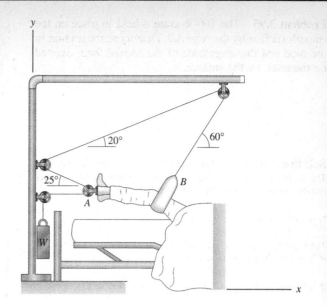

Solution: Isolate the leg. Express the tensions at A and B in scalar components. Solve the equilibrium conditions. The pulleys change the direction but not the magnitude of the force $|\mathbf{W}|$. The force at B is

$$\mathbf{F}_B = |\mathbf{W}|(\mathbf{i}\cos 60° + \mathbf{j}\sin 60°).$$

$$\mathbf{F}_B = |\mathbf{W}|(0.5\mathbf{i} + 0.866\mathbf{j}).$$

The angles at A relative to the positive x axis are: $180°$ and $180° - 25° = 155°$. The force at A is the sum of the two forces:

$$\mathbf{F}_A = |\mathbf{W}|(\mathbf{i}\cos 180° + \mathbf{j}\sin 180°) + |\mathbf{W}|(\mathbf{i}\cos 155° + \mathbf{j}\sin 155°)$$

$$\mathbf{F}_A = |\mathbf{W}|(-1.906\mathbf{i} + 0.4226\mathbf{j}).$$

The total force exerted by the patient's leg is $\mathbf{F}_P = F_H\mathbf{i} - 32.2\mathbf{j}$, where F_H is an unknown component. The equilibrium conditions are

$$\sum \mathbf{F} = \mathbf{F}_A + \mathbf{F}t_B + \mathbf{F}_P = 0,$$

from which: $\sum \mathbf{F}_X = (0.5|\mathbf{W}| - 1.906|\mathbf{W}| + F_H)\mathbf{i} = 0$

and $\sum \mathbf{F}_Y = (0.866|\mathbf{W}| + 0.4226|\mathbf{W}| - 32.2)\mathbf{j} = 0.$

Solve for the weight: $\boxed{|\mathbf{W}| = \dfrac{32.2}{1.2886} = 25 \text{ lb}}$.

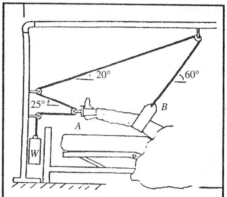

Problem 3.97 A heavy rope used as a hawser for a cruise ship sags as shown. If it weighs 200 lb, what are the tensions in the rope at A and B?

Solution: Resolve the tensions at A and B into scalar components. Solve the equilibrium equations. The tension at B is

$$\mathbf{T}_B = |\mathbf{T}_B|(\mathbf{i}\cos 40° + \mathbf{j}\sin 40°)$$

$$\mathbf{T}_B = |\mathbf{T}_B|(0.7660\mathbf{i} + 0.6428\mathbf{j}).$$

The angle at A relative to the positive x axis is $180° - 55° = 125°$.

The tension at A:

$$\mathbf{T}_A = |\mathbf{T}_A|(\mathbf{i}\cos 125° + \mathbf{j}\sin 125°) = |\mathbf{T}_A|(-0.5736\mathbf{i} + 0.8192\mathbf{j}).$$

The weight is: $\mathbf{W} = 0\mathbf{i} - 200\mathbf{j}$. The equilibrium conditions are

$$\sum \mathbf{F} = \mathbf{T}_A + \mathbf{T}_B + \mathbf{W} = 0,$$

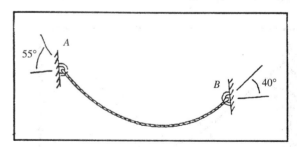

from which $\sum \mathbf{F}_x = (0.766|\mathbf{T}_B| - 0.5736|\mathbf{T}_A|)\mathbf{i} = 0$

$$\sum \mathbf{F}_y = (0.6428|\mathbf{T}_B| - 0.8192|\mathbf{T}_A| - 200)\mathbf{i} = 0.$$

Solve: $|\mathbf{T}_B| = 115.1$ lb, $\quad |\mathbf{T}_A| = 153.8$ lb.

Problem 3.98 The cable *AB* is horizontal, and the box on the right weighs 100 lb. The surfaces are smooth.

(a) What is the tension in the cable?
(b) What is the weight of the box on the left?

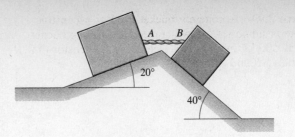

Solution: Isolate the right hand box, resolve the forces into components, and solve the equilibrium conditions. Repeat for the box on the left.

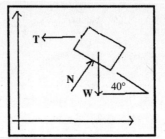

(a) For right hand box. The weight is $\mathbf{W} = 0\mathbf{i} - 100\mathbf{j}$. The angle between the normal force and the positive x axis is $(90° - 40°) = 50°$. The force:

$$\mathbf{N} = |\mathbf{N}|(\mathbf{i}\cos 50° + \mathbf{j}\sin 50°) = |\mathbf{N}|(0.6428\mathbf{i} + 0.7660\mathbf{j}).$$

The cable tension is $\mathbf{T} = -|\mathbf{T}|\mathbf{i} + 0\mathbf{j}$. The equilibrium conditions are

$$\sum \mathbf{F} = \mathbf{T} + \mathbf{N} + \mathbf{W} = 0,$$

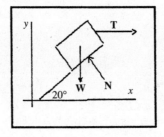

from which $\sum \mathbf{F}_x = (0.6428|\mathbf{N}| - |\mathbf{T}|)\mathbf{i} = 0$

and $\qquad \sum \mathbf{F}_y = (0.7660|\mathbf{N}| - 100)\mathbf{j} = 0$

Solve: $|\mathbf{T}| = 83.9$ lb

(b) For left hand box: The weight $\mathbf{W} = 0\mathbf{i} - |\mathbf{W}|\mathbf{j}$. The angle between the normal force and the positive x axis is $(90° + 20° = 110°$. The normal force:

$$\mathbf{N} = |\mathbf{N}|(-0.3420\mathbf{i} + 0.9397\mathbf{j}).$$

The cable tension is: $\mathbf{T} = |\mathbf{T}|\mathbf{i} + 0\mathbf{j}$. The equilibrium conditions are:

$$\sum \mathbf{F} = \mathbf{W} + \mathbf{N} + \mathbf{T} = 0,$$

from which: $\sum \mathbf{F}_x = (-0.342|\mathbf{N}| + 83.9)\mathbf{i} = 0$

and $\qquad \sum \mathbf{F}_y = (-0.940|\mathbf{N}| - |\mathbf{W}|)\mathbf{j} = 0.$

Solving for the weight of the box, we get $\boxed{|\mathbf{W}| = 230.6 \text{ lb.}}$

Problem 3.99 A concrete bucket used at a construction site is supported by two cranes. The 100-kg bucket contains 500 kg of concrete. Determine the tensions in the cables AB and AC.

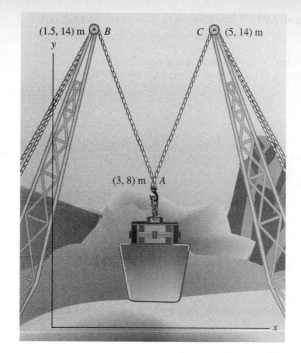

Solution: We need unit vectors $\mathbf{e}_{AB}$ and $\mathbf{e}_{AC}$. The coordinates of A, B, and C are

$$\begin{cases} \mathbf{e}_{AB} = -0.243\mathbf{i} + 0.970\mathbf{j} \\ \mathbf{e}_{AC} = 0.316\mathbf{i} + 0.949\mathbf{j} \end{cases}$$

The forces are

$$\begin{cases} \mathbf{T}_{AB} = -0.243 T_{AB}\mathbf{i} + 0.970 T_{AB}\mathbf{j} \\ \mathbf{T}_{AC} = 0.316 T_{AC}\mathbf{i} + 0.949 T_{AC}\mathbf{j} \\ \mathbf{W} = -5886\mathbf{j} \text{ N} \end{cases}$$

$$\begin{cases} \sum F_x = -0.243 T_{AB} + 0.316 T_{AC} = 0 \\ \sum F_y = 0.970 T_{AB} + 0.949 T_{AC} - 5886 = 0 \end{cases}$$

Solving, $T_{AB} = 3.47$ kN, $T_{AC} = 2.66$ kN

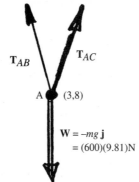

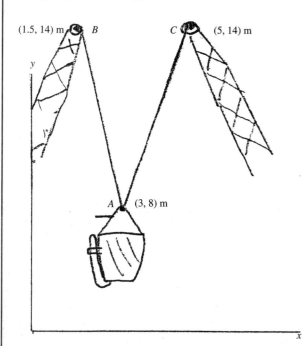

Problem 3.100 The mass of the suspended object A is m_A and the masses of the pulleys are negligible. Determine the force T necessary for the system to be in equilibrium.

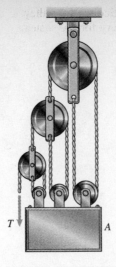

Solution: Break the system into four free body diagrams as shown. Carefully label the forces to ensure that the tension in any single cord is uniform. The equations of equilibrium for the four objects, starting with the leftmost pulley and moving clockwise, are:

$$S - 3T = 0, \quad R - 3S = 0, \quad F - 3R = 0,$$

and $2T + 2S + 2R - m_A g = 0$.

We want to eliminate S, R, and F from our result and find T in terms of m_A and g. From the first two equations, we get $S = 3T$, and $R = 3S = 9T$. Substituting these into the last equilibrium equation results in $2T + 2(3T) + 2(9T) = m_A g$.

Solving, we get $\boxed{T = m_A g/26}$.

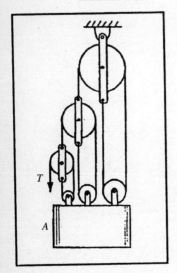

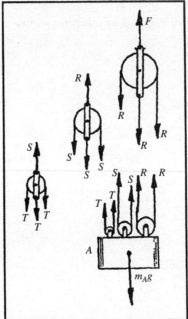

Note: We did not have to solve for F to find the appropriate value of T. The final equation would give us the value of F in terms of m_A and g. We would get $F = 27 m_A g/26$. If we then drew a free body diagram of the entire assembly, the equation of equilibrium would be $F - T - m_A g = 0$. Substituting in the known values for T and F, we see that this equation is also satisfied. Checking the equilibrium solution by using the "extra" free body diagram is often a good procedure.

Problem 3.101 The assembly A, including the pulley, weighs 60 lb. What force F is necessary for the system to be in equilibrium?

Solution: From the free body diagram of the assembly A, we have
$3F - 60 = 0$, or $\boxed{F = 20 \text{ lb}}$

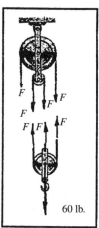

F F F

F F F

60 lb.

Problem 3.102 The mass of block A is 42 kg, and the mass of block B is 50 kg. The surfaces are smooth. If the blocks are in equilibrium, what is the force F?

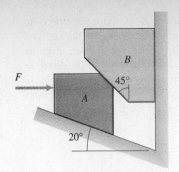

Solution: Isolate the top block. Solve the equilibrium equations. The weight is. The angle between the normal force N_1 and the positive x axis is. The normal force is. The force N_2 is. The equilibrium conditions are

$$\sum F = N_1 + N_2 + W = 0$$

from which $\sum F_x = (0.7071|N_1| - |N_2|)i = 0$

$$\sum F_y = (0.7071|N_1| - 490.5)j = 0.$$

Solve: $N_1 = 693.7$ N, $|N_2| = 490.5$ N

Isolate the bottom block. The weight is

$$W = 0i - |W|j = 0i - (42)(9.81)j = 0i - 412.02j \text{ (N)}.$$

The angle between the normal force N_1 and the positive x axis is $(270° - 45°) = 225°$.

The normal force:

$$N_1 = |N_1|(i\cos 225° + j\sin 225°) = |N_1|(-0.7071i - 0.7071j).$$

The angle between the normal force N_3 and the positive x-axis is $(90° - 20°) = 70°$.

The normal force is

$$N_1 = |N_3|(i\cos 70° + j\sin 70°) = |N_3|(0.3420i - 0.9397j).$$

The force is $\ldots F = |F|i + 0j$. The equilibrium conditions are

$$\sum F = W + N_1 + N_3 + F = 0,$$

from which: $\sum F_x = (-0.7071|N_1| + 0.3420|N_3| + |F|)i = 0$

$$\sum F_y = (-0.7071|N_1| + 0.9397|N_3| - 412)j = 0$$

For $|N_1| = 693.7$ N from above: $\boxed{|F| = 162 \text{ N}}$

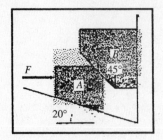

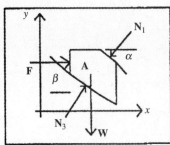

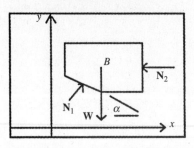

Problem 3.103 The climber A is being helped up an icy slope by two friends. His mass is 80 kg, and the direction cosines of the force exerted on him by the slope are $\cos\theta_x = -0.286$, $\cos\theta_y = 0.429$, $\cos\theta_z = 0.857$. The y axis is vertical. If the climber is in equilibrium in the position shown, what are the tensions in the ropes AB and AC and the magnitude of the force exerted on him by the slope?

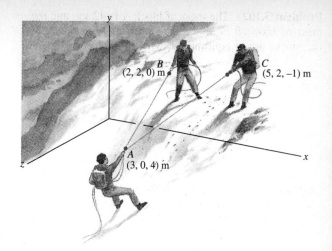

Solution: Get the unit vectors parallel to the ropes using the coordinates of the end points. Express the tensions in terms of these unit vectors, and solve the equilibrium conditions. The rope tensions, the normal force, and the weight act on the climber. The coordinates of points A, B, C are given by the problem, $A(3, 0, 4)$, $B(2, 2, 0)$, $C(5, 2, -1)$.

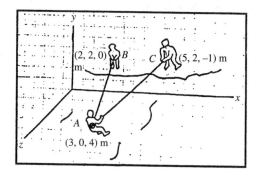

The vector locations of the points A, B, C are:

$$\mathbf{r}_A = 3\mathbf{i} + 0\mathbf{j} + 4\mathbf{k}, \quad \mathbf{r}_B = 2\mathbf{i} + 2\mathbf{j} + 0\mathbf{k}, \quad \mathbf{r}_C = 5\mathbf{i} + 2\mathbf{j} + 1\mathbf{k}.$$

The unit vector parallel to the tension acting between the points A, B in the direction of B is

$$\mathbf{e}_{AB} = \frac{\mathbf{r}_B - \mathbf{r}_A}{|\mathbf{r}_B - \mathbf{r}_A|}$$

The unit vectors are

$$\mathbf{e}_{AB} = -0.2182\mathbf{i} + 0.4364\mathbf{j} - 0.8729\mathbf{k},$$

$$\mathbf{e}_{AC} = 0.3482\mathbf{i} + 0.3482\mathbf{j} - 0.8704\mathbf{k},$$

and $\mathbf{e}_N = -0.286\mathbf{i} + 0.429\mathbf{j} + 0.857\mathbf{k}$.

where the last was given by the problem statement. The forces are expressed in terms of the unit vectors,

$$\mathbf{T}_{AB} = |\mathbf{T}_{AB}|\mathbf{e}_{AB}, \quad \mathbf{T}_{AC} = |\mathbf{T}_{AC}|\mathbf{e}_{AC}, \quad \mathbf{N} = |\mathbf{N}|\mathbf{e}_N.$$

The weight is

$$\mathbf{W} = 0\mathbf{i} - |\mathbf{W}|\mathbf{j} + 0\mathbf{k} = 0\mathbf{i} - (80)(9.81)\mathbf{j} + 0\mathbf{k} - 0\mathbf{i} - 784.8\mathbf{j} + 0\mathbf{k}.$$

The equilibrium conditions are

$$\sum \mathbf{F} = 0 = \mathbf{T}_{AB} + \mathbf{T}_{AC} + \mathbf{N} + \mathbf{W} = 0.$$

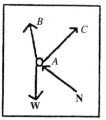

Substitute and collect like terms,

$$\sum F_x = (0.2182|\mathbf{T}_{AB}| + 0.3482|\mathbf{T}_{AC}| - 0.286|\mathbf{N}|)\mathbf{i} = 0$$

$$\sum F_y = (0.4364|\mathbf{T}_{AB}| + 0.3482|\mathbf{T}_{AC}| - 0.429|\mathbf{N}| - 784.8)\mathbf{j} = 0$$

$$\sum F_z = (0.8729|\mathbf{T}_{AB}| + 0.8704|\mathbf{T}_{AC}| - 0.857|\mathbf{N}|)\mathbf{k} = 0$$

We have three linear equations in three unknowns. The solution is:

$$\boxed{|\mathbf{T}_{AB}| = 100.7 \text{ N}}, \quad \boxed{|\mathbf{T}_{AC}| = 889.0 \text{ N}}, \quad \boxed{|\mathbf{N}| = 1005.5 \text{ N}}.$$

Problem 3.104 Consider the climber A being helped by his friends in Problem 3.103. To try to make the tensions in the ropes more equal, the friend at B moves to the position $(4, 2, 0)$ m. What are the new tensions in the ropes AB and AC and the magnitude of the force exerted on the climber by the slope?

Solution: Get the unit vectors parallel to the ropes using the coordinates of the end points. Express the tensions in terms of these unit vectors, and solve the equilibrium conditions. The coordinates of points A, B, C are $A(3, 0, 4)$, $B(4, 2, 0)$, $C(5, 2, -1)$. The vector locations of the points A, B, C are:

$$\mathbf{r}_A = 3\mathbf{i} + 0\mathbf{j} + 4\mathbf{k}, \quad \mathbf{r}_B = 4\mathbf{i} + 2\mathbf{j} + 0\mathbf{k}, \quad \mathbf{r}_C = 5\mathbf{i} + 2\mathbf{j} + 1\mathbf{k}.$$

The unit vectors are

$$\mathbf{e}_{AB} = -0.2182\mathbf{i} + 0.4364\mathbf{j} - 0.8729\mathbf{k},$$

$$\mathbf{e}_{AC} = +0.3482\mathbf{i} + 0.3482\mathbf{j} - 0.8704\mathbf{k},$$

$$\mathbf{e}_N = -0.286\mathbf{i} + 0.429\mathbf{j} + 0.857\mathbf{k}.$$

where the last was given by the problem statement. The forces are expressed in terms of the unit vectors,

$$\mathbf{T}_{AB} = |\mathbf{T}_{AB}|\mathbf{e}_{AB}, \quad \mathbf{T}_{AC} = |\mathbf{T}_{AC}|\mathbf{e}_{AC}, \quad \mathbf{N} = |\mathbf{N}|\mathbf{e}_N.$$

The weight is

$$\mathbf{W} = 0\mathbf{i} - |\mathbf{W}|\mathbf{j} + 0\mathbf{k} = 0\mathbf{i} - (80)(9.81)\mathbf{j} + 0\mathbf{k} - 0\mathbf{i} - 784.8\mathbf{j} + 0\mathbf{k}.$$

The equilibrium conditions are

$$\sum \mathbf{F} = 0 = \mathbf{T}_{AB} + \mathbf{T}_{AC} + \mathbf{N} + \mathbf{W} = 0.$$

Substitute and collect like terms,

$$\sum F_x = (+0.281|\mathbf{T}_{AB}| + 0.3482|\mathbf{T}_{AC}| - 0.286|\mathbf{N}|)\mathbf{i} = 0$$

$$\sum F_y = (0.4364|\mathbf{T}_{AB}| + 0.3482|\mathbf{T}_{AC}| - 0.429|\mathbf{N}| - 784.8)\mathbf{j} = 0$$

$$\sum F_z = (0.8729|\mathbf{T}_{AB}| + 0.8704|\mathbf{T}_{AC}| - 0.857|\mathbf{N}|)\mathbf{k} = 0$$

The HP-28S hand held calculator was used to solve these simultaneous equations. The solution is:

$$\boxed{|\mathbf{T}_{AB}| = 420.5 \text{ N}}, \quad \boxed{|\mathbf{T}_{AC}| = 532.5 \text{ N}}, \quad \boxed{|\mathbf{N}| = 969.3 \text{ N}}.$$

Problem 3.105 A climber helps his friend up an icy slope. His friend is hauling a box of supplies. If the mass of the friend is 90 kg and the mass of the supplies is 22 kg, what are the tensions in the ropes AB and CD? Assume that the slope is smooth.

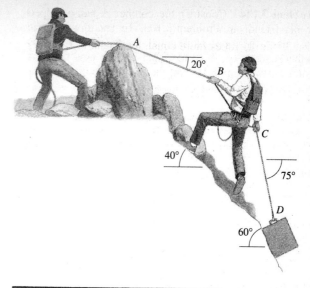

Solution: Isolate the box. The weight vector is

$\mathbf{W}_2 = (22)(9.81)\mathbf{j} = -215.8\mathbf{j}$ (N).

The angle between the normal force and the positive x axis is $(90° - 60°) = 30°$.

The normal force is $\mathbf{N}_B = |\mathbf{N}_B|(0.866\mathbf{i} - 0.5\mathbf{j})$.

The angle between the rope CD and the positive x axis is $(180° - 75°) = 105°$; the tension is:

$\mathbf{T}_2 = |\mathbf{T}_2|(\mathbf{i}\cos 105° + \mathbf{j}\sin 105°) = |\mathbf{T}_2|(-0.2588\mathbf{i} + 0.9659\mathbf{j})$

The equilibrium conditions are

$\sum \mathbf{F}_x = (0.866|\mathbf{N}_B| + 0.2588|\mathbf{T}_2|)\mathbf{i} = 0,$

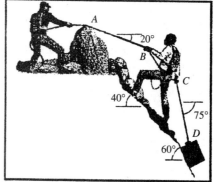

$\sum \mathbf{F}_y = (0.5|\mathbf{N}_B| + 0.9659|\mathbf{T}_2| - 215.8)\mathbf{j} = 0.$

Solve: $N_B = 57.8$ N, $|\mathbf{T}_2| = 193.5$ N.

Isolate the friend. The weight is

$\mathbf{W} = -(90)(9.81)\mathbf{j} = -882.9\mathbf{j}$ (N).

The angle between the normal force and the positive x axis is $(90° - 40°) = 50°$. The normal force is:

$\mathbf{N}_F = |\mathbf{N}_F|(0.6428\mathbf{i} + 0.7660\mathbf{j}).$

The angle between the lower rope and the x axis is $-75°$; the tension is

$\mathbf{T}_2 = |\mathbf{T}_2|(0.2588\mathbf{i} + 0.9659\mathbf{j}).$

The angle between the tension in the upper rope and the positive x axis is $(180° - 20°) = 160°$, the tension is

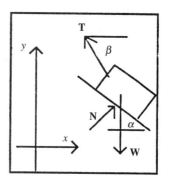

$\mathbf{T}_1 = |\mathbf{T}_1|(0.9397\mathbf{i} + 0.3420\mathbf{j}).$

The equilibrium conditions are

$\sum \mathbf{F} = \mathbf{W} + \mathbf{T}_1 + \mathbf{T}_2 + \mathbf{N}_F = 0.$

From which:

$\sum \mathbf{F}_x = (0.6428|\mathbf{N}_F| + 0.2588|\mathbf{T}_2| - 0.9397|\mathbf{T}_1|)\mathbf{i} = 0$

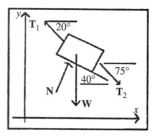

$\sum \mathbf{F}_y = (-0.7660|\mathbf{N}_F| - 0.9659|\mathbf{T}_2| + 0.3420|\mathbf{T}_1| - 882.9)\mathbf{j} = 0$

Solve, for $|T_2| = 193.5$ N. The result:

$\boxed{|\mathbf{N}_F| = 1051.6 \text{ N}}$, $\boxed{|\mathbf{T}_1| = 772.6 \text{ N}}$.

Problem 3.106 The small sphere of mass m is attached to a string of length L and rests on the smooth surface of a sphere of radius R. Determine the tension in the string in terms of m, L, h, and R.

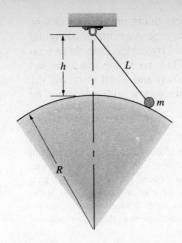

Solution: Isolate the small sphere. Use the law of sines to determine the interior angles that appear in the solution.

The weight is $\mathbf{W} = 0\mathbf{i} - mg\mathbf{j}$.

The angle between the normal force and the positive $\mathbf{x}$ axis is $(90° - \beta)$; the normal force is $\mathbf{N} = |\mathbf{N}|(\mathbf{i}\sin\beta + \mathbf{j}\cos\beta)$.

The angle between the string tension and the positive $\mathbf{x}$ axis is $(90° + \alpha)$ (use the rule of equality of opposite interior angles from geometry), hence the string tension is $\mathbf{T} = |\mathbf{T}|(-\mathbf{i}\sin\alpha + \mathbf{j}\cos\alpha)$.

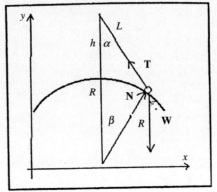

The equilibrium conditions are

$$\sum \mathbf{F} = \mathbf{T} + \mathbf{N} + \mathbf{W} = 0,$$

from which: $\sum \mathbf{F}_x = (|\mathbf{N}|\sin\beta - |\mathbf{T}|\sin\alpha)\mathbf{i} = 0$

$$\sum \mathbf{F}_y = (|\mathbf{N}|\cos\beta - |\mathbf{T}|\cos\alpha - mg)\mathbf{j} = 0$$

Solve: $|\mathbf{T}| = \left(\dfrac{mg\sin\beta}{\sin(\alpha + \beta)}\right)$.

From the law of sines for the triangle with sides R, $R + h$, and L,

$$\frac{(R + h)}{\sin(\alpha + \beta)} = \frac{L}{\sin\beta}.$$

Substitute into the tension:

$$\boxed{|\mathbf{T}| = \left(\frac{mgL}{(R + h)}\right)}$$

Problem 3.107 An engineer doing preliminary design studies for a new radio telescope envisions a triangular receiving platform suspended by cables from three equally spaced 40-m towers. The receiving platform has a mass of 20 Mg (megagrams) and is 10 m below the tops of the towers. What tension would the cables be subjected to?

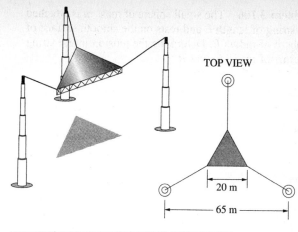

TOP VIEW

Solution: Isolate the platform. Choose a coordinate system with the origin at the center of the platform, with the z axis vertical, and the x,y axes as shown. Express the tensions in terms of unit vectors, and solve the equilibrium conditions. The cable connections at the platform are labeled a, b, c, and the cable connections at the towers are labeled A, B, C. The horizontal distance from the origin (center of the platform) to any tower is given by

$$L = \frac{65}{2\sin(60)} = 37.5 \text{ m}.$$

The coordinates of points A, B, C are

$A(37.5, 0, 10)$, $B(37.5\cos(120°), 37.5\sin(120°).10)$,

$C(37.5\cos(240°), 37.5\sin(240°), 10)$,

The vector locations are:

$\mathbf{r}_A = 37.5\mathbf{i} + 0\mathbf{j} + 10\mathbf{k}$, $\mathbf{r}_B = 18.764\mathbf{i} + 32.5\mathbf{j} + 10\mathbf{k}$,

$\mathbf{r}_C = 18.764\mathbf{i} + -32.5\mathbf{j} + 10\mathbf{k}$.

The distance from the origin to any cable connection on the platform is

$$d = \frac{20}{2\sin(60°)} = 11.547 \text{ m}.$$

The coordinates of the cable connections are

$a(11.547, 0, 0)$, $b(11.547\cos(120°), 11547\sin(120°), 0)$,

$c(11.547\cos(240°), 11.547\sin(240°), 0)$.

The vector locations of these points are,

$\mathbf{r}_a = 11.547\mathbf{i} + 0\mathbf{j} + 0\mathbf{k}$, $\mathbf{r}_b = 5.774\mathbf{i} + 10\mathbf{j} + 0\mathbf{k}$,

$\mathbf{r}_c = 5.774\mathbf{i} + 10\mathbf{j} + 0\mathbf{k}$.

The unit vector parallel to the tension acting between the points A, a in the direction of A is by definition

$$\mathbf{e}_{aA} = \frac{\mathbf{r}_A - \mathbf{r}_a}{|\mathbf{r}_A - \mathbf{r}_a|}.$$

Perform this operation for each of the unit vectors to obtain

$\mathbf{e}_{aA} = +0.9333\mathbf{i} + 0\mathbf{j} - 0.3592\mathbf{k}$

$\mathbf{e}_{bB} = -0.4667\mathbf{i} + 0.8082\mathbf{j} - 0.3592\mathbf{k}$

$\mathbf{e}_{cC} = -0.4667\mathbf{i} + 0.8082\mathbf{j} + 0.3592\mathbf{k}$

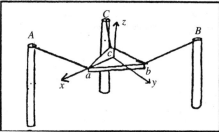

The tensions in the cables are expressed in terms of the unit vectors,

$$\mathbf{T}_{aA} = |\mathbf{T}_{aA}|\mathbf{e}_{aA}, \quad \mathbf{T}_{bB} = |\mathbf{T}_{bB}|\mathbf{e}_{bB}, \quad \mathbf{T}_{cC} = |\mathbf{T}_{cC}|\mathbf{e}_{cC}.$$

The weight is $\mathbf{W} = 0\mathbf{i} - 0\mathbf{j} - (20000)(9.81)\mathbf{k} = 0\mathbf{i} + 0\mathbf{j} - 196200\mathbf{k}$.

The equilibrium conditions are

$$\sum \mathbf{F} = 0 = \mathbf{T}_{aA} + \mathbf{T}_{bB} + \mathbf{T}_{cC} + \mathbf{W} = 0,$$

from which:

$$\sum \mathbf{F}_x = (0.9333|\mathbf{T}_{aA}| - 0.4666|\mathbf{T}_{bB}| - 0.4666|\mathbf{T}_{cC}|)\mathbf{i} = 0$$

$$\sum \mathbf{F}_y = (0|\mathbf{T}_{aA}| + 0.8082|\mathbf{T}_{bB}| - 0.8082|\mathbf{T}_{cC}|)\mathbf{j} = 0$$

$$\sum \mathbf{F}_z = (0.3592|\mathbf{T}_{aA}| - 0.3592|\mathbf{T}_{bB}|$$

$$+ 0.3592|\mathbf{T}_{cC}| - 196200|)\mathbf{k} = 0$$

The commercial package **TK Solver Plus** was used to solve these equations. The results:

$\boxed{|\mathbf{T}_{aA}| = 182.1 \text{ kN}}$, $\boxed{|\mathbf{T}_{bB}| = 182.1 \text{ kN}}$, $\boxed{|\mathbf{T}_{cC}| = 182.1 \text{ kN}}$.

Check: For this geometry, where from symmetry all cable tensions may be assumed to be the same, only the z-component of the equilibrium equations is required:

$$\sum F_z = 3|\mathbf{T}|\sin\theta - 196200 = 0,$$

where $\theta = \tan^{-1}\left(\frac{10}{37.5 - 11.547}\right) = 21.07°$,

from which each tension is $|\mathbf{T}| = 182.1$ kN.   *check.*

Problem 3.108 The metal disk A weighs 10 lb. It is held in place at the center of the smooth inclined surface by the strings AB and AC. What are the tensions in the strings?

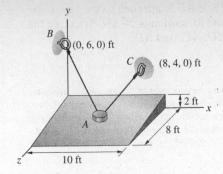

Solution: Isolate the disk, express the tensions in terms of the unit vectors, and solve the equilibrium equations. The coordinates of points A, B, C are: $A(5, 1, 4)$, $B(0, 6, 0)$, $C(8, 4, 0)$, where the coordinates of A are determined from the geometry of the inclined plane. The radius vectors corresponding to these coordinates are

$$\mathbf{r}_A = 5\mathbf{i} + 1\mathbf{j} + 4\mathbf{k}, \quad \mathbf{r}_B = 0\mathbf{i} + 6\mathbf{j} + 0\mathbf{k}, \quad \mathbf{r}_C = 8\mathbf{i} + 4\mathbf{j} + 0\mathbf{k}.$$

The unit vector $\mathbf{e}_{AB}$ is, by definition,

$$\mathbf{e}_{AB} = \frac{\mathbf{r}_B - \mathbf{r}_A}{|\mathbf{r}_B - \mathbf{r}_A|}.$$

Apply this to find the unit vectors parallel to the cables,

$$\mathbf{e}_{AB} = -0.6155\mathbf{i} + 0.6155\mathbf{j} - 0.4924\mathbf{k},$$

$$\mathbf{e}_{AC} = 0.5145\mathbf{i} + 0.5145\mathbf{j} - 0.6860\mathbf{k}.$$

The weight is $\mathbf{W} = 0\mathbf{i} - 10\mathbf{j} + 0\mathbf{k}$. The normal force acts normally to the inclined surface,

$$\mathbf{N} = |\mathbf{N}|(0\mathbf{i} + \mathbf{j}\cos\alpha + \mathbf{k}\sin\alpha$$

where $\tan\alpha = \left(\dfrac{2}{8}\right) - 0.25$, $\alpha = 14°$.

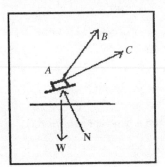

The tensions in the cables are expressed in terms of the unit vectors,

$$\mathbf{T}_{AB} = |\mathbf{T}_{AB}|\mathbf{e}_{AB}, \quad \mathbf{T}_{AC} = |\mathbf{T}_{AC}|\mathbf{e}_{AC}.$$

The equilibrium conditions are

$$\sum \mathbf{F} = 0 = \mathbf{T}_{AB} + \mathbf{T}_{AC} + \mathbf{W} + \mathbf{N} = 0.$$

From which

$$\sum \mathbf{F}_x = (-0.6155|\mathbf{T}_{AB}| + 0.5145|\mathbf{T}_{AC}|)\mathbf{i} = 0$$

$$\sum \mathbf{F}_y = (0.6155|\mathbf{T}_{AB}| + 0.5145|\mathbf{T}_{AC}| + 0.9703|\mathbf{N}| - 10)\mathbf{j} = 0$$

The solution to this set of simultaneous equations was obtained using the commercial program **TK Solver 2.** The result:

$$\boxed{|\mathbf{N}| = 8.35 \text{ lb}}, \quad \boxed{|\mathbf{T}_{AB}| = 1.54 \text{ lb}}, \quad \boxed{|\mathbf{T}_{AC}| = 1.85 \text{ lb}}.$$

Problem 3.109 Cable AB is attached to the top of the vertical 3-m post, and its tension is 50 kN. What are the tensions in cables AO, AC, and AD?

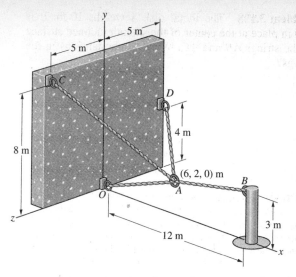

Solution: Get the unit vectors parallel to the cables using the coordinates of the end points. Express the tensions in terms of these unit vectors, and solve the equilibrium conditions. The coordinates of points A, B, C, D, O are found from the problem sketch: The coordinates of the points are $A(6, 2, 0)$, $B(12, 3, 0)$, $C(0, 8, 5)$, $D(0, 4, -5)$, $O(0, 0, 0)$.

The vector locations of these points are:

$$\mathbf{r}_A = 6\mathbf{i} + 2\mathbf{j} + 0\mathbf{k}, \quad \mathbf{r}_B = 12\mathbf{i} + 3\mathbf{j} + 0\mathbf{k}, \quad \mathbf{r}_C = 0\mathbf{i} + 8\mathbf{j} + 5\mathbf{k},$$

$$\mathbf{r}_D = 0\mathbf{i} + 4\mathbf{j} - 5\mathbf{k}, \quad \mathbf{r}_O = 0\mathbf{i} + 0\mathbf{j} + 0\mathbf{k}.$$

The unit vector parallel to the tension acting between the points A, B in the direction of B is by definition

$$\mathbf{e}_{AB} = \frac{\mathbf{r}_B - \mathbf{r}_A}{|\mathbf{r}_B - \mathbf{r}_A|}.$$

Perform this for each of the unit vectors

$$\mathbf{e}_{AB} = +0.9864\mathbf{i} + 0.1644\mathbf{j} + 0\mathbf{k}$$

$$\mathbf{e}_{AC} = -0.6092\mathbf{i} + 0.6092\mathbf{j} + 0.5077\mathbf{k}$$

$$\mathbf{e}_{AD} = -0.7442\mathbf{i} + 0.2481\mathbf{j} - 0.6202\mathbf{k}$$

$$\mathbf{e}_{AO} = -0.9487\mathbf{i} - 0.3162\mathbf{j} + 0\mathbf{k}$$

The tensions in the cables are expressed in terms of the unit vectors,

$$\mathbf{T}_{AB} = |\mathbf{T}_{AB}|\mathbf{e}_{AB} = 50\mathbf{e}_{AB}, \quad \mathbf{T}_{AC} = |\mathbf{T}_{AC}|\mathbf{e}_{AC},$$

$$\mathbf{T}_{AD} = |\mathbf{T}_{AD}|\mathbf{e}_{AD}, \quad \mathbf{T}_{AO} = |\mathbf{T}_{AO}|\mathbf{e}_{AO}.$$

The equilibrium conditions are

$$\sum \mathbf{F} = 0 = \mathbf{T}_{AB} + \mathbf{T}_{AC} + \mathbf{T}_{AD} + \mathbf{T}_{AO} = 0.$$

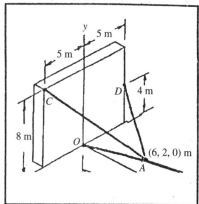

Substitute and collect like terms,

$$\sum F_x = (0.9864(50) - 0.6092|\mathbf{T}_{AC}| - 0.7422|\mathbf{T}_{AD}|$$

$$- 0.9487|\mathbf{T}_{AO}|)\mathbf{i} = 0$$

$$\sum F_y = (0.1644(50) + 0.6092|\mathbf{T}_{AC}| + 0.2481|\mathbf{T}_{AD}|$$

$$- 0.3162|\mathbf{T}_{AO}|)\mathbf{j} = 0$$

$$\sum F_z = (+0.5077|\mathbf{T}_{AC}| - 0.6202|\mathbf{T}_{AD}|)\mathbf{k} = 0.$$

This set of simultaneous equations in the unknown forces may be solved using any of several standard algorithms. The results are:

$$|\mathbf{T}_{AO}| = 43.3 \text{ kN}, \quad |\mathbf{T}_{AC}| = 6.8 \text{ kN}, \quad |\mathbf{T}_{AD}| = 5.5 \text{ kN}.$$

Problem 3.110 The 1350-kg car is at rest on a plane surface with its brakes locked. The unit vector $\mathbf{e}_n = 0.231\mathbf{i} + 0.923\mathbf{j} + 0.308\mathbf{k}$ is perpendicular to the surface. The y axis points upward. The direction cosines of the cable from A to B are $\cos\theta_x = -0.816$, $\cos\theta_y = 0.408$, $\cos\theta_z = -0.408$, and the tension in the cable is 1.2 kN. Determine the magnitudes of the normal and friction forces the car's wheels exert on the surface.

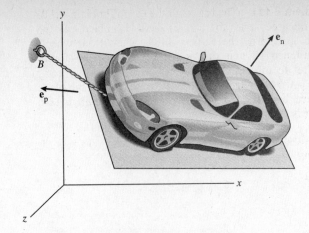

Solution: Assume that all forces act at the center of mass of the car. The vector equation of equilibrium for the car is

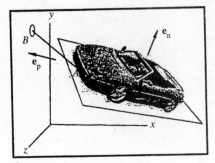

$$\mathbf{F}_S + \mathbf{T}_{AB} + \mathbf{W} = 0.$$

Writing these forces in terms of components, we have

$$\mathbf{W} = -mg\mathbf{j} = -(1350)(9.81) = -13240\mathbf{j} \text{ N},$$

$$\mathbf{F}_S = F_{Sx}\mathbf{i} + F_{Sy}\mathbf{j} + F_{Sz}\mathbf{k},$$

and $\mathbf{T}_{AB} = T_{AB}\mathbf{e}_{AB}$,

where

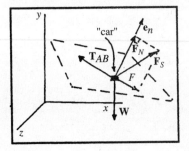

$$\mathbf{e}_{AB} = \cos\theta_x\mathbf{i} + \cos\theta_y\mathbf{j} + \cos\theta_z\mathbf{k} = -0.816\mathbf{i} + 0.408\mathbf{j} - 0.408\mathbf{k}.$$

Substituting these values into the equations of equilibrium and solving for the unknown components of $\mathbf{F}_S$, we get three scalar equations of equilibrium. These are:

$$F_{Sx} - T_{ABx} = 0, \quad F_{Sy} - T_{ABy} - W = 0,$$

and $F_{Sz} - T_{ABz} = 0.$

Substituting in the numbers and solving, we get

$$F_{Sx} = 979.2 \text{ N}, \quad F_{Sy} = 12,754 \text{ N},$$

and $F_{Sz} = 489.6$ N.

The next step is to find the component of $\mathbf{F}_S$ normal to the surface. This component is given by

$$F_N = \mathbf{F}_N \cdot \mathbf{e}_n = F_{Sx}\mathbf{e}_{ny} + F_{Sx}\mathbf{e}_{ny} + F_{Sz}\mathbf{e}_{nz}.$$

Substitution yields

$$\boxed{F_N = 12149 \text{ N}}.$$

From its components, the magnitude of $\mathbf{F}_S$ is $F_S = 12800$ N. Using the Pythagorean theorem, the friction force is

$$\boxed{f = \sqrt{F_S^2 - F_N^2} = 4033 \text{ N}.}$$

Problem 3.111 The brakes of the car in Problem 3.110 are released, and the car is held in place on the plane surface by the cable AB. The car's front wheels are aligned so that the tires exert no friction forces parallel to the car's longitudinal axis. The unit vector $\mathbf{e}_p = -0.941\mathbf{i} + 0.131\mathbf{j} + 0.314\mathbf{k}$ is parallel to the plane surface and aligned with the car's longitudinal axis. What is the tension in the cable?

Solution: Only the cable and the car's weight exert forces in the direction parallel to $\mathbf{e}_p$. Therefore

$\mathbf{e}_p \cdot (\mathbf{T} - mg\mathbf{j}) = 0$: $(-0.941\mathbf{i} + 0.131\mathbf{j} + 0.314\mathbf{k})$

$\cdot [T(-0.816\mathbf{i} + 0.408\mathbf{j} - 0.408\mathbf{k}) - mg\mathbf{j}] = 0$,

$(0.941)(0.816)T$

$\quad + (0.131)(0.408T - mg) + (0.314)(-0.408T) = 0.$

Solving, we obtain $T = 2.50$ kN.

Problem 4.1 Determine the moment of the 50-N force about (a) point A, (b) point B.

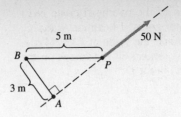

Solution: Use 2-dimensional moment strategy: determine normal distance to line of action D; calculate magnitude DF; determine sign.

(a) The perpendicular distance from A to line of action is $D = 0$, hence the moment $M_A = DF = 0$.

(b) The perpendicular distance from B to line of action is 3 m (the triangle is a 3-4-5 right triangle), and the action is counter clockwise, hence $M_B = +(3)(50) = +150$ N-m.

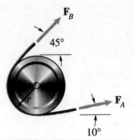

Problem 4.2 The radius of the pulley is $r = 0.2$ m and it is not free to rotate. The magnitudes of the forces are $|\mathbf{F}_A| = 140$ N and $|\mathbf{F}_B| = 180$ N.

(a) What is the moment about the center of the pulley due to the force $\mathbf{F}_A$?

(b) What is the sum of the moments about the center of the pulley due to the forces $\mathbf{F}_A$ and $\mathbf{F}_B$?

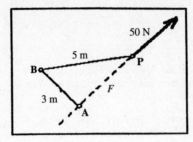

Solution:

$$+M_A = r|\mathbf{F}_A| = (0.2)140 \text{ N-m}$$

$$M_A = 28 \text{ N-m}$$

$$+M_B = -r|\mathbf{F}_B| = -(0.2)180$$

$$+M_B = -36 \text{ N-m}$$

$$+M_A + M_B = 28 - 36 = -8 \text{ Nm}$$

$$+(M_A + M_B) = -8 \text{ N-m}$$

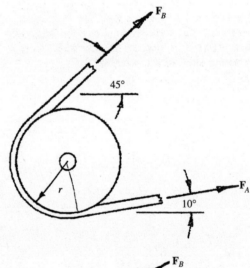

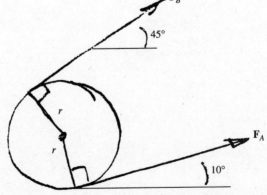

Problem 4.3 The wheels of the overhead crane exert downward forces on the horizontal I-beam at B and C. If the force at B is 40 kip and the force at C is 44 kip, determine the sum of the moments of the forces on the beam about (a) point A, (b) point D.

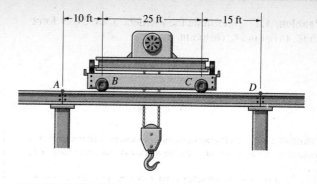

Solution: Use 2-dimensional moment strategy: determine normal distance to line of action D; calculate magnitude DF; determine sign. Add moments.

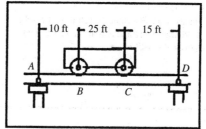

(a) The normal distances from A to the lines of action are $D_{AB} = 10$ ft, and $D_{AC} = 35$ ft. The moments are clockwise (negative). Hence,

$$\sum M_A = -10(40) - 35(44) = -1940 \text{ ft-kip}$$

(b) The normal distances from D to the lines of action are $D_{DB} = 40$ ft, and $D_{DC} = 15$ ft. The actions are positive; hence

$$\sum M_D = +(40)(40) + (15)(44) = 2260 \text{ ft-kip}$$

Problem 4.4 If you exert a 90-N force on the wrench in the direction shown, what moment do you exert about the center of the nut? Compare your answer to the moment exerted if you exert the 90-N force perpendicular to the shaft of the wrench.

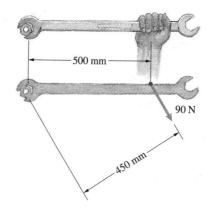

Solution:

$$M = d_1 \cdot F = (.45)\underset{\substack{\text{clockwise} \\ \text{for direction shown}}}{90 = 40.5 \text{ N-m}}$$

$$M_P = d_2 \cdot F = (0.5)\underset{\substack{\text{clockwise} \\ \text{for perpendicular force}}}{90 = 45 \text{ N-m}}$$

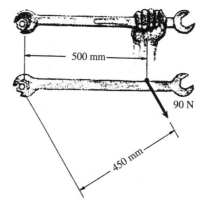

Problem 4.5 If you exert a force F on the wrench in the direction shown and a 50 N-m moment is required to loosen the nut, what force F must you apply?

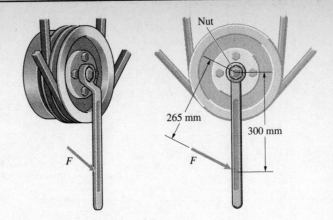

Solution: Use 2-dimensional moment strategy: determine normal distance to line of action D; calculate magnitude DF; determine sign. Solve for unknown force.

The normal distance from the nut center to the line of action is $D = 0.265$ m.

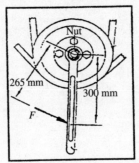

Thus to loosen the nut, $50 = D|\mathbf{F}| = 0.265|\mathbf{F}|$. Solve: $|\mathbf{F}| = \dfrac{50}{0.265} = 188.7$ N in the direction shown.

Problem 4.6 The support at the left end of the beam will fail if the moment about P due to the 20-kN force exceeds 35 kN-m. Based on this criterion, what is the maximum safe value of the angle α in the range $0 \le \alpha \le 90°$?

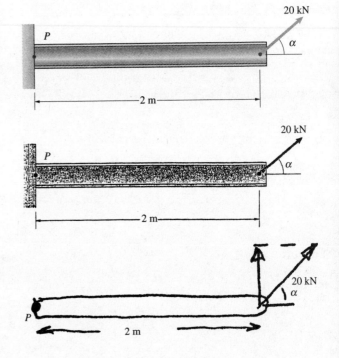

Solution:

$$M_P = dF \sin \alpha$$

$$M_P = (2)(20 \text{ kN}) \sin \alpha \text{ kN-m}$$

Set $\quad M_P = 35$ kN-m and solve

for $\quad \alpha \quad \sin \alpha = \dfrac{35}{40}$

$$\alpha_{\max} = 61.0°$$

Problem 4.7 The gears exert 200-N forces on each other at their point of contact.

(a) Determine the moment about A due to the force exerted on the left gear.
(b) Determine the moment about B due to the force exerted on the right gear.

Solution: Use 2-dimensional moment strategy: resolve the forces into components normal to the radii; calculate magnitude DF, where F is the normal component; determine sign. The angles between the forces and the x-axis are $(270 - 20) = 250°$ for the left gear and $(90 - 20) = 70°$ for the right gear. The forces are $F_{AY} = 200|\sin 250°| = 187.9$ N, and $F_{BY} = 200|\sin 70°| = 187.9$ N. These magnitudes are normal to the radii. The distances between the points A and B and their respective action lines are the radii. The radii are $R_A = 0.120$ m, and $R_B = 0.080$ m. The actions are negative. Thus

$$M_A = -0.120(|187.9|) = -22.55 \text{ N-m},$$

and $M_B = -0.080(|187.9|) = -15.0$ N-m.

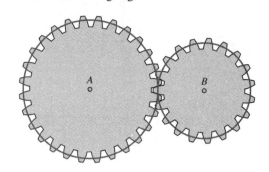

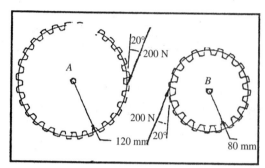

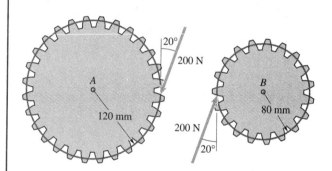

Problem 4.8 The support at the left end of the beam will fail if the moment about A of the 15-kN force F exceeds 18 kN-m. Based on this criterion, what is the largest allowable length of the beam?

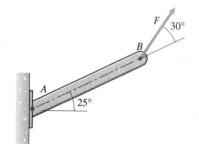

Solution:

$$M_A = L \cdot F \sin 30° = L\left(\frac{15}{2}\right)$$

$$M_A = 7.5 \text{ L kN} \cdot \text{m}$$

set $M_A = M_{A\text{max}} = 18 \text{ kN} \cdot \text{m} = 7.5 \text{ L}_{\text{max}}$

$L_{\text{max}} = 2.4$ m

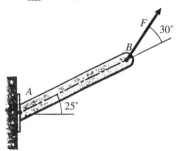

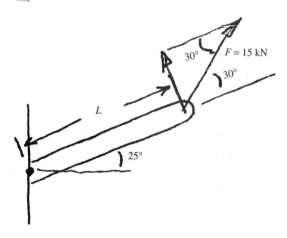

Problem 4.9 Determine the moment of the 80-lb force about P.

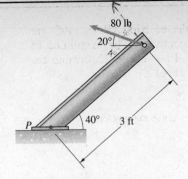

Solution: Use 2-dimensional moment strategy: resolve the force into a component normal to the beam; calculate magnitude DF, where F is the component normal to the beam; determine sign.

The angle between the beam and the force is $(180° - 40° - 20°) = 120°$. The component of the force normal to the beam is

$$F_N = |\mathbf{F}| \sin 120° = (80)(0.866) = 69.3 \text{ lb}.$$

The normal distance from P to the action line is the length of the beam, and the action is positive. Thus

$$M = (3)(69.3) = 207.8 \text{ ft-lb}$$

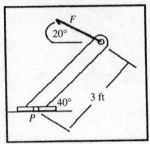

Problem 4.10 The 20-N force F exerts a 20 N-m counterclockwise moment about P.

(a) What is the perpendicular distance from P to the line of action of F?

(b) What is the angle α?

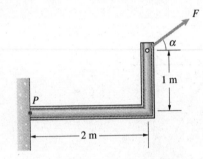

Solution: Use 2-dimensional moment strategy: determine normal distance to line of action D; calculate magnitude DF; determine sign.

(a) The moment is $|\mathbf{M}| = 20 = 20\,D$, from which the perpendicular distance is $D = \dfrac{20 \text{ N-m}}{20 \text{ N}} = 1 \text{ m}$

(b) The angle between the force and the line from P is $(\alpha - \beta)$, where $\beta = \tan^{-1}\left(\frac{1}{2}\right) = 26.6°$. The component of the force normal to the line from P is $F_N = |\mathbf{F}| \sin(\alpha - \beta)$, thus $M = 20 = \sqrt{1^2 + 2^2}|\mathbf{F}| \sin(\alpha - \beta) = \sqrt{5}(20) \sin(\alpha - \beta)$. Solve: $\alpha = \beta + \sin^{-1}(0.4472)$. Thus $\alpha = 26.6° + 26.6° = 53.1°$, $\alpha = 26.6° + 153.4° = 180°$.

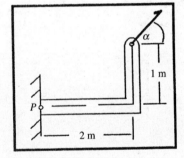

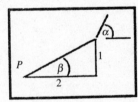

Problem 4.11 The lengths of bars AB and AC are 350 mm and 450 mm respectively. The magnitude of the vertical force at A is $|\mathbf{F}| = 600$ N. Determine the moment of $\mathbf{F}$ about B and about C.

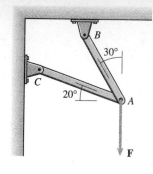

Solution: The geometry is the key to this problem

$$\sin 30° = \frac{d_1}{0.35 \text{ m}}$$

$$d_1 = 0.175 \text{ m}$$

$$\cos 20° = \frac{d_2}{0.45 \text{ m}}$$

$$d_2 = 0.423 \text{ m}$$

$\curvearrowleft +M_B = -d_1 F = -(0.175)(600)^-$

$\curvearrowleft +M_B = -105$ N-m $= 105$ N-m clockwise

$\curvearrowleft +M_C = -d_2 F = -(0.423)(600)$ N-m

$\curvearrowleft +M_C = -254$ N-m

$\qquad = 254$ N-m clockwise

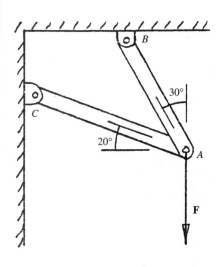

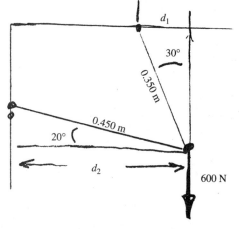

189

Problem 4.12 Two students attempt to loosen a lug nut with a lug wrench. One of the students exerts the two 60-lb forces; the other, having to reach around his friend, can only exert the two 30-lb forces. What torque (moment) do they exert on the nut?

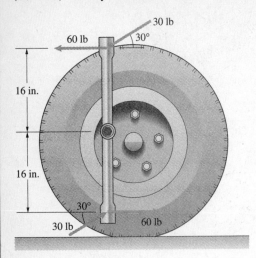

Solution: Determine the normal distance from line of action of the normal force to the lug nut. Calculate moment; determine sign. The two 60 lb forces act in a positive direction at a distance of 16 in from the lug nut. The moment due to the 60 lb forces is

$$M_{60} = 2(60 \text{ lb})(16 \text{ in})\left(\frac{1 \text{ ft}}{12 \text{ in}}\right) = 160 \text{ ft-lb}.$$

The normal component of the 30 lb force is $F_{30} = 30\cos 30° = 26$ lb. This force acts at a distance of 16 in from the lug nut. The action is positive. The moment due to the 30 lb forces is

$$M_{30} = 2(26 \text{ lb})(16 \text{ in})\left(\frac{1 \text{ ft}}{12 \text{ in}}\right) = 69.3 \text{ ft-lb}.$$

The total moment is $M_T = 69.3 + 160 = 229.3$ ft-lb

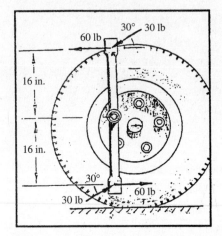

Problem 4.13 The two students described in Problem 4.12, having failed to loosen the lug nut, try a different tactic. One of them stands on the lug wrench, exerting a 150-lb force on it. The other pulls on the wrench with the force F. If a torque of 245 ft-lb is required to loosen the lug nut, what force F must the student exert?

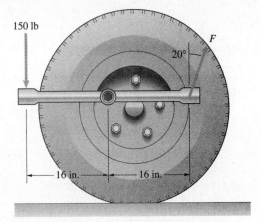

Solution: The normal component of the force is

$$F_N = |\mathbf{F}|\cos 20° = 0.9397|\mathbf{F}|$$

The total moment is

$$M = (150)(16 \text{ in})\left(\frac{1 \text{ ft}}{12 \text{ in}}\right) + (|\mathbf{F}|)(0.9397)(16 \text{ in})\left(\frac{1 \text{ ft}}{12 \text{ in}}\right)$$

$$= 200 + 1.253|\mathbf{F}| \text{ ft-lb}.$$

If the moment required is 245 ft-lb, then

$$|\mathbf{F}| = \left(\frac{1}{1.253}\right)(245 - 200) = 35.9 \text{ lb}$$

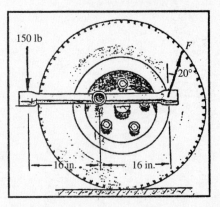

Problem 4.14 The moment exerted about point E by the weight is 299 in-lb. What moment does the weight exert about point S?

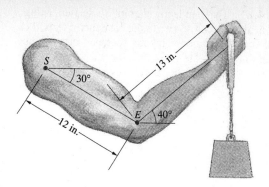

Solution: The key is the geometry

From trigonometry,

$$\cos 40° = \frac{d_2}{13 \text{ in}}, \quad \cos 30° = \frac{d_1}{12 \text{ in}}$$

Thus $d_1 = (12 \text{ in}) \cos 30°$

$\quad d_1 = 10.39''$

and $d_2 = (13 \text{ in}) \cos 40°$

$\quad d_2 = 9.96''$

We are given that

$299 \text{ in-lb} = d_2 W = 9.96 \, W$

$\quad W = 30.0 \text{ lb}$

Now,

$M_s = (d_1 + d_2)W$

$M_s = (20.35)(30.0)$

$M_s = 611$ in-lb clockwise

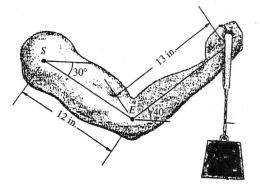

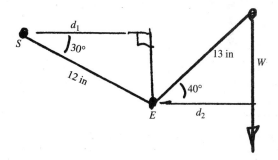

Problem 4.15 Three forces act on the square plate. Determine the sum of the moments of the forces (a) about A, (b) about B, (c) about C.

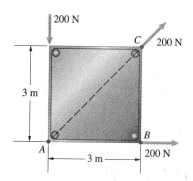

Solution: Determine the perpendicular distance between the points and the lines of action. Determine sign, and calculate moment. (a) The distances from point A to the lines of action is zero, hence the moment about A is $M_A = 0$. (b) The perpendicular distances of the lines of action from B are: 3 m for the force through A, with a positive action, and for the force through C, $D_C = \left(\frac{1}{2}\right)\sqrt{3^2 + 3^2} = 2.12$ m with a negative action. The moment about B is $M_B = (3)(200) - 2.12(200) = 175.74$ N-m (c) The distance of the force through A from C is 3 m, with a positive action, and the distance of the force through B from C is 3 m, with a positive action. The moment about C is $M_C = 2(3)(200) = 1200$ N-m.

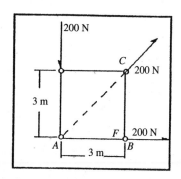

191

Problem 4.16 Determine the sum of moments of the three forces about (a) point A, (b) point B, (c) point C.

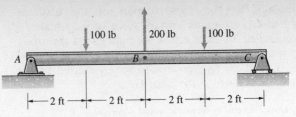

Solution:

(a) The sum of the moments about A:

$$\sum M_A = -(2)(100) + (4)(200) - (6)(100) = 0.$$

(b) The sum of the moments about B:

$$\sum M_B = +(2)(100) - (2)(100) = 0$$

(c) The sum of the moments about C:

$$\sum M_C = +(6)(100) - (4)(200) + (2)(100) = 0.$$

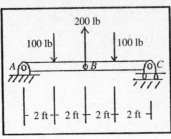

Problem 4.17 Determine the sum of the moments of the five forces acting on the Howe truss about point A.

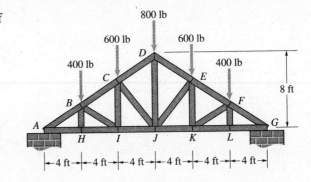

Solution: All of the moments about A are clockwise (negative). The equation for the sum of the moments about A in units of ft-lb is given by:

$$\sum M_A = -4(400) - 8(600) - 12(800) - 16(600) - 20(400)$$

or $\boxed{\sum M_A = -33,600 \text{ ft-lb.}}$

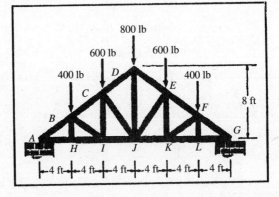

Problem 4.18 The right support of the truss in Problem 4.17 exerts an upward force of magnitude G. (Assume that the force acts at the right end of the truss). The sum of the moments about A due to the upward force G and the five downward forces exerted on the truss is zero. What is the force G?

Solution: Summing moments around A, we get (ALL UNITS IN lbs)

$$+M_A = -(4)(400) - (8)(600) - (12)(800)$$

$$- (16)(600) - (20)(400) + 24\,G = 0$$

Solving, we get

$$G = 1400 \text{ lbs}$$

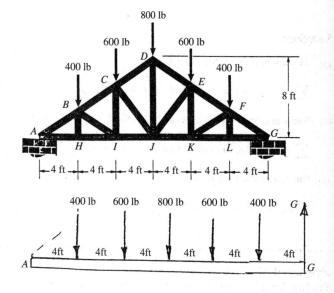

Problem 4.19 The sum of the forces F_1 and F_2 is 250 N and the sum of the moments of F_1 and F_2 about B is 700 N-m. What are F_1 and F_2?

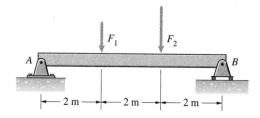

Solution:

$$\sum F = F_1 + F_2 = 250 \text{ N}$$

$$+\sum M_B = 4F_1 + 2F_2 = 700 \text{ N-m}$$

We have two equations in two unknowns. Solving, we have

$$F_1 = 100 \text{ N}, \quad F_2 = 150 \text{ N}$$

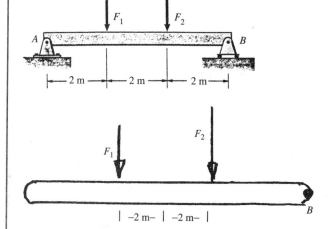

Problem 4.20 Consider the beam shown in Problem 4.19. If the two forces exert a 140 kN-m clockwise moment about A and a 20 kN-m clockwise moment about B, what are F_1 and F_2?

Solution: Sum of the moments about A:

$$\sum M_{(ptA)} = -2F_1 - 4F_2 = -140 \text{ kN-m}.$$

Sum of the moments about B:

$$\sum M_{(ptB)} = 4F_1 + 2F_2 = -20 \text{ kN-m}.$$

Solving these equations, we obtain

$$F_1 = -30 \text{ kN}, \quad F_2 = 50 \text{ kN}.$$

Problem 4.21 The force $|\mathbf{F}| = 140$ lb. The vector sum of the forces acting on the beam is zero, and the sum of the moments about the left end of the beam is zero.

(a) What are the forces A_x, A_y, and B?
(b) What is the sum of the moments about the right end of the beam?

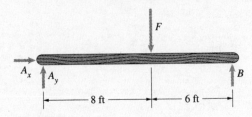

Solution: The forces are:

$$\mathbf{A}_X = |\mathbf{A}_X|(1\mathbf{i} + 0\mathbf{j}), \quad \mathbf{A}_Y = |\mathbf{A}_Y|(0\mathbf{i} + 1\mathbf{j})$$

$$\mathbf{B} = |\mathbf{B}|(0\mathbf{i} + 1\mathbf{j}), \quad \mathbf{F} = 140(0\mathbf{i} - 1\mathbf{j}).$$

(a) The sum of the forces: $\sum \mathbf{F} = \mathbf{A}_X + \mathbf{A}_Y + \mathbf{B} + \mathbf{F} = 0$. Substitute and collect like terms:

$$\sum \mathbf{F}_X = (|\mathbf{A}_X|)\mathbf{i} = 0.$$

$$\sum \mathbf{F}_Y = (\mathbf{A}_Y + \mathbf{B} - 140)\mathbf{j} = 0.$$

It follows that $|\mathbf{A}_X| = 0$.

The sum of the moments about the left end is

$$\sum M = (+0|\mathbf{A}_Y| - 140(8) + |\mathbf{B}|14) = 0.$$

Solve: $|\mathbf{B}| = 80$ lb, from which the sum of forces equation yields $|\mathbf{A}_Y| = 60$ lb

(b) The moments about the right end are:

$$\sum M = (+6)((140)) - (14)(60) = 0$$

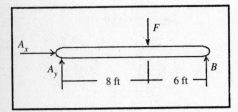

Problem 4.22 The vector sum of the three forces is zero, and the sum of the moments of the three forces about A is zero.

(a) What are F_A and F_B?
(b) What is the sum of the moments of the three forces about B?

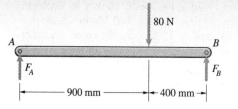

80 N

A B

F_A F_B

— 900 mm — — 400 mm —

Solution: The forces are:

$$\mathbf{F}_A = |\mathbf{F}_A|(0\mathbf{i} + 1\mathbf{j}), \mathbf{F}_B = |\mathbf{F}_B|(0\mathbf{i} + 1\mathbf{j}),$$

and $\mathbf{F} = 80(0\mathbf{i} - 1\mathbf{j})$.

The sum of the forces is:

$$\sum \mathbf{F} = \mathbf{F}_A + \mathbf{F}_B + \mathbf{F} = 0,$$

from which

$$\sum \mathbf{F}_Y = (|\mathbf{F}_A| + |\mathbf{F}_B| - 80)\mathbf{j} = 0.$$

The sum of the moments:

$$\sum M_A = -(0.9)(80) + (1.3)(|\mathbf{F}_B|) = 0.$$

(a) Solve these two equations to obtain: $|\mathbf{F}_B| = 55.4$ N, and $|\mathbf{F}_A| = 24.6$ N (b) The moments about B:

$$\sum M_B = (80)(0.4) - (1.3)|\mathbf{F}_A| = 0$$

Problem 4.23 The weights (in ounces) of fish A, B, and C are 2.7, 8.1, and 2.1, respectively. The sum of the moments due to the weights of the fish about the point where the mobile is attached to the ceiling is zero. What is the weight of fish D?

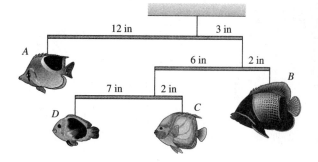

12 in   3 in

A 6 in   2 in

           B

7 in   2 in

D C

Solution:

$$\sum M_O = (12)(2.7) - 3(10.2 + D)$$

Solving $D = 0.6$ oz

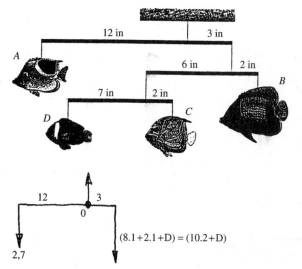

12 in   3 in

A 6 in   2 in

           B

7 in   2 in

D C

12   3
0
2,7

$(8.1 + 2.1 + D) = (10.2 + D)$

Problem 4.24 The weight $W = 1.2$ kN. The sum of the moments about A due to W and the force exerted at the end of the bar by the rope is zero. What is the tension in the rope?

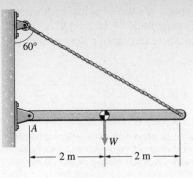

Solution:

$$\circlearrowleft + \sum M_A = -(2)(1.2) + 4(T\sin 30°) = 0$$

$$-2.4 + 2T = 0$$

$$T = 1.2 \text{ kN}$$

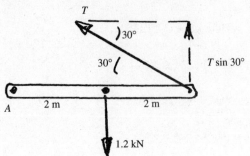

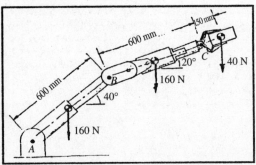

Problem 4.25 The 160-N weights of the arms AB and BC of the robotic manipulator act at their midpoints. Determine the sum of the moments of the three weights about A.

Solution: The strategy is to find the perpendicular distance from the points to the line of action of the forces, and determine the sum of the moments, using the appropriate sign of the action.

The distance from A to the action line of the weight of the arm AB is:

$$d_{AB} = (0.300)\cos 40° = 0.2298 \text{ m}$$

The distance from A to the action line of the weight of the arm BC is

$$d_{BC} = (0.600)(\cos 40°) + (0.300)(\cos 20°) = 0.7415 \text{ m}.$$

The distance from A to the line of action of the force is

$$d_F = (0.600)(\cos 40°) + (0.600)(\cos 20°) + (0.150)(\cos 20°)$$

$$= 1.1644 \text{ m}.$$

The sum of the moments about A is

$$\sum M_A = -d_{AB}(160) - d_{BC}(160) - d_F(40) = -202 \text{ N-m}$$

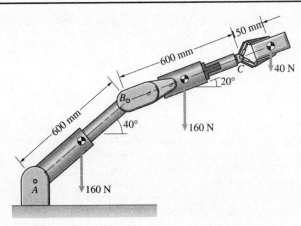

Problem 4.26 The space shuttle's attitude thrusters exert two forces of magnitude $F = 7.70$ kN. What moment do the thrusters exert about the center of mass G?

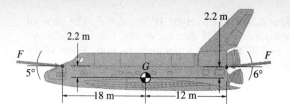

Solution: The key to this problem is getting the geometry correct. The simplest way to do this is to break each force into components parallel and perpendicular to the axis of the shuttle and then to sum the moments of the components. (This will become much easier in the next section)

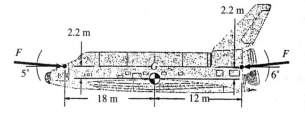

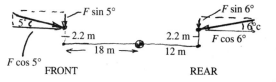

$+M_{\text{FRONT}_\oplus} = (18)F \sin 5° - (2.2)F \cos 5°$

$+M_{\text{REAR}_\oplus} = (2.2)F \cos 6° - (12)F \sin 6°$

$+M_{\text{TOTAL}} = M_{\text{FRONT}} + M_{\text{REAR}}$

$+M_{\text{TOTAL}} = -4.80 + 7.19$ N-m

$+M_{\text{TOTAL}} = 2.39$ N-m

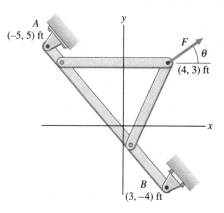

Problem 4.27 The force F exerts a 200 ft-lb counterclockwise moment about A and a 100 ft-lb clockwise moment about B. What are F and θ?

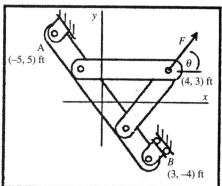

Solution: The strategy is to resolve $\mathbf{F}$ into x- and y-components, and compute the perpendicular distance to each component from A and B. The components of $\mathbf{F}$ are: $\mathbf{F} = \mathbf{i}F_X + \mathbf{j}F_Y$. The vector from A to the point of application is:

$\mathbf{r}_{AF} = (4 - (-5))\mathbf{i} + (3 - 5)\mathbf{j} = 9\mathbf{i} - 2\mathbf{j}.$

The perpendicular distances are $d_{AX} = 9$ ft, and $d_{AY} = 2$ ft, and the actions are positive. The moment about A is $M_A = (9)F_Y + (2)F_X = 200$ ft-lb. The vector from B to the point of application is $\mathbf{r}_{BF} = (4 - 3)\mathbf{i} + (3 - (-4))\mathbf{j} = 1\mathbf{i} + 7\mathbf{j}$; the distances $d_{BX} = 1$ ft and $d_{BY} = 7$ ft, the action of F_Y is positive and the action of F_X is negative. The moment about B is $M_B = (1)F_Y - (7)F_X = -100$ ft-lb. The two simultaneous equations have solution: $F_Y = 18.46$ lb and $F_X = 16.92$ lb. Take the ratio to find the angle:

$\theta = \tan^{-1}\left(\frac{F_Y}{F_X}\right) = \tan^{-1}\left(\frac{18.46}{16.92}\right) = \tan^{-1}(1.091) = 47.5°.$

From the Pythagorean theorem

$|\mathbf{F}| = \sqrt{F_Y^2 + F_X^2} = \sqrt{18.46^2 + 16.92^2} = 25.04$ lb

Problem 4.28 Five forces act on a link in the gear-shifting mechanism of a lawn mower. The vector sum of the five forces on the bar is zero. The sum of their moments about the point where the forces A_x and A_y act is zero.

(a) Determine the forces A_x, A_y, and B.
(b) Determine the sum of the moments of the forces about the point where the force B acts.

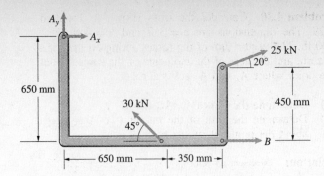

Solution: The strategy is to resolve the forces into x- and y-components, determine the perpendicular distances from B to the line of action, determine the sign of the action, and compute the moments.

The angles are measured counterclockwise from the x-axis. The forces are

$$\mathbf{F}_2 = 30(\mathbf{i}\cos 135° + \mathbf{j}\sin 135°) = -21.21\mathbf{i} + 21.21\mathbf{j}$$

$$\mathbf{F}_1 = 25(\mathbf{i}\cos 20° + \mathbf{j}\sin 20°) = 23.50\mathbf{i} + 8.55\mathbf{j}.$$

(a) The sum of the forces is

$$\sum \mathbf{F} = \mathbf{A} + \mathbf{B} + \mathbf{F}_1 + \mathbf{F}_2 = 0.$$

Substituting:

$$\sum \mathbf{F}_X = (A_X + B_X + 23.5 - 21.2)\mathbf{i} = 0,$$

and $\sum \mathbf{F}_Y = (A_Y + 21.2 + 8.55)\mathbf{j} = 0.$

Solve the second equation: $A_Y = -29.76$ kN. The distances of the forces from A are: the triangle has equal base and altitude, hence the angle is $45°$, so that the line of action of $\mathbf{F}_1$ passes through A. The distance to the line of action of $\mathbf{B}$ is 0.65 m, with a positive action. The distance to the line of action of the y-component of $\mathbf{F}_2$ is $(0.650 + 0.350) = 1$ m, and the action is positive. The distance to the line of action of the x-component of $\mathbf{F}_2$ is $(0.650 - 0.450) = 0.200$ m, and the action is positive. The moment about A is

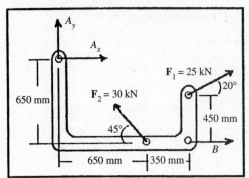

$$\sum M_A = (8.55)(1) + (23.5)(0.2) + (B_X)(0.65) = 0.$$

Solve: $B_X = -20.38$ kN. Substitute into the force equation to obtain $A_X = 18.09$ kN

(b) The distance from B to the line of action of the y-component of $\mathbf{F}_1$ is 0.350 m, and the action is negative. The distance from B to the line of action of A_X is 0.650 m and the action is negative. The distance from B to the line of action of A_Y is 1 m and the action is positive. The distance from B to the line of action of the x-component of $\mathbf{F}_2$ is 0.450 m and the action is negative. The sum of the moments about B:

$$\sum M_B = -(0.350)(21.21) - (0.650)(18.09)$$

$$+ (1)(29.76) - (0.450)(23.5) = 0$$

Problem 4.29 Five forces act on a model truss built by a civil engineering student as part of a design project. The dimensions are $b = 300$ mm and $h = 400$ mm; $F = 100$ N. The sum of the moments of the forces about the point where A_x and A_y act is zero. If the weight of the truss is negligible, what is the force B?

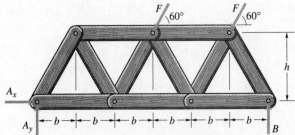

Solution: The x- and y-components of the force $\mathbf{F}$ are

$$\mathbf{F} = -|\mathbf{F}|(\mathbf{i}\cos 60° + \mathbf{j}\sin 60°) = -|\mathbf{F}|(0.5\mathbf{i} + 0.866\mathbf{j}).$$

The distance from A to the x-component is h and the action is positive. The distances to the y-component are $3b$ and $5b$. The distance to B is $6b$. The sum of the moments about A is

$$\sum M_A = 2|\mathbf{F}|(0.5)(h) - 3b|\mathbf{F}|(0.866) - 5b|\mathbf{F}|(0.866) + 6bB = 0.$$

Substitute and solve: $B = \dfrac{1.6784|\mathbf{F}|}{1.8} = 93.2$ N

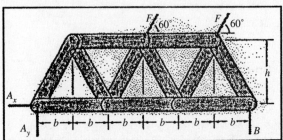

Problem 4.30   Consider the truss shown in Problem 4.29. The dimensions are $b = 3$ ft and $h = 4$ ft; $F = 300$ lb. The vector sum of the forces acting on the truss is zero, and the sum of the moments of the forces about the point where A_x and A_y act is zero.

(a)   Determine the forces A_x, A_y, and B.
(b)   Determine the sum of the moments of the forces about the point where the force B acts.

Solution: The forces are resolved into x- and y-components:

$$\mathbf{F} = -300(\mathbf{i}\cos 60° + \mathbf{j}\sin 60°) = -150\mathbf{i} - 259.8\mathbf{j}.$$

(a)   The sum of the forces:

$$\sum \mathbf{F} = 2\mathbf{F} + \mathbf{A} + \mathbf{B} = 0.$$

The x- and y-components:

$$\sum \mathbf{F}_x = (A_x - 300)\mathbf{i} = 0,$$

$$\sum \mathbf{F}_y = (-519.6 + A_y + B)\mathbf{j} = 0.$$

Solve the first: $A_x = 300$ lb. The distance from point A to the x-components of the forces is h, and the action is positive. The distances between the point A and the lines of action of the y-components of the forces are $3b$ and $5b$. The actions are negative. The distance to the line of action of the force B is $6b$. The action is positive. The sum of moments about point A is

$$\sum M_A = 2(150)\,h - 3b(259.8) - 5b(259.8) + 6b\,B = 0.$$

Substitute and solve: $B = 279.7$ lb. Substitute this value into the force equation and solve: $A_x = 519.6 - 279.7 = 239.9$ lb

(b)   The distances from B and the line of action of A_Y is $6b$ and the action is negative. The distance between B and the x-component of the forces is h and the action is positive. The distance between B and the y-components of the forces is b and $3b$, and the action is positive. The sum of the moments about B:

$$\sum M_B = -6b(239.9) + 2(150)\,h + b(259.8) + 3b(259.8) = 0$$

Problem 4.31   The mass $m = 70$ kg. What is the moment about A due to the force exerted on the beam at B by the cable?

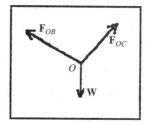

Solution: The strategy is to resolve the force at B into components parallel to and normal to the beam, and solve for the moment using the normal component of the force. The force at B is to be determined from the equilibrium conditions on the cable juncture O. Angles are measured from the positive x-axis. The forces at the cable juncture are:

$$\mathbf{F}_{OB} = |\mathbf{F}_{OB}|(\mathbf{i}\cos 150° + \mathbf{j}\sin 150°) = |\mathbf{F}_{OB}|(-0.866\mathbf{i} + 0.5\mathbf{j})$$

$$\mathbf{F}_{OC} = |\mathbf{F}_{OC}|(\mathbf{i}\cos 45° + \mathbf{j}\sin 45°) = |\mathbf{F}_{OC}|(0.707\mathbf{i} + 0.707\mathbf{j}).$$

$$\mathbf{W} = (70)(9.81)(0\mathbf{i} - 1\mathbf{j}) = -686.7\mathbf{j} \text{ (N)}.$$

The equilibrium conditions are:

$$\sum \mathbf{F}_x = (-0.866|\mathbf{F}_{OB}| + 0.7070|\mathbf{F}_{OC}|)\mathbf{i} = 0$$

$$\sum \mathbf{F}_Y = (0.500|\mathbf{F}_{OB}| + (.707|\mathbf{F}_{OC}|) - 686.7)\mathbf{j} = 0.$$

Solve: $|\mathbf{F}_{OB}| = 502.70$ N. This is used to resolve the cable tension at B:
$\mathbf{F}_B = 502.7(\mathbf{i}\cos 330° + \mathbf{j}\sin 330°) = 435.4\mathbf{i} - 251.4\mathbf{j}$. The distance from A to the action line of the y-component at B is 3 m, and the action is negative. The x-component at passes through A, so that the action line distance is zero. The moment at A is $M_A = -3(251.4) = -754.0$ N-m

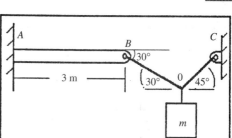

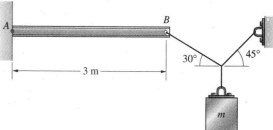

Problem 4.32 Consider the system shown in Problem 4.31. The beam will collapse at A if the magnitude of the moment about A due to the force exerted on the beam at B by the cable exceeds 2 kN-m. What is the largest mass m that can be suspended?

Solution: The strategy is to determine the tension in the cable at B that corresponds to the 2 kN-m moment at A, and then determine the mass that will exert this tension. From the solution to Problem 4.31, the y-component of the cable tension at B that corresponds to the 2 kN moment is

$$-0.5|\mathbf{F}_{OB}| = \frac{-2000 \text{ N-m}}{3 \text{ m}} = 666.67 \text{ N},$$

from which $|\mathbf{F}_{OB}| = 1333$ N. The two equilibrium equations for the cable juncture O in the solution for Problem 4.31 are:

$$\sum \mathbf{F}_X = (-0.866|\mathbf{F}_{OB}| + 0.7070|\mathbf{F}_{OC}|)\mathbf{i} = 0$$

$$\sum \mathbf{F}_Y = (0.500|\mathbf{F}_{OB}| + (.707|\mathbf{F}_{OC}|) - |\mathbf{W}|)\mathbf{j} = 0.$$

Substitute the value of $|\mathbf{F}_{OB}|$, and rewrite these in the form of simultaneous equations in two unknowns:

$$(0.707|\mathbf{F}_{OC}| + 0|\mathbf{W}|) = 1154.3$$

$$(0.707|\mathbf{F}_{OC}| - |\mathbf{W}|) = -666.7.$$

Solve: $|\mathbf{W}| = 1821$ N, from which: $m = \dfrac{1821}{9.81} = 185.66$ kg

---

Problem 4.33 The bar AB exerts a force at B that helps support the vertical retaining wall. The force is parallel to the bar. The civil engineer wants the bar to exert a 38 kN-m moment about O. What is the magnitude of the force the bar must exert?

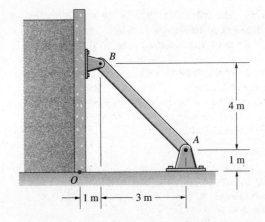

Solution: The strategy is to resolve the force at B into components parallel to and normal to the wall, determine the perpendicular distance from O to the line of action, and compute the moment about O in terms of the magnitude of the force exerted by the bar.

By inspection, the bar forms a 3, 4, 5 triangle. The angle the bar makes with the horizontal is $\cos \theta = \frac{3}{5} = 0.600$, and $\sin \theta = \frac{4}{5} = 0.800$. The force at B is $\mathbf{F}_B = |\mathbf{F}_B|(-0.600\mathbf{i} + 0.800\mathbf{j})$. The perpendicular distance from O to the line of action of the x-component is $(4 + 1) = 5$ m, and the action is positive. The distance from O to the line of action of the y-component is 1 m, and the action is positive. The moment about O is $\sum M_O = 5(0.600)|\mathbf{F}_B| + 1(0.800)|\mathbf{F}_B| = 3.8|\mathbf{F}_B| = 38$ kN, from which $|\mathbf{F}_B| = 10$ kN

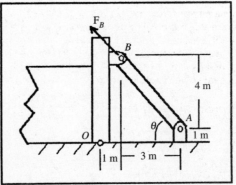

Problem 4.34 A contestant in a fly-casting contest snags his line in some grass. If the tension in the line is 5 lb, what moment does the force exerted on the rod by the line exert about point H, where he holds the rod?

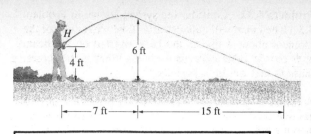

Solution: The strategy is to resolve the line tension into a component normal to the rod; use the length from H to tip as the perpendicular distance; determine the sign of the action, and compute the moment.

The line and rod form two right triangles, as shown in the sketch. The angles are:

$$\alpha = \tan^{-1}\left(\frac{2}{7}\right) = 15.95°$$

$$\beta = \tan^{-1}\left(\frac{6}{15}\right) = 21.8°.$$

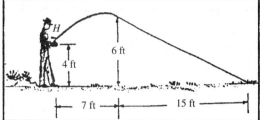

The angle between the perpendicular distance line and the fishing line is $\theta = \alpha + \beta = 37.7°$. The force normal to the distance line is $F = 5(\sin 37.7°) = 3.061$ lb. The distance is $d = \sqrt{2^2 + 7^2} = 7.28$ ft, and the action is negative. The moment about H is $M_H = -7.28(3.061) = -22.3$ ft-lb *Check:* The tension can be resolved into x and y components,

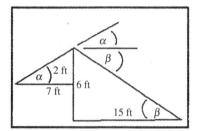

$$F_x = F\cos\beta = 4.642 \text{ lb}, \quad F_y = -F\sin\beta = -1.857 \text{ lb.}$$

The moment is

$$M = -2F_x + 7F_y = -22.28 = -22.3 \text{ ft-lb. } \textit{check.}$$

Problem 4.35 The cables AB and AC help support the tower. The tension in cable AB is 5 kN. The points A, B, C, and O are contained in the same vertical plane.

(a) What is the moment about O due to the force exerted on the tower by cable AB?
(b) If the sum of the moments about O due to the forces exerted on the tower by the two cables is zero, what is the tension in cable AC?

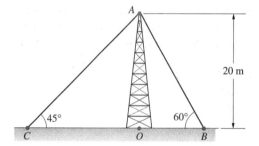

Solution: The strategy is to resolve the cable tensions into components normal to the vertical line through OA; use the height of the tower as the perpendicular distance; determine the sign of the action, and compute the moments.

(a) The component normal to the line OA is $F_{BN} = 5(\cos 60°) = 2.5$ kN. The action is negative. The moment about O is $M_{OA} = -2.5(20) = -50$ kN-m
(b) By a similar process, the normal component of the tension in the cable AC is $F_{CN} = |\mathbf{F}_C|\cos 45° = 0.707|\mathbf{F}_C|$. The action is positive. If the sum of the moments is zero,

$$\sum M_O = (0.707(20)|\mathbf{F}_C| - 50) = 0,$$

from which

$$|\mathbf{F}_C| = \frac{50 \text{ kN m}}{(0.707)(20 \text{ m})} = 3.54 \text{ kN}$$

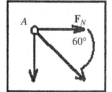
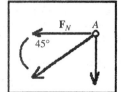

Problem 4.36 The cable from B to A (the sailboat's forestay) exerts a 230-N force at B. The cable from B to C (the backstay) exerts a 660-N force at B. The bottom of the sailboat's mast is located at $x = 4$ m, $y = 0$. What is the sum of the moments about the bottom of the mast due to the forces exerted at B by the forestay and backstay?

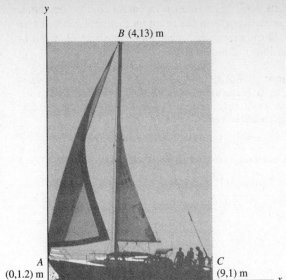

Solution: Triangle ABP

$$\tan\alpha = \frac{4}{11.8}, \quad \alpha = 18.73°$$

Triangle BCQ

$$\tan\beta = \frac{5}{12}, \quad \beta = 22.62°$$

$+M_O = (13)(230)\sin\alpha - (13)(660)\sin\beta$

$+M_O = -2340$ N-m

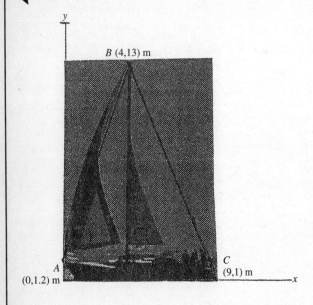

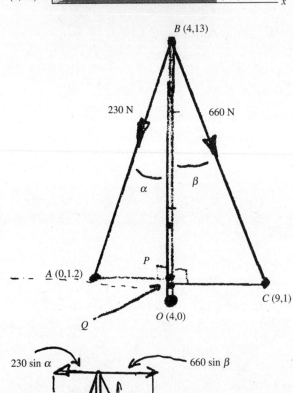

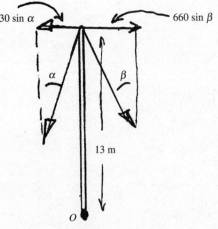

Problem 4.37 The tension in each cable is the same. The forces exerted on the beam by the three cables exert a 1.2 kN-m counterclockwise moment about O. What is the tension in the cables?

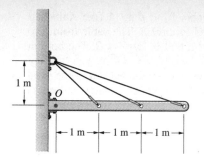

Solution: The strategy is to resolve cable tensions into components normal to the beam; use the distances from O to attachment point; determine action, and compute the moment in terms of cable tensions. From the known moment, solve for the tensions.

Denote the cables as 1, 2, and 3, starting near the root.

The angle formed by the first cable with the beam is

$$\theta_1 = \tan^{-1}\left(\tfrac{1}{1}\right) = 45°.$$

The component normal to the beam is: $F_1 = |\mathbf{T}|\sin 45° = 0.707|\mathbf{T}|$. Similarly,

$$\theta_2 = \tan^{-1}\left(\tfrac{1}{2}\right) = 26.57°,$$

$$F_2 = |\mathbf{T}|\sin 26.57° = 0.4472|\mathbf{T}|,$$

$$\theta_3 = \tan^{-1}\left(\tfrac{1}{3}\right) = 18.43°,$$

and $F_3 = |\mathbf{T}|\sin 18.43° = 0.3162|\mathbf{T}|$.

The actions are positive. The sum of the moments about O

$$\sum M_O = (1)(0.707|\mathbf{T}|) + 2(0.4472|\mathbf{T}|) + 3(0.3162|\mathbf{T}|)$$

$$= 1.2 \text{ kN m}.$$

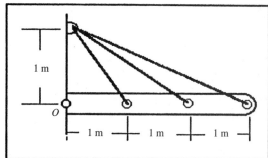

Solving:

$$|\mathbf{T}| = \frac{1.2}{2.55} = 0.4706 \text{ kN}$$

Problem 4.38 The tension in cable AB is 300 lb. The sum of the moments about O due to the forces exerted on the beam by the two cables is zero. What is the magnitude of the sum of the forces exerted on the beam by the two cables?

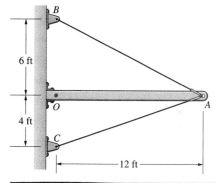

Solution: The strategy is to resolve the cable tensions into a components parallel to and normal to the beam; use the length of the beam as the distance; determine the sign of the action, and compute the moments about O. The moment balance is solved for the unknown force in CA. The parallel components are used to find the magnitude of the force.

The angle formed by cable AB is

$$\theta_{AB} = \tan^{-1}\left(\frac{6}{12}\right) = 26.6°.$$

The component normal to the beam is

$$F_{NB} = |\mathbf{T}_{AB}|\sin 26.6° = (300)(0.4472) = 134.16 \text{ lb}.$$

The parallel component is

$$F_{PB} = |\mathbf{T}_{AB}|\cos 26.6° = (300)(0.8944) = 268.32 \text{ lb}.$$

Similarly for the cable AC,

$$\theta_{CA} = \tan^{-1}\left(\frac{4}{12}\right) = 18.43°,$$

$$F_{NC} = |\mathbf{T}_{AC}|\sin 18.43° = 0.3162|\mathbf{T}_{AC}|,$$

$$F_{PC} = |\mathbf{T}_{AC}|\cos 18.43° = 0.9487|\mathbf{T}_{AC}|$$

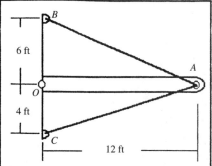

The action of AB is positive, the action of AC is negative. The moments about O

$$\sum M_O = 12(134.16) - 12(0.3162)(|\mathbf{T}_{AC}|) = 0.$$

Solve: $|\mathbf{T}_{AC}| = 424.3$ lb. The sum of the forces acting on the beam is

$$\sum F_P = 268.32 + (0.9487)(424.3) = 670.8 \text{ lb}$$

Problem 4.39 The beam shown in Problem 4.38 will safely support the force exerted by the two cables at A if the magnitude of the horizontal component of the total force exerted at A does not exceed 1000 lb and the sum of the moments about O due to the forces exerted by the cables equals zero. Based on these criteria, what are the maximum permissible tensions in the two cables?

Solution: From Problem 4.38, the forces are

$$\mathbf{F}_{AC} = -F_{AC} \cos 18.43°\mathbf{i} - F_{AC} \sin 18.43°\mathbf{j}, \text{ and}$$

$$\mathbf{F}_{AB} = -F_{AB} \cos 26.57°\mathbf{i} + F_{AB} \sin 26.57°\mathbf{j}.$$

The vector from O to A is given by $\mathbf{r}_{OA} = 12\mathbf{i}$ ft. The equation for the sum of the horizontal components is $-F_{AC} \cos 18.43° - F_{AB} \cos 26.57° = -1000$ lb. The moment equation is

$$\sum \mathbf{M}_O = \mathbf{r}_{OA} \times \mathbf{F}_{AC} + \mathbf{r}_{OA} \times \mathbf{F}_{AB} = \mathbf{r}_{OA} \times (\mathbf{F}_{AC} + \mathbf{F}_{AB}) = 0, \text{ or}$$

$$\sum \mathbf{M}_O = 12\mathbf{i} \times ((-F_{AC} \cos 18.43°\mathbf{i} - F_{AC} \sin 18.43°\mathbf{j}$$

$$- F_{AB} \cos 26.57°\mathbf{i} + F_{AB} \sin 26.57°\mathbf{j})) = 0.$$

Carrying out the vector operations, we get

$$\sum \mathbf{M}_O = 12(-F_{AC} \sin 18.43° + F_{AB} \sin 26.57°)\mathbf{k} = 0.$$

gives $\sum \mathbf{M}_O = 12(-F_{AC} \sin 18.43° + F_{AB} \sin 26.57°)\mathbf{k} = 0$

Solving the force equation and the moment equation simultaneously, we obtain $F_{AB} = 447$ lb and $F_{AC} = 632$ lb.

Problem 4.40 The hydraulic cylinder BC exerts a 300-kN force on the boom of the crane at C. The force is parallel to the cylinder. What is the moment of the force about A?

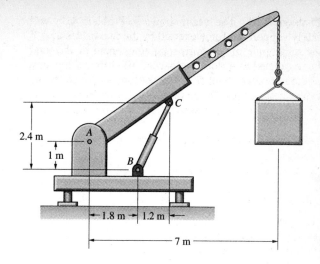

Solution: The strategy is to resolve the force exerted by the hydraulic cylinder into the normal component about the crane; determine the distance; determine the sign of the action, and compute the moment.

Two right triangles are constructed: The angle formed by the hydraulic cylinder with the horizontal is

$$\beta = \tan^{-1}\left(\frac{2.4}{1.2}\right) = 63.43°.$$

The angle formed by the crane with the horizontal is

$$\alpha = \tan^{-1}\left(\frac{1.4}{3}\right) = 25.02°.$$

The angle between the hydraulic cylinder and the crane is $\theta = \beta - \alpha = 38.42°$. The normal component of the force is: $F_N = (300)(\sin 38.42°) = 186.42$ kN. The distance from point A is $d = \sqrt{1.4^2 + 3^2} = 3.31$ m. The action is positive. The moment about A is $M_O = +3.31(186.42) = 617.15$ kN-m *Check:* The force exerted by the actuator can be resolved into x- and y-components, $F_x = F \cos\beta = 134.16$ kN, $F_y = F \sin\beta = 268.33$ kN. The moment about the point A is $M = -1.4F_x + 3.0 F_y = 617.15$ kN m. *check.*

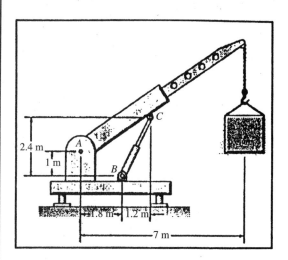

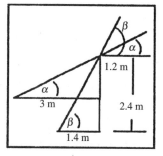

Problem 4.41 The hydraulic cylinder BC exerts a 2200-lb force on the boom of the crane at C. The force is parallel to the cylinder. The angle $\alpha = 40°$. What is the moment of the force about A?

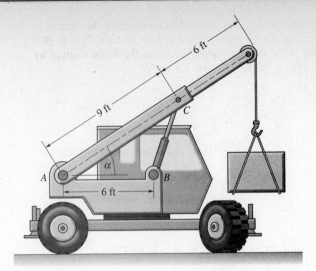

Solution: Define the positive x direction to the right and the positive y direction as upward. Place a coordinate origin at A. The vector from A to B is given as $\mathbf{r}_{AB} = 6\mathbf{i}$ ft. The location of point C in the xy coordinates is given by

$$\mathbf{r}_{AC} = 9\cos 40°\mathbf{i} + 9\sin 40°\mathbf{j} = 6.89\mathbf{i} + 5.79\mathbf{j} \text{ ft.}$$

The unit vector from B to C is given by

$$\mathbf{e}_{BC} = \frac{(x_C - x_B)\mathbf{i} + (y_C - y_B)\mathbf{j}}{\sqrt{(x_C - x_B)^2 + (y_C - y_B)^2}}$$

$$= 0.153\mathbf{i} + 0.988\mathbf{j}.$$

Thus, the force along BC is $\mathbf{F}_{BC} = 2200\mathbf{e}_{BC} = 337\mathbf{i} + 2174\mathbf{j}$ lb. The moment of this force about point A is $M_A = 6(2174) = 13040$ ft-lb

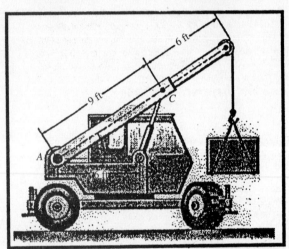

Problem 4.42 The hydraulic cylinder BC in Problem 4.41 exerts a 2200-lb force on the boom of the crane at C. The force is parallel to the cylinder. The cable supporting the suspended crate exerts a downward force at the end of the boom equal to the weight of the crate. The angle $\alpha = 35°$. If the sum of the moments about A due to the two forces exerted on the boom is zero, what is the weight of the crate?

Solution: Define the positive x direction to the right and the positive y direction as upward. Place a coordinate origin at A. The vector from A to B is given as $\mathbf{r}_{AB} = 6\mathbf{i}$ ft. The location of point C in the xy coordinates is given by $\mathbf{r}_{AC} = 9\cos 35°\mathbf{i} + 9\sin 35°\mathbf{j} = 7.37\mathbf{i} + 5.16\mathbf{j}$ ft. The unit vector from B to C is given by

$$\mathbf{e}_{BC} = \frac{(x_C - x_B)\mathbf{i} + (y_C - y_B)\mathbf{j}}{\sqrt{(x_C - x_B)^2 + (y_C - y_B)^2}}$$

$$= 0.257\mathbf{i} + 0.966\mathbf{j}.$$

Thus, the force along BC is

$$\mathbf{F}_{BC} = 2200$$

$$\mathbf{e}_{BC} = 565\mathbf{i} + 2126\mathbf{j} \text{ lb.}$$

The moment of the force in BC about point A is $M_A = 6(2126) = 12756$ ft-lb. The moment of the weight of the crate about A is given by $M_{AW} = (15\cos 35°)(-W) = -12.29W$ ft-lb. Summing the two moments and setting the sum to zero, we get

$$\sum M = (-12.29W + 12756)\mathbf{k} \text{ ft-lb} = 0.$$

Solving, we get $W = 1038$ lb.

Problem 4.43 The unstretched length of the spring is 1 m, and the spring constant is $k = 20$ N/m. If $\alpha = 30°$, what is the moment about A due to the force exerted by the spring on the circular bar at B?

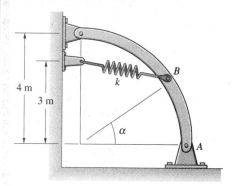

Solution: Assume that the bar is a quarter circle, with a radius of 4 m. The stretched length of the spring is found from the Pythagorean Theorem: The vertical height from the floor to the attachment point on the bar is $h = 4 \sin \alpha = 2$ m, and the distance from the wall is $4 \cos \alpha$. The stretched length of the spring is $L = \sqrt{(3-h)^2 + (4 \cos \alpha)^2} = 3.6055$ m. The spring force is $F = (20)(3.6055 - 1) = 52.1$ N. The angle that the spring makes with the horizontal is

$$\beta = \tan^{-1}\left(\frac{3-h}{4 \cos \alpha}\right)$$

$$= \tan^{-1}(0.2887) = 16.1°.$$

The horizontal component of the spring force is $F_X = F \cos 16.1° = (52.1)(0.9608) = 50.07$ N. The vertical component of the force is $F_Y = F \sin 16.1° = (52.1)(0.2773) = 14.45$ N.

The distance from A to the spring attachment point to the left of A is $d = 4(1 - \cos \alpha) = 0.536$ m, hence the action of the vertical component is negative, and the action of the horizontal component is positive. The moment about A is $M_A = -0.536(14.45) + 2(50.07) = 92.4$ N-m.

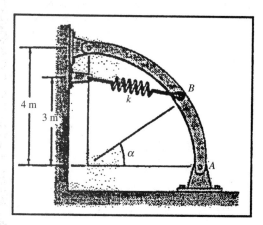

Problem 4.44 The hydraulic cylinder exerts an 8-kN force at B that is parallel to the cylinder and points from C toward B. Determine the moments of the force about points A and D.

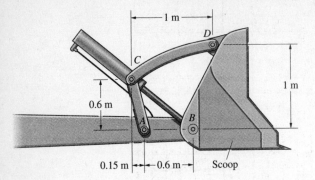

Solution: Use x, y coords with origin A. We need the unit vector from C to B, $\mathbf{e}_{CB}$. From the geometry,

$$\mathbf{e}_{CB} = 0.780\mathbf{i} - 0.625\mathbf{j}$$

The force $\mathbf{F}_{CB}$ is given by

$$\mathbf{F}_{CB} = (0.780)8\mathbf{i} - (0.625)8\mathbf{j} \text{ kN}$$

$$\mathbf{F}_{CB} = 6.25\mathbf{i} - 5.00\mathbf{j} \text{ kN}$$

For the moments about A and D, treat the components of F_{CB} as two separate forces.

$$\curvearrowleft +M_A = (5,00)(0.15) - (0.6)(6.25) \text{ kN} \cdot \text{m}$$

$$\curvearrowleft +M_A = -3.00 \text{ kN} \cdot \text{m}$$

For the moment about D

$$\curvearrowleft +\sum M_D = (5 \text{ kN})(1 \text{ m}) + (6.25 \text{ kN})(0.4 \text{ m})$$

$$\curvearrowleft +M_D = 7.5 \text{ kN} \cdot \text{m}$$

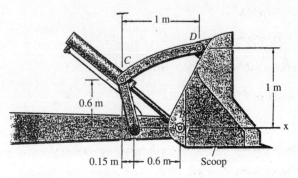

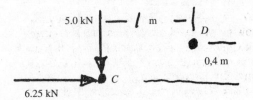

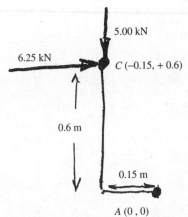

Problem 4.45 Use Eq. (4.2) to determine the moment of the 50-lb force about the origin O. Compare your answer with the two-dimensional description of the moment.

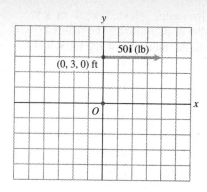

Solution:

$\mathbf{M} = \mathbf{r} \times \mathbf{F} = 3\mathbf{j} \times 50\mathbf{i}$

$\mathbf{M} = -150\mathbf{k}$ ft-lb

Two dimensional description

$\curvearrowleft +M_O = -dF = -(3)(50) = -150$ ft-lb

The descriptions match.

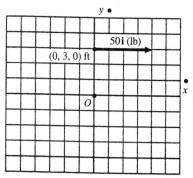

Problem 4.46 Use Eq. (4.2) to determine the moment of the 80-N force about the origin O letting $\mathbf{r}$ be the vector (a) from O to A; (b) from O to B.

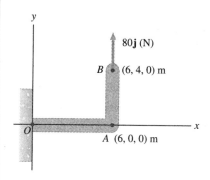

Solution:

(a) $\mathbf{M}_O = \mathbf{r}_{OA} \times \mathbf{F}$

$= 6\mathbf{i} \times 80\mathbf{j} = 480\mathbf{k}$ (N-m).

(b) $\mathbf{M}_O = \mathbf{r}_{OB} \times \mathbf{F}$

$= (6\mathbf{i} + 4\mathbf{j}) \times 80\mathbf{j}$

$= 480\mathbf{k}$ (N-m).

Problem 4.47 A bioengineer studying an injury sustained in throwing the javelin estimates that the magnitude of the maximum force exerted was $|\mathbf{F}| = 360$ N and the perpendicular distance from O to the line of action of $\mathbf{F}$ was 550 mm. The vector $\mathbf{F}$ and point O are contained in the $x - y$ plane. Express the moment of $\mathbf{F}$ about the shoulder joint at O as a vector.

Solution: The magnitude of the moment is $|\mathbf{F}|(0.55 \text{ m}) = (360 \text{ N}) (0.55 \text{ m}) = 198$ N-m. The moment vector is perpendicular to the $x - y$ plane, and the right-hand rule indicates it points in the positive z direction. Therefore $\mathbf{M}_O = 198\mathbf{k}$ (N-m).

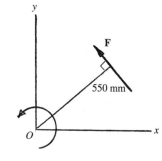

Problem 4.48 Use Eq. (4.2) to determine the moment of the 100-kN force (a) about A, (b) about B.

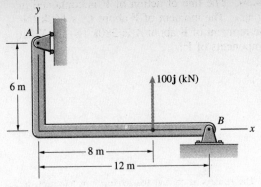

Solution: (a) The coordinates of A are $(0,6,0)$. The coordinates of the point of application of the force are $(8,0,0)$. The position vector from A to the point of application of the force is $\mathbf{r}_{AF} = (8-0)\mathbf{i} + (0-6)\mathbf{j} = 8\mathbf{i} - 6\mathbf{j}$. The force is $\mathbf{F} = 100\mathbf{j}$ (kN). The cross product is

$$\mathbf{r}_{AF} \times \mathbf{F} = \begin{vmatrix} \mathbf{i} & \mathbf{j} & \mathbf{k} \\ 8 & -6 & 0 \\ 0 & 100 & 0 \end{vmatrix} = 800\mathbf{k} \text{ (kN-m)}$$

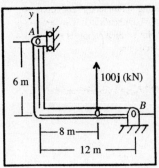

(b) The coordinates of B are $(12,0,0)$. The position vector from B to the point of application of the force is $\mathbf{r}_{BF} = (8-12)\mathbf{i} = -4\mathbf{i}$. The cross product is:

$$\mathbf{r}_{BF} \times \mathbf{F} = \begin{vmatrix} \mathbf{i} & \mathbf{j} & \mathbf{k} \\ -4 & 0 & 0 \\ 0 & 100 & 0 \end{vmatrix} = -400\mathbf{k} \text{ (kN-m)}$$

Problem 4.49 The line of action of the 100-lb force is contained in the $x - y$ plane.

(a) Use Eq. (4.2) to determine the moment of the force about the origin O.
(b) Use the result of (a) to determine the perpendicular distance from O to the line of action of the force.

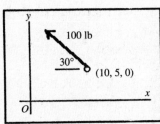

Solution: The resolved force is $\mathbf{F} = 100(\mathbf{i}\cos 150° + \mathbf{j}\sin 150°) = -86.6\mathbf{i} + 50\mathbf{j}$. The position vector to the point of application: $\mathbf{r} = 10\mathbf{i} + 5\mathbf{j}$.

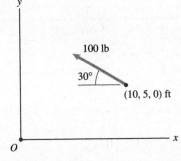

(a) The cross product:

$$\mathbf{r} \times \mathbf{F} = \begin{vmatrix} \mathbf{i} & \mathbf{j} & \mathbf{k} \\ 10 & 5 & 0 \\ -86.6 & 50 & 0 \end{vmatrix} = (500 + 433)\mathbf{k}. = 933\mathbf{k} \text{ ft-lb}$$

(b) The magnitude of the moment is $|\mathbf{M}| = 933$ ft-lb. The magnitude of the force is $|\mathbf{F}| = 100$ lb. The distance is

$$D = \frac{933 \text{ ft-lb}}{100 \text{ lb}} = 9.33 \text{ ft.}$$

Problem 4.50 The line of action of **F** is contained in the $x - y$ plane. The moment of **F** about O is 140**k** (N-m), and the moment of **F** about A is 280**k** (N-m). What are the components of **F**?

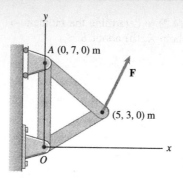

Solution: The strategy is to find the moments in terms of the components of **F** and solve the resulting simultaneous equations. The position vector from O to the point of application is $\mathbf{r}_{OF} = 5\mathbf{i} + 3\mathbf{j}$. The position vector from A to the point of application is $\mathbf{r}_{AF} = (5 - 0)\mathbf{i} + (3 - 7)\mathbf{j} = 5\mathbf{i} - 4\mathbf{j}$. The cross products:

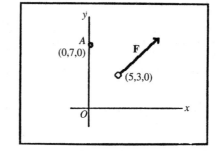

$$\mathbf{r}_{OF} \times \mathbf{F} = \begin{vmatrix} \mathbf{i} & \mathbf{j} & \mathbf{k} \\ 5 & 3 & 0 \\ F_X & F_Y & 0 \end{vmatrix} = (5F_Y - 3F_X)\mathbf{k} = 140\mathbf{k}, \text{ and}$$

$$\mathbf{r}_{AF} \times \mathbf{F} = \begin{vmatrix} \mathbf{i} & \mathbf{j} & \mathbf{k} \\ 5 & -4 & 0 \\ F_X & F_Y & 0 \end{vmatrix} = (5F_Y + 4F_X)\mathbf{k} = 280\mathbf{k}.$$

Take the dot product of both sides with **k** to eliminate **k**. The simultaneous equations are:

$$5F_Y - 3F_X = 140, \quad 5F_Y + 4F_X = 280.$$

Solving: $F_Y = 40, \quad F_X = 20,$ from which $\mathbf{F} = 20\mathbf{i} + 40\mathbf{j}$ (N)

Problem 4.51 To test the bending stiffness of a light composite beam, engineering students subject it to the vertical forces shown. Use Eq. (4.2) to determine the moment of the 6-kN force about A.

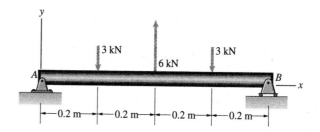

Solution:

$$\mathbf{M}_A = \mathbf{r} \times \mathbf{F}$$

$$= 0.4\mathbf{i} \times 6\mathbf{j}$$

$$= 2.4\mathbf{k} \text{ (kN-m)}.$$

Problem 4.52 Consider the beam and forces shown in Problem 4.51. Use Eq. (4.2) to determine the sum of the moments of the three forces (a) about A, (b) about B.

Solution:

(a) $\mathbf{M}_A = 0.2\mathbf{i} \times (-3\mathbf{j}) + 0.4\mathbf{i} \times 6\mathbf{j} + 0.6\mathbf{i} \times (-3\mathbf{j})$

$$= \mathbf{0}.$$

(b) $\mathbf{M}_B = (-0.2\mathbf{i}) \times (-3\mathbf{j}) + (-0.4\mathbf{i}) \times 6\mathbf{j} + (-0.6\mathbf{i}) \times (-3\mathbf{j})$

$$= \mathbf{0}.$$

211

Problem 4.53 Three forces are applied to the plate. Use Eq. (4.2) to determine the sum of the moments of the three forces about the origin O.

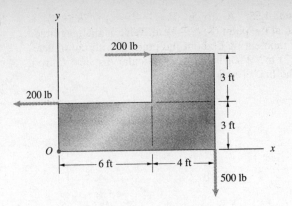

Solution: The position vectors from O to the points of application of the forces are: $\mathbf{r}_{O1} = 3\mathbf{j}$, $\mathbf{F}_1 = -200\mathbf{i}$; $\mathbf{r}_{O2} = 10\mathbf{i}$, $\mathbf{F}_2 = -500\mathbf{j}$; $\mathbf{r}_{O3} = 6\mathbf{i} + 6\mathbf{j}$, $\mathbf{F}_3 = 200\mathbf{i}$.

The sum of the moments about O is

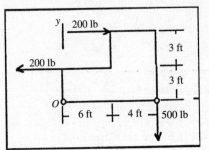

$$\sum \mathbf{M}_O = \begin{vmatrix} \mathbf{i} & \mathbf{j} & \mathbf{k} \\ 0 & 3 & 0 \\ -200 & 0 & 0 \end{vmatrix} + \begin{vmatrix} \mathbf{i} & \mathbf{j} & \mathbf{k} \\ 10 & 0 & 0 \\ 0 & -500 & 0 \end{vmatrix} + \begin{vmatrix} \mathbf{i} & \mathbf{j} & \mathbf{k} \\ 6 & 6 & 0 \\ 200 & 0 & 0 \end{vmatrix} \text{ lb}$$

$$= 600\mathbf{k} - 5000\mathbf{k} - 1200\mathbf{k} = -5600\mathbf{k} \text{ ft-lb}$$

Problem 4.54 (a) Determine the magnitude of the moment of the 150-N force about A by calculating the perpendicular distance from A to the line of action of the force.

(b) Use Eq. (4.2) to determine the magnitude of the moment of the 150-N force about A.

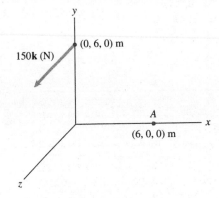

Solution:

(a) The perpendicular from A to the line of action of the force lies in the $x - y$ plane

$$d = \sqrt{6^2 + 6^2} = 8.485 \text{ m}$$

$$|\mathbf{M}| = dF = (8.485)(150) = 1270 \text{ N-m}$$

(b) $\mathbf{M} = (-6\mathbf{i} + 6\mathbf{j}) \times (150\mathbf{k}) = -900\mathbf{j} + 900\mathbf{i}$ N-m

$$|\mathbf{M}| = \sqrt{900^2 + 900^2} = 1270 \text{ N-m}$$

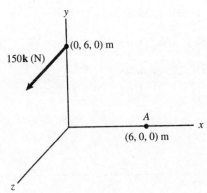

Problem 4.55 A force $\mathbf{F} = -4\mathbf{i} + 6\mathbf{j} - 2\mathbf{k}$ (kN) is applied at the point $(8, 4, -4)$ m. What is the magnitude of the moment of $\mathbf{F}$ about the point P with coordinates $(2, 2, 2)$ m? What is the perpendicular distance D from P to the line of action of $\mathbf{F}$?

Solution: The vector from P $(2, 2, 2)$ m, to the point of application of the force $(8, 4, -4)$ m, is

$$\mathbf{r} = 6\mathbf{i} + 2\mathbf{j} - 6\mathbf{k} \text{ m}$$

The moment of the force $\mathbf{F}$ about P is

$$\mathbf{M}_P = \mathbf{r} \times \mathbf{F} = \begin{vmatrix} \mathbf{i} & \mathbf{j} & \mathbf{k} \\ 6 & 2 & -6 \\ -4 & 6 & -2 \end{vmatrix} = 32\mathbf{i} + 36\mathbf{j} + 44\mathbf{k} \text{ kN-m}$$

$$|\mathbf{M}_P| = \sqrt{32^2 + 36^2 + 44^2} = 65.2 \text{ kN-m}$$

$$|\mathbf{F}| = \sqrt{4^2 + 6^2 + 2^2} = 7.48 \text{ kN}$$

$$|\mathbf{M}_P| = |\mathbf{F}|D \qquad D = \frac{|\mathbf{M}_P|}{|\mathbf{F}|} = 8.72 \text{ m}$$

Problem 4.56 A force $\mathbf{F} = 20\mathbf{i} - 30\mathbf{j} + 60\mathbf{k}$ (N) is applied at the point $(2, 3, 6)$ m. What is the magnitude of the moment of $\mathbf{F}$ about the point P with coordinates $(-2, -1, -1)$ m? What is the perpendicular distance D from P to the line of action of $\mathbf{F}$?

Solution: The vector from P $(2, 3, 6)$ m. to the point of application of the force $(-2, -1, -1)$ m is

$$\mathbf{r} = -4\mathbf{i} - 4\mathbf{j} - 7\mathbf{k} \text{ m}$$

The moment of the force about P is

$$\mathbf{M}_P = \mathbf{r} \times \mathbf{F} = \begin{vmatrix} \mathbf{i} & \mathbf{j} & \mathbf{k} \\ -4 & -4 & -7 \\ 20 & -30 & 60 \end{vmatrix} = -450\mathbf{i} + 100\mathbf{j} + 200\mathbf{k} \text{ N-m}$$

$$|\mathbf{M}_P| = \sqrt{450^2 + 100^2 + 200^2} = 502 \text{ N-m}$$

$$|\mathbf{F}| = \sqrt{20^2 + 30^2 + 60^2} = 70 \text{ N}$$

$$|\mathbf{M}_P| = |\mathbf{F}|D \quad D = |\mathbf{M}_P|/|\mathbf{F}| = 7.18 \text{ m}$$

Problem 4.57 A force $\mathbf{F} = 20\mathbf{i} - 30\mathbf{j} + 60\mathbf{k}$ (lb). The moment of $\mathbf{F}$ about a point P is $\mathbf{M}_P = 450\mathbf{i} - 100\mathbf{j} - 200\mathbf{k}$ (ft-lb). What is the perpendicular distance from point P to the line of action of $\mathbf{F}$?

Solution: The magnitude of the moment is

$$|\mathbf{M}_P| = \sqrt{450^2 + 100^2 + 200^2} = 502.5 \text{ (ft-lb)}.$$

The magnitude of the force is

$$|\mathbf{F}| = \sqrt{20^2 + 30^2 + 60^2} = 70 \text{ (lb)}.$$

The perpendicular distance is

$$D = \frac{|\mathbf{M}_P|}{|\mathbf{F}|} = \frac{502.5 \text{ ft-lb}}{70 \text{ lb}} = 7.18 \text{ ft}$$

Problem 4.58 A force **F** is applied at the point (8, 6, 13) m. Its magnitude is $|\mathbf{F}| = 90$ N, and the moment of **F** about the point (4, 2, 6) is zero. What are the components of **F**?

Solution:

$$\mathbf{r} \times \mathbf{F} = \begin{vmatrix} \mathbf{i} & \mathbf{j} & \mathbf{k} \\ 8-4 & 6-2 & 13-6 \\ F_x & F_y & F_z \end{vmatrix} = \mathbf{0}.$$

Therefore

$$4F_z - 7F_y = 0, \quad (1)$$

$$7F_x - 4F_z = 0, \quad (2)$$

$$4F_y - 4F_x = 0. \quad (3)$$

From Eq. (3), $F_y = F_x$, and from Eqs. (1) and (2), $F_z = \frac{7}{4}F_x$. The magnitude is

$$90 \text{ N} = \sqrt{F_x^2 + F_y^2 + F_z^2}$$

$$= \sqrt{F_x^2 + F_x^2 + \left(\frac{7}{4}F_x\right)^2}.$$

Solving, we obtain $F_x = \pm 40$ N. we see that

$$\mathbf{F} = 40\mathbf{i} + 40\mathbf{j} + 70\mathbf{k} \text{ (N)}$$

or

$$\mathbf{F} = -40\mathbf{i} - 40\mathbf{j} - 70\mathbf{k} \text{ (N)}.$$

Problem 4.59 The force $\mathbf{F} = 30\mathbf{i} + 20\mathbf{j} - 10\mathbf{k}$ (N).

(a) Determine the magnitude of the moment of **F** about A.

(b) Suppose that you can change the direction of **F** while keeping its magnitude constant, and you want to choose a direction that maximizes the moment of **F** about A. What is the magnitude of the resulting maximum moment?

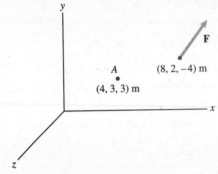

Solution: The vector from A to the point of application of **F** is

$$\mathbf{r} = 4\mathbf{i} - 1\mathbf{j} - 7\mathbf{k} \text{ m}$$

and

$$|\mathbf{r}| = \sqrt{4^2 + 1^2 + 7^2} = 8.12 \text{ m}$$

(a) The moment of **F** about A is

$$\mathbf{M}_A = \mathbf{r} \times \mathbf{F} = \begin{vmatrix} \mathbf{i} & \mathbf{j} & \mathbf{k} \\ 4 & -1 & -7 \\ 30 & 20 & -10 \end{vmatrix} = 150\mathbf{i} - 170\mathbf{j} + 110\mathbf{k} \text{ N-m}$$

$$|\mathbf{M}_A| = \sqrt{150^2 + 170^2 + 110^2} = 252 \text{ N-m}$$

(b) The maximum moment occurs when $\mathbf{r} \perp \mathbf{F}$. In this case

$$|\mathbf{M}_{A_{\max}}| = |\mathbf{r}||\mathbf{F}|$$

Hence, we need $|\mathbf{F}|$.

$$|\mathbf{F}| = \sqrt{30^2 + 20^2 + 10^2} = 37.4 \text{ (N)}$$

Thus,

$$|\mathbf{M}_{A_{\max}}| = (8.12)(37.4) = 304 \text{ N-m}$$

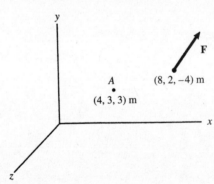

Problem 4.60 The direction cosines of the force $\mathbf{F}$ are $\cos\theta_x = 0.818$, $\cos\theta_y = 0.182$, and $\cos\theta_z = -0.545$. The support of the beam at O will fail if the magnitude of the moment of $\mathbf{F}$ about O exceeds 100 kN-m. Determine the magnitude of the largest force $\mathbf{F}$ that can safely be applied to the beam.

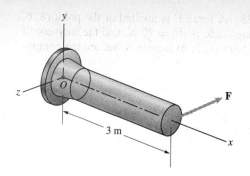

Solution: The strategy is to determine the perpendicular distance from O to the action line of $\mathbf{F}$, and to calculate the largest magnitude of $\mathbf{F}$ from $M_O = D|\mathbf{F}|$. The position vector from O to the point of application of $\mathbf{F}$ is $\mathbf{r}_{OF} = 3\mathbf{i}$ (m). Resolve the position vector into components parallel and normal to $\mathbf{F}$. The component parallel to $\mathbf{F}$ is $\mathbf{r}_P = (\mathbf{r}_{OF} \cdot \mathbf{e}_F)\mathbf{e}_F$, where the unit vector $\mathbf{e}_F$ parallel to $\mathbf{F}$ is $\mathbf{e}_F = \mathbf{i}\cos\theta_X + \mathbf{j}\cos\theta_Y + \mathbf{k}\cos\theta_Z = 0.818\mathbf{i} + 0.182\mathbf{j} - 0.545\mathbf{k}$. The dot product is $\mathbf{r}_{OF} \cdot \mathbf{e}_F = 2.454$. The parallel component is $\mathbf{r}_P = 2.007\mathbf{i} + 0.4466\mathbf{j} - 1.3374\mathbf{k}$. The component normal to $\mathbf{F}$ is $\mathbf{r}_N = \mathbf{r}_{OF} - \mathbf{r}_P = (3-2)\mathbf{i} - 0.4466\mathbf{j} + 1.3374\mathbf{k}$. The magnitude of the normal component is the perpendicular distance: $D = \sqrt{1^2 + 0.4466^2 + 1.337^2} = 1.7283$ m. The maximum moment allowed is $M_O = 1.7283|\mathbf{F}| = 100$ kN-m, from which

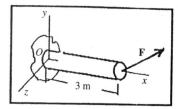

$$|\mathbf{F}| = \frac{100 \text{ kN-m}}{1.7283 \text{ m}} = 57.86 \cong 58 \text{ kN}$$

Problem 4.61 The force $\mathbf{F}$ exerted on the grip of the exercise machine points in the direction of the unit vector $\mathbf{e} = \frac{2}{3}\mathbf{i} - \frac{2}{3}\mathbf{j} + \frac{1}{3}\mathbf{k}$ and its magnitude is 120 N. Determine the magnitude of the moment of $\mathbf{F}$ about the origin O.

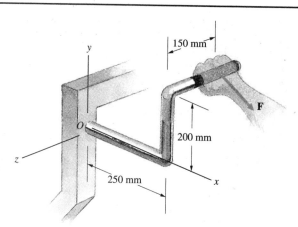

Solution: The vector from O to the point of application of the force is

$$\mathbf{r} = 0.25\mathbf{i} + 0.2\mathbf{j} - 0.15\mathbf{k} \text{ m}$$

and the force is $\mathbf{F} = |\mathbf{F}|\mathbf{e}$

or

$$\mathbf{F} = 80\mathbf{i} - 80\mathbf{j} + 40\mathbf{k} \text{ N}.$$

The moment of $\mathbf{F}$ about O is

$$\mathbf{M}_O = \mathbf{r} \times \mathbf{F} = \begin{vmatrix} \mathbf{i} & \mathbf{j} & \mathbf{k} \\ 0.25 & 0.2 & -0.15 \\ 80 & -80 & 40 \end{vmatrix} \text{ N-m}$$

or

$$\mathbf{M}_O = -4\mathbf{i} - 22\mathbf{j} - 36\mathbf{k} \text{ N-m}$$

and

$$|\mathbf{M}_O| = \sqrt{4^2 + 22^2 + 36^2} \text{ N-m}$$

$$|\mathbf{M}_O| = 42.4 \text{ N-m}$$

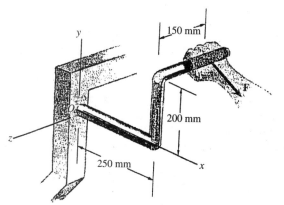

Problem 4.62 The force $\mathbf{F}$ in Problem 4.61 points in the direction of the unit vector $\mathbf{e} = \frac{2}{3}\mathbf{i} - \frac{2}{3}\mathbf{j} + \frac{1}{3}\mathbf{k}$. The support at O will safely support a moment of 560 N-m magnitude.

(a) Based on this criterion, what is the largest safe magnitude of $\mathbf{F}$?

(b) If the force $\mathbf{F}$ may be exerted in any direction, what is its largest safe magnitude?

Solution: See the figure of Problem 4.61.

The moment in Problem 4.61 can be written as

$$\mathbf{M}_O = \begin{vmatrix} \mathbf{i} & \mathbf{j} & \mathbf{k} \\ 0.25 & 0.2 & -0.15 \\ \frac{2}{3}F & -\frac{2}{3}F & +\frac{1}{3}F \end{vmatrix} \text{ where } F = |\mathbf{F}|$$

$$\mathbf{M}_O = (-0.0333\mathbf{i} - 0.1833\mathbf{j} - 0.3\mathbf{k})\mathbf{F}$$

And the magnitude of $\mathbf{M}_O$ is

$$|\mathbf{M}_O| = (\sqrt{0.0333^2 + 0.1833^2 + 0.3^2})F$$

$$|\mathbf{M}_O| = 0.353\ F$$

If we set $|\mathbf{M}_O| = 560$ N-m, we can solve for $|\mathbf{F}_{max}|$

$$560 = 0.353|\mathbf{F}_{max}|$$

$$|\mathbf{F}_{max}| = 1586\text{ N}$$

(b) If $\mathbf{F}$ can be in any direction, then the worst case is when $\mathbf{r} \perp \mathbf{F}$. The moment in this case is $|\mathbf{M}_O| = |\mathbf{r}||\mathbf{F}_{worst}|$

$$|\mathbf{r}| = \sqrt{0.25^2 + 0.2^2 + 0.15^2} = 0.3536\text{ m}$$

$$560 = (0.3536)|\mathbf{F}_{WORST}|$$

$$|\mathbf{F}_{worst}| = 1584\text{ N}$$

Problem 4.63 An engineer estimates that under the most adverse expected weather conditions, the total force on the highway sign will be $\mathbf{F} = \pm1.4\mathbf{i} - 2.0\mathbf{j}$ (kN). What moment does this force exert about the base O?

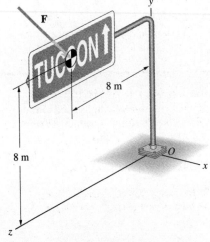

Solution: The coordinates of the point of application of the force are: (0, 8, 8). The position vector is $\mathbf{r}_{OF} = 8\mathbf{j} + 8\mathbf{k}$. The cross product is

$$\mathbf{r}_{OF} \times \mathbf{F} = \begin{vmatrix} \mathbf{i} & \mathbf{j} & \mathbf{k} \\ 0 & 8 & 8 \\ \pm1.4 & -2 & 0 \end{vmatrix} = 16\mathbf{i} - (\mp1.4)(8)\mathbf{j} + (\mp1.4)(8)\mathbf{k}$$

$$\mathbf{M}_O = 16\mathbf{i} \pm 11.2\mathbf{j} \mp 11.2\mathbf{k} \text{ (N-m)}$$

Check: Use perpendicular distances to forces:

$$M_X = 8(2) = 16,$$

$$M_Y = 8(\pm1.4) = \pm11.2,$$

$$\boxed{M_Z = -8(\pm1.4) = \mp11.2}$$

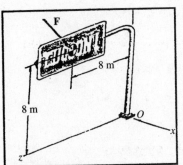

216

Problem 4.64 The weights of the arms *OA* and *AB* of the robotic manipulator act at their midpoints. The direction cosines of the centerline of arm *OA* are $\cos\theta_x = 0.500$, $\cos\theta_y = 0.866$, and $\cos\theta_z = 0$, and the direction cosines of the centerline of arm *AB* are $\cos\theta_x = 0.707$, $\cos\theta_y = 0.619$, and $\cos\theta_z = -0.342$. What is the sum of the moments about *O* due to the two forces?

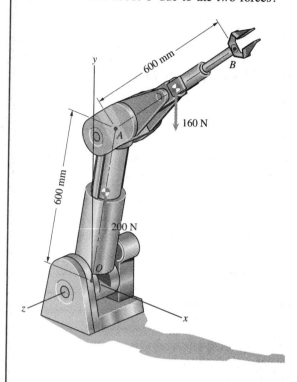

Solution: By definition, the direction cosines are the scalar components of the unit vectors. Thus the unit vectors are $\mathbf{e}_1 = 0.5\mathbf{i} + 0.866\mathbf{j}$, and $\mathbf{e}_2 = 0.707\mathbf{i} + 0.619\mathbf{j} - 0.342\mathbf{k}$. The position vectors of the midpoints of the arms are

$$\mathbf{r}_1 = 0.3\mathbf{e}_1 = 0.3(0.5\mathbf{i} + 0.866\mathbf{j}) = 0.15\mathbf{i} + 0.2598\mathbf{j}$$

$$\mathbf{r}_2 = 0.6\mathbf{e}_1 = 0.3\mathbf{e}_2 = 0.512\mathbf{i} + 0.7053\mathbf{j} - 0.0943\mathbf{k}.$$

The sum of moments is

$$\mathbf{M} = \mathbf{r}_1 \times \mathbf{W}_1 \mathbf{r}_2 \times \mathbf{W}_2$$

$$= \begin{vmatrix} \mathbf{i} & \mathbf{j} & \mathbf{k} \\ 0.15 & 0.2598 & 0 \\ 0 & -200 & 0 \end{vmatrix} + \begin{vmatrix} \mathbf{i} & \mathbf{j} & \mathbf{k} \\ 0.512 & 0.7053 & -0.1026 \\ 0 & -160 & 0 \end{vmatrix}$$

$$= -16.42\mathbf{i} - 111.92\mathbf{k} \text{ (N-m)}$$

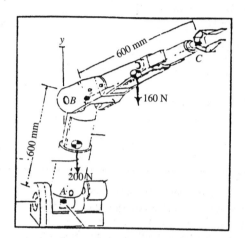

Problem 4.65 The tension in cable *AC* is 100 lb. Determine the moment about the origin *O* due to the force exerted at *A* by cable *AC*. Use the cross product, letting **r** be the vector (a) from *O* to *A*, (b) from *O* to *C*

Solution: The position vectors of the point *A* and *C* are:

$\mathbf{r}_{OA} = 8\mathbf{j}$, $\mathbf{r}_{OC} = 14\mathbf{i} + 14\mathbf{k}$. The vector parallel to cable *AC* is $\mathbf{r}_{AC} = \mathbf{r}_{OC} - \mathbf{r}_{OA} = 14\mathbf{i} - 8\mathbf{j} + 14\mathbf{k}$, with magnitude $|\mathbf{r}_{AC}| = 21.3542$ ft. The unit vector parallel to *AC* is

$$\mathbf{e}_{AC} = \frac{\mathbf{r}_{AC}}{|\mathbf{r}_{AC}|} = 0.6556\mathbf{i} - 0.3746\mathbf{j} + 0.6556\mathbf{k}$$

The tension in cable *AC* is $\mathbf{T}_{AC} = 100\mathbf{e}_{AC} = 65.56\mathbf{i} - 37.46\mathbf{j} + 65.56\mathbf{k}$.

(a) The moment using the vector from *O* to *A* is

$$\mathbf{M}_O = \mathbf{r}_{OA} \times \mathbf{T}_{AC} = \begin{vmatrix} \mathbf{i} & \mathbf{j} & \mathbf{k} \\ 0 & 8 & 0 \\ 65.56 & -37.46 & 65.56 \end{vmatrix}$$

$$= 524.4\mathbf{i} - 524.4\mathbf{k} \text{ (ft-lb)}$$

(b) The moment using the vector from *O* to *C* is

$$\mathbf{M}_O = \mathbf{r}_{OC} \times \mathbf{T}_{AC} = \begin{vmatrix} \mathbf{i} & \mathbf{j} & \mathbf{k} \\ 14 & 0 & 14 \\ 65.56 & -37.46 & 65.56 \end{vmatrix}$$

$$= 524.4\mathbf{i} - 524.4\mathbf{k} \text{ (ft-lb)}$$

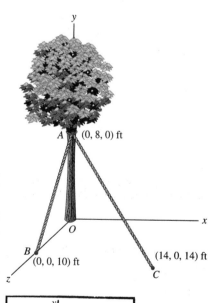

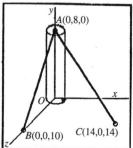

Problem 4.66 Consider the tree in Problem 4.65. The tension in cable AB is 100 lb, and the tension in cable AC is 140 lb. Determine the magnitude of the sum of the moments about O due to the forces exerted at A by the two cables.

Solution: From the solution to Problem 4.65 the unit vector parallel to AC is $\mathbf{e}_{AC} = 0.6556\mathbf{i} - 0.3746\mathbf{j} + 0.6556\mathbf{k}$. The tension in cable AC is $\mathbf{T}_{AC} = 140\mathbf{e}_{AC} = 91.784\mathbf{i} - 52.444\mathbf{j} + 91.784\mathbf{k}$. The position vector parallel to cable AB is $\mathbf{r}_{AB} = -8\mathbf{j} + 10\mathbf{k}$. The magnitude is $|\mathbf{r}_{AB}| = 12.8062$ ft. The unit vector is $\mathbf{e}_{AB} = -0.6247\mathbf{j} + 0.7809\mathbf{k}$. The tension in cable AB is $\mathbf{T}_{AB} = 100\mathbf{e}_{AB} = -62.47\mathbf{j} + 78.09\mathbf{k}$ (lb). The sum of the moments is

$$\sum \mathbf{M}_O = (\mathbf{r}_{OA} \times \mathbf{T}_{AB}) + (\mathbf{r}_{OA} \times \mathbf{T}_{AC}) = (\mathbf{r}_{OA} \times (\mathbf{T}_{AB} + \mathbf{T}_{AC}))$$

$$= \begin{vmatrix} \mathbf{i} & \mathbf{j} & \mathbf{k} \\ 0 & 8 & 0 \\ 91.78 & -114.91 & 169.87 \end{vmatrix} = 1359\mathbf{i} - 734.2\mathbf{k}$$

The magnitude of the sum of moments: $|\mathbf{M}_O| = 1544.65$ ft lb

---

Problem 4.67 The force $\mathbf{F} = 5\mathbf{i}$ (kN) acts on the ring A where the cables AB, AC, and AD are joined. What is the sum of the moments about point D due to the force $\mathbf{F}$ and the three forces exerted on the ring by the cables?

Strategy: The ring is in equilibrium. Use what you know about the four forces acting on it.

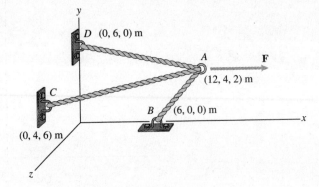

Solution: The vector from D to A is

$\mathbf{r}_{DA} = 12\mathbf{i} - 2\mathbf{j} + 2\mathbf{k}$ m.

The sum of the moments about point D is given by

$$\sum \mathbf{M}_D = \mathbf{r}_{DA} \times \mathbf{F}_{AD} + \mathbf{r}_{DA} \times \mathbf{F}_{AC} + \mathbf{r}_{DA} \times \mathbf{F}_{AB} + \mathbf{r}_{DA} \times \mathbf{F}$$

$$\sum \mathbf{M}_D = \mathbf{r}_{DA} \times (\mathbf{F}_{AD} + \mathbf{F}_{AC} + \mathbf{F}_{AB} + \mathbf{F})$$

However, we are given that ring A is in equilibrium and this implies that

$$(\mathbf{F}_{AD} + \mathbf{F}_{AC} + \mathbf{F}_{AB} + \mathbf{F}) = \mathbf{O} = 0$$

Thus,

$$\sum \mathbf{M}_D = \mathbf{r}_{DA} \times (\mathbf{O}) = 0$$

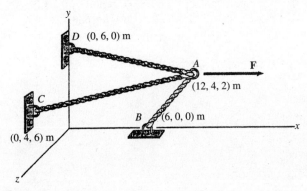

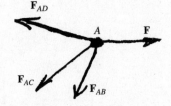

Problem 4.68 In Problem 4.67, determine the moment about point D due to the force exerted on the ring A by the cable AB.

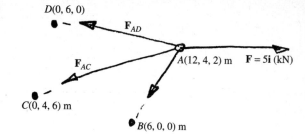

Solution: We need to write the forces as magnitudes times the appropriate unit vectors, write the equilibrium equations for A in component form, and then solve the resulting three equations for the three unknown magnitudes. The unit vectors are of the form

$$\mathbf{e}_{AP} = \frac{(x_P - x_A)\mathbf{i} + (y_P - y_A)\mathbf{j} + (z_P - z_A)\mathbf{k}}{|\mathbf{r}_{AP}|}$$

Where P takes on values B, C, and D

Calculating the unit vectors, we get

$$\begin{cases} \mathbf{e}_{AB} = -0.802\mathbf{i} - 0.535\mathbf{j} - 0.267\mathbf{k} \\ \mathbf{e}_{AC} = -0.949\mathbf{i} + 0\mathbf{j} + 0.316\mathbf{k} \\ \mathbf{e}_{AD} = -0.973\mathbf{i} + 0.162\mathbf{j} - 0.162\mathbf{k} \end{cases}$$

From equilibrium, we have

$$F_{AB}\mathbf{e}_{AB} + F_{AC}\mathbf{e}_{AC} + F_{AD}\mathbf{e}_{AD} + 5\mathbf{i} \text{ (kN)} = 0$$

In component form, we get

$$\begin{cases} \mathbf{i}: \ -0.802F_{AB} - 0.949F_{AC} - 0.973F_{AD} + 5 = 0 \\ \mathbf{j}: \ -0.535F_{AB} + (0)F_{AC} + 0.162F_{AD} = 0 \\ \mathbf{k}: \ -0.267F_{AB} + 0.316F_{AC} - 0.162F_{AD} = 0 \end{cases}$$

Solving, we get

$$F_{AB} = 779.5 \text{ N}, \ F_{AC} = 1976 \text{ N}$$

$$F_{AD} = 2569 \text{ N}$$

The vector from D to A is

$$\mathbf{r}_{DA} = 12\mathbf{i} - 2\mathbf{j} + 2\mathbf{k} \text{ m}$$

The force $\mathbf{F}_{AB}$ is given by

$$\mathbf{F}_{AB} = F_{AB}\mathbf{e}_{AB}$$

$$\mathbf{F}_{AB} = -0.625\mathbf{i} - 0.417\mathbf{j} - 0.208\mathbf{k} \text{ (kN)}$$

The moment about D is given by

$$\mathbf{M}_D = \mathbf{r}_{DA} \times \mathbf{F}_{AB} = \begin{vmatrix} \mathbf{i} & \mathbf{j} & \mathbf{k} \\ 12 & -2 & 2 \\ -0.625 & -0.417 & -0.208 \end{vmatrix}$$

$$\mathbf{M}_D = 1.25\mathbf{i} + 1.25\mathbf{j} - 6.25\mathbf{k} \text{ (kN-m)}$$

Problem 4.69 The tower is 70 m tall. The tensions in cables AB, AC, and AD are 4 kN, 2 kN, and 2 kN, respectively. Determine the sum of the moments about the origin O due to the forces exerted by the cables at point A.

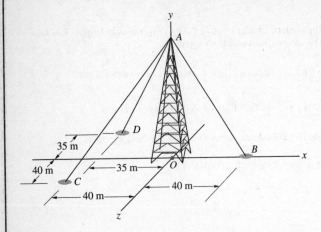

Solution: The coordinates of the points are A $(0, 70, 0)$, B $(40, 0, 0)$, C $(-40, 0, 40)$ $D(-35, 0, -35)$. The position vectors corresponding to the cables are:

$$\mathbf{r}_{AD} = (-35 - 0)\mathbf{i} + (0 - 70)\mathbf{j} + (-35 - 0)\mathbf{k}$$

$$\mathbf{r}_{AD} = -35\mathbf{i} - 70\mathbf{k} - 35\mathbf{k}$$

$$\mathbf{r}_{AC} = (-40 - 0)\mathbf{i} + (0 - 70)\mathbf{j} + (40 - 0)\mathbf{k}$$

$$\mathbf{r}_{AC} = -40\mathbf{i} - 70\mathbf{j} + 40\mathbf{k}$$

$$\mathbf{r}_{AB} = (40 - 0)\mathbf{i} + (0 - 70)\mathbf{j} + (0 - 0)\mathbf{k}$$

$$\mathbf{r}_{AB} = 40\mathbf{i} - 70\mathbf{j} + 0\mathbf{k}$$

The unit vectors corresponding to these position vectors are:

$$\mathbf{e}_{AD} = \frac{\mathbf{r}_{AD}}{|\mathbf{r}_{AD}|} = \frac{-35}{85.73}\mathbf{i} - \frac{70}{85.73}\mathbf{j} - \frac{35}{85.73}$$

$$= -0.4082\mathbf{i} - 0.8165\mathbf{j} - 0.4082\mathbf{k}$$

$$\mathbf{e}_{AC} = \frac{\mathbf{r}_{AC}}{|\mathbf{r}_{AC}|} = -\frac{40}{90}\mathbf{i} - \frac{70}{90}\mathbf{j} + \frac{40}{90}\mathbf{k}$$

$$= -0.4444\mathbf{i} - 0.7778\mathbf{j} + 0.4444\mathbf{k}$$

$$\mathbf{e}_{AB} = \frac{\mathbf{r}_{AB}}{|\mathbf{r}_{AB}|} = \frac{40}{80.6}\mathbf{i} - \frac{70}{80.6}\mathbf{j} + 0\mathbf{k} = 0.4962\mathbf{i} - 0.8682\mathbf{j} + 0\mathbf{k}$$

The forces at point A are

$$\mathbf{T}_{AB} = 4\mathbf{e}_{AB} = 1.9846\mathbf{i} - 3.4729\mathbf{j} + 0\mathbf{k}$$

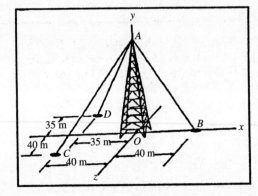

$$\mathbf{T}_{AC} = 2\mathbf{e}_{AB} = -0.8889\mathbf{i} - 1.5556\mathbf{j} + 0.8889\mathbf{k}$$

$$\mathbf{T}_{AD} = 2\mathbf{e}_{AD} = -0.8165\mathbf{i} - 1.6330\mathbf{j} - 0.8165\mathbf{k}.$$

The sum of the forces acting at A are

$$\mathbf{T}_A = 0.2792\mathbf{i} - 6.6615\mathbf{j} + 0.07239\mathbf{k} \ (\text{kN-m})$$

The position vector of A is $\mathbf{r}_{OA} = 70\mathbf{j}$. The moment about O is $\mathbf{M} = \mathbf{r}_{OA} \times \mathbf{T}_A$

$$\mathbf{M} = \begin{vmatrix} \mathbf{i} & \mathbf{j} & \mathbf{k} \\ 0 & 70 & 0 \\ 0.2792 & -6.6615 & 0.07239 \end{vmatrix}$$

$$= (70)(0.07239)\mathbf{i} - \mathbf{j}0 - \mathbf{k}(70)(0.2792) = 5.067\mathbf{i} - 19.54\mathbf{k}$$

Problem 4.70 Consider the 70-m tower in Problem 4.69. Suppose that the tension in cable AB is 4 kN, and you want to adjust the tensions in cables AC and AD so that the sum of the moments about the origin O due to the forces exerted by the cables at point A is zero. Determine the tensions.

Solution: From Varignon's theorem, the moment is zero only if the resultant of the forces normal to the vector $\mathbf{r}_{OA}$ is zero. From Problem 4.69 the unit vectors are:

$$\mathbf{e}_{AD} = \frac{\mathbf{r}_{AD}}{|\mathbf{r}_{AD}|} = \frac{-35}{85.73}\mathbf{i} - \frac{70}{85.73}\mathbf{j} - \frac{35}{85.73}\mathbf{k}$$

$$= -0.4082\mathbf{i} - 0.8165\mathbf{j} - 0.4082\mathbf{k}$$

$$\mathbf{e}_{AC} = \frac{\mathbf{r}_{AC}}{|\mathbf{r}_{AC}|} = -\frac{40}{90}\mathbf{i} - \frac{70}{90}\mathbf{j} + \frac{40}{90}\mathbf{k}$$

$$= -0.4444\mathbf{i} - 0.7778\mathbf{j} + 0.4444\mathbf{k}$$

$$\mathbf{e}_{AB} = \frac{\mathbf{r}_{AB}}{|\mathbf{r}_{AB}|} = \frac{40}{80.6}\mathbf{i} - \frac{70}{80.6}\mathbf{j} + 0\mathbf{k} = 0.4963\mathbf{i} - 0.8685\mathbf{j} + 0\mathbf{k}$$

The tensions are $\mathbf{T}_{AB} = 4\mathbf{e}_{AB}$, $\mathbf{T}_{AC} = |\mathbf{T}_{AC}|\mathbf{e}_{AC}$, and $\mathbf{T}_{AD} = |\mathbf{T}_{AD}|\mathbf{e}_{AD}$. The components normal to $\mathbf{r}_{OA}$ are

$$\sum F_X = (-0.4082|\mathbf{T}_{AD}| - 0.4444|\mathbf{T}_{AC}| + 1.9846)\mathbf{i} = 0$$

$$\sum F_Z = (-0.4082|\mathbf{T}_{AD}| + 0.4444|\mathbf{T}_{AC}|)\mathbf{k} = 0.$$

The HP-28S calculator was used to solve these equations:

$$|\mathbf{T}_{AC}| = 2.23 \text{ kN}, \quad |\mathbf{T}_{AD}| = 2.43 \text{ kN}$$

Problem 4.71 The tension in cable AB is 150 N. The tension in cable AC is 100 N. Determine the sum of the moments about D due to the forces exerted on the wall by the cables.

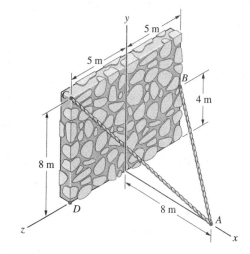

Solution: The coordinates of the points A, B, C are A (8, 0, 0), B (0, 4, -5), C (0, 8, 5), $D(0, 0, 5)$. The point A is the intersection of the lines of action of the forces. The position vector DA is

$$\mathbf{r}_{DA} = 8\mathbf{i} + 0\mathbf{j} - 5\mathbf{k}.$$

The position vectors AB and AC are

$$\mathbf{r}_{AB} = -8\mathbf{i} + 4\mathbf{j} - 5\mathbf{k}, \quad r_{AB} = \sqrt{8^2 + 4^2 + 5^2} = 10.247 \text{ m}.$$

$$\mathbf{r}_{AC} = -8\mathbf{i} + 8\mathbf{j} + 5\mathbf{k}, \quad r_{AC} = \sqrt{8^2 + 8^2 + 5^2} = 12.369 \text{ m}.$$

The unit vectors parallel to the cables are:

$$\mathbf{e}_{AB} = -0.7807\mathbf{i} + 0.3904\mathbf{j} - 0.4879\mathbf{k},$$

$$\mathbf{e}_{AC} = -0.6468\mathbf{i} + 0.6468\mathbf{j} - 0.4042\mathbf{k}.$$

The tensions are

$$\mathbf{T}_{AB} = 150\mathbf{e}_{AB} = -117.11\mathbf{i} + 58.56\mathbf{j} - 73.19\mathbf{k},$$

$$\mathbf{T}_{AC} = 100\mathbf{e}_{AC} = -64.68\mathbf{i} + 64.68\mathbf{j} - 40.42\mathbf{k}.$$

The sum of the forces *exerted by the wall on A* is

$$\mathbf{T}_A = -181.79\mathbf{i} + 123.24\mathbf{j} - 32.77\mathbf{k}.$$

The force exerted on the wall by the cables is $-\mathbf{T}_A$. The moment about D is $\mathbf{M}_D = -\mathbf{r}_{DA} \times \mathbf{T}_A$,

$$\mathbf{M}_D = \begin{vmatrix} \mathbf{i} & \mathbf{j} & \mathbf{k} \\ 8 & 0 & -5 \\ 181.79 & -123.24 & +32.77 \end{vmatrix} = (-123.24)(5)\mathbf{i}$$

$$- ((8)(+32.77) - (-5)(181.79))\mathbf{j} + (8)(-123.24)\mathbf{k}$$

$$\mathbf{M}_D = -616.2\mathbf{i} - 117.11\mathbf{j} - 985.9\mathbf{k} \text{ (N-m)}$$

(*Note*: An alternate method of solution is to express the moment in terms of the sum: $\mathbf{M}_D = (\mathbf{r}_{DC} \times \mathbf{T}_C + (\mathbf{r}_{DB} \times \mathbf{T}_B).)$

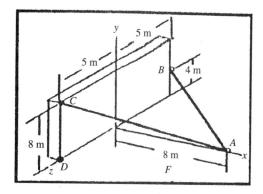

Problem 4.72 Consider the wall shown in Problem 4.71. The total force exerted by the two cables in the direction perpendicular to the wall is 2 kN. The magnitude of the sum of the moments about D due to the forces exerted on the wall by the cables is 18 kN-m. What are the tensions in the cables?

Solution: From the solution of Problem 4.71, we have $\mathbf{r}_{DA} = 8\mathbf{i} + 0\mathbf{j} - 5\mathbf{k}$. Forces in both cables pass through point A and we can use this vector to determine moments of both forces about D. The position vectors AB and AC are

$$\mathbf{r}_{AB} = -8\mathbf{i} + 4\mathbf{j} - 5\mathbf{k}, \quad |\mathbf{r}_{AB}| = \sqrt{8^2 + 4^2 + 5^2} = 10.247 \text{ m}.$$

$$\mathbf{r}_{AC} = -8\mathbf{i} + 8\mathbf{j} + 5\mathbf{k}, \quad |\mathbf{r}_{AC}| = \sqrt{8^2 + 8^2 + 5^2} = 12.369 \text{ m}.$$

The unit vectors parallel to the cables are:

$$\mathbf{e}_{AB} = -0.7807\mathbf{i} + 0.3904\mathbf{j} - 0.4879\mathbf{k},$$

$$\mathbf{e}_{AC} = -0.6468\mathbf{i} + 0.6468\mathbf{j} + 0.4042\mathbf{k}.$$

The tensions are

$$\mathbf{T}_{BA} = -T_{BA}\mathbf{e}_{AB} = -T_{BA}(-0.7807\mathbf{i} + 0.3904\mathbf{j} - 0.4879\mathbf{k}), \text{ and}$$

$$\mathbf{T}_{CA} = -T_{CA}\mathbf{e}_{AC} = -T_{CA}(-0.6468\mathbf{i} + 0.6468\mathbf{j} + 0.4042\mathbf{k}).$$

The sum of the forces exerted by the cables perpendicular to the wall ﹀ is given by

$$T_{\text{Perpendicular}} = T_{AB}(0.7807) + T_{AC}(0.6468) = 2 \text{ kN}.$$

The moments of these two forces about D are given by

$$\mathbf{M}_D = (\mathbf{r}_{DA} \times \mathbf{T}_{CA}) + (\mathbf{r}_{DA} \times \mathbf{T}_{BA}) = \mathbf{r}_{DA} \times (\mathbf{T}_{CA} + \mathbf{T}_{BA}).$$

The sum of the two forces is given by

$$\mathbf{M}_D = \begin{vmatrix} \mathbf{i} & \mathbf{j} & \mathbf{k} \\ 8 & 0 & -5 \\ (T_{CA} + T_{CB})_X & (T_{CA} + T_{CB})_Y & (T_{CA} + T_{CB})_Z \end{vmatrix}.$$

This expression can be expanded to yield

$$\mathbf{M}_D = 5(T_{CA} + T_{CB})_Y\mathbf{i} + [-8(T_{CA} + T_{CB})_Z - 5(T_{CA} + T_{CB})_X]\mathbf{j}$$

$$+ 8(T_{CA} + T_{CB})_Y\mathbf{k}.$$

The magnitude of this vector is given as 18 kN-m. Thus, we obtain the relation

$$|\mathbf{M}_D| = \sqrt{\begin{array}{l} 25(T_{CA} + T_{CB})_Y^2 + [-8(T_{CA} + T_{CB})_Z \\ -5(T_{CA} + T_{CB})_X]^2 + 64(T_{CA} + T_{CB})_Y^2 \end{array}} = 18 \text{ kN-m}.$$

We now have two equations in the two tensions in the cables. Either algebraic substitution or a numerical solver can be used to give

$$\boxed{T_{BA} = 1.596 \text{ kN}, \text{ and } T_{CA} = 1.166 \text{ kN}.}$$

Problem 4.73   The force $F = 800$ lb. The sum of the moments about O due to the force F and the forces exerted at A by the cables AB and AC is zero. What are the tensions in the cables?

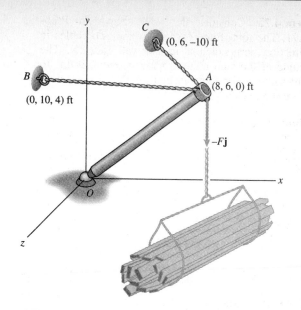

Solution: The coordinates of the points O, A, B, C are O $(0, 0, 0)$, A $(8, 6, 0)$, B $(0, 10, 4)$, C $(0, 6, -10)$. The position vectors are:

$$\mathbf{r}_{OA} = 8\mathbf{i} + 6\mathbf{j} + 0\mathbf{k}. |\mathbf{r}_{OA}| = 10 \text{ ft}$$

$$\mathbf{r}_{AB} = (0 - 8)\mathbf{i} + (10 - 6)\mathbf{j} + (4 - 0)\mathbf{k}$$

$$= -8\mathbf{i} + 4\mathbf{j} + 4\mathbf{k} |\mathbf{r}_{AB}| = 9.798 \text{ ft}$$

$$\mathbf{r}_{AC} = (0 - 8)\mathbf{i} + (6 - 6)\mathbf{j} + (-10 - 0)\mathbf{k}$$

$$= -8\mathbf{i} + 0\mathbf{j} - 10\mathbf{k}. |\mathbf{r}_{AC}| = 12.806 \text{ ft}.$$

The line of action of the forces intersect at point A. By Varignon's theorem, the forces at point A are in equilibrium if the moments vanish about O. The unit vectors are

$$\mathbf{e}_{OA} = 0.8\mathbf{i} + 0.6\mathbf{j} + 0\mathbf{k},$$

$$\mathbf{e}_{AB} = -0.8165\mathbf{i} + 0.4082\mathbf{j} + 0.4082\mathbf{k},$$

$$\mathbf{e}_{AC} = -0.6247\mathbf{i} + 0\mathbf{j} - 0.7809\mathbf{k}.$$

The forces are:

$$\mathbf{F}_{OA} = |\mathbf{F}_{OA}|\mathbf{e}_{OA}, \quad \mathbf{F}_{AB} = |\mathbf{F}_{AB}|\mathbf{e}_{AB}, \quad \mathbf{F}_{AC} = |\mathbf{F}_{AC}|\mathbf{e}_{AC}.$$

The equilibrium conditions are

$$\sum \mathbf{F} = \mathbf{F} + \mathbf{F}_{OA} + \mathbf{F}_{AB} + \mathbf{F}_{AC} = 0.$$

Combining and collecting terms

$$\sum \mathbf{F}_X = (0.8|\mathbf{F}_{OA}| - 0.8165|\mathbf{F}_{AB}| - 0.6247|\mathbf{F}_{AC}|)\mathbf{i} = 0$$

$$\sum \mathbf{F}_Y = (0.6|\mathbf{F}_{OA}| + 0.4082|\mathbf{F}_{AB}| - 800)\mathbf{j} = 0$$

$$\sum \mathbf{F}_Z = (0.4082|\mathbf{F}_{AB}| - 0.7809|\mathbf{F}_{AC}|)\mathbf{k} = 0.$$

These equations were solved using the **TK Solver Plus** commercial software package. The result:

$$|\mathbf{F}_{OA}| = 903.23 \text{ lb}, \quad |\mathbf{F}_{AB}| = 632.13 \text{ lb}, \quad |\mathbf{F}_{AC}| = 330.48 \text{ lb}.$$

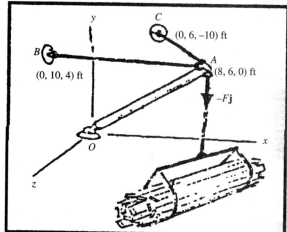

Problem 4.74 In Problem 4.73, the sum of the moments about O due to the force F and the forces exerted at A by the cables AB and AC is zero. Each cable will safely support a tension of 2000 lb. Based on this criterion, what is the largest safe value of the force F?

Solution: For Problem 4.73, the loads, for a value of $|F| = 800$ lb, we get $|F_{OA}| = 903.23$ lb. $|F_{AB}| = 632.13$ lb, and $|F_{AC}| = 330.48$ lb. To scale the problem, we must make $|F_{AB}| = 2000$ lb. The problem is linear, so we may scale everything up. The scaling factor is $k = 2000/632.13 = 3.164$. Scaling the 800 lb load by this factor gives

$$F_{MAX} = 2531 \text{ lb.}$$

Problem 4.75 The 200-kg slider at A is held in place on the smooth vertical bar by the cable AB. Determine the moment about the bottom of the bar (point C with coordinates $x = 2$ m, $y = z = 0$) due to the force exerted on the slider by the cable.

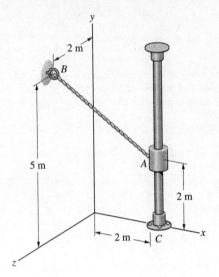

Solution: The slider is in equilibrium. The smooth bar exerts no vertical forces on the slider. Hence, the vertical component of $\mathbf{F}_{AB}$ supports the weight of the slider.

The unit vector from A to B is determined from the coordinates of points A and B $A(2, 2, 0)$, $B(0, 5, 2)$ m

Thus, $\mathbf{r}_{AB} = -2\mathbf{i} + 3\mathbf{j} + 2\mathbf{k}$ m

$\mathbf{e}_{AB} = -0.485\mathbf{i} + 0.728\mathbf{j} + 0.485\mathbf{k}$

and $\mathbf{F}_{AB} = F_{AB}\mathbf{e}_{AB}$

The horizontal force exerted by the bar on the slider is

$\mathbf{H} = H_x\mathbf{i} + H_z\mathbf{k}$

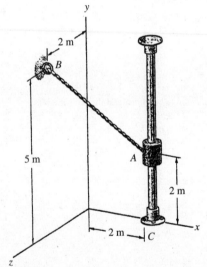

Equilibrium requires $\mathbf{H} + \mathbf{F}_{AB} - mg\mathbf{j} = 0$

$\mathbf{i}: H_x - 0.485F_{AB} = 0 \quad m = 200$ kg

$\mathbf{j}: 0.728F_{AB} - mg = 0 \quad g = 9.81$ m/s^2

$\mathbf{k}: H_z + 0.485F_{AB} = 0$

Solving, we get

$F_{AB} = 2697$N $= 2, 70$ kN

$H_x = 1308$N $= 1.31$ kN

$H_z = -1308$N $= -1.31$ kN

$\mathbf{r}_{CA} = 2\mathbf{j}$ m

$\mathbf{F}_{AB} = F_{AB}\mathbf{e}_{AB}$

$\mathbf{F}_{AB} = -1308\mathbf{i} + 1962\mathbf{j} + 1308\mathbf{k}$ N

$$\mathbf{M}_c = \begin{vmatrix} \mathbf{i} & \mathbf{j} & \mathbf{k} \\ 0 & 2 & 0 \\ -1308 & 1962 & 1308 \end{vmatrix}$$

$\mathbf{M}_c = 2616\mathbf{i} + 0\mathbf{j} + 2616\mathbf{k}$ N-m

$\mathbf{M}_c = 2.62\mathbf{i} + 2.62\mathbf{i}$ kN-m

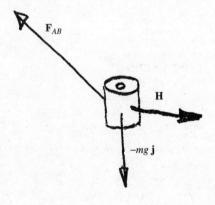

Problem 4.76 To evaluate the adequacy of the design of the vertical steel post, you must determine the moment about the bottom of the post due to the force exerted on the post at B by the cable AB. A calibrated strain gauge mounted on cable AC indicates that the tension in cable AC is 22 kN. What is the moment?

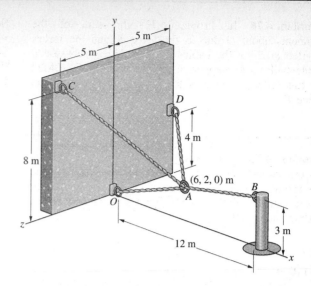

Solution: To find the moment, we must find the force in cable AB. In order to do this, we must find the forces in cables AO and AD also. This requires that we solve the equilibrium problem at A.

Our first task is to write unit vectors e_{AB}, e_{AO}, e_{AC}, and e_{AD}. Each will be of the form

$$e_{Ai} = \frac{(x_i - x_A)\mathbf{i} + (y_i - y_A)\mathbf{j} + (z_i - z_A)\mathbf{k}}{\sqrt{(x_i - x_A)^2 + (y_i - y_A)^2 + (z_i - z_A)^2}}$$

where i takes on the values B, C, D, and O. We get

$$e_{AB} = 0.986\mathbf{i} + 0.164\mathbf{j} + 0\mathbf{k}$$

$$e_{AC} = -0.609\mathbf{i} + 0.609\mathbf{j} + 0.508\mathbf{k}$$

$$e_{AD} = -0.744\mathbf{i} + 0.248\mathbf{j} - 0.620\mathbf{k}$$

$$e_{AO} = -0.949\mathbf{i} - 0.316\mathbf{j} + 0\mathbf{k}$$

We now write the forces as

$$\mathbf{T}_{AB} = T_{AB}e_{AB}$$

$$\mathbf{T}_{AC} = T_{AC}e_{AC}$$

$$\mathbf{T}_{AD} = T_{AD}e_{AD}$$

$$\mathbf{T}_{AO} = T_{AO}e_{AO}$$

We then sum the forces and write the equilibrium equations in component form.

For equilibrium at A, $\sum \mathbf{F}_A = 0$

$$\sum \mathbf{F}_A = \mathbf{T}_{AB} + \mathbf{T}_{AC} + \mathbf{T}_{AD} + \mathbf{T}_{AO} = 0.$$

In component form,

$$\begin{cases} T_{AB}e_{ABx} + T_{AC}e_{ACx} + T_{AD}e_{ADx} + T_{AO}e_{AOx} = 0 \\ T_{AB}e_{ABy} + T_{AC}e_{ACy} + T_{AD}e_{ADy} + T_{AO}e_{AOy} = 0 \\ T_{AB}e_{ABz} + T_{AC}e_{ACz} + T_{AD}e_{ADz} + T_{AO}e_{AOz} = 0 \end{cases}$$

We know $T_{AC} = 22$ kN. Substituting this in, we have 3 eqns in 3 unknowns. Solving, we get

$$T_{AB} = 163.05 \text{ kN}, \quad T_{AD} = 18.01 \text{ kN} \quad T_{AO} = 141.28 \text{ kN}$$

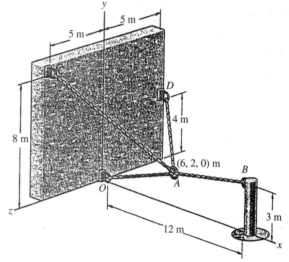

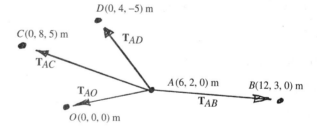

We now know that $\mathbf{T}_{AB}$ is given as

$$\mathbf{T}_{AB} = T_{AB}e_{AB} = 160.8\mathbf{i} + 26.8\mathbf{j} \text{ (kN)}$$

and that the force acting at B is $(-\mathbf{T}_{AB})$.

The moment about the bottom of the post is given by

$$\mathbf{M}_{\text{BOTTOM}} = \mathbf{r} \times (-\mathbf{T}_{AB}) = 3\mathbf{j} \times (-\mathbf{T}_{AB})$$

Solving, we get

$$\mathbf{M}_{\text{BOTTOM}} = 482\mathbf{k} \text{ (kN-m)}$$

Problem 4.77 Use Eqs. (4.5) and (4.6) to determine the moment of the 40-N force about the z axis. (First see if you can write down the result without using the equations.)

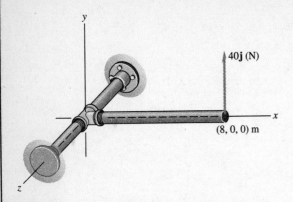

40**j** (N)

(8, 0, 0) m

Solution: By inspection, the moment should be 8 m × 40 N in the negative z direction (using the right hand rule). Thus, we expect the result to be

$$M_{zaxis} = -320\mathbf{k} \ \text{(N-m)}$$

Equation (4.5) is

$$\mathbf{M}_L = [\mathbf{e} \cdot (\mathbf{r} \times \mathbf{F})]\mathbf{e}$$

where Eq. (4.6) can be used to evaluate $\mathbf{e} \cdot (\mathbf{r} \times \mathbf{F})$. Eqn. (4.6) is

$$\mathbf{e} \cdot (\mathbf{r} \times \mathbf{F}) = \begin{vmatrix} e_x & e_y & e_z \\ r_x & r_y & r_z \\ F_x & F_y & F_z \end{vmatrix}$$

For our problem, $\mathbf{e} = \mathbf{kr} = 8\mathbf{i}$ and $\mathbf{F} = -40\mathbf{j}$

Thus, from Eq. (4.6)

$$\mathbf{e} \cdot (\mathbf{r} \times \mathbf{F}) = \begin{vmatrix} 0 & 0 & 1 \\ 8 & 0 & 0 \\ 0 & -40 & 0 \end{vmatrix} = -320 \ \text{(N-m)}$$

and from Eq. (4.5)

$$\mathbf{M}_L = (\mathbf{e} \cdot (\mathbf{r} \times \mathbf{F}))\mathbf{e} = -320\mathbf{k}$$

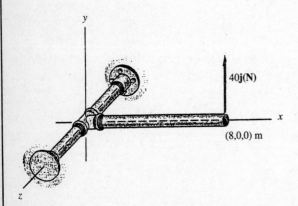

40j(N)

(8,0,0) m

Problem 4.78 Use Eqs. (4.5) and (4.6) to determine the moment of the 20-N force about (a) the x axis, (b) the y axis, (c) the z axis. (First see if you can write down the results without using the equations.)

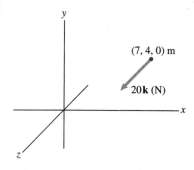

Solution: The force is parallel to the z-axis. The perpendicular distance from the x axis to the line of action of the force is 4 m. The perpendicular distance from the y axis is 7 m and the perpendicular distance from the z axis is $\sqrt{4^2 + 7^2} = \sqrt{65}$ m.

By inspection, the moment about the x axis is

$$\mathbf{M}_x = (4)(20)\mathbf{i} \ (\text{N-m})$$

$$\mathbf{M}_x = 80\mathbf{i} \ (\text{N-m})$$

By inspection, the moment about the y axis is $\mathbf{M}_y = (7)(20)(-\mathbf{j})$ N-m

$$\mathbf{M}_y = -140\mathbf{j} \ (\text{N-m})$$

By inspection, the moment about the z-axis is zero since $\mathbf{F}$ is parallel to the z-axis.

$$\mathbf{M}_z = 0 \ (\text{N-m})$$

Now for the calculations using (4.5) and (4.6)

$$\mathbf{M}_L = [\mathbf{e} \cdot (\mathbf{r} \times \mathbf{F})]\mathbf{e}$$

$$\mathbf{M}_x = \begin{vmatrix} 1 & 0 & 0 \\ 7 & 4 & 0 \\ 0 & 0 & 20 \end{vmatrix} \mathbf{i} = 80\mathbf{i} \ (\text{N-m})$$

$$\mathbf{M}_y = \begin{vmatrix} 0 & 1 & 0 \\ 7 & 4 & 0 \\ 0 & 0 & 20 \end{vmatrix} \mathbf{j} = -140\mathbf{j} \ (\text{N-m})$$

$$\mathbf{M}_z = \begin{vmatrix} 0 & 0 & 1 \\ 7 & 4 & 0 \\ 0 & 0 & 20 \end{vmatrix} \mathbf{k} = 0\mathbf{k} \ (\text{N-m})$$

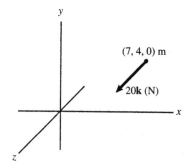

Problem 4.79 Three forces parallel to the y axis act on the rectangular plate. Use Eqs. (4.5) and (4.6) to determine the sum of the moments of the forces about the x axis. (First see if you can write down the result without using the equations.)

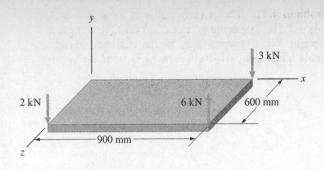

Solution: By inspection, the 3 kN force has no moment about the x-axis since it acts through the x axis. The perpendicular distances of the other two forces from the x axis is 0.6 m. The H 2 kN force has a positive moment and the 6 kN force has a negative about the x axis.

$$\sum M_x = [(2)(0.6) - (6)(0.6)]\mathbf{i} \text{ kN}$$

$$\sum M_x = -2.4\mathbf{i} \text{ kN}$$

Calculating the result:

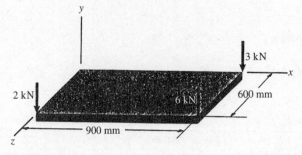

$$\mathbf{M}_{3\ kN} = \begin{vmatrix} 1 & 0 & 0 \\ 0 & 0 & 0 \\ 0 & -3 & 0 \end{vmatrix} \mathbf{i} = 0\mathbf{i} \text{ kN}$$

$$\mathbf{M}_{2\ kN} = \begin{vmatrix} 1 & 0 & 0 \\ 0 & 0 & .6 \\ 0 & -2 & 0 \end{vmatrix} \mathbf{i} = 1.2\mathbf{i} \text{ kN}$$

$$\mathbf{M}_{6\ kN} = \begin{vmatrix} 1 & 0 & 0 \\ 0 & 0 & .6 \\ 0 & 6 & 0 \end{vmatrix} \mathbf{i} = -3.6\mathbf{i} \text{ kN}$$

$$\sum \mathbf{M}_x = \mathbf{M}_{3\ kN} + \mathbf{M}_{2\ kN} + \mathbf{M}_{6\ kN}$$

$$\sum \mathbf{M}_x = 0 + 1.2\mathbf{i} - 3.6\mathbf{i} \text{ (kN)}$$

$$\sum \mathbf{M}_x = -2.4\mathbf{i} \text{ (kN)}$$

Problem 4.80 Consider the rectangular plate shown in Problem 4.79. The three forces are parallel to the y axis. Determine the sum of the moments of the forces (a) about the y axis, (b) about the z axis.

Solution: (a) The magnitude of the moments about the y-axis is $M = \mathbf{e}_Y \cdot (\mathbf{r} \times \mathbf{F})$. The position vectors of the three forces are given in the solution to Problem 4.79. The magnitude for each force is:

$$\mathbf{e}_Y \cdot (\mathbf{r} \times \mathbf{F}) = \begin{vmatrix} 0 & 1 & 0 \\ 0.9 & 0 & 0 \\ 0 & -3 & 0 \end{vmatrix} = 0,$$

$$\mathbf{e}_Y \cdot (\mathbf{r} \times \mathbf{F}) = \begin{vmatrix} 0 & 1 & 0 \\ 0.9 & 0 & 0.6 \\ 0 & 6 & 0 \end{vmatrix} = 0,$$

$$\mathbf{e}_Y \cdot (\mathbf{r} \times \mathbf{F}) = \begin{vmatrix} 0 & 1 & 0 \\ 0 & 0 & 0.6 \\ 0 & -2 & 0 \end{vmatrix} = 0$$

Thus the moment about the y-axis is zero, since the magnitude of each moment is zero.

(b) The magnitude of each moment about the z-axis is

$$\mathbf{e}_Z \cdot (\mathbf{r} \times \mathbf{F}) = \begin{vmatrix} 0 & 1 & 0 \\ 0.9 & 0 & 0 \\ 0 & -3 & 0 \end{vmatrix} = -2.7,$$

$$\mathbf{e}_Z \cdot (\mathbf{r} \times \mathbf{F}) = \begin{vmatrix} 0 & 0 & 1 \\ 0.9 & 0 & 0.6 \\ 0 + & 6 & 0 \end{vmatrix} = 5.4,$$

$$\mathbf{e}_Z \cdot (\mathbf{r} \times \mathbf{F}) = \begin{vmatrix} 0 & 0 & 1 \\ 0 & 0 & 0.6 \\ 0 & -2 & 0 \end{vmatrix} = 0.$$

Thus the moment about the z-axis is

$$\sum \mathbf{M}_Z = -2.7\mathbf{e}_Z + 5.4\mathbf{e}_Z = 2.7\mathbf{k} \text{ (kN-m)}$$

Problem 4.81 The person exerts a force $\mathbf{F} = 0.2\mathbf{i} - 0.4\mathbf{j} + 1.2\mathbf{k}$ (lb) on the gate at C. Point C lies in the $x - y$ plane. What moment does the person exert about the gate's hinge axis, which is coincident with the y axis?

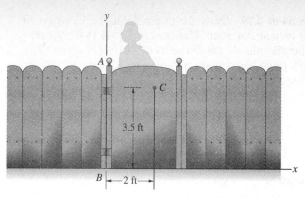

Solution:

$$\mathbf{M} = [\mathbf{e} \cdot (\mathbf{r} \times \mathbf{F})]\mathbf{e}$$

$$\mathbf{e} = \mathbf{j}, \quad \mathbf{r} = 2\mathbf{i} \text{ ft}, \quad \mathbf{F} \text{ is given}$$

$$M_Y = \begin{vmatrix} 0 & 1 & 0 \\ 2 & 0 & 0 \\ .2 & -.4 & 1.2 \end{vmatrix} \mathbf{j} = -2.4\mathbf{j} \text{ (ft-lb)}$$

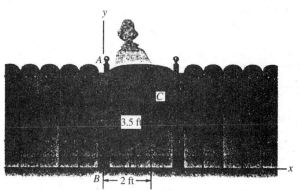

Problem 4.82 Four forces parallel to the y axis act on the rectangular plate. The sum of the forces in the positive y direction is 200 lb. The sum of the moments of the forces about the x axis is $-300\mathbf{i}$ (ft-lb) and the sum of the moments about the z axis is $400\mathbf{k}$ (ft-lb). What are the magnitudes of the forces?

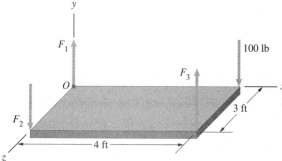

Solution: Sum of forces in y-direction:

$$F_1 - F_2 + F_3 - 100 = 200 \text{ lb} \quad (1)$$

Sum of Moments about x-axis:

$$\sum \mathbf{M}_x = \begin{vmatrix} 1 & 0 & 0 \\ 0 & 0 & 3 \\ 0 & -F_2 & 0 \end{vmatrix} \mathbf{i} + \begin{vmatrix} 1 & 0 & 0 \\ 0 & 0 & 3 \\ 0 & F_3 & 0 \end{vmatrix} \mathbf{i} + 0 + 0$$

$$\sum \mathbf{M}_x = 3F_2\mathbf{i} - 3F_3\mathbf{i} = -300\mathbf{i}$$

or $\quad 3F_2 - 3F_3 = -300$ (ft-lb) $\quad\quad\quad$ (2)

Sum of moments about the z-axis:

$$\sum \mathbf{M}_z = \begin{vmatrix} 0 & 0 & 1 \\ 4 & 0 & 0 \\ 0 & -100 & 0 \end{vmatrix} \mathbf{k} + \begin{vmatrix} 0 & 0 & 1 \\ 4 & 0 & 0 \\ 0 & F_3 & 0 \end{vmatrix} \mathbf{k} + 0 + 0$$

$$\sum \mathbf{M}_z = -400\mathbf{k} + 4F_3\mathbf{k} = 400\mathbf{k} \text{ (ft-lb)}$$

or $\quad -400 + 4F_3 = 400$ (ft-lb) $\quad\quad\quad$ (3)

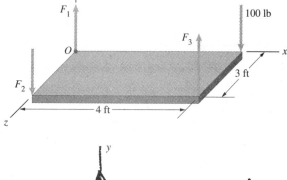

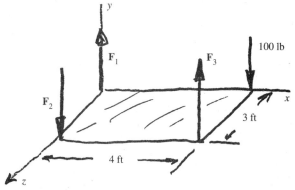

Solving (1), (2), and (3) simultaneously, we get

$F_1 = 200$ lb, $F_2 = 100$ lb, $F_3 = 200$ lb.

Problem 4.83 The force $\mathbf{F} = 100\mathbf{i} + 60\mathbf{j} - 40\mathbf{k}$ (lb). What is the moment of $\mathbf{F}$ about the y axis? Draw a sketch to indicate the sense of the moment.

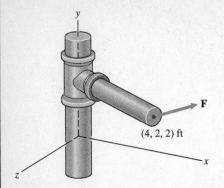

Solution: The radius vector to the point of application of the force is $\mathbf{r} = 4\mathbf{i} + 2\mathbf{j} - 2\mathbf{k}$. The magnitude of the moment is

$$\mathbf{e}_Y \cdot (\mathbf{r} \times \mathbf{F}) = \begin{vmatrix} 0 & 1 & 0 \\ 4 & 2 & -2 \\ 100 & 60 & -40 \end{vmatrix} = -40 \text{ ft lb}$$

The moment is $\mathbf{M}_Y = -40\mathbf{e}_Y = -40\mathbf{j}$. The sense of the moment is the direction of the curled fingers of the right hand if the thumb is held parallel to the negative y-axis (pointing thumb down in the sketch).

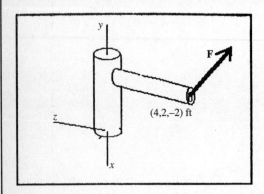

(4,2,−2) ft

Problem 4.84 Suppose that the moment of the force $\mathbf{F}$ shown in Problem 4.83 about the x axis is $-80\mathbf{i}$ (ft-lb), the moment about the y axis is zero, and the moment about the z axis is $160\mathbf{k}$ (ft-lb). If $F_y = 80$ lb, what are F_x and F_z?

Solution: The magnitudes of the moments:

$$\mathbf{e} \bullet (\mathbf{r} \times \mathbf{F}) = \begin{vmatrix} e_X & e_Y & e_Z \\ r_X & r_Y & r_Z \\ F_X & F_Y & F_Z \end{vmatrix},$$

$$\mathbf{e}_Z \cdot (\mathbf{r} \times \mathbf{F}) = \begin{vmatrix} 0 & 0 & 1 \\ 4 & 2 & -2 \\ F_X & 80 & F_Z \end{vmatrix} = 320 - 2F_X = 160$$

Solve: $F_X = 80$ lb, $F_Z = 40$ lb, from which the force vector is $\mathbf{F} = 80\mathbf{i} + 80\mathbf{j} + 40\mathbf{k}$

Problem 4.85 The robotic manipulator is stationary. The weights of the arms AB and BC act at their midpoints. The direction cosines of the centerline of arm AB are $\cos\theta_x = 0.500$, $\cos\theta_y = 0.866$, $\cos\theta_z = 0$, and the direction cosines of the centerline of arm BC are $\cos\theta_x = 0.707$, $\cos\theta_y = 0.619$, $\cos\theta_z = -0.342$. What total moment is exerted about the z axis by the weights of the arms?

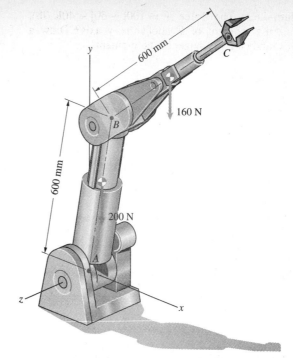

Solution: The unit vectors along AB and AC are of the form

$$\mathbf{e} = \cos\theta_x\mathbf{i} + \cos\theta_y\mathbf{j} + \cos\theta_z\mathbf{k}.$$

The unit vectors are

$$\mathbf{e}_{AB} = 0.500\mathbf{i} + 0.866\mathbf{j} + 0\mathbf{k} \text{ and } \mathbf{e}_{BC} = 0.707\mathbf{i} + 0.619\mathbf{j} - 0.342\mathbf{k}.$$

The vector to point G at the center of arm AB is

$$\mathbf{r}_{AG} = 300(0.500\mathbf{i} + 0.866\mathbf{j} + 0\mathbf{k}) = 150\mathbf{i} + 259.8\mathbf{j} + 0\mathbf{k} \text{ mm},$$

and the vector from A to the point H at the center of arm BC is given by

$$\mathbf{r}_{AH} = \mathbf{r}_{AB} + \mathbf{r}_{BH} = 600\mathbf{e}_{AB} + 300\mathbf{e}_{BC}$$

$$= 512.1\mathbf{i} + 705.3\mathbf{j} - 102.6\mathbf{k} \text{ mm}.$$

The weight vectors acting at G and H are $\mathbf{W}_G = -200\mathbf{j}$ N, and $\mathbf{W}_H = -160\mathbf{j}$ N. The moment vectors of these forces about the z axis are of the form

$$\mathbf{e} \bullet (\mathbf{r} \times \mathbf{F}) = \begin{vmatrix} e_X & e_Y & e_Z \\ r_X & r_Y & r_Z \\ F_X & F_Y & F_Z \end{vmatrix}.$$

Here, $\mathbf{W}_G$ and $\mathbf{W}_H$ take on the role of $\mathbf{F}$, and $\mathbf{e} = \mathbf{k}$.

Substituting into the form for the moment of the force at G, we get

$$\mathbf{e} \bullet (\mathbf{r} \times F) = \begin{vmatrix} 0 & 0 & 1 \\ 0.150 & 0.260 & 0 \\ 0 & -200 & 0 \end{vmatrix} = -30 \text{ N-m}.$$

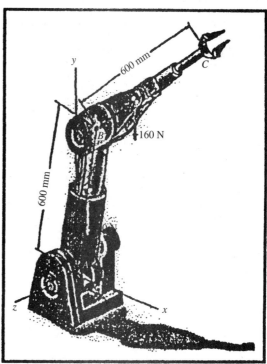

Similarly, for the moment of the force at H, we get

$$\mathbf{e} \bullet (\mathbf{r} \times F) = \begin{vmatrix} 0 & 0 & 1 \\ 0.512 & 0.705 & -0.103 \\ 0 & -160 & 0 \end{vmatrix} = -81.9 \text{ N-m}.$$

The total moment about the z axis is the sum of the two moments. Hence, $M_{z-\text{axis}} = -111.9$ N-m

Problem 4.86 In Problem 4.85, what total moment is exerted about the x axis by the weights of the arms?

Solution: The solution is identical to that of Problem 4.85 except that $\mathbf{e} = \mathbf{i}$. Substituting into the form for the moment of the force at G, we get

$$\mathbf{e} \cdot (\mathbf{r} \times \mathbf{F}) = \begin{vmatrix} 1 & 0 & 0 \\ 0.150 & 0.260 & 0 \\ 0 & -200 & 0 \end{vmatrix} = 0 \text{ N-m.}$$

Similarly, for the moment of the force at H, we get

$$\mathbf{e} \cdot (\mathbf{r} \times \mathbf{F}) = \begin{vmatrix} 1 & 0 & 0 \\ 0.512 & 0.705 & -0.103 \\ 0 & -160 & 0 \end{vmatrix} = -16.4 \text{ N-m.}$$

The total moment about the x axis is the sum of the two moments. Hence, $M_{x-\text{axis}} = -16.4$ N-m

---

Problem 4.87 Two forces are exerted on the crankshaft by the connecting rods. The direction cosines of F_A are $\cos\theta_x = -0.182$, $\cos\theta_y = 0.818$, and $\cos\theta_z = 0.545$, and its magnitude is 4 kN. The direction cosines of F_B are $\cos\theta_x = 0.182$, $\cos\theta_y = 0.818$, and $\cos\theta_z = -0.545$, and its magnitude is 2 kN. What is the sum of the moments of the two forces about the x axis? (This is the moment that causes the crankshaft to rotate.)

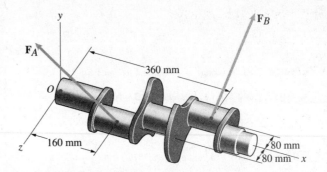

Solution: The coordinates of the points of action of the two forces are A (0.16, 0, 0.08), B (0.36, 0, −0.08). The position vectors are

$$\mathbf{r}_{OA} = 0.16\mathbf{i} + 0\mathbf{j} + 0.08\mathbf{k} \text{ (m)},$$

$$\mathbf{r}_{OB} = 0.36\mathbf{i} + 0\mathbf{j} - 0.08\mathbf{k} \text{ (m)}.$$

The unit vectors parallel to the forces are given by the direction cosines:

$$\mathbf{e}_{FA} = -0.182\mathbf{i} + 0.818\mathbf{j} + 0.545\mathbf{k},$$

$$\mathbf{e}_{FB} = 0.182\mathbf{i} + 0.818\mathbf{j} - 0.545\mathbf{k}$$

The forces are

$$\mathbf{F}_A = -0.728\mathbf{i} + 3.272\mathbf{j} + 2.18\mathbf{k} \text{ (kN)}$$

$$\mathbf{F}_B = 0.364\mathbf{i} + 1.636\mathbf{j} - 1.09\mathbf{k} \text{ (kN)}$$

The magnitude of the moments:

$$\mathbf{e}_X \cdot (\mathbf{r}_A \times \mathbf{F}_A) = \begin{vmatrix} 1 & 0 & 0 \\ 0.16 & 0 & 0.08 \\ -0.728 & 3.272 & 2.18 \end{vmatrix} = -0.2618,$$

$$\mathbf{e}_X \cdot (\mathbf{r}_B \times \mathbf{F}_B) = \begin{vmatrix} 1 & 0 & 0 \\ 0.36 & 0 & -0.08 \\ 0.364 & 1.636 & -1.09 \end{vmatrix} = 0.1309$$

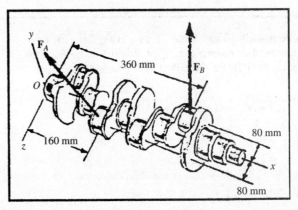

The sum of the moments about the x-axis is

$$\mathbf{M}_X = -0.2618\mathbf{e}_X + 0.1309\mathbf{e}_X = -0.1309\mathbf{i} \text{ kN-m.}$$

Problem 4.88   Determine the moment of the 20-N force about the line AB. Use Eqs. (4.5) and (4.6), letting the unit vector **e** point (a) from A toward B, (b) from B toward A.

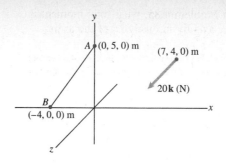

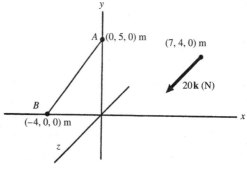

Solution: First, we need the unit vector

$$\mathbf{e}_{AB} = \frac{(x_B - x_A)\mathbf{i} + (y_B - y_A)\mathbf{j} + (z_B - z_A)\mathbf{k}}{\sqrt{(x_B - x_A)^2 + (y_B - y_A)^2 + (z_B - z_A)^2}}$$

$$\mathbf{e}_{AB} = -0.625\mathbf{i} - 0.781\mathbf{j} = -\mathbf{e}_{BA}$$

Now, the moment of the $20\mathbf{k}$ (N) force about AB is given as

$$M_L = \begin{vmatrix} e_x & e_y & e_z \\ r_x & r_y & r_z \\ F_x & F_y & F_z \end{vmatrix} \mathbf{e} \quad \text{where } \mathbf{e} \text{ is } \mathbf{e}_{AB} \text{ or } \mathbf{e}_{BA}$$

For this problem, **r** must go from line AB to the point of application of the force. Let us use point A.

$$\mathbf{r} = (7 - 0)\mathbf{i} + (4 - 5)\mathbf{j} + (0 - 0)\mathbf{k} \text{ m}$$

$$\mathbf{r} = 7\mathbf{i} - 1\mathbf{j} + 0\mathbf{k} \text{ m}$$

Using $\mathbf{e}_{AB}$

$$\mathbf{M}_L = \begin{vmatrix} -0.625 & -0.781 & 0 \\ 7 & -1 & 0 \\ 0 & 0 & 20 \end{vmatrix} (-0.625\mathbf{i} - 0.781\mathbf{j})$$

$$\mathbf{M}_L = -76.1\mathbf{i} - 95.1\mathbf{j} \text{ (N-m)}$$

Using $\mathbf{e}_{BA}$

$$\mathbf{M}_L = \begin{vmatrix} 0.625 & 0.781 & 0 \\ 7 & -1 & 0 \\ 0 & 0 & 20 \end{vmatrix} (0.625\mathbf{i} + 0.781\mathbf{j})$$

$$\mathbf{M}_L = -76.1\mathbf{i} - 95.1\mathbf{j} \text{ (N-m)}$$

*Results are the same

Problem 4.89   The force $\mathbf{F} = -10\mathbf{i} + 5\mathbf{j} - 5\mathbf{k}$ (kip). Determine the moment of **F** about the line AB. Draw a sketch to indicate the sense of the moment.

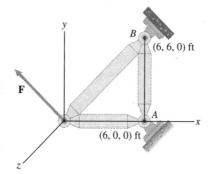

Solution: The moment of **F** about pt. A is

$$\mathbf{M}_A = -6\mathbf{i} \times \mathbf{F}$$

$$= \begin{vmatrix} \mathbf{i} & \mathbf{j} & \mathbf{k} \\ -6 & 0 & 0 \\ -10 & 5 & -5 \end{vmatrix}$$

$$= -30\mathbf{j} - 30\mathbf{k} \text{ (ft-kip)}.$$

The unit vector **j** is parallel to line AB, so the moment about AB is

$$\mathbf{M}_{AB} = (\mathbf{j} \cdot \mathbf{M}_A)\mathbf{j}$$

$$= -30\mathbf{j} \text{ (ft-kip)}.$$

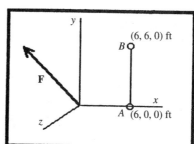

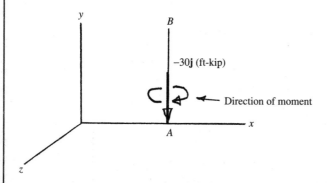

Problem 4.90 The force $\mathbf{F} = 10\mathbf{i} + 12\mathbf{j} - 6\mathbf{k}$ (N). What is the moment of $\mathbf{F}$ about the line OA? Draw a sketch to indicate the sense of the moment.

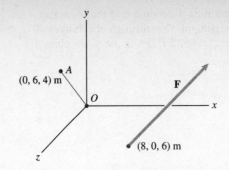

Solution: The strategy is to determine a unit vector parallel to OA and to use this to determine the moment about OA. The vector parallel to OA is $\mathbf{r}_{OA} = 6\mathbf{j} + 4\mathbf{k}$. The magnitude: $\mathbf{F}$. The unit vector parallel to OA is $\mathbf{e}_{OA} = 0.8321\mathbf{j} + 0.5547\mathbf{k}$. The vector from O to the point of application of $\mathbf{F}$ is $\mathbf{r}_{OF} = 8\mathbf{i} + 6\mathbf{k}$. The magnitude of the moment about OA is

$$|\mathbf{M}_O| = \mathbf{e}_{OA} \cdot (\mathbf{r}_{OF} \times \mathbf{F}) = \begin{vmatrix} 0 & 0.8321 & 0.5547 \\ 8 & 0 & 6 \\ 10 & 12 & -6 \end{vmatrix}$$

$$= 89.8614 + 53.251 = 143.1 \text{ N-m.}$$

The moment about OA is $\mathbf{M}_{OA} = |\mathbf{M}_{OA}|\mathbf{e}_{OA} = 119.1\mathbf{j} + 79.4\mathbf{k}$ (N-m). The sense of the moment is in the direction of the curled fingers of the right hand when the thumb is parallel to OA, pointing to A.

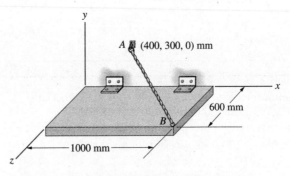

Problem 4.91 The tension in the cable AB is 1 kN. Determine the moment about the x axis due to the force exerted on the hatch by the cable at point B. Draw a sketch to indicate the sense of the moment.

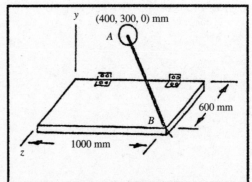

Solution: The vector parallel to BA is

$$\mathbf{r}_{BA} = (0.4 - 1)\mathbf{i} + 0.3\mathbf{j} - 0.6\mathbf{k} = -0.6\mathbf{i} + 0.3\mathbf{j} - 0.6\mathbf{k}.$$

The unit vector parallel to BA is

$$\mathbf{e}_{BA} = -0.6667\mathbf{i} + 0.3333\mathbf{j} - 0.6667\mathbf{k}.$$

The moment about O is

$$\mathbf{M}_O = \mathbf{r}_{OB} \times \mathbf{T} = \begin{vmatrix} \mathbf{i} & \mathbf{j} & \mathbf{k} \\ 1 & 0 & 0.6 \\ -0.6667 & 0.3333 & -0.66667 \end{vmatrix}$$

$$\mathbf{M}_O = -0.2\mathbf{i} + 0.2667\mathbf{j} + 0.3333\mathbf{k}.$$

The magnitude is

$$|M_X| = \mathbf{e}_X \cdot \mathbf{M}_O = -0.2 \text{ kN-m.}$$

The moment is $\mathbf{M}_X = -0.2\mathbf{i}$ kN-m. The sense is clockwise when viewed along the x-axis toward the origin.

234

Problem 4.92 Determine the moment of the force applied at D about the straight line through the hinges A and B. (The line through A and B lies in the $y - z$ plane.)

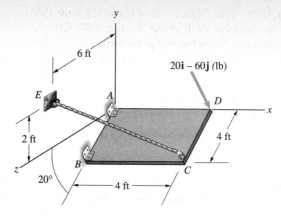

Solution: From the figure, we see that the unit vector along the line from A toward B is given by $\mathbf{e}_{AB} = -\sin 20°\mathbf{j} + \cos 20°\mathbf{k}$. The position vector is $\mathbf{r}_{AD} = 4\mathbf{i}$ ft, and the force vector is as shown in the figure. The moment vector of a force about an axis is of the form

$$\mathbf{e} \bullet (\mathbf{r} \times \mathbf{F}) = \begin{vmatrix} e_X & e_y & e_z \\ r_X & r_Y & r_Z \\ F_X & F_Y & F_Z \end{vmatrix}.$$

For this case,

$$\mathbf{e} \bullet (\mathbf{r} \times \mathbf{F}) = \begin{vmatrix} 0 & -\sin 20° & \cos 20° \\ 4 & 0 & 0 \\ 20 & -60 & 0 \end{vmatrix} = -240 \cos 20° \text{ ft-lb}$$

$$= -225.5 \text{ ft-lb}.$$

The negative sign is because the moment is opposite in direction to the unit vector from A to B.

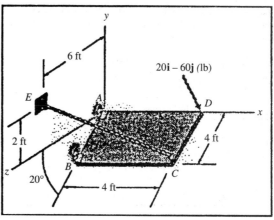

Problem 4.93 In Problem 4.92, the tension in the cable CE is 160 lb. Determine the moment of the force exerted by the cable on the hatch at C about the straight line through the hinges A and B.

Solution: From the figure, we see that the unit vector along the line from A toward B is given by $\mathbf{e}_{AB} = -\sin 20°\mathbf{j} + \cos 20°\mathbf{k}$. The position vector is $\mathbf{r}_{BC} = 4\mathbf{i}$ ft. The coordinates of point C are $(4, -4\sin 20°, 4\cos 20°)$. The unit vector along CE is and the force vector is as shown in the figure.

The moment vector is a force about an axis is of the form

$$\mathbf{e} \bullet (\mathbf{r} \times \mathbf{F}) = \begin{vmatrix} e_X & e_y & e_z \\ r_X & r_Y & r_Z \\ F_X & F_Y & F_Z \end{vmatrix}.$$

For this case,

$$\mathbf{e} \bullet (\mathbf{r} \times \mathbf{F}) = \begin{vmatrix} 0 & -\sin 20° & \cos 20° \\ 4 & 0 & 0 \\ 20 & -60 & 0 \end{vmatrix} = -240 \cos 20° \text{ ft-lb}$$

$$= -225.5 \text{ ft-lb}.$$

The negative sign is because the moment is opposite in direction to the unit vector from A to B.

Problem 4.94 The coordinates of A are $(-2.4, 0, -0.6)$ m, and the coordinates of B are $(-2.2, 0.7, -1.2)$ m. The force exerted at B by the sailboat's main sheet AB is 130 N. Determine the moment of the force about the centerline of the mast (the y axis). Draw a sketch to indicate the sense of the moment.

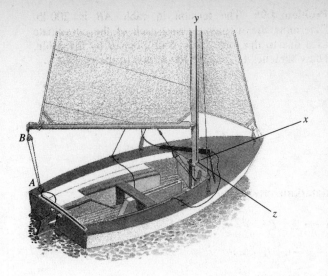

Solution: The position vectors:

$\mathbf{r}_{OA} = -2.4\mathbf{i} - 0.6\mathbf{k}$ (m), $\mathbf{r}_{OB} = -2.2\mathbf{i} + 0.7\mathbf{j} - 1.2\mathbf{k}$ (m),

$\mathbf{r}_{BA} = (-2.4 + 2.2)\mathbf{i} + (0 - 0.7)\mathbf{j} + (-0.6 + 1.2)\mathbf{k}$ (m)

$\quad = -0.2\mathbf{i} - 0.7\mathbf{j} + 0.6\mathbf{k}$ (m).

The magnitude is $|\mathbf{r}_{BA}| = 0.9434$ m.

The unit vector parallel to BA is

$\mathbf{e}_{BA} = -0.2120\mathbf{i} - 0.7420\mathbf{j} + 0.6360\mathbf{k}$.

The tension is $\mathbf{T}_{BA} = 130\mathbf{e}_{BA}$.

The moment of $\mathbf{T}_{BA}$ about the origin is

$$\mathbf{M}_O = \mathbf{r}_{OB} \times \mathbf{T}_{BA} = \begin{vmatrix} \mathbf{i} & \mathbf{j} & \mathbf{k} \\ -2.2 & 0.7 & -1.2 \\ -27.56 & -96.46 & 82.68 \end{vmatrix},$$

or $\mathbf{M}_O = -57.88\mathbf{i} + 214.97\mathbf{j} + 231.5\mathbf{k}$.

The magnitude of the moment about the y-axis is

$|\mathbf{M}_Y| = \mathbf{e}_Y \cdot \mathbf{M}_O = 214.97$ N-m.

The moment is $\boxed{\mathbf{M}_Y = \mathbf{e}_Y(214.97) = 214.97\mathbf{j} \text{ N-m.}}$

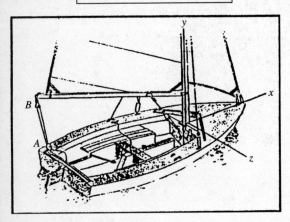

Problem 4.95 The tension in cable AB is 200 lb. Determine the moments about each of the coordinate axes due to the force exerted on point B by the cable. Draw sketches to indicate the senses of the moments.

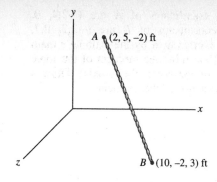

Solution: The position vector from B to A is

$$\mathbf{r}_{BA} = (2-10)\mathbf{i} + [5-(-2)]\mathbf{j} + (-2-3)\mathbf{k}$$

$$= -8\mathbf{i} + 7\mathbf{j} - 5\mathbf{k} \text{ (ft)},$$

So the force exerted on B is

$$\mathbf{F} = 200 \frac{\mathbf{r}_{BA}}{|\mathbf{r}_{BA}|} = -136.2\mathbf{i} + 119.2\mathbf{j} - 85.1\mathbf{k} \text{ (lb)}.$$

The moment of $\mathbf{F}$ about the origin O is

$$\mathbf{r}_{OB} \times \mathbf{F} = \begin{vmatrix} \mathbf{i} & \mathbf{j} & \mathbf{k} \\ 10 & -2 & 3 \\ -136.2 & 119.2 & -85.1 \end{vmatrix}$$

$$= -187\mathbf{i} + 443\mathbf{j} + 919\mathbf{k} \text{ (ft-lb)}.$$

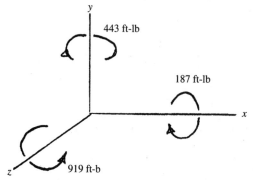

The moments about the x, y, and z axes are

$$[(\mathbf{r}_{OB} \times \mathbf{F}) \cdot \mathbf{i}]\mathbf{i} = -187\mathbf{i} \text{ (ft-lb)},$$

$$[(\mathbf{r}_{OB} \times \mathbf{F}) \cdot \mathbf{j}]\mathbf{j} = 443\mathbf{j} \text{ (ft-lb)},$$

$$[(\mathbf{r}_{OB} \times \mathbf{F}) \cdot \mathbf{k}]\mathbf{k} = 919\mathbf{k} \text{ (ft-lb)}.$$

Problem 4.96 The total force exerted on the blades of the turbine by the steam nozzle is $\mathbf{F} = 20\mathbf{i} - 120\mathbf{j} + 100\mathbf{k}$ (N), and it effectively acts at the point (100, 80, 300) mm. What moment is exerted about the axis of the turbine (the x axis)?

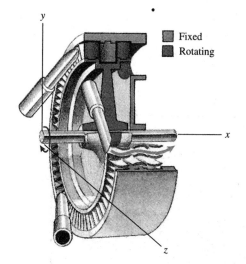

Solution: The moment about the origin is

$$\mathbf{M}_O = \begin{vmatrix} \mathbf{i} & \mathbf{j} & \mathbf{k} \\ 0.1 & 0.08 & 0.3 \\ 20 & -120 & 100 \end{vmatrix}$$

$$= 44.0\mathbf{i} - 4.0\mathbf{j} - 13.6\mathbf{k} \text{ (N-m)}.$$

The moment about the x axis is

$$(\mathbf{M}_O \cdot \mathbf{i})\mathbf{i} = 44.0\mathbf{i} \text{ (N-m)}.$$

Problem 4.97 The tension in cable AB is 50 N. Determine the moment about the line OC due to the force exerted by the cable at B. Draw a sketch to indicate the sense of the moment.

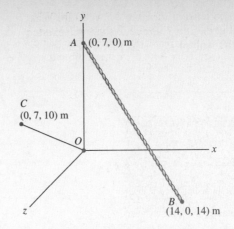

Solution: The vector OC is $\mathbf{r}_{OC} = 7\mathbf{j} + 10\mathbf{k}$. The unit vector parallel to OC is $\mathbf{e}_{OC} = 0.573\mathbf{j} + 0.819\mathbf{k}$. The position vectors of A and B are

$\mathbf{r}_{OA} = 7\mathbf{j}$ (m), and $\mathbf{r}_{OB} = 14\mathbf{i} + 0\mathbf{j} + 14\mathbf{k}$ (m).

The vector parallel to BA is

$\mathbf{r}_{BA} = (0 - 14)\mathbf{i} + (7 - 0)\mathbf{j} + (0 - 14)\mathbf{k} = -14\mathbf{i} + 7\mathbf{j} - 14\mathbf{k}$.

The magnitude:

$|\mathbf{r}_{BA}| = \sqrt{14^2 + 7^2 + 14^2} = 21$ m.

The unit vector parallel to BA is

$\mathbf{e}_{BA} = -0.6667\mathbf{i} + 0.3333\mathbf{j} - 0.6667\mathbf{k}$.

The tension acting on B is

$\mathbf{T}_{BA} = -33.335\mathbf{i} + 16.665\mathbf{j} - 33.335\mathbf{k}$ (N).

The moment about the origin is

$$\mathbf{M}_O = \mathbf{r}_{OB} \times \mathbf{T}_{BA} = \begin{vmatrix} \mathbf{i} & \mathbf{j} & \mathbf{k} \\ 14 & 0 & 14 \\ -33.335 & 16.665 & -33.335 \end{vmatrix}$$

$= -233.31\mathbf{i} + 233.31\mathbf{k}$.

The magnitude of the moment about the line OC is

$|\mathbf{M}_{OC}| = \mathbf{e}_{OC} \cdot \mathbf{M}_O = 191.2$ N-m.

The moment about the line OC is

$\mathbf{M}_{OC} = 191.1\mathbf{e}_{OC} = 109.6\mathbf{j} + 156.5\mathbf{k}$ (N-m).

The sense of the moment is in the direction of the curled fingers of the right hand when the thumb points from O toward C.

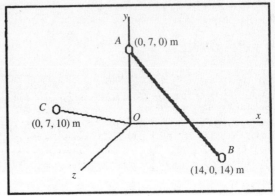

Problem 4.98 The tension in cable AB is 80 lb. What is the moment about the line CD due to the force exerted by the cable on the wall at B?

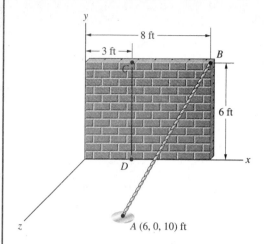

Solution: The strategy is to find the moment about the point C exerted by the force at B, and then to find the component of that moment acting along the line CD. The coordinates of the points B, C, D are B (8, 6, 0), C (3, 6, 0), D(3, 0, 0). The position vectors are: $\mathbf{r}_{OB} = 8\mathbf{i} + 6\mathbf{j}$, $\mathbf{r}_{OC} = 3\mathbf{i} + 6\mathbf{j}$, $\mathbf{r}_{OD} = 3\mathbf{i}$. The vector parallel to CD is $\mathbf{r}_{CD} = \mathbf{r}_{OD} - \mathbf{r}_{OC} = -6\mathbf{j}$. The unit vector parallel to CD is $\mathbf{e}_{CD} = -1\mathbf{j}$. The vector from point C to B is $\mathbf{r}_{CB} = \mathbf{r}_{OB} - \mathbf{r}_{OC} = 5\mathbf{i}$.

The position vector of A is $\mathbf{r}_{OA} = 6\mathbf{i} + 10\mathbf{k}$. The vector parallel to BA is $\mathbf{r}_{BA} = \mathbf{r}_{OA} - \mathbf{r}_{OB} = -2\mathbf{i} - 6\mathbf{j} + 10\mathbf{k}$. The magnitude is $|\mathbf{r}_{BA}| = 11.832$ ft. The unit vector parallel to BA is

$$\mathbf{e}_{BA} = -0.1690\mathbf{i} - 0.5071\mathbf{j} + 0.8452\mathbf{k}.$$

The tension acting at B is

$$\mathbf{T}_{BA} = 80\mathbf{e}_{BA} = -13.52\mathbf{i} - 40.57\mathbf{j} + 67.62\mathbf{k}.$$

The magnitude of the moment about CD due to the tension acting at B is

$$|\mathbf{M}_{CD}| = \mathbf{e}_{CD} \cdot (\mathbf{r}_{CB} \times \mathbf{T}_{BA}) = \begin{vmatrix} 0 & -1 & 0 \\ 5 & 0 & 0 \\ -13.52 & -40.57 & 67.62 \end{vmatrix}$$

$$= 338.1 \text{ (ft lb)}.$$

The moment about CD is $\mathbf{M}_{CD} = 338.1\mathbf{e}_{CD} = -338.1\mathbf{j}$ (ft lb). The sense of the moment is along the curled fingers of the right hand when the thumb is parallel to CD, pointing toward D.

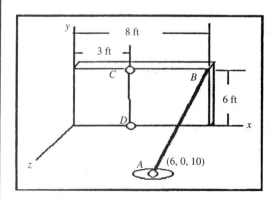

Problem 4.99 The universal joint is connected to the drive shaft at A and A'. The coordinates of A are $(0, 40, 0)$ mm, and the coordinates of A' are $(0, -40, 0)$ mm. The forces exerted on the drive shaft by the universal joint are $-30\mathbf{j} + 400\mathbf{k}$ (N) at A and $30\mathbf{j} - 400\mathbf{k}$ (N) at A'. What is the magnitude of the torque (moment) exerted by the universal joint on the drive shaft about the shaft axis $O\text{-}O'$?

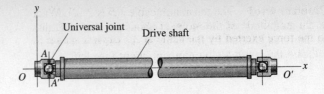

Solution: The position vectors of A and A' are $\mathbf{r}_{OA} = 40\mathbf{j}$ (mm), and $\mathbf{r}_{OA'} = -40\mathbf{j}$ (mm). The magnitudes of the moments about the origin are:

$$|\mathbf{M}_{OO}| = \mathbf{e}_X \cdot (\mathbf{r}_{OA} \times \mathbf{F}) = \begin{vmatrix} 1 & 0 & 0 \\ 0 & 40 & 0 \\ 0 & -30 & 400 \end{vmatrix} = 16000 \text{ (N-mm)},$$

$$\mathbf{M}_{OO} = 16000\mathbf{e}_X = 16000\mathbf{i}$$

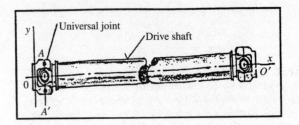

$$|\mathbf{M}_{OO}| = \mathbf{e}_X \cdot (\mathbf{r}_{OA'} \times \mathbf{F}) = \begin{vmatrix} 1 & 0 & 0 \\ 0 & -40 & 0 \\ 0 & 30 & -400 \end{vmatrix} = 16000 \text{ (N-mm)}$$

$$\mathbf{M}_{OO} = 16000\mathbf{e}_X = 16000\mathbf{i}$$

The sum of the moments is

$$\sum \mathbf{M}_{OO} = 32000\mathbf{i} \text{ (N-mm)} \quad \boxed{= 32\mathbf{i} \text{ (N-m)}}$$

Problem 4.100 A motorist applies the two forces shown to loosen a lug nut. The direction cosines of $\mathbf{F}$ are $\cos\theta_x = \frac{4}{13}$, $\cos\theta_y = \frac{12}{13}$, and $\cos\theta_z = \frac{3}{13}$. If the magnitude of the moment about the x axis must be 32 ft-lb to loosen the nut, what is the magnitude of the forces the motorist must apply?

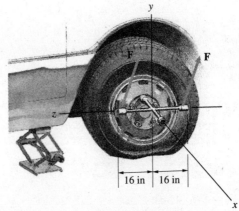

Solution: The unit vectors for the forces are the direction cosines. The position vector of the force $\mathbf{F}$ is $\mathbf{r}_{OF} = -1.333\mathbf{k}$ ft. The magnitude of the moment due to $\mathbf{F}$ is

$$|\mathbf{M}_{OF}| = \mathbf{e}_X \cdot (\mathbf{r}_{OF} \times \mathbf{F}) = \begin{vmatrix} 1 & 0 & 0 \\ 0 & 0 & -1.333 \\ 0.3077F & 0.9231F & 0.2308F \end{vmatrix}$$

$$|\mathbf{M}_{OF}| = 1.230F \text{ ft lb.}$$

The magnitude of the moment due to $-\mathbf{F}$ is

$$|\mathbf{M}_{-OF}| = \mathbf{e}_X \cdot (\mathbf{r}_{-OF} \times -\mathbf{F})$$

$$= \begin{vmatrix} 1 & 0 & 0 \\ 0 & 0 & 1.333 \\ -.3077F & -0.9231F & -0.2308F \end{vmatrix} = 1.230F \text{ ft lb.}$$

The total moment about the x-axis is

$$\sum \mathbf{M}_X = 1.230F\mathbf{i} + 1.230F\mathbf{i} = 2.46F\mathbf{i},$$

from which, for a total magnitude of 32 ft lb, the force to be applied is

$$F = \frac{32}{2.46} = 13 \text{ lb}$$

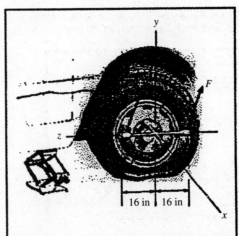

Problem 4.101 The tension in cable AB is 2 kN. What is the magnitude of the moment about the shaft CD due to the force exerted by the cable at A? Draw a sketch to indicate the sense of the moment about the shaft.

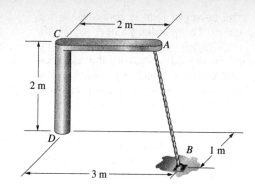

Solution: The strategy is to determine the moment about C due to A, and determine the component parallel to CD. The moment is determined from the distance CA and the components of the tension, which is to be found from the magnitude of the tension and the unit vector parallel to AB. The coordinates of the points A, B, C, and D are: A (2, 2, 0), B (3, 0, 1), C (0, 2, 0), and D (0,0,0). The unit vector parallel to CD is by inspection $\mathbf{e}_{CD} = -1\mathbf{j}$. The position vectors parallel to DC, DA, and DB:

$$\mathbf{r}_{DC} = 2\mathbf{j}, \quad \mathbf{r}_{DA} = 2\mathbf{i} + 2\mathbf{j}, \quad \mathbf{r}_{DB} = 3\mathbf{i} + 1\mathbf{k}.$$

The vector parallel to CA is $\mathbf{r}_{CA} = 2\mathbf{i}$. The vector parallel to AB is

$$\mathbf{r}_{AB} = \mathbf{r}_{DB} - \mathbf{r}_{DA} = 1\mathbf{i} - 2\mathbf{j} + 1\mathbf{k}.$$

The magnitude: $|\mathbf{r}_{AB}| = 2.4495$ m. The unit vector parallel to AB is

$$\mathbf{e}_{AB} = 0.4082\mathbf{i} - 0.8165\mathbf{j} + 0.4082\mathbf{k}.$$

The tension is

$$\mathbf{T}_{AB} = 2\mathbf{e}_{AB} = 0.8165\mathbf{i} - 1.633\mathbf{j} + 0.8165\mathbf{k}.$$

The magnitude of the moment about CD is

$$|\mathbf{M}_{CD}| = \mathbf{e}_{CD} \cdot (\mathbf{r}_{CA} \times \mathbf{T}_{AB}) = \begin{vmatrix} 0 & -1 & 0 \\ 2 & 0 & 0 \\ 0.8164 & -1.633 & 0.8165 \end{vmatrix}$$

$$= 1.633 \text{ kN-m}.$$

The moment about CD is

$$\mathbf{M}_{CD} = \mathbf{e}_{CD}|\mathbf{M}_{CD}| = -1.633\mathbf{j} \text{ (kN-m)}.$$

The sense is in the direction of the curled fingers of the right hand when the thumb is parallel to DC, pointed toward D.

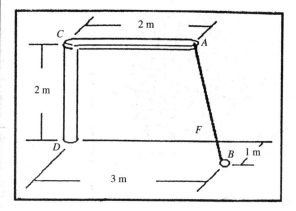

Problem 4.102 The axis of the car's wheel passes through the origin of the coordinate system and its direction cosines are $\cos\theta_x = 0.940$, $\cos\theta_y = 0$, $\cos\theta_z = 0.342$. The force exerted on the tire by the road effectively acts at the point $x = 0$, $y = -0.36$ m, $z = 0$ and has components $\mathbf{F} = -720\mathbf{i} + 3660\mathbf{j} + 1240\mathbf{k}$ (N). What is the moment of $\mathbf{F}$ about the wheel's axis?

Solution: We have to determine the moment about the axle where a unit vector along the axle is

$\mathbf{e} = \cos\theta_x\mathbf{i} + \cos\theta_y\mathbf{j} + \cos\theta_z\mathbf{k}$

$\mathbf{e} = 0.940\mathbf{i} + 0\mathbf{j} + 0.342\mathbf{k}$

The vector from the origin to the point of contact with the road is

$\mathbf{r} = 0\mathbf{i} - 0.36\mathbf{j} + 0\mathbf{k}$ m

The force exerted at the point of contact is

$\mathbf{F} = -720\mathbf{i} + 3660\mathbf{j} + 1240\mathbf{k}$ N

The moment of the force $\mathbf{F}$ about the axle is

$M_{\text{AXLE}} = [\mathbf{e} \cdot (\mathbf{r} \times \mathbf{F})]\mathbf{e}$

$$M_{\text{AXLE}} = \begin{vmatrix} 0.940 & 0 & 0.342 \\ 0 & -0.36 & 0 \\ -720 & +3660 & +1240 \end{vmatrix} (0.940\mathbf{i} + 0.342\mathbf{k}) \text{ (N-m)}$$

$M_{\text{AXLE}} = (-508.26)(0.940\mathbf{i} + 0.342\mathbf{k})$ (N-m)

$M_{\text{AXLE}} = -478\mathbf{i} - 174\mathbf{k}$ (N-m)

Problem 4.103 The direction cosines of the centerline OA are $\cos\theta_x = 0.500$, $\cos\theta_y = 0.866$, and $\cos\theta_z = 0$, and the direction cosines of the line AG are $\cos\theta_x = 0.707$, $\cos\theta_y = 0.619$, and $\cos\theta_z = -0.342$. What is the moment about OA due to the 250-N weight? Draw a sketch to indicate the sense of the moment about the shaft.

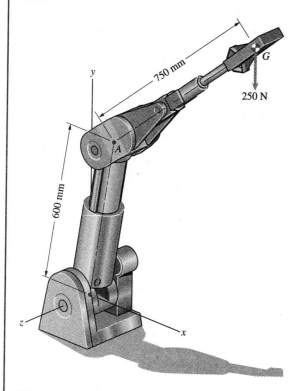

Solution: By definition, the direction cosines are the scalar components of the unit vectors. Thus the unit vectors are

$\mathbf{e}_1 = 0.5\mathbf{i} + 0.866\mathbf{j}$, and $\mathbf{e}_2 = 0.707\mathbf{i} + 0.619\mathbf{j} - 0.341\mathbf{k}$.

The force is $\mathbf{W} = 250\mathbf{j}$ (N). The position vector of the 250 N weight is

$\mathbf{r}_W = 0.600\mathbf{e}_1 + 0.750\mathbf{e}_2 = 0.8303\mathbf{i} + 0.9839\mathbf{j} - 0.2565\mathbf{k}$

The moment about OA is

$\mathbf{M}_{OA} = \mathbf{e}_{OA}(\mathbf{e}_{OA} \cdot (\mathbf{r}_W \times \mathbf{W}))$

$$= \begin{vmatrix} 0.5 & 0.866 & 0 \\ 0.8303 & 0.9839 & -0.2565 \\ 0 & -250 & 0 \end{vmatrix} \mathbf{e}_1 = -32.06\mathbf{e}_1$$

$= -16\mathbf{i} - 27.77\mathbf{j}$ (N-m)

The moment is anti parallel to the unit vector parallel to OA, with the sense of the moment in the direction of the curled fingers when the thumb of the right hand is directed oppositely to the direction of the unit vector.

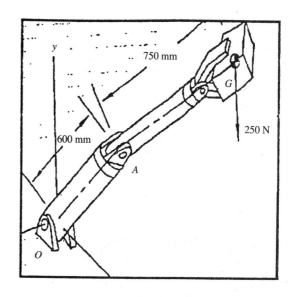

Problem 4.104 The radius of the steering wheel is 200 mm. The distance from O to C is 1 m. The center C of the steering wheel lies in the $x - y$ plane. The driver exerts a force $\mathbf{F} = 10\mathbf{i} + 10\mathbf{j} - 5\mathbf{k}$ (N) on the wheel at A. If the angle $\alpha = 0$, what is the magnitude of the moment about the shaft OC? Draw a sketch to indicate the sense of the moment about the shaft.

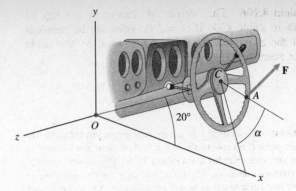

Solution: The strategy is to determine the moment about C, and then determine its component about OC. The radius vectors parallel to OC and CA are:

$$\mathbf{r}_{OC} = 1(\mathbf{i}\cos 20° + \mathbf{j}\sin 20° + 0\mathbf{k}) = 0.9397\mathbf{i} + 0.3420\mathbf{j}.$$

The line from C to the x-axis is perpendicular to OC since it lies in the plane of the steering wheel. The unit vector from C to the x-axis is

$$\mathbf{e}_{CX} = \mathbf{i}\cos(20 - 90) + \mathbf{j}\sin(20 - 90) = 0.3420\mathbf{i} - 0.9397\mathbf{j},$$

where the angle is measured positive counterclockwise from the x-axis. The vector parallel to CA is

$$\mathbf{r}_{CA} = 0.2\mathbf{e}_{CX} = +0.0684\mathbf{i} - 0.1879\mathbf{j} \text{ (m)}.$$

The magnitude of the moment about OC

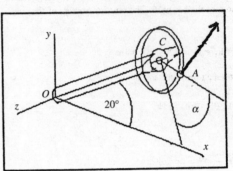

$$|\mathbf{M}_{OC}| = \mathbf{e}_{OC} \cdot (\mathbf{r}_{CA} \times \mathbf{F}) = \begin{vmatrix} 0.9397 & 0.3420 & 0 \\ 0.0684 & -0.1879 & 0 \\ 10 & 10 & -5 \end{vmatrix}$$

$$= 0.9998 = 1 \text{ N-m}.$$

The sense of the moment is in the direction of the curled fingers of the right hand if the thumb is parallel to OC, pointing from O to C.

Problem 4.105 Consider the steering wheel in Problem 4.104. Determine the moment of $\mathbf{F}$ about the shaft OC of the steering wheel if $\alpha = 30°$. Draw a sketch to indicate the sense of the moment about the shaft.

Solution: The position vector of A relative to C is

$$\mathbf{r}_{CA} = R\cos\alpha\sin 20°\mathbf{i} - R\cos\alpha\cos 20°\mathbf{j} - R\sin\alpha\mathbf{k}$$

$$= 0.0592\mathbf{i} - 0.1628\mathbf{j} - 0.1\mathbf{k} \text{ (m)}.$$

The moment about pt. C is

$$\mathbf{M}_C = \begin{vmatrix} \mathbf{i} & \mathbf{j} & \mathbf{k} \\ 0.0592 & -0.1628 & -0.1 \\ 10 & 10 & -5 \end{vmatrix}$$

$$= 1.814\mathbf{i} - 0.704\mathbf{j} + 2.220\mathbf{k} \text{ (N-m)}.$$

A unit vector parallel to the shaft is

$$\mathbf{e}_{OC} = \cos 20°\mathbf{i} + \sin 20°\mathbf{j},$$

and $\mathbf{e}_{OC} \cdot \mathbf{M}_C = 1.464$ N-m

The sense of the moment is in the direction of the curled fingers of the right hand with the thumb pointing from 0 to C.

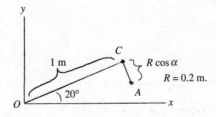

244

Problem 4.106 The weight W causes a tension of 100 lb in cable CD. If $d = 2$ ft, what is the moment about the z axis due to the force exerted by the cable CD at point C?

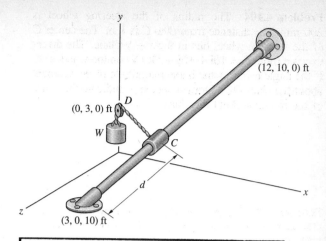

Solution: The strategy is to use the unit vector parallel to the bar to locate point C relative to the origin, and then use this location to find the unit vector parallel to the cable CD. With the tension resolved into components about the origin, the moment about the origin can be resolved into components along the z-axis. Denote the top of the bar by T and the bottom of the bar by B. The position vectors of the ends of the bar are:

$$\mathbf{r}_{OB} = 3\mathbf{i} + 0\mathbf{j} + 10\mathbf{k}, \quad \mathbf{r}_{OT} = 12\mathbf{i} + 10\mathbf{j} + 0\mathbf{k}.$$

The vector from the bottom to the top of the bar is

$$\mathbf{r}_{BT} = \mathbf{r}_{OT} - \mathbf{r}_{OB} = 9\mathbf{i} + 10\mathbf{j} - 10\mathbf{k}.$$

The magnitude:

$$|\mathbf{r}_{BT}| = \sqrt{9^2 + 10^2 + 10^2} = 16.763 \text{ ft}.$$

The unit vector parallel to the bar, pointing toward the top, is

$$\mathbf{e}_{BT} = 0.5369\mathbf{i} + 0.5965\mathbf{j} - 0.5965\mathbf{k}.$$

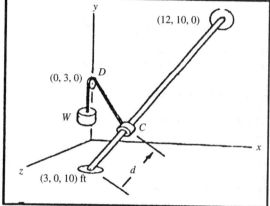

The position vector of the point C relative to the bottom of the bar is

$$\mathbf{r}_{BC} = 2\mathbf{e}_{BT} = 1.074\mathbf{i} + 1.193\mathbf{j} - 1.193\mathbf{k}.$$

The position vector of point C relative to the origin is

$$\mathbf{r}_{OC} = \mathbf{r}_{OB} + \mathbf{r}_{BC} = 4.074\mathbf{i} + 1.193\mathbf{j} + 8.807\mathbf{k}.$$

The position vector of point D is

$$\mathbf{r}_{OD} = 0\mathbf{i} + 3\mathbf{j} + 0\mathbf{k}.$$

The vector parallel to CD is

$$\mathbf{r}_{CD} = \mathbf{r}_{OD} - \mathbf{r}_{OC} = -4.074\mathbf{i} + 1.807\mathbf{j} - 8.807\mathbf{k}.$$

The magnitude is

$$|\mathbf{r}_{CD}| = \sqrt{4.074^2 + 1.807^2 + 8.807^2} = 9.87 \text{ ft}.$$

The unit vector parallel to CD is

$$\mathbf{e}_{CD} = -0.4127\mathbf{i} + 0.1831\mathbf{j} - 0.8923\mathbf{k}.$$

The tension is

$$\mathbf{T}_{CD} = 100\mathbf{e}_{CD} = -41.27\mathbf{i} + 18.31\mathbf{j} - 89.23\mathbf{k} \text{ lb}.$$

The magnitude of the moment about the z-axis is

$$|\mathbf{M}_O| = \mathbf{e}_Z \cdot (\mathbf{r}_{OC} \times \mathbf{T}_{CD}) = \begin{vmatrix} 0 & 0 & 1 \\ 4.074 & 1.193 & 8.807 \\ -41.27 & 18.31 & -89.23 \end{vmatrix}$$

$$= 123.83 \text{ ft lb}$$

Problem 4.107 The rod AB supports the open hood of the car. The force exerted by the rod on the hood at B is parallel to the rod. If the rod must exert a moment of 100 ft-lb magnitude about the x axis to support the hood and the distance $d = 2$ ft, what is the magnitude of the force the rod must exert on the hood?

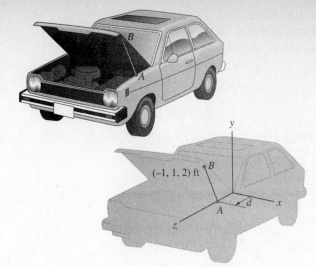

Solution: The coordinates of B are $B\,(-1,\,1,\,2)$. The position vectors of A, B are

$$\mathbf{r}_{OA} = 2\mathbf{k}, \quad \mathbf{r}_{OB} = -1\mathbf{i} + 1\mathbf{j} + 2\mathbf{k}.$$

The vector parallel to AB is

$$\mathbf{r}_{AB} = \mathbf{r}_{OB} - \mathbf{r}_{OA} = -1\mathbf{i} + 1\mathbf{j}.$$

The unit vector is $\mathbf{e}_{AB} = -0.7071\mathbf{i} + 0.7071\mathbf{j}$. The force is $\mathbf{F}_{AB} = F\mathbf{e}_{AB}$. The moment about the origin is

$$|\mathbf{M}_X| = \mathbf{e}_X \cdot (\mathbf{r}_{OA} \times \mathbf{F}_{AB}) = \begin{vmatrix} 1 & 0 & 0 \\ 0 & 0 & 2 \\ -0.7071F & 0.7071F & 0 \end{vmatrix} = -1.414F,$$

from which, for

$$|\mathbf{M}_X| = 100 \text{ ft lb}, \quad F = \frac{100}{1.414} = 70.71 \text{ lb}$$

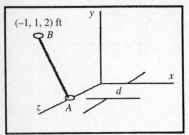

Problem 4.108   Determine the moment of the couple and represent it as shown in Fig. 4.28(c).

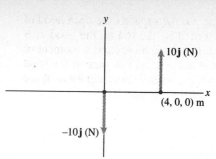

Solution: The moment of the couple is

$$\mathbf{M} = \mathbf{r} \times \mathbf{F} = 4\mathbf{i} \times 10\mathbf{j} = 40\mathbf{k} \text{ (N-m)}$$

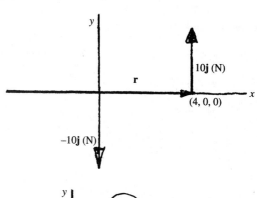

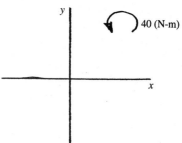

Problem 4.109   The forces are contained in the $x - y$ plane.

(a)   Determine the moment of the couple and represent it as shown in Fig. 4.28c.
(b)   What is the sum of the moments of the two forces about the point $(10, -40, 20)$ ft?

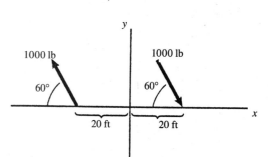

Solution: The right hand force is

$$\mathbf{F} = [1000 \text{ (lb)}](\cos 60°\mathbf{i} - \sin 60°\mathbf{j})$$

$$\mathbf{F} = +500\mathbf{i} - 867\mathbf{j} \text{ lb.}$$

The vector from the x intercept of the left force to that of the right force is $\mathbf{r} = 40\mathbf{i}$ ft.

The moment is $\mathbf{M}_C = \mathbf{r} \times \mathbf{F}$

$$\mathbf{M}_C = 40\mathbf{i} \times (500\mathbf{i} - 867\mathbf{j}) \text{ (ft-lb)}$$

$$\mathbf{M}_C = -34700 \text{ (ft-lb) } \mathbf{k}$$

or $\mathbf{M}_C = -34700$ (ft-lb) clockwise

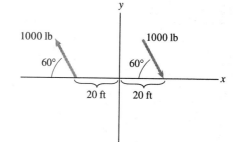

Problem 4.110 The forces are contained in the $x - y$ plane and the moment of the couple is $-110\mathbf{k}$ (N-m).

(a) What is the distance b?
(b) What is the sum of the moments of the two forces about the point $(3, -3, 2)$ m?

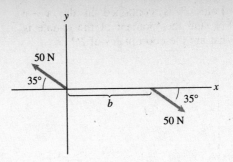

Solution: The right hand-force is

$$\mathbf{F}_R = 50(\cos 35°\mathbf{i} - \sin 35°\mathbf{j})$$

$$\mathbf{F}_R = 40.96\mathbf{i} - 28.68\mathbf{j} \text{ N}$$

The moment of the couple is -110 (N-m). Also,

$$\mathbf{M}_C = b\mathbf{i} \times (40.96\mathbf{i} - 28.6\mathbf{j}) :$$

$$-110\mathbf{k} = -28.68 \, b\mathbf{k},$$

$$b = 3.84 \text{ m}$$

The moment of the couple about any point is the same, $-110\mathbf{k}$ (N-m) To show this, we can find the moments about a point $(3, -3, 2)$ m. Use the following as the points of application of the two forces.

Left force $(0, 0, 0)$ m

Right force $(3.48, 0, 0)$ m

Moment of Left force

$$\mathbf{M}_L = \mathbf{r}_{PO} \times \mathbf{F}_L$$

$$\mathbf{M}_L = (-3\mathbf{i} + 3\mathbf{j} - 2\mathbf{k}) \times (-40.96\mathbf{i} + 28.68\mathbf{j})$$

$$\mathbf{M}_L = 57.36\mathbf{i} + 81.92\mathbf{j} + 36.9\mathbf{k} \text{ (N-m)}$$

Moment of Right Force

$$\mathbf{M}_R = (0.84\mathbf{i} + 3\mathbf{j} - 2\mathbf{k}) \times (40.96\mathbf{i} - 28.68\mathbf{j})$$

$$\mathbf{M}_R = -57.36\mathbf{i} - 81.92\mathbf{j} - 146.9\mathbf{k} \text{ (N-m)}$$

$$\sum \mathbf{M} = -110\mathbf{k} \text{ (N-m)}$$

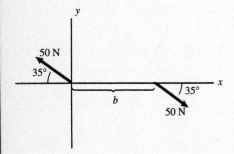

Problem 4.111 Point P is contained in the $x - y$ plane, $|\mathbf{F}| = 100$ N, and the moment of the couple is $-500\mathbf{k}$ (N-m). What are the coordinates of P?

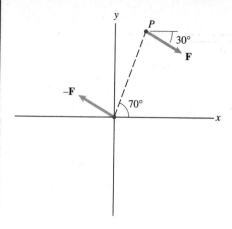

Solution: The force is

$$\mathbf{F} = 100(\mathbf{i}\cos(-30°) + \mathbf{j}\sin(-30°)) = 86.6\mathbf{i} - 50\mathbf{j}.$$

Let r be the distance OP. The vector parallel to OP is

$$\mathbf{r} = r(\mathbf{i}\cos 70° + \mathbf{j}\sin 70°) = r(0.3420\mathbf{i} + 0.9397\mathbf{j}).$$

The moment is

$$\mathbf{M} = \mathbf{r} \times \mathbf{F} = \begin{vmatrix} \mathbf{i} & \mathbf{j} & \mathbf{k} \\ 0.3420r & 0.9397r & 0 \\ 86.6 & -50.0 & 0 \end{vmatrix} = -98.48r\mathbf{k}.$$

From which, $r = \dfrac{500}{98.48} = 5.077$ m. From above,

$$\mathbf{r} = 5.077(0.3420\mathbf{i} + 0.9397\mathbf{j}).$$

The coordinates of P are

$$x = 5.077(0.3420) = 1.74 \text{ m}, \quad y = 5.077(0.9397) = 4.77 \text{ m}$$

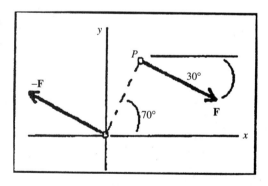

Problem 4.112 The forces are contained in the $x - y$ plane.

(a) Determine the sum of the moments of the two couples.
(b) What is the sum of the moments of the four forces about the point $(-6, -6, 2)$ m?
(c) Represent the result of (a) as shown in Fig. 4.28c.

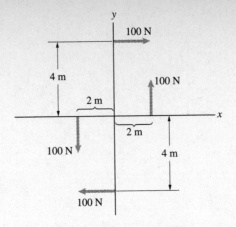

Solution: The position vectors for the forces on the x-axis are $\mathbf{r}_{X1} = 2\mathbf{i}$, $\mathbf{r}_{X2} = -2\mathbf{i}$. The position vectors for the forces on the y-axis are $\mathbf{r}_{Y1} = 4\mathbf{j}$, $\mathbf{r}_{Y2} = -4\mathbf{j}$. The force on the positive x-axis is $\mathbf{F}_X = +100\mathbf{j}$ (N). The force on the positive y-axis is $\mathbf{F}_Y = +100\mathbf{i}$ (N).

(a) The sum of the moments is

$$\sum \mathbf{M} = (\mathbf{r}_{X1} - \mathbf{r}_{X2}) \times \mathbf{F}_X + (\mathbf{r}_{Y1} - \mathbf{r}_{Y2}) \times \mathbf{F}_Y$$

$$= \begin{vmatrix} \mathbf{i} & \mathbf{j} & \mathbf{k} \\ 4 & 0 & 0 \\ 0 & 100 & 0 \end{vmatrix} + \begin{vmatrix} \mathbf{i} & \mathbf{j} & \mathbf{k} \\ 0 & 8 & 0 \\ 100 & 0 & 0 \end{vmatrix} = -400\mathbf{k} \text{ (N-m)}$$

(b) The vector from the point $P(-6, -6, 2)$ to the force on the positive x-axis is

$$\mathbf{r}_{PX1} = \mathbf{r}_{X1} - \mathbf{r}_p = (2+6)\mathbf{i} + 6\mathbf{j} - 2\mathbf{k}.$$

The vector from the point P to the force on the negative x-axis is

$$\mathbf{r}_{pX2} = \mathbf{r}_{X2} - \mathbf{r}_p = (-2+6)\mathbf{i} + 6\mathbf{j} - 2\mathbf{k}.$$

The vector from point P to the force on the positive y-axis is

$$\mathbf{r}_{pY1} = \mathbf{r}_{Y1} - \mathbf{r}_p = +6\mathbf{i} + (4+6)\mathbf{j} - 2\mathbf{k} = 6\mathbf{i} + 10\mathbf{j} - 2\mathbf{k}.$$

The vector from P to the force on the negative y-axis is

$$\mathbf{r}_{PY2} = \mathbf{r}_{Y2} - \mathbf{r}_P = 6\mathbf{i} + (-4+6)\mathbf{j} - 2\mathbf{k} = 6\mathbf{i} + 2\mathbf{j} - 2\mathbf{k}.$$

The sum of the moments:

$$\sum \mathbf{M} = (\mathbf{r}_{pX1} - \mathbf{r}_{pX2}) \times \mathbf{F}_X + (\mathbf{r}_{pY1} - \mathbf{r}_{pY2}) \times \mathbf{F}_Y$$

$$= \begin{vmatrix} \mathbf{i} & \mathbf{j} & \mathbf{k} \\ 4 & 0 & 0 \\ 0 & 100 & 0 \end{vmatrix} + \begin{vmatrix} \mathbf{i} & \mathbf{j} & \mathbf{k} \\ 0 & 8 & 0 \\ 100 & 0 & 0 \end{vmatrix} = -400\mathbf{k} \text{ (N-m)}$$

(c) The figure is shown.

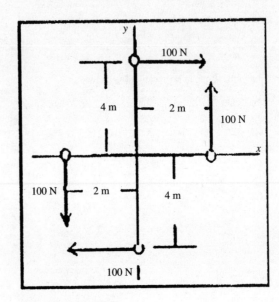

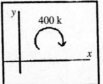

Problem 4.113 The moment of the couple is 40 kN-m counterclockwise.

(a) Express the moment of the couple as a vector.
(b) Draw a sketch showing two equal and opposite forces that exert the given moment.

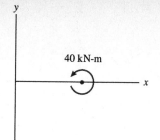

Solution:

(a) The moment is directed along the positive z-axis,
$$\mathbf{M} = 40\mathbf{k} \ (\text{kN-m})$$
(b) A candidate pair of forces is shown in the sketch: 40 kN forces directed oppositely at 1 m apart.

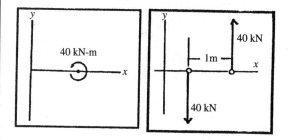

Problem 4.114 The moments of two couples are shown. What is the sum of the moments about point P?

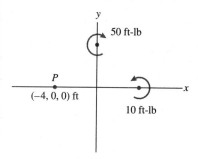

Solution: The moment of a couple is the same anywhere in the plane. Hence the sum about the point P is

$$\sum \mathbf{M} = -50\mathbf{k} + 10\mathbf{k} = -40\mathbf{k} \text{ ft lb}$$

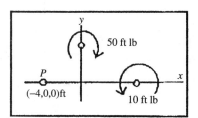

Problem 4.115 Determine the sum of the moments exerted on the plate by the two couples.

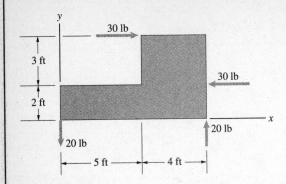

Solution: The moment due to the 30 lb couple, which acts in a clockwise direction is

$$M_{30} = -3(30)k = -90k \text{ ft lb.}$$

The moment due to the 20 lb couple, which acts in a counterclockwise direction, is

$$M_{20} = 9(20)k = 180k \text{ ft lb.}$$

The sum of the moments is

$$\sum M = -90k + 180k = +90k \text{ ft lb.}$$

The sum of the moments is the same anywhere on the plate.

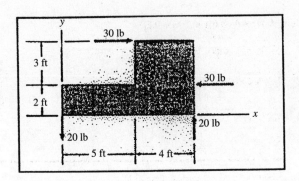

Problem 4.116 Determine the sum of the moments exerted about A by the couple and the two forces.

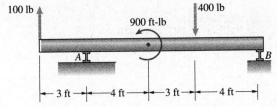

Solution: Let the x axis point to the right and the y axis point upward in the plane of the page. The moments of the forces are

$$M_{100} = (-3i) \times (100j) = -300k \text{ (ft-lb)},$$

and $M_{400} = (7i) \times (-400j) = -2800k$ (ft-lb).

The moment of the couple is $M_C = 900k$ (ft-lb). Summing the moments, we get

$$\boxed{M_{\text{Total}} = -2200k \text{ (ft-lb)}}$$

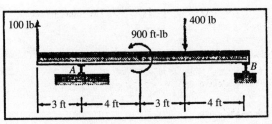

Problem 4.117 Determine the sum of the moments exerted about A by the couple and the two forces.

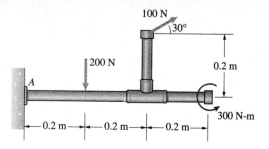

Solution:

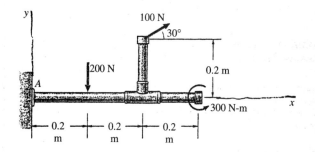

$$\sum M_A = (0.2\mathbf{i}) \times (-200\mathbf{j}) + (0.4\mathbf{i} + 0.2\mathbf{j})$$

$$\times (86.7\mathbf{i} + 50\mathbf{j}) + 300\mathbf{k} \text{ (N-m)}$$

$$\sum M_A = -40\mathbf{k} + 2.66\mathbf{k} + 300\mathbf{k} \text{ (N-m)}$$

$$\sum M_A = 262.7\mathbf{k} \text{ (N-m)} \simeq 263\mathbf{k} \text{ (N-m)}$$

Problem 4.118 What is the sum of the moment exerted on the object?

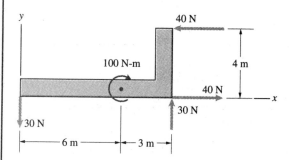

Solution: Three couples act on the object. The moments due to the couples are:

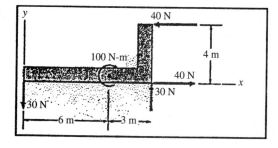

$\mathbf{M}_1 = -100\mathbf{k}$ N-m.

$\mathbf{M}_2 = 9(30)\mathbf{k} = 270\mathbf{k}$ N-m,

$\mathbf{M}_3 = 4(40)\mathbf{k} = 160\mathbf{k}$ N-m

The sum of the moments:

$$\sum \mathbf{M} = -100\mathbf{k} + 270\mathbf{k} + 160\mathbf{k} = 330\mathbf{k} \text{ N-m}$$

Problem 4.119 Four forces and a couple act on the beam. The vector sum of the forces is zero, and the sum of the moments about the left end of the beam is zero. What are the forces A_x, A_y, and B?

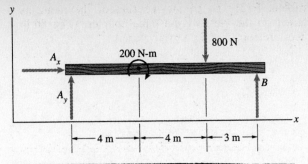

Solution: The sum of the forces about the y-axis is

$$\sum F_X = A_Y + B - 800 = 0.$$

The sum of the forces about the x-axis is

$$\sum F_X = A_X = 0.$$

The sum of the moments about the left end of the beam is

$$\sum M_L = 11B - 8(800) - 200 = 0.$$

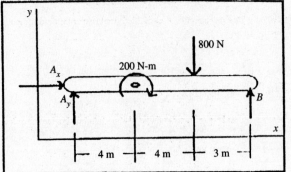

From the moments:

$$B = \frac{6600}{11} = 600 \text{ N}.$$

Substitute into the forces balance equation to obtain:

$$A_Y = 800 - 600 = 200 \text{ N}$$

Problem 4.120 The force $\mathbf{F} = 40\mathbf{i} + 24\mathbf{j} + 12\mathbf{k}$ (N).

(a) What is the moment of the couple?
(b) Determine the perpendicular distance between the lines of action of the two forces.

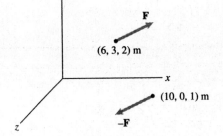

Solution:

(a) The moment of the couple is given

$$\mathbf{M}_C = \mathbf{r}_{AB} \times \mathbf{F}$$

$$\mathbf{M}_C = (-4\mathbf{i} + 3\mathbf{j} + 1\mathbf{k}) \times (40\mathbf{i} + 24\mathbf{j} + 12\mathbf{k})$$

$$\mathbf{M}_C = 12\mathbf{i} + 88\mathbf{j} - 216\mathbf{k} \text{ (N-m)}$$

(b) $|\mathbf{M}_C| = |\mathbf{d}||\mathbf{F}| \sin 90°$

$$|\mathbf{F}| = \sqrt{F_x^2 + F_y^2 + F_z^2} = 48.2 \text{ N}$$

$$|\mathbf{M}_C| = \sqrt{M_x^2 + M_y^2 + M_z^2} = 233.5 \text{ N}$$

$|\mathbf{d}| = $ perpendicular distance

$$|\mathbf{d}| = |\mathbf{M}_C|/|\mathbf{F}|$$

$$|\mathbf{d}| = 4.85 \text{ m}$$

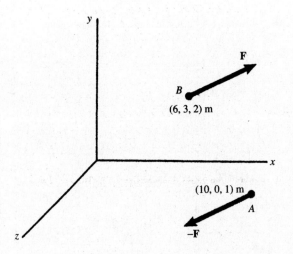

Problem 4.121 Determine the sum of the moments exerted on the plate by the three couples. (The 80-lb forces are contained in the x-z plane.)

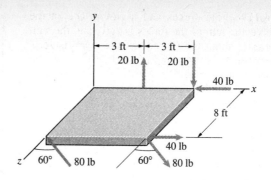

Solution: The moments of two of the couples can be determined from inspection:

$$M_1 = -(3)(20)k = -60k \text{ ft lb.}$$

$$M_2 = (8)(40)j = 320j \text{ ft lb}$$

The forces in the 3rd couple are resolved:

$$F = (80)(i \sin 60° + k \cos 60°) = 69.282i + 40k$$

The two forces in the third couple are separated by the vector

$$r_3 = (6i + 8k) - (8k) = 6i$$

The moment is

$$M_3 = r_3 \times F_3 = \begin{vmatrix} i & j & k \\ 6 & 0 & 0 \\ 69.282 & 0 & 40 \end{vmatrix} = -240j.$$

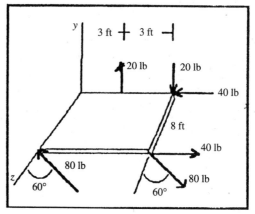

The sum of the moments due to the couples:

$$\sum M = -60k + 320j - 240j = 80j - 60k \text{ ft lb}$$

Problem 4.122 What is the magnitude of the sum of the moments exerted on the T-shaped structure by the two couples?

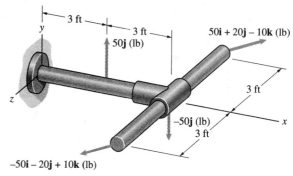

Solution: The moment of the 50 lb couple can be determined by inspection:

$$M_1 = -(50)(3)k = -150k \text{ ft lb.}$$

The vector separating the other two force is $r = 6k$. The moment is

$$M_2 = r \times F = \begin{vmatrix} i & j & k \\ 0 & 0 & 6 \\ 50 & 20 & -10 \end{vmatrix} = -120i + 300j.$$

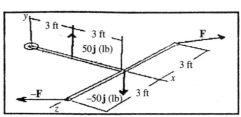

The sum of the moments is

$$\sum M = -120i + 300j - 150k.$$

The magnitude is

$$|M| = \sqrt{120^2 + 300^2 + 150^2} = 356.23 \text{ ft lb}$$

Problem 4.123 The tension in cables AB and CD is 500 N.

(a) Show that the two forces exerted by the cables on the rectangular hatch at B and C form a couple.

(b) What is the moment exerted on the plate by the cables?

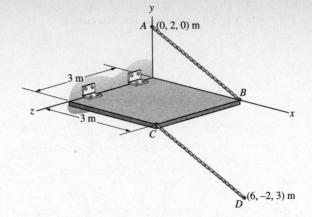

Solution: One condition for a couple is that the sum of a pair of forces vanish; another is for a non-zero moment to be the same anywhere. The first condition is demonstrated by determining the unit vectors parallel to the action lines of the forces. The vector position of point B is $\mathbf{r}_B = 3\mathbf{i}$ m. The vector position of point A is $\mathbf{r}_A = 2\mathbf{j}$. The vector parallel to cable AB is

$$\mathbf{r}_{BA} = \mathbf{r}_A - \mathbf{r}_B = -3\mathbf{i} + 2\mathbf{j}.$$

The magnitude is:

$$|\mathbf{r}_{AB}| = \sqrt{3^2 + 2^2} = 3.606 \text{ m}.$$

The unit vector:

$$\mathbf{e}_{AB} = \frac{\mathbf{r}_{AB}}{|\mathbf{r}_{AB}|} = -0.8321\mathbf{i} + 0.5547\mathbf{j}.$$

The tension is

$$\mathbf{T}_{AB} = |\mathbf{T}_{AB}|\mathbf{e}_{AB} = -416.05\mathbf{i} + 277.35\mathbf{j}.$$

The vector position of points C and D are:

$$\mathbf{r}_C = 3\mathbf{i} + 3\mathbf{k}, \quad \mathbf{r}_D = 6\mathbf{i} - 2\mathbf{j} + 3\mathbf{k}.$$

The vector parallel to the cable CD is $\mathbf{r}_{CD} = \mathbf{r}_D - \mathbf{r}_C = 3\mathbf{i} - 2\mathbf{j}$. The magnitude is $|\mathbf{r}_{CD}| = 3.606$ m, and the unit vector parallel to the cable CD is $\mathbf{e}_{CD} = +0.8321\mathbf{i} - 0.5547\mathbf{j}$. The magnitude of the tension in the two cables is the same, and $\mathbf{e}_{BA} = -\mathbf{e}_{CD}$, hence the sum of the tensions vanish on the plate. The second condition is demonstrated by determining the moment at any point on the plate. By inspection, the distance between the action lines of the forces is

$$\mathbf{r}_{CB} = \mathbf{r}_B - \mathbf{r}_C = 3\mathbf{i} - 3\mathbf{i} - 3\mathbf{k} = -3\mathbf{k}.$$

The moment is

$$\mathbf{M} = \mathbf{r}_{CB} \times \mathbf{T}_{AB} = \begin{vmatrix} \mathbf{i} & \mathbf{j} & \mathbf{k} \\ 0 & 0 & -3 \\ -416.05 & 277.35 & 0 \end{vmatrix}$$

$$= 832.05\mathbf{i} - 1248.15\mathbf{j} \text{ (N-m)}.$$

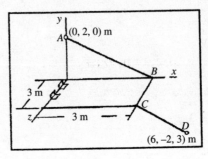

The moment about the origin is

$$\mathbf{M}_O = (\mathbf{r}_B - \mathbf{r}_C) \times \mathbf{T}_{AB} = \mathbf{r}_{CB} \times \mathbf{T}_{AB},$$

which is identical with the above expression for the moment. Let $\mathbf{r}_{PC}$ and $\mathbf{r}_{PB}$ be the distances to points C and B from an arbitrary point P on the plate. Then $\mathbf{M}_P = (\mathbf{r}_{PB} - \mathbf{r}_{PC}) \times \mathbf{T}_{AB} = \mathbf{r}_{CB} \times \mathbf{T}_{AB}$ which is identical to the above expression. Thus the moment is the same everywhere on the plate, and the forces form a couple.

Problem 4.124 Determine the sum of the moments exerted about P by the couple and the two forces.

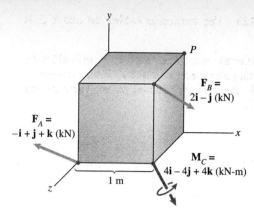

Solution:

$$\sum M_P = \mathbf{r}_{PA} \times \mathbf{F}_A + \mathbf{r}_{PB} \times \mathbf{F}_B + \mathbf{M}_C$$

$$\sum M_P = (-1\mathbf{i} - 1\mathbf{j} + 1\mathbf{k}) \times (-1\mathbf{i} + 1\mathbf{j} + 1\mathbf{k}) \text{ (kN-m)}$$

$$+ (0\mathbf{i} + 0\mathbf{j} + 1\mathbf{k}) \times (2\mathbf{i} - 1\mathbf{j} + 0\mathbf{k}) \text{ (kN-m)}$$

$$+ 4\mathbf{i} - 4\mathbf{j} + 4\mathbf{k} \text{ (kN-m)}$$

$$\sum M_P = (-2\mathbf{i} + 0\mathbf{j} - 2\mathbf{k})$$

$$+ (1\mathbf{i} + 2\mathbf{j} + 0\mathbf{k})$$

$$+ (4\mathbf{i} - 4\mathbf{j} + 4\mathbf{k}) \text{ (kN-m)}$$

$$\sum M_P = 3\mathbf{i} - 2\mathbf{j} + 2\mathbf{k} \text{ (kN-m)}$$

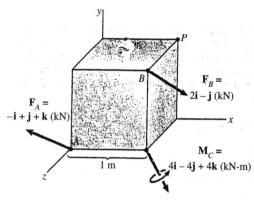

Problem 4.125 The bar is loaded by the forces

$$\mathbf{F}_B = 2\mathbf{i} + 6\mathbf{j} + 3\mathbf{k} \text{ (kN)},$$

$$\mathbf{F}_C = \mathbf{i} - 2\mathbf{j} + 2\mathbf{k} \text{ (kN)},$$

and the couple

$$\mathbf{M}_C = 2\mathbf{i} + \mathbf{j} - 2\mathbf{k} \text{ (kN-m)}.$$

Determine the sum of the moments of the two forces and the couple about A.

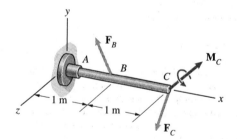

Solution: The moments of the two forces about A are given by

$$\mathbf{M}_{FB} = (1\mathbf{i}) \times (2\mathbf{i} + 6\mathbf{j} + 3\mathbf{k}) \text{ (kN-m)} = 0\mathbf{i} - 3\mathbf{j} + 6\mathbf{k} \text{ (kN-m) and}$$

$$\mathbf{M}_{FC} = (2\mathbf{i}) \times (1\mathbf{i} - 2\mathbf{j} + 2\mathbf{k}) \text{ (kN-m)} = 0\mathbf{i} - 4\mathbf{j} - 4\mathbf{k} \text{ (kN-m)}.$$

Adding these two moments and

$$\mathbf{M}_C = 2\mathbf{i} + 1\mathbf{j} - 2\mathbf{k} \text{ (kN-m)},$$

we get $\boxed{\mathbf{M}_{TOTAL} = 2\mathbf{i} - 6\mathbf{j} + 0\mathbf{k} \text{ (kN-m)}}$

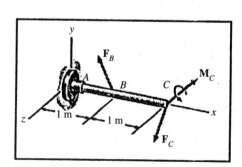

Problem 4.126 In Problem 4.125, the forces

$$\mathbf{F}_B = 2\mathbf{i} + 6\mathbf{j} + 3\mathbf{k} \ (kN),$$

$$\mathbf{F}_C = \mathbf{i} - 2\mathbf{j} + 2\mathbf{k} \ (kN),$$

and the couple

$$\mathbf{M}_C = M_{Cy}\mathbf{j} + M_{Cz}\mathbf{k} \ (kN\text{-}m).$$

Determine the values for M_{Cy} and M_{Cz}, so that the sum of the moments of the two forces and the couple about A is zero.

Solution: From the solution to Problem 4.125, the sum of the moments of the two forces about A is

$$\mathbf{M}_{\text{Forces}} = 0\mathbf{i} - 7\mathbf{j} + 2\mathbf{k} \ (kN\text{-}m).$$

The required moment, $\mathbf{M}_C$, must be the negative of this sum.

Thus $\boxed{M_{Cy} = 7 \ (kN\text{-}m), \ \text{and} \ M_{Cz} = -2 \ (kN\text{-}m).}$

Problem 4.127 Two wrenches are used to tighten an elbow fitting. The force $\mathbf{F} = 10\mathbf{k}$ (lb) on the right wrench is applied at $(6, -5, -3)$ in., and the force $-\mathbf{F}$ on the left wrench is applied at $(4, -5, 3)$ in.

(a) Determine the moment about the x axis due to the force exerted on the right wrench.
(b) Determine the moment of the couple formed by the forces exerted on the two wrenches.
(c) Based on the results of (a) and (b), explain why two wrenches are used.

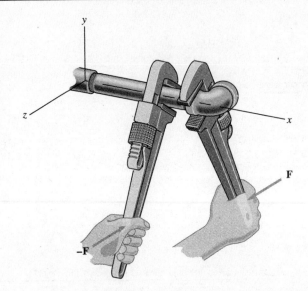

Solution: The position vector of the force on the right wrench is $\mathbf{r}_R = 6\mathbf{i} - 5\mathbf{j} - 3\mathbf{k}$. The magnitude of the moment about the x-axis is

$$|\mathbf{M}_R| = \mathbf{e}_X \cdot (\mathbf{r}_R \times \mathbf{F}) = \begin{vmatrix} 1 & 0 & 0 \\ 6 & -5 & -3 \\ 0 & 0 & 10 \end{vmatrix} = -50 \ \text{in lb}$$

(a) The moment about the x-axis is

$$\mathbf{M}_R = |\mathbf{M}_R|\mathbf{e}_X = -50\mathbf{i} \ (\text{in lb}).$$

(b) The moment of the couple is

$$\mathbf{M}_C = (\mathbf{r}_R - \mathbf{r}_L) \times \mathbf{F}_R = \begin{vmatrix} \mathbf{i} & \mathbf{j} & \mathbf{k} \\ 2 & 0 & -6 \\ 0 & 0 & 10 \end{vmatrix} = -20\mathbf{j} \ \text{in lb}$$

(c) The objective is to apply a moment to the elbow relative to connecting pipe, and zero resultant moment to the pipe itself. A resultant moment about the x-axis will affect the joint at the origin. However the use of two wrenches results in a net zero moment about the x-axis the moment is absorbed at the juncture of the elbow and the pipe. This is demonstrated by calculating the moment about the x-axis due to the left wrench:

$$|\mathbf{M}_X| = \mathbf{e}_X \cdot (\mathbf{r}_L \times \mathbf{F}_L) = \begin{vmatrix} 1 & 0 & 0 \\ 4 & -5 & 3 \\ 0 & 0 & -10 \end{vmatrix} = 50 \ \text{in lb}$$

from which $\mathbf{M}_{XL} = 50\mathbf{i}$ in lb, which is opposite in direction and equal in magnitude to the moment exerted on the x-axis by the right wrench. The left wrench force is applied 2 in nearer the origin than the right wrench force, hence the moment must be absorbed by the space between, where it is wanted.

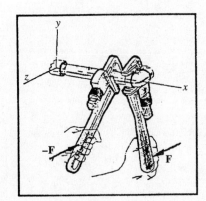

Problem 4.128 Two systems of forces act on the beam. Are they equivalent?

Strategy: Check the two conditions for equivalence. The sums of the forces must be equal, and the sums of the moments about an arbitrary point must be equal.

System 1

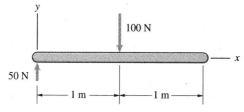

System 2

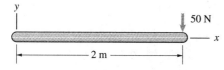

Solution: The strategy is to check the two conditions for equivalence: (a) the sums of the forces must be equal and (b) the sums of the moments about an arbitrary point must be equal. The sums of the forces of the two systems: $\sum F_X = 0$, (both systems) and

$$\sum \mathbf{F}_{Y1} = -100\mathbf{j} + 50\mathbf{j} = -50\mathbf{j} \text{ (N)}$$

$$\sum \mathbf{F}_{Y2} = -50\mathbf{j} \text{ (N)}.$$

The sums of the forces are equal. The sums of the moments about the left end are:

$$\sum \mathbf{M}_1 = -(1)(100)\mathbf{k} = -100\mathbf{k} \text{ (N-m)}$$

$$\sum \mathbf{M}_2 = -(2)(50)\mathbf{k} = -100\mathbf{k} \text{ (N-m)}.$$

The sums of the moments about the left end are equal. Choose any point P at the same distance $\mathbf{r} = x\mathbf{i}$ from the left end on each beam. The sums of the moments about the point P are

$$\sum \mathbf{M}_1 = (-50x + 100(x-1))\mathbf{k} = (50x - 100)\mathbf{k} \text{ (N-m)}$$

$$\sum \mathbf{M}_2 = (-50(2-x))\mathbf{k} = (50x - 100)\mathbf{k} \text{ (N-m)}.$$

Thus the sums of the moments about any point on the beam are equal for the two sets of forces; the systems are equivalent. Yes

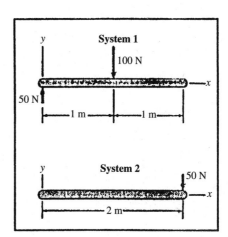

Problem 4.129 Two systems of forces and moments act on the beam. Are they equivalent?

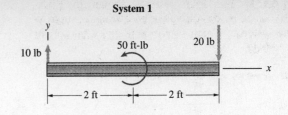

System 1

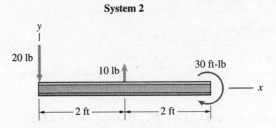

System 2

Solution: The sums of the forces are:

$$\sum F_X = 0 \text{ (both systems)}$$

$$\sum F_{Y1} = 10\mathbf{j} - 20\mathbf{j} = -10\mathbf{j} \text{ (lb)}$$

$$\sum F_{Y2} = -20\mathbf{j} + 10\mathbf{j} = -10\mathbf{j} \text{ (lb)}$$

Thus the sums of the forces are equal. The sums of the moments about the left end are:

$$\sum M_1 = (-20)(4)\mathbf{k} + 50\mathbf{k} = -30\mathbf{k} \text{ (ft lb)}$$

$$\sum M_2 = (+10(2))\mathbf{k} - 30\mathbf{k} = -10\mathbf{k} \text{ (ft lb)}$$

The sums of the moments are not equal, hence the systems are not equivalent. No

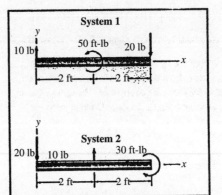

Problem 4.130 Four systems of forces and moments act on an 8-m beam. Which systems are equivalent?

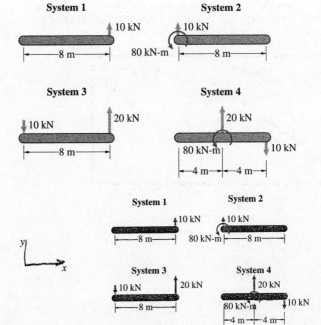

Solution: For equivalence, the sum of the forces and the sum of the moments about some point (the left end will be used) must be the same.

	System 1	System 2	System 3	System 4
$\sum F$ (kN)	10j	10j	10j	10j
$\sum M_L$ (kN-m)	80k	80k	160k	80k

Systems 1, 2, and 4 are equivalent.

260

Problem 4.131 The four systems shown in Problem 4.130 can be made equivalent by adding a couple to one of the systems. Which system is it, and what couple must be added?

Solution: From the solution to 4.130, All systems have

$$\sum \mathbf{F} = 10\mathbf{j} \text{ kN}$$

and systems 1, 2, and 4 have

$$\sum \mathbf{M}_L = 80\mathbf{k} \text{ (kN-m)}$$

system 3 has

$$\sum \mathbf{M}_L = 160\mathbf{k} \text{ (kN-m)}$$

Thus, we need to add a couple $\mathbf{M} = -80\mathbf{k}$ (kN-m) to system 3. (clockwise moment)

Problem 4.132 System 1 is a force $\mathbf{F}$ acting at a point O. System 2 is the force $\mathbf{F}$ acting at a different point O' along the same line of action. Explain why these systems are equivalent. (This simple result is called the *principle of transmissibility*.)

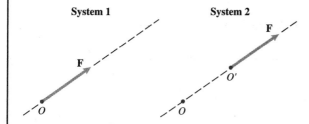

Solution: The sum of forces is obviously equal for both systems. Let P be any point on the beam. The moment about P is the cross product of the distance from P to the line of action of a force times the force, that is, $\mathbf{M} = \mathbf{r}_{PL} \times \mathbf{F}$, where $\mathbf{r}_{PL}$ is the distance from P to the line of action of $\mathbf{F}$. Since both systems have the same line of action, and the forces are equal, the systems are equivalent.

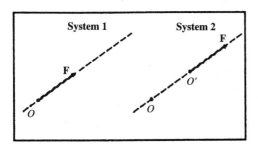

Problem 4.133 The vector sum of the forces exerted on the log by the cables is the same in the two cases. Show that the systems of forces exerted on the log are equivalent.

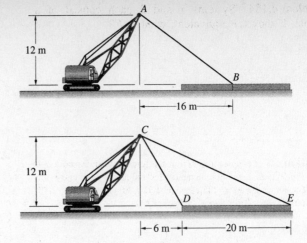

Solution: The angle formed by the single cable with the positive x-axis is

$$\theta = 180° - \tan^{-1}\left(\frac{12}{16}\right) = 143.13°.$$

The single cable tension is

$$\mathbf{T}_1 = |\mathbf{T}|(\mathbf{i}\cos 143.13° + \mathbf{j}\sin 143.13°)$$

$$= |\mathbf{T}|(-0.8\mathbf{i} + 0.6\mathbf{j}).$$

The position vector to the center of the log from the left end is $\mathbf{r}_c = 10\mathbf{i}$. The moment about the end of the log is

$$\mathbf{M} = \mathbf{r} \times \mathbf{T}_1 = |\mathbf{T}_1|\begin{vmatrix} \mathbf{i} & \mathbf{j} & \mathbf{k} \\ 10 & 0 & 0 \\ -0.8 & 0.6 & 0 \end{vmatrix} = |\mathbf{T}|(6)\mathbf{k} \text{ (N-m)}.$$

For the two cables, the angles relative to the positive x-axis are

$$\theta_1 = 180° - \tan^{-1}\left(\frac{12}{6}\right) = 116.56°, \text{ and}$$

$$\theta_2 = 180 - \tan^{-1}\left(\frac{12}{26}\right) = 155.22°.$$

The two cable vectors are

$$\mathbf{T}_L = |\mathbf{T}_L|(\mathbf{i}\cos 116.56° + \mathbf{j}\sin 116.56°)$$

$$= |\mathbf{T}_L|(-0.4472\mathbf{i} + 0.8945\mathbf{j}),$$

$$\mathbf{T}_R = |\mathbf{T}_R|(\mathbf{i}\cos 155.22° + \mathbf{j}\sin 155.22°)$$

$$= |\mathbf{T}_R|(-0.9079\mathbf{i} + 0.4191\mathbf{j}).$$

Since the vector sum of the forces in the two systems is equal, two simultaneous equations are obtained:

$$0.4472|\mathbf{T}_L| + 0.9079|\mathbf{T}_R| = 0.8|\mathbf{T}_1|, \text{ and}$$

$$0.8945|\mathbf{T}_L| + 0.4191|\mathbf{T}_R| = 0.6|\mathbf{T}_1|$$

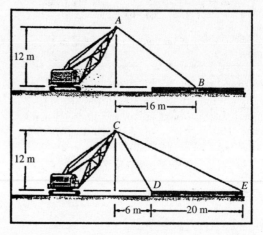

Solve:

$$|\mathbf{T}_L| = 0.3353|\mathbf{T}_1|, \text{ and}$$

$$|\mathbf{T}_R| = 0.7160|\mathbf{T}_1|.$$

The tension in the right hand cable is $\mathbf{T}_R = |\mathbf{T}_1|(0.7160)(-0.9079\mathbf{i} + 0.4191\mathbf{j}) = |\mathbf{T}_1|(-0.6500\mathbf{i} + 0.3000)$. The position vector of the right end of the log is $\mathbf{r}_R = 20\mathbf{i}$ m relative to the left end. The moments about the left end of the log for the second system are

$$\mathbf{M}_2 = \mathbf{r}_R \times \mathbf{T}_R = |\mathbf{T}_1|\begin{vmatrix} \mathbf{i} & \mathbf{j} & \mathbf{k} \\ 20 & 0 & 0 \\ -0.6500 & 0.3000 & 0 \end{vmatrix} = |\mathbf{T}_1|(6)\mathbf{k} \text{ (N-m)}.$$

This is equal to the moment about the left end of the log for System 1, hence the systems are equivalent.

Problem 4.134 Systems 1 and 2 each consist of a couple. If they are equivalent, what is F?

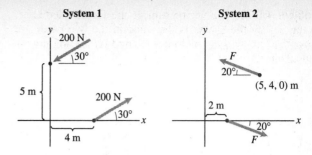

Solution: For couples, the sum of the forces vanish for both systems. For System 1, the two forces are located at $\mathbf{r}_{11} = 4\mathbf{i}$, and $\mathbf{r}_{12} = +5\mathbf{j}$. The forces are $\mathbf{F}_1 = 200(\mathbf{i}\cos 30° + \mathbf{j}\sin 30°) = 173.21\mathbf{i} + 100\mathbf{j}$. The moment due to the couple in System 1 is

$$\mathbf{M}_1 = (\mathbf{r}_{11} - \mathbf{r}_{12}) \times \mathbf{F}_1 = \begin{vmatrix} \mathbf{i} & \mathbf{j} & \mathbf{k} \\ 4 & -5 & 0 \\ 173.21 & 100 & 0 \end{vmatrix} = 1266.05\mathbf{k} \text{ (N-m)}.$$

For System 2, the positions of the forces are $\mathbf{r}_{21} = 2\mathbf{i}$, and $\mathbf{r}_{22} = 5\mathbf{i} + 4\mathbf{j}$. The forces are

$$\mathbf{F}_2 = F(\mathbf{i}\cos(-20°) + \mathbf{j}\sin(-20°)) = F(0.9397\mathbf{i} - 0.3420\mathbf{j}).$$

The moment of the couple in System 2 is

$$\mathbf{M}_2 = (\mathbf{r}_{21} - \mathbf{r}_{22}) \times \mathbf{F}_2 = F\begin{vmatrix} \mathbf{i} & \mathbf{j} & \mathbf{k} \\ -3 & -4 & 0 \\ 0.9397 & -0.3420 & 0 \end{vmatrix} = 4.7848F\mathbf{k},$$

from which, if the systems are to be equivalent,

$$F = \frac{1266}{4.7848} = 264.6 \text{ N}$$

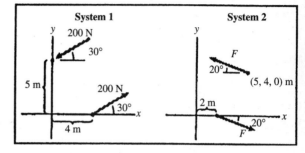

Problem 4.135 Two equivalent systems of forces and moments act on the L-shaped bar. Determine the forces F_A and F_B and the couple M.

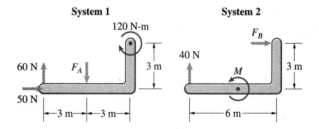

Solution: The sums of the forces for System 1 are

$$\sum F_X = 50, \text{ and}$$

$$\sum F_Y = -F_A + 60.$$

The sums of the forces for System 2 are

$$\sum F_X = F_B, \text{ and}$$

$$\sum F_Y = 40.$$

For equivalent systems: $F_B = 50$ N, and $F_A = 60 - 40 = 20$ N. The sum of the moments about the left end for

System 1 is

$$\sum M_1 = -(3)F_A - 120 = -180 \text{ N-m}.$$

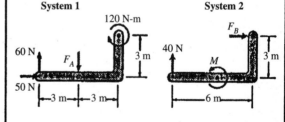

The sum of the moments about the left end for

System 2 is

$$\sum M_2 = -(3)F_B + M = -150 + M \text{ N-m}.$$

Equating the sums of the moments, $M = 150 - 180 = -30$ N-m

Problem 4.136 Two equivalent systems of forces and moments act on the plate. Determine the force F and the couple M.

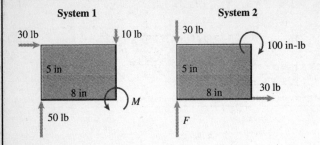

Solution: The sums of the forces for System 1 are

$$\sum F_X = 30 \text{ lb},$$

$$\sum F_Y = 50 - 10 = 40 \text{ lb}.$$

The sums of the forces for System 2 are

$$\sum F_X = 30 \text{ lb},$$

$$\sum F_Y = F - 30 \text{ lb}.$$

For equivalent forces, $F = 30 + 40 = 70$ lb. The sum of the moments about the lower left corner for System 1 is

$$\sum M_1 = -(5)(30) - (8)(10) + M = -230 + M \text{ in lb}.$$

The sum of the moments about the lower left corner for System 2 is

$$\sum M_2 = -100 \text{ in lb}.$$

Equating the sum of moments, $M = 230 - 100 = 130$ in lb

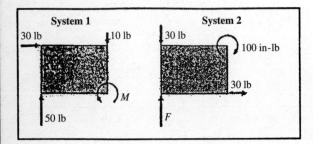

Problem 4.137 In system 1, four forces act on the rectangular flat plate. The forces are perpendicular to the plate and the 400-kN force acts at its midpoint. In system 2, no forces or couples act on the plate. Systems 1 and 2 are equivalent. What are the forces F_1, F_2, and F_3.

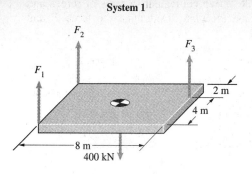

System 1

System 2

Solution: For the two systems to be equivalent

$$\sum \mathbf{F}_1 = \sum \mathbf{F}_2 \text{ and}$$

$$\sum \mathbf{M}_{A_1} = \sum \mathbf{M}_{A_2}$$

From system 2,

$$\sum \mathbf{F}_2 = 0 \text{ and}$$

$$\sum \mathbf{M}_{A_2} = 0$$

This

$$\sum \mathbf{F}_1 = \mathbf{F}_1 + \mathbf{F}_2 + \mathbf{F}_3 - 400\mathbf{j} = 0 \text{ or}$$

$$\sum F_{1Y} = F_1 + F_2 + F_3 - 400 = 0 \quad (1)$$

Summing Moments around A, we get

$$\sum \mathbf{M}_A = (4\mathbf{i} + 3\mathbf{k}) \times (-400\mathbf{j}) + (6\mathbf{k} \times F_1\mathbf{j})$$

$$+ (8\mathbf{i} + 2\mathbf{k}) \times F_2\mathbf{j}$$

$$\sum \mathbf{M}_A = (-1600\mathbf{k} + 1200\mathbf{i}) - 6F_1\mathbf{i}$$

$$+ 8F_3\mathbf{k} - 2F_3\mathbf{i} \text{ (kN-m)} = 0$$

In component form, we have

x: $-6F_1 - 2F_3 + 1200 = 0$ (kN-m)

z: $8F_3 - 1600 = 0$ (kN-m)

And the Force equation $F_1 + F_2 + F_3 - 400 = 0$ kN

Solving, we get

$F_3 = 200$ kN

$F_1 = \dfrac{800}{6} = 133.3$ kN

$F_2 = 66.7$ kN

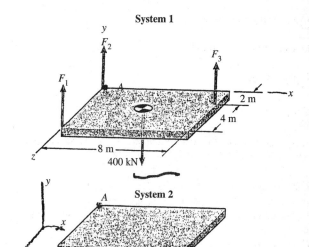

Problem 4.138   Three forces and a couple are applied to a beam (system 1).

(a)   If you represent system 1 by a force applied at A and a couple (system 2), what are $\mathbf{F}$ and M?

(b)   If you represent system 1 by the force $\mathbf{F}$ (system 3), what is the distance D?

System 1

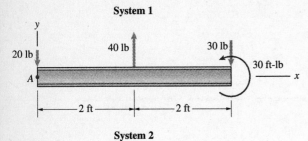

System 2

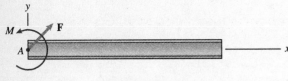

System 3

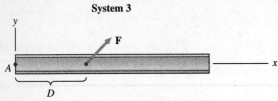

Solution: The sum of the forces in System 1 is

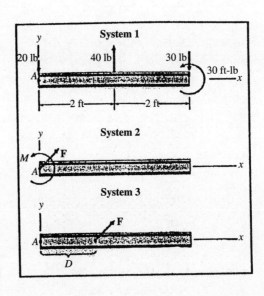

$$\sum \mathbf{F}_X = 0\mathbf{i},$$

$$\sum \mathbf{F}_Y = (-20 + 40 - 30)\mathbf{j} = -10\mathbf{j} \text{ lb}.$$

The sum of the moments about the left end for System 1 is

$$\sum \mathbf{M}_1 = (2(40) - 4(30) + 30)\mathbf{k} = -10\mathbf{k} \text{ ft lb}.$$

(a)   For System 2, the force at A is $\mathbf{F} = -10\mathbf{j}$ lb
      The moment at A is $\mathbf{M}_2 = -10\mathbf{k}$ ft lb

(b)   For System 3 the force at D is $\mathbf{F} = -10\mathbf{j}$ lb. The distance D is the ratio of the magnitude of the moment to the magnitude of the force, where the magnitudes are those in System 1:

$$D = \frac{10}{10} = 1 \text{ ft}$$

Problem 4.139 Represent the two forces and couple acting on the beam by a force $\mathbf{F}$. Determine $\mathbf{F}$ and determine where its line of action intersects the x axis.

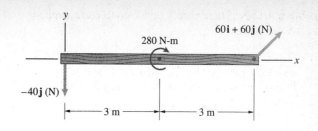

Solution: We first represent the system by an equivalent system consisting of a force $\mathbf{F}$ at the origin and a couple M:

This system is equivalent if

$\mathbf{F} = -40\mathbf{j} + 60\mathbf{i} + 60\mathbf{j}$

$\quad = 60\mathbf{i} + 20\mathbf{j}$ (N),

$M = -280 + (6)(60)$

$\quad = 80$ N-m.

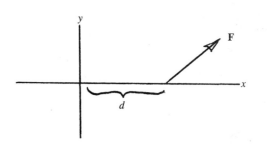

We then represent this system by an equivalent system consisting of $\mathbf{F}$ alone:

For equivalence, $M = d(F_y)$, so

$d = \dfrac{M}{F_y} = \dfrac{80}{20} = 4$ m.

Problem 4.140 The vector sum of the forces acting on the beam is zero, and the sum of the moments about the left end of the beam is zero.

(a) Determine the forces A_x, A_y, and B.
(b) If you represent the forces A_x, A_y, and B by a force $\mathbf{F}$ acting at the right end of the beam and a couple M, what are $\mathbf{F}$ and M?

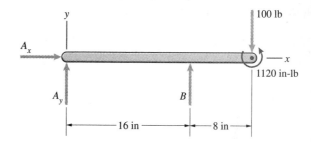

Solution: (a) The sum of the forces

$\sum F_X = A_X = 0$

$\sum F_Y = (A_Y + B - 100) = 0.$

The sum of the moments:

$\sum \mathbf{M} = ((16)B - 24(100) + 1120)\mathbf{k} = (16B - 1280)\mathbf{k} = 0,$

from which $B = 80$ lb. From the force balance equation: $A_Y = -80 + 100 = 20$ lb. (b) The force at the right end of the beam must balance the 100 lb force, $\mathbf{F} = 100\mathbf{j}$ lb. The couple must balance the existing couple $\mathbf{M} = -1120\mathbf{k}$ in lb

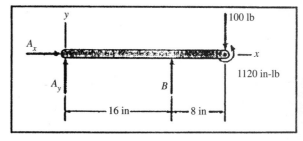

Problem 4.141 The vector sum of the forces acting on the beam is zero, and the sum of the moments about the left end of the beam is zero.

(a) Determine the forces A_x and A_y, and the couple M_A.
(b) Determine the sum of the moments about the right end of the beam.
(c) If you represent the 600-N force, the 200-N force, and the 30 N-m couple by a force $\mathbf{F}$ acting at the left end of the beam and a couple M, what are $\mathbf{F}$ and M?

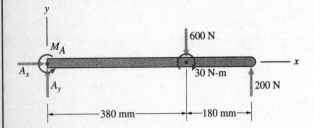

Solution: (a) The sum of the forces is

$$\sum \mathbf{F}_X = A_X\mathbf{i} = 0 \text{ and}$$

$$\sum \mathbf{F}_Y = (A_Y - 600 + 200)\mathbf{j} = 0,$$

from which $A_Y = 400$ N. The sum of the moments is

$$\sum \mathbf{M}_L = (M_A - 0.38(600) - 30 + 0.560(200))\mathbf{k} = 0,$$

from which $M_A = 146$ N-m. (b) The sum of the moments about the right end of the beam is

$$\sum \mathbf{M}_L = 0.18(600) - 30 + 146 - 0.56(400) = 0.$$

(c) The sum of the forces for the new system is

$$\sum \mathbf{F}_Y = (A_Y + F)\mathbf{j} = 0,$$

from $F = -A_Y = -400$ N, or $\mathbf{F} = -400\mathbf{j}$ N. The sum of the moments for the new system is

$$\sum M = (M_A + M) = 0,$$

from which $M = -M_A = -146$ N-m

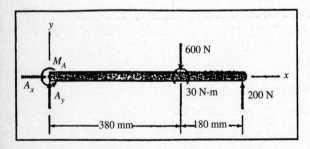

Problem 4.142 The vector sum of the forces acting on the truss is zero, and the sum of the moments about the origin O is zero.

(a) Determine the forces A_x, A_y, and B.
(b) If you represent the 2-kip, 4-kip, and 6-kip forces by a force $\mathbf{F}$, what is $\mathbf{F}$, and where does its line of action intersect the y axis?
(c) If you replace the 2-kip, 4-kip, and 6-kip forces by the force you determined in (b), what are the vector sum of the forces acting on the truss and the sum of the moments about O?

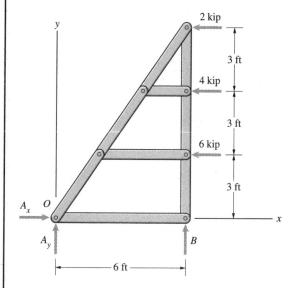

Solution: (a) The sum of the forces is

$$\sum \mathbf{F}_X = (A_X - 2 - 4 - 6)\mathbf{i} = 0,$$

from which $A_X = 12$ kip

$$\sum \mathbf{F}_Y = (A_Y + B)\mathbf{j} = 0.$$

The sum of the moments about the origin is

$$\sum M_O = (3)(6) + (6)(4) + (9)(2) + 6(B) = 0,$$

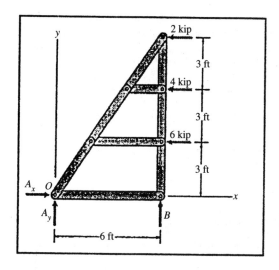

from which $\mathbf{B} = -10\mathbf{j}$ kip. (b) Substitute into the force balance equation to obtain $A_Y = -B = 10$ kip. (b) The force in the new system will replace the 2, 4, and 6 kip forces, $\mathbf{F} = (-2 - 4 - 6)\mathbf{i} = -12\mathbf{i}$ kip. The force must match the moment due to these forces: $FD = 3(6) + (6)(4) + (9)(2) = 60$ kip ft, from which $D = \dfrac{60}{12} = 5$ ft, or the action line intersects the y-axis 5 ft above the origin. (c) The new system is equivalent to the old one, hence *the sum of the forces vanish and the sum of the moments about O are zero.*

Problem 4.143 The distributed force exerted on part of a building foundation by the soil is represented by five forces. If you represent them by a force **F**, what is **F**, and where does its line of action intersect the x axis?

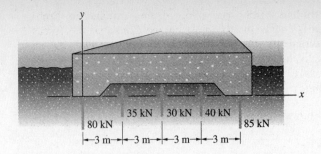

Solution: The equivalent force must equal the sum of the forces exerted by the soil:

$$\mathbf{F} = (80 + 35 + 30 + 40 + 85)\mathbf{j} = 270\mathbf{j} \text{ kN}$$

The sum of the moments about any point must be equal for the two systems. The sum of the moments are

$$\sum M = 3(35) + 6(30) + 9(40) + 12(85) = 1665 \text{ kN-m.}$$

Equating the moments for the two systems $FD = 1665$ kN-m from which

$$D = \frac{1665 \text{ kN-m}}{270 \text{ kN}} = 6.167 \text{ m.}$$

Thus the action line intersects the x axis at a distance $D = 6.167$ m to the right of the origin.

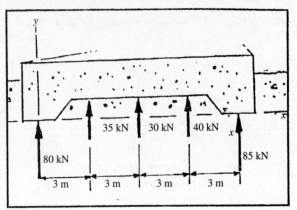

Problem 4.144 After landing, the pilot engages the airplane's thrust reversers and engines 1, 2, 3, and 4 exert forces toward the right of magnitudes 39 kN, 40 kN, 42 kN, and 40 kN, respectively. If you represent the four forces by an equivalent force **F**, what is **F**, and what is the y coordinate of its line of action?

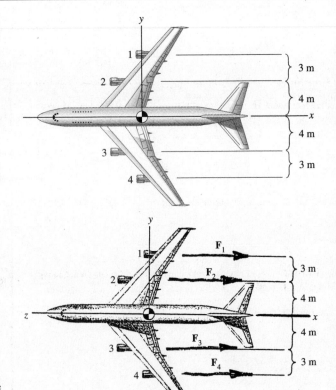

Solution: We must find the sum of the forces and the sum of the moments around the center of mass. We must then find the moment arm at which the sum of the forces would create the same moment as the four individual forces.

$$\sum \mathbf{F} = 39\mathbf{i} + 40\mathbf{i} + 42\mathbf{i} + 40\mathbf{i} \text{ (kN)}$$

$$\sum \mathbf{F} = 161\mathbf{i} \text{ (kN)}$$

$$\sum \mathbf{M}_\oplus = +7\mathbf{j} \times 39\mathbf{i} + 4\mathbf{j} \times 40\mathbf{i} - 4\mathbf{j} \times 42\mathbf{i} - 7\mathbf{j} \times 40\mathbf{i}$$

$$\sum \mathbf{M}_\oplus = -273\mathbf{k} - 160\mathbf{k} + 168\mathbf{k} + 280\mathbf{k}$$

$$\sum \mathbf{M}_\oplus = 15\mathbf{k} \text{ (kN-m)}$$

We Now need to find the moment arm for the sum of the forces. We require

$$4\mathbf{j} \times 161\mathbf{i} = 15\mathbf{k}$$

$$-161y = 15$$

$$y = -0.0932 \text{ m}$$

Problem 4.145 The pilot of the airplane in Problem 4.144 wants to adjust engine 2 so that the forces exerted by the engines can be represented by an equivalent force whose line of action intersects the z axis. When this is done, what force is exerted by engine 2?

Solution: Here we have F_2 unknown and know that

$$\sum \mathbf{M}_\oplus = 0.$$

All else is unchanged from the solution to Problem 4.144. Hence, we have

$$\sum \mathbf{F} = 39\mathbf{i} + F_2\mathbf{i} + 42\mathbf{i} + 40\mathbf{i} \text{ (kN)}$$

$$\sum F = 121\mathbf{i} + F_2\mathbf{i} \text{ (kN)}$$

and $\sum \mathbf{M}_\oplus = 7\mathbf{j} \times 39\mathbf{i} + 4\mathbf{j} \times F_2\mathbf{i} - 4\mathbf{j} \times 42\mathbf{i} - 7\mathbf{j} \times 40\mathbf{i} = 0$

$$\sum \mathbf{M}_\oplus = -273\mathbf{k} - 4F_2\mathbf{k} + 168\mathbf{k} + 280\mathbf{k} = 0$$

or $\sum \mathbf{M}_\oplus = (175 - 4F_2)\mathbf{k} = 0$

Solving:

$F_2 = 43.75$ (kN-m)

$\mathbf{F}_2 = 43.75\mathbf{i}$ (kN-m)

Problem 4.146 The system is in equilibrium. If you represent the forces $\mathbf{F}_{AB}$ and $\mathbf{F}_{AC}$ by a force $\mathbf{F}$ acting at A and a couple $\mathbf{M}$, what are $\mathbf{F}$ and $\mathbf{M}$?

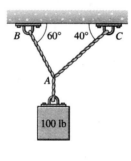
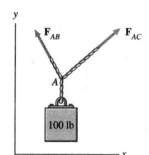

Solution: The sum of the forces acting at A is in opposition to the weight, or $\mathbf{F} = |\mathbf{W}|\mathbf{j} = 100\mathbf{j}$ lb.

The moment about point A is zero.

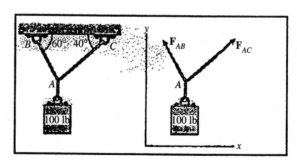

Problem 4.147 Three forces act on a beam.

(a) Represent the system by a force **F** acting at the origin O and a couple M.

(b) Represent the system by a single force. Where does the line of action of the force intersect the x axis?

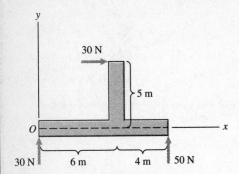

Solution: (a) The sum of the forces is

$$\sum F_X = 30\mathbf{i} \text{ N, and}$$

$$\sum F_Y = (30 + 50)\mathbf{j} = 80\mathbf{j} \text{ N.}$$

The equivalent at O is $\mathbf{F} = 30\mathbf{i} + 80\mathbf{j}$ (N). The sum of the moments about O:

$$\sum M = (-5(30) + 10(50)) = 350 \text{ N-m}$$

(b) The solution of Part (a) is the single force. The intersection is the moment divided by the y-component of force: $D = \dfrac{350}{80} = 4.375$ m

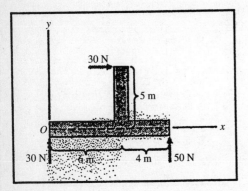

Problem 4.148 The tension in cable AB is 400 N, and the tension in cable CD is 600 N.

(a) If you represent the forces exerted on the left post by the cables by a force $\mathbf{F}$ acting at the origin O and a couple M, what are $\mathbf{F}$ and M?

(b) If you represent the forces exerted on the left post by the cables by the force $\mathbf{F}$ alone, where does its line of action intersect the y axis?

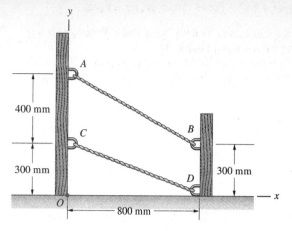

Solution: From the right triangle, the angle between the positive x-axis and the cable AB is

$$\theta = -\tan^{-1}\left(\frac{400}{800}\right) = -26.6°.$$

The tension in AB is

$$\mathbf{T}_{AB} = 400(\mathbf{i}\cos(-26.6°) + \mathbf{j}\sin(-26.6°)) = 357.77\mathbf{i} - 178.89\mathbf{j} \text{ (N)}.$$

The angle between the positive x-axis and the cable CD is

$$\alpha = -\tan^{-1}\left(\frac{300}{800}\right) = -20.6°.$$

The tension in CD is

$$\mathbf{T}_{CD} = 600(\mathbf{i}\cos(-20.6°) + \mathbf{j}\sin(-20.6°)) = 561.8\mathbf{i} - 210.67\mathbf{j}.$$

The equivalent force acting at the origin O is the sum of the forces acting on the left post:

$$\mathbf{F} = (357.77 + 561.8)\mathbf{i} + (-178.89 - 210.67)\mathbf{j}$$

$$= 919.6\mathbf{i} - 389.6\mathbf{j} \text{ (N)}.$$

The sum of the moments acting on the left post is the product of the moment arm and the x-component of the tensions:

$$\sum \mathbf{M} = -0.7(357.77)\mathbf{k} - 0.3(561.8)\mathbf{k} = -419\mathbf{k} \text{ N-m}$$

Check: The position vectors at the point of application are $\mathbf{r}_{AB} = 0.7\mathbf{j}$, and $\mathbf{r}_{CD} = 0.3\mathbf{j}$. The sum of the moments is

$$\sum \mathbf{M} = (\mathbf{r}_{AB} \times T_{AB}) + (\mathbf{r}_{CD} \times \mathbf{T}_{CD})$$

$$= \begin{vmatrix} \mathbf{i} & \mathbf{j} & \mathbf{k} \\ 0 & 0.7 & 0 \\ 357.77 & -178.89 & 0 \end{vmatrix} + \begin{vmatrix} \mathbf{i} & \mathbf{j} & \mathbf{k} \\ 0 & 0.3 & 0 \\ 561.8 & -210.67 & 0 \end{vmatrix}$$

$$= -0.7(357.77)\mathbf{k} - 0.3(561.8)\mathbf{k} = -419\mathbf{k}$$

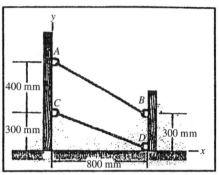

Check. (b) The equivalent single force retains the same scalar components, but must act at a point that duplicates the sum of the moments. The distance on the y-axis is the ratio of the sum of the moments to the x-component of the equivalent force. Thus

$$D = \frac{419}{919.6} = 0.456 \text{ m}$$

Check: The moment is

$$\mathbf{M} = \mathbf{r}_F \times \mathbf{F} = \begin{vmatrix} \mathbf{i} & \mathbf{j} & \mathbf{k} \\ 0 & D & 0 \\ 919.6 & -389.6 & 0 \end{vmatrix} = -919.6D\mathbf{k} = -419\mathbf{k},$$

from which $D = \dfrac{419}{919.6} = 0.456$ m, *Check.*

Problem 4.149 Consider the system shown in Problem 4.148. The tension in each of the cables AB and CD is 400 N. If you represent the forces exerted on the right post by the cables by a force $\mathbf{F}$, what is $\mathbf{F}$, and where does its line of action intersect the y axis?

Solution: From the solution of Problem 4.148, the tensions are

$$\mathbf{T}_{AB} = -400(\mathbf{i}\cos(-26.6°)+\mathbf{j}\sin(-26.6°)) = -357.77\mathbf{i} + 178.89\mathbf{j},$$

and

$$\mathbf{T}_{CD} = -400(\mathbf{i}\cos(-20.6°)+\mathbf{j}\sin(-20.6°)) = -374.42\mathbf{i} + 140.74\mathbf{j}.$$

The equivalent force is equal to the sum of these forces:

$$\mathbf{F} = (-357.77 - 374.42)\mathbf{i} + (178.77 + 140.74)\mathbf{j}$$

$$= -732.19\mathbf{i} + 319.5\mathbf{j} \text{ (N)}.$$

The sum of the moments about O is

$$\sum \mathbf{M} = 0.3(357.77) + 0.8(140.74 + 178.89)\mathbf{k} = 363\mathbf{k} \text{ (N-m)}.$$

The intersection is $D = \dfrac{363}{732.19} = 0.496$ m on the positive y-axis.

Problem 4.150 If you represent the three forces acting on the beam cross section by a force $\mathbf{F}$, what is $\mathbf{F}$, and where does its line of action intersect the x axis?

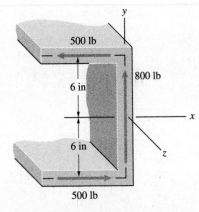

Solution: The sum of the forces is

$$\sum \mathbf{F}_X = (500 - 500)\mathbf{i} = 0.$$

$$\sum \mathbf{F}_Y = 800\mathbf{j}.$$

Thus a force and a couple with moment $\mathbf{M} = 500\mathbf{k}$ ft lb act on the cross section. The equivalent force is $\mathbf{F} = 800\mathbf{j}$ which acts at a positive x-axis location of $D = \dfrac{500}{800} = 0.625$ ft $= 7.5$ in to the right of the origin.

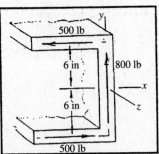

Problem 4.151 The two systems of forces and moments acting on the beam are equivalent. Determine the force **F** and the couple **M**.

System 1

System 2

Solution: The sum of the forces on the two systems are equivalent: the force on System 1 is $\mathbf{F}_1 = 4\mathbf{i} + 4\mathbf{j} - 2\mathbf{k}$ (kN). The moments on the two systems are equivalent: the moment about the origin for System 1 is the product of the moment arm and the y- and z-components of the force:

$\mathbf{M} = 3(2)\mathbf{j} + 3(4)\mathbf{k} = 6\mathbf{j} + 12\mathbf{k}$. Hence the couple moment on System 2 is $\mathbf{M}_2 = 6\mathbf{j} + 12\mathbf{k}$ (kN-m)

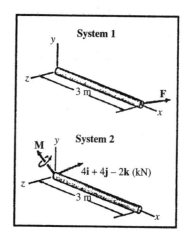

Problem 4.152 The wall bracket is subjected to the force shown.

(a) Determine the moment exerted by the force about the z axis.
(b) Determine the moment exerted by the force about the y axis.
(c) If you represent the force by a force **F** acting at O and a couple **M**, what are **F** and **M**?

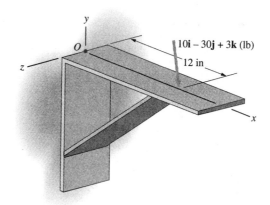

Solution:

(a) The moment about the z-axis is negative,

$$M_Z = -1(30) = -30 \text{ ft lb,}$$

(b) The moment about the y-axis is negative,

$$M_Y = -1(3) = -3 \text{ ft lb}$$

(c) The equivalent force at O must be equal to the force at $x = 12$ in, thus $\mathbf{F}_{EQ} = 10\mathbf{i} - 30\mathbf{j} + 3\mathbf{k}$ (lb)

The couple moment must equal the moment exerted by the force at $x = 12$ in. This moment is the product of the moment arm and the y- and z-components of the force: $\mathbf{M} = -1(30)\mathbf{k} - 1(3)\mathbf{j} = -3\mathbf{j} - 30\mathbf{k}$ (ft lb).

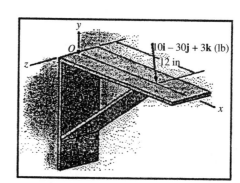

Problem 4.153 A basketball player executes a "slam dunk" shot, then hangs momentarily on the rim, exerting the two 100-lb forces shown. The dimensions are $h = 14\frac{1}{2}$ in., and $r = 9\frac{1}{2}$ in., and the angle $\alpha = 120°$.

(a) If you represent the forces he exerts by a force **F** acting at O and a couple **M**, what are **F** and **M**?
(b) The glass backboard will shatter if $|\mathbf{M}| > 4000$ in-lb. Does it break?

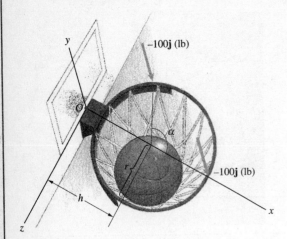

Solution: The equivalent force at the origin must equal the sum of the forces applied: $\mathbf{F}_{EQ} = -200\mathbf{j}$. The position vectors of the points of application of the forces are $\mathbf{r}_1 = (h + r)\mathbf{i}$, and $\mathbf{r}_2 = \mathbf{i}(h + r\cos\alpha) - \mathbf{k}r\sin\alpha$. The moments about the origin are

$$\mathbf{M} = (\mathbf{r}_1 \times \mathbf{F}_1) + (\mathbf{r}_2 \times \mathbf{F}_2) = (\mathbf{r}_1 + \mathbf{r}_2) \times \mathbf{F}$$

$$= \begin{vmatrix} \mathbf{i} & \mathbf{j} & \mathbf{k} \\ 2h + r(1 + \cos\alpha) & 0 & -r\sin\alpha \\ 0 & -100 & 0 \end{vmatrix}$$

$$= -100(r\sin\alpha)\mathbf{i} - 100(2h + r(1 + \cos\alpha))\mathbf{k}.$$

For the values of h, r, and α given, the moment is $\mathbf{M} = -822.72\mathbf{i} - 3375\mathbf{k}$ in lb. This is the couple moment required. (b) The magnitude of the moment is $|\mathbf{M}| = \sqrt{822.72^2 + 3375^2} = 3473.8$ in lb. *The backboard does not break.*

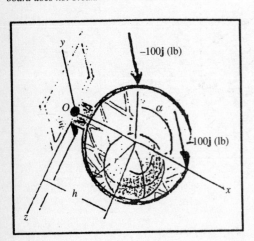

276

Problem 4.154 The three forces are parallel to the x axis.

(a) If you represent the three forces by a force $\mathbf{F}$ acting at the origin O and a couple $\mathbf{M}$, what are $\mathbf{F}$ and $\mathbf{M}$?

(b) If you represent the forces by a single force, what is the force, and where does its line of action intersect the $y - z$ plane?

Strategy: In (b), assume that the force acts at a point $(0, y, z)$ of the $y - z$ plane, and use the conditions for equivalence to determine the force and the coordinates y and z. (See Example 4.20.)

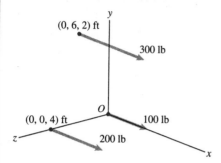

Solution:

(a) $\mathbf{F} = 100\mathbf{i} + 200\mathbf{i} + 300\mathbf{i}$

$= 600\mathbf{i} \ (\text{lb}).$

$$
\mathbf{M} = \begin{vmatrix} \mathbf{i} & \mathbf{j} & \mathbf{k} \\ 0 & 0 & 4 \\ 200 & 0 & 0 \end{vmatrix} + \begin{vmatrix} \mathbf{i} & \mathbf{j} & \mathbf{k} \\ 0 & 6 & 2 \\ 300 & 0 & 0 \end{vmatrix}
$$

$= 800\mathbf{j} + 600\mathbf{j} - 1800\mathbf{k}$

$= 1400\mathbf{j} - 1800\mathbf{k} \ (\text{ft-lb}).$

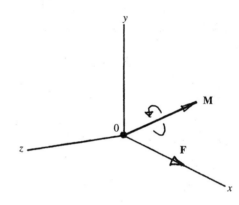

(b) $\mathbf{F} = 600\mathbf{i} \ (\text{lb}).$

To determine y and z, require that

$$
\mathbf{M} = 1400\mathbf{j} - 1800\mathbf{k} = \begin{vmatrix} \mathbf{i} & \mathbf{j} & \mathbf{k} \\ 0 & y & z \\ 600 & 0 & 0 \end{vmatrix}
$$

$1400 = 600\ z,$

$-1800 = -600\ y.$

Solving, $y = 3$ ft and $z = 2.33$ ft.

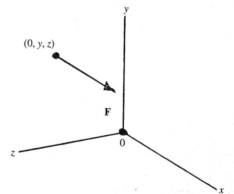

Problem 4.155 The positions and weights of three particles are shown. If you represent the weights by a single force **F**, determine **F** and show that its line of action intersects the x-z plane at

$$x = \frac{\sum_{i=1}^{3} x_i W_i}{\sum_{i=1}^{3} W_i}, \quad z = \frac{\sum_{i=1}^{3} z_i W_i}{\sum_{i=1}^{3} W_i}.$$

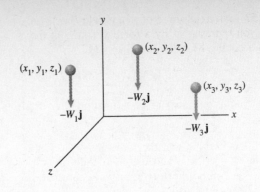

Solution: The single equivalent force must be equal to the sum of the forces:

$$\mathbf{F} = (-W_1 - W_2 - W_3)\mathbf{j} = -\sum_{i=1}^{3} W_i$$

The moment about the x-axis is

$$\sum M_X = \mathbf{e}_X \cdot (\mathbf{r}_1 \times \mathbf{W}_1) + \mathbf{e}_X \cdot (\mathbf{r}_2 \times \mathbf{W}_2) + \mathbf{e}_X \cdot (\mathbf{r}_3 \times \mathbf{W}_3)$$

$$= \begin{vmatrix} 1 & 0 & 0 \\ x_1 & y_1 & z_1 \\ 0 & -W_1 & 0 \end{vmatrix} + \begin{vmatrix} 1 & 0 & 0 \\ x_2 & y_2 & z_2 \\ 0 & -W_2 & 0 \end{vmatrix} + \begin{vmatrix} 1 & 0 & 0 \\ x_3 & y_3 & z_3 \\ 0 & -W_3 & 0 \end{vmatrix}$$

$$= \sum_{i=1}^{3} W_i z_i.$$

Similarly, the moment about the z-axis is

$$\sum M_Z = -\sum_{i=1}^{3} W_i x_i.$$

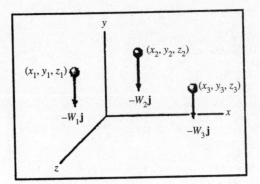

The moment arm is the ratio of the magnitude of the moment to the magnitude of the force,

$$D_X = \frac{\sum_{i=1}^{3} W_i z_i}{\sum_{i=1}^{3} W_i}, \quad D_Z = \frac{\sum_{i=1}^{3} W_i x_i}{\sum_{i=1}^{3} W_i}$$

Problem 4.156 Two forces act on the beam. If you represent them by a force **F** acting at C and a couple **M**, what are **F** and **M**?

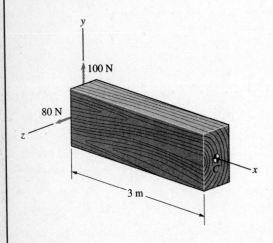

Solution: The equivalent force must equal the sum of forces: $\mathbf{F} = 100\mathbf{j} + 80\mathbf{k}$. The equivalent couple is equal to the moment about C:

$$\sum \mathbf{M} = (3)(80)\mathbf{j} - (3)(100)\mathbf{k} = 240\mathbf{j} - 300\mathbf{k}$$

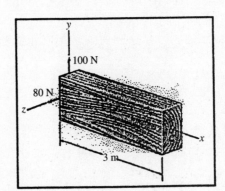

Problem 4.157 An axial force of magnitude P acts on the beam. If you represent it by a force $\mathbf{F}$ acting at the origin O and a couple $\mathbf{M}$, what are $\mathbf{F}$ and $\mathbf{M}$?

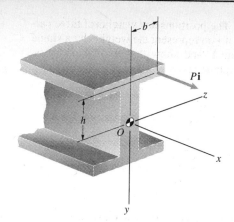

Solution: The equivalent force at the origin is equal to the applied force $\mathbf{F} = P\mathbf{i}$. The position vector of the applied force is $\mathbf{r} = -h\mathbf{j} + b\mathbf{k}$. The moment is

$$\mathbf{M} = (\mathbf{r} \times \mathbf{P}) = \begin{vmatrix} \mathbf{i} & \mathbf{j} & \mathbf{k} \\ 0 & -h & +b \\ P & 0 & 0 \end{vmatrix} = bP\mathbf{j} + hP\mathbf{k}.$$

This is the couple at the origin.

(Note that in the sketch the axis system has been rotated 180 about the x-axis; so that up is negative and right is positive for y and z.)

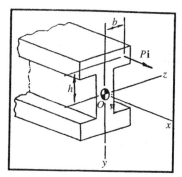

Problem 4.158 The brace is being used to remove a screw.

(a) If you represent the forces acting on the brace by a force $\mathbf{F}$ acting at the origin O and a couple $\mathbf{M}$, what are $\mathbf{F}$ and $\mathbf{M}$?

(b) If you represent the forces acting on the brace by a force $\mathbf{F}'$ acting at a point P with coordinates (x_P, y_P, z_P) and a couple $\mathbf{M}'$, what are $\mathbf{F}'$ and $\mathbf{M}'$?

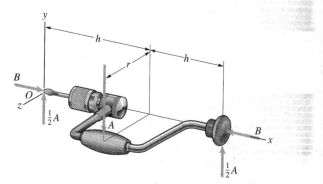

Solution: (a) Equivalent force at the origin O has the same value as the sum of forces,

$$\sum \mathbf{F}_X = (B - B)\mathbf{i} = 0,$$

$$\sum \mathbf{F}_Y = \left(-A + \tfrac{1}{2}A + \tfrac{1}{2}A\right)\mathbf{j} = 0,$$

thus $\mathbf{F} = 0$. The equivalent couple moment has the same value as the moment exerted on the brace by the forces,

$$\sum \mathbf{M}_O = (rA)\mathbf{i}.$$

Thus the couple at O has the moment $\mathbf{M} = rA\mathbf{i}$. (b) The equivalent force at (x_P, y_P, z_P) has the same value as the sum of forces on the brace, and the equivalent couple at (x_P, y_P, z_P) has the same moment as the moment exerted on the brace by the forces: $\mathbf{F} = 0$, $\mathbf{M} = rA\mathbf{i}$.

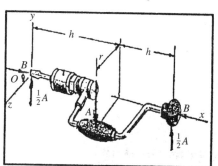

Problem 4.159 Two forces and a couple act on the cube. If you represent them by a force **F** acting at point P and a couple **M**, what are **F** and **M**?

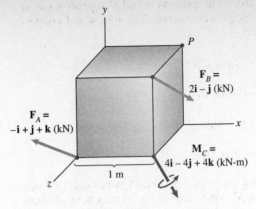

Solution: The equivalent force at P has the value of the sum of forces,

$$\sum F = (2-1)i + (1-1)j + k, \quad F_P = i + k \text{ (kN)}.$$

The equivalentcouple at P has the moment exerted by the forces and moment about P. The position vectors of the forces relative to P are:

$r_A = -i - j + k$, and $r_B = +k$. The moment of the couple:

$$\sum M = (r_A \times F_A) + (r_B \times F_B) + M_C$$

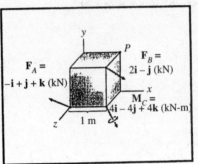

$$= \begin{vmatrix} i & j & k \\ -1 & -1 & 1 \\ -1 & 1 & 1 \end{vmatrix} + \begin{vmatrix} i & j & k \\ 0 & 0 & 1 \\ 2 & -1 & 0 \end{vmatrix} + M_C$$

$$= 3i - 2j + 2k \text{ (kN-m)}.$$

Problem 4.160 The two shafts are subjected to the torques (couples) shown.

(a) If you represent the two couples by a force **F** acting at the origin O and a couple **M**, what are **F** and **M**?
(b) What is the magnitude of the total moment exerted by the two couples?

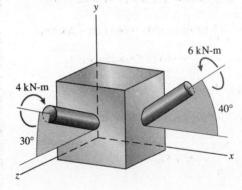

Solution: The equivalent force at the origin is zero, **F** = 0 since there is no resultant force on the system. Represent the couples of 4 kN-m and 6 kN-m magnitudes by the vectors M_1 and M_2. The couple at the origin must equal the sum:

$$\sum M = M_1 + M_2.$$

The sense of M_1 is (see sketch) negative with respect to both y and z, and the sense of M_2 is positive with respect to both x and y.

$$M_1 = 4(-j \sin 30° - k \cos 30°) = -2j - 3.464k,$$

$$M_2 = 6(i \cos 40° + j \sin 40°) = 4.5963i + 3.8567j.$$

Thus the couple at the origin is $M_O = 4.6i + 1.86j - 3.46k$ (kN-m)
(b) The magnitude of the total moment exerted by the two couples is
$$|M_O| = \sqrt{4.6^2 + 1.86^2 + 3.46^2} = 6.05 \text{ (kN-m)}$$

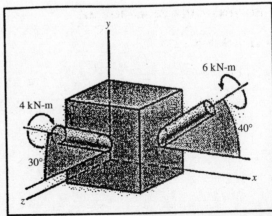

Problem 4.161 The persons A and B support a bar to which three dogs are tethered. The forces and couples they exert are

$$\mathbf{F}_A = -5\mathbf{i} + 15\mathbf{j} - 10\mathbf{k} \text{ (lb)},$$

$$\mathbf{M}_A = 15\mathbf{j} + 10\mathbf{k} \text{ (ft-lb)},$$

$$\mathbf{F}_B = 5\mathbf{i} + 10\mathbf{j} - 10\mathbf{k} \text{ (lb)},$$

$$\mathbf{M}_B = -10\mathbf{j} - 15\mathbf{k} \text{ (ft-lb)}.$$

If person B let go, person A would have to exert a force $\mathbf{F}$ and couple $\mathbf{M}$ equivalent to the system both of them were exerting together. What are $\mathbf{F}$ and $\mathbf{M}$?

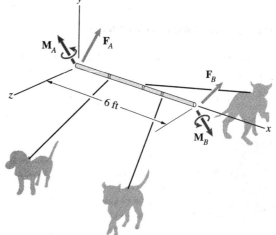

Solution: The equivalent force at B is the sum of the forces:

$$\sum \mathbf{F} = (-5+5)\mathbf{i} + (15+10)\mathbf{j} + (-10-10)\mathbf{k} = 25\mathbf{j} - 20\mathbf{k} \text{ (lb)}.$$

The equivalent couple at A is the sum of the moments at A

$$\sum \mathbf{M} = (\mathbf{r}_B \times \mathbf{F}_B) + \mathbf{M}_A + \mathbf{M}_B.$$

The position vector of B relative to A is $\mathbf{r}_B = 6\mathbf{i}$. Thus:

$$\sum \mathbf{M}_B = \begin{vmatrix} \mathbf{i} & \mathbf{j} & \mathbf{k} \\ 6 & 0 & 0 \\ 5 & 10 & -10 \end{vmatrix} + \mathbf{M}_A + \mathbf{M}_B$$

$$\sum \mathbf{M}_B = (60\mathbf{j} + 60\mathbf{k}) + (15\mathbf{j} + 10\mathbf{k}) + (-10\mathbf{j} - 15\mathbf{k})$$

$$= 65\mathbf{j} + 55\mathbf{k} \text{ (ft-lb)}$$

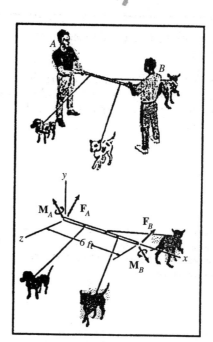

Problem 4.162 Point G is at the center of the block. The forces are

$$\mathbf{F}_A = -20\mathbf{i} + 10\mathbf{j} + 20\mathbf{k} \text{ (lb)},$$

$$\mathbf{F}_B = 10\mathbf{j} - 10\mathbf{k} \text{ (lb)}.$$

If you represent the two forces by a force $\mathbf{F}$ acting at G and a couple $\mathbf{M}$, what are $\mathbf{F}$ and $\mathbf{M}$?

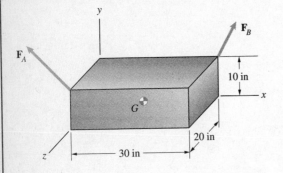

Solution: The equivalent force is the sum of the forces:

$$\sum \mathbf{F} = (-20)\mathbf{i} + (10 + 10)\mathbf{j} + (20 - 10)\mathbf{k}$$

$$= -20\mathbf{i} + 20\mathbf{j} + 10\mathbf{k} \text{ (lb)}.$$

The equivalent couple is the sum of the moments about G. The position vectors are:

$$\mathbf{r}_A = -15\mathbf{i} + 5\mathbf{j} + 10\mathbf{k} \text{ (in)},$$

$$\mathbf{r}_B = 15\mathbf{i} + 5\mathbf{j} - 10\mathbf{k}.$$

The sum of the moments:

$$\sum \mathbf{M}_G = (\mathbf{r}_A \times \mathbf{F}_A) + (\mathbf{r}_B \times \mathbf{F}_B)$$

$$= \begin{vmatrix} \mathbf{i} & \mathbf{j} & \mathbf{k} \\ -15 & 5 & 10 \\ -20 & 10 & 20 \end{vmatrix} + \begin{vmatrix} \mathbf{i} & \mathbf{j} & \mathbf{k} \\ 15 & 5 & -10 \\ 0 & 10 & -10 \end{vmatrix}$$

$$= 50\mathbf{i} + 250\mathbf{j} + 100\mathbf{k} \text{ (in lb)}$$

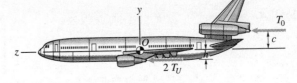

Problem 4.163 The engine above the airplane's fuselage exerts a thrust $T_0 = 16$ kip, and each of the engines under the wings exerts a thrust $T_U = 12$ kip. The dimensions are $h = 8$ ft, $c = 12$ ft, and $b = 16$ ft. If you represent the three thrust forces by a force $\mathbf{F}$ acting at the origin O and a couple $\mathbf{M}$, what are $\mathbf{F}$ and $\mathbf{M}$?

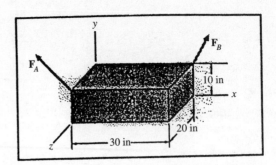

Solution: The equivalent thrust at the point G is equal to the sum of the thrusts:

$$\sum T = 16 + 12 + 12 = 40 \text{ kip}$$

The sum of the moments about the point G is

$$\sum \mathbf{M} = (\mathbf{r}_{1U} \times \mathbf{T}_U) + (\mathbf{r}_{2U} \times \mathbf{T}_U) + (\mathbf{r}_O \times \mathbf{T}_O)$$

$$= (\mathbf{r}_{1U} + \mathbf{r}_{2U}) \times \mathbf{T}_U + (\mathbf{r}_O \times \mathbf{T}_O).$$

The position vectors are $\mathbf{r}_{1U} = +b\mathbf{i} - h\mathbf{j}$, $\mathbf{r}_{2U} = -b\mathbf{i} - h\mathbf{j}$, and $\mathbf{r}_O = +c\mathbf{j}$. For $h = 8$ ft, $c = 12$ ft, and $b = 16$ ft, the sum of the moments is

$$\sum \mathbf{M} = \begin{vmatrix} \mathbf{i} & \mathbf{j} & \mathbf{k} \\ 0 & -16 & 0 \\ 0 & 0 & 12 \end{vmatrix} + \begin{vmatrix} \mathbf{i} & \mathbf{j} & \mathbf{k} \\ 0 & 12 & 0 \\ 0 & 0 & 16 \end{vmatrix} = (-192 + 192)\mathbf{i} = 0.$$

Thus the equivalent couple is $\mathbf{M} = 0$

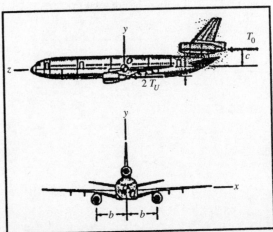

Problem 4.164 Consider the airplane described in Problem 4.163 and suppose that the engine under the wing to the pilot's right loses thrust.

(a) If you represent the two remaining thrust forces by a force **F** acting at the origin O and a couple **M**, what are **F** and **M**?

(b) If you represent the two remaining thrust forces by the force **F** alone, where does its line of action intersect the $x - y$ plane?

Solution: The sum of the forces is now

$$\sum \mathbf{F} = 12 + 16 = 28\mathbf{k} \text{ (kip).}$$

The sum of the moments is now:

$$\sum \mathbf{M} = (\mathbf{r}_{2U} \times \mathbf{T}_U) + (\mathbf{r}_O \times \mathbf{T}_O).$$

For $h = 8$ ft, $c = 12$ ft, and $b = 16$ ft, using the position vectors for the engines given in Problem 4.147, the equivalent couple is

$$\mathbf{M} = \begin{vmatrix} \mathbf{i} & \mathbf{j} & \mathbf{k} \\ 16 & -8 & 0 \\ 0 & 0 & 12 \end{vmatrix} + \begin{vmatrix} \mathbf{i} & \mathbf{j} & \mathbf{k} \\ 0 & 12 & 0 \\ 0 & 0 & 16 \end{vmatrix} = 96\mathbf{i} - 192\mathbf{j} \text{ (ft kip)}$$

(b) The moment of the single force is

$$\mathbf{M} = \begin{vmatrix} \mathbf{i} & \mathbf{j} & \mathbf{k} \\ x & y & z \\ 0 & 0 & 28 \end{vmatrix} = 28y\mathbf{i} - 28x\mathbf{j} = 96\mathbf{i} - 192\mathbf{j}.$$

From which

$$x = \frac{192}{28} = 6.86 \text{ ft, and } y = \frac{96}{28} = 3.43 \text{ ft.}$$

As to be expected, z can have any value, corresponding to any point on the line of action. Arbitrarily choose $z = 0$, so that the coordinates of the point of action are $(6.86, 3.43, 0)$.

Problem 4.165 The tension in cable AB is 100 lb, and the tension in cable CD is 60 lb. Suppose that you want to replace these two cables by a single cable EF so that the force exerted on the wall at E is equivalent to the two forces exerted by cables AB and CD on the walls at A and C. What is the tension in cable EF, and what are the coordinates of points E and F?

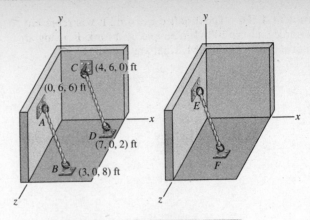

Solution: The position vectors of the points A, B, C, and D are

$$\mathbf{r}_A = 0\mathbf{i} + 6\mathbf{j} + 6\mathbf{k},$$

$$\mathbf{r}_B = 3\mathbf{i} + 0\mathbf{j} + 8\mathbf{k},$$

$$\mathbf{r}_C = 4\mathbf{i} + 6\mathbf{j} + 0\mathbf{k}, \text{ and}$$

$$\mathbf{r}_D = 7\mathbf{i} + 0\mathbf{j} + 2\mathbf{k}.$$

The unit vectors parallel to the cables are obtained as follows:

$$\mathbf{r}_{AB} = \mathbf{r}_B - \mathbf{r}_A = 3\mathbf{i} - 6\mathbf{j} + 2\mathbf{k},$$

$$|\mathbf{r}_{AB}| = \sqrt{3^2 + 6^2 + 2^2} = 7,$$

from which

$$\mathbf{e}_{AB} = 0.4286\mathbf{i} - 0.8571\mathbf{j} + 0.2857\mathbf{k}.$$

$$\mathbf{r}_{CD} = \mathbf{r}_D - \mathbf{r}_C = 3\mathbf{i} - 6\mathbf{j} + 2\mathbf{k},$$

$$|\mathbf{r}_{CD}| = \sqrt{3^2 + 6^2 + 2^2} = 7,$$

from which

$$\mathbf{e}_{CD} = 0.4286\mathbf{i} - 0.8571\mathbf{j} + 0.2857\mathbf{k}.$$

Since $\mathbf{e}_{AB} = \mathbf{e}_{CD}$, *the cables are parallel*. To duplicate the force, the single cable EF must have the same unit vector.

The force on the wall at point A is

$$\mathbf{F}_A = 100\mathbf{e}_{AB} = 42.86\mathbf{i} - 85.71\mathbf{j} + 28.57\mathbf{k} \text{ (lb)}.$$

The force on the wall at point C is

$$\mathbf{F}_C = 60\mathbf{e}_{CD} = 25.72\mathbf{i} - 51.43\mathbf{j} + 17.14\mathbf{k} \text{ (lb)}.$$

The total force is

$$\mathbf{F}_{EF} = 68.58\mathbf{i} - 137.14\mathbf{j} + 45.71\mathbf{k} \text{ (lb)},$$

$$|\mathbf{F}_{EF}| = 160 \text{ lb}.$$

For the systems to be equivalent, the moments about the origin must be the same. The moments about the origin are

$$\sum \mathbf{M}_O = (\mathbf{r}_A \times \mathbf{F}_A) + (\mathbf{r}_C \times \mathbf{F}_C)$$

$$= \begin{vmatrix} \mathbf{i} & \mathbf{j} & \mathbf{k} \\ 0 & 6 & 6 \\ 42.86 & -85.71 & 28.57 \end{vmatrix} + \begin{vmatrix} \mathbf{i} & \mathbf{j} & \mathbf{k} \\ 4 & 6 & 0 \\ 25.72 & -51.43 & 17.14 \end{vmatrix}$$

$$= 788.57\mathbf{i} + 188.57\mathbf{j} - 617.14\mathbf{k}.$$

This result is used to establish the coordinates of the point E. For the one cable system, the end E is located at $x = 0$. The moment is

$$\mathbf{M}_1 = \mathbf{r} \times \mathbf{F}_{EF} = \begin{vmatrix} \mathbf{i} & \mathbf{j} & \mathbf{k} \\ 0 & y & z \\ 68.58 & -137.14 & 45.71 \end{vmatrix}$$

$$= (45.71y + 137.14z)\mathbf{i} + (68.58z)\mathbf{j} - (68.58y)\mathbf{k}$$

$$= 788.57\mathbf{i} + 188.57\mathbf{j} - 617.14\mathbf{k},$$

from above. From which

$$y = \frac{617.14}{68.58} = 8.999\ldots = 9 \text{ ft}$$

$$z = \frac{188.57}{68.58} = 2.75 \text{ ft}.$$

Thus the coordinates of point E are E (0, 9, 2.75) ft. The coordinates of the point F are found as follows: Let L be the length of cable EF. Thus, from the definition of the unit vector, $y_F - y_E = Le_y$ with the condition that $y_F = 0$, $L = \dfrac{9}{0.8571} = 10.5$ ft. The other coordinates are $x_F - x_E = Le_X$, from which $x_F = 0 + 10.5(0.4286) = 4.5$ ft $z_F - z_E = Le_Z$, from which $z_F = 2.75 + 10.5(0.2857) = 5.75$ ft The coordinates of F are F (4.5, 0, 5.75) ft

Problem 4.166   The distance $s = 4$ m. If you represent the force and the 200-N-m couple by a force **F** acting at origin O and a couple **M**, what are **F** and **M**?

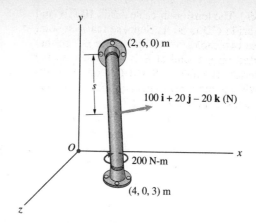

(2, 6, 0) m

s

$100\,\mathbf{i} + 20\,\mathbf{j} - 20\,\mathbf{k}$ (N)

O

x

200 N-m

(4, 0, 3) m

z

Solution: The equivalent force at the origin is

$$\mathbf{F} = 100\mathbf{i} + 20\mathbf{j} - 20\mathbf{k}.$$

The strategy is to establish the position vector of the action point of the force relative to the origin O for the purpose of determining the moment exerted by the force about the origin. The position of the top of the bar is

$\mathbf{r}_T = 2\mathbf{i} + 6\mathbf{j} + 0\mathbf{k}$. The vector parallel to the bar, pointing toward the base, is $\mathbf{r}_{TB} = 2\mathbf{i} - 6\mathbf{j} + 3\mathbf{k}$, with a magnitude of $|\mathbf{r}_{TB}| = 7$. The unit vector parallel to the bar is

$$\mathbf{e}_{TB} = 0.2857\mathbf{i} - 0.8571\mathbf{j} + 0.4286\mathbf{k}.$$

The vector from the top of the bar to the action point of the force is

$$\mathbf{r}_{TF} = s\mathbf{e}_{TB} = 4\mathbf{e}_{TB} = 1.1429\mathbf{i} - 3.4286\mathbf{j} + 1.7143\mathbf{k}.$$

The position vector of the action point from the origin is

$$\mathbf{r}_F = \mathbf{r}_T + \mathbf{r}_{TF} = 3.1429\mathbf{i} + 2.5714\mathbf{j} + 1.7143\mathbf{k}.$$

The moment of the force about the origin is

$$\mathbf{M}_F = \mathbf{r} \times \mathbf{F} = \begin{vmatrix} \mathbf{i} & \mathbf{j} & \mathbf{k} \\ 3.1429 & 2.5714 & 1.7143 \\ 100 & 20 & -20 \end{vmatrix}$$

$$= -85.71\mathbf{i} + 234.20\mathbf{j} - 194.3\mathbf{k}.$$

The couple is obtained from the unit vector and the magnitude. The sense of the moment is directed positively toward the top of the bar.

$$\mathbf{M}_C = -200\mathbf{e}_{TB} = -57.14\mathbf{i} + 171.42\mathbf{j} - 85.72\mathbf{k}.$$

The sum of the moments is

$$\mathbf{M} = \mathbf{M}_F + \mathbf{M}_C = -142.86\mathbf{i} + 405.72\mathbf{j} - 280\mathbf{k}.$$

This is the moment of the equivalent couple at the origin.

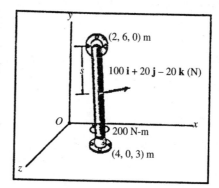

(2, 6, 0) m

s

$100\,\mathbf{i} + 20\,\mathbf{j} - 20\,\mathbf{k}$ (N)

O

x

200 N-m

(4, 0, 3) m

z

Problem 4.167 The force **F** and couple **M** in system 1 are

$$\mathbf{F} = 12\mathbf{i} + 4\mathbf{j} - 3\mathbf{k} \text{ (lb)},$$

$$\mathbf{M} = 4\mathbf{i} + 7\mathbf{j} + 4\mathbf{k} \text{ (ft-lb)}.$$

Suppose you want to represent system 1 by a wrench (system 2). Determine the couple $\mathbf{M}_p$ and the coordinates x and z where the line of action of the force intersects the $x - z$ plane.

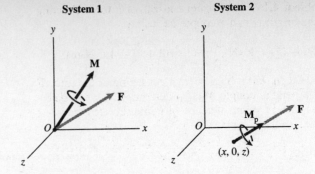

Solution: The component of **M** that is parallel to **F** is found as follows: The unit vector parallel to **F** is

$$\mathbf{e}_F = \frac{\mathbf{F}}{|\mathbf{F}|} = 0.9231\mathbf{i} + 0.3077\mathbf{j} - 0.2308\mathbf{k}.$$

The component of **M** parallel to **F** is

$$\mathbf{M}_P = (\mathbf{e}_F \cdot \mathbf{M})\mathbf{e}_F = 4.5444\mathbf{i} + 1.5148\mathbf{j} - 1.1361\mathbf{k} \text{ (ft-lb)}.$$

The component of **M** normal to **F** is

$$\mathbf{M}_N = \mathbf{M} - \mathbf{M}_P = -0.5444\mathbf{i} + 5.4858\mathbf{j} + 5.1361\mathbf{k} \text{ (ft-lb)}.$$

The moment of **F** must produce a moment equal to the normal component of **M**. The moment is

$$\mathbf{M}_F = \mathbf{r} \times \mathbf{F} = \begin{vmatrix} \mathbf{i} & \mathbf{j} & \mathbf{k} \\ x & 0 & z \\ 12 & 4 & -3 \end{vmatrix} = -(4z)\mathbf{i} + (3x + 12z)\mathbf{j} + (4x)\mathbf{k},$$

from which

$$z = \frac{-0.5444}{-4} = 0.1361 \text{ ft}$$

$$x = \frac{5.1362}{4} = 1.2840 \text{ ft}$$

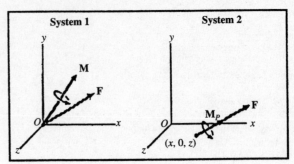

Problem 4.168 A system consists of a force **F** acting at the origin O and a couple **M**, where

$$\mathbf{F} = 10\mathbf{i} \text{ (lb)}, \quad \mathbf{M} = 20\mathbf{j} \text{ (ft-lb)}.$$

If you represent the system by a wrench consisting of the force **F** and a parallel couple $\mathbf{M}_p$, what is $\mathbf{M}_p$, and where does the line of action **F** intersect the y-z plane?

Solution: The component of **M** parallel to **F** is zero, since $\mathbf{M}_P = (\mathbf{e}_F \cdot \mathbf{M})\mathbf{e}_F = 0$. The normal component is equal to **M**. The equivalent force must produce the same moment as the normal component

$$\mathbf{M} = \mathbf{r} \times \mathbf{F} = \begin{vmatrix} \mathbf{i} & \mathbf{j} & \mathbf{k} \\ 0 & y & z \\ 10 & 0 & 0 \end{vmatrix} = (10z)\mathbf{j} - (10y)\mathbf{k} = 20\mathbf{j},$$

from which $z = \dfrac{20}{10} = 2$ ft and $y = 0$

Problem 4.169   A system consists of a force **F** acting at the origin O and a couple **M**, where

$$\mathbf{F} = \mathbf{i} + 2\mathbf{j} + 5\mathbf{k} \text{ (N)}, \quad \mathbf{M} = 10\mathbf{i} + 8\mathbf{j} - 4\mathbf{k} \text{ (N-m)}.$$

If you represent it by a wrench consisting of the force **F** and a parallel couple $\mathbf{M_p}$, (a) determine $\mathbf{M_p}$, and determine where the line of action of **F** intersects (b) the $x - z$ plane, (c) the y-z plane.

Solution: The unit vector parallel to **F** is

$$\mathbf{e}_F = \frac{\mathbf{F}}{|\mathbf{F}|} = 0.1826\mathbf{i} + 0.3651\mathbf{j} + 0.9129\mathbf{k}.$$

(a) The parallel component of $\mathbf{M}_t$ is

$$\mathbf{M}_P = (\mathbf{e}_F \cdot \mathbf{M})\mathbf{e}_F = 0.2\mathbf{i} + 0.4\mathbf{j} + 1.0\mathbf{k} \text{ (N-m)}.$$

The normal component is

$$\mathbf{M}_N = \mathbf{M} - \mathbf{M}_P = 9.8\mathbf{i} + 7.6\mathbf{j} - 5\mathbf{k}.$$

The moment of the force about the origin must be equal to the normal component of the moment. (b) The intersection with the $x - z$ plane:

$$\mathbf{M}_N = \mathbf{r} \times \mathbf{F} = \begin{vmatrix} \mathbf{i} & \mathbf{j} & \mathbf{k} \\ x & 0 & z \\ 1 & 2 & 5 \end{vmatrix} = -(2z)\mathbf{i} - (5x - z)\mathbf{j} + (2x)\mathbf{k}$$

$$= 9.8\mathbf{i} + 7.6\mathbf{j} - 5\mathbf{k},$$

from which

$$z = \frac{9.8}{-2} = -4.9 \text{ m, and } x = \frac{5}{-2} = -2.5 \text{ m}$$

(c) The intersection with the y-z plane is

$$\mathbf{M}_N = \mathbf{r} \times \mathbf{F} = \begin{vmatrix} \mathbf{i} & \mathbf{j} & \mathbf{k} \\ 0 & y & z \\ 1 & 2 & 5 \end{vmatrix} = (5y - 2z)\mathbf{i} + (z)\mathbf{j} - (y)\mathbf{k}$$

$$= 9.8\mathbf{i} + 7.6\mathbf{j} - 5\mathbf{k},$$

from which

$$y = 5 \text{ m and } z = 7.6 \text{ m}$$

Problem 4.170   Consider the force **F** acting at the origin O and the couple **M** given in Example 4.21. If you represent this system by a wrench, where does the line of action of the force intersect the $x - y$ plane?

Solution: From Example 4.21 the force and moment are $\mathbf{F} = 3\mathbf{i} + 6\mathbf{j} + 2\mathbf{k}$ (N), and $\mathbf{M} = 12\mathbf{i} + 4\mathbf{j} + 6\mathbf{k}$ (N-m).

The normal component of the moment is

$$\mathbf{M}_N = 7.592\mathbf{i} - 4.816\mathbf{j} + 3.061\mathbf{k} \text{ (N-m)}.$$

The moment produced by the force must equal the normal component:

$$\mathbf{M}_N = \mathbf{r} \times \mathbf{F} = \begin{vmatrix} \mathbf{i} & \mathbf{j} & \mathbf{k} \\ x & y & 0 \\ 3 & 6 & 2 \end{vmatrix}$$

$$= (2y)\mathbf{i} - (2x)\mathbf{j} + (6x - 3y)\mathbf{k} = 7.592\mathbf{i} - 4.816\mathbf{j} + 3.061\mathbf{k},$$

from which

$$x = \frac{4.816}{2} = 2.408 \text{ m and } y = \frac{7.592}{2} = 3.796 \text{ m}$$

Problem 4.171 Consider the force **F** acting at the origin O and the couple **M** given in Example 4.21. If you represent this system by a wrench, where does the line of action of the force intersect the plane $y = 3$ m?

Solution: From Example 4.21 (see also Problem 4.170) the force is $\mathbf{F} = 3\mathbf{i} + 6\mathbf{j} + 2\mathbf{k}$, and the normal component of the moment is

$$\mathbf{M}_N = 7.592\mathbf{i} - 4.816\mathbf{j} + 3.061\mathbf{k}.$$

The moment produced by the force must be equal to the normal component:

$$\mathbf{M}_N = \mathbf{r} \times \mathbf{F} = \begin{vmatrix} \mathbf{i} & \mathbf{j} & \mathbf{k} \\ x & 3 & z \\ 3 & 6 & 2 \end{vmatrix} = (6 - 6z)\mathbf{i} - (2x - 3z)\mathbf{j} + (6x - 9)\mathbf{k}$$

$$= 7.592\mathbf{i} - 4.816\mathbf{j} + 3.061\mathbf{k},$$

from which

$$x = \frac{9 + 3.061}{6} = 2.01 \text{ m and } z = \frac{6 - 7.592}{6} = -0.2653 \text{ m}$$

Problem 4.172 A wrench consists of a force of magnitude 100 N acting at the origin O and a couple of magnitude 60 N-m. The force and couple point in the direction from O to the point $(1, 1, 2)$ m. If you represent the wrench by a force **F** acting at point $(5, 3, 1)$ m and a couple **M**, what are **F** and **M**?

Solution: The vector parallel to the force is $\mathbf{r}_F = \mathbf{i} + \mathbf{j} + 2\mathbf{k}$, from which the unit vector parallel to the force is $\mathbf{e}_F = 0.4082\mathbf{i} + 0.4082\mathbf{j} + 0.8165\mathbf{k}$. The force and moment at the origin are

$$\mathbf{F} = |\mathbf{F}|\mathbf{e}_{OF} = 40.82\mathbf{i} + 40.82\mathbf{j} + 81.65\mathbf{k} \text{ (N)}, \text{ and}$$

$$\mathbf{M} = 24.492\mathbf{i} + 24.492\mathbf{j} + 48.99\mathbf{k} \text{ (N-m)}.$$

The force and moment are parallel. At the point $(5, 3, 1)$ m the equivalent force is equal to the force at the origin, given above. The moment of this force about the origin is

$$\mathbf{M}_F = \mathbf{r} \times \mathbf{F} = \begin{vmatrix} \mathbf{i} & \mathbf{j} & \mathbf{k} \\ 5 & 3 & 1 \\ 40.82 & 40.82 & 81.65 \end{vmatrix}$$

$$= 204.13\mathbf{i} - 367.43\mathbf{j} + 81.64\mathbf{k}.$$

For the moments to be equal in the two systems, the added equivalent couple must be

$$\mathbf{M}_C = \mathbf{M} - \mathbf{M}_F = -176.94\mathbf{i} + 391.92\mathbf{j} - 32.65\mathbf{k} \text{ (N-m)}$$

Problem 4.173 System 1 consists of two forces and a couple. Suppose that you want to represent it by a wrench (system 2). Determine the force **F**, the couple $\mathbf{M_p}$, and the coordinates x and z where the line of action of **F** intersects the $x - z$ plane.

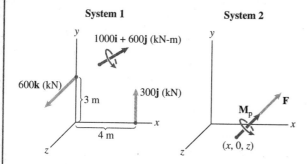

Solution: The sum of the forces in System 1 is $\mathbf{F} = 300\mathbf{j} + 600\mathbf{k}$ (N). The equivalent force in System 2 must have this value. The unit vector parallel to the force is $\mathbf{e}_F = 0.4472\mathbf{j} + 0.8944\mathbf{k}$. The sum of the moments in System 1 is

$$\mathbf{M} = 600(3)\mathbf{i} + 300(4)\mathbf{k} + 1000\mathbf{i} + 600\mathbf{j}$$

$$= 2800\mathbf{i} + 600\mathbf{j} + 1200\mathbf{k} \text{ (kN m)}.$$

The component parallel to the force is

$$\mathbf{M}_P = 599.963\mathbf{j} + 1199.93\mathbf{k} \text{ (kN-m)} = 600\mathbf{j} + 1200\mathbf{k} \text{ (kN-m)}.$$

The normal component is $\mathbf{M}_N = \mathbf{M} - \mathbf{M}_P = 2800\mathbf{i}$. The moment of the force

$$\mathbf{M}_N = \begin{vmatrix} \mathbf{i} & \mathbf{j} & \mathbf{k} \\ x & 0 & z \\ 0 & 300 & 600 \end{vmatrix} = -300z\mathbf{i} - 600x\mathbf{j} + 300x\mathbf{k} = 2800\mathbf{i},$$

from which

$$x = 0, \ z = \frac{2800}{-300} = -9.333 \text{ m}$$

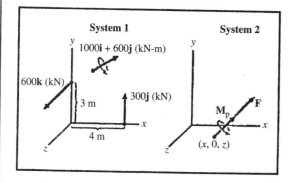

Problem 4.174 A plumber exerts the two forces shown to loosen a pipe.

(a) What total moment does he exert about the axis of the pipe?

(b) If you represent the two forces by a force **F** acting at O and a couple **M**, what are **F** and **M**?

(c) If you represent the two forces by a wrench consisting of the force **F** and a parallel couple $\mathbf{M}_p$, what is $\mathbf{M}_p$, and where does the line of action of **F** intersect the $x - y$ plane?

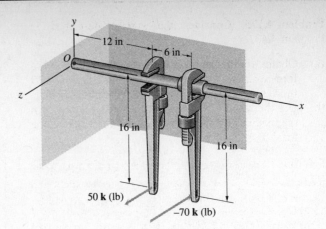

Solution: The sum of the forces is

$$\sum \mathbf{F} = 50\mathbf{k} - 70\mathbf{k} = -20\mathbf{k} \text{ (lb).}$$

(a) The total moment exerted on the pipe is

$$\mathbf{M} = 16(20)\mathbf{i} = 320\mathbf{i} \text{ (ft lb).}$$

(b) The equivalent force at O is $\mathbf{F} = -20\mathbf{k}$. The sum of the moments about O is

$$\sum \mathbf{M}_O = (\mathbf{r}_1 \times \mathbf{F}_1) + (\mathbf{r}_2 \times \mathbf{F}_2)$$

$$= \begin{vmatrix} \mathbf{i} & \mathbf{j} & \mathbf{k} \\ 12 & -16 & 0 \\ 0 & 0 & 50 \end{vmatrix} + \begin{vmatrix} \mathbf{i} & \mathbf{j} & \mathbf{k} \\ 18 & -16 & 0 \\ 0 & 0 & -70 \end{vmatrix}$$

$$= 320\mathbf{i} + 660\mathbf{j}.$$

(c) The unit vector parallel to the force is $\mathbf{e}_F = \mathbf{k}$, hence the moment parallel to the force is $\mathbf{M}_P = (\mathbf{e}_F \cdot \mathbf{M})\mathbf{e}_F = 0$, and the moment normal to the force is $\mathbf{M}_N = \mathbf{M} - \mathbf{M}_P = 320\mathbf{i} + 660\mathbf{j}$. The force at the location of the wrench must produce this moment for the wrench to be equivalent.

$$\mathbf{M}_N = \begin{vmatrix} \mathbf{i} & \mathbf{j} & \mathbf{k} \\ x & y & 0 \\ 0 & 0 & -20 \end{vmatrix} = -20y\mathbf{i} + 20x\mathbf{j} = 320\mathbf{i} + 660\mathbf{j},$$

from which $x = \dfrac{660}{20} = 33$ in, $y = \dfrac{320}{-20} = -16$ in

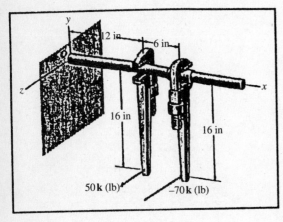

Problem 4.175 Consider the system described in Problem 4.43.

(a) Obtain a graph of the moment about A due to the force exerted by the spring on the circular bar at B for values of the angle α from zero to 90°.

(b) Use the result of (a) to estimate the angle at which the maximum moment occurs and the value of the maximum moment.

Solution: The unstretched length of spring is 1 m and the spring constant is $k = 20\,\dfrac{\text{N}}{\text{m}}$. Assume that the bar is a quarter circle, with a radius of 4 m. The stretched length of the spring is found from the Pythagorean Theorem: The height of the attachment point is $h = 4\sin\alpha$ m, and the distance from the center is $4\cos\alpha$. The stretched length of the spring is

$$L = \sqrt{(3-h)^2 + (4\cos\alpha)^2}\ \text{m}.$$

The spring force is $F = (20)(L-1)$ N. The angle that the spring makes with a vertical line parallel to A is

$$\beta = \tan^{-1}\left(\frac{3-h}{4\cos\alpha}\right).$$

The horizontal component of the spring force is $F_X = F\cos\beta$ N. The vertical component of the force is $F_Y = F\sin\beta$ N. The displacement of the attachment point to the left of point A is $d = 4(1-\cos\alpha)$ m, hence the action of the vertical component is negative, and the action of the horizontal component is positive. The moment about A is

$$\sum M_A = -dF_Y + hF_X.$$

Collecting terms and equations,

$$h = 4\sin\alpha\ \text{m},$$

$$F_Y = F\sin\beta\ \text{N},$$

$$F_X = F\cos\beta\ \text{N},$$

$$F = (20)(L-1)\ \text{N},$$

$$L = \sqrt{(3-h)^2 + (4\cos\alpha)^2}\ \text{m},$$

$$\beta = \tan^{-1}\left(\frac{3-h}{4\cos\alpha}\right).$$

A programmable calculator or a commercial package such as **TK Solver®** or **Mathcad®** is almost essential to the solution of this and the following problems. The commercial package **TK Solver PLUS** was used here to plot the graph of M against α. Using the graph as a guide, the following tabular values were taken about the maximum:

α, deg	Moment, N-m
41.5	101.463
42.0	101.483
42.5	101.472

The maximum value of the moment is estimated at $M_B = 101.49$ N-m, which occurs at approximately $\alpha = 42.2°$

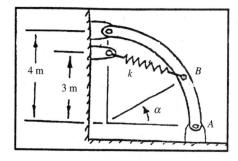

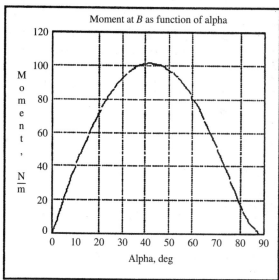

Moment at B as function of alpha

291

Problem 4.176 The exercise equipment shown is used by resting the elbow on the fixed pad and rotating the forearm to stretch the elastic cord AB. The cord behaves like a linear spring, and its unstretched length is 1 ft. Suppose you want to design the equipment so that the maximum moment that will be exerted about the elbow joint E as the forearm is rotated will be 60 ft-lb. What should the spring constant k of the elastic cord be?

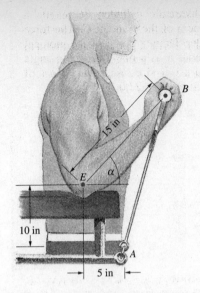

Solution: The strategy is to determine the position of maximum moment as a function of the angle α for a known spring constant and then from the system linearity use the fact that ratio of the desired moment to the actual maximum moment is equal to the ratio of the spring constants, for the same cord elongation. It is convenient to use $k_1 = 1$ for the initial spring constant. The steps in the algorithm are:

(1) The position vectors are $\mathbf{r}_{EB} = 15(\mathbf{i}\cos\alpha + \mathbf{j}\sin\alpha)$, and $\mathbf{r}_{EA} = 5\mathbf{i} - 10\mathbf{j}$.

(2) The vector parallel to the cord is $\mathbf{r}_{BA} = \mathbf{r}_{EA} - \mathbf{r}_{EB}$; its magnitude is the stretched length of the cord.

(3) The unit vector parallel to the cord is $\mathbf{e}_{BA} = \dfrac{\mathbf{r}_{BA}}{|\mathbf{r}_{BA}|}$.

(4) The (unknown) force is $\mathbf{F} = |\mathbf{F}|\mathbf{e}_{BA}$.

(5) The moment about the z-axis is $M_Z = \mathbf{k} \cdot (\mathbf{r}_{EB} \times \mathbf{F})$.

(6) For spring constant $k = 1$, graph the moment against angle α to find the maximum moment.

The **TK Solver PLUS** program was used to graph the moment against the angle for $k = 1\ \dfrac{\text{lb}}{\text{ft}}$.

The maximum moment occurs at about $\alpha = 49°$, as shown by the tabulated values at the maximum point, shown to four significant figures below.

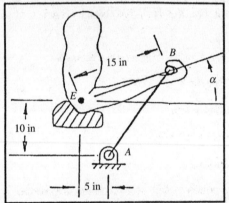

α, deg	Moment, ft lb
48	0.4856
49	0.4856
50	0.4856

Since the system is linear, the ratio of the moments is equal to the ratio of the applied forces *for the same angular position*. Thus

$$\frac{60 \text{ ft lb}}{0.4856 \text{ ft lb}} = \frac{k_2 \Delta L}{k_1 \Delta L},$$

from which, since ΔL cancels for the same angular position, and

$$k_1 = 1, k_2 = \left(\frac{60}{0.4856}\right)k_1 = 123.54\ \frac{\text{lb}}{\text{ft}}.$$

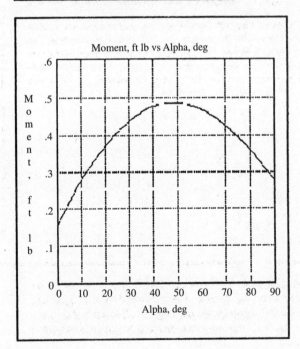

Moment, ft lb vs Alpha, deg

Problem 4.177 The hydraulic cylinder *BC* exerts a 2200-lb force on the boom of the crane at *C*. The force is parallel to the cylinder. Draw a graph of the moment exerted by the force about *A* as a function of the angle α for $0 \leq \alpha \leq 90°$, and use it to estimate the values of α for which the moment equals 12,000 ft-lb.

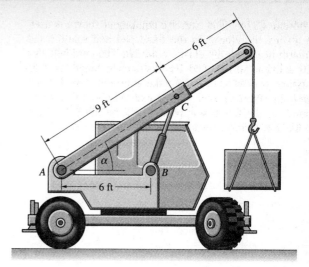

Solution: Set the coordinate origin at *A* and the *x* axis along *AB*. The *y* axis is upward. In these coordinates, with units in feet, *B* is at (6,0) and *C* is at $(9\cos\alpha, 9\sin\alpha)$. The vector from *B* to *C* is given by

$$\mathbf{e}_{BC} = (x_C - x_B)\mathbf{i} + (y_C - y_B)\mathbf{j} = (9\cos\alpha - 6)\mathbf{i} + (9\sin\alpha)\mathbf{j}.$$

The force along *BC* is given by

$$\mathbf{F}_{BC} = |\mathbf{F}_{BC}|\mathbf{e}_{BC} = 2200\mathbf{e}_{BC} \quad \text{(lb)}$$

and the moment about *A* is given by

$$\mathbf{M}_A = \mathbf{r}_{AB} \times \mathbf{F}_{BC} = 6\mathbf{i} \times \mathbf{F}_{BC}.$$

The magnitude of the moment is given by its magnitude, and since the problem is planar, the magnitude is the coefficient of the unit vector **k**.

The **TK Solver Plus** software package was used to solve this problem for values of α over the range $0 \leq \alpha \leq 90$. Solutions were evaluated at one degree intervals. The resulting plot of the magnitude of the moment versus the angle α is shown at the right. From the plot, there are two values of α where the value of the moment is 12,000 ft-lb. These values are $\alpha \cong 29°$ and $\alpha \cong 88°$.

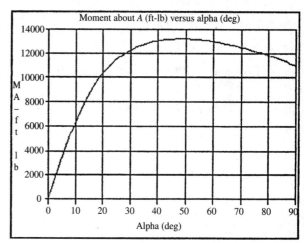

Moment about *A* (ft-lb) versus alpha (deg)

Problem 4.178 In Problem 4.177, the moment about *A* exerted by the 2200-lb force exerted by the hydraulic cylinder *BC* depends on the angle α. Estimate the maximum value of the moment and the angle α at which it occurs.

Solution: From the solution plot developed for Problem 4.177, the maximum value of the moment occurs somewhere near $\alpha = 48°$. The maximum value for the moment about *A* is just over 13,000 ft-lb. We would expect the maximum to occur at the configuration where *AB* and *BC* are perpendicular. In this case, the maximum value for the moment would be $M_{MAX} = (6)(2200) = 13,200$ ft-lb.

Problem 4.179 The support cable extends from the top of the 3-m column at A to a point B on the line L. The tension in the cable is 2 kN. The line L intersects the ground at the point (3, 0, 1) m and is parallel to the unit vector $\mathbf{e} = \frac{2}{7}\mathbf{i} + \frac{6}{7}\mathbf{j} - \frac{3}{7}\mathbf{k}$. The distance along L from the ground to point B is denoted s. What is the range of values of s for which the magnitude of the moment about O due to the force exerted by the cable at A exceeds 5.6 kN-m?

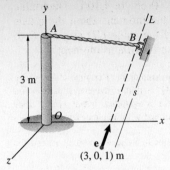

(3, 0, 1) m

Solution: A programmable calculator or a commercial package such as **TK Solver®** or **Mathcad®** is almost essential in the solution to this Problem. The **TK Solver Plus** package was used here. The algorithm for computation is outlined as computational steps, which may be programmed or performed with a calculator:

(1) The position vectors are:

$$\mathbf{r}_{OG} = 3\mathbf{i} + 0\mathbf{j} + 1\mathbf{k}, \mathbf{r}_{OA} = 0\mathbf{i} + 3\mathbf{j} + 0\mathbf{k}.$$

(2) The vector parallel to the line L is

$$\mathbf{r}_{GB} = s\mathbf{e}_{GB} = \left(\frac{2}{7}\mathbf{i} + \frac{6}{7}\mathbf{j} - \frac{2}{7}\mathbf{k}\right)s.$$

(3) The vector from O to B is the sum $\mathbf{r}_{OB} = \mathbf{r}_{OG} + \mathbf{r}_{GB}$.

(4) The vector parallel to AB is $\mathbf{r}_{AB} = \mathbf{r}_{OB} - \mathbf{r}_{OA}$.

(5) The unit vector parallel to AB is $\mathbf{e}_{AB} = \dfrac{\mathbf{r}_{AB}}{|\mathbf{r}_{AB}|}$.

(6) The tension at A is $\mathbf{T}_{AB} = 2\mathbf{e}_{AB}$.

(7) The moment about O due to the force applied at A is $\mathbf{M}_O = \mathbf{r}_{OA} \times \mathbf{T}_{AB}$. *Completes the computation for a given value of s.*

A plot of moment against s obtained using **TK Solver 2.0** is shown. The graph is relatively flat near the values of interest, which leads to inaccuracies in determining the limits on s. Using the graph as a guide, the following values were generated by **TK Solver**.

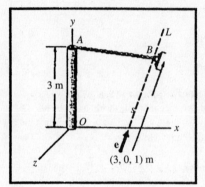

(3, 0, 1) m

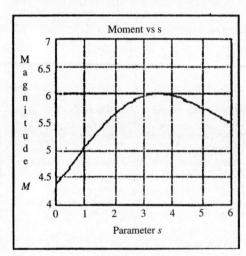

Moment vs s

s, meters	Moment, kN m
1.89	5.596
1.90	5.601
5.57	5.602
5.58	5.5996

Thus the limits occur at about $\boxed{1.895 < s < 5.575 \text{ m.}}$

Problem 4.180 Consider Problem 4.106. Determine the distance d that causes the moment about the z axis due to the force exerted by the cable CD at point C to be a maximum. What is the maximum moment?

Solution: A programmable calculator or a commercial package such as **TK Solver®** or **Mathcad®** is almost essential in the solution to this Problem. The algorithm for computation is outlined as steps that may be programmed or performed with a calculator:

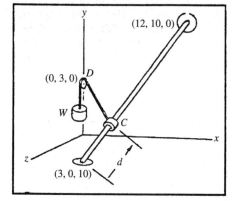

(1) The position vectors for the bottom and top of the bar, and the pulley D are:

$$\mathbf{r}_{OB} = 3\mathbf{i} + 0\mathbf{j} + 10\mathbf{k},$$

$$\mathbf{r}_{OT} = 12\mathbf{i} + 10\mathbf{j} + 0\mathbf{k}$$

$$\mathbf{r}_{OD} = 0\mathbf{i} + 3\mathbf{j} + 0\mathbf{k}.$$

(2) The vector parallel to the bar, pointing to the top, is $\mathbf{r}_{BT} = \mathbf{r}_{OT} - \mathbf{r}_{OB}$.

(3) The unit vector parallel to the bar is $\mathbf{e}_{BT} = \dfrac{\mathbf{r}_{BT}}{|\mathbf{r}_{BT}|}$.

(4) The vector from the bottom of the bar to the point C is $\mathbf{r}_{BC} = d\mathbf{e}_{BT}$.

(5) The vector position of the collar C is $\mathbf{r}_{OC} = \mathbf{r}_{OB} + \mathbf{r}_{BC}$.

(6) The vector parallel to CD is $\mathbf{r}_{CD} = \mathbf{r}_{OD} - \mathbf{r}_{OC}$.

(7) The unit vector parallel to CD is $\mathbf{e}_{CD} = \dfrac{\mathbf{r}_{CD}}{|\mathbf{r}_{CD}|}$.

(8) The tension acting at the collar is $\mathbf{T}_{CD} = 100\mathbf{e}_{CD}$ lb.

(9) The moment about the z-axis is $\mathbf{M} = \mathbf{k} \cdot (\mathbf{r}_{OC} \times \mathbf{T}_{CD})$.

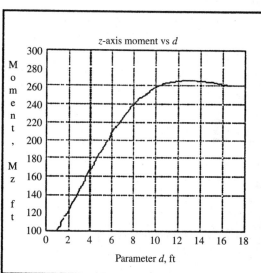

A graph of the moment about the z-axis against the parameter d obtained using **TK Solver Plus** is shown.

Using the graph as a guide, the values from a table in the **TK Solver** solution were selected:

d, ft	z-axis Moment, ft lb
12.8	265.38
13.0	265.41
13.2	265.38

The maximum appears to occur exactly at $\boxed{d = 13 \text{ ft}}$, with a maximum value of $\boxed{M_Z = 265.41 \text{ ft lb}}$.

295

Problem 4.181 Consider Problem 4.107. The rod AB must exert a moment of magnitude 100 ft-lb about the x axis to support the hood of the car. Draw a graph of the magnitude of the force the rod must exert on the hood at B as a function of d for $1 \leq d \leq 4$ ft. If you were designing the support AB, what value of d would you choose, and what is the magnitude of the force AB must exert on the hood?

Solution: The steps in an algorithm for computing the magnitude of the force as a function of the distance d are: (the detailed computations for one value of d are given in the solution to Problem 4.107.)

(1) The position coordinates of A and B are $\mathbf{r}_B = -1\mathbf{i} + 1\mathbf{j} + 2\mathbf{k}$, and $\mathbf{r}_A = 0\mathbf{i} + 0\mathbf{j} + d\mathbf{k}$.

(2) The vector parallel to AB is $\mathbf{r}_{AB} = \mathbf{r}_{OB} - \mathbf{r}_{OA}$.

(3) The unit vector parallel to AB is $\mathbf{e}_{AB} = \dfrac{\mathbf{r}_{AB}}{|\mathbf{r}_{AB}|}$.

(4) The force exerted by the rod AB is $\mathbf{F} = |\mathbf{F}|\mathbf{e}_{AB}$. The moment about the x-axis is $M_X = \mathbf{i} \cdot (\mathbf{r}_{OA} \times \mathbf{F})$.

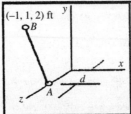

The commercial program **TK Solver Plus** was used to graph the magnitude of the force as a function of the distance d. Using the graph as a guide, the following three values were taken from the table computed by **TK Solver**.

d, ft	Force, lb
2.8	58.02
3.0	57.74
3.2	57.96

The minimum force for the required moment occurs at $\boxed{d = 3 \text{ ft}}$, with a value of $\boxed{|\mathbf{F}| = 57.74 \text{ lb}}$

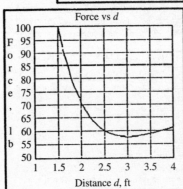

Force vs d

Problem 4.182 Consider the system shown in Problem 4.148. The forces exerted on the left post by cables AB and CD can be represented by a single force $\mathbf{F}$. Determine the tensions in the cables so that $|\mathbf{F}| = 600$ N and the line of action of $\mathbf{F}$ intersects the y axis at $y = 400$ mm.

Solution: The strategy is to solve by iteration the simultaneous conditions on the forces and moments. Equating the horizontal and vertical components of the forces for the two systems:

$$T_{AB}\cos\alpha + T_{CD}\cos\beta = 600\cos\theta$$

$$T_{AB}\sin\alpha + T_{CD}\sin\beta = 600\sin\theta.$$

where the angles are

$$\alpha = -\tan^{-1}\left(\frac{400}{800}\right) = -26.6°$$

for cable AB, and

$$\beta = -\tan^{-1}\left(\frac{300}{800}\right) = -20.6°$$

for cable CD., and the unknown angle θ applies to the single cable system. A guess at the unknown angle θ will yield a solution for the tensions which may not satisfy the equality of moments condition for the two systems. This difficulty is resolved as follows: denote the error in the equality of moments about the origin of the left post as

$$\varepsilon = 0.3(T_{AB}\cos\alpha) + 0.7(T_{CD}\cos\beta) - 0.5(600\cos\theta).$$

Plot the error as a function of the angle θ over the allowed interval. For an angle θ at which $\varepsilon = 0$ the three conditions are satisfied.

The **TK Solver** software package was used to graph the error as a function of the angle. The range of allowed angles θ was determined by assuming that the single cable could be attached on the right post at any point between the ground and the 300 mm height.

The zero crossing for the error occurs at about $\theta = 22°$. A closer look at tabulated values near this value yields an angle of $\theta = 22.11°$. At this angle the tensions in the two cables are $\boxed{T_{AB} = 155.4 \text{ N}}$, and $\boxed{T_{CD} = 445.25 \text{ N}}$

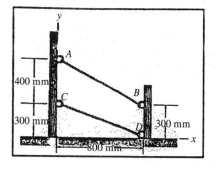

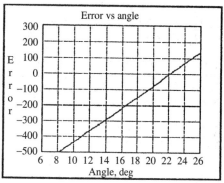

Error vs angle

Problem 4.183 Suppose you want to represent the force and the 200-N-m couple in Problem 4.166 by a force **F** and a couple **M**, and choose the distance s so that the magnitude of **M** is a minimum. Determine s, **F**, and **M**.

Solution: The steps in an algorithm for entering into a programmable calculator or a commercial software package such as **TK Solver®** or **Mathcad®** are given: (The details of a computation for one value of s are given in the solution to Problem 4.150)

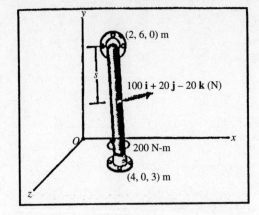

(1) The position vectors for the top and bottom of the bar are:

$$\mathbf{r}_T = 2\mathbf{i} + 6\mathbf{j} + 0\mathbf{k} \text{ m,}$$

$$\mathbf{r}_B = 4\mathbf{i} + 0\mathbf{j} + 3\mathbf{k} \text{ m.}$$

(2) The vector parallel to the bar, pointing top to bottom, is

$$\mathbf{r}_{TB} = \mathbf{r}_B - \mathbf{r}_T = 2\mathbf{i} - 6\mathbf{j} + 3\mathbf{k} \text{ m.}$$

(3) The unit vector parallel to the bar, pointing top to bottom is
$$\mathbf{e}_{TB} = \frac{\mathbf{r}_{TB}}{|\mathbf{r}_{TB}|}.$$

(4) The distance from the top of the bar to the point of application of the force is $\mathbf{r}_{TF} = s\mathbf{e}_{TB}$ m.

(5) The vector from the origin to the point of application of the force is $\mathbf{r}_{OF} = \mathbf{r}_T + \mathbf{r}_{TF}$ m.

(6) The moment about the origin due to the action of the force is $\mathbf{M}_{OF} = \mathbf{r}_{OF} \times \mathbf{F}$ N-m.

(7) The couple moment is $\mathbf{M}_C = M_C\mathbf{e}_{BT} = -M_C\mathbf{e}_{TB}$ N-m.

(8) The total moment is the sum of the moments due to the force and the couple, $\mathbf{M}_T = \mathbf{M}_{OF} + \mathbf{M}_C$.

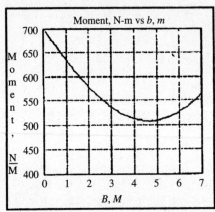

The force is given: $\mathbf{F} = 100\mathbf{i} + 20\mathbf{j} - 20\mathbf{k}$ N. The couple moment magnitude is given: $M_C = 200$ N-m.

The strategy is to graph the total moment as a function of s to determine the minimum value of the moment, and the value of s at the minimum. The **TK Solver 2.0** package was used to graph the total moment as a function of s. Using the graph as a guide, tabulated values near the minimum were examined. The minimum magnitude of the moment occurs at $\boxed{s = 4.66 \text{ m}}$. The equivalent force at the origin is $\boxed{\mathbf{F} = 100\mathbf{i} + 20\mathbf{j} - 20\mathbf{k} \text{ N}}$. At $s = 4.66$ m the equivalent moment at the origin is

$$\boxed{\mathbf{M}_T = \mathbf{M}_{OF} + \mathbf{M}_C = -137.2\mathbf{i} + 437.77\mathbf{j} - 219.66\mathbf{k} \text{ N-m}}$$

Problem 4.184 Determine the moment of the 200-N force about A.

(a) What is the two-dimensional description of the moment?
(b) Express the moment as a vector.

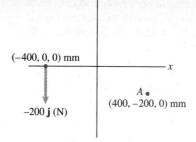

Solution:

(a) The two dimensional description. By inspection, the perpendicular distance to the line of action from A is

$$d = (400 - (-400)) \text{ mm} = 0.8 \text{ m}.$$

The moment is positive, since it is counterclockwise. Thus $M_A = (0.8)(200) = 160$ N-m

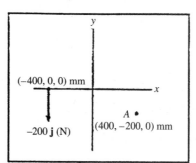

(b) The vector description. The position vectors of A and the point of action are $\mathbf{r}_{OA} = 0.4\mathbf{i} - 0.2\mathbf{j}$ m, and $\mathbf{r}_{OF} = -0.4\mathbf{i}$ m. The distance from A to the point of action is $\mathbf{r}_{AF} = \mathbf{r}_{OF} - \mathbf{r}_{OA} = (-0.4 - 0.4)\mathbf{i} - (-0.2)\mathbf{j} = -0.8\mathbf{i} + 0.2\mathbf{j}$ m. The moment is

$$\mathbf{M}_A = \mathbf{r}_{AF} \times \mathbf{F} = \begin{vmatrix} \mathbf{i} & \mathbf{j} & \mathbf{k} \\ -0.8 & 0.2 & 0 \\ 0 & -200 & 0 \end{vmatrix} = 160\mathbf{k} \text{ N-m}$$

Problem 4.185 The Leaning Tower of Pisa is approximately 55 m tall and 7 m in diameter. The horizontal displacement of the top of the tower from the vertical is approximately 5 m. Its mass is approximately 3.2×10^6 kg. If you model the tower as a cylinder and assume that its weight acts at the center, what is the magnitude of the moment exerted by the weight about the point at the center of the tower's base?

Solution: The position vector of the center of mass, in the coordinates shown, is

$$\mathbf{r}_{CM} = 2.5\mathbf{i} + 27.5\mathbf{j} \text{ m}$$

The weight acting at the center of mass is $\mathbf{W} = -mg\mathbf{j}$

$$\mathbf{W} = -\left(9.81 \frac{m}{52}\right)(3.2 \times 10^6 \text{ kg})\mathbf{j} = -31.4\mathbf{j} \text{ MN}$$

The moment is $\mathbf{r}_{CM} \times W$

$$\mathbf{M} = (2.5\mathbf{i} + 27.5\mathbf{j}) \times (-31.4\mathbf{j}) \text{ (MN-m)}$$

$$\mathbf{M} = -78.5\mathbf{k} \text{ (MN-m)}$$

Problem 4.186 The device shown has been suggested as a design for a perpetual motion machine. Determine the moment about the axis of rotation due to the four masses as a function of the angle as the device rotates 90° clockwise from the position shown, and indicate whether gravity could cause rotation in that direction.

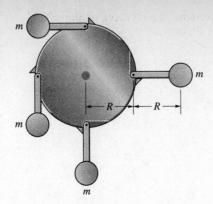

Solution: *Preliminary Remarks:* The problem is put in perspective by noting that the masses contribute zero moment in the configuration shown. The action line of the bottom weight passes through the wheel center, so that it contributes zero moment. The perpendicular distance from the wheel center to the line of action of the right hand weight is $2R$. Its moment about the wheel center due to the action of gravity is $\mathbf{M}_{RM} = -2Rmg\mathbf{j}$. The left hand and top weights are located at perpendicular distances R from the center. The sum of their moments is $\mathbf{M}_{LM} = 2Rmg\mathbf{j}$. The sum of these moments is zero: $\mathbf{M}_{RM} + \mathbf{M}_M = 0$. Thus *the wheel has no resulting moment to cause rotation* when in the configuration shown.

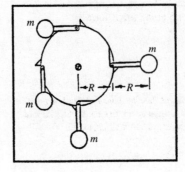

The problem, however, addresses another issue: what happens when the wheel is rotated from the current configuration through $-90°$? One can guess beforehand that the bottom weight will act like a pendulum weight, producing a restoring moment, that is, a moment opposed to the rotation. That this is indeed the case is shown in the following analysis. *End of preliminary remarks.* The vector positions of the masses are the sum of two vectors: the position on the rim of the wheel, and the position of the mass. The angle is measured counterclockwise. The vector positions of the masses relative to the rim of the wheel are discontinuous with angle, with an abrupt discontinuity at $\alpha = 0°$:

$\mathbf{r}_m = R(\mathbf{i}\cos\alpha + \mathbf{j}\sin\alpha)\ (270° < \alpha < 360°)$

$\mathbf{r}_m = -R\mathbf{j}\,(180° < \alpha < 270°)$

$\mathbf{r}_m = R(-\mathbf{i}\sin\alpha + \mathbf{j}\cos\alpha)\ (0° < \alpha < 180°)$

These vectors are to be added to the wheel rim positions:

$\mathbf{r}_W = R(\mathbf{i}\cos\alpha + \mathbf{j}\sin\alpha)\ (0 < \alpha < 360°)$.

Adding the vectors, the positions with respect to the center of the wheel for the three intervals are:

$\mathbf{R}_1 = 2R(\mathbf{i}\cos\alpha + \mathbf{j}\sin\alpha)\ (270° < \alpha < 360°)$

$\mathbf{R}_2 = R(\mathbf{i}\cos\alpha - \mathbf{j}(1 - \sin\alpha))\ (180 < \alpha < 270°)$

$\mathbf{R}_3 = R(\mathbf{i}(\cos\alpha - \sin\alpha) + \mathbf{j}(\cos\alpha + \sin\alpha))\ (0° < \alpha < 180°)$.

(a) The four masses are located 90° apart on the wheel. Start with a near but greater than zero. The positions of the masses are obtained by adding multiples of 90° to the angle.

Mass No 1: $\mathbf{R}_1 = 2R(\mathbf{i}\cos\alpha + \mathbf{j}\sin\alpha)\ (\alpha \cong 0°)$

Mass No 2: $\mathbf{R}_2 = R(\mathbf{i}\sin\alpha - \mathbf{j}(1 + \cos\alpha))\ (\alpha \cong 0°)$

Mass No 3: $\mathbf{R}_3 = R(\mathbf{i}(\sin\alpha - \cos\alpha) - \mathbf{j}(\sin\alpha + \cos\alpha))\ (\alpha \cong 0°)$

Mass No 4: $\mathbf{R}_4 = -R(\mathbf{i}(\sin\alpha + \cos\alpha) + \mathbf{j}(\sin\alpha - \cos\alpha))\ (\alpha \cong 0°)$

The weight vectors are $\mathbf{W} = -mg\mathbf{j}$. The sums of the moments:

$$\sum \mathbf{M}_O = (\mathbf{R}_1 \times \mathbf{W}) + (\mathbf{R}_2 \times \mathbf{W}) + (\mathbf{R}_3 \times \mathbf{W}) + (\mathbf{R}_4 \times \mathbf{W})$$

$$= (\mathbf{R}_1 + \mathbf{R}_2 + \mathbf{R}_3 + \mathbf{R}_4) \times \mathbf{W} = \left(\sum_1^4 \mathbf{R}_i\right) \times \mathbf{W}.$$

Collecting terms in the sum:

$$\sum_1^4 \mathbf{R}_i = +\mathbf{i}R\sin\alpha - \mathbf{j}R(1 + \cos\alpha),$$

from which

$$\sum \mathbf{M}_O = \begin{vmatrix} \mathbf{i} & \mathbf{j} & \mathbf{k} \\ R\sin\alpha & -R(1+\cos\alpha) & 0 \\ 0 & -mg & 0 \end{vmatrix} = -\mathbf{k}mgR\sin\alpha$$

This is a clockwise moment for $\alpha > 0°$, and a counterclockwise moment for $\alpha < 0°$. The moment vanishes at exactly $\alpha = 0°$, and reverses sign on either side in a manner that tries to restore the angle to zero. An attempt to rotate in the negative direction will be opposed by a counterclockwise moment, and conversely an attempt to rotate in a clockwise manner will be opposed. This is analogous to a pendulum.

Problem 4.187 In Problem 4.186, determine whether gravity could cause rotation in the counterclockwise direction.

Solution: The solution is contained in the discussion and solution to Problem 4.186. *Gravity will not cause the system to rotate.*

Problem 4.188 Determine the moment of the 400-N force (a) about A, (b) about B.

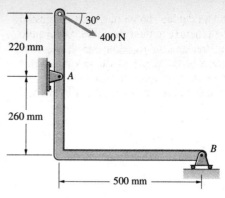

Solution: Use the two dimensional description of the moment. The vertical and horizontal components of the 200 N force are

$$F_Y = -400 \sin 30° = -200 \text{ N},$$

$$F_X = +400 \cos 30° = 346.41 \text{ N}.$$

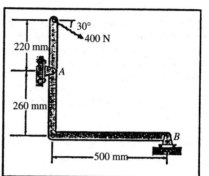

(a) The moment arm from A to the line of action of the horizontal component is 0.22 m. The moment arm from A to the vertical component is zero. The moment about A is negative,

$$M_A = -0.22(346.41) = -76.21 \text{ N-m}$$

(b) The perpendicular distances to the lines of action of the vertical and horizontal components of the force from B are $d_1 = 0.5$ m, and $d_2 = 0.48$ m. The action of the vertical component is positive, and the action of the horizontal component is negative. The sum of the moments: $M_B = +0.5(200) - 0.48(346.41) = -66.28$ N-m

---

Problem 4.189 Determine the sum of the moments exerted about A by the three forces and the couple.

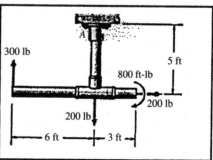

Solution: Establish coordinates with origin at A, x horizontal, and y vertical with respect to the page. The moment exerted by the couple is the same about any point. The moment of the 300 lb force about A is $M_{300} = (-6\mathbf{i} - 5\mathbf{j}) \times (300\mathbf{j}) = -1800\mathbf{k}$ ft-lb.

The moment of the downward 200 lb force about A is zero since the line of action of the force passes through A. The moment of the 200 lb force which pulls to the right is

$$M_{200} = (3\mathbf{i} - 5\mathbf{j}) \times (200\mathbf{i}) = 1000\mathbf{k} \text{ (ft-lb)}.$$

The moment of the couple is $\mathbf{M}_C = -800\mathbf{k}$ (ft-lb). Summing the four moments, we get

$$\boxed{\mathbf{M}_A = (-1800 + 0 + 1000 - 800)\mathbf{k} = -1600\mathbf{k} \text{ (ft-lb)}}$$

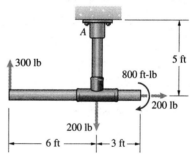

Problem 4.190 In Problem 4.189, if you represent the three forces and the couple by an equivalent system consisting of a force **F** acting at A and a couple **M**, what are the magnitudes of **F** and **M**?

Solution: The equivalent force will be equal to the sum of the forces and the equivalent couple will be equal to the sum of the moments about A. From the solution to Problem 4.189, the equivalent couple will be $C = \mathbf{M}_A = -1600\mathbf{k}$ (ft-lb). The equivalent force will be $\mathbf{F}_{EQUIV.} = 200\mathbf{i} - 200\mathbf{j} + 300\mathbf{j} = 200\mathbf{i} + 100\mathbf{j}$ (lb)

Problem 4.191 The vector sum of the forces acting on the beam is zero, and the sum of the moments about A is zero.

(a) What are the forces A_x, A_y, and B?
(b) What is the sum of the moments about B?

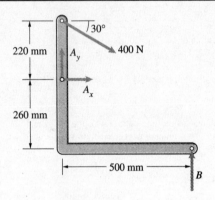

Solution: The vertical and horizontal components of the 400 N force are:

$F_X = 400 \cos 30° = 346.41$ N,

$F_Y = 400 \sin 30° = 200$ N.

The sum of the forces is

$\sum F_X = A_X + 346.41 = 0,$

from which $A_X = -346.41$ N

$\sum F_Y = A_Y + B - 200 = 0.$

The sum of the moments about A is

$\sum M_A = 0.5B - 0.22(346.41) = 0,$

from which $B = 152.42$ N. Substitute into the force equation to get $A_Y = 200 - B = 47.58$ N

(b) The moments about B are

$M_B = -0.5A_Y - 0.48(346.41) - 0.26A_X + 0.5(200) = 0$

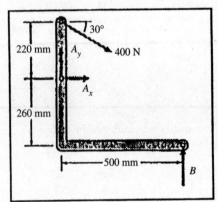

Problem 4.192 To support the ladder, the force exerted at B by the hydraulic piston AB must exert a moment about C equal in magnitude to the moment about C due to the ladder's 450-lb weight. What is the magnitude of the force exerted at B?

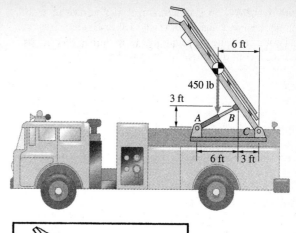

Solution: The moment about C exerted by the weight is

$$M_C = 450(6) = 2700 \text{ ft lb.}$$

The ladder is at an elevation of $45°$ from the horizontal. The cylinder is at an angle

$$\theta = \tan^{-1}\left(\frac{3}{6}\right) = 26.56°.$$

The vertical and horizontal components of the force at B due to the cylinder are

$$F_X = F \cos 26.57° = 0.8944F \text{ lb}$$

$$F_Y = F \sin 26.57° = 0.4472F \text{ lb.}$$

The moment about C due to these forces is

$$M_C = -3(0.4472)F - 3(0.8944)F + 2700 = 0.$$

Solving:

$$F = \frac{2700}{4.0249} = 670.82 \text{ lb}$$

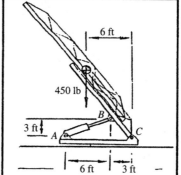

Problem 4.193 The force $\mathbf{F} = -60\mathbf{i} + 60\mathbf{j}$ (lb).

(a) Determine the moment of $\mathbf{F}$ about point A.
(b) What is the perpendicular distance from point A to the line of action of $\mathbf{F}$?

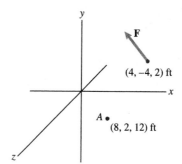

Solution: The position vector of A and the point of action are

$$\mathbf{r}_A = 8\mathbf{i} + 2\mathbf{j} + 12\mathbf{k} \text{ (ft), and } \mathbf{r}_F = 4\mathbf{i} - 4\mathbf{j} + 2\mathbf{k}.$$

The vector from A to F is

$$\mathbf{r}_{AF} = \mathbf{r}_F - \mathbf{r}_{OA} = (4 - 8)\mathbf{i} + (-4 - 2)\mathbf{j} + (2 - 12)\mathbf{k}$$

$$= -4\mathbf{i} - 6\mathbf{j} - 10\mathbf{k}.$$

(a) The moment about A is

$$\mathbf{M}_A = \mathbf{r}_{AF} \times \mathbf{F} = \begin{vmatrix} \mathbf{i} & \mathbf{j} & \mathbf{k} \\ -4 & -6 & -10 \\ -60 & 60 & 0 \end{vmatrix}$$

$$= 600\mathbf{i} + 600\mathbf{j} - 600\mathbf{k} \text{ (ft lb)}$$

(b) The magnitude of the moment is

$$|\mathbf{M}_A| = \sqrt{600^2 + 600^2 + 600^2} = 1039.3 \text{ ft lb.}$$

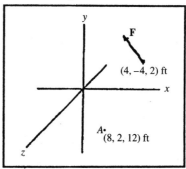

The magnitude of the force is $|\mathbf{F}| = \sqrt{60^2 + 60^2} = 84.8528$ lb. The perpendicular distance from A to the line of action is

$$D = \frac{1039.3}{84.8528} = 12.25 \text{ ft}$$

Problem 4.194 The 20-kg mass is suspended by cables attached to three vertical 2-m posts. Point A is at $(0, 1.2, 0)$ m. Determine the moment about the base E due to the force exerted on the post BE by the cable AB.

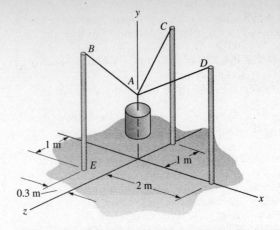

Solution: The strategy is to develop the simultaneous equations in the unknown tensions in the cables, and use the tension in AB to find the moment about E. This strategy requires the unit vectors parallel to the cables. The position vectors of the points are:

$$\mathbf{r}_{OA} = 1.2\mathbf{j},$$

$$\mathbf{r}_{OB} = -0.3\mathbf{i} + 2\mathbf{j} + 1\mathbf{k},$$

$$\mathbf{r}_{OC} = 2\mathbf{j} - 1\mathbf{k},$$

$$\mathbf{r}_{OD} = 2\mathbf{i} + 2\mathbf{j},$$

$$\mathbf{r}_{OE} = -0.3\mathbf{i} + 1\mathbf{k}.$$

The vectors parallel to the cables are:

$$\mathbf{r}_{AB} = \mathbf{r}_{OB} - \mathbf{r}_{OA} = -0.3\mathbf{i} + 0.8\mathbf{j} + 1\mathbf{k},$$

$$\mathbf{r}_{AC} = \mathbf{r}_{OC} - \mathbf{r}_{OA} = +0.8\mathbf{j} - 1\mathbf{k},$$

$$\mathbf{r}_{AD} = \mathbf{r}_{OD} - \mathbf{r}_{OA} = +2\mathbf{i} + 0.8\mathbf{j}.$$

The unit vectors parallel to the cables are:

$$\mathbf{e}_{AB} = \frac{\mathbf{r}_{AB}}{|\mathbf{r}_{AB}|} = -0.2281\mathbf{i} + 0.6082\mathbf{j} + 0.7603\mathbf{k} :$$

$$\mathbf{e}_{AC} = 0\mathbf{i} + 0.6247\mathbf{j} - 0.7809\mathbf{k},$$

$$\mathbf{e}_{AD} = +0.9284\mathbf{i} + 0.3714\mathbf{j} + 0\mathbf{k}.$$

The tensions in the cables are

$$\mathbf{T}_{AB} = T_{AB}\mathbf{e}_{AB},$$

$$\mathbf{T}_{AC} = T_{AC}\mathbf{e}_{AC}, \text{ and}$$

$$\mathbf{T}_{AD} = T_{AD}\mathbf{e}_{AD}.$$

The equilibrium conditions are $\mathbf{T}_{AB} + \mathbf{T}_{AC} + \mathbf{T}_{AD} = \mathbf{W}$. Collect like terms in $\mathbf{i}, \mathbf{j}, \mathbf{k}$:

$$\sum F_X = (-0.2281 T_{AB} + 0T_{AC} + 0.9284 T_{AD})\mathbf{i} = 0$$

$$\sum F_Y = (+0.6082 \cdot T_{AB} + 0.6247 \cdot T_{AC}$$

$$+ 0.3714 \cdot T_{AD} - 196.2)\mathbf{j} = 0$$

$$\sum F_Z = (+0.7603 \cdot T_{AB} - 0.7809 \cdot T_{AC} + 0 \cdot T_{AD})\mathbf{k} = 0$$

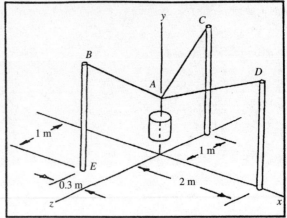

Solve:

$$T_{AB} = 150.04 \text{ N},$$

$$T_{AC} = 146.08 \text{ N},$$

$$T_{AD} = 36.86 \text{ N}.$$

The moment about E is

$$\mathbf{M}_E = \mathbf{r}_{EB} \times (-T_{AB}\mathbf{e}_{AB}) = -T_{AB}(\mathbf{r}_{EB} \times \mathbf{e}_{AB})$$

$$= -150 \begin{vmatrix} \mathbf{i} & \mathbf{j} & \mathbf{k} \\ 0 & 2 & 0 \\ -0.2281 & +0.6082 & +0.7603 \end{vmatrix}$$

$$= -228\mathbf{i} - 68.43\mathbf{k} \text{ (N-m)}$$

Problem 4.195 Three forces of equal magnitude are applied parallel to the sides of an equilateral triangle.

(a) Show that the sum of the moments of the forces is the same about any point.
(b) Determine the magnitude of the moment.

Strategy: To do (a), resolve one of the forces into vector components parallel to the other two forces.

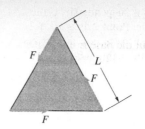

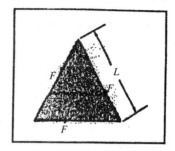

Solution: The interior angles of an equilateral triangle are 60°. Assume that the x-axis is coincident with the lower side, with the origin at the lower left corner. Denote the forces by labels 1, 2, 3 counterclockwise beginning with the one coincident with the lower side, and label the corners 1, 2, 3 beginning with the lower left corner. The vectors to the lower corners are $\mathbf{r}_1 = 0$, and $\mathbf{r}_2 = L\mathbf{i}$. Let $P(x, y)$ be any point in the space. The vector distances from P to the lower corners are

$$\mathbf{r}_{P1} = \mathbf{r}_1 - \mathbf{r}_P = -x\mathbf{i} - y\mathbf{j},$$

$$\mathbf{r}_{P2} = \mathbf{r}_2 - \mathbf{r}_p = (L - x)\mathbf{i} - y\mathbf{j}.$$

The unit vectors parallel to the forces are:

$$\mathbf{e}_1 = 1\mathbf{i},$$

$$\mathbf{e}_2 = -\frac{1}{2}\mathbf{i} + \frac{\sqrt{3}}{2}\mathbf{j}, \text{ and}$$

$$\mathbf{e}_3 = -\frac{1}{2}\mathbf{i} - \frac{\sqrt{3}}{2}\mathbf{j}.$$

The sum of the moments about P is

$$\sum \mathbf{M} = (\mathbf{r}_{P1} \times \mathbf{F}_1) + (\mathbf{r}_{P1} \times \mathbf{F}_3) + (\mathbf{r}_{P2} \times \mathbf{F}_2)$$

$$= F[\mathbf{r}_{P1} \times (\mathbf{e}_1 + \mathbf{e}_3) + (\mathbf{r}_{P2} \times \mathbf{e}_2)]$$

$$\sum \mathbf{M}_P = F \begin{vmatrix} \mathbf{i} & \mathbf{j} & \mathbf{k} \\ -x & -y & 0 \\ \frac{1}{2} & -\frac{\sqrt{3}}{2} & 0 \end{vmatrix} + F \begin{vmatrix} \mathbf{i} & \mathbf{j} & \mathbf{k} \\ L-x & -y & 0 \\ -\frac{1}{2} & \frac{\sqrt{3}}{2} & 0 \end{vmatrix}$$

$$= \mathbf{k}F\left(\frac{\sqrt{3}}{2}x + \frac{1}{2}y\right) + \mathbf{k}F\left(\frac{\sqrt{3}}{2}L - \frac{\sqrt{3}}{2}x - \frac{1}{2}y\right)$$

$$= \frac{\sqrt{3}}{2}FL\mathbf{k}$$

Since the result is independent of the coordinates of P, the moment about any point is the same.

Problem 4.196 The bar AB supporting the lid of the grand piano exerts a force $\mathbf{F} = -6\mathbf{i} + 35\mathbf{j} - 12\mathbf{k}$ (lb) at B. The coordinates of B are $(3, 4, 3)$ ft. What is the moment of the force about the hinge line of the lid (the x axis)?

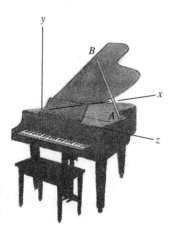

Solution: The position vector of point B is $\mathbf{r}_{OB} = 3\mathbf{i} + 4\mathbf{j} + 3\mathbf{k}$. The moment about the x-axis due to the force is

$$M_X = \mathbf{e}_X \cdot (\mathbf{r}_{OB} \times \mathbf{F}) = \mathbf{i} \cdot (\mathbf{r}_{OB} \times \mathbf{F})$$

$$M_X = \begin{vmatrix} 1 & 0 & 0 \\ 3 & 4 & 3 \\ -6 & 35 & -12 \end{vmatrix} = -153 \text{ ft lb}$$

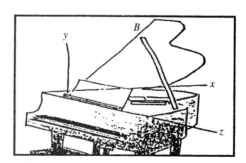

Problem 4.197 Determine the moment of the vertical 800-lb force about point C.

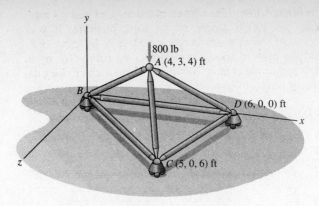

Solution: The force vector acting at A is $\mathbf{F} = -800\mathbf{j}$ (lb) and the position vector from C to A is

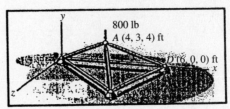

$$\mathbf{r}_{CA} = (x_A - x_C)\mathbf{i} + (y_A - y_C)\mathbf{j} + (z_A - z_C)\mathbf{k}$$

$$= (4 - 5)\mathbf{i} + (3 - 0)\mathbf{j} + (4 - 6)\mathbf{k} = -1\mathbf{i} + 3\mathbf{j} - 2\mathbf{k} \text{ (ft)}.$$

The moment about C is

$$M_C = \begin{vmatrix} \mathbf{i} & \mathbf{j} & \mathbf{k} \\ -1 & 3 & -2 \\ 0 & -800 & 0 \end{vmatrix} = -1600\mathbf{i} + 0\mathbf{j} + 800\mathbf{k} \text{ (ft-lb)}$$

Problem 4.198 In Problem 4.197, determine the moment of the vertical 800-lb force about the straight line through points C and D.

Solution: In Problem 4.197, we found the moment of the 800 lb force about point C to be given by

$$\mathbf{M}_C = -1600\mathbf{i} + 0\mathbf{j} + 800\mathbf{j} \text{ (ft-lb)}.$$

The vector from C to D is given by

$$r_{CD} = (x_D - x_C)\mathbf{i} + (y_D - y_C)\mathbf{j} + (z_D - z_C)\mathbf{k}$$

$$= (6 - 5)\mathbf{i} + (0 - 0)\mathbf{j} + (0 - 6)\mathbf{k}$$

$$= 1\mathbf{i} + 0\mathbf{j} - 6\mathbf{j} \text{ (ft)},$$

and its magnitude is

$$|r_{CD}| = \sqrt{1^2 + 6^2} = \sqrt{37} \text{ (ft)}.$$

The unit vector from C to D is given by

$$e_{CD} = \frac{1}{\sqrt{37}}\mathbf{i} - \frac{6}{\sqrt{37}}\mathbf{k}.$$

The moment of the 800 lb vertical force about line CD is given by

$$M_{CD} = \left(\frac{1}{\sqrt{37}}\mathbf{i} - \frac{6}{\sqrt{37}}\mathbf{k}\right) \cdot (-1600\mathbf{i} + 0\mathbf{j} + 800\mathbf{j} \text{ (ft-lb)})$$

$$= \left(\frac{-1600 - 4800}{\sqrt{37}}\right) \text{ (ft-lb)}.$$

Carrying out the calculations, we get $\boxed{M_{CD} = -1052 \text{ (ft-lb)}}$

Problem 4.199 The system of cables and pulleys supports the 300-lb weight of the work platform. If you represent the upward force exerted at E by cable EF and the upward force exerted at G by cable GH by a single equivalent force $\mathbf{F}$, what is $\mathbf{F}$, and where does its line of action intersect the x axis?

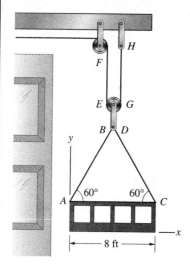

Solution: The cable-pulley combination does not produce a moment. Hence the equivalent force does not. The equivalent force is equal to the total supported weight, or $\mathbf{F} = +\dfrac{600}{2}\mathbf{j} = 300\mathbf{j}$ (lb). The force occurs at midpoint of the platform width, $x = \dfrac{8}{2} = 4$ ft

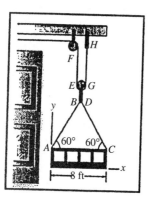

Problem 4.200 Consider the system in Problem 4.199.

(a) What are the tensions in cables AB and CD?
(b) If you represent the forces exerted by the cables at A and C by a single equivalent force $\mathbf{F}$, what is $\mathbf{F}$, and where does its line of action intersect the x axis?

Solution: The vertical component of the tension is each cable must equal half the weight supported.

$T_{AB} \sin 60° = 150$ lb, from which $T_{AB} = \dfrac{150}{\sin 60°} = 173.2$ lb. By symmetry, the tension $T_{CD} = 173.2$ lb.

The single force must equal the sum of the vertical components; since there is no resultant moment produced by the cables, the force is $\mathbf{F} = 300\mathbf{j}$ lb and it acts at the platform width midpoint $x = 4$ ft.

Problem 4.201   The two systems are equivalent. Determine the forces A_x and A_y, and the couple M_A.

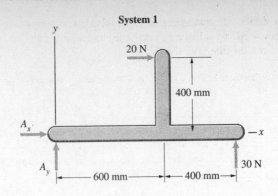

System 1

20 N

400 mm

A_x

A_y

—x

30 N

600 mm — 400 mm

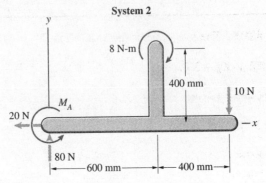

System 2

8 N-m

400 mm

10 N

M_A

20 N

—x

80 N

600 mm — 400 mm

Solution: The sum of the forces for System 1 is

$$\sum \mathbf{F}_X = (A_X + 20)\mathbf{i},$$

$$\sum \mathbf{F}_Y = (A_Y + 30)\mathbf{j}.$$

The sum of forces for System 2 is

$$\sum \mathbf{F}_X = (-20)\mathbf{i} \text{ and}$$

$$\sum \mathbf{F}_Y = (80 - 10)\mathbf{j}.$$

Equating the two systems:

$A_X + 20 = -20$ from which $A_X = -40$ N

$A_Y + 30 = 80 - 10$ from which $A_Y = 40$ N

The sum of the moments about the left end for System 1 is

$$\sum M_1 = -(0.4)(20) + 30(1) = 22 \text{ N-m}.$$

The sum of moments about the left end for System 2 is

$$\sum M_2 = M_A - 10(1) - 8 = M_A - 18.$$

Equating the moments for the two systems:

$M_A = 18 + 22 = 40$ N-m

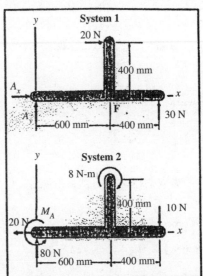

Problem 4.202   If you represent the equivalent systems in Problem 4.201 by a force $\mathbf{F}$ acting at the origin and a couple M, what are $\mathbf{F}$ and M?

Solution: Summing the forces in System 1, $\mathbf{F} = (A_X + 20)\mathbf{i} + (A_Y + 30)\mathbf{j}$. Substituting from the solution in Problem 4.179, $\mathbf{F} = -20\mathbf{i} + 70\mathbf{j}$. The moment is $\mathbf{M} = -20(0.4)\mathbf{k} + 30\mathbf{k} = 22\mathbf{k}$ (N-m)

Problem 4.203 If you represent the equivalent systems in Problem 4.201 by a force **F**, what is **F**, and where does its line of action intersect the x axis?

Solution: The force is $\mathbf{F} = -20\mathbf{i} + 70\mathbf{j}$. The moment to be represented is

$$\mathbf{M} = (\mathbf{r} \times \mathbf{F}) = 22\mathbf{k} = \begin{vmatrix} \mathbf{i} & \mathbf{j} & \mathbf{k} \\ x & 0 & 0 \\ -20 & 70 & 0 \end{vmatrix} = 70x\mathbf{k},$$

from which $x = \dfrac{22}{70} = 0.3143$ m

Problem 4.204 The two systems are equivalent. If

$$\mathbf{F} = -100\mathbf{i} + 40\mathbf{j} + 30\mathbf{k} \text{ (lb)},$$

$$\mathbf{M}' = -80\mathbf{i} + 120\mathbf{j} + 40\mathbf{k} \text{ (in-lb)},$$

determine **F'** and **M**.

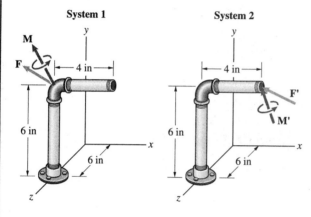

Solution: The sum of forces in the two systems must be equal, thus $\mathbf{F}' = \mathbf{F} = -100\mathbf{i} + 40\mathbf{j} + 30\mathbf{k}$ (lb).

The moment for the unprimed system is $\mathbf{M}_T = \mathbf{r} \times \mathbf{F} + \mathbf{M}$.

The moment for the primed system is $\mathbf{M}'_T = \mathbf{r}' \times \mathbf{F} + \mathbf{M}'$.

The position vectors are $\mathbf{r} = 0\mathbf{i} + 6\mathbf{j} + 6\mathbf{k}$, and $\mathbf{r}' = 4\mathbf{i} + 6\mathbf{j} + 6\mathbf{k}$. Equating the moments and solving for the unknown moment

$$\mathbf{M} = \mathbf{M}' + (\mathbf{r}' - \mathbf{r}) \times \mathbf{F} = -80\mathbf{i} + 120\mathbf{j} + 40\mathbf{k} + \begin{vmatrix} \mathbf{i} & \mathbf{j} & \mathbf{k} \\ 4 & 0 & 0 \\ -100 & 40 & 30 \end{vmatrix}$$

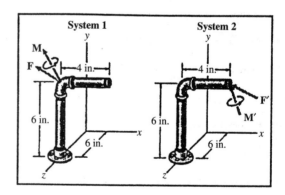

$$= -80\mathbf{i} + 120\mathbf{j} + 40\mathbf{k} - 120\mathbf{j} + 160\mathbf{k}$$

$$= -80\mathbf{i} + 200\mathbf{k} \text{ (in-lb)}$$

Problem 4.205 The tugboats A and B exert forces $F_A = 1$ kN and $F_B = 1.2$ kN on the ship. The angle $\theta = 30°$. If you represent the two forces by a force $\mathbf{F}$ acting at the origin O and a couple M, what are $\mathbf{F}$ and M?

Solution: The sums of the forces are:

$$\sum \mathbf{F}_X = (1 + 1.2\cos 30°)\mathbf{i} = 2.0392\mathbf{i} \text{ (kN)}$$

$$\sum \mathbf{F}_Y = (1.2\sin 30°)\mathbf{j} = 0.6\mathbf{j} \text{ (kN)}.$$

The equivalent force at the origin is

$$\mathbf{F}_{EQ} = 2.04\mathbf{i} + 0.6\mathbf{j}$$

The moment about O is $\mathbf{M}_O = \mathbf{r}_A \times \mathbf{F}_A + \mathbf{r}_B \times \mathbf{F}_B$. The vector positions are

$$\mathbf{r}_A = -25\mathbf{i} + 60\mathbf{j} \text{ (m)}, \text{ and}$$

$$\mathbf{r}_B = -25\mathbf{i} - 60\mathbf{j} \text{ (m)}.$$

The moment:

$$\mathbf{M}_O = \begin{vmatrix} \mathbf{i} & \mathbf{j} & \mathbf{k} \\ -25 & 60 & 0 \\ 1 & 0 & 0 \end{vmatrix} + \begin{vmatrix} \mathbf{i} & \mathbf{j} & \mathbf{k} \\ -25 & -60 & 0 \\ 1.0392 & 0.6 & 0 \end{vmatrix}$$

$$= -12.648\mathbf{k} = -12.6\mathbf{k} \text{ (kN-m)}$$

Check: Use a two dimensional description: The moment is

$$M_O = -(25)F_B \sin 30° + (60)(F_B \cos 30°) - (60)(F_A)$$

$$= 39.46F_B - 60F_A = -12.6 \text{ kN-m}$$

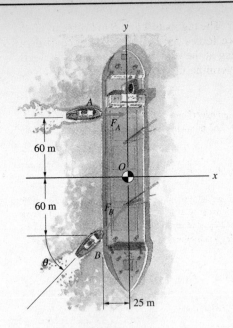

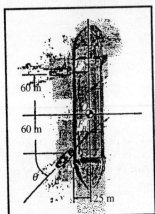

Problem 4.206 The tugboats A and B in Problem 4.205 exert forces $F_A = 600$ N and $F_B = 800$ N on the ship. The angle $\theta = 45°$. If you represent the two forces by a force $\mathbf{F}$, what is $\mathbf{F}$, and where does its line of action intersect the y axis?

Solution: The equivalent force is

$$\mathbf{F} = (0.6 + 0.8\cos 45°)\mathbf{i} + 0.8\sin 45°\mathbf{j} = 1.1656\mathbf{i} + 0.5656\mathbf{j} \text{ (kN)}.$$

The moment produced by the two forces is

$$\mathbf{M}_O = \mathbf{r}_A \times \mathbf{F}_A + \mathbf{r}_B \times \mathbf{F}_B.$$

The vector positions are

$$\mathbf{r}_A = -25\mathbf{i} + 60\mathbf{j} \text{ (m)}, \text{ and } \mathbf{r}_B = -25\mathbf{i} - 60\mathbf{j} \text{ (m)}.$$

The moment:

$$\mathbf{M}_O = \begin{vmatrix} \mathbf{i} & \mathbf{j} & \mathbf{k} \\ -25 & 60 & 0 \\ 0.6 & 0 & 0 \end{vmatrix} + \begin{vmatrix} \mathbf{i} & \mathbf{j} & \mathbf{k} \\ -25 & -60 & 0 \\ 0.5656 & 0.5656 & 0 \end{vmatrix} = -16.20\mathbf{k} \text{ (kN-m)}$$

Check: Use a two dimensional description:

$$M_O = -(25)F_B \sin 45° + (60)F_B \cos 45° - 60F_A$$

$$= 24.75F_B - 60F_A = -16.20 \text{ kN-m}.$$

The single force must produce this moment.

$$\mathbf{M}_O = \begin{vmatrix} \mathbf{i} & \mathbf{j} & \mathbf{k} \\ 0 & y & 0 \\ 1.1656 & 0.5656 & 0 \end{vmatrix} = -1.1656y\mathbf{k} = -16.20\mathbf{k},$$

from which

$$y = \frac{16.20}{1.1656} = 13.90 \text{ m}$$

Problem 4.207 The tugboats A and B in Problem 4.205 want to exert two forces on the ship that are equivalent to a force $\mathbf{F}$ acting at the origin O of 2-kN magnitude. If $F_A = 800$ N, determine the necessary values of F_B and angle θ.

Solution: The equivalent force at the origin is $(F_A + F_B \cos\theta)^2 + (F_B \sin\theta)^2 = 2000^2$. The moment about the origin due to F_A and F_B must be zero:

$$\sum M_O = -60F_A + 60F_B \cos\theta - 25F_B \sin\theta = 0.$$

These are two equations in two unknowns $F_B \sin\theta$ and $F_B \cos\theta$. For brevity write $x = F_B \cos\theta$, $y = F_B \sin\theta$, so that the two equations become $x^2 + 2F_A x + F_A^2 + y^2 = 2000^2$ and $60x - 25y - 60F_A = 0$. Eliminate y by solving each equation for y^2 and equating the results:

$$y^2 = 2000^2 - x^2 - 2F_A x - F_A^2 = \left(-\frac{60}{25}F_A + \frac{60}{25}x\right)^2.$$

Reduce to obtain the quadratic in x:

$$\left[1 + \left(\frac{60}{25}\right)^2\right]x^2 + 2F_A\left[1 - \left(\frac{60}{25}\right)^2\right]x$$

$$+ \left[1 + \left(\frac{60}{25}\right)^2\right]F_A^2 - 2000^2 = 0.$$

Substitute $F_A = 800$ N to obtain $6.76x^2 - 7616x + 326400 = 0$. In canonical form: $x^2 + 2bx + c = 0$, where $b = -563.31$, and $c = 48284.0$, with the solutions $x = -b \pm \sqrt{b^2 - c} = 1082.0$, $= 44.62$. From the second equation, $y = -1812.9$, $= 676.81$. The force F_B has two solutions: Solve for F_B and θ: (1)

$$F_B = \sqrt{44.6^2 + 1812.9^2} = 1813.4 \text{ N}$$

at the angle

$$\theta = \tan^{-1}\left(\frac{-1812.9}{44.6}\right) = -88.6°, \text{ and (2)}$$

$$F_B = \sqrt{676.8^2 + 1082.0^2} = 1276.2 \text{ N},$$

at the angle

$$\theta = \tan^{-1}\left(\frac{676.8}{1082.0}\right) = 32.0°$$

Problem 4.208 If you represent the forces exerted by the floor on the table legs by a force $\mathbf{F}$ acting at the origin O and a couple $\mathbf{M}$, what are $\mathbf{F}$ and $\mathbf{M}$?

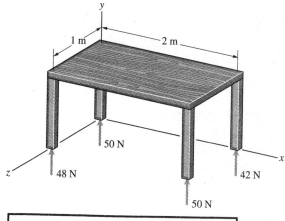

Solution: The sum of the forces is the equivalent force at the origin. $\mathbf{F} = (50 + 48 + 50 + 42)\mathbf{j} = 190\mathbf{j}$ (N). The position vectors of the legs are, numbering the legs counterclockwise from the lower left in the sketch:

$\mathbf{r}_1 = +1\mathbf{k}$,

$\mathbf{r}_2 = 2\mathbf{i} + 1\mathbf{k}$,

$\mathbf{r}_3 = 2\mathbf{i}$,

$\mathbf{r}_4 = 0$.

The sum of the moments about the origin is

$$\mathbf{M}_O = \begin{vmatrix} \mathbf{i} & \mathbf{j} & \mathbf{k} \\ 0 & 0 & 1 \\ 0 & 48 & 0 \end{vmatrix} + \begin{vmatrix} \mathbf{i} & \mathbf{j} & \mathbf{k} \\ 2 & 0 & 1 \\ 0 & 50 & 0 \end{vmatrix} + \begin{vmatrix} \mathbf{i} & \mathbf{j} & \mathbf{k} \\ 2 & 0 & 0 \\ 0 & 42 & 0 \end{vmatrix}$$

$$= -98\mathbf{i} + 184\mathbf{k} \text{ (N-m)}.$$

This is the couple that acts at the origin.

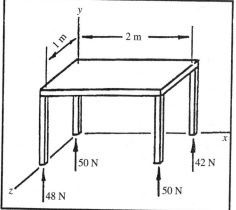

Problem 4.209 If you represent the forces exerted by the floor on the table legs in Problem 4.208 by a force **F**, what is **F**, and where does its line of action intersect the $x - z$ plane?

Solution: From the solution to Problem 4.208 the equivalent force is $\mathbf{F} = 190\mathbf{j}$. This force must produce the moment $\mathbf{M} = -98\mathbf{i} + 184\mathbf{k}$ obtained in Problem 4.208.

$$M = \begin{vmatrix} \mathbf{i} & \mathbf{j} & \mathbf{k} \\ x & 0 & z \\ 0 & 190 & 0 \end{vmatrix} = -190z\mathbf{i} + 190x\mathbf{k} = -98\mathbf{i} + 184\mathbf{k},$$

from which

$$x = \frac{184}{190} = 0.9684 \text{ m and}$$

$$z = \frac{98}{190} = 0.5158 \text{ m}$$

Problem 4.210 Two forces are exerted on the crankshaft by the connecting rods. The direction cosines of $\mathbf{F}_A$ are $\cos\theta_x = -0.182$, $\cos\theta_y = 0.818$, and $\cos\theta_z = 0.545$, and its magnitude is 4 kN. The direction cosines of $\mathbf{F}_B$ are $\cos\theta_x = 0.182$, $\cos\theta_y = 0.818$, and $\cos\theta_z = -0.545$, and its magnitude is 2 kN. If you represent the two forces by a force **F** acting at the origin O and a couple **M**, what are **F** and **M**?

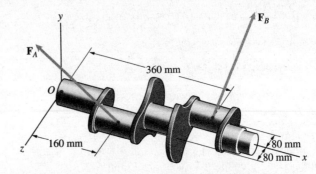

Solution: The equivalent force is the sum of the forces:

$$\mathbf{F}_A = 4(-0.182\mathbf{i} + 0.818\mathbf{j} + 0.545\mathbf{k})$$

$$= -0.728\mathbf{i} + 3.272\mathbf{j} + 2.18\mathbf{k} \text{ (kN)}$$

$$\mathbf{F}_B = 2(0.182\mathbf{i} + 0.818\mathbf{j} - 0.545\mathbf{k}) = 0.364\mathbf{i} + 1.636\mathbf{j} - 1.09\mathbf{k} \text{ (kN)}.$$

The sum: $\mathbf{F}_A + \mathbf{F}_B = -0.364\mathbf{i} + 4.908\mathbf{j} + 1.09\mathbf{k}$ (kN)

The equivalent couple is the sum of the moments. $M = \mathbf{r}_A \times \mathbf{F}_A + \mathbf{r}_B \times \mathbf{F}_B$. The position vectors are:

$$\mathbf{r}_A = 0.16\mathbf{i} + 0.08\mathbf{k},$$

$$\mathbf{r}_B = 0.36\mathbf{i} - 0.08\mathbf{k}.$$

The sum of the moments:

$$M = \begin{vmatrix} \mathbf{i} & \mathbf{j} & \mathbf{k} \\ 0.16 & 0 & 0.08 \\ -0.728 & 3.272 & 2.180 \end{vmatrix} + \begin{vmatrix} \mathbf{i} & \mathbf{j} & \mathbf{k} \\ 0.36 & 0 & -0.08 \\ 0.364 & 1.636 & -1.090 \end{vmatrix}$$

$$M = -0.1309\mathbf{i} - 0.0438\mathbf{j} + 1.1125\mathbf{k} \text{ (kN-m)}$$

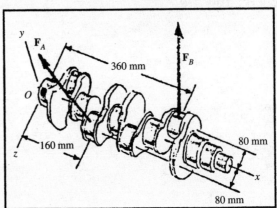

Problem 4.211 If you represent the two forces exerted on the crankshaft in Problem 4.210 by a wrench consisting of a force $\mathbf{F}$ and a parallel couple $\mathbf{M_p}$, what are $\mathbf{F}$ and $\mathbf{M_p}$, and where does the line of action of $\mathbf{F}$ intersect the $x - z$ plane?

Solution: From the solution to Problem 4.210,

$\mathbf{F} = -0.364\mathbf{i} + 4.908\mathbf{j} + 1.09\mathbf{k}$ (kN) and

$\mathbf{M} = -0.1309\mathbf{i} - 0.0438\mathbf{j} + 1.1125\mathbf{k}$ (kN-m).

The unit vector parallel to $\mathbf{F}$ is

$\mathbf{e}_F = \dfrac{\mathbf{F}}{|\mathbf{F}|} = -0.0722\mathbf{i} + 0.9737\mathbf{j} + 0.2162\mathbf{k}.$

The moment parallel to the force is

$\mathbf{M}_P = (\mathbf{e}_F \cdot \mathbf{M})\mathbf{e}_F.$

Carrying out the operations:

$\mathbf{M}_P = 0.2073\mathbf{e}_F = -0.01497\mathbf{i} + 0.2019\mathbf{j} + 0.0448\mathbf{k}$ (kN-m).

This is the equivalent couple parallel to $\mathbf{F}$.

The component of the moment perpendicular to $\mathbf{F}$ is

$\mathbf{M}_N = \mathbf{M} - \mathbf{M}_P = -0.1159\mathbf{i} - 0.2457\mathbf{j} + 1.0688\mathbf{k}.$

The force exerts this moment about the origin.

$$\mathbf{M}_N = \begin{vmatrix} \mathbf{i} & \mathbf{j} & \mathbf{k} \\ x & 0 & z \\ -0.364 & 4.908 & 1.09 \end{vmatrix}$$

$= (-4.908z)\mathbf{i} - (1.09x + 0.364z)\mathbf{j} + (4.908x)\mathbf{k}$

$= -0.1159\mathbf{i} - 0.2457\mathbf{j} + 1.06884\mathbf{k}.$

From which

$x = \dfrac{1.0688}{4.908} = 0.2178$ m,

$z = \dfrac{0.1159}{4.908} = 0.0236$ m

Problem 5.1 The beam has pin and roller supports and is subjected to a 4-kN load.

(a) Draw the free-body diagram of the beam.
(b) Determine the reactions at the supports.

Strategy: (a) Draw a diagram of the beam isolated from its supports. Complete the free-body diagram of the beam by adding the 4-kN load and the reactions due to the pin and roller supports (see Table 5.1). (b) Use the scalar equilibrium equations (5.4)–(5.6) to determine the reactions.

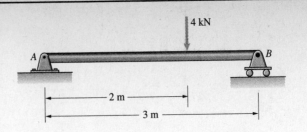

Solution:

$$\sum F_X = 0: \quad A_X = 0$$

$$\sum F_Y = 0: \quad A_Y + B_Y - 4 \text{ kN} = 0$$

$$\sum M_A = 0: \quad -2(4 \text{ kN}) + 3B_Y = 0$$

$$B_Y = 8/3 \text{ kN}$$

$$A_Y = 4/3 \text{ kN}$$

$$A_X = 0, \quad A_Y = 1.33 \text{ kN}, \quad B_Y = 2.67 \text{ kN}$$

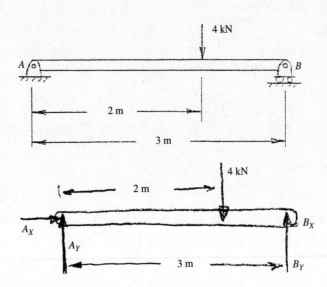

Problem 5.2 The beam has a built-in support and is loaded by a 2-kN force and a 6 kN-m couple.

(a) Draw the free-body diagram of the beam.
(b) Determine the reactions at the supports.

Solution:

(a)

(b) $\sum F_X = 0: \quad A_X = 0$

$\sum F_Y = 0: \quad A_Y - 2 \text{ kN} = 0$

$\sum M_A = 0: \quad M_A - (2)(2 \text{ kN}) + 6 \text{ kN-m} = 0$

$M_A = -2 \text{ kNm}$

$A_X = 0$

$A_Y = 2 \text{ kN}$

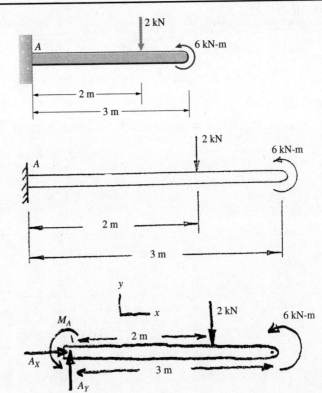

Problem 5.3 The beam is subjected to a load $F = 400$ N and is supported by the rope and the smooth surfaces at A and B.

(a) Draw the free-body diagram of the beam.
(b) What are the magnitudes of the reactions at A and B?

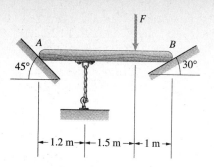

Solution:

$$\sum F_X = 0: \quad A\cos 45° - B\sin 30° = 0$$

$$\sum F_Y = 0: \quad A\sin 45° + B\cos 30° - T - 400 \text{ N} = 0$$

$$\curvearrowleft + \sum M_A = 0: \quad -1.2T - 2.7(400) + 3.7B\cos 30° = 0$$

Solving, we get

$A = 271$ N

$B = 383$ N

$T = 124$ N

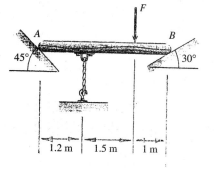

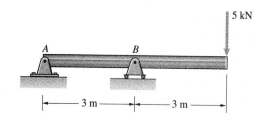

Problem 5.4 (a) Draw the free-body diagram of the beam.

(b) Determine the reactions at the supports.

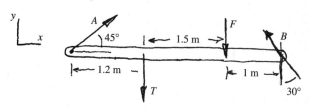

Solution:

(a)

(b) $\sum F_X = 0: \quad A_X = 0$

$$\sum F_Y = 0: \quad A_Y + B_Y - 5 \text{ kN} = 0$$

$$\curvearrowleft + \sum M_A = 0: \quad 3B_Y - 6(5 \text{ kN}) = 0$$

Solving: $A_X = 0$

$B_Y = 10$ kN

$A_Y = -5$ kN

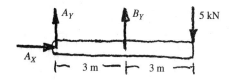

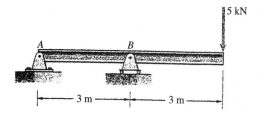

315

Problem 5.5 (a) Draw the free-body diagram of the 60-lb drill press, assuming that the surfaces at A and B are smooth.

(b) Determine the reactions at A and B.

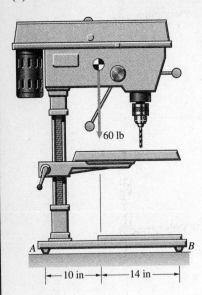

60 lb

A B

|— 10 in —|— 14 in —|

Solution: The system is in equilibrium.

(a) The free body diagram is shown.

(b) The sum of the forces:

$$\sum F_X = 0, \quad \sum F_Y = F_A + F_B - 60 = 0$$

The sum of the moments about point A:

$$\sum M_A = -10(60) + 24(F_B) = 0,$$

from which $F_B = \dfrac{600}{24} = 25$ lb

Substitute into the force balance equation:

$F_A = 60 - F_B = 35$ lb

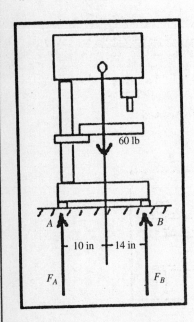

60 lb

A B

|— 10 in —|— 14 in —|

F_A F_B

Problem 5.6 The masses of the person and the diving board are 54 kg and 36 kg, respectively. Assume that they are in equilibrium.

(a) Draw the free-body diagram of the diving board.
(b) Determine the reactions at the supports A and B.

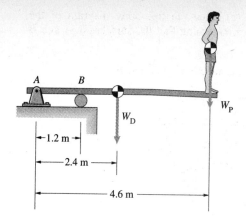

Solution:

(a)

(b) (N) $\sum F_X = 0$: $A_X = 0$

(N) $\sum F_Y = 0$: $A_Y + B_Y - (54)(9.81) - 36(9.81) = 0$

$\sum M_A = 0$: $1.2B_Y - (2.4)(36)(9.81)$

$\qquad\qquad - (4.6)(54)(9.81) = 0$

Solving: $A_X = 0$ N

$A_Y = -1.85$ kN

$B_Y = 2.74$ kN

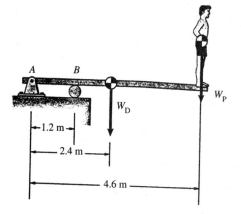

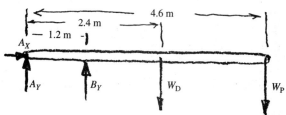

Problem 5.7 The ironing board has supports at A and B that can be modeled as roller supports.

(a) Draw the free-body diagram of the ironing board.
(b) Determine the reactions at A and B.

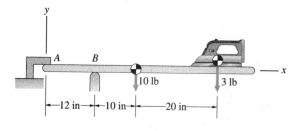

Solution: The system is in equilibrium.

(a) The free-body diagram is shown.
(b) The sums of the forces are:

$\sum F_X = 0,$

$\sum F_Y = F_A + F_B - 10 - 3 = 0.$

The sum of the moments about A is

$\sum M_A = 12F_B - 22(10) - 42(3) = 0,$

from which $F_B = \dfrac{346}{12} = 28.833$ in.

Substitute into the force balance equation:

$F_A = 13 - F_B = -15.833$ lb

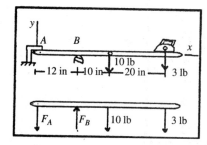

Problem 5.8 The distance $x = 2$ m.

(a) Draw the free-body diagram of the beam.
(b) Determine the reactions at the supports.

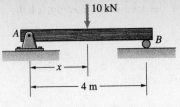

Solution: The system is in equilibrium. The point A is a pinned support. The point B is a roller support. (a) The free body diagram is shown. (b) The sums of the forces:

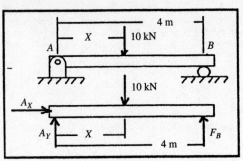

$$\sum F_X = A_X = 0,$$

$$\sum F_Y = A_Y - 10 + F_B = 0.$$

The sum of the moments about A is

$$\sum M_A = -2(10) + 4F_B = 0,$$

from which $F_B = \dfrac{20}{4} = 5$ kN.

Substitute into the force balance equation to obtain

$$A_Y = 10 - F_B = 5 \text{ kN}$$

Problem 5.9 Consider the beam in Problem 5.8. An engineer determines that each support will safely support a force of 7.5 kN. What is the range of values of the distance x at which the 10-kN force can safely be applied?

Solution: From the solution to Problem 5.8 the equations for $\mathbf{F_B}$ and A_Y are:

$$\sum M_A = 4F_B - 10x = 0,$$

from which $F_B = \dfrac{10x}{4} = 2.5x.$

$$\sum F_Y = A_Y - 10 + F_B = 0,$$

from which $A_Y = 10 - F_B = 10 - 2.5x$

Solve for the value of x:

$$x = \frac{F_B}{2.5},$$

and $x = \dfrac{10 - A_Y}{2.5}.$

Let $F_B = 7.5$ kN,

then $A_Y = 2.5$ kN

and $x = \dfrac{7.5}{2.5} = 3$ m.

Let $A_Y = 7.5$ kN,

then $F_B = 2.5$ kN,

and $x = \dfrac{10 - 7.5}{2.5} = 1$ m.

Thus $1 \le x \le 3$ m

Problem 5.10 (a) Draw the free-body diagram of the beam.
(b) Determine the reactions at the supports.

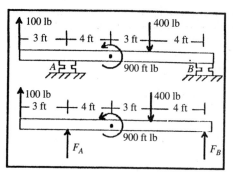

Solution: (a) Both supports are roller supports. The free body diagram is shown. (b) The sum of the forces:

$$\sum F_X = 0,$$

and $\sum F_Y = F_A + F_B + 100 - 400 = 0.$

The sum of the moments about A is

$$\sum M_A = -3(100) + 900 - 7(400) + 11F_B = 0.$$

From which $F_B = \dfrac{2200}{11} = 200$ lb

Substitute into the force balance equation to obtain

$F_A = 300 - F_B = 100$ lb

Problem 5.11 Consider the beam in Problem 5.10. First represent the loads (the 100-lb force, the 400-lb force, and the 900 ft-lb couple) by a single equivalent force; and then determine the reactions at the supports.

Solution: The equivalent force is the sum of the applied force:

$$\sum F_Y = 100 - 400 = -300 \text{ lb}.$$

The applied moment about the point A is

$$\sum M_A = -3(100) + 900 - 7(400) = -2200 \text{ ft lb}.$$

The equivalent force must be applied at a point that produces this moment about A.

Let x be the distance to the line of action from A: then

$-300x = -2200$ ft lb from which x

$$= \frac{2200}{300} = 7.33 \text{ ft}$$

to the right of A. The equivalent system is shown. The sum of the forces:

$$\sum F_X = 0,$$

$$\sum F_Y = F_A + F_B - 300 = 0.$$

The sum of moments about A is

$$\sum M_A = -(7.33)(300) + 11F_B = 0,$$

from which $F_B = \dfrac{2200}{11} = 200$ lb.

Substitute into the force balance equation to obtain:

$F_A = 300 - F_B = 100$ lb.

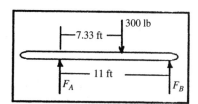

Problem 5.12 (a) Draw the free-body diagram of the beam.
(b) Determine the reactions at the support.

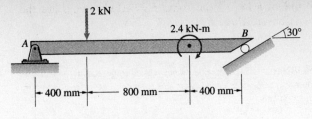

Solution: The equilibrium equations are

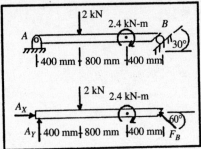

$$\sum F_X = A_X - F_B \cos 60° = 0,$$

$$\sum F_Y = A_Y - 2 + F_B \sin 60° = 0,$$

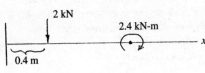

$$\sum M_{(pt\ A)} = -2.4 - (0.4)(2) + (1.6)F_B \sin 60° = 0.$$

Solving, we obtain

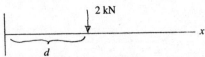

$A_X = 1.15$ kN,

$A_Y = 0,$

$F_B = 2.31$ kN.

Problem 5.13 Consider the beam in Problem 5.12. First represent the loads (the 2-kN force and the 24-kN-m couple) by a single equivalent force; then determine the reactions at the supports.

Solution: The single force is equivalent to the force and couple if

$$d(2) = (0.4)(2) + 2.4,$$

so $d = 1.6$ m.

From the equilibrium equations

$$\sum F_X = A_X - F_B \cos 60° = 0,$$

$$\sum F_Y = A_Y - 2 + F_B \sin 60° = 0,$$

$$\sum M_{(pt\ B)} = -1.6 A_Y = 0,$$

we obtain

$A_X = 1.15$ kN,

$A_Y = 0,$

$F_B = 2.31$ kN.

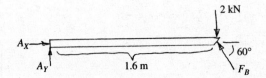

Problem 5.14 If the force $F = 40$ kN, what are the reactions at A and B?

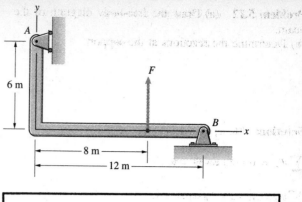

Solution: There are two force equilibrium equations and one moment equilibrium equation for this Problem. The force equilibrium equations are

$$\sum F_x = F_{AX} + F_{BX} = 0,$$

and $\sum F_y = F_{BY} + F$ kN $= 0.$

The moment equilibrium equation around point B is

$$\sum M_B = -(4 \text{ m})(F \text{ kN})$$

$$- (6 \text{ m})F_{AX} = 0.$$

Since we know that $F = 40$ kN, We have three scalar equations in the three unknowns. The moment equation can be solved alone, giving $F_{AX} = -26.7$ kN. Substituting this value into the force equilibrium equation in the x direction yields $F_{BX} = 26.7$ kN. Finally, the y direction force equation yields $F_{BY} = -40$ kN.

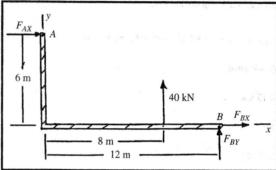

Problem 5.15 In Problem 5.14, the structural designer determines that the magnitude of the force exerted on the support A by the beam must not exceed 80 kN, and the magnitude of the force exerted on the support B must not exceed 140 kN. Based on these criteria, what is the largest allowable value of the upward load F?

Solution: From Problem 5.14, we have

$$\sum F_x = F_{AX} + F_{BX} = 0,$$

$$\sum F_y = F_{BY} + F \text{ kN} = 0,$$

and $\sum M_B = -(4 \text{ m})(F \text{ kN}) - (6 \text{ m})F_{AX} = 0.$

We also know that

$$|\mathbf{F}_A| = F_{AX}$$

and $|\mathbf{F}_B| = \sqrt{F_{BX}^2 + F_{BY}^2}.$

Thus we have five equations relating the six variables F, F_{AX}, F_{BX}, F_{BY}, $|\mathbf{F}_A|$, and $|\mathbf{F}_B|$.

Case 1: If we set $|\mathbf{F}_A| = F_{AX} = 80$ kN and solve the equations, we get answers for all of the forces in the system. The one answer that concerns us is that we get $|\mathbf{F}_B| = 144.2$ kN, which violates the force condition at B. Thus, the loading in Case 1 cannot be allowed for this system. *Case 2:* If we set

$$|\mathbf{F}_B| = \sqrt{F_{BX}^2 + F_{BY}^2} = 140 \text{ kN}$$

and solve the equations, we again get answers for all of the forces in the system. In this case, we get

$$|\mathbf{F}_A| = |F_{AX}| = -77.65 \text{ kN},$$

which is under the 80 kN limit for this force. This is the situation we wanted — one force at its limit and the other under its limit. In this case, the solution of the equation set yields $F = 116.4$ kN. Note: The actual answer for F can be rounded up to $F = 116.5$ kN, but if we round up, we exceed the load limits set in our Problem. Be very careful in such cases. (In the real world, we have safety factors that eliminate the possibility of such situations)

Problem 5.16 The person doing push-ups pauses in the position shown. His mass is 80 kg. Assume that his weight W acts at the point shown. The dimensions shown are $a = 250$ mm, $b = 740$ mm, and $c = 300$ mm. Determine the normal force exerted by the floor (a) on each hand, (b) on each foot.

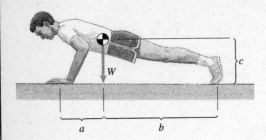

Solution: We assume that each hand and each foot carries an equal load.

$\sum F_X = 0:$ No forces in x-direction

$\sum F_Y = 0:$ $2F_H + 2F_F - W = 0$

$\sum M_H = 0:$ $-aW + (a + b)(2F_F) = 0$

Solving, we get

$W = 784.8$ N

$F_H = 293.3$ N

$F_F = 99.1$ N

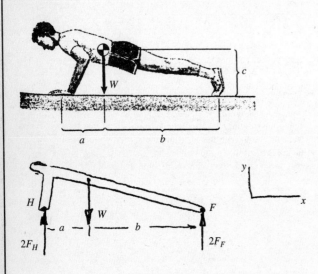

Problem 5.17   With each of the devices shown you can support a load R by applying a force F. They are called levers of the first, second, and third class.

(a)   The ratio R/F is called the *mechanical advantage*. Determine the mechanical advantage of each lever.

(b)   Determine the magnitude of the reaction at A for each lever. (Express your answer in terms of F.)

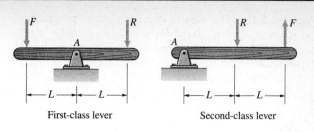

First-class lever   Second-class lever

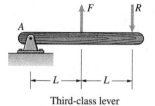

Third-class lever

Solution: *Lever of first kind.*

(a)   The sum of the forces is

$$\sum F_Y = -F + A - R = 0.$$

The sum of the moments about A is

$$\sum M_A = FL - RL = 0,$$

from which $\dfrac{R}{F} = \dfrac{L}{L} = 1$

(b)   The reaction at A is obtained from the force balance equation:

$$A = R + F = 2F$$

Lever of second kind.

(a)   The sum of forces is

$$\sum F_Y = A - R + F = 0.$$

The sum of the moments about A is

$$\sum M_A = -LR + 2LF = 0,$$

from which $\dfrac{R}{F} = \dfrac{2L}{L} = 2$

(b)   The reaction at A is obtained from the force balance equation:

$$A = -F + R = -F + 2F = F$$

Lever of third kind.

(a)   The sum of forces is

$$\sum F_Y = A - R + F = 0.$$

The sum of moments about A is:

$$\sum M_A = -2LR + LF = 0,$$

from which: $\dfrac{R}{F} = \dfrac{L}{2L} = \dfrac{1}{2}$

(b)   From the force balance equation

$$A = -F + R = -F + \frac{F}{2} = -\frac{F}{2},$$

$$|A| = \frac{F}{2}$$

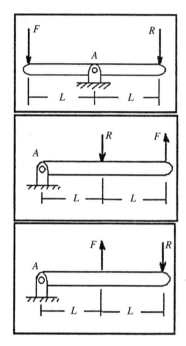

Problem 5.18 (a) Draw the free-body diagram of the beam. (b) Determine the reactions at the support.

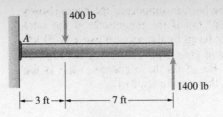

Solution:

$$\sum F_X = 0: \quad A_X + 200 \text{ N} = 0$$

$$\sum F_Y = 0: \quad A_Y + 300 \text{ N} - 200 \text{ N} = 0$$

$$\sum M_A = 0: \quad M_A - 180 - (0.6)(300) + (0.5)(200) = 0$$

Solving: $A_X = -200$ N

$A_Y = -100$ N

$M_A = 260$ N-m

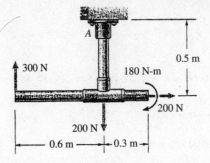

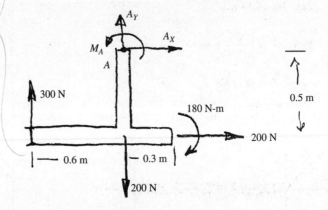

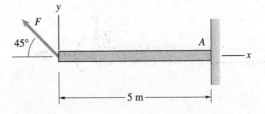

Problem 5.19 The force $F = 12$ kN. Determine the reactions at A.

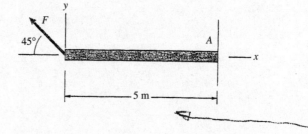

Solution:

$$\sum F_X: \quad A_X - 12\cos(45°) = 0$$

$$\sum F_Y: \quad A_Y + 12\sin(45°) = 0$$

$$\sum M_A: \quad M_A - (5)(12)(\sin 45°) = 0$$

Solving: $A_X = 8.49$ kN

$A_Y = -8.49$ kN

$M_A = 42.4$ kN-m

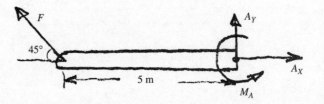

Problem 5.20 The built-in support of the beam shown in Problem 5.19 will fail if the magnitude of the total force exerted on the beam by the support exceeds 20 kN or if the magnitude of the couple exerted by the support exceeds 65 kN-m. Based on these criteria, what is the maximum force F that can be applied?

Solution:

(a) Assume the limit is a force limit.

$$\sum \mathbf{F} = 0 \quad \mathbf{A} + \mathbf{F} = 0$$

Thus, $|\mathbf{A}| = |\mathbf{F}|$ and if $|\mathbf{A}| = 20$ kN, the force limit for $|\mathbf{F}|$ is 20 kN.

(b) Assume the limit is a moment limit

$$\sum M = M_A - 5(F \sin 45°) = 0$$

and $M_A = 65$ kN-m

Here, $F = \left(\dfrac{65}{5} \right) \Big/ \sin 45°$

$F = 18.38$ kN

The limit is $|\mathbf{F}| = 18.38$ kN

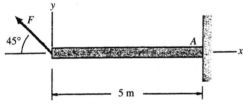

Problem 5.21 The mobile is in equilibrium. The fish B weighs 27 oz. Determine the weights of the fish A, C, and D. (The weights of the crossbars are negligible.)

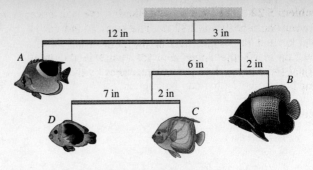

Solution: Denote the reactions at the supports by F_{AB}, F_{CD}, and F_{BCD} as shown. Start with the crossbar supporting the weights C and D. The sum of the forces is

$$\sum F_Y = -C - D + F_{CD} = 0,$$

from which $F_{CD} = C + D$.

For the cross bar supporting the weight B, the sum of the forces is

$$\sum F_Y = -B + F_{BCD} - F_{CD} = 0,$$

from which, substituting, $F_{BCD} = B + C + D$.

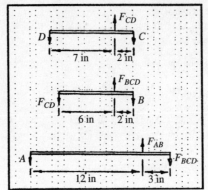

For the crossbar supporting C and D, the sum of the moments about the support is

$$\sum M_{CD} = 7D + 2C = 0,$$

from which $D = \dfrac{2C}{7}$.

For the crossbar supporting B, the sum of the moments is

$$\sum M_{BCD} = 6F_{CD} - 2B = 0,$$

from which, substituting from above

$$F_{CD} = \frac{2B}{6} = C + D = C + \frac{2C}{7} = \frac{9C}{7},$$

or $C = 7B/27 = 7$ oz,

and $D = 2C/7 = 2$ oz.

The sum of the moments about the crossbar supporting A is

$$\sum M_{AB} = 12A - 3F_{BCD} = 0,$$

from which, substituting from above,

$$A = \frac{3(B + C + D)}{12} = \frac{27 + 7 + 2}{4} = 9 \text{ oz}$$

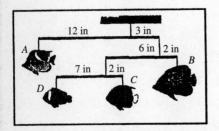

326

Problem 5.22 The car's wheelbase (the distance between the wheels) is 2.82 m. The mass of the car is 1760 kg and its weight acts at the point $x = 2.00$ m, $y = 0.68$ m. If the angle $\alpha = 15°$, what is the total normal force exerted on the two rear tires by the sloped ramp?

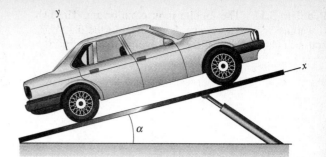

Solution: Split W into components:

$W \cos \alpha$ acts $\perp$ to the incline

$W \sin \alpha$ acts parallel to the incline

$\sum F_X$: $\quad f - W \sin \alpha = 0$

$\sum F_Y$: $\quad N_R + N_F - W \cos \alpha = 0$

$\sum M_R$: $\quad (-2)(W \cos \alpha) + (0.68)W \sin \alpha + 2.82 N_F = 0$

Solving: $N_R = 5930$ N, $N_F = 10750$ N

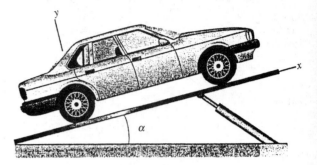

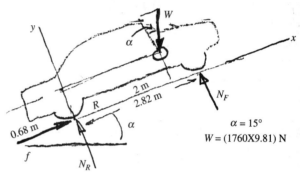

$\alpha = 15°$
$W = (1760 \times 9.81)$ N

Problem 5.23 The car in Problem 5.22 can remain in equilibrium on the sloped ramp only if the total friction force exerted on its tires does not exceed 0.8 times the total normal force exerted on the two rear tires. What is the largest angle α for which it can remain in equilibrium?

Solution: The solution to Problem 5.22 yielded

$$\begin{cases} f = W \sin \alpha \\ N_R + N_F - W \cos \alpha = 0 \\ -2W \cos \alpha + 0.68W \sin \alpha + 2.82 N_F = 0 \end{cases}$$

Our limit is $f/N_R \leq 0.8$, so let us set $f = 0.8 N_R$ and solve the resulting relations for α_{max}

$$\begin{cases} 0.8 N_R = W \sin \alpha_{max} \\ N_R + N_F - W \cos \alpha_{max} = 0 \\ -2W \cos \alpha + 6.68 \ W \sin \alpha_{max} + 2.82 N_F = 0 \end{cases}$$

Solving, we get

$\alpha_{max} = 16.1°$,

$f = 4788$ N,

$N_R = 5985$ N,

$N_F = 10603$ N.

327

Problem 5.24 The 14.5-lb chain saw is subjected to the loads at A by the log it cuts. Determine the reactions R, B_x, and B_y that must be applied by the person using the saw to hold it in equilibrium.

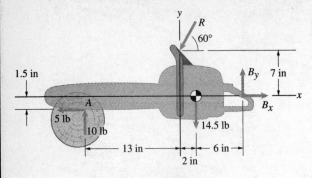

Solution: The sum of the forces are

$$\sum F_X = -5 + B_X - R\cos 60° = 0.$$

$$\sum F_Y = 10 - 14.5 + B_Y - R\sin 60° = 0.$$

The sum of the moments about the origin is

$$\sum M_O = 7R\cos 60° + 8B_Y - 2(14.5) - 13(10) - 5(1.5) = 0.$$

From which $7R\cos 60° + 8B_Y - 166.5 = 0$. Collecting equations and reducing to 3 equations in 3 unknowns:

$$B_X + 0B_Y - 0.5R = 5$$

$$0B_X + B_Y - 0.866R = 4.5$$

$$0B_X + 8B_Y + 3.5R = 166.5.$$

Solving:

$$B_X = 11.257 \text{ lb,}$$

$$B_Y = 15.337 \text{ lb,}$$

and $R = 12.514$ lb

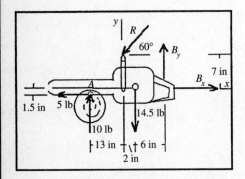

Problem 5.25 The mass of the trailer is 2.2 Mg (mega-grams). The distances $a = 2.5$ m and $b = 5.5$ m. The truck is stationary, and the wheels of the trailer can turn freely, which means that the road exerts no horizontal force on them. The hitch at B can be modeled as a pin support.

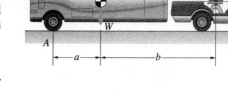

(a) Draw the free-body diagram of the trailer.
(b) Determine the total normal force exerted on the rear tires at A and the reactions exerted on the trailer at the pin support B.

Solution:

(a) The free body diagram is shown.
(b) The sum of forces:

$$\sum F_X = B_X = 0.$$

$$\sum F_Y = F_A - W + F_B = 0.$$

The sum of the moments about A:

$$\sum M_A = -aW + (a+b)F_B = 0,$$

from which

$$F_B = \frac{aW}{a+b} = \frac{2.5(2.2 \times 10^3)(9.81)}{(2.5+5.5)} = 6.744 \text{ kN}$$

Substitute into the force equation:

$$F_A = W - F_B = 14.838 \text{ kN}$$

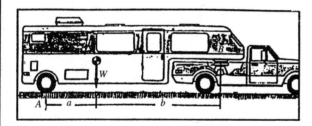

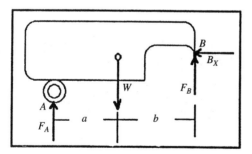

Problem 5.26 The total weight of the wheelbarrow and its load is $W = 100$ lb.

(a) If $F = 0$, what are the vertical reactions at A and B?
(b) What force F is necessary to lift the support at A off the ground?

Solution: (a) The sum of the forces:

$$\sum F_X = A_X = 0$$

$$\sum F_Y = A_Y - W + F_B = 0.$$

The sum of the moments about A is

$$\sum M_A = -W(12) + F_B(26) = 0,$$

from which

$$F_B = \frac{12W}{26} = 46.1538 \text{ lb} = 46.2 \text{ lb}.$$

Substitute into the force equation to obtain:

$$A_Y = W - F_B = 53.8462 \text{ lb} = 53.8 \text{ lb}$$

(b) The sum of the moments about B when the point A is not making contact with the ground:

$$\sum M_B = (14)(100) - (66)F = 0,$$

from which

$$F = \frac{(14)(100)}{66} = 21.2121 = 21.2 \text{ lb}$$

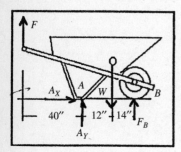

Problem 5.27   The airplane's weight is $W = 2400$ lb. Its brakes keep the rear wheels locked. The front (nose) wheel can turn freely, and so the ground exerts no horizontal force on it. The force T exerted by the airplane's propeller is horizontal.

(a)   Draw the free-body diagram of the airplane. Determine the reaction exerted on the nose wheel and the total normal reaction on the rear wheels

(b)   when $T = 0$,

(c)   when $T = 250$ lb.

Solution: (a) The free body diagram is shown. (b) The sum of the forces:

$$\sum F_X = B_X = 0$$

$$\sum F_Y = A_Y - W + B_Y = 0.$$

The sum of the moments about A is

$$\sum M_A = -5W + 7B_Y = 0,$$

from which $B_Y = \dfrac{5W}{7} = 1714.3$ lb

Substitute from the force balance equation:

$$A_Y = W - B_Y = 685.7 \text{ lb}$$

(c) The sum of the forces:

$$\sum F_X = -250 + B_X = 0,$$

from which $B_X = 250$ lb

$$\sum F_Y = A_Y - W + B_Y = 0.$$

The sum of the moments about A:

$$\sum M_A = (250)(4) - 5W + 7B_Y = 0,$$

from which $B_Y = 1571.4$ lb. Substitute into the force balance equation to obtain: $A_Y = 828.6$ lb

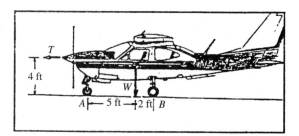

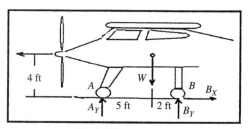

Problem 5.28 The forklift is stationary. The front wheels are free to turn, and the rear wheels are locked. The distances are $a = 1.25$ m, $b = 0.50$ m, and $c = 1.40$ m. The weight of the load is $W_L = 2$ kN, and the weight of the truck and operator is $W_F = 8$ kN. What are the reactions at A and B?

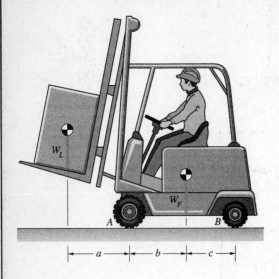

Solution: The sum of the forces:

$$\sum F_X = B_X = 0$$

$$\sum F_Y = A_Y - W_L - W_F + B_Y = 0.$$

The sum of the moments about A is

$$\sum M_A = +aW_L - bW_F + (b+c)B_Y = 0,$$

from which

$$B_Y = \frac{bW_F - aW_L}{b+c} = 0.7895 \text{ kN}.$$

Substitute into the force equation to obtain:

$$A_Y = W_L + W_F - B_Y = 9.211 \text{ kN}$$

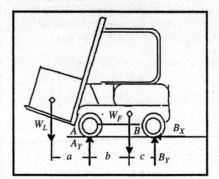

Problem 5.29 Consider the stationary forklift shown in Problem 5.28. The front wheels are free to turn, and the rear wheels are locked. The distances are $a = 45$ in., $b = 20$ in., and $c = 50$ in. The weight of the truck and operator is $W_F = 3000$ lb. For safety reasons, a rule is established that the reaction at the rear wheels must be at least 400 lb. If the weight W_L of the load acts at the position shown, what is the maximum safe load?

Solution: From the solution to Problem 5.26, $B_X = 0$, and the sum of the moments:

$$\sum M_A = +aW_L - bW_F + (b+c)B_Y = 0,$$

from which

$$W_L = \frac{bW_F - (b+c)B_Y}{a} = 1333.33 - 1.5555B_Y.$$

Since B_Y is positive, the maximum load for $B_Y = 400$ lb is $W_L = 711.1$ lb

Problem 5.30 The weight of the fan is $W = 20$ lb. Its base has four equally spaced legs of length $b = 12$ in., and $h = 36$ in. What is the largest thrust T exerted by the fan's propeller for which the fan will remain in equilibrium?

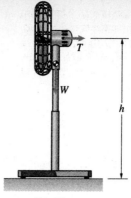

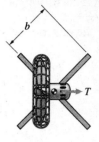

Side View

Top View

Solution: Each leg is assumed to be in contact with a rough surface, with (in two dimensions) two force components each.

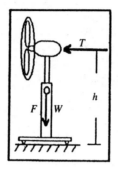

The four equally spaced legs can be in two positions relative to the thrust line of action: In the first the distance to the center is b. In the second, the distance is $b \sin 45° = 0.707b$. Tipping will occur when the leftmost (or rightmost) leg(s) has zero reaction on the floor.

For each position the sum of the moments about the center is:

$$\sum M_T = -bW + Th = 0, \text{ and}$$

$$\sum M_T = -0.707bW + Th = 0.$$

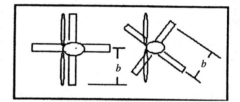

From which the two tipping moment thrusts are:

$$T_1 = \frac{bW}{h} = 6.67 \text{ lbs,}$$

$$T_2 = \frac{0.707bW}{h} = 4.71 \text{ lb}$$

which is the maximum thrust allowed.

Problem 5.31 Consider the fan described in Problem 5.30. As a safety criterion, an engineer decides that the vertical reaction on any of the fan's legs should not be less than 20% of the fan's weight. If the thrust T is 1 lb when the fan is set on its highest speed, what is the maximum safe value of h?

Solution: The total upward reaction of the legs is equal to the weight of the fan, so that each leg normally bears one quarter of the weight. Under the condition of maximum tipping moment, with the legs in the position such that the distance to the center is $0.707b$, the legs in the outer position will each have the reaction of 20 percent of the weight, so that both will carry 40 percent of the weight. Thus the legs on the other side must bear 60 percent of the weight. The sum of the moments at the maximum tipping condition allowed is

$$\sum M_T = (0.707b)(0.4W) + Th - (0.707b)(0.6W) = 0,$$

from which:

$$h = \frac{0.707b(0.2W)}{T} = 33.94 \text{ in}$$

Problem 5.32 To decrease costs, an engineer considers supporting a fan with three equally spaced legs instead of the four-leg configuration shown in Problem 5.30. For the same values of b, h, and W, show that the largest thrust T for which the fan will remain in equilibrium with three legs is related to the value with four legs by

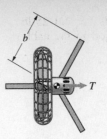

$$T_{(\text{three legs})} = (1/\sqrt{2})T_{(\text{four legs})}.$$

Solution: From the solution to Problem 5.30 the maximum thrust is

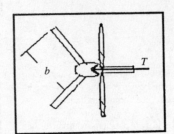

$$T_{\text{four legs}} = \frac{bW \sin 45°}{h} = \frac{bW}{\sqrt{2}h}.$$

For three legs assume that the legs are in the position shown with respect to the line of action of the thrust. The distance to the center is $b \cos 60° = \dfrac{b}{2}$. When the outermost leg has zero reaction, the other legs must bear the weight of the fan. The sum of the moments about the center when the outer most leg has zero reaction is

$$\sum M_T = -\frac{bW}{2} + Th = 0,$$

from which $T_{\text{three legs}} = \dfrac{bW}{2h} = \dfrac{1}{\sqrt{2}} T_{\text{four legs}}.$

Problem 5.33 A force $F = 400$ N acts on the bracket. What are the reactions at A and B?

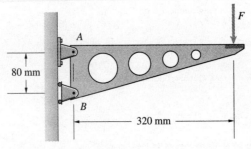

Solution: The joint A is a pinned joint; B is a roller joint. The pinned joint has two reaction forces A_X, A_Y. The roller joint has one reaction force B_X. The sum of the forces is

$$\sum F_X = A_X + B_X = 0,$$

$$\sum F_Y = A_Y - F = 0,$$

from which

$$A_Y = F = 400 \text{ N}.$$

The sum of the moments about A is

$$\sum M_A = 0.08 B_X - 0.320 F = 0,$$

from which

$$B_X = \frac{0.320(400)}{0.08} = 1600 \text{ N}.$$

Substitute into the sum of forces equation to obtain:

$$A_X = -B_X = -1600 \text{ N}$$

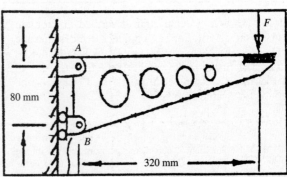

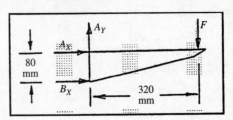

Problem 5.34 The hanging sign exerts vertical 25-lb forces at A and B. Determine the tension in the cable and the reactions at the support at C.

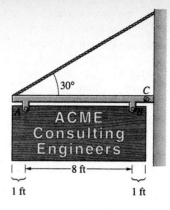

8 ft

1 ft   1 ft

Solution: The joint C is pinned joint, with two forces, C_X, C_Y. The sum of the vertical forces is

$$\sum F_X = T_C \cos 30° + C_X = 0.$$

$$\sum F_Y = T_C \sin 30° - A_Y - B_Y + C_Y = 0.$$

The sum of the moments about C is

$$\sum M_C = 9A_Y + 1B_Y - 10T_C \sin 30° = 0$$

from which

$$T_C = \frac{9A_Y + B_Y}{10 \sin 30°} = \frac{250}{5} = 50 \text{ lb}.$$

Substitute into the vertical forces sum to obtain:

$$C_Y = A_Y + B_Y - T_C \sin 30° = 25 \text{ lb}.$$

Substitute into the horizontal forces sum to obtain

$$C_X = -T_C \cos 30° = -43.3 \text{ lb}$$

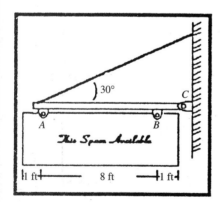

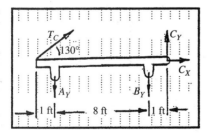

335

Problem 5.35 This device, called a *swape* or *shadoof*, is used to help a person lift a heavy load. (It was used in Egypt at least as early as 1550 B.C. and is still in use in various parts of the world today.) The distances are $a = 12$ ft and $b = 4$ ft. If the load being lifted weighs 100 lb and $W = 200$ lb, determine the vertical force the person must exert to support the stationary load (a) when the load is just above the ground (the position shown); (b) when the load is 3 ft above the ground. (Assume that the rope remains vertical.)

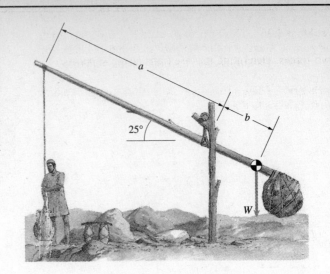

Solution: Denote the vertical force exerted by the laborer by F.

(a) The sum of the moments about the fulcrum point is

$$\sum M_F = -aF \cos 25° + aW_L \cos 25° - bW \cos 25° = 0$$

from which

$$F = \frac{(aW_L - bW)}{a},$$

or $F = \dfrac{1200 - 800}{12} = 33.33$ lb.

the force exerted by the laborer is independent of the angle.

(b) When the load is three feet above the ground, the swape is at a new angle. But since the force is independent of the angle, $F = 33.33$ lb

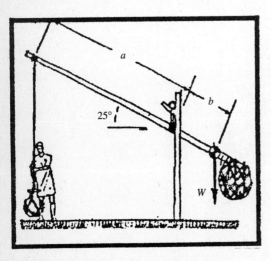

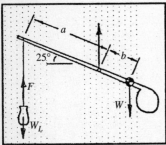

Problem 5.36 This structure, called a *truss*, has a pin support at A and a roller support at B and is loaded by two forces. Determine the reactions at the supports.

Strategy: Draw a free-body diagram, treating the entire truss as a single object.

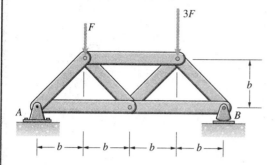

Solution: The truss can be treated as a single member. The pinned joint at A is a two force support; the roller support at B is a single force support. The sum of the forces:

$$\sum F_X = A_X = 0.$$

$$\sum F_Y = A_Y + B_Y - F - 3F = 0.$$

The sum of moments about A is

$$\sum M_A = -bF - 3b(3F) + 4bB_Y = 0,$$

from which $B_Y = 2.5F$.

From the vertical force sum,

$$A_Y = 4F - 2.5F = 1.5F$$

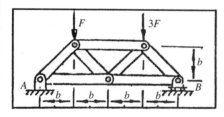

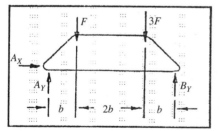

Problem 5.37 An Olympic gymnast is stationary in the "iron cross" position. The weight of his left arm and the weight of his body *not including his arms* are shown. The distances are $a = b = 9$ in. and $c = 13$ in. Treat his shoulder S as a built-in support, and determine the magnitudes of the reactions at his shoulder. That is, determine the force and couple his shoulder must support.

144 lb   8 lb

a   b   c

Solution: The shoulder as a built-in joint has two-force and couple reactions. The left hand must support the weight of the left arm and half the weight of the body:

$$F_H = \frac{144}{2} + 8 = 80 \text{ lb.}$$

The sum of the forces on the left arm is the weight of his left arm and the vertical reaction at the shoulder and hand:

$$\sum F_X = S_X = 0.$$

$$\sum F_Y = F_H - S_Y - 8 = 0,$$

from which $S_Y = F_H - 8 = 72$ lb. The sum of the moments about the shoulder is

$$\sum M_S = M + (b + c)F_H - b8 = 0,$$

where M is the couple reaction at the shoulder. Thus

$$M = b8 - (b + c)F_H = -1688 \text{ in lb} = 1688 \text{ (in lb)} \left(\frac{1 \text{ ft}}{12 \text{ in}}\right)$$

$$= 140.67 \text{ ft lb}$$

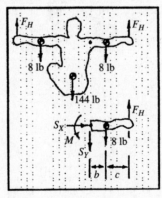

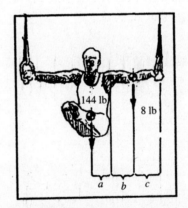

Problem 5.38 Determine the reactions at A.

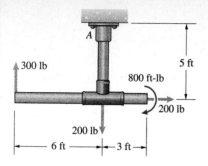

Solution: The built-in support at A is a two-force and couple reaction support. The sum of the forces for the system is

$$\sum F_X = A_X + 200 = 0,$$

from which

$$A_X = -200 \text{ lb}$$

$$\sum F_Y = A_Y + 300 - 200 = 0,$$

from which $A_Y = -100$ lb

The sum of the moments about A:

$$\sum M = -6(300) + 5(200) - 800 + M_A = 0,$$

from which $M_A = 1600$ ft lb which is the couple at A.

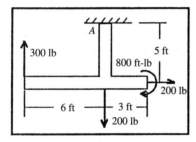

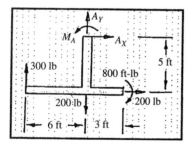

Problem 5.39 The car's brakes keep the rear wheels locked, and the front wheels are free to turn. Determine the forces exerted on the front and rear wheels by the road when the car is parked (a) on an up slope with $\alpha = 15°$; (b) on a down slope with $\alpha = -15°$.

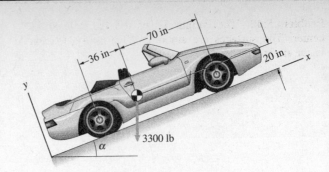

Solution: The rear wheels are two force reaction support, and the front wheels are a one force reaction support. Denote the rear wheels by A and the front wheels by B, and define the reactions as being parallel to and normal to the road. The sum of forces:

$$\sum F_X = A_X - 3300 \sin 15° = 0,$$

from which

$$A_X = 854.1 \text{ lb.}$$

$$\sum F_Y = A_Y - 3300 \cos 15° + B_Y = 0.$$

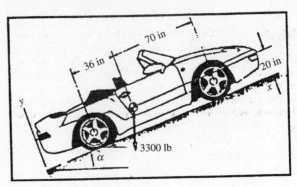

Since the mass center of the vehicle is displaced above the point A, a component of the weight $(20W \sin \alpha)$ produces a positive moment about A, whereas the other component $(36W \cos \alpha)$ produces a negative moment about A. The sum of the moments about A:

$$\sum M_A = -36(3300 \cos 15°) + 20(3300 \sin 15°) + B_Y(106) = 0,$$

from which

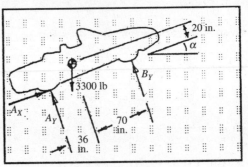

$$B_Y = \frac{+97669}{106} = 921.4 \text{ lb.}$$

Substitute into the sum of forces equation to obtain $A_Y = 2266.1$ lb

(b) For the car parked down-slope the sum of the forces is

$$\sum F_X = A_X + 3300 \sin 15° = 0,$$

from which $A_X = -854$ lb

$$\sum F_Y = A_Y - 3300 \cos 15° + B_Y = 0.$$

The component $(20W \sin \alpha)$ now produces a negative moment about A. The sum of the moments about A is

$$\sum M_A = -3300(36) \cos 15° - 3300(20) \sin 15° + 106 B_Y = 0,$$

from which

$$B_Y = \frac{131834}{106} = 1243.7 \text{ lb.}$$

Substitute into the sum of forces equation to obtain $A_Y = 1943.8$ lb

Problem 5.40 The weight W of the bar acts at its center. The surfaces are smooth. What is the tension in the horizontal string?

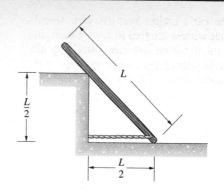

Solution: The surfaces are roller supports, with only one reaction force, which is normal to the contact surface. Denote the reaction at the top of the bar by B, the tension in the string by T, and the reaction at the base of the bar by A. The angle formed by the bar at the base is $\alpha = 45°$, since the altitude and base of the triangle are equal. The reaction at the top of the bar forms the angle $(90 - \alpha)$ with the horizontal, and the reaction at the base is vertical. The sum of the forces is

$$\sum F_X = -T + B\cos(90 - \alpha) = -T + B\sin\alpha = 0.$$

$$\sum F_Y = -W + A_Y + B\cos\alpha = 0.$$

The sum of the moments about the lower end is

$$\sum M_A = \left(\frac{WL}{2}\right)\cos\alpha - B\left(\frac{L}{\sqrt{2}}\right) = 0,$$

from which

$$B = \frac{W\cos\alpha}{\sqrt{2}}.$$

Substitute into the horizontal force equation to obtain the string tension

$$T = \frac{W}{\sqrt{2}}\sin\alpha\cos\alpha$$

$$= \frac{W}{2\sqrt{2}} = 0.3536W$$

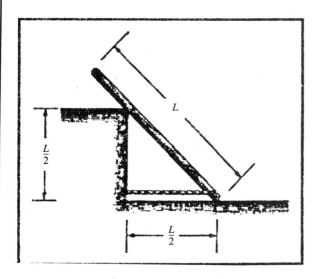

Problem 5.41 The mass of the bar is 36 kg and its weight acts at its midpoint. The spring is unstretched when $\alpha = 0$. The bar is in equilibrium when $\alpha = 30°$. Determine the spring constant k.

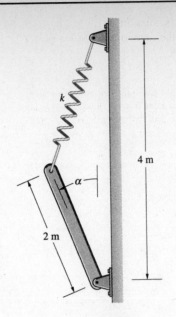

Solution:

$l^2 = 4^2 + 2^2 - 2(4)(2)\cos 30°$

Solving, $l = 2.48$ m

The force acting at the top end of the bar is $F = k(\delta)$ where $\delta = l - l_0$.

We also need ϕ when $\alpha = 30°$

$$\frac{\sin \phi}{z} = \frac{\sin \alpha}{l} = \frac{\sin 30°}{2.48}$$

$\phi = 23,78°$ when $\alpha = 30°$

Equilibrium equations:

$\overset{+}{\rightarrow} \sum F_X = 0: \quad k\delta \sin \phi + A_X = 0$

$+\uparrow \sum F_Y = 0: \quad k\delta \cos \phi + A_Y - mg = 0$

$\curvearrowright + \sum M_B = 0: \quad A_Y(2\sin\alpha) - mg(1\sin\alpha)$

$\qquad\qquad\qquad + A_X(2\cos\alpha) = 0$

Substituting δ, ϕ, and α into the equations and solving, we get

$A_X = -44.1$ N

$A_Y = 253.0$ N

$k = 229$ N/m

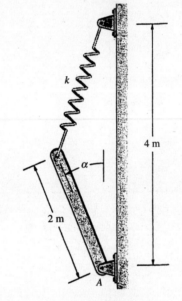

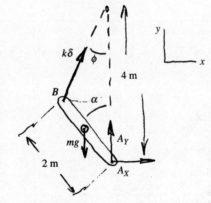

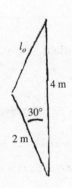

Problem 5.42 The plate is supported by a pin in a smooth slot at B. What are the reactions at the supports?

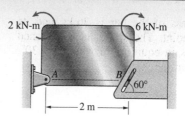

Solution: The pinned support is a two force reaction support. The smooth pin is a roller support, with a one force reaction. The reaction at B forms an angle of $90° + 60° = 150°$ with the positive x-axis. The sum of the forces:

$$\sum F_X = A_X + B \cos 150° = 0$$

$$\sum F_Y = A_Y + B \sin 150° = 0$$

The sum of the moments about B is

$$\sum M_B = -2A_Y + 2 - 6 = 0,$$

from which

$$A_Y = -\frac{4}{2} = -2 \text{ kN}.$$

Substitute into the force equations to obtain

$$B = \frac{A_Y}{\sin 150°} = 4 \text{ kN},$$

and $A_X = -B \cos 150° = 3.464$ kN.

The horizontal and vertical reactions at B are

$$B_X = 4 \cos 150° = -3.464 \text{ kN},$$

and $B_Y = 4 \sin 150° = 2$ kN.

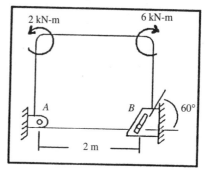

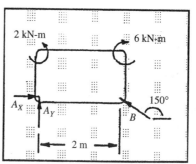

Problem 5.43 The force $F = 800$ N, and the couple $M = 200$ N-m. The distance $L = 2$ m. What are the reactions at A and B?

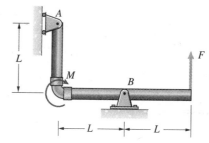

Solution: The sum of the forces:

$$\sum F_X = A_X + B_X = 0$$

$$\sum F_Y = B_Y + F = 0,$$

from which $B_Y = -F = -800$ N.

The sum of the moments about B is

$$\sum M_B = -LA_X + LF - M = 0,$$

from which $A_X = \dfrac{LF - M}{L} = 700$ N.

Substitute into the force equations to obtain $B_X = -700$ N.

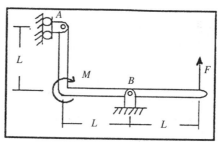

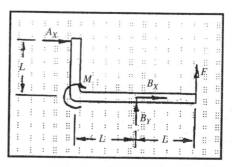

Problem 5.44 The mass of the bar is 40 kg and its weight acts at its midpoint. Determine the tension in the cable and the reactions at A.

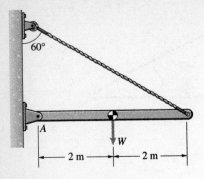

Solution: *Equations of equilibrium*:

$$\sum F_X = 0: \quad A_X - T\cos 30° = 0$$

$$\sum F_Y = 0: \quad A_Y + T\sin 30° - mg = 0$$

$$\sum M_A = 0: \quad -2\,mg + 4(T\sin 30°) = 0$$

Solving, we get

$A_X = 340$ N,

$A_Y = 196$ N,

$T = 392$ N.

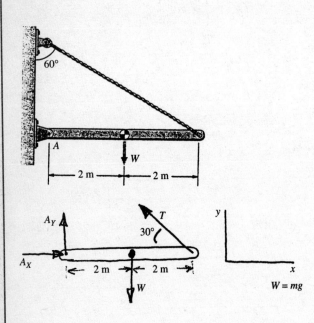

Problem 5.45 If the length of the cable in Problem 5.44 is increased by 1 m, what are the tension in the cable and the reactions at A?

Solution: We first need the cable length in Problem 5.44.

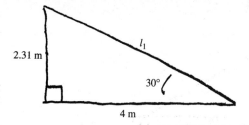

$$\cos 30° = \frac{4}{l_1}$$

$$l_1 = \frac{4}{\cos 30°} = 4.62 \text{ m}$$

In the new problem,

$$l_2 = l_1 + 1 \text{ m}$$

$$l_2 = 5.62$$

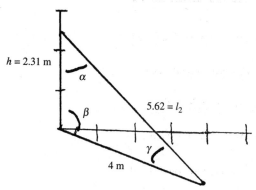

From the law of cosines,

$$4^2 = 5.62^2 + 2.31^2 - 2(5.62)(2.31)\cos\alpha$$

$$\alpha = 36.3°$$

From the law of sines

$$\frac{\sin\alpha}{4} = \frac{\sin\gamma}{h}$$

$$\gamma = 20.0°$$

Now $\alpha + \beta + \gamma = 180°$

$$\beta = 123.7°$$

We now have the geometry defined and can draw a free body diagram and write the equilibrium eqns.

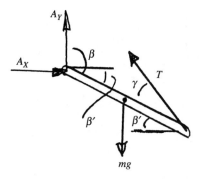

$$\beta' = \beta - 90° = 33.7°$$

$$\sum F_X = A_X - T\cos(\gamma + \beta') = 0$$

$$\sum F_Y = A_Y + T\sin(\gamma + \beta') - mg = 0$$

$$\sum M_A = -mg(2\cos\beta') + T\sin(\gamma + \beta')(4\cos\beta')$$

$$- T\cos(\gamma + \beta')(4\sin\beta') = 0$$

Solving, we get

$$A_X = 282.88 \text{ N}(282.55)$$

$$A_Y = 7.89 \text{ N}(7.76)$$

$$T = 477.36 \text{ N}(477.28)$$

Problem 5.46 The mass of each of the suspended boxes is 80 kg. Determine the reactions at the supports at A and E.

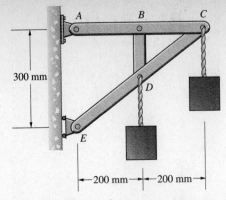

Solution: From the free body diagram, the equations of equilibrium for the rigid body are

$$\sum F_x = A_X + E_X = 0,$$

$$\sum F_y = A_Y - 2(80)(9.81) = 0,$$

and $\sum M_A = 0.3 E_X - 0.2(80)(9.81) - 0.4(80)(9.81) = 0.$

We have three equations in the three components of the support reactions. Solving for the unknowns, we get the values

$$A_X = -1570 \text{ N},$$

$$A_Y = 1570 \text{ N},$$

and $E_X = 1570$ N.

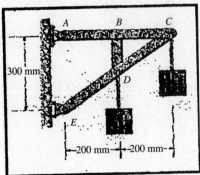

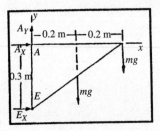

Problem 5.47 The suspended boxes in Problem 5.46 are each of mass m. The supports at A and E will each safely support a force of 6 kN magnitude. Based on this criterion, what is the largest safe value of m?

Solution: Written with the mass value of 80 kg replaced by the symbol m, the equations of equilibrium from Problem 5.46 are

$$\sum F_x = A_X + E_X = 0,$$

$$\sum F_y = A_Y - 2\,m(9.81) = 0,$$

and $\sum M_A = 0.3 E_X - 0.2\,m(9.81) - 0.4\,m(9.81) = 0.$

We also need the relation

$$|A| = \sqrt{A_X^2 + A_Y^2} = 6000 \text{ N}.$$

We have four equations in the three components of the support reactions plus the magnitude of A. This is four equations in four unknowns. Solving for the unknowns, we get the values

$$A_X = -4243 \text{ N},$$

$$A_Y = 4243 \text{ N},$$

$$E_X = 4243 \text{ N},$$

and $m = 216.5$ kg.

Note: We could have gotten this result by a linear scaling of all of the numbers in Problem 5.46.

Problem 5.48 The tension in cable BC is 100 lb. Determine the reactions at the built-in support.

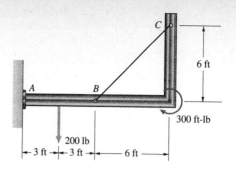

Solution: The cable does not exert an external force on the system, and can be ignored in determining reactions. The built-in support is a two-force and couple reaction support. The sum of forces:

$$\sum F_X = A_X = 0.$$

$$\sum F_Y = A_Y - 200 = 0,$$

from which $A_Y = 200$ lb.

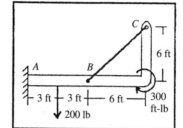

The sum of the moments about A is

$$\sum M = M_A - (3)(200) - 300 = 0,$$

from which $M_A = 900$ ft lb

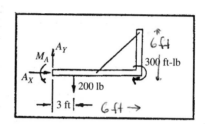

Problem 5.49 The tension in cable AB is 2 kN. What are the reactions at C in the two cases?

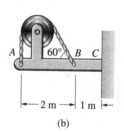

(a)   (b)

Solution: *First Case:* The sum of the forces:

$$\sum F_X = C_X - T \cos 60° = 0,$$

from which $C_X = 2(0.5) = 1$ kN

$$\sum F_Y = C_Y + T \sin 60° + T = 0,$$

from which $C_Y = -1.866(2) = -3.732$ kN.

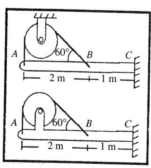

The sum of the moments about C is

$$\sum M = M_C - T \sin 60° - 3T = 0,$$

from which $M_C = 3.866(2) = 7.732$ kN

Second Case: The weight of the beam is ignored, hence there are no external forces on the beam, and the reactions at C are zero.

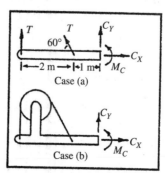

347

Problem 5.50 Determine the reactions at the supports.

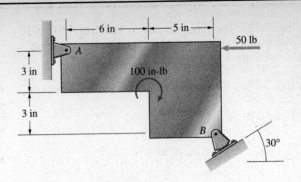

Solution: The reaction at A is a two-force reaction. The reaction at B is one-force, normal to the surface.

The sum of the forces:

$$\sum F_X = A_X - B\cos 60° - 50 = 0.$$

$$\sum F_Y = A_Y + B\sin 60° = 0.$$

The sum of the moments about A is

$$\sum M_A = -100 + 11B\sin 60° - 6B\cos 60° = 0,$$

from which

$$B = \frac{100}{(11\sin 60° - 6\cos 60°)} = 15.3 \text{ lb.}$$

Substitute into the force equations to obtain

$$A_Y = -B\sin 60° = -13.3 \text{ lb}$$

and $A_X = B\cos 60° + 50 = 57.7$ lb

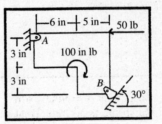

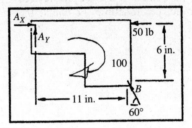

Problem 5.51 The weight $W = 2$ kN. Determine the tension in the cable and the reactions at A.

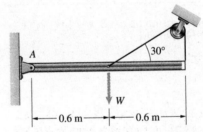

Solution: *Equilibrium Eqns:*

$$\sum F_X = 0: \quad A_X + T\cos 30° = 0$$

$$\sum F_Y = 0: \quad A_Y + T + T\sin 30° - W = 0$$

$$\curvearrowleft + \sum M_A = 0: \quad (-0, 6)(W) + (0.6)(T\sin 30°)$$

$$+ (1, 2)(T) = 0$$

Solving, we get

$A_X = -693$ N,

$A_Y = 800$ N,

$T = 800$ N

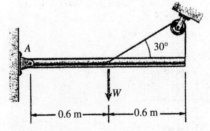

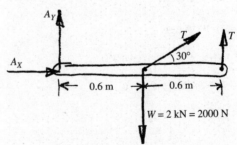

Problem 5.52 The cable shown in Problem 5.51 will safely support a tension of 6 kN. Based on this criterion, what is the largest safe value of the weight W?

Solution: The equilibrium equations in the solution of problem are

$$\sum F_X = 0: \quad A_X + T\cos 30° = 0$$

$$\sum F_Y = 0: \quad A_Y + T + T\sin 30° - W = 0$$

$$\curvearrowleft + \sum M_A = 0: \quad (-0,6)(W) + (0,6)(T\sin 30°)$$

$$+ (1,2)(T) = 0$$

We previously had 3 equations in the 3 unknowns A_X, A_Y and T (we knew W). In the current problem, we know T but don't know W. We again have three equations in three unknowns (A_X, A_Y, and W). Setting $T = 6$ kN, we solve to get

$A_X = -5.2$ kN

$A_Y = 6.0$ kN

$W = 15.0$ kN

Problem 5.53 The spring constant is $k = 9600$ N/m and the unstretched length of the spring is 30 mm. Treat the bolt at A as a pin support and assume that the surface at C is smooth. Determine the reactions at A and the normal force at C.

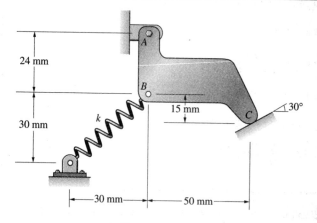

Solution: The length of the spring is

$$l = \sqrt{30^2 + 30^2} \text{ mm} = \sqrt{1800} \text{ mm}$$

$$l = 42.4 \text{ mm} = 0.0424 \text{ m}$$

The spring force is $k\delta$ where $\delta = l - l_0$. l_0 is give as 30 mm. (We must be careful because the units for k are given as N/m) We need to use length units as all mm or all meters). k is given as 9600 N/m. Let us use $l_0 = 0.0300$ m and $l = 0.0424$ m

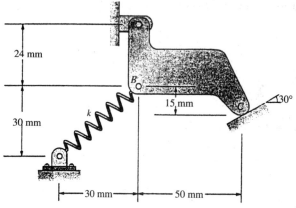

Equilibrium equations:

$$\sum F_X = 0: \quad A_X - k(l - l_0)\sin 45°$$

$$- N_C \cos 60° = 0$$

$$\sum F_Y = 0: \quad A_Y - k(l - l_0)\cos 45°$$

$$+ N_C \sin 60° = 0$$

$$\sum M_B = 0: \quad (-0.024)A_X + (0.050)(N_C \sin 60°)$$

$$- (0.015)(N_C \cos 60°) = 0$$

Solving, we get

$A_X = 126.7$ N

$A_Y = 10.5$ N

$N_C = 85.1$ N

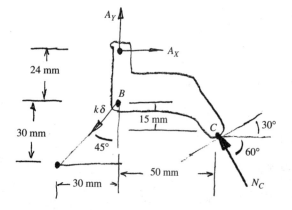

Problem 5.54 The engineer designing the release mechanism shown in Problem 5.53 wants the normal force exerted at C to be 120 N. If the unstretched length of the spring is 30 mm, what is the necessary value of the spring constant k?

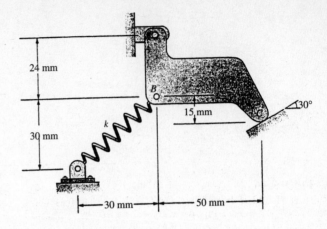

Solution: Refer to the solution of Problem 5.53. The equilibrium equations derived were

$$\sum F_X = 0: \quad A_X - k(l - l_0)\sin 45 - N_C \cos 60° = 0$$

$$\sum F_Y = 0: \quad A_Y - k(l - l_0)\cos 45 + N_C \sin 60° = 0$$

$$\sum M_B = 0: \quad -0.024 A_X + 0.050 N_C \sin 60°$$

$$-0.015 N_C \cos 60° = 0$$

where $l = 0.0424$ m, $l_0 = 0.030$ m, $N_C = 120$ N, and A_X, A_Y, and k are unknowns.

Solving, we get

$A_X = 179.0$ N,

$A_Y = 15.1$ N,

$k = 13500$ N/m

Problem 5.55 Suppose that you want to design the safety valve to open when the difference between the pressure p in the circular pipe (diameter = 150 mm) and the atmospheric pressure is 10 MPa (megapascals; a pascal is 1 N/m²). The spring is compressed 20 mm when the valve is closed. What should the value of the spring constant be?

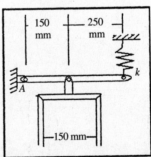

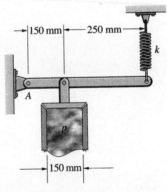

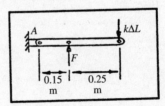

Solution: The area of the valve is

$$a = \pi \left(\frac{0.15}{2}\right)^2 = 17.671 \times 10^{-3} \text{ m}^2.$$

The force at opening is

$$F = 10a \times 10^6 = 1.7671 \times 10^5 \text{ N}.$$

The force on the spring is found from the sum of the moments about A,

$$\sum M_A = 0.15 F - (0.4)k\Delta L = 0.$$

Solving,

$$k = \frac{0.15 F}{(0.4)\Delta L} = \frac{0.15(1.7671 \times 10^5)}{(0.4)(0.02)}$$

$$= 3.313 \times 10^6 \; \frac{\text{N}}{\text{m}}$$

Problem 5.56 The bar AB is of length L and weight W, and the weight acts at its midpoint. The angle $\alpha = 30°$. What is the tension in the string?

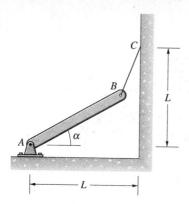

Solution: The strategy is to determine the angle formed by the string on the end of the rod (see sketch). The vertical distance from the pinned joint to the end of the rod is $D = L\sin\alpha$. The horizontal distance is $H = L\cos\alpha$. The sides of the small triangle formed by the string is $X = L - L\cos\alpha$ and $Y = L - L\sin\alpha$. The angle formed by the string with the horizontal is

$$\beta = \tan^{-1}\left(\frac{1 - \sin\alpha}{1 - \cos\alpha}\right) = 75°.$$

The angle relative to the rod is $\theta = \beta - \alpha = 45°$. The moment about the pinned joint is

$$\sum M = -\left(\frac{L}{2}\right)W\cos\alpha + TL\sin\theta = 0,$$

from which

$$T = \frac{W\cos\alpha}{2\sin\theta} = \frac{W(0.866)}{2(0.707)} = \frac{\sqrt{3}W}{2\sqrt{2}} = 0.61237W$$

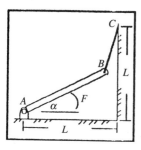

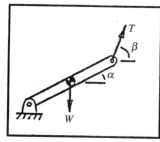

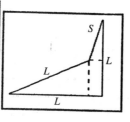

351

Problem 5.57 The crane's arm has a pin support at A. The hydraulic cylinder BC exerts a force on the arm at C in the direction parallel to BC. The crane's arm has a mass of 200 kg, and its weight can be assumed to act at a point 2 m to the right of A. If the mass of the suspended box is 800 kg and the system is in equilibrium, what is the magnitude of the force exerted by the hydraulic cylinder?

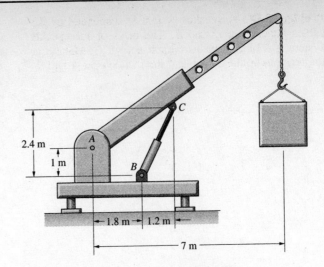

Solution: The geometry gives

$$\tan \theta = 2.4/1.2,$$

or $\theta = 63.4°$.

From the diagram,

$$F_{HX} = |\mathbf{F}_H| \cos \theta,$$

and $F_{HY} = |\mathbf{F}_H| \sin \theta$.

The force equilibrium equations are

$$\sum F_x = A_X + F_{HX} = 0,$$

$$\sum F_y = A_Y + F_{HY} - (200)g - (800)g = 0,$$

and the moment equation is

$$\sum M_A = -(2)(200)g - (7)(800)g + (3)F_{HY} - (2.4)F_{HX} = 0.$$

Solving the five equations simultaneously, we get $|\mathbf{F}_H| = 36.56$ kN, which is the result called for in this problem. Other values obtained in the solution are

$$A_X = -16.35 \text{ kN},$$

and $A_Y = -22.89$ kN.

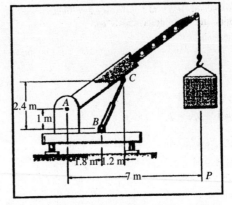

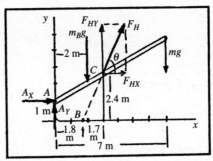

Problem 5.58 In Problem 5.57, what is the magnitude of the force exerted on the crane's arm by the pin support at A?

Solution: The values for the components of A were determined in the solution to Problem 5.57. The magnitude of the force is

$$|\mathbf{A}| = \sqrt{A_X^2 + A_Y^2} = 28.13 \text{ kN}.$$

Problem 5.59 A speaker system is suspended by the cables attached at D and E. The mass of the speaker system is 130 kg, and its weight acts at G. Determine the tensions in the cables and the reactions at A and C.

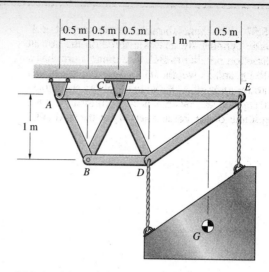

Solution: The weight of the speaker is $W = mg = 1275$ N. The equations of equilibrium for the entire assembly are

$$\sum F_x = C_X = 0,$$

$$\sum F_y = A_Y + C_Y - mg = 0$$

(where the mass $m = 130$ kg), and

$$\sum M_C = -(1)A_Y - (1.5)mg = 0.$$

Solving these equations, we get

$$C_X = 0,$$

$$C_Y = 3188 \text{ N},$$

and $A_Y = -1913$ N.

From the free body diagram of the speaker alone, we get

$$\sum F_y = T_1 + T_2 - mg = 0,$$

and $\sum M_{\text{left support}} = -(1)mg + (1.5)T_2 = 0.$

Solving these equations, we get

$$T_1 = 425. \text{ N}$$

and $T_2 = 850$ N

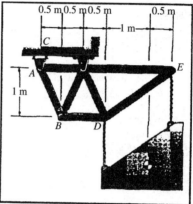

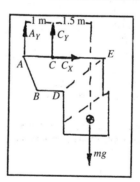

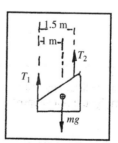

353

Problem 5.60 The weight $W_1 = 1000$ lb. Neglect the weight of the bar AB. The cable goes over a pulley at C. Determine the weight W_2 and the reactions at the pin support A.

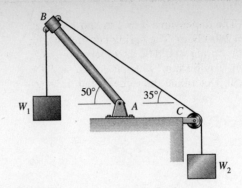

Solution: The strategy is to resolve the tensions at the end of bar AB into x- and y-components, and then set the moment about A to zero. The angle between the cable and the positive x axis is $-35°$. The tension vector in the cable is

$$\mathbf{T}_2 = W_2(\mathbf{i}\cos(-35°) + \mathbf{j}\sin(-35°)).$$

$$= W_2(0.8192\mathbf{i} - 0.5736\mathbf{j})(\text{lb}).$$

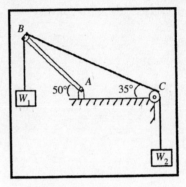

Assume a unit length for the bar. The angle between the bar and the positive x-axis is $180° - 50° = 130°$. The position vector of the tip of the bar relative to A is

$$\mathbf{r}_B = \mathbf{i}\cos(130°) + \mathbf{j}\sin(130°), = -0.6428\mathbf{i} + 0.7660\mathbf{j}.$$

The tension exerted by W_1 is $\mathbf{T}_1 = -1000\mathbf{j}$. The sum of the moments about A is:

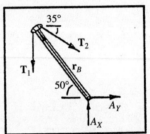

$$\sum \mathbf{M}_A = (\mathbf{r}_B \times \mathbf{T}_1) + (\mathbf{r}_B \times \mathbf{T}_2) = \mathbf{r}_B \times (\mathbf{T}_1 + \mathbf{T}_2)$$

$$= L\begin{vmatrix} \mathbf{i} & \mathbf{j} \\ -0.6428 & 0.7660 \\ 0.8191W_2 & -0.5736W_2 - 1000 \end{vmatrix}$$

$$\sum \mathbf{M}_A = (-0.2587W_2 + 642.8)\mathbf{k} = 0,$$

from which $W_2 = 2483.5$ lb

The sum of the forces:

$$\sum \mathbf{F}_X = (A_X + W_2(0.8192))\mathbf{i} = 0,$$

from which $A_X = -2034.4$ lb

$$\sum \mathbf{F}_Y = (A_Y - W_2(0.5736) - 1000)\mathbf{j} = 0,$$

from which $A_Y = 2424.5$ lb

Problem 5.61   The dimensions $a = 2$ m and $b = 1$ m. The couple $M = 2400$ N-m. The spring constant is $k = 6000$ N/m, and the spring would be unstretched if $h = 0$. The system is in equilibrium when $h = 2$ m and the beam is horizontal. Determine the force F and the reactions at A.

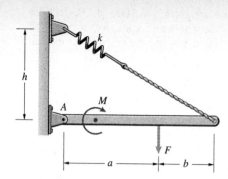

Solution: We need to know the unstretched length of the spring, l_0

$$l_0 = a + b = 3 \text{ m}$$

We also need the stretched length

$$l^2 = h^2 + (a + b)^2$$

$$l = 3.61 \text{ m}$$

$$F_S = k(l - l_0)$$

$$\tan\theta = \frac{h}{(a + b)}$$

$$\theta = 33.69°$$

Equilibrium eqns:

$$\sum F_X : \quad A_X - F_S \cos\theta = 0$$

$$\sum F_Y : \quad A_Y + F_S \sin\theta - F = 0$$

$$\curvearrowleft + \sum M_A : \quad -M - aF + (a + b)F_S \sin\theta = 0$$

$$a = 2 \text{ m}, \quad b = 1 \text{ m}, \quad M = 2400 \text{ N-m},$$

$$h = 2 \text{ m}, \quad k = 6000 \text{ N/m}.$$

Substituting in and solving, we get

$$F_S = 6000(l - l_0) = 3633 \text{ N}$$

and the equilibrium equations yield

$$A_X = 3023 \text{ N}$$

$$A_Y = -192 \text{ N}$$

$$F = 1823 \text{ N}$$

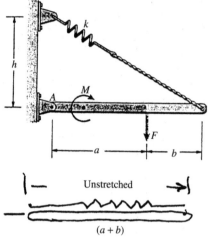

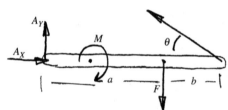

Problem 5.62 The bar is 1 m long, and its weight W acts at its midpoint. The distance $b = 0.75$ m, and the angle $\alpha = 30°$. The spring constant is $k = 100$ N/m, and the spring is unstretched when the bar is vertical. Determine W and the reactions at A.

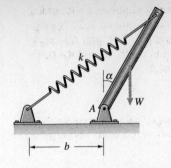

Solution: The unstretched length of the spring is $L = \sqrt{b^2 + 1^2} = 1.25$ m. The obtuse angle is $90 + \alpha$, so the stretched length can be determined from the cosine law:

$$L_2^2 = 1^2 + 0.75^2 - 2(0.75)\cos(90 + \alpha) = 2.3125 \text{ m}^2$$

from which $L_2 = 1.5207$ m. The force exerted by the spring is

$$T = k\Delta L = 100(1.5207 - 1.25) = 27.1 \text{ N}.$$

The angle between the spring and the bar can be determined from the sine law:

$$\frac{b}{\sin\beta} = \frac{1.5207}{\sin(90 + \alpha)},$$

from which $\sin\beta = 0.4271$,

$$\beta = 25.28°.$$

The angle the spring makes with the horizontal is $180 - 25.28 - 90 - \alpha = 34.72°$. The sum of the forces:

$$\sum F_X = A_X - T\cos 34.72° = 0,$$

from which $A_X = 22.25$ N.

$$\sum F_Y = A_Y - W - T\sin 34.72° = 0.$$

The sum of the moments about A is

$$\sum M_A = T\sin 25.28° - \left(\frac{W}{2}\right)\sin\alpha = 0,$$

from which

$$W = \frac{2T\sin 25.28°}{\sin\alpha} = 46.25 \text{ N}.$$

Substitute into the force equation to obtain: $A_Y = W + T\sin 34.72° = 61.66$ N

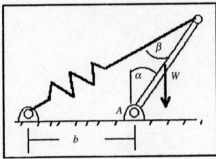

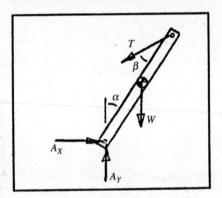

Problem 5.63 The boom derrick supports a suspended 15-kip load. The booms *BC* and *DE* are each 20 ft long. The distances are $a = 15$ ft and $b = 2$ ft, and the angle $\theta = 30°$. Determine the tension in cable *AB* and the reactions at the pin supports *C* and *D*.

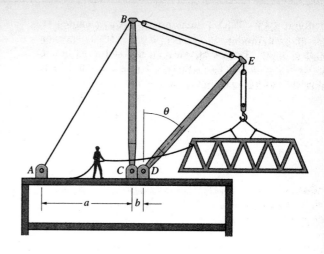

Solution: Choose a coordinate system with origin at point *C*, with the *y* axis parallel to *CB*. The position vectors of the labeled points are:

$$\mathbf{r}_D = 2\mathbf{i}$$

$$\mathbf{r}_E = \mathbf{r}_D + 20(\mathbf{i}\sin 30° + \mathbf{j}\cos 30°)$$

$$= 12\mathbf{i} + 17.3\mathbf{j},$$

$$\mathbf{r}_B = 20\mathbf{j},$$

$$\mathbf{r}_A = -15\mathbf{i}.$$

The unit vectors are:

$$\mathbf{e}_{DE} = \frac{\mathbf{r}_E - \mathbf{r}_D}{|\mathbf{r}_E - \mathbf{r}_D|} = 0.5\mathbf{i} + 0.866\mathbf{j},$$

$$\mathbf{e}_{EB} = \frac{\mathbf{r}_B - \mathbf{r}_E}{|\mathbf{r}_B - \mathbf{r}_E|} = -0.976\mathbf{i} + 0.2179\mathbf{j}.$$

$$\mathbf{e}_{CB} = \frac{\mathbf{r}_B - \mathbf{r}_C}{|\mathbf{r}_B - \mathbf{r}_C|} = 1\mathbf{j},$$

$$\mathbf{e}_{AB} = \frac{\mathbf{r}_A - \mathbf{r}_B}{|\mathbf{r}_A - \mathbf{r}_B|} = -0.6\mathbf{i} - 0.8\mathbf{j}.$$

Isolate the juncture at E: The equilibrium conditions are

$$\sum F_x = 0.5|\mathbf{D}| - 0.976|\mathbf{T}_{EB}| = 0,$$

$$\sum F_y = 0.866|\mathbf{D}| + 0.2179|\mathbf{T}_{EB}| - 15 = 0,$$

from which

$$|\mathbf{D}| = 15.34 \text{ kip}$$

and $|\mathbf{T}_{EB}| = 7.86$ kip.

Isolate the juncture at B: The equilibrium conditions are:

$$\sum F_x = 0|\mathbf{C}| - 0.6|\mathbf{T}_{AB}| + 0.976|\mathbf{T}_{EB}|,$$

and $\sum F_y = 1|\mathbf{C}| - 0.6|\mathbf{T}_{AB}| - 0.2179|\mathbf{T}_{EB}| = 0,$

from which

$$|\mathbf{T}_{AB}| = 12.79 \text{ kip},$$

and $|\mathbf{C}| = 11.94$ kip.

The components:

$$D_x = 0.6|\mathbf{D}| = 7.67 \text{ kip},$$

$$D_y = 0.866|\mathbf{D}| = 13.287 \text{ kip},$$

and $C_y = 1|\mathbf{C}| = 11.94$ kip

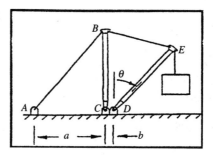

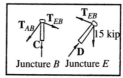

Juncture *B*   Juncture *E*

Problem 5.64 The arrangement shown controls the elevators of an airplane. (The elevators are the horizontal control surfaces in the airplane's tail.) The elevators are attached to member *EDG*. Aerodynamic pressures on the elevators exert a clockwise couple of 120 in.-lb. Cable *BG* is slack, and its tension can be neglected. Determine the force *F* and the reactions at pin support *A*.

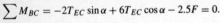

Solution: Begin at the elevator. The moment arms at *E* and *G* are 6 in. The angle of the cable *EC* with the horizontal is

$$\alpha = \tan^{-1}\frac{12}{119.5} = 5.734°.$$

Denote the horizontal and vertical components of the force on point *E* by F_X and F_Y. The sum of the moments about the pinned support on the member *EG* is

$$\sum M_{EG} = 2.5F_Y + 6F_X - 120 = 0.$$

This is the tension in the cable *EC*. Noting that

$$F_X = T_{EC}\cos\alpha,$$

and $F_Y = T_{EC}\sin\alpha$,

then $T_{EC} = \dfrac{120}{2.5\sin\alpha + 6\cos\alpha}.$

The sum of the moments about the pinned support *BC* is

$$\sum M_{BC} = -2T_{EC}\sin\alpha + 6T_{EC}\cos\alpha - 2.5F = 0.$$

Substituting:

$$F = \left(\frac{120}{2.5}\right)\left(\frac{6\cos\alpha - 2\sin\alpha}{6\cos\alpha + 2.5\sin\alpha}\right)$$

$$= (48)(0.9277) = 44.53 \text{ lb}.$$

The sum of the forces about the pinned joint *A*:

$$\sum F_x = A_x - F + T_{EC}\cos\alpha = 0$$

from which $A_x = 25.33$ lb,

$$\sum F_y = A_y + T_{EC}\sin\alpha = 0$$

from which $A_y = -1.93$ lb

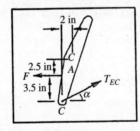
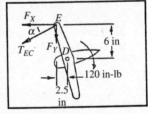

Problem 5.65 In Fig. 5.17, suppose that $\alpha = 40°$, $d = 1$ m, $a = 200$ mm, $b = 500$ mm, $R = 75$ mm, and the mass of the luggage is 40 kg. Determine F and N.

Solution: (See Example 5.5.)

The sum of the moments about the center of the wheel:

$$\sum M_C = dF\cos\alpha + aW\sin\alpha - bW\cos\alpha = 0,$$

from which $F = \dfrac{(b - a\tan\alpha)W}{d} = 130.35$ N.

The sum of the forces:

$$\sum F_Y = N - W + F = 0,$$

from which $N = 262.1$ N

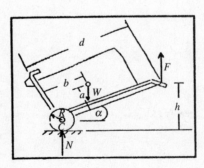

Problem 5.66 In Fig. 5.17, suppose that $\alpha = 35°$, $d = 46$ in., $a = 10$ in., $b = 14$ in., $R = 3$ in., and you don't want the user to have to exert a force F larger than 20 lb. What is the largest luggage weight that can be placed on the carrier?

Solution: (See Example 5.5.) From the solution to Problem 5.65, the force is

$$F = \frac{(b - a\tan\alpha)W}{d}.$$

Solve for W:

$$W = \frac{Fd}{(b - a\tan\alpha)}.$$

For $F = 20$ lb,

$$W = 131.47 = 131.5 \text{ lb}$$

Problem 5.67 One of the difficulties in making design decisions is that you don't know how the user will place the luggage on the carrier in Example 5.5. Suppose you assume that the point where the weight acts may be anywhere within the "envelope" $R \le a \le 0.75c$ and $0 \le b \le 0.75d$. If $\alpha = 30°$, $c = 14$ in., $d = 48$ in., $R = 3$ in., and $W = 80$ lb, what is the largest force F the user will have to exert for any luggage placement?

Solution: (See Example 5.5.) From the solution to Problem 5.65, the force is

$$F = \frac{(b - a\tan\alpha)W}{d}.$$

The force is maximized as

$$b \to 0.75d,$$

and $a \to R$.

Thus

$$F_{MAX} = \frac{(0.75d - R\tan\alpha)W}{d} = 57.11 \text{ lb}$$

Problem 5.68 In our design of the luggage carrier in Example 5.5, we assumed a user that would hold the carrier's handle at $h = 36$ in. above the floor. We assumed that $R = 3$ in., $a = 6$ in., and $b = 12$ in., and we chose the dimension $d = 4$ ft. The resulting ratio of the force the user must exert to the weight of the luggage is $F/W = 0.132$. Suppose that people with a range of heights use this carrier. Obtain a graph of F/W as a function of h for $24 \le h \le 36$ in.

Solution: (See Example 5.5.) From the solution to Problem 5.67, the force that must be exerted is

$$F = \frac{(b - a\tan\alpha)W}{d},$$

from which $\dfrac{F}{W} = \dfrac{(b - a\tan\alpha)}{d}.$

The angle a is given by

$$\alpha = \sin^{-1}\left(\frac{h - R}{d}\right).$$

The commercial package **TK Solver Plus** was used to plot a graph of $\dfrac{F}{W}$ as a function of h.

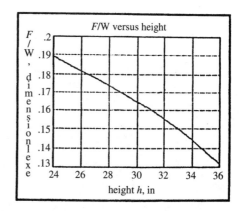

F/W versus height

Problem 5.69 (a) Draw the free-body diagram of the beam and show that it is statically indeterminate.
(b) Determine as many of the reactions as possible.

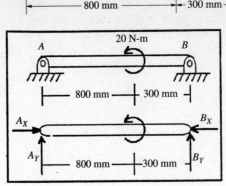

Solution: (a) The free body diagram shows that there are four unknowns, whereas only three equilibrium equations can be written.
(b) The sum of moments about A is

$$\sum M_A = M + 1.1 B_Y = 0,$$

from which $B_Y = -\dfrac{20}{1.1} = -18.18$ N.

The sum of forces in the vertical direction is

$$\sum F_Y = A_Y + B_Y = 0,$$

from which $A_Y = -B_Y = 18.18$ N.

The sum of forces in the horizontal direction is

$$\sum F_X = A_X + B_X = 0,$$

from which the values of A_X and B_X are indeterminate.

Problem 5.70 Consider the beam in Problem 5.69. Choose supports at A and B so that it is not statically indeterminate. Determine the reactions at the supports.

Solution: One possibility is shown: the pinned support at B is replaced by a roller support. The equilibrium conditions are:

$$\sum F_X = A_X = 0.$$

The sum of moments about A is

$$\sum M_A = M + 1.1 B_Y = 0,$$

from which $B_Y = -\dfrac{20}{1.1} = -18.18$ N.

The sum of forces in the vertical direction is

$$\sum F_Y = A_Y + B_Y = 0,$$

from which $A_Y = -B_Y = 18.18$ N.

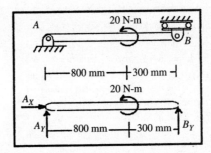

Problem 5.71 (a) Draw the free-body diagram of the beam and show that it is statically indeterminate. (The external couple M_0 is known.)

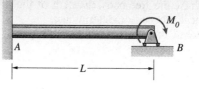

(b) By an analysis of the beam's deflection, it is determined that the vertical reaction B exerted by the roller support is related to the couple M_0 by $B = 2M_0/L$. What are the reactions at A?

Solution:

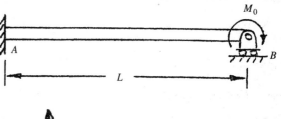

(a) $\sum F_X$: $A_X = 0$ **(1)**

    $\sum F_Y$: $A_Y + B = 0$ **(2)**

$\curvearrowleft + \sum M_A$: $M_A - M_O + BL = 0$ **(3)**

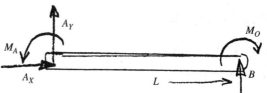

Unknowns: M_A, A_X, A_Y, B.

3 Eqns in 4 unknowns

$\therefore$ *Statistically indeterminate*

(b) Given $B = 2M_O/L$ **(4)**

We now have 4 eqns in 4 unknowns and can solve.

Eqn (1) yields $A_X = 0$

Eqn (2) and Eqn (4) yield

$A_Y = -2M_O/L$

Eqn (3) and Eqn (4) yield

$M_A = M_O - 2M_O$

$M_A = -M_O$

M_A was assumed counterclockwise

$\boxed{\begin{array}{l} M_A = |M_O| \text{ clockwise} \\ A_X = 0 \\ A_Y = -2M_O/L \end{array}}$

Problem 5.72 Consider the beam in Problem 5.71. Choose supports at A and B so that it is not statically indeterminate. Determine the reactions at the supports.

Solution: This result is not unique. There are several possible answers

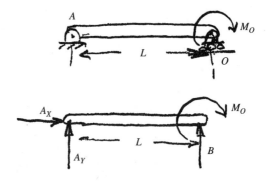

$\sum F_X$: $A_X = 0$

$\sum F_Y$: $A_Y + B_Y = 0$

$\sum M_A$: $-M_o + BL = 0$

     $A_X = 0$

     $B = M_O/L$

     $A_Y = -M_O/L$

Problem 5.73 Draw the free-body diagram of the L-shaped pipe assembly and show that it is statically indeterminate. Determine as many of the reactions as possible.

Strategy: Place the coordinate system so that the x axis passes through points A and B.

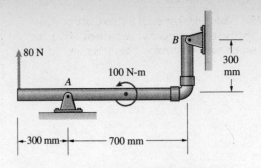

Solution: The free body diagram shows that there are four reactions, hence the system is statically indeterminate. The sum of the forces:

$$\sum F_X = (A_X + B_X) = 0,$$

and $\sum F_Y = A_Y + B_Y + F = 0.$

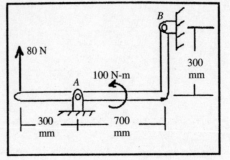

A strategy for solving some statically indeterminate problems is to select a coordinate system such that the indeterminate reactions vanish from the sum of the moment equations. The choice here is to locate the x-axis on a line passing through both A and B, with the origin at A. Denote the reactions at A and B by A_N, A_P, B_N, and B_P, where the subscripts indicate the reactions are normal to and parallel to the new x-axis. Denote

$F = 80$ N,

$M = 100$ N-m.

The length from A to B is

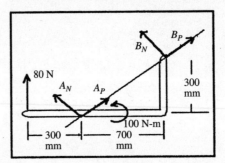

$L = \sqrt{0.3^2 + 0.7^2} = 0.76157$ m.

The angle between the new axis and the horizontal is

$$\theta = \tan^{-1}\left(\frac{0.3}{0.7}\right) = 23.2°.$$

The moment about the point A is

$$M_A = LB_N - 0.3F + M = 0,$$

from which $B_N = \dfrac{-M + 0.3F}{L} = \dfrac{-76}{0.76157} = -99.79$ N,

from which

The sum of the forces normal to the new axis is

$$\sum F_N = A_N + B_N + F\cos\theta = 0,$$

from which

$A_N = -B_N - F\cos\theta = 26.26$ lb

The reactions parallel to the new axis are indeterminate.

Problem 5.74 Consider the pipe assembly in Problem 5.73. Choose supports at A and B so that it is not statically indeterminate. Determine the reactions at the supports.

Solution: This problem has no unique solution. Please just leave it out.

Problem 5.75 State whether each of the L-shaped bars shown is properly or improperly supported. If a bar is properly supported, determine the reactions at its supports.

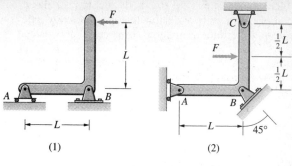

(1)

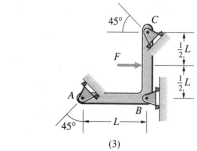

(2)

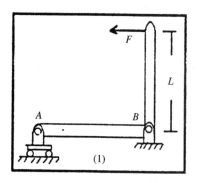

(3)

Solution:

(1) *is properly constrained.* The sum of the forces

$$\sum F_X = -F + B_X = 0,$$

from which $B_X = F$.

$$\sum F_Y = B_Y + A_y = 0,$$

from which $B_y = -A_y$. The sum of the moments about B:

$$\sum M_B = -LA_Y + LF = 0,$$

from which $A_Y = F$, and $B_y = -F$

(2) *is improperly constrained.* The reactions intersect at B, while the force produces a moment about B.

(3) *is properly constrained.* The forces are neither concurrent nor parallel. The sum of the forces:

$$\sum F_X = -C\cos 45° - B - A\cos 45° + F = 0.$$

$$\sum F_Y = C\sin 45° - A\sin 45° = 0$$

from which $A = C$. The sum of the moments about A:

$$\sum M_A = -\tfrac{1}{2}LF + LC\cos 45° + LC\sin 45° = 0,$$

from which $C = \dfrac{F}{2\sqrt{2}}$. Substituting and combining: $A = \dfrac{F}{2\sqrt{2}}$, $B = \dfrac{F}{2}$

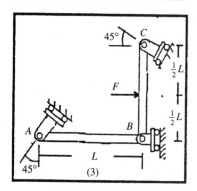

(1)

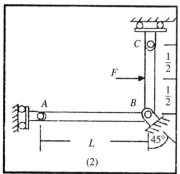

(2)

(3)

363

Problem 5.76 State whether each of the L-shaped bars shown is properly or improperly supported. If a bar is properly supported, determine the reactions at its supports.

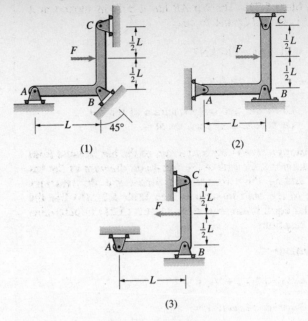

(1)

(2)

(3)

Solution:

(1) *is improperly constrained.* The reactions intersect at a point P, and the force exerts a moment about that point.

(2) *is improperly constrained.* The reactions intersect at a point P and the force exerts a moment about that point.

(3) *is properly constrained.* The sum of the forces:

$$\sum F_X = C - F = 0,$$

from which $C = F$.

$$\sum F_Y = -A + B = 0,$$

from which $A = B$. The sum of the moments about B: $LA + \frac{L}{2}F - LC = 0$, from which $A = \frac{1}{2}F$, and $B = \frac{1}{2}F$

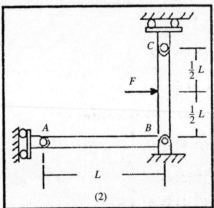

(2)

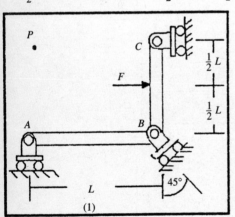

(1)

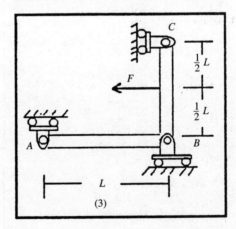

(3)

364

Problem 5.77 The bar AB has a built-in support at A and is loaded by the forces

$$\mathbf{F}_B = 2\mathbf{i} + 6\mathbf{j} + 3\mathbf{k} \text{ (kN)},$$

$$\mathbf{F}_C = \mathbf{i} - 2\mathbf{j} + 2\mathbf{k} \text{ (kN)}.$$

(a) Draw the free-body diagram of the bar.
(b) Determine the reactions at A.

Strategy: (a) Draw a diagram of the bar isolated from its supports. Complete the free-body diagram of the bar by adding the two external forces and the reactions due to the built-in support (see Table 5.2). (b) Use the scalar equilibrium equations (5.16)–(5.21) to determine the reactions.

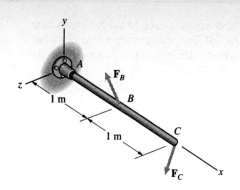

Solution:

$$\mathbf{M}_A = M_{Ax}\mathbf{i} + M_{Ay}\mathbf{j} + M_{Az}\mathbf{k}$$

(b) Equilibrium Eqns (Forces)

$$\sum F_X: \quad A_X + F_{B_X} + F_{C_X} = 0$$

$$\sum F_Y: \quad A_Y + F_{B_Y} + F_{C_Y} = 0$$

$$\sum F_Z: \quad A_Z + F_{B_Z} + F_{C_Z} = 0$$

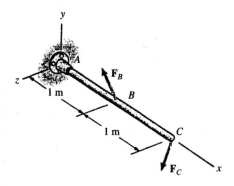

Equilibrium Equations (Moments) Sum moments about A

$$\mathbf{r}_{AB} \times \mathbf{F}_B = 1\mathbf{i} \times (2\mathbf{i} + 6\mathbf{j} + 3\mathbf{k}) \text{ kN-m}$$

$$\mathbf{r}_{AB} \times \mathbf{F}_B = -3\mathbf{j} + 6\mathbf{k} \text{ (kN-m)}$$

$$\mathbf{r}_{AC} \times \mathbf{F}_C = 2\mathbf{i} \times (1\mathbf{i} - 2\mathbf{j} + 2\mathbf{k}) \text{ kN-m}$$

$$\mathbf{r}_{AC} \times \mathbf{F}_C = -4\mathbf{j} - 4\mathbf{k} \text{ (kN-m)}$$

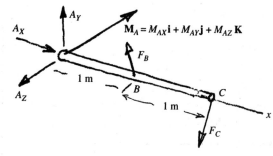

$$x: \sum M_A: \quad M_{Ax} = 0$$

$$y: \sum M_A: \quad M_{Ay} - 3 - 4 = 0$$

$$z: \sum M_A: \quad M_{Az} + 6 - 4 = 0$$

Solving, we get

$$A_X = -3 \text{ kN},$$

$$A_Y = -4 \text{ kN},$$

$$A_Z = -5 \text{ kN}$$

$$M_{Ax} = 0,$$

$$M_{Ay} = 7 \text{ kN-m},$$

$$M_{Az} = -2 \text{ kN-m}$$

Problem 5.78 The bar AB has a built-in support at A. The tension in cable BC is 8 kN. Determine the reactions at A.

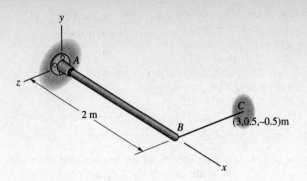

Solution:

$$\mathbf{M}_A = M_{Ax}\mathbf{i} + M_{Ay}\mathbf{j} + M_{Az}\mathbf{k}$$

We need the unit vector $\mathbf{e}_{BC}$

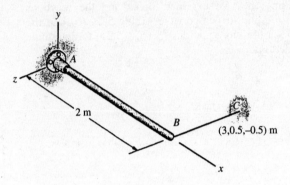

$$\mathbf{e}_{BC} = \frac{(x_C - x_B)\mathbf{i} + (y_C - y_B)\mathbf{j} + (z_C - z_B)\mathbf{k}}{\sqrt{(x_C - x_B)^2 + (y_C - y_B)^2 + (z_C - z_B)^2}}$$

$$\mathbf{e}_{BC} = 0.816\mathbf{i} + 0.408\mathbf{j} - 0.408\mathbf{k}$$

$$\mathbf{T}_{BC} = (8 \text{ kN})\mathbf{e}_{BC}$$

$$\mathbf{T}_{BC} = 6.53\mathbf{i} + 3.27\mathbf{j} - 3.27\mathbf{k} \text{ (kN)}$$

The moment of $\mathbf{T}_{BC}$ about A is

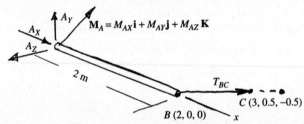

$$\mathbf{M}_{BC} = \mathbf{r}_{AB} \times \mathbf{T}_{BC} = \begin{vmatrix} \mathbf{i} & \mathbf{j} & \mathbf{k} \\ 2 & 0 & 0 \\ 6.53 & 3.27 & -3.27 \end{vmatrix}$$

$$\mathbf{M}_{BC} = \mathbf{r}_{AB} \times \mathbf{T}_{BC} = 0\mathbf{i} + 6.53\mathbf{j} + 6.53\mathbf{k} \text{ (kN-m)}$$

Equilibrium Eqns.

$$\sum F_X: \quad A_X + T_{BC_X} = 0$$

$$\sum F_Y: \quad A_Y + T_{BC_Y} = 0$$

$$\sum F_Z: \quad A_Z + T_{BC_Z} = 0$$

$$\sum M_X: \quad M_{AX} + M_{BC_X} = 0$$

$$\sum M_Y: \quad M_{AY} + M_{BC_Y} = 0$$

$$\sum M_Z: \quad M_{AZ} + M_{BC_Z} = 0$$

Solving, we get

$$A_X = -6.53 \text{ (kN)},$$

$$A_Y = -3.27 \text{ (kN)},$$

$$A_Z = 3.27 \text{ (kN)}$$

$$M_{Ax} = 0,$$

$$M_{Ay} = -6.53 \text{ (kN-m)},$$

$$M_{Az} = -6.53 \text{ (kN-m)}$$

Problem 5.79 The bar AB has a built-in support at A. The collar at B is fixed to the bar. The tension in the cable BC is 10 kN.

(a) Draw the free-body diagram of the bar.
(b) Determine the reactions at A.

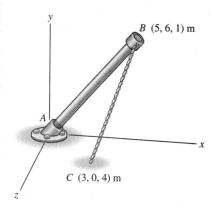

C (3, 0, 4) m

Solution: The position vectors of the ends of the cable are

$$\mathbf{r}_B = 5\mathbf{i} + 6\mathbf{j} + \mathbf{k},$$

and $\mathbf{r}_C = 3\mathbf{i} + 0\mathbf{j} + 4\mathbf{k}.$

The vector parallel to the cable is

$$\mathbf{r}_{BC} = \mathbf{r}_C - \mathbf{r}_B = -2\mathbf{i} - 6\mathbf{j} + 3\mathbf{k},$$

$$|\mathbf{r}_{BC}| = \sqrt{2^2 + 6^2 + 3^2} = 7 \text{ m}.$$

The unit vector parallel to the cable is

$$\mathbf{e} = \frac{\mathbf{r}_{BC}}{|\mathbf{r}_{BC}|} = -0.2857\mathbf{i} - 0.8571\mathbf{j} + 0.4286\mathbf{k}.$$

The tension vector is

$$\mathbf{T}_{BC} = 10\mathbf{e}_{BC} = -2.857\mathbf{i} - 8.571\mathbf{j} + 4.286\mathbf{k}.$$

The force reaction at A is determined by

$$\sum \mathbf{F}_R = \mathbf{F}_A + \mathbf{T}_{BC} = 0,$$

from which $\mathbf{F}_A = 2.857\mathbf{i} + 8.571\mathbf{j} - 4.286\mathbf{k}$ (kN)

The moment reaction at A is given by

$$\sum \mathbf{M}_R = \mathbf{M}_A + \mathbf{r}_B \times \mathbf{T}_{BC}$$

$$= \mathbf{M}_A + \begin{vmatrix} \mathbf{i} & \mathbf{j} & \mathbf{k} \\ 5 & 6 & 6 \\ -2.857 & -8.571 & 4.286 \end{vmatrix} = 0$$

From which $\boxed{\mathbf{M}_A = -34.287\mathbf{i} + 24.287\mathbf{j} + 25.713\mathbf{k} \text{ (kN-m)}}$

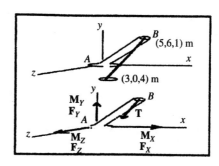

Problem 5.80 Consider the bar in Problem 5.79. The magnitude of the couple exerted on the bar by the built-in support is 100 kN-m. What is the tension in the cable?

Solution: From the solution to Problem 5.79, the moment reaction at A is the solution to the moment equilibrium equation:

$$\sum \mathbf{M}_R = \mathbf{M}_A + \mathbf{r}_B \times \mathbf{T}_{BC} = 0,$$

from which $\mathbf{M}_A = -\mathbf{r}_B \times \mathbf{T}_{BC}$.

Noting that $\mathbf{T}_{BC} = |\mathbf{T}_{BC}|\mathbf{e}_{BC}$, then using the unit vector developed in the solution to Problem 5.79,

$$\mathbf{e} = \frac{\mathbf{r}_{BC}}{|\mathbf{r}_{BC}|} = -0.2857\mathbf{i} - 0.8571\mathbf{j} + 0.4286\mathbf{k}$$

and the position vector of the end of the bar:

$\mathbf{r}_B = 5\mathbf{i} + 6\mathbf{j} + \mathbf{k}$

$$\mathbf{M}_A = -\mathbf{r}_B \times |\mathbf{T}_{BC}|\mathbf{e}_{BC} = -|\mathbf{T}_{BC}| \begin{vmatrix} \mathbf{i} & \mathbf{j} & \mathbf{k} \\ 5 & 6 & 6 \\ -0.2857 & -0.8571 & 0.4286 \end{vmatrix}$$

$$= -|\mathbf{T}_{BC}|(3.4287\mathbf{i} - 2.4287\mathbf{j} - 2.5713\mathbf{k})$$

Take the magnitude of both sides

$$|\mathbf{M}_A| = 100 = |\mathbf{T}_{BC}|\sqrt{3.4287^2 + 2.4287^2 + 2.5713^2}$$

$$= |\mathbf{T}_{BC}|(4.2961).$$

Solve: $|\mathbf{T}_{BC}| = \dfrac{100}{4.2961} = 20.300$ kN

Problem 5.81 The force exerted on the highway sign by wind and the sign's weight is $\mathbf{F} = 800\mathbf{i} - 600\mathbf{j}$ (N). Determine the reactions at the built-in support at O.

Solution: The force acting on the sign is

$$\mathbf{F} = F_X\mathbf{i} + F_Y\mathbf{j} + F_Z\mathbf{k} = 800\mathbf{i} - 600\mathbf{j} + 0\mathbf{k} \text{ N},$$

and the position from O to the point on the sign where $\mathbf{F}$ acts is

$$\mathbf{r} = 0\mathbf{i} + 8\mathbf{j} + 8\mathbf{k} \text{ m}.$$

The force equations of equilibrium for the sign are

$$O_X + F_X = 0,$$

$$O_Y + F_Y = 0,$$

and $O_Z + F_Z = 0$.

Note that the weight of the sign is included in the components of $\mathbf{F}$. The moment equation, in vector form, is

$$\sum \mathbf{M} = \mathbf{M}_O + \mathbf{r} \times \mathbf{F}.$$

Expanded, we get

$$\sum \mathbf{M} = M_{OX}\mathbf{i} + M_{OY}\mathbf{j} + M_{OZ}\mathbf{k} + \begin{vmatrix} \mathbf{i} & \mathbf{j} & \mathbf{k} \\ 0 & 8 & 8 \\ 800 & -600 & 0 \end{vmatrix} = 0.$$

The corresponding scalar equations are

$$M_{OX} - (8)(-600) = 0,$$

$$M_{OY} + (8)(800) = 0,$$

and $M_{OZ} - (8)(800) = 0$.

Solving for the support reactions, we get

$$O_X = -800 \text{ N},$$

$$O_Y = 600 \text{ N},$$

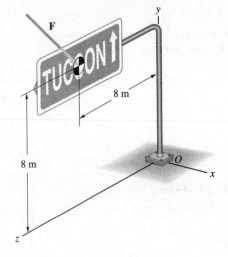

$$O_Z = 0,$$

$$M_{OX} = -4800 \text{ N-m},$$

$$M_{OY} = -6400 \text{ N-m},$$

and $M_{OZ} = 6400$ N-m.

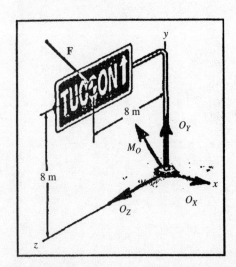

Problem 5.82 In Problem 5.81, the force exerted on the sign by wind and the sign's weight is $\mathbf{F} = \pm 4.4 v^2 \mathbf{i} - 600\mathbf{j}$ (N), where v is the component of the wind's velocity perpendicular to the sign in meters per second (m/s). If you want to design the sign to remain standing in hurricane winds with velocities v as high as 70 m/s, what reactions must the built-in support at O be designed to withstand?

Solution: The magnitude of the wind component of the force on the sign is $(4.4)(70)^2$ N = 21.56 kN. The force acting on the sign is

$$\mathbf{F} = F_X \mathbf{i} + F_Y \mathbf{j} + F_Z \mathbf{k} = \pm 21560\mathbf{i} - 600\mathbf{j} + 0\mathbf{k} \text{ N,}$$

and the position from O to the point on the sign where $\mathbf{F}$ acts is $\mathbf{r} = 0\mathbf{i} + 8\mathbf{j} + 8\mathbf{k}$ m. The force equations of equilibrium for the sign are

$$O_X + F_X = 0,$$

$$O_Y + F_Y = 0,$$

and $O_Z + F_Z = 0$.

Note that the weight of the sign is included in the components of $\mathbf{F}$. The moment equation, in vector form, is

$$\sum \mathbf{M} = \mathbf{M}_O + \mathbf{r} \times \mathbf{F}.$$

Expanded, we get

$$\sum \mathbf{M} = M_{OX}\mathbf{i} + M_{OY}\mathbf{j} + M_{OZ}\mathbf{k} + \begin{vmatrix} \mathbf{i} & \mathbf{j} & \mathbf{k} \\ 0 & 8 & 8 \\ \pm 21560 & -600 & 0 \end{vmatrix} = 0.$$

The corresponding scalar equations are

$$M_{OX} - (8)(-600) = 0,$$

$$M_{OY} + (8)(\pm 21560) = 0,$$

and $M_{OZ} - (8)(\pm 21560) = 0$.

Solving for the support force reactions, we get

$O_X = \pm 21560$ N,

$O_Y = 600$ N,

$O_Z = 0$,

and for moments,

$$M_{OX} = -4800 \text{ N-m,}$$

$$M_{OY} = \pm 172{,}500 \text{ N-m,}$$

and $M_{OZ} = \pm 172{,}500$ N-m.

Problem 5.83 The tension in cable AB is 24 kN. Determine the reactions in the built-in support D.

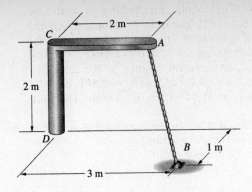

Solution: The force acting on the device is

$$\mathbf{F} = F_X\mathbf{i} + F_Y\mathbf{j} + F_Z\mathbf{k} = (24 \text{ kN})\mathbf{e}_{AB},$$

and the unit vector from A toward B is given by

$$\mathbf{e}_{AB} = \frac{1\mathbf{i} - 2\mathbf{j} + 1\mathbf{k}}{\sqrt{6}}.$$

The force, then, is given by

$$\mathbf{F} = 9.80\mathbf{i} - 19.60\mathbf{j} + 9.80\mathbf{k} \text{ kN}.$$

The position from D to A is

$$\mathbf{r} = 2\mathbf{i} + 2\mathbf{j} + 0\mathbf{k} \text{ m}.$$

The force equations of equilibrium are

$$D_X + F_X = 0,$$

$$D_Y + F_Y = 0,$$

and $D_Z + F_Z = 0.$

The moment equation, in vector form, is

$$\sum \mathbf{M} = \mathbf{M}_D + \mathbf{r} \times \mathbf{F}.$$

Expanded, we get

$$\sum \mathbf{M} = M_{DX}\mathbf{i} + M_{DY}\mathbf{j} + M_{DZ}\mathbf{k} + \begin{vmatrix} \mathbf{i} & \mathbf{j} & \mathbf{k} \\ 2 & 2 & 0 \\ 9.80 & -19.60 & 9.80 \end{vmatrix} = 0.$$

The corresponding scalar equations are

$$M_{DX} + (2)(9.80) = 0,$$

$$M_{DY} - (2)(9.80) = 0,$$

and $M_{DZ} + (2)(-19.60) - (2)(9.80) = 0.$

Solving for the support reactions, we get

$$D_X = -9.80 \text{ kN},$$

$$O_Y = 19.60 \text{ kN},$$

$$O_Z = -9.80 \text{ kN}.$$

$$M_{DX} = -19.6 \text{ kN-m},$$

$$M_{DY} = 19.6 \text{ kN-m},$$

and $M_{DZ} = 58.8 \text{ kN-m}.$

Problem 5.84 The robotic manipulator is stationary and the y axis is vertical. The weights of the arms AB and BC act at their midpoints. The direction cosines of the centerline of arm AB are $\cos\theta_x = 0.174$, $\cos\theta_y = 0.985$, $\cos\theta_z = 0$, and the direction cosines of the centerline of arm BC are $\cos\theta_x = 0.743$, $\cos\theta_y = 0.557$, $\cos\theta_z = -0.371$. The support at A behaves like a built-in support.

(a) What is the sum of the moments about A due to the weights of the two arms?

(b) What are the reactions at A?

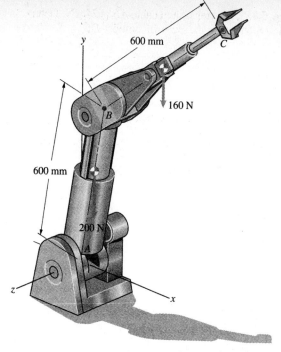

Solution: Denote the center of mass of arm AB as D_1 and that of BC as D_2. We need

$$r_{AD},$$

$$r_{AB},$$

and r_{BD_2}.

To get these, use the direction cosines to get the unit vectors e_{AB} and e_{BC}. Use the relation

$$e = \cos\theta_X i + \cos\theta_Y j + \cos\theta_Z k$$

$$e_{AB} = 0.174i + 0.985j + 0k$$

$$e_{BC} = 0.743i + 0.557j - 0.371k$$

$$r_{AD_1} = 0.3e_{AB} \text{ m}$$

$$r_{AB} = 0.6e_{AB} \text{ m}$$

$$r_{BC} = 0.6e_{BC} \text{ m}$$

$$r_{BD_2} = 0.3e_{BC} \text{ m}$$

$$W_{AB} = -200j \text{ N}$$

$$W_{BC} = -160j \text{ N}$$

Thus $r_{AD_1} = 0.0522i + 0.2955j$ m

$$r_{AB} = 0.1044i + 0.5910j \text{ m}$$

$$r_{BD_2} = 0.2229i + 0.1671j - 0.1113k \text{ m}$$

$$r_{BC} = 0.4458i + 0.3342j - 0.2226k \text{ m}$$

and $r_{AD_2} = r_{AB} + r_{BD_2}$

$$r_{AD_2} = 0.3273i + 0.7581j - 0.1113k \text{ m}$$

(a) We now have the geometry determined and are ready to determine the moments of the weights about A.

$$\sum M_W = r_{AD1} \times W_1 + r_{AD2} \times W_2$$

where

$$r_{AD1} \times W_1 = \begin{vmatrix} i & j & k \\ 0.0522 & 0.2955 & 0 \\ 0 & -200 & 0 \end{vmatrix}$$

$$r_{AD1} \times W_1 = -10.44k \text{ N-m}$$

and

$$r_{AD2} \times W_2 = \begin{vmatrix} i & j & k \\ 0.3273 & 0.7581 & -0.1113 \\ 0 & -160 & 0 \end{vmatrix}$$

$$r_{AD2} \times W_2 = -17.81i - 52.37k$$

Thus,

$$\sum M_W = -17.81i - 62.81k \text{ (N-m)}$$

(b) Equilibrium Eqns

$$\sum F_X: \quad A_X = 0$$

$$\sum F_Y: \quad A_Y - W_1 - W_2 = 0$$

$$\sum F_Z: \quad A_Z = 0$$

Sum Moments about

$$A: M_A + \sum M_W = 0$$

$$\sum M_X: \quad M_{Ax} - 17.81 = 0 \text{ (N-m)}$$

$$\sum M_Y: \quad M_{Ay} + 0 = 0$$

$$\sum M_Z: \quad M_Z - 62.81 = 0 \text{ (N-m)}$$

5.84 *Contd.*

Thus: $A_X = 0$, $A_Y = 360$ (N), $A_Z = 0$,

$M_{Ax} = 17.81$ (N-m), $M_{Ay} = 0$, $M_{Az} = 62.81$ (N-m)

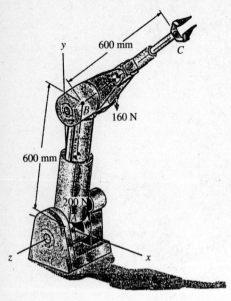

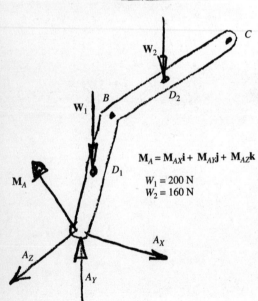

$$M_A = M_{Ax}\mathbf{i} + M_{Ay}\mathbf{j} + M_{Az}\mathbf{k}$$

$W_1 = 200$ N
$W_2 = 160$ N

Problem 5.85 The force exerted on the grip of the exercise machine is $\mathbf{F} = 260\mathbf{i} - 130\mathbf{j}$ (N). What are the reactions at the built-in support at O?

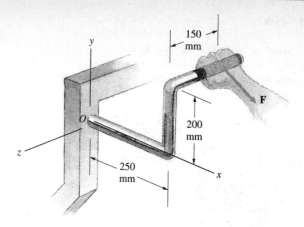

Solution:

$$\mathbf{M}_O = M_{Ox}\mathbf{i} + M_{Oy}\mathbf{j} + M_{Oz}\mathbf{k}$$

$$\mathbf{r}_{OP} = 0.25\mathbf{i} + 0.2\mathbf{j} - 0.15\mathbf{k}$$

Equilibrium (Forces)

$$\sum F_X: \quad O_X + F_X = O_X + 260 = 0 \text{ (N)}$$

$$\sum F_Y: \quad O_Y + F_Y = O_Y - 130 = 0 \text{ (N)}$$

$$\sum F_Z: \quad O_Z + F_Z = O_Z = 0 \text{ (N)}$$

Thus, $O_X = -260$ N, $O_Y = 130$ N, $O_Z = 0$

Summing Moments about O

$$\sum M_X: \quad M_{Ox} + M_{Fx} = 0$$

$$\sum M_Y: \quad M_{Oy} + M_{Fy} = 0$$

$$\sum M_Z: \quad M_{Oz} + M_{Fz} = 0$$

where

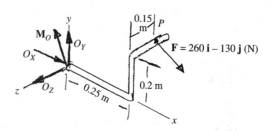

$$\mathbf{M}_F = \mathbf{r}_{OP} \times \mathbf{F} = \begin{vmatrix} \mathbf{i} & \mathbf{j} & \mathbf{k} \\ 0.25 & 0.2 & -0.15 \\ 260 & -130 & 0 \end{vmatrix}$$

$$\mathbf{M}_F = -19.5\mathbf{i} - 39\mathbf{j} - 84.5\mathbf{k} \text{ (N-m)}$$

and from the moment equilibrium eqns,

$$M_{Ox} = 19.5 \text{ (N-m)}$$

$$M_{Oy} = 39.0 \text{ (N-m)}$$

$$M_{Oz} = 84.5 \text{ (N-m)}$$

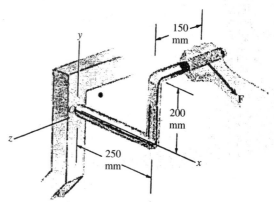

Problem 5.86 The designer of the exercises machine in Problem 5.85 assumes that the force **F** exerted on the grip will be parallel to the $x - y$ plane and that its magnitude will not exceed 900 N. Based on these criteria, what reactions must the built-in support at O be designed to withstand?

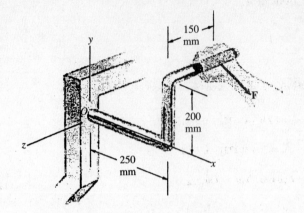

Solution: The solution to this problem is similar to that of Problem 5.85. The free-body diagram and the equilibrium equations are similar, but there are significant differences. For that reason, the solution will be presented as if Problem 5.35 had not been solved previously.

$$\mathbf{M}_O = M_{Ox}\mathbf{i} + M_{Oy}\mathbf{j} + M_{Oz}\mathbf{k}$$

$$\mathbf{F} = F\cos\theta\mathbf{i} + F\sin\theta\mathbf{j}$$

$$0 \le \theta \le 360°$$

$$|\mathbf{F}| = 900 \text{ N}$$

$$\mathbf{r}_{OP} = 0.25\mathbf{i} + 0.2\mathbf{j} - 0.15\mathbf{k} \text{ m}$$

$$\sum F_X: \quad O_X + F_X = O_X + F\cos\theta = 0$$

$$\sum F_Y: \quad O_Y + F_Y = O_Y + F\sin\theta = 0$$

$$\sum F_Z: \quad O_Z + F_Z = O_Z + 0 = 0$$

Thus $O_X = -F\cos\theta$

$$O_Y = -F\sin\theta$$

$$O_Z = 0$$

$$\sqrt{O_X^2 + O_Y^2} = |\mathbf{F}| = 900 \text{ N}$$

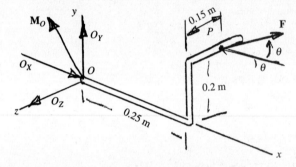

The moment equilibrium equations are

$$\sum M_X: \quad M_{Ox} + M_{Fx} = 0$$

$$\sum M_Y: \quad M_{Oy} + M_{Fy} = 0$$

$$\sum M_Z: \quad M_{Oz} + M_{Fz} = 0$$

where $\mathbf{M}_F = \mathbf{r}_{OP} \times \mathbf{F} = \begin{vmatrix} \mathbf{i} & \mathbf{j} & \mathbf{k} \\ 0.25 & 0.2 & -0.15 \\ F\cos\theta & F\sin\theta & 0 \end{vmatrix}$

$$\mathbf{M}_F = +0.15\,F\sin\theta\mathbf{i}$$

$$- 0.15\,F\cos\theta\mathbf{j}$$

$$+ (0.25\,F\sin\theta - 0.2\,F\cos\theta)\mathbf{k}$$

and $\mathbf{M}_O = -\mathbf{M}_F$

The first plot on the next page shows $|\mathbf{M}_O|$ vs θ for $0 \le \theta \le 360°$. The second plot shows the three components of $\mathbf{M}_O$ as functions of θ.

From the analysis and the plot, the support at 0 must be able to exert a force of 900 N in any direction in the $x - y$ plane *and* it must be able to exert a moment $|\mathbf{M}_O| \ge 320$ (N-m) From the component plots, we see that the support must provide

$$-135 \text{ (N-m)} \le M_{Ox} \le 135 \text{ (N-m)}$$

$$-135 \text{ (N-m)} \le M_{Oy} \le 135 \text{ (N-m)}$$

$$-288 \text{ (N-m)} \le M_{Oz} \le 288 \text{ (N-m)}$$

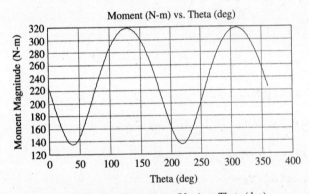

Moment (N-m) vs. Theta (deg)

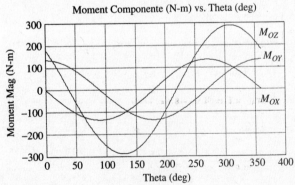

Moment Componente (N-m) vs. Theta (deg)

Problem 5.87 The boom ABC is subjected to a force $\mathbf{F} = -8\mathbf{j}$ (kN) at C and is supported by a ball and socket at A and the cables BD and BE.

(a) Draw the free-body diagram of the boom.
(b) Determine the tension in the cables and the reactions at A.

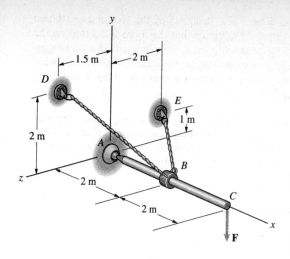

Solution: First, we need the unit vectors $\mathbf{e}_{BD}$ and $\mathbf{e}_{BE}$, use $\mathbf{e} = \dfrac{\mathbf{r}}{|\mathbf{r}|}$

$\mathbf{e}_{BD} = -0.625\mathbf{i} + 0.625\mathbf{j} + 0.469\mathbf{k}$

$\mathbf{e}_{BE} = -0.667\mathbf{i} + 0.333\mathbf{j} - 0.667\mathbf{k}$

$\mathbf{T}_{BD} = T_{BD}\,\mathbf{e}_{BD}, \quad \mathbf{T}_{BE} = T_{BE}\,\mathbf{e}_{BE}$

$\mathbf{T}_{BD} = -0.625T_{BD}\mathbf{i} + 0.625T_{BD}\mathbf{j} + 0.469T_{BD}\mathbf{k}$

$\mathbf{T}_{BE} = -0.667T_{BE}\mathbf{i} + 0.333T_{BE}\mathbf{j} - 0.667T_{BE}\mathbf{k}$

$\mathbf{A} = A_X\mathbf{i} + A_Y\mathbf{j} + A_Z\mathbf{k}$

$\mathbf{F} = 0\mathbf{i} - 8\mathbf{j} + 0\mathbf{k}$ (kN)

Force Equilibrium requires:

$\mathbf{A} + \mathbf{T}_{BD} + \mathbf{T}_{BE} + \mathbf{F} = 0$

$\sum F_X: \quad A_X + T_{BD_X} + T_{BE_X} = 0 \qquad (1)$

$\sum F_Y: \quad A_Y + T_{BD_Y} + T_{BE_Y} - 8 = 0 \quad (2)$

$\sum F_Z: \quad A_Z + T_{BD_Z} + T_{BE_Z} = 0 \qquad (3)$

Moment equilibrium (about A) requires

$\sum M = \mathbf{r}_{AB} \times \mathbf{T}_{BD} + \mathbf{r}_{AB} \times \mathbf{T}_{BE} + \mathbf{r}_{AC} \times \mathbf{F} = 0$

or $\mathbf{r}_{AB} \times (\mathbf{T}_{BD} + \mathbf{T}_{BE}) + \mathbf{r}_{AC} \times \mathbf{F} = 0$

$\mathbf{r}_{AB} \times (\mathbf{T}_{BD} + \mathbf{T}_{BE})$

$$= \begin{vmatrix} \mathbf{i} & \mathbf{j} & \mathbf{k} \\ 2 & 0 & 0 \\ (T_{BD_X} + T_{BE_X}) & (T_{BD_Y} + T_{BE_Y}) & (T_{BD_Z} + T_{BE_Z}) \end{vmatrix}$$

$\mathbf{r}_{AB} \times (\mathbf{T}_{BD} + \mathbf{T}_{BE}) = -2(T_{BD_Z} + T_{BE_Z})\mathbf{j} + 2(T_{BD_Y} + T_{BE_Y})\mathbf{k}$

$\mathbf{r}_{AC} \times \mathbf{F} = 4\mathbf{i} \times (-8\mathbf{j}) = -32\mathbf{k}$

$\sum M_X: \quad 0 = 0 \qquad\qquad\qquad (4)$

$\sum M_Y: \quad -2T_{BD_Z} - 2T_{BE_Z} = 0 \qquad (5)$

$\sum M_Z: \quad 2T_{BD_Y} + 2T_{BE_Y} - 32 = 0 \quad (6)$

Eqns (1), (2), (3), (5) and (6) are 5 eqns in the 5 unknowns A_X, A_Y, A_Z, T_{BD}, and T_{BE} (considering the definitions of $\mathbf{T}_{BD}$ and $\mathbf{T}_{BE}$ in terms of their unit vectors. Solving, we get

$A_X = 20.4$ kN, $A_Y = -8$ kN, $A_Z = 0$

$T_{BD} = 18.6$ kN, $T_{BE} = 13.1$ kN

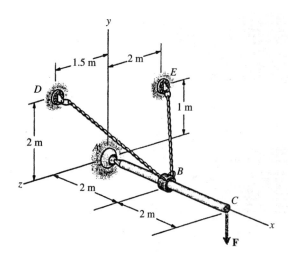

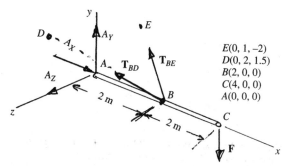

E(0, 1, −2)
D(0, 2, 1.5)
B(2, 0, 0)
C(4, 0, 0)
A(0, 0, 0)

Problem 5.88 The cables supporting the boom ABC in Problem 5.87 will each safely support a tension of 25 kN. Based on this criterion, what is the largest safe magnitude of the downward force F?

Solution: Note that the solution of Problem 5.87 is linear in all of the force and moment components. This means that we can find the largest cable tension, scale it up to 25 kN, and then scale the F of Problem 5.87 up by the same factor. In 5.87, $T_{BD} = 18.6$ kN was the largest tension. Let $F = \dfrac{25}{18.6}$

$$\mathbf{F}_{max} = (-8)f = -10.7 \text{ kN}$$

$$|\mathbf{F}_{max}| = 10.7 \text{ kN}$$

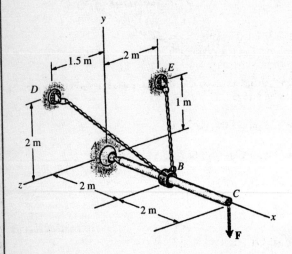

Problem 5.89 The suspended load exerts a force $F = 600$ lb at A, and the weight of the bar OA is negligible. Determine the tensions in the cables and the reactions at the ball and socket support O.

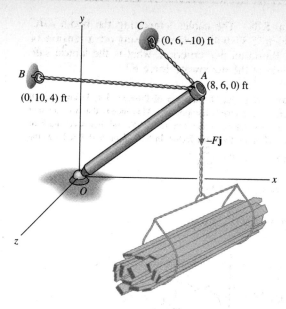

Solution: From the diagram, the important points in this problem are A (8, 6, 0), B (0, 10, 4), C (0, 6, −10), and the origin O (0, 0, 0) with all dimensions in ft. We need unit vectors in the directions A to B and A to C. Both vectors are of the form

$$\mathbf{e}_{AP} = (x_P - x_A)\mathbf{i} + (y_P - y_A)\mathbf{j} + (z_P - z_A)\mathbf{k},$$

where P can be either A or B. The forces in cables AB and AC are

$$\mathbf{T}_{AB} = T_{AB}\,\mathbf{e}_{AB} = T_{ABX}\mathbf{i} + T_{ABY}\mathbf{j} + T_{ABZ}\mathbf{k},$$

and $\mathbf{T}_{AC} = T_{AC}\,\mathbf{e}_{AB} = T_{ACX}\mathbf{i} + T_{ACY}\mathbf{j} + T_{ACZ}\mathbf{k}.$

The weight force is

$$\mathbf{F} = 0\mathbf{i} - 600\mathbf{j} + 0\mathbf{k},$$

and the support force at the ball joint is

$$\mathbf{S} = S_X\mathbf{i} + S_Y\mathbf{j} + S_Z\mathbf{k}.$$

The vector form of the force equilibrium equation (which gives three scalar equations) for the bar is

$$\mathbf{T}_{AB} + \mathbf{T}_{AC} + \mathbf{F} + \mathbf{S} = 0.$$

Let us take moments about the origin. The moment equation, in vector form, is given by

$$\sum \mathbf{M}_O = \mathbf{r}_{OA} \times \mathbf{T}_{AB} + \mathbf{r}_{OA} \times \mathbf{T}_{AC}$$

$$+ \,\mathbf{r}_{OA} \times \mathbf{F} = 0,$$

where $\mathbf{r}_{OA} = 8\mathbf{i} + 6\mathbf{j} + 0\mathbf{k}.$

The cross products are evaluated using the form

$$\mathbf{M} = \mathbf{r} \times \mathbf{H} = \begin{vmatrix} \mathbf{i} & \mathbf{j} & \mathbf{k} \\ 8 & 6 & 0 \\ H_X & H_Y & H_Z \end{vmatrix},$$

where $\mathbf{H}$ can be any of the three forces acting at point A. The vector moment equation provides another three equations of equilibrium. Once we have evaluated and applied the unit vectors, we have six vector equations of equilibrium in the five unknowns $T_{AB}, T_{AC}, S_X, S_Y,$ and S_Z (there is one redundant equation since all forces pass through the line OA). Solving these equations yields the required values for the support reactions at the origin.

If we carry through these operations in the sequence described, we get the following vectors:

$$\mathbf{e}_{AB} = -0.816\mathbf{i} + 0.408\mathbf{j} + 0.408\mathbf{k},$$

$$\mathbf{e}_{AC} = -0.625\mathbf{i} + 0\mathbf{j} - 0.781\mathbf{k},$$

$$\mathbf{T}_{AB} = -387.1\mathbf{i} + 193.5\mathbf{j} + 193.5\mathbf{k} \text{ lb},$$

$$|\mathbf{T}_{AB}| = 474.1 \text{ lb},$$

$$\mathbf{T}_{AC} = -154.8\mathbf{i} + 0\mathbf{j} - 193.5\mathbf{k} \text{ lb},$$

$$|\mathbf{T}_{AC}| = 247.9 \text{ lb},$$

$$\mathbf{M}_{AB} = \mathbf{r}_{OA} \times \mathbf{T}_{AB} = 1161\mathbf{i} - 1548\mathbf{j} + 3871\mathbf{k} \text{ ft-lb},$$

$$\mathbf{M}_{AC} = \mathbf{r}_{OA} \times \mathbf{T}_{AC} = -1161\mathbf{i} + 1548\mathbf{j} + 929\mathbf{k} \text{ ft-lb},$$

and $\mathbf{S} = 541.9\mathbf{i} + 406.5\mathbf{j} + 0\mathbf{k}$ lb

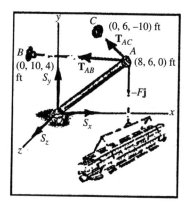

Problem 5.90 In Problem 5.89, suppose that the suspended load exerts a force $F = 600$ lb at A and bar OA weighs 200 lb. Assume that the bar's weight acts at its midpoint. Determine the tensions in the cables and the reactions at the ball and socket support O.

Solution: Point G is located at $(4, 3, 0)$ and the position vector of G with respect to the origin is

$$\mathbf{r}_{OG} = 4\mathbf{i} + 3\mathbf{j} + 0\mathbf{k} \text{ ft.}$$

The weight of the bar is

$$\mathbf{W}_B = 0\mathbf{i} - 200\mathbf{j} + 0\mathbf{k} \text{ lb,}$$

and its moment around the origin is

$$\mathbf{M}_{WB} = 0\mathbf{i} + 0\mathbf{j} - 800\mathbf{k} \text{ ft-lb.}$$

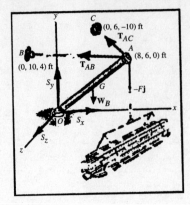

The mathematical representation for all other forces and moments from Problem 5.89 remain the same (the numbers change!). Each equation of equilibrium has a new term reflecting the addition of the weight of the bar. The new force equilibrium equation is

$$\mathbf{T}_{AB} + \mathbf{T}_{AC} + \mathbf{F} + \mathbf{S} + \mathbf{W}_B = 0.$$

The new moment equilibrium equation is

$$\sum \mathbf{M}_O = \mathbf{r}_{OA} \times \mathbf{T}_{AB} + \mathbf{r}_{OA} \times \mathbf{T}_{AC}$$

$$+ \mathbf{r}_{OA} \times \mathbf{F} + \mathbf{r}_{OG} \times \mathbf{W}_B = 0.$$

As in Problem 5.89, the vector equilibrium conditions can be reduced to six scalar equations of equilibrium. Once we have evaluated and applied the unit vectors, we have six vector equations of equilibrium in the five unknowns $T_{AB}, T_{AC}, S_X, S_Y,$ and S_Z (As before, there is one redundant equation since all forces pass through the line OA). Solving these equations yields the required values for the support reactions at the origin.

If we carry through these operations in the sequence described, we get the following vectors:

$$\mathbf{e}_{AB} = -0.816\mathbf{i} + 0.408\mathbf{j} + 0.408\mathbf{k},$$

$$\mathbf{e}_{AC} = -0.625\mathbf{i} + 0\mathbf{j} - 0.781\mathbf{k},$$

$$\mathbf{T}_{AB} = -451.6\mathbf{i} + 225.8\mathbf{j} + 225.8\mathbf{k} \text{ lb,}$$

$$|\mathbf{T}_{AB}| = 553.1 \text{ lb,}$$

$$\mathbf{T}_{AC} = -180.6\mathbf{i} + 0\mathbf{j} - 225.8\mathbf{k} \text{ lb,}$$

$$|\mathbf{T}_{AC}| = 289.2 \text{ lb,}$$

$$\mathbf{M}_{AB} = \mathbf{r}_{OA} \times \mathbf{T}_{AB} = 1355\mathbf{i} - 1806\mathbf{j} + 4516\mathbf{k} \text{ ft-lb,}$$

$$\mathbf{M}_{AC} = \mathbf{r}_{OA} \times \mathbf{T}_{AC} = -1354\mathbf{i} + 1806\mathbf{j} + 1084\mathbf{k} \text{ ft-lb,}$$

and $\mathbf{S} = 632.3\mathbf{i} + 574.2\mathbf{j} + 0\mathbf{k}$ lb

Problem 5.91 The 158,000-kg airplane is at rest on the ground ($z = 0$ is ground level). The landing gear carriages are at A, B, and C. The coordinates of the point G at which the weight of the plane acts are $(3, 0.5, 5)$ m. What are the magnitudes of the normal reactions exerted on the landing gear by the ground?

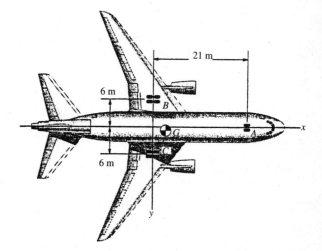

Solution:

$$\sum F_Y = (N_L + N_R) + N_F - W = 0$$

$$\sum M_R = -3 \text{ mg} + 21 N_F = 0$$

Solving,

$$N_F = 221.4 \text{ kN} \quad \textbf{(1)}$$

$$(N_L + N_R) = 1328.6 \text{ kN} \quad \textbf{(2)}$$

$$\sum F_Y = N_R + N_L + N_F - W = 0$$

(same equation as before)

$$\curvearrowleft + \sum M_O = 0.5 \text{ W} - 6(N_R) + 6(N_L) = 0 \quad \textbf{(3)}$$

Solving (1), (2), and (3), we get

$$N_F = 221.4 \text{ kN}$$

$$N_R = 728.9 \text{ kN}$$

$$N_L = 599.7 \text{ kN}$$

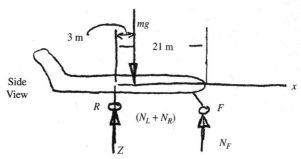

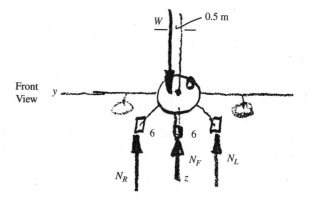

Problem 5.92 The 800-kg horizontal wall section is supported by the three vertical cables, A, B, and C. What are the tensions in the cables?

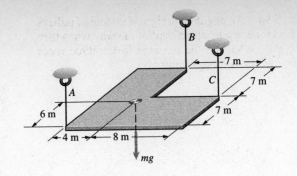

Solution: All dimensions are in m and all forces are in N. Forces A, B, C, and W act on the wall at (0, 0, 0), (5, 14, 0), (12, 7, 0), and (4, 6, 0), respectively. All forces are in the z direction. The force equilibrium equation in the z direction is $A + B + C - W = 0$. The moments are calculated from

$$\mathbf{M}_B = \mathbf{r}_{OB} \times B\mathbf{k},$$

$$\mathbf{M}_C = \mathbf{r}_{OC} \times C\mathbf{k},$$

and $\mathbf{M}_G = \mathbf{r}_{OG} \times (-W)\mathbf{k}.$

The moment equilibrium equation is

$$\sum \mathbf{M}_O = \mathbf{M}_B + \mathbf{M}_C + \mathbf{M}_G = 0.$$

Carrying out these operations, we get

$A = 3717$ N,

$B = 2596$ N,

$C = 1534$ N,

and $W = 7848$ N.

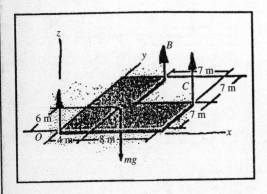

Problem 5.93 The cables in Problem 5.92 will each safely support a tension of 10 kN. Based on this criterion, what is the largest safe mass of the horizontal wall section?

Solution: The solution for this problem involves exactly the same equations as Problem 5.92. The unknowns and knowns just shift a bit. We no longer know the mass of the wall section, but we do know the tension in one of the cables. From the solution to Problem 5.92, we see that the cable carrying the largest load is the cable at A. We set $A = 10$ kN, make m (or W) an unknown, and solve the exact same equations as above. The result is $A = 10$ kN, $B = 6.984$ kN, $C = 4.127$ kN, $W = 21.114$ kN, and $m = 2152$ kg.

Problem 5.94 An engineer designs a system of pulleys to pull his model trains up and out of the way when they aren't in use. What are the tensions in the three ropes when the system is in equilibrium?

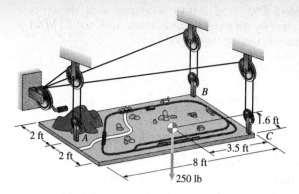

Solution: Take the origin as the point C on the platform. The position vectors are

$$\mathbf{r}_A = -2\mathbf{i} + 8\mathbf{k},$$

$$\mathbf{r}_B = -4\mathbf{i},$$

$$\mathbf{r}_G = -1.6\mathbf{i} + 3.5\mathbf{k}.$$

The sum of the moments about C is

$$\sum \mathbf{M}_C = \begin{vmatrix} \mathbf{i} & \mathbf{j} & \mathbf{k} \\ -2 & 0 & 8 \\ 0 & A & 0 \end{vmatrix} + \begin{vmatrix} \mathbf{i} & \mathbf{j} & \mathbf{k} \\ -4 & 0 & 0 \\ 0 & B & 0 \end{vmatrix}$$

$$+ \begin{vmatrix} \mathbf{i} & \mathbf{j} & \mathbf{k} \\ -1.6 & 0 & 3.5 \\ 0 & -250 & 0 \end{vmatrix} = 0$$

$$\sum \mathbf{M}_C = -(8A\mathbf{i} + 2A\mathbf{k}) - 4B\mathbf{k} + (875\mathbf{i} + 400\mathbf{k}) = 0.$$

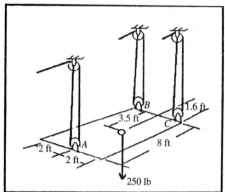

Collecting like terms:

$$(-8A + 875)\mathbf{i} = 0,$$

$$(-2A - 2B + 400)\mathbf{k} = 0,$$

from which $A = \dfrac{875}{8} = 109.375$ lb,

$$B = \frac{200 - A}{2} = 45.3125 \text{ lb}.$$

The value of the reaction at C is found from the sum of the vertical forces:

$$\sum \mathbf{F}_Y = (-250 + A + B + C)\mathbf{j} = 0,$$

from which $C = 95.3125$ lb. Two pulley ropes support each point, so the tension in each rope is one-half the reaction at the point supported:

$$T_A = \frac{A}{2} = 54.67 \text{ lb},$$

$$T_B = \frac{B}{2} = 22.65 \text{ lb},$$

$$T_C = \frac{C}{2} = 47.66 \text{ lb}$$

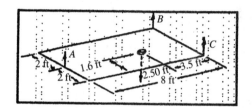

Problem 5.95 The L-shaped bar is supported by a bearing at A and rests on a smooth horizontal surface at B. The vertical force $F = 4$ kN and the distance $b = 0.15$ m. Determine the reactions at A and B.

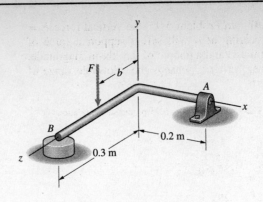

Solution: *Equilibrium Eqns:*

$$\sum F_X: \quad 0 = 0$$

$$\sum F_Y: \quad A_Y + B - F = 0$$

$$\sum F_Z: \quad A_Z = 0$$

Sum moments around A

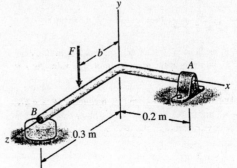

$x: \quad Fb - 0.3B = (4)(0.15) - 0.3B = 0$

$y: \quad M_{AY} = 0$

$z: \quad M_{AZ} + 0.2F - 0.2B = 0$

Solving,

$A_X = 0,$

$A_Y = 2$ (kN),

$A_Z = 0$

$M_{AX} = 0,$

$M_{AY} = 0,$

$M_{AZ} = -0.4$ (kN-m)

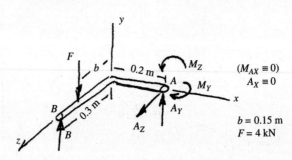

Problem 5.96 In Problem 5.95, the vertical force $F = 4$ kN and the distance $b = 0.15$ m. If you represent the reactions at A and B by an equivalent system consisting of a single force, what is the force and where does its line of action intersect the $x - z$ plane?

Solution: We want to represent the forces at A & B by a single force. From Prob. 5.96

$\mathbf{A} = +2\mathbf{j}$ (kN),

$\mathbf{B} = +2\mathbf{j}$ (kN)

$\mathbf{M}_A = -0.4\mathbf{k}$ (kN-m)

We want a single equivalent force, $\mathbf{R}$ that has the same resultant force and moment about A as does the set $\mathbf{A}$, $\mathbf{B}$, and $\mathbf{M}_A$.

$\mathbf{R} = \mathbf{A} + \mathbf{B} = 4\mathbf{j}$ (kN)

Let $\mathbf{R}$ pierce the x, z plane at (x_R, z_R)

$$\sum M_X: \quad -z_R R = -0.3B$$

$$\sum M_Z: \quad -x_R R = 0.2A_Y$$

$z_R(4) = (+0.3)(2)$

$z_R = +0.15$ m

$x_R(4) = 0.2(2)$

$x_R = 0.1$ m

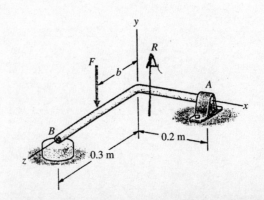

Problem 5.97 In Problem 5.95, the vertical force $F = 4$ kN. The bearing at A will safely support a force of 2.5-kN magnitude and a couple of 0.5 kN-m magnitude. Based on these criteria, what is the allowable range of the distance b?

Solution: The solution to Prob. 5.95 produced the relations

$$A_Y + B - F = 0 \quad (F = 4 \; kN)$$

$$Fb - 0.3B = 0$$

$$M_{Az} + 0.2F - 0.2B = 0$$

$$A_X = A_Z = M_{Ax} = M_{Ay} = 0$$

Set the force at A to its limit of 2.5 kN and solve for b. In this case, $M_{Az} = -0.5$ (kN-m) which is at the moment limit. The value for b is $b = 0.1125$ m

We make A_Y unknown, b unknown, and B unknown $(F = 4$ kN, $M_{Ay} = +0.5$ (kN-m), and solve we get $A_Y = -2.5$ at $b = 0.4875$ m However, 0.3 is the physical limit of the device.

Thus, $0.1125 \; m \le b \le 0.3 \; m$

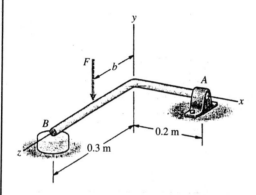

Problem 5.98 The 1.1-m bar is supported by a ball and socket support at A and the two smooth walls. The tension in the vertical cable CD is 1 kN.

(a) Draw the free-body diagram of the bar.
(b) Determine the reactions at A and B.

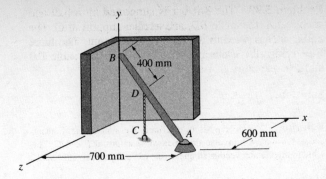

Solution:

(a) The ball and socket cannot support a couple reaction, but can support a three force reaction. The smooth surface supports one-force normal to the surface. The cable supports one force parallel to the cable.

(b) The strategy is to determine the moments about A, which will contain only the unknown reaction at B. This will require the position vectors of B and D relative to A, which in turn will require the unit vector parallel to the rod. The angle formed by the bar with the horizontal is required to determine the coordinates of B:

$$\alpha = \cos^{-1}\left(\frac{\sqrt{0.6^2 + 0.7^2}}{1.1}\right) = 33.1°.$$

The coordinates of the points are: A (0.7, 0, 0.6), B (0, 1.1 (sin 33.1°), 0) = (0, 0.6, 0), from which the vector parallel to the bar is

$$\mathbf{r}_{AB} = \mathbf{r}_B - \mathbf{r}_A = -0.7\mathbf{i} + 0.6\mathbf{j} - 0.6\mathbf{k} \text{ (m)}.$$

The unit vector parallel to the bar is

$$\mathbf{e}_{AB} = \frac{\mathbf{r}_{AB}}{1.1} = -0.6364\mathbf{i} + 0.5455\mathbf{j} - 0.5455\mathbf{k}.$$

The vector location of the point D relative to A is

$$\mathbf{r}_{AD} = (1.1 - 0.4)\mathbf{e}_{AB} = 0.7\mathbf{e}_{AB}$$

$$= -0.4455\mathbf{i} + 0.3819\mathbf{j} - 0.3819\mathbf{k}.$$

The reaction at B is horizontal, with unknown x-component and z-components. The sum of the moments about A is

$$\sum \mathbf{M}_A = \mathbf{r}_{AB} \times \mathbf{B} + \mathbf{r}_{AD} \times \mathbf{D} = 0 = \begin{vmatrix} \mathbf{i} & \mathbf{j} & \mathbf{k} \\ -0.7 & 0.6 & -0.6 \\ B_X & 0 & B_Z \end{vmatrix}$$

$$+ \begin{vmatrix} \mathbf{i} & \mathbf{j} & \mathbf{k} \\ -0.4455 & 0.3819 & -0.3819 \\ 0 & -1 & 0 \end{vmatrix} = 0$$

Expand and collect like terms:

$$\sum \mathbf{M}_A = (0.6B_Z - 0.3819)\mathbf{i} - (0.6B_X - 0.7B_Z)\mathbf{j}$$

$$+ (-0.6B_X + 0.4455)\mathbf{k} = 0.$$

From which,

$$B_Z = \frac{0.3819}{0.6} = 0.6365 \text{ kN},$$

$$B_X = \frac{0.4455}{0.6} = 0.7425 \text{ kN}$$

The reactions at A are determined from the sums of the forces:

$$\sum \mathbf{F}_X = (B_X + A_X)\mathbf{i} = 0, \text{ from which } A_X = -0.7425 \text{ kN}.$$

$$\sum \mathbf{F}_Y = (A_Y - 1)\mathbf{j} = 0, \text{ from which } A_Y = 1 \text{ kN}.$$

$$\sum \mathbf{F}_Z = (B_Z + A_Z)\mathbf{k} = 0, \text{ from which } A_Z = -0.6365 \text{ kN}$$

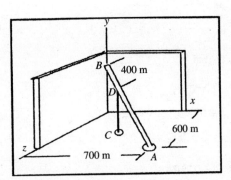

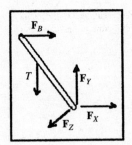

Problem 5.99 The 8-ft bar is supported by a ball and socket at A, the cable BD, and a roller support at C. The collar at B is fixed to the bar at its midpoint. The force $\mathbf{F} = -50\mathbf{k}$ (lb). Determine the tension in the cable BD and the reactions at A and C.

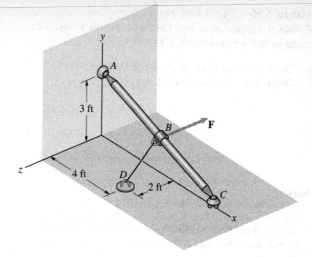

Solution: The strategy is to determine the sum of the moments about A, which will involve the unknown reactions at B and C. This will require the unit vectors parallel to the rod and parallel to the cable.

The angle formed by the rod is

$$\alpha = \sin^{-1}\left(\frac{3}{8}\right) = 22°.$$

The vector positions are:

$$\mathbf{r}_A = 3\mathbf{j},$$

$$\mathbf{r}_D = 4\mathbf{i} + 2\mathbf{k}$$

and $\mathbf{r}_C = (8\cos 22°)\mathbf{i} = 7.4162\mathbf{i}$.

The vector parallel to the rod is

$$\mathbf{r}_{AC} = \mathbf{r}_C - \mathbf{r}_A = 7.4162\mathbf{i} - 3\mathbf{j}.$$

The unit vector parallel to the rod is

$$\mathbf{e}_{AC} = 0.9270\mathbf{i} - 0.375\mathbf{j}.$$

The location of B is

$$\mathbf{r}_{AB} = 4\mathbf{e}_{AC} = 3.7081\mathbf{i} - 1.5\mathbf{j}.$$

The vector parallel to the cable is

$$\mathbf{r}_{BD} = \mathbf{r}_D - (\mathbf{r}_A + \mathbf{r}_{AB}) = 0.2919\mathbf{i} - 1.5\mathbf{j} + 2\mathbf{k}.$$

The unit vector parallel to the cable is

$$\mathbf{e}_{BD} = 0.1160\mathbf{i} - 0.5960\mathbf{j} + 0.7946\mathbf{k}.$$

The tension in the cable is $\mathbf{T} = |\mathbf{T}|\mathbf{e}_{BD}$. The reaction at the roller support C is normal to the $x-z$ plane. The sum of the moments about A

$$\sum \mathbf{M}_A = \mathbf{r}_{AB} \times \mathbf{F} + \mathbf{r}_{AB} \times \mathbf{T} + \mathbf{r}_{AC} \times \mathbf{C} = 0$$

$$= \begin{vmatrix} \mathbf{i} & \mathbf{j} & \mathbf{k} \\ 3.7081 & -1.5 & 0 \\ 0 & 0 & -50 \end{vmatrix}$$

$$+ |\mathbf{T}| \begin{vmatrix} \mathbf{i} & \mathbf{j} & \mathbf{k} \\ 3.7081 & -1.5 & 0 \\ 0.1160 & -0.5960 & 0.7946 \end{vmatrix}$$

$$+ \begin{vmatrix} \mathbf{i} & \mathbf{j} & \mathbf{k} \\ 7.4162 & -3 & 0 \\ 0 & C_Y & 0 \end{vmatrix} = 0$$

$$= 75\mathbf{i} + 185.4\mathbf{j} + |\mathbf{T}|(-1.192\mathbf{i} - 2.9466\mathbf{j} - 2.036\mathbf{k})$$

$$+ 7.4162 C_Y \mathbf{k} = 0,$$

from which $|\mathbf{T}| = \dfrac{75}{1.192} = 62.92$ lb

$$C_Y = \frac{2.036|\mathbf{T}|}{7.4162} = 17.27 \text{ lb}.$$

The reaction at A is determined from the sums of forces:

$$\sum \mathbf{F}_X = (A_X + 0.1160|\mathbf{T}|)\mathbf{i} = 0,$$

from which $A_X = -7.29$ lb,

$$\sum \mathbf{F}_Y = (A_Y - 0.5960|\mathbf{T}| + C_Y)\mathbf{j} = 0,$$

from which $A_Y = 20.23$ lb

$$\sum \mathbf{F}_Z = (A_Z + 0.7946|\mathbf{T}| - 50)\mathbf{k} = 0,$$

from which $A_Z = 0$ lb

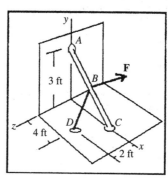

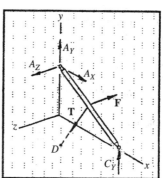

Problem 5.100 Consider the 8-ft bar in Problem 5.99. The force $\mathbf{F} = F_y\mathbf{j} - 50\mathbf{k}$ (lb). What is the largest value of F_y for which the roller support at C will remain on the floor?

Solution: From the solution to Problem 5.99, the sum of the moments about A is

$$\sum \mathbf{M}_A = \begin{vmatrix} \mathbf{i} & \mathbf{j} & \mathbf{k} \\ 3.7081 & -1.5 & 0 \\ 0 & F_Y & -50 \end{vmatrix}$$

$$+ |\mathbf{T}| \begin{vmatrix} \mathbf{i} & \mathbf{j} & \mathbf{k} \\ 3.7081 & -1.5 & 0 \\ 0.1160 & -0.5960 & 0.7946 \end{vmatrix}$$

$$+ \begin{vmatrix} \mathbf{i} & \mathbf{j} & \mathbf{k} \\ 7.4162 & -3 & 0 \\ 0 & C_Y & 0 \end{vmatrix} = 0$$

$$= 75\mathbf{i} + 185.4\mathbf{j} + 3.7081 F_Y\mathbf{k}$$

$$+ |\mathbf{T}|(-1.192\mathbf{i} - 2.9466\mathbf{j} - 2.036\mathbf{k})$$

$$+ 7.4162 C_Y\mathbf{k} = 0,$$

from which, $|\mathbf{T}| = \dfrac{75}{1.192} = 62.92$ lb.

Collecting terms in $\mathbf{k}$, $3.7081 F_Y + 2.384|\mathbf{T}| - 7.4162 C_Y = 0$.

For $C_Y = 0$, $F_Y = \dfrac{128.11}{3.708} = 34.54$ lb

Problem 5.101 The tower is 70 m tall. The tension in each cable is 2 kN. Treat the base of the tower A as a built-in support. What are the reactions at A?

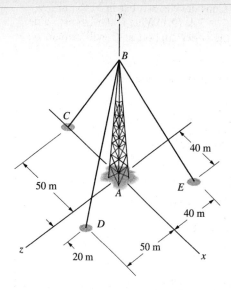

Solution: The strategy is to determine moments about A due to the cables. This requires the unit vectors parallel to the cables.

The coordinates of the points are:

$A(0, 0, 0)$, $B(0, 70, 0)$, $C(-50, 0, 0)$,

$D(20, 0, 50)$, $E(40, 0, -40)$.

The unit vectors parallel to the cables, directed from B to the points E, D, and C

$\mathbf{r}_{BE} = 40\mathbf{i} - 70\mathbf{j} - 40\mathbf{k}$,

$\mathbf{r}_{BD} = 20\mathbf{i} - 70\mathbf{j} + 50\mathbf{k}$,

$\mathbf{r}_{BC} = -50\mathbf{i} - 70\mathbf{j}$.

The unit vectors parallel to the cables, pointing from B, are:

$\mathbf{e}_{BE} = 0.4444\mathbf{i} - 0.7778\mathbf{j} - 0.4444\mathbf{k}$,

$\mathbf{e}_{BD} = 0.2265\mathbf{i} - 0.7926\mathbf{j} + 0.5661\mathbf{k}$,

$\mathbf{e}_{BC} = -0.5812\mathbf{i} - 0.8137\mathbf{j} + 0\mathbf{k}$.

The tensions in the cables are:

$\mathbf{T}_{BD} = 2\mathbf{e}_{BD} = 0.4529\mathbf{i} - 1.5852\mathbf{j} + 1.1323\mathbf{k}$ (kN),

$\mathbf{T}_{BE} = 2\mathbf{e}_{BE} = 0.8889\mathbf{i} - 1.5556\mathbf{j} - 0.8889\mathbf{k}$ (kN),

$\mathbf{T}_{BC} = 2\mathbf{e}_{BC} = -1.1625\mathbf{i} - 1.6275\mathbf{j} - 0\mathbf{k}$.

The sum of the moments about A is

$$\sum \mathbf{M}_A = \mathbf{M}^A + \mathbf{r}_{AB} \times \mathbf{T}_{BE}$$

$$+ \quad \mathbf{r}_{AB} \times \mathbf{T}_{BD} + \mathbf{r}_{AB} \times \mathbf{T}_{BC} = 0$$

$$= \mathbf{M}^A + \mathbf{r}_{AB} \times (\mathbf{T}_{BE} + \mathbf{T}_{BC} + \mathbf{T}_{BD})$$

$$\sum \mathbf{M}_A = \mathbf{M}^A + \begin{vmatrix} \mathbf{i} & \mathbf{j} & \mathbf{k} \\ 0 & 70 & 0 \\ 0.1793 & -4.7682 & 0.2434 \end{vmatrix} = 0$$

$$= (M_X^A + 17.038)\mathbf{i} + (M_Y^A + 0)\mathbf{j}$$

$$+ (M_Z^A - 12.551)\mathbf{k} = 0$$

from which

$M_X^A = -17.038$ kN-m,

$M_Y^A = 0$,

$M_Z^A = 12.551$ kN-m.

The force reactions at A are determined from the sums of forces. (Note that the sums of the cable forces have already been calculated and used above.)

$$\sum \mathbf{F}_X = (A_X + 0.17932)\mathbf{i} = 0,$$

from which $A_X = -0.179$ kN,

$$\sum \mathbf{F}_Y = (A_Y - 4.7682)\mathbf{j} = 0,$$

from which $A_Y = 4.768$ kN,

$$\sum \mathbf{F}_Z = (A_Z + 0.2434)\mathbf{k} = 0,$$

from which $A_Z = -0.2434$ kN

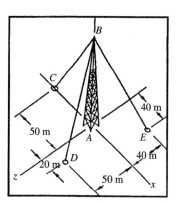

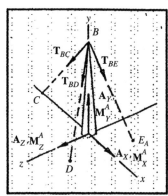

Problem 5.102 Consider the tower in Problem 5.101. If the tension in cable BC is 2 kN, what must the tensions in cables BD and BE be if you want the couple exerted on the tower by the built-in support at A to be zero? What are the resulting reactions at A?

Solution: From the solution to Problem 5.101, the sum of the moments about A is given by

$$\sum \mathbf{M}_A = \mathbf{M}^A + \mathbf{r}_{AB} \times (\mathbf{T}_{BE} + \mathbf{T}_{BC} + \mathbf{T}_{BD}) = 0.$$

If the couple $\mathbf{M}^A = 0$, then the cross product is zero, which is possible only if the vector sum of the cable tensions is zero in the x and z directions. Thus, from Problem 5.101,

$$\mathbf{e}_x \cdot (\mathbf{T}_{BC} + |\mathbf{T}_{BE}|\mathbf{e}_{BE} + |\mathbf{T}_{BD}|\mathbf{e}_{BD}) = 0,$$

and $\mathbf{e}_z \cdot (\mathbf{T}_{BC} + |\mathbf{T}_{BE}|\mathbf{e}_{BE} + |\mathbf{T}_{BD}|\mathbf{e}_{BD}) = 0.$

Two simultaneous equations in two unknowns result;

$$0.4444|\mathbf{T}_{BE}| + 0.2265|\mathbf{T}_{BD}| = 1.1625$$

$$-0.4444|\mathbf{T}_{BE}| + 0.5661|\mathbf{T}_{BD}| = 0.$$

Solve:

$$|\mathbf{T}_{BE}| = 1.868 \text{ kN},$$

$$|\mathbf{T}_{BD}| = 1.467 \text{ kN}.$$

The reactions at A oppose the sum of the cable tensions in the x-, y-, and z-directions.

$$A_X = 0, \quad A_Y = 4.243 \text{ kN}, \quad A_Z = 0.$$

(These results are to be expected if there is no moment about A.)

Problem 5.103 The space truss has roller supports at B, C, and D and is subjected to a vertical force $F = 20$ kN at A. What are the reactions at the roller supports?

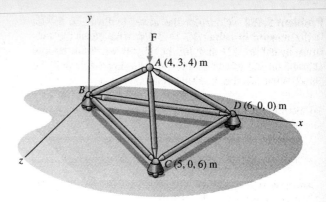

Solution: The key to this solution is expressing the forces in terms of unit vectors and magnitudes-then using the method of joints in three dimensions. The points A, B, C, and D are located at

$A(4, 3, 4)$ m, $B(0, 0, 0)$ m,

$C(5, 0, 6)$ m, $D(6, 0, 0)$ m

we need $\mathbf{e}_{AB}$, $\mathbf{e}_{AC}$, $\mathbf{e}_{AD}$, $\mathbf{e}_{BC}$, $\mathbf{e}_{BD}$, and $\mathbf{e}_{CD}$. Use the form

$$\mathbf{e}_{PQ} = \frac{(x_Q - x_P)\mathbf{i} + (y_Q - y_P)\mathbf{j} + (z_Q - z_P)\mathbf{k}}{[(x_Q - x_P)^2 + (y_Q - y_P)^2 + (z_Q - z_P)^2]^{1/2}}$$

$\mathbf{e}_{AB} = -0.625\mathbf{i} - 0.469\mathbf{j} - 0.625\mathbf{k}$

$\mathbf{e}_{AC} = 0.267\mathbf{i} - 0.802\mathbf{j} + 0.535\mathbf{k}$

$\mathbf{e}_{AD} = 0.371\mathbf{i} - 0.557\mathbf{j} - 0.743\mathbf{k}$

$\mathbf{e}_{BC} = 0.640\mathbf{i} + 0\mathbf{j} + 0.768\mathbf{k}$

$\mathbf{e}_{BD} = 1\mathbf{i} + 0\mathbf{j} + 0\mathbf{k}$

$\mathbf{e}_{CD} = 0.164\mathbf{i} + 0\mathbf{j} - 0.986\mathbf{k}$

We will write each force as a magnitude times the appropriate unit vector.

$\mathbf{T}_{AB} = T_{AB}\mathbf{e}_{AB}$, $\mathbf{T}_{AC} = T_{AC}\mathbf{e}_{AC}$

$\mathbf{T}_{AD} = T_{AD}\mathbf{e}_{AD}$, $\mathbf{T}_{BC} = T_{BC}\mathbf{e}_{BC}$

$\mathbf{T}_{BD} = T_{BD}\mathbf{e}_{BD}$, $\mathbf{T}_{CD} = T_{CD}\mathbf{e}_{CD}$

Each force will be written in component form, i.e.

$$\left.\begin{array}{l} T_{AB_X} = T_{AB}e_{AB_X} \\ T_{AB_Y} = T_{AB}e_{AB_Y} \\ T_{AB_Z} = T_{AB}e_{AB_Z} \end{array}\right\} \text{ etc.}$$

Joint A: $\mathbf{T}_{AB} + \mathbf{T}_{AC} + \mathbf{T}_{AD} + \mathbf{F} = 0$

$\qquad T_{AB_X} + T_{AC_X} + T_{AD_X} = 0$

$\qquad T_{AB_Y} + T_{AC_Y} + T_{AD_Y} - 20 = 0$

$\qquad T_{AB_Z} + T_{AC_Z} + T_{AD_Z} = 0$

Joint B: $-\mathbf{T}_{AB} + \mathbf{T}_{BC} + \mathbf{T}_{BD} + N_B\mathbf{j} = 0$

Joint C: $-\mathbf{T}_{AC} - \mathbf{T}_{BC} + \mathbf{T}_{CD} + N_C\mathbf{j} = 0$

Joint D: $-\mathbf{T}_{AD} - \mathbf{T}_{BD} - \mathbf{T}_{CD} + N_D\mathbf{j} = 0$

Solving for all the unknowns, we get

$N_B = 4.44$ kN
$N_C = 2.22$ kN
$N_D = 13.33$ kN

Also, $T_{AB} = -9.49$ kN, $T_{AC} = -16.63$ kN

$\qquad T_{AD} = -3.99$ kN, $T_{BC} = 7.71$ kN

$\qquad T_{BD} = 0.99$ kN, $T_{CD} = 3.00$ kN

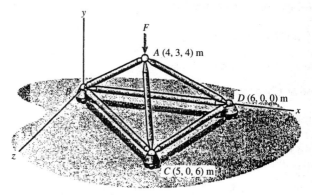

Joint A :

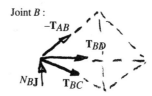

Joint B :

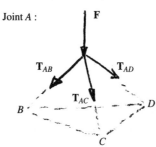

Joint C :

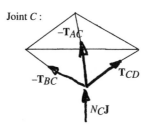

Joint D :

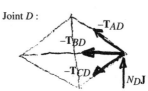

Problem 5.104 In Problem 5.103, suppose that you don't want the reaction at any of the roller supports to exceed 15 kN. What is the largest force F the truss can support?

Solution: The solution to Problem 5.103 is linear in the force components-hence, it can be scaled. The largest roller reaction is at C, $N_C = 13.33$ kN. The maximum value is 15 kN. Scaling the force by the factor 15/13.33 gives

$$F_{max} = \left(\frac{15}{13.33}\right)(20 \text{ kN}) = 22.5 \text{ kN}$$

$$F_{max} = 22.5 \text{ kN}$$

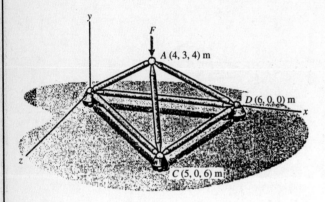

Problem 5.105 The 40-lb door is supported by hinges at A and B. The y axis is vertical. The hinges do not exert couples on the door, and the hinge at B does not exert a force parallel to the hinge axis. The weight of the door acts at its midpoint. What are the reactions at A and B?

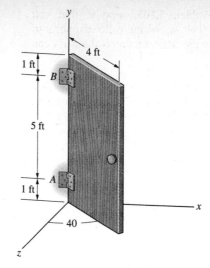

Solution: The position vector of the midpoint of the door:

$$\mathbf{r}_{CM} = (2\cos 50°)\mathbf{i} + 3.5\mathbf{j} + (2\cos 40°)\mathbf{k}$$

$$= 1.2856\mathbf{i} + 3.5\mathbf{j} + 1.532\mathbf{k}.$$

The position vectors of the hinges:

$$\mathbf{r}_A = \mathbf{j}, \quad \mathbf{r}_B = 6\mathbf{j}.$$

The forces are: $\mathbf{W} = -40\mathbf{j}$,

$$\mathbf{A} = A_X\mathbf{i} + A_Y\mathbf{j} + A_Z\mathbf{k},$$

$$\mathbf{B} = B_X\mathbf{i} + B_Z\mathbf{k}.$$

The position vectors relative to A are

$$\mathbf{r}_{ACM} = \mathbf{r}_{CM} - \mathbf{r}_A = 1.2856\mathbf{i} + 2.5\mathbf{j} + 1.532\mathbf{k},$$

$$\mathbf{r}_{AB} = \mathbf{r}_B - \mathbf{r}_A = 5\mathbf{j}.$$

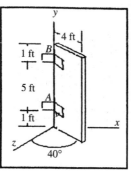

The sum of the moments about A

$$\sum \mathbf{M}_A = \mathbf{r}_{ACM} \times \mathbf{W} + \mathbf{r}_{AB} \times \mathbf{B}$$

$$= \begin{vmatrix} \mathbf{i} & \mathbf{j} & \mathbf{k} \\ 1.2856 & 2.5 & 1.532 \\ 0 & -40 & 0 \end{vmatrix} + \begin{vmatrix} \mathbf{i} & \mathbf{j} & \mathbf{k} \\ 0 & 5 & 0 \\ B_X & 0 & B_Z \end{vmatrix} = 0$$

$$\sum \mathbf{M}_A = (5B_Z + 40(1.532))\mathbf{i} + (-5B_X - 40(1.285))\mathbf{k} = 0,$$

from which $B_Z = \dfrac{-40(1.532)}{5} = -12.256$ lb

and $\quad B_X = \dfrac{-40(1.285)}{5} = -10.28$ lb.

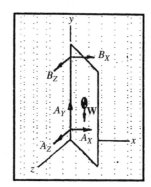

The reactions at A are determined from the sums of forces:

$$\sum \mathbf{F}_X = (A_X + B_X)\mathbf{i} = 0,$$

from which $A_X = 10.28$ lb,

$$\sum \mathbf{F}_Y = (A_Y - 40)\mathbf{j} = 0,$$

from which $A_Y = 40$ lb,

$$\sum \mathbf{F}_Z = (A_Z + B_Z)\mathbf{k} = 0,$$

from which $A_Z = 12.256$ lb

Problem 5.106 The vertical cable is attached at A. Determine the tension in the cable and the reactions at the bearing B due to the force $\mathbf{F} = 10\mathbf{i} - 30\mathbf{j} - 10\mathbf{k}$ (N).

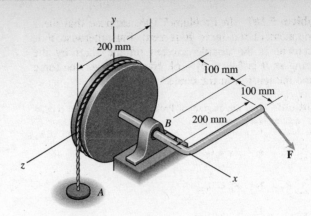

Solution: The position vector of the point of application of the force is

$$\mathbf{r}_F = 0.2\mathbf{i} - 0.2\mathbf{k}.$$

The position vector of the bearing is

$$\mathbf{r}_B = 0.1\mathbf{i}.$$

The position vector of the cable attachment to the wheel is

$$\mathbf{r}_C = 0.1\mathbf{k}.$$

he position vectors relative to B are:

$$\mathbf{r}_{BC} = \mathbf{r}_C - \mathbf{r}_B = -0.1\mathbf{i} + 0.1\mathbf{k},$$

$$\mathbf{r}_{BF} = \mathbf{r}_F - \mathbf{r}_B = 0.1\mathbf{i} - 0.2\mathbf{k}.$$

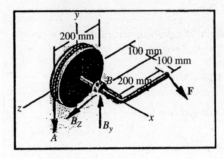

The sum of the moments about the bearing B is

$$\sum \mathbf{M}_B = M_B + \mathbf{r}_{BF} \times \mathbf{F} + \mathbf{r}_{BC} \times \mathbf{C} = 0,$$

or $\sum \mathbf{M}_B = M_B + \begin{vmatrix} \mathbf{i} & \mathbf{j} & \mathbf{k} \\ 0.1 & 0 & -0.2 \\ 10 & -30 & -10 \end{vmatrix} + \begin{vmatrix} \mathbf{i} & \mathbf{j} & \mathbf{k} \\ -0.1 & 0 & 0.1 \\ 0 & -T & 0 \end{vmatrix}$

$$= (-6 + 0.1T)\mathbf{i} + (M_{BY} - 1)\mathbf{j}$$

$$+ (M_{BZ} - 3 + 0.1T)\mathbf{k} = 0,$$

from which $T = \dfrac{6}{0.1} = 60$ N,

$$M_{BY} = +1 \text{ N-m},$$

$$M_{BZ} = -0.1T + 3 = -3 \text{ N-m}.$$

The force reactions at the bearing are determined from the sums of forces:

$$\sum \mathbf{F}_X = (B_X + 10)\mathbf{i} = 0,$$

from which $B_X = -10$ N.

$$\sum \mathbf{F}_Y = (B_Y - 30 - 60)\mathbf{j} = 0,$$

from which $B_Y = 90$ N.

$$\sum \mathbf{F}_Z = (B_Z - 10)\mathbf{j} = 0,$$

from which $B_Z = 10$ N.

Problem 5.107 In Problem 5.106, suppose that the z component of the force $\mathbf{F}$ is zero, but otherwise $\mathbf{F}$ is unknown. If the couple exerted on the shaft by the bearing at B is $\mathbf{M}_B = 6\mathbf{j} - 6\mathbf{k}$ N-m, what are the force $\mathbf{F}$ and the tension in the cable?

Solution: From the diagram of Problem 5.106, the force equilibrium equation components are

$$\sum F_x = B_X + F_X = 0,$$

$$\sum F_y = B_Y + F_Y = 0,$$

and $\sum F_z = B_Z + F_Z = 0,$

where $F_Z = 0$ is given in the problem statement. The moment equations can be developed by inspection of the figure also. They are

$$\sum M_x = M_{BX} + M_{AX} + M_{FX} = 0,$$

$$\sum M_Y = M_{BY} + M_{AY} + M_{FY} = 0,$$

and $\sum M_Z = M_{BZ} + M_{AZ} + M_{FZ} = 0,$

where $M_B = 6\mathbf{j} - 6\mathbf{k}$ N-m. Note that $M_{BX} = 0$ can be inferred. The moments which need to be substituted into the moment equations are

$$M_A = (0.1)A\mathbf{i} + 0\mathbf{j} + (0.1)A\mathbf{k} \text{ N-m},$$

and $M_F = (0.2)F_Y\mathbf{i} - (0.2)F_X\mathbf{j} + (0.1)F_Y\mathbf{k}$ N-m.

Substituting these values into the equilibrium equations, we get $\mathbf{F} = 30\mathbf{i} - 60\mathbf{j} + 0\mathbf{k}$ N, and $A = 120$ N.

Problem 5.108 The device in Problem 5.106 is badly designed because of the couples that must be supported by the bearing at B, which would cause the bearing to "bind". (Imagine trying to open a door supported by only one hinge.) In this improved design, the bearings at B and C support no couples, and the bearing at C does not exert a force in the x direction. If the force $\mathbf{F} = 10\mathbf{i} - 30\mathbf{j} - 10\mathbf{k}$ (N), what are the tension in the vertical cable and the reactions at the bearings B and C?

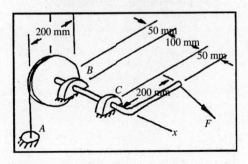

Solution: The position vectors relative to the bearing B are: the position vector of the cable attachment to the wheel is

$$\mathbf{r}_{BT} = -0.05\mathbf{i} + 0.1\mathbf{k}.$$

The position vector of the bearing C is:

$$\mathbf{r}_{BC} = 0.1\mathbf{i}.$$

The position vector of the point of application of the force is:

$$\mathbf{r}_{BF} = 0.15\mathbf{i} - 0.2\mathbf{k}.$$

The sum of the moments about B is

$$\sum \mathbf{M}_B = \mathbf{r}_{BT} \times \mathbf{T} + \mathbf{r}_{BC} \times \mathbf{C} + \mathbf{r}_{BF} \times \mathbf{F} = 0$$

$$\sum \mathbf{M}_B = \begin{vmatrix} \mathbf{i} & \mathbf{j} & \mathbf{k} \\ -0.05 & 0 & 0.1 \\ 0 & -T & 0 \end{vmatrix} + \begin{vmatrix} \mathbf{i} & \mathbf{j} & \mathbf{k} \\ 0.1 & 0 & 0 \\ 0 & C_Y & C_Z \end{vmatrix}$$

$$+ \begin{vmatrix} \mathbf{i} & \mathbf{j} & \mathbf{k} \\ 0.15 & 0 & -0.2 \\ 10 & -30 & -10 \end{vmatrix} = 0$$

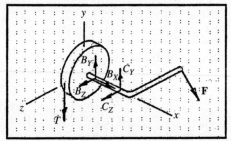

$$\sum \mathbf{M}_B = (0.1T - 6)\mathbf{i} + (-0.1C_Z + 1.5 - 2)\mathbf{j}$$

$$+ (0.05T + 0.1C_Y - 4.5)\mathbf{k} = 0.$$

From which: $T = 60$ N,

$$C_Z = \frac{-0.5}{0.1} = -5 \text{ N},$$

$$C_Y = \frac{4.5 - 0.05T}{0.1} = 15 \text{ N}.$$

The reactions at B are found from the sums of forces:

$$\sum \mathbf{F}_X = (B_X + 10)\mathbf{i} = 0,$$

from which $B_X = -10$ N.

$$\sum \mathbf{F}_Y = (B_Y + C_Y - T - 30)\mathbf{j} = 0,$$

from which $B_Y = 75$ N.

$$\sum \mathbf{F}_Z = (B_Z + C_Z - 10)\mathbf{k} = 0,$$

from which $B_Z = 15$ N

Problem 5.109 The rocket launcher is supported by the hydraulic jack *DE* and the bearings *A* and *B*. The bearings lie on the *x* axis and supports shafts parallel to the *x* axis. The hydraulic cylinder *DE* exerts a force on the launcher that points along the line from *D* to *E*. The coordinates of *D* are (7, 0, 7) ft, and the coordinates of *E* are (9, 6, 4) ft. The weight *W* = 30 kip acts at (4.5, 5, 2) ft. What is the magnitude of the reaction on the launcher at *E*?

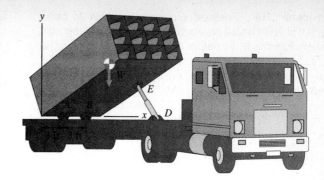

Solution: The position vectors of the points *D*, *E* and *W* are

$$\mathbf{r}_D = 7\mathbf{i} + 7\mathbf{k},$$

$$\mathbf{r}_E = 9\mathbf{i} + 6\mathbf{j} + 4\mathbf{k} \text{ (ft)},$$

$$\mathbf{r}_W = 4.5\mathbf{i} + 5\mathbf{j} + 2\mathbf{k} \text{ (ft)}.$$

The vector parallel to *DE* is

$$\mathbf{r}_{DE} = \mathbf{r}_E - \mathbf{r}_D = 2\mathbf{i} + 6\mathbf{j} - 3\mathbf{k}.$$

The unit vector parallel to *DE* is

$$\mathbf{e}_{DE} = 0.2857\mathbf{i} + 0.8571\mathbf{j} - 0.4286\mathbf{k}.$$

Since the bearings cannot exert a moment about the *x*-axis, the sum of the moments due to the weight and the jack force must be zero about the *x*-axis. The sum of the moments about the *x*-axis is:

$$\sum M_X = \begin{vmatrix} 1 & 0 & 0 \\ 4.5 & 5 & 2 \\ 0 & -30 & 0 \end{vmatrix} + |\mathbf{F}_{DE}| \begin{vmatrix} 1 & 0 & 0 \\ 9 & 6 & 4 \\ 0.2857 & 0.8571 & -0.4286 \end{vmatrix} = 0$$

$$= 60 - 6|\mathbf{F}_{DE}| = 0.$$

From which

$$|\mathbf{F}_{DE}| = \frac{60}{6} = 10 \text{ kip}$$

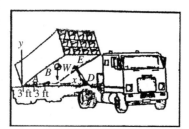

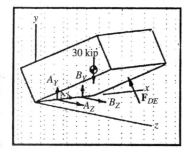

Problem 5.110 Consider the rocket launcher described in Problem 5.109. The bearings at A and B do not exert couples, and the bearing B does not exert a force in the x direction. Determine the reactions at A and B.

Solution: See the solution of Problem 5.109. The force $\mathbf{F}_{DE}$ can be written

$$\mathbf{F}_{DE} = F_{DE}(0.2857\mathbf{i} + 0.8571\mathbf{j} - 0.4286\mathbf{k}).$$

The equilibrium equations are

$$\sum F_X = A_X + 0.2857F_{DE} = 0,$$

$$\sum F_Y = A_Y + B_Y + 0.8571F_{DE} - 30 = 0,$$

$$\sum F_Z = A_Z + B_Z - 0.4286F_{DE} = 0,$$

$$\sum M_{(origin)} = \begin{vmatrix} \mathbf{i} & \mathbf{j} & \mathbf{k} \\ 3 & 0 & 0 \\ A_X & A_Y & A_Z \end{vmatrix} + \begin{vmatrix} \mathbf{i} & \mathbf{j} & \mathbf{k} \\ 6 & 0 & 0 \\ 0 & B_Y & B_Z \end{vmatrix}$$

$$+ F_{DE} \begin{vmatrix} \mathbf{i} & \mathbf{j} & \mathbf{k} \\ 7 & 0 & 7 \\ 0.2857 & 0.8571 & -0.4286 \end{vmatrix}$$

$$+ \begin{vmatrix} \mathbf{i} & \mathbf{j} & \mathbf{k} \\ 4.5 & 5 & 2 \\ 0 & -30 & 0 \end{vmatrix} = 0$$

The components of the moment eq. are

$$-5.9997F_{DE} + 60 = 0,$$

$$-3A_Z - 6B_Z + 5.0001F_{DE} = 0,$$

$$3A_Y + 6B_Y + 5.9997F_{DE} - 135 = 0.$$

Solving, we obtain

$$F_{DE} = 10.00 \text{ kip}, \quad A_X = -2.86 \text{ kip},$$

$$A_Y = 17.86 \text{ kip}, \quad A_Z = -8.09 \text{ kip},$$

$$B_Y = 3.57 \text{ kip}, \quad B_Z = 12.38 \text{ kip}.$$

Problem 5.111 The crane's cable CD is attached to a stationary object at D. The crane is supported by the bearings E and F and the horizontal cable AB. The tension in cable AB is 8 kN. Determine the tension in the cable CD.

Strategy: Since the reactions exerted on the crane by the bearings do not exert moments about the z axis, the sum of the moments about the z axis due to the forces exerted on the crane by the cables AB and CD equals zero. (See the discussion at the end of Example 5.10.)

Solution: The position vector from C to D is

$$\mathbf{r}_{CD} = 3\mathbf{i} - 6\mathbf{j} - 3\mathbf{k} \text{ (m)},$$

so we can write the force exerted at C by cable CD as

$$\mathbf{T}_{CD} = T_{CD}\frac{\mathbf{r}_{CD}}{|\mathbf{r}_{CD}|} = T_{CD}(0.408\mathbf{i} - 0.816\mathbf{j} - 0.408\mathbf{k}).$$

The coordinates of pt. B are $x = \dfrac{4}{6}(3) = 2$ m, $y = 4$ m.

The moment about the origin due to the forces exerted by the two cables is

$$\mathbf{M}_O = \begin{vmatrix} \mathbf{i} & \mathbf{j} & \mathbf{k} \\ 2 & 4 & 0 \\ -8 & 0 & 0 \end{vmatrix} + \begin{vmatrix} \mathbf{i} & \mathbf{j} & \mathbf{k} \\ 3 & 6 & 0 \\ 0.408T_{CD} & -0.816T_{CD} & -0.408T_{CD} \end{vmatrix}$$

$$= 32\mathbf{k} - 2.448T_{CD}\mathbf{i} + 1.224T_{CD}\mathbf{j} - 4.896T_{CD}\mathbf{k}.$$

The moment about the z axis is

$$\mathbf{k} \cdot \mathbf{M}_O = 32 - 4.896T_{CD} = 0,$$

so $T_{CD} = 6.54$ kN.

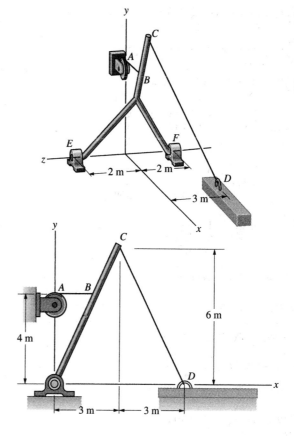

Problem 5.112 The crane in Problem 5.111 is supported by the horizontal cable AB and the bearings at E and F. The bearings do not exert couples, and the bearing at F does not exert a force in the z direction. The tension in cable AB is 8 kN. Determine the reactions at E and F.

Solution: See the solution of Problem 5.111. The force exerted at C can be written

$$\mathbf{T}_{CD} = T_{CD}(0.408\mathbf{i} - 0.816\mathbf{j} - 0.408\mathbf{k})$$

and the coordinates of pt. B are $(2, 4, 0)$ m.

The equilibrium equations are

$$\sum F_X = E_X + F_X - 8 + 0.408T_{CD} = 0,$$

$$\sum F_Y = E_Y + F_Y - 0.816T_{CD} = 0,$$

$$\sum F_Z = E_Z - 0.408T_{CD} = 0,$$

$$\sum \mathbf{M}_O = \begin{vmatrix} \mathbf{i} & \mathbf{j} & \mathbf{k} \\ 0 & 0 & 2 \\ E_X & E_Y & E_Z \end{vmatrix} + \begin{vmatrix} \mathbf{i} & \mathbf{j} & \mathbf{k} \\ 0 & 0 & -2 \\ F_X & F_Y & 0 \end{vmatrix} + \begin{vmatrix} \mathbf{i} & \mathbf{j} & \mathbf{k} \\ 2 & 4 & 0 \\ -8 & 0 & 0 \end{vmatrix}$$

$$+ \begin{vmatrix} \mathbf{i} & \mathbf{j} & \mathbf{k} \\ 3 & 6 & 0 \\ 0.408T_{CD} & -0.816T_{CD} & -0.408T_{CD} \end{vmatrix} = 0.$$

The components of the moment equation are

$$\sum M_X = -2E_Y + 2F_Y - 2.448T_{CD} = 0,$$

$$\sum M_Y = 2E_X - 2F_X + 1.224T_{CD} = 0,$$

$$\sum M_Z = 32 - 4.896T_{CD} = 0.$$

From the last equation, $T_{CD} = 6.54$ kN. Solving the other eqs, we obtain

$$E_X = 667 \text{ N},$$

$$E_Y = -1,333 \text{ N},$$

$$E_Z = 2,667 \text{ N},$$

$$F_X = 4,667 \text{ N},$$

$$F_Y = 6,667 \text{ N}.$$

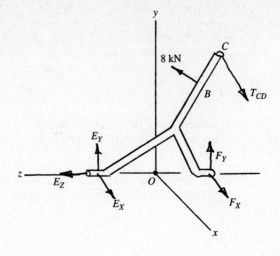

Problem 5.113 The plate is supported by hinges at A and B and the cable CE, and it is loaded by the force at D. The edge of the plate to which the hinges are attached lies in the $y - z$ plane, and the axes of the hinges are parallel to the line through points A and B. The hinges do not exert couples on the plate. What is the tension in cable CE?

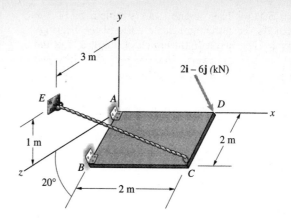

Solution:

$$\sum F = A + B + F_D + T_{CE} = 0$$

However, we just want tension in CE. This quantity is the only unknown in the moment equation about the line AB. To get this, we need the unit vector along CE.

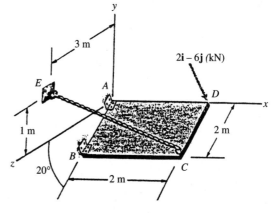

Point C is at $(2, -2\sin 20°, 2\cos 20°)$ Point E is at $(0, 1, 3)$

$$e_{CE} = \frac{r_{CE}}{|r_{CE}|}$$

$$e_{CE} = -0.703i + 0.592j + 0.394k$$

We also need the unit vector e_{AB}. $A(0, 0, 0)$, $B(0, -2\sin 20°, 2\cos 20°)$

$$e_{AB} = 0i - 0.342j + 0.940k$$

The moment of F_D about A (a point on AB) is

$$M_{F_D} = r_{AD} \times F_{D_1} = (2i) \times (2i - 6j)$$

$$M_{F_D} = -12k$$

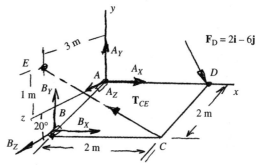

The moment of T_{CE} about B (another point on line CE) is

$$M_{T_{CE}} = r_{BC} \times T_{CE}e_{CE} = 2i \times T_{CE}e_{CE},$$

where e_{CE} is given above.

The moment of F_D about line AB is

$$M_{FD_{AB}} = M_{FD} \cdot e_{AB}$$

$$M_{FD_{AB}} = -11.27 \text{ N-m}$$

The moment of T_{CE} about line AB is

$$M_{CE_{AB}} = T_{CE}(2i \times e_{CE}) \cdot e_{AB}$$

$$M_{CE_{AB}} = T_{CE}(-0.788j + 1.184k) \cdot e_{AB}$$

$$M_{CE_{AB}} = 1.382T_{CE}$$

The sum of the moments about line AB is zero. Hence

$$M_{FD_{AB}} + M_{CE_{AB}} = 0$$

$$-11.27 + 1.382T_{CE} = 0$$

$$T_{CE} = 8.15 \text{ kN}$$

Problem 5.114 In Problem 5.113, the hinge at B does not exert a force on the plate in the direction of the hinge axis. What are the magnitudes of the forces exerted on the plate by the hinges at A and B?

Solution: From the solution to Problem 5.113, $T_{CE} = 8.15$ kN Also, from that solution,

$$\mathbf{e}_{AB} = 0\mathbf{i} - 0.342\mathbf{j} + 0.940\mathbf{k}$$

We are given that the force at force at hinge B does not exert a force parallel to AB at B. This implies

$$\mathbf{B} \cdot \mathbf{e}_{AB} = 0.$$

$$\mathbf{B} \cdot \mathbf{e}_{AB} = -0.342B_Y + 0.940B_Z = 0 \quad \textbf{(1)}$$

We also had, in the solution to Problem 5.113

$$\mathbf{e}_{CE} = -0.703\mathbf{i} + 0.592\mathbf{j} + 0.394\mathbf{k}$$

and $\quad \mathbf{T}_{CE} = T_{CE}\mathbf{e}_{CE}$ (kN)

For Equilibrium,

$$\sum \mathbf{F} = \mathbf{A} + \mathbf{B} + \mathbf{T}_{CE} + \mathbf{F} = 0$$

$$\sum F_X: \quad A_X + B_X + T_{CE}e_{CE_X} + 2 = 0 \text{ (kN)} \quad \textbf{(2)}$$

$$\sum F_Y: \quad A_Y + B_Y + T_{CE}e_{CE_Y} - 6 = 0 \text{ (kN)} \quad \textbf{(3)}$$

$$\sum F_Z: \quad A_Z + B_Z + T_{CE}e_{CE_Z} = 0 \text{ (kN)} \quad \textbf{(4)}$$

Summing Moments about A, we have

$$\mathbf{r}_{AD} \times \mathbf{F} + \mathbf{r}_{AC} \times \mathbf{T}_{CE} + \mathbf{r}_{AB} \times \mathbf{B} = 0$$

$$\mathbf{r}_{AD} \times \mathbf{F} = 2\mathbf{i} \times (2\mathbf{i} - 6\mathbf{j}) = -12\mathbf{k} \text{ (kN)}$$

$$\mathbf{r}_{AC} \times \mathbf{T}_{CE} = (-2 \sin \theta T_Z - 2 \cos \theta T_Y)\mathbf{i}$$

$$+ (2 \cos \theta T_X - 2T_Z)\mathbf{j}$$

$$+ (2T_Y + 2T_X \sin \theta)\mathbf{k}$$

$$\mathbf{r}_{CE} \times \mathbf{B} = (-2B_Z \sin \theta - 2B_Y \cos \theta)\mathbf{i}$$

$$+ (2B_X \cos \theta)\mathbf{j} + (+2B_X \sin \theta)\mathbf{k}$$

$$\sum \mathbf{M}_A = 0,$$

Hence

x: $\quad -2 \sin \theta T_Z - 2 \cos \theta T_Y - 2B_Z \sin \theta$

$\quad - 2B_Y \cos \theta = 0 \quad \textbf{(5)}$

y: $\quad 2 \cos \theta T_X - 2T_Z + 2B_X \cos \theta = 0 \quad \textbf{(6)}$

z: $\quad -12 + 2T_Y + 2T_X \sin \theta + 2B_X \sin \theta = 0 \quad \textbf{(7)}$

Solving Eqns (1)–(7), we get

$$|\mathbf{A}| = 8.53 \text{ (kN)}, \quad |\mathbf{B}| = 10.75 \text{ (kN)}$$

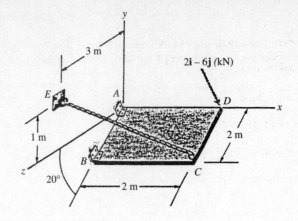

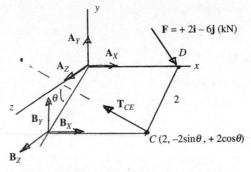

Problem 5.115 The bar ABC is supported by ball and socket supports at A and C and the cable BD, and is loaded by the 200-lb suspended weight. What is the tension in cable BD?

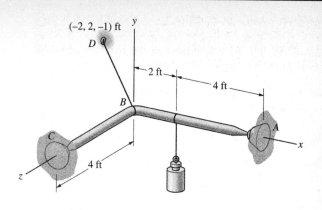

(−2, 2, −1) ft

Solution: The strategy is to take the moments about A. Note that a ball and socket cannot support a couple reaction. The vector parallel to the cable is

• $\mathbf{r}_{BD} = -2\mathbf{i} + 2\mathbf{j} - \mathbf{k}$.

The unit vector parallel to the cable is

$\mathbf{e}_{BD} = -0.6667\mathbf{i} + 0.6667\mathbf{j} - 0.3333\mathbf{k}$.

The vector positions of the weight, point B and point C relative to point A are:

$\mathbf{r}_{AW} = -4\mathbf{i}$,

$\mathbf{r}_{AB} = -6\mathbf{i}$,

and $\mathbf{r}_{AC} = -6\mathbf{i} + 4\mathbf{k}$.

The sum of the moments about A is

$$\sum \mathbf{M}_A = \mathbf{r}_{AW} \times \mathbf{W} + \mathbf{r}_{AB} \times \mathbf{T}$$
$$+ \, \mathbf{r}_{AC} \times \mathbf{C} = 0$$

$$\sum \mathbf{M}_A = \begin{vmatrix} \mathbf{i} & \mathbf{j} & \mathbf{k} \\ -4 & 0 & 0 \\ 0 & -200 & 0 \end{vmatrix} + |\mathbf{T}| \begin{vmatrix} \mathbf{i} & \mathbf{j} & \mathbf{k} \\ -6 & 0 & 0 \\ -0.6667 & 0.6667 & -0.3333 \end{vmatrix}$$

$$+ \begin{vmatrix} \mathbf{i} & \mathbf{j} & \mathbf{k} \\ -6 & 0 & 4 \\ C_X & C_Y & C_Z \end{vmatrix} = 0$$

$$= -4C_Y\mathbf{i} + (-2|\mathbf{T}| + 4C_X + 6C_Z)\mathbf{j}$$

$$+ \, (800 - 4|\mathbf{T}| - 6C_Y)\mathbf{k} = 0.$$

From which:

$C_Y = 0$,

$$|\mathbf{T}| = \frac{800}{4} = 200 \text{ lb}$$

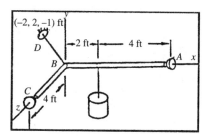

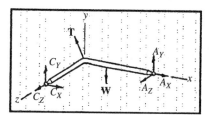

Problem 5.116 In Problem 5.115, determine the y components of the reactions exerted on the bar ABC by the ball and socket supports at A and C.

Solution: From the figure in Problem 5.115, we see that there are seven unknowns (3 reaction components each at A and C plus the magnitude of the tension force in the cable). Equilibrium in three dimensions gives us only six equations. Thus, statics alone will not give us information sufficient to find all of the unknowns. However, we are often able to find values for some of the variables. In Problem 5.115, we found that the cable tension was 200 lb and the value for the y component of the force at C is zero. We are now asked to determine the values of the y components of the forces at A and C. We have already determined $C_Y = 0$, and

$T_Y = Te_{BDY} = 200(0.667) = 133.3 \text{ lb}$.

Since we also know the weight, we know all of the vertical forces except the vertical support force at A. The vertical equilibrium equation is

$C_Y + A_Y + T_Y - W = 0$.

Substituting and solving results in

$A_Y = W - T_Y = 200 - 133.33 = 66.67 \text{ lb}$.

Problem 5.117 The bearings at A, B, and C do not exert couples on the bar and do not exert forces in the direction of the axis of the bar. Determine the reactions at the bearings due to the two forces on the bar.

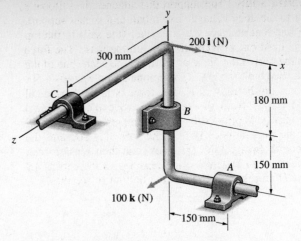

Solution: The strategy is to take the moments about A and solve the resulting simultaneous equations. The position vectors of the bearings relative to A are:

$$\mathbf{r}_{AB} = -0.15\mathbf{i} + 0.15\mathbf{j},$$

$$\mathbf{r}_{AC} = -0.15\mathbf{i} + 0.33\mathbf{j} + 0.3\mathbf{k}.$$

Denote the lower force by subscript 1, and the upper by subscript 2:

$$\mathbf{r}_{A1} = -0.15\mathbf{i},$$

$$\mathbf{r}_{A2} = -0.15\mathbf{i} + 0.33\mathbf{j}.$$

The sum of the moments about A is:

$$\sum \mathbf{M}_A = \mathbf{r}_{A1} \times \mathbf{F}_1 + \mathbf{r}_{AB} \times \mathbf{B} + \mathbf{r}_{A2} \times \mathbf{F}_2 + \mathbf{r}_{AC} \times \mathbf{C} = 0$$

$$\sum \mathbf{M}_A = \begin{vmatrix} \mathbf{i} & \mathbf{j} & \mathbf{k} \\ -0.15 & 0 & 0 \\ 0 & 0 & 100 \end{vmatrix} + \begin{vmatrix} \mathbf{i} & \mathbf{j} & \mathbf{k} \\ -0.15 & 0.15 & 0 \\ B_X & 0 & B_Z \end{vmatrix}$$

$$+ \begin{vmatrix} \mathbf{i} & \mathbf{j} & \mathbf{k} \\ -0.15 & 0.33 & 0 \\ 200 & 0 & 0 \end{vmatrix} + \begin{vmatrix} \mathbf{i} & \mathbf{j} & \mathbf{k} \\ -0.15 & 0.33 & 0.3 \\ C_X & C_Y & 0 \end{vmatrix} = 0$$

$$\sum \mathbf{M}_A = (0.15B_Z - 0.3C_Y)\mathbf{i} + (15 + 0.15B_Z + 0.3C_X)\mathbf{j}$$

$$+ (-0.15B_X - 66 - 0.15C_Y - 0.33C_X)\mathbf{k} = 0.$$

This results in three equations in four unknowns; an additional equation is provided by the sum of the forces in the x-direction (which cannot have a reaction term due to A)

$$\sum \mathbf{F}_X = (B_X + C_X + 200)\mathbf{i} = 0.$$

The four equations in four unknowns:

$$0B_X + 0.15B_Z + 0C_X - 0.3C_Z = 0$$

$$0B_X + 0.15B_Z + 0.3C_X + 0C_Y = -15$$

$$-0.15B_X + 0B_Z - 0.33C_X - 0.15C_Y = 66$$

$$B_X + 0B_Z + C_X + 0C_Z = -200.$$

(The HP-28S hand held calculator was used to solve these equations.) The solution:

$$B_X = 750 \text{ N},$$

$$B_Z = 1800 \text{ N},$$

$$C_X = -950 \text{ N},$$

$$C_Y = 900 \text{ N}.$$

The reactions at A are determined by the sums of forces:

$$\sum \mathbf{F}_Y = (A_Y + C_Y)\mathbf{j} = 0, \text{ from which } A_Y = -C_Y = -900 \text{ N}$$

$$\sum \mathbf{F}_Z = (A_Z + B_Z + 100)\mathbf{k} = 0, \text{ from which } A_Z = -1900 \text{ N}$$

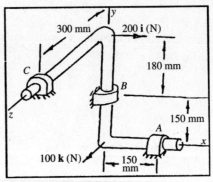

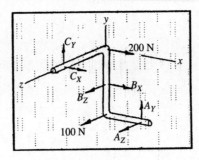

Problem 5.118 The support that attaches the sailboat's mast to the deck behaves like a ball and socket support. The line that attaches the spinnaker (the sail) to the top of the mast exerts a 200-lb force on the mast. The force is in the horizontal plane at 15° from the centerline of the boat. (See the top view.) The spinnaker pole exerts a 50-lb force on the mast at P. The force is in the horizontal plane at 45° from the centerline. (See the top view.) The mast is supported by two cables, the back stay AB and the port shroud ACD. (The fore stay AE and the starboard shroud AFG are slack, and their tensions can be neglected.) Determine the tensions in the cables AB and CD and the reactions at the bottom of the mast.

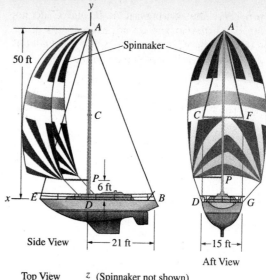

Side View

Aft View

Top View z (Spinnaker not shown)

Solution: Although the dimensions are not given in the sketch, assume that the point C is at the midpoint of the mast (25 ft above the deck). The position vectors for the points A, B, C, D, and P are:

$$\mathbf{r}_A = 50\mathbf{j},$$

$$\mathbf{r}_B = -21\mathbf{i},$$

$$\mathbf{r}_P = 6\mathbf{j},$$

$$\mathbf{r}_C = 25\mathbf{j} - 7.5\mathbf{k}.$$

The vector parallel to the backstay AB is

$$\mathbf{r}_{AB} = \mathbf{r}_B - \mathbf{r}_A = -21\mathbf{i} - 50\mathbf{j}.$$

The unit vector parallel to backstay AB is

$$\mathbf{e}_{AB} = -0.3872\mathbf{i} - 0.9220\mathbf{j}.$$

The vector parallel to AC is

$$\mathbf{r}_{AC} = \mathbf{r}_C - \mathbf{r}_A = -25\mathbf{j} - 7.5\mathbf{k}.$$

The forces acting on the mast are: (1) The force due to the spinnaker at the top of the mast:

$$\mathbf{F}_A = 200(\mathbf{i}\cos 15° + \mathbf{k}\cos 75°) = 193.19\mathbf{i} + 51.76\mathbf{k}.$$

(2) The reaction due to the backstay:

$$\mathbf{T}_{AB} = |\mathbf{T}_{AB}|\mathbf{e}_{AB}$$

(3) The reaction due to the shroud:

$$\mathbf{T}_{AC} = |\mathbf{T}_{AC}|\mathbf{e}_{AC}$$

(4) The force acting on the cross spar CE:

$$\mathbf{T}_{CE} = -(\mathbf{k} \cdot \mathbf{T}_{AC})\mathbf{k} = 0.2873|\mathbf{T}_{AC}|\mathbf{k}.$$

(5) The force due to the spinnaker pole:

$$\mathbf{F}_P = 50(-0.707\mathbf{i} + 0.707\mathbf{k}) = -35.35\mathbf{i} + 35.35\mathbf{k}.$$

The sum of the moments about the base of the mast is

$$\mathbf{M}_Q = \mathbf{r}_A \times \mathbf{F}_A + \mathbf{r}_A \times \mathbf{T}_{AB} + \mathbf{r}_A \times \mathbf{T}_{AC} + \mathbf{r}_C \times \mathbf{T}_{CE}$$

$$+ \mathbf{r}_P \times \mathbf{F}_P = 0$$

$$\sum \mathbf{M}_Q = \mathbf{r}_A \times (\mathbf{F}_A + \mathbf{T}_{AB} + \mathbf{T}_{AC}) + \mathbf{r}_C \times \mathbf{T}_{CE} + \mathbf{r}_P \times \mathbf{F}_P = 0.$$

From above,

$$\mathbf{F}_A + \mathbf{T}_{AB} + \mathbf{T}_{AC} = F_{TX}\mathbf{i} + F_{TY}\mathbf{j} + F_{TZ}\mathbf{k}$$

$$= (193.2 - (0.3872)|\mathbf{T}_{AB}|)\mathbf{i} + (-0.922|\mathbf{T}_{AB}|$$

$$- 0.9578|\mathbf{T}_{AC}|)\mathbf{j} + (51.76 - 0.2873|\mathbf{T}_{AC}|)\mathbf{k}$$

$$\sum \mathbf{M}_Q = \begin{vmatrix} \mathbf{i} & \mathbf{j} & \mathbf{k} \\ 0 & 50 & 50 \\ F_{TX} & F_{TY} & F_{TZ} \end{vmatrix} + \begin{vmatrix} \mathbf{i} & \mathbf{j} & \mathbf{k} \\ 0 & 25 & -7.5 \\ 0 & 0 & 0.2873|\mathbf{T}_{AC}| \end{vmatrix}$$

$$+ \begin{vmatrix} \mathbf{i} & \mathbf{j} & \mathbf{k} \\ 0 & 6 & 6 \\ -35.35 & 0 & 35.35 \end{vmatrix} = 0$$

$$= (50F_{TZ} + (25)(0.2873)|\mathbf{T}_{AC}| + 212.1)\mathbf{i}$$

$$+ (-50F_{TX} + 212.1)\mathbf{k} = 0.$$

Substituting and collecting terms:

$$(2800 - 7.1829|\mathbf{T}_{AC}|)\mathbf{i} + (-9447.9 + 19.36|\mathbf{T}_{AB}|)\mathbf{k} = 0,$$

from which

$$|\mathbf{T}_{AC}| = \frac{2800}{7.1829} = 389.81 \text{ lb},$$

$$|\mathbf{T}_{AB}| = 488.0 \text{ lb}.$$

5.118 *Contd.*

The tension in cable *CD* is the vertical component of the tension
in *AC*,

$$|\mathbf{T}_{CD}| = |\mathbf{T}_{AC}|(\mathbf{j} \cdot \mathbf{e}_{AC}) = |\mathbf{T}_{AC}|(0.9578) = 373.37 \text{ lb.}$$

The reaction at the base is found from the sums of the forces:

$$\sum \mathbf{F}_X = (Q_X + 193.19 - 35.35 - |\mathbf{T}_{AB}|(0.3872)) = 0,$$

from which $Q_X = 31.11$ lb

$$\sum \mathbf{F}_Y = (Q_Y - 0.922|\mathbf{T}_{AB}| - 0.9578|\mathbf{T}_{AC}|)\mathbf{j} = 0,$$

from which $Q_Y = 823.24$ lb

$$\sum \mathbf{F}_Z = (Q_Z + 51.76 + (0.2873|\mathbf{T}_{AC}|$$

$$- 0.2873|\mathbf{T}_{AC}| + 35.35))\mathbf{k} = 0,$$

from which $Q_Z = -87.11$ lb

Collecting the terms, the reaction is

$$\mathbf{Q} = 31.14\mathbf{i} + 823.26\mathbf{j} - 87.12\mathbf{k} \text{ (lb)}$$

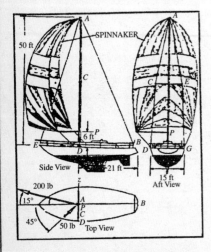

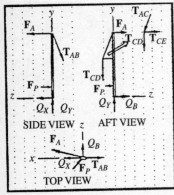

Problem 5.119 The door is supported by the cable DE and hinges at A and B, and is subjected to a 2-kN force at C. The door's weight is negligible. The hinges do not exert couples on the door, and their axes are aligned with the line from A to B. Determine the tension in the cable.

Solution: We will sum moments around the origin. There are two unit vectors that we need to find. We need the unit vector along the hinge line AB and the unit vector along the cable DE. These unit vectors are

$$\mathbf{e}_{AB} = 0.545\mathbf{i} - 0.182\mathbf{j} + 0.818\mathbf{k}$$

and $\mathbf{e}_{DE} = -0.545\mathbf{i} + 0.182\mathbf{j} + 0.818\mathbf{k}$.

We also need to know the vectors from the origin, A, to each of the points involved. Each of these vectors is of the form

$$\mathbf{r}_{AP} = x_P\mathbf{i} + y_P\mathbf{j} + z_p\mathbf{k},$$

where the point is at (x_P, y_P, z_P). The force in the cable is of the form

$$\mathbf{T}_{DE} = T_{DE}\mathbf{e}_{DE} = T_{DEX}\mathbf{i} + T_{DEY}\mathbf{j} + T_{DEZ}\mathbf{k}\ \text{N}.$$

The force at C is of the form $C = -2\mathbf{j}$ kN, and the forces at A and B are

$$\mathbf{A} = A_X\mathbf{i} + A_Y\mathbf{j} + A_Z\mathbf{k}$$

and $\mathbf{B} = B_X\mathbf{i} + B_Y\mathbf{j} + B_Z\mathbf{k}$.

With these definitions, the force and moment vector equations of equilibrium are

$$\mathbf{A} + \mathbf{B} + \mathbf{C} + \mathbf{T} = 0$$

and $\mathbf{M}_T + \mathbf{M}_B + \mathbf{M}_C = 0$.

Writing these in scalar form yields six equations in seven unknowns. To find the magnitude T, we need another condition. If we look at the picture, we see that the moments around the hinge line AB must be balanced or the door will move. Furthermore, this equation does not involve forces at either A or B. We get one equation in the one unknown we are looking for. To get the equation for the moment about line AB, we find the sum of the moments of the forces around any point on AB (choose A) and then dot this into the unit vector along AB. The condition is

$$(\mathbf{M}_T + \mathbf{M}_B + \mathbf{M}_C) \bullet \mathbf{e}_{AB} = 0.$$

If we write the equations in scalar form and add this to our equations and solve, we get $T = 2.44$ N.

Problem 5.120 Determine the reactions at the hinges supporting the door in Problem 5.119. Assume that the hinge at B exerts no force parallel to the hinge axis.

Strategy: Express the reactions at the hinges as

$$\mathbf{A} = A_x\mathbf{i} + A_y\mathbf{j} + A_z\mathbf{k}$$

and $\mathbf{B} = B_x\mathbf{i} + B_y\mathbf{j} + B_z\mathbf{k}$.

Let $\mathbf{e}_{AB}$ be a unit vector parallel to the hinge axes. Since the hinge at B exerts no force parallel to the hinge axis, you know that $\mathbf{e}_{AB} \bullet \mathbf{B} = 0$.

Solution: We have done much of this problem in Problem 5.119. The extra equation that we found, summing moments around the hinge axis, did not give us an additional equation to count in the equations versus unknowns balancing process. It was merely a handy linear combination of the equations we already had. — However, now we have been given additional information. The force B does not act parallel to the hinge axis, and it a hinge axis coordinate system, would have only two components. This, in effect, removes one unknown (or adds a new equation), balancing equations and unknowns. The equation that we add is

$$\mathbf{e}_{AB} \bullet \mathbf{B} = e_{ABX}B_X + e_{ABY}B_Y + e_{ABZ}B_Z = 0.$$

Adding this to the force and moment equations from above and solving, we get

$$\mathbf{A} = 0.474\mathbf{i} - 0.825\mathbf{j} - 1.956\mathbf{k} \text{ N and}$$

$$\mathbf{B} = 0.860\mathbf{i} + 2.380\mathbf{j} - 0.044\mathbf{k} \text{ N}.$$

Note that in these coordinates, the force at B has components parallel to all three axes. If we rotated into coordinates parallel and perpendicular to the hinge axis AB, one of the components of the force at B would disappear.

Problem 5.121 The horizontal bar has a mass of 10 kg. Its weight acts at the midpoint of the bar, and it is supported by a roller support at A and the cable BC. Use the fact that the bar is a three-force member to determine the angle α, the tension in the cable BC, and the magnitude of the reaction at A.

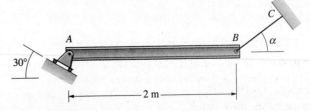

Solution: The roller support at A and the cable support at B are one-force supports. The reaction at A is

$$\mathbf{A} = A(\mathbf{i}\cos 60° + \mathbf{j}\sin 60°) = A(0.5\mathbf{i} + 0.866\mathbf{j}).$$

The reaction at B is

$$\mathbf{B} = B(\mathbf{i}\cos\alpha + \mathbf{j}\sin\alpha).$$

The sum of the moments about B is

$$\sum M_B = +W(1) - A(0.866)(2) = 0,$$

from which

$$A = \frac{W}{(0.866)(2)} = \frac{(9.81)(10)}{1.732} = 56.64 \text{ N}$$

The sums of the forces:

$$\sum F_X = A(0.5) + B(\cos\alpha) = 0,$$

from which

$$B\cos\alpha = -56.64(0.5) = -28.32.$$

$$\sum F_Y = A(0.866) - W + B\sin\alpha = 0,$$

from which

$$B\sin\alpha = 98.1 - 45.09 = 49.05.$$

Combining:

$$\tan\alpha = \frac{49.05}{-28.32} = -1.732,$$

from which

$$\alpha = 120°$$

or $\alpha = 300°$.

Since

$$\cos\alpha \leq 0$$

and $\sin\alpha \geq 0$,

the angle is in the second quadrant, hence $\alpha = 120°$, and $B = \dfrac{49.05}{\sin\alpha} = 56.64$ N

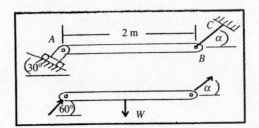

Problem 5.122 The horizontal bar is of negligible weight. Use the fact that the bar is a three-force member to determine the angle α necessary for equilibrium.

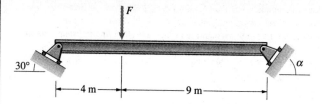

Solution: When the action lines of the reactions meet at a point, and the force does not produce a moment about that point, the system is in equilibrium. This situation occurs when all three action lines meet at the point P. Construct the two triangles shown. The hypotenuse of the left triangle is

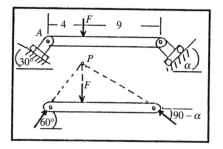

$$h = \frac{4}{\cos 60°} = 8.$$

The vertical distance to the point P is $D = \sqrt{8^2 - 4^2} = 6.9282$. The angle α is:

$$90° - \alpha = \tan^{-1}\left(\frac{6.9282}{9}\right),$$

from which $\alpha = 90° - 37.589° = 52.4°$

Problem 5.123 The suspended load weighs 1000 lb. If you neglect its weight, the structure is a three-force member. Use this fact to determine the magnitudes of the reactions at A and B.

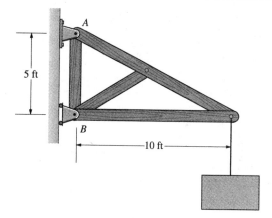

Solution: The pin support at A is a two-force reaction, and the roller support at B is a one force reaction. The moment about A is $M_A = 5B - 10(1000) = 0$, from which the magnitude at B is $B = 2000$ lb. The sums of the forces:

$$\sum F_X = A_X + B = A_X + 2000 = 0, \text{ from which } A_X = -2000 \text{ lb.}$$

$$\sum F_Y = A_Y - 1000 = 0, \text{ from which } A_Y = 1000 \text{ lb.}$$

The magnitude at A is $A = \sqrt{2000^2 + 1000^2} = 2236$ lb

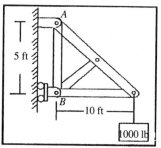

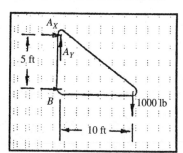

Problem 5.124 The weight $W = 50$ lb acts at the center of the disk. Use the fact that the disk is a three-force member to determine the tension in the cable and the magnitude of the reaction at the pin support.

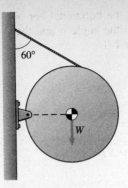

Solution: Denote the magnitude of the reaction at the pinned joint by B. The sums of the forces are:

$$\sum F_X = B_X - T \sin 60° = 0,$$

and $\sum F_Y = B_Y + T \cos 60° - W = 0.$

The perpendicular distance to the action line of the tension from the center of the disk is the radius R. The sum of the moments about the center of the disk is $M_C = -RB_Y + RT = 0$, from which $B_Y = T$. Substitute into the sum of the forces to obtain: $T + T(0.5) - W = 0$, from which

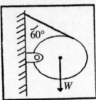

$$T = \frac{2}{3}W = 33.33 \text{ lb.}$$

Substitute into the sum of forces to obtain

$$B_X = T \sin 60° = 28.86 \text{ lb.}$$

The magnitude of the reaction at the pinned joint is

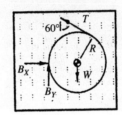

$$B = \sqrt{33.33^2 + 28.86^2} = 44.1 \text{ lb}$$

Problem 5.125 The weight $W = 40$ N acts at the center of the disk. The surfaces are rough. What force F is necessary to lift the disk off the floor?

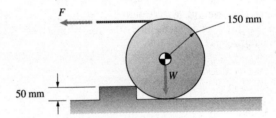

Solution: The reaction at the obstacle acts through the center of the disk (see sketch) Denote the contact point by B. When the moment is zero about the point B, the disk is at the verge of leaving the floor, hence the force at this condition is the force required to lift the disk. The perpendicular distance from B to the action line of the weight is $d = R \cos \alpha$, where α is given by (see sketch)

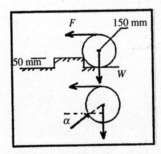

$$\alpha = \sin^{-1}\left(\frac{R - h}{R}\right) = \sin^{-1}\left(\frac{150 - 50}{150}\right) = 41.81°.$$

The perpendicular distance to the action line of the force is

$$D = 2R - h = 300 - 50 = 250 \text{ mm.}$$

The sum of the moments about the contact point is

$$M_B = -(R \cos \alpha)W + (2R - h)F = 0,$$

from which $\boxed{F = \dfrac{(150 \cos 41.81°)W}{250} = 0.4472W = 17.88 \text{ N}}$

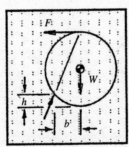

Problem 5.126 Use the fact that the horizontal bar is a three-force member to determine the angle α and the magnitudes of the reactions at A and B.

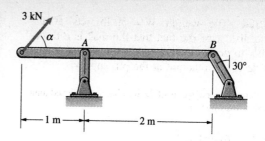

Solution: The sum of the moments about B is

$$M_B = -(3)(3\sin\alpha) + (2)A = 0,$$

from which $A = \dfrac{9\sin\alpha}{2} = 4.5\sin\alpha.$

The sum of the forces:

$$\sum F_X = 3\cos\alpha - B\sin 30° = 0,$$

and $\sum F_Y = 3\sin\alpha - A + B\cos 30° = 0.$

Eliminate B as follows: solve each equation for B, and substitute the value for A:

$$B = \frac{1.5\sin\alpha}{\cos 30°},$$

and $B = \dfrac{3\cos\alpha}{\sin 30°},$

from which

$$\frac{1.5\sin\alpha}{\cos 30°} = \frac{3\cos\alpha}{\sin 30°},$$

or $\tan\alpha = \dfrac{3\cos 30°}{1.5\sin 30°}$

$$= 3.4641,$$

$$\alpha = 73.9°.$$

Substitute into the force equations to obtain

$B = 1.66$ kN,

$A = 4.32$ kN

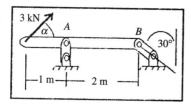

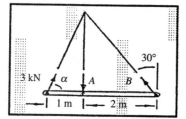

Problem 5.127 The suspended load weighs 600 lb. Use the fact that ABC is a three-force member to determine the magnitudes of the reactions at A and B.

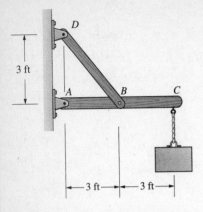

Solution: Isolate the member ABC. The angle ABD is $45°$ since the base and altitude of the triangle are equal. The sum of the moments about A is

$$M_A = +3B \sin 45° - 6(600) = 0$$

from which $B = \dfrac{6(600)}{3 \sin 45°} = 1697.1$ lb.

The sum of the forces

$$\sum F_X = A_X - B \cos 45° = 0,$$

from which $A_X = 1199.8$ lb.

$$\sum F_Y = A_Y + B \sin 45° - 600 = 0,$$

from which $A_Y = 600 - 1199.82 = -599.82$.

The magnitude at A is

$$A = \sqrt{1199.8^2 + 599.8^2} = 1341.4 \text{ lb}$$

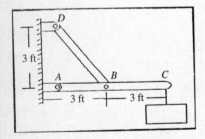

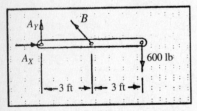

Problem 5.128 (a) Is the L-shaped bar a three-force member?

(b) Determine the magnitudes of the reactions at A and B.

(c) Are the three forces acting on the L-shaped bar concurrent?

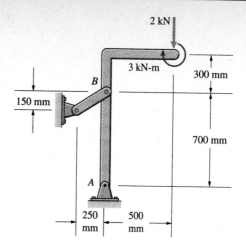

Solution: (a) No. The reaction at B is one-force, and the reaction at A is two-force. The couple keeps the L-shaped bar from being a three force member.(b) The angle of the member at B with the horizontal is

$$\alpha = \tan^{-1}\left(\frac{150}{250}\right) = 30.96°.$$

The sum of the moments about A is

$$\sum M_A = -3 - 0.5(2) + 0.7B\cos\alpha = 0,$$

from which $B = 6.6637$ kN. The sum of forces:

$$\sum F_X = A_X + B\cos\alpha = 0,$$

from which $A_X = -5.7143$ kN.

$$\sum F_Y = A_Y - B\sin\alpha - 2 = 0,$$

from which $A_Y = 5.4281$ kN. The magnitude at A:

$$A = \sqrt{5.71^2 + 5.43^2} = 7.88 \text{ kN (c) No, by inspection.}$$

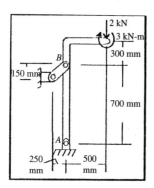

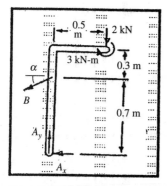

Problem 5.129 The bucket of the excavator is supported by the two-force member AB and the pin support at C. Its weight is $W = 1500$ lb. What are the reactions at C?

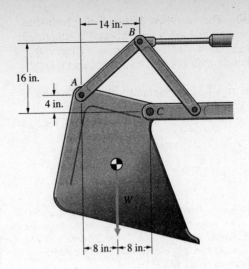

Solution: The angle of the member AB relative to the positive x axis is

$$\alpha = \tan^{-1}\left(\frac{12}{14}\right) = 40.6°.$$

The moment about the point C is

$$M_C = 4A\cos 40.6° + 16A\sin 40.6° + 8W = 0,$$

from which $A = -0.5948W = -892.23$ lb. The sum of forces:

$$\sum F_X = C_X - A\cos 40.6° = 0,$$

from which: $C_X = -677.4$ lb

$$\sum F_Y = C_Y - A\sin 40.6° - W = 0,$$

from which $C_Y = 919.4$ lb

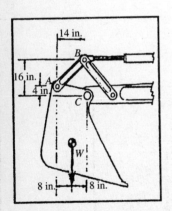

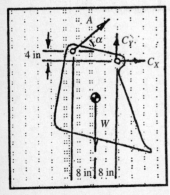

Problem 5.130 The member ACG of the front-end loader is subjected to a load $W = 2$ kN and is supported by a pin support at A and the hydraulic cylinder BC. Treat the hydraulic cylinder as a two-force member.

(a) Draw a free-body diagrams of the hydraulic cylinder and the member ACG.
(b) Determine the reactions on the member ACG.

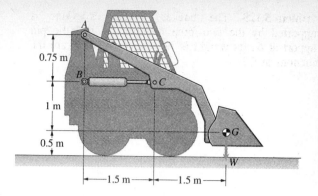

Solution: This is a very simple Problem. The free body diagrams are shown at the right. From the free body diagram of the hydraulic cylinder, we get the equation $B_X + C_X = 0$. This will enable us to find B_X once the loads on member ACG are known. From the diagram of ACG, the equilibrium equations are

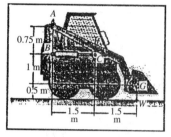

$$\sum F_x = A_X + C_X = 0,$$

$$\sum F_y = A_Y - W = 0,$$

and $\sum M_A = (0.75)C_X - (3)W = 0.$

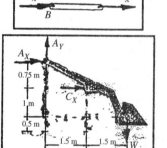

Using the given value for W and solving these equations, we get

$A_X = -8$ kN,

$A_Y = 2$ kN,

$C_X = 8$ kN,

and $B_X = -8$ kN.

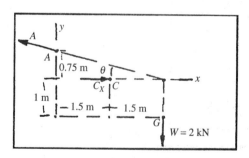

Problem 5.131 In Problem 5.130, determine the reactions of the member ACG by using the fact that it is a three-force member.

Solution: The easiest way to do this is take advantage of the fact that for a three force member, the three forces must be concurrent. The fact that the force at C is horizontal and the weight is vertical make it very easy to find the point of concurrency. We then use this point to determine the direction of the force through A. We can even know which direction this force must take along its line — it must have an upward component to support the weight — which is down. From the geometry, we can determine the angle between the force A and the horizontal.

$\tan \theta = 0.75/3,$

or $\theta = 14.04°.$

Using this, we can write force equilibrium equations in the form

$$\sum F_x = -A \cos \theta + C_X = 0, \quad \text{and}$$

$$\sum F_y = A \sin \theta - W = 0.$$

Solving these equations, we get $A = 8.246$ kN, and $C_X = 8$ kN. The components of A are as calculated in Problem 5.130.

Problem 5.132 A rectangular plate is subjected to two forces A and B (Fig. a). In Fig. b, the two forces are resolved into components. By writing equilibrium equations in terms of the components A_x, A_y, B_x, and B_y, show that the two forces A and B are equal in magnitude, opposite in direction, and directed along the line between their points of application.

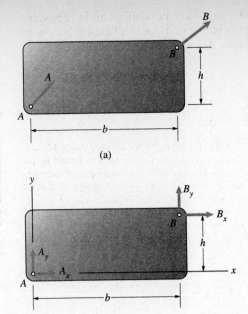

(a)

(b)

Solution: The sum of forces:

$$\sum F_X = A_X + B_X = 0,$$

from which $A_X = -B_X$

$$\sum F_Y = A_Y + B_Y = 0,$$

from which $A_Y = -B_y$. These last two equations show that A and B are equal and opposite in direction, (if the components are equal and opposite, the vectors are equal and opposite). To show that the two vectors act along the line connecting the two points, determine the angle of the vectors relative to the positive x-axis. The sum of the moments about A is

$$M_A = B_x(h) - bB_y = 0,$$

from which the angle of direction of B is

$$\tan^{-1}\left(\frac{B_Y}{B_X}\right) = \tan^{-1}\left(\frac{h}{b}\right) = \alpha_B.$$

or $(180 + \alpha_B)$. Similarly, by substituting A:

$$\tan^{-1}\left(\frac{A_Y}{A_X}\right) = \tan^{-1}\left(\frac{h}{b}\right) = \alpha_A,$$

or $(180 + \alpha_A)$. But

$$\alpha = \tan^{-1}\left(\frac{h}{b}\right)$$

describes direction of the line from A to B. The two vectors are opposite in direction, therefore the angles of direction of the vectors is one of two possibilities: B is directed along the line from A to B, and A is directed along the same line, oppositely to B.

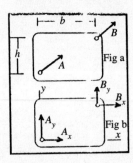

Problem 5.133 An object in equilibrium is subjected to three forces whose points of application lie on a straight line. Prove that the forces are coplanar.

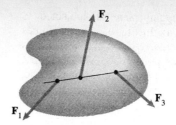

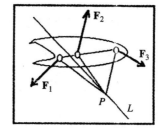

Solution: The strategy is to show that for a system in equilibrium under the action of forces alone, any two of the forces must lie in the same plane, hence all three must be in the same plane, since the choice of the two was arbitrary. Let P be a point in a plane containing the straight line and one of the forces, say $\mathbf{F}_2$. Let L also be a line, not parallel to the straight line, lying in the same plane as $\mathbf{F}_2$, passing through P. Let $\mathbf{e}$ be a vector parallel to this line L. First we show that the sum of the moments about any point in the plane is equal to the sum of the moments about one of the points of application of the forces. The sum of the moments about the point P:

$$\mathbf{M} = \mathbf{r}_1 \times \mathbf{F}_1 + \mathbf{r}_2 \times \mathbf{F}_2 + \mathbf{r}_3 \times \mathbf{F}_3 = 0,$$

where the vectors are the position vectors of the points of the application of the forces relative to the point P. (The position vectors lie in the plane.) Define

$$\mathbf{d}_{12} = \mathbf{r}_2 - \mathbf{r}_1,$$

and $\mathbf{d}_{13} = \mathbf{r}_3 - \mathbf{r}_1$.

Then the sum of the moments can be rewritten,

$$\mathbf{M} = \mathbf{r}_1 \times (\mathbf{F}_1 + \mathbf{F}_2 + \mathbf{F}_3)$$
$$+ \mathbf{d}_{12} \times \mathbf{F}_2 + \mathbf{d}_{13} \times \mathbf{F}_3 = 0.$$

Since the system is in equilibrium,

$$\mathbf{F}_1 + \mathbf{F}_2 + \mathbf{F}_3 = 0,$$

and the sum of moments reduces to

$$\mathbf{M} = \mathbf{d}_{12} \times \mathbf{F}_2 + \mathbf{d}_{13} \times \mathbf{F}_3 = 0,$$

which is the moment about the point of application of $\mathbf{F}_1$. (The vectors $\mathbf{d}_{12}$, $\mathbf{d}_{13}$ are parallel to the line L.) The component of the moment parallel to the line L is

$$\mathbf{e} \cdot (\mathbf{d}_{12} \times \mathbf{F}_2)\mathbf{e} + \mathbf{e} \cdot (\mathbf{d}_{13} \times \mathbf{F}_3)\mathbf{e} = 0,$$

or $\mathbf{F}_2 \cdot (\mathbf{d}_{12} \times \mathbf{e})\mathbf{e} + \mathbf{F}_3 \cdot (\mathbf{d}_{13} \times \mathbf{e})\mathbf{e} = 0$.

But by definition, $\mathbf{F}_2$ lies in the same plane as the line L, hence it is normal to the cross product $\mathbf{d}_{12} \times \mathbf{e} \neq 0$, and the term

$$\mathbf{F}_2 \cdot (\mathbf{d}_{12} \times \mathbf{e}) = 0.$$

But this means that

$$\mathbf{F}_3 \cdot (\mathbf{d}_{13} \times \mathbf{e})\mathbf{e} = 0,$$

which implies that $\mathbf{F}_3$ also lies in the same plane as $\mathbf{F}_2$, since

$$\mathbf{d}_{13} \times \mathbf{e} \neq 0.$$

Thus the two forces lie in the same plane. Since the choice of the point about which to sum the moments was arbitrary, this process can be repeated to show that $\mathbf{F}_1$ lies in the same plane as $\mathbf{F}_2$. *Thus all forces lie in the same plane.*

Problem 5.134 The rectangular plate is held in equilibrium by the horizontal force F. The weight W acts at the midpoint of the plate. The ratio $b/h = 4$. Determine the angle α at which the plate is in equilibrium for five values of the ratio F/W: 0, 0.5, 1.0, 1.5, and 2. (Assume that $0 \le \alpha \le 90°$.)

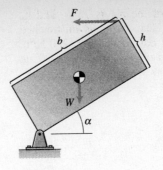

Solution: The moment about the pinned joint of the force is $M_F = HF$, where y is the vertical distance from the pinned joint to the action line of the force. This distance is the projection of the diagonal of the rectangle on the vertical axis, as shown in the second sketch:

$$H = \sqrt{b^2 + h^2}\sin(\alpha + \beta),$$

where $\beta = \tan^{-1}\dfrac{h}{b}$.

By a similar construction, the horizontal distance to the action line of the weight is

$$X = (\tfrac{1}{2})\sqrt{b^2 + h^2}\cos(\alpha + \beta).$$

The sum of the moments about the pinned joint is

$$\sum M = F(\sqrt{b^2 + h^2})\sin(\alpha + \beta)$$

$$-\left(\frac{W}{2}\right)(\sqrt{b^2 + h^2})\cos(\alpha + \beta) = 0.$$

Noting that

$$\cos\beta = \frac{b}{\sqrt{b^2 + h^2}},$$

and $\sin\beta = \dfrac{h}{\sqrt{b^2 + h^2}},$

using the double angle formulas:

$$\cos(\alpha + \beta) = \cos\alpha\cos\beta - \sin\alpha\sin\beta,$$

and $\sin(\alpha + \beta) = \sin\alpha\cos\beta + \cos\alpha\sin\beta,$

the moment equation reduces to

$$\sum M = F(b\sin\alpha + h\cos\alpha) - \left(\frac{W}{2}\right)$$

$$(b\cos\alpha - h\sin\alpha) = 0,$$

from which

$$\frac{F}{W} = \frac{\left(\dfrac{b}{h}\cos\alpha - \sin\alpha\right)}{2\left(\cos\alpha + \dfrac{b}{h}\sin\alpha\right)}$$

$$= \frac{\left(\dfrac{b}{h} - \tan\alpha\right)}{2\left(1 + \dfrac{b}{h}\tan\alpha\right)}.$$

Inverting:

$$\tan\alpha = \frac{\left(\dfrac{b}{h} - 2\dfrac{F}{W}\right)}{\left(2\dfrac{F}{W}\dfrac{b}{h} + 1\right)}.$$

Substituting $\dfrac{b}{h} = 4$, the results are for

$$\frac{F}{W} = 0, 0.5, 1.0, 1.5, 2.0,$$

$$\alpha = 75.96°, 30.96°, 12.53°, 4.40, 0$$

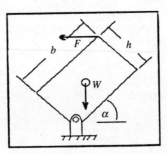

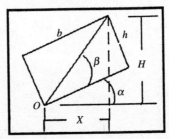

416

Problem 5.135 The mass of the bar is 36 kg and its weight acts at its midpoint. The spring is unstretched when $\alpha = 0$, and the spring constant is $k = 200$ N/m. Determine the values of α in the range $0 \le \alpha \le 90°$ at which the bar is in equilibrium.

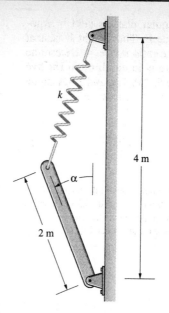

Solution:

$$l_{BC}^2 = 2^2 + 4^2 - 2(2)(4)\cos\alpha$$

$$\sin\alpha / l_{BC} = \sin\beta / 2$$

$$\sum F_X = A_X + T\sin\beta = 0$$

$$\sum F_Y = A_Y + T\cos\beta - W = 0$$

$$\sum M_A = (W\% \sin\alpha)\mathbf{k} + \mathbf{r}_{AB} \times \mathbf{T} = 0$$

where $\mathbf{r}_{AB} = -2\sin\alpha\mathbf{i} + 2\cos\alpha\mathbf{j}$

$$\mathbf{T} = T\sin\beta\mathbf{i} + T\cos\beta\mathbf{j}$$

$$\mathbf{k} : \sum M_A = W\sin\alpha - 2T\sin\alpha\cos\beta - 2T\cos\alpha\sin\beta = 0$$

Solving, we get two roots

$$\begin{pmatrix} \alpha = 0° \\ T = 0 \\ \delta = 0 \end{pmatrix} \text{ and } \begin{pmatrix} \alpha = 33.0° \\ T = 113.3 \text{ N} \\ \delta = 0.566 \text{ m} \end{pmatrix}$$

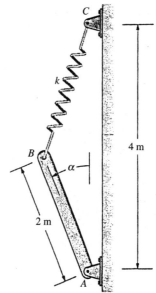

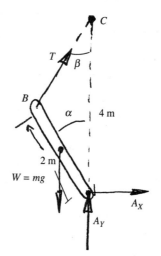

Problem 5.136 Consider the system shown in Problem 5.61. The distances are $a = 2$ m and $b = 1$ m. The couple $M = 1$ kN-m and the force $F = 2$ kN. The spring constant is $k = 3$ kN/m. The spring would be unstretched if $h = 0$. Determine the distance h for equilibrium of the horizontal bar and the reactions at A.

Solution: Loss of equilibrium occurs when the moment about A does not equal zero. The angle of the spring relative to the beam is

$$\alpha = \tan^{-1}\left(\frac{h}{a+b}\right).$$

The unstretched length of the spring is $a + b = 3$ m. The stretched length is

$$L = \sqrt{h^2 + (a+b)^2} \text{ m.}$$

The force exerted by the spring is

$$T = k\Delta L = 3(L - (a+b)) \text{ kN.}$$

The sum of the forces:

$$\sum F_X = A_X - T\cos\alpha = 0,$$

from which $A_X = T\cos\alpha$.

$$\sum F_Y = A_Y - F + T\sin\alpha = 0,$$

from which $A_Y = F - T\sin\alpha$. The sum of the moments about A is

$$\sum M_A = -M - aF + (a+b)T\sin\alpha = 0,$$

from which $F = \dfrac{(a+b)T\sin\alpha - M}{a}$.

The threshold of equilibrium is determined by

$$f(h) = -M - aF + (a+b)T\sin\alpha \geq 0.$$

Graph $f(h)$ against h to determine the value of h at the zero crossing of $f(h)$, from which the other unknowns can be determined. The commercial package **TK Solver Plus** was used to graph $f(h)$ against h. The equations are:

$$f(h) = -M - aF + (a+b)T\sin\alpha \geq 0,$$

$$\alpha = \tan^{-1}\left(\frac{h}{a+b}\right),$$

$$L = \sqrt{h^2 + (a+b)^2} \text{ m,}$$

$$T = k\Delta L = 3(L - (a+b)) \text{ kN,}$$

$$A_X = T\cos\alpha,$$

and $A_Y = F - T\sin\alpha$.

The value of h at the zero crossing is $h \geq 2.456$ m. The reactions are

$$A_X = 2.03 \text{ kN}$$

and $A_Y = 0.338$ kN.

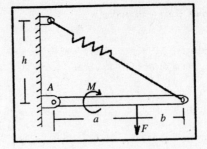

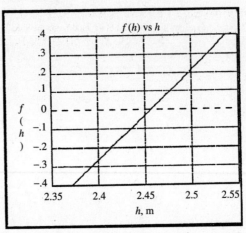

$f(h)$ vs h

Problem 5.137 Consider the system shown in Problem 5.62. The bar is 1 m long, and its weight $W = 35$ N acts at its midpoint. The distance $b = 0.75$ m. The spring constant is $k = 100$ N/m, and the spring is unstretched when the bar is vertical. Determine the angle α and the reactions at A.

Solution: The unstretched length of the spring is

$$L = \sqrt{b^2 + 1^2} = 1.25 \text{ m.}$$

The obtuse angle is $90 + \alpha$, so the stretched length can be determined from the cosine law:

$$L_2^2 = 1^2 + 0.75^2 - 2(0.75)\cos(90 + \alpha)$$

$$= 1.5625 + 1.5\sin\alpha.$$

The force exerted by the spring is $T = k\Delta L = 100(L_2 - 1.25)$ N. The angle between the spring and the bar can be determined from the sine law:

$$\frac{b}{\sin\beta} = \frac{L_2}{\sin(90 + \alpha)},$$

from which $\sin\beta = \dfrac{b\cos\alpha}{L_2}$.

The angle the spring makes with the horizontal is

$$\theta = 180 - \beta - 90 - \alpha = 90 - \beta - \alpha.$$

The sum of the forces:

$$\sum F_X = A_X - T\cos\theta = 0,$$

from which $A_X = T\cos\theta$ N.

$$\sum F_Y = A_Y - W - T\sin\theta = 0,$$

from which $A_Y = W + T\sin\theta$. The sum of the moments about A is

$$\sum M_A = T\sin\beta - \left(\frac{W}{2}\right)\sin\alpha = 0.$$

The function

$$f(\alpha) = T\sin\beta - \left(\frac{W}{2}\right)\sin\alpha$$

is to be graphed against α to determine the value of α at the zero crossing. The commercial package **TK Solver Plus** was used to graph the function. At the zero crossing $\alpha = 44.1°$.

$$A_X = 32.6 \text{ N,}$$

and $A_Y = 51.2$ N

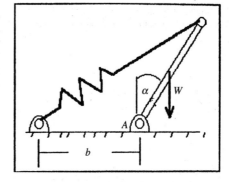

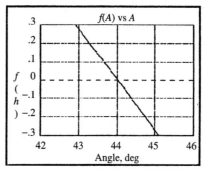

f(A) vs A

Problem 5.138 The hydraulic actuator BC exerts a force at C that points along the line from B to C. Treat A as a pin support. The mass of the suspended load is 4000 kg. If the actuator BC can exert a maximum force of 90 kN, what is the smallest permissible value of α?

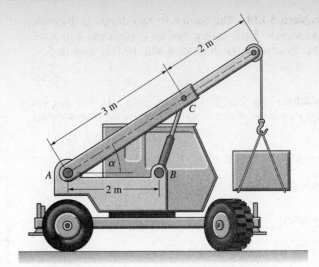

Solution: Note $\gamma > 90°$, $\therefore$ most adjust γ from law of sines

$$\sum F_X = A_X + F_{BC}\cos(180° - \gamma) = 0$$

$$\sum F_Y = A_Y + F_{BC}\sin(180° - \gamma) - W = 0$$

$$\sum M_A = \mathbf{r}_{AC} \times \mathbf{F}_{BC} + \mathbf{r}_{AD} \times \mathbf{W} = 0$$

where $\mathbf{r}_{AC} = 3\cos\alpha\mathbf{i} + 3\sin\alpha\mathbf{j}$ m

$\quad \mathbf{r}_{AD} = 5\cos\alpha\mathbf{i} + 5\sin\alpha\mathbf{j}$ m

$\quad \mathbf{F}_{BC} = F_{BC}\cos(180° - \gamma)\mathbf{i} + F_{BC}\sin(180° - \gamma)\mathbf{j}$

$\quad \mathbf{W} = -(4000)(9.81)\mathbf{j}$ N

or $\mathbf{k}: \sum M_A = 3F_{BC}\cos\alpha\sin(180 - \gamma)$

$\qquad\qquad - 3\sin\alpha F_{BC}\cos(180° - \gamma)$

$\qquad\qquad + 5(\cos\alpha)(W) = 0$

Set $F_{BC} = 90000$ N

Solving-we get

$A_X = 31.63$ kN

$A_Y = -45.02$ kN

$\alpha_{min} = 30.8°$

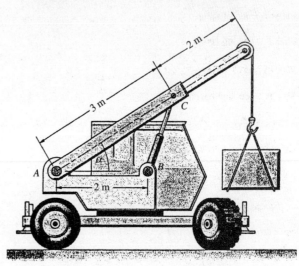

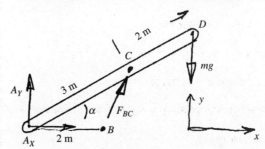

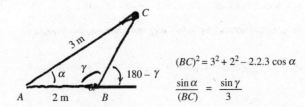

$(BC)^2 = 3^2 + 2^2 - 2.2.3\cos\alpha$

$\dfrac{\sin\alpha}{(BC)} = \dfrac{\sin\gamma}{3}$

Problem 5.139 The beam is in equilibrium in the position shown. Each spring has an unstretched length of 1 m. Determine the distance b and the reactions at A.

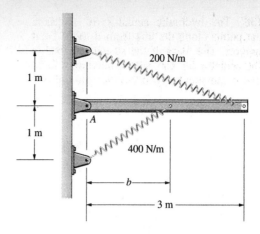

Solution: The strategy is to determine the value of b that will cause the moment about A to equal zero. The angle of the top spring is

$$\alpha = \tan^{-1}(\tfrac{1}{3}) = 18.435°.$$

The angle of the bottom spring is

$$\beta = \tan^{-1}\left(\frac{1}{b}\right).$$

The stretched length of the top spring is

$$L_T = \sqrt{1^2 + 3^2} = 3.1623 \text{ m}.$$

The tension in the top spring is

$$T_T = (200)(3.1623 - 1) = 432.456 \text{ N}.$$

The tension in the bottom spring is

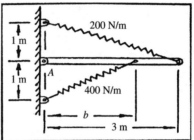

$$T_B = 400(\sqrt{b^2 + 1} - 1) \text{ N}.$$

The sum of the moments about the point A:

$$M_A = -bT_B \sin\beta + 3(432.456)\sin 18.435°$$

$$= -bT \sin\beta + 410.26 = 0.$$

The sum of the forces:

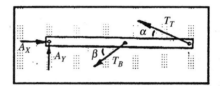

$$\sum F_X = A_X - T_B \cos\beta - 432.456\cos 18.435 = 0,$$

from which $A_X = T_B \cos\beta - 410.264$ N.

$$\sum F_Y = A_Y - T_B \sin\beta + 432.456\sin 18.435° = 0,$$

from which $A_Y = T_B \sin\beta - 136.755$ N.

The solution is obtained by graphing the sum of moments equation,

$$f(b) = -bT_B \sin\beta + 410.26,$$

against b to determine the value of b at the zero crossing.

The commercial package **TK Solver Plus** was used to graph the function.

At the zero crossing the value of b is $b = 1.91$ N The reactions at A are:

$$A_X = 820 \text{ N},$$

and $A_Y = 77.8$ N

The values of A_X, A_Y are changing rapidly in the neighborhood of the zero crossing, so that the results are good only to three significant figures, at best.

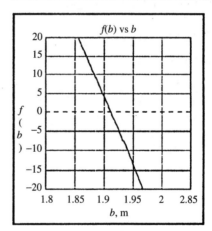

Problem 5.140 Determine the reactions at A and B.

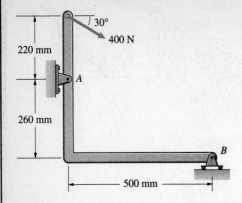

Solution: From the free body diagram at the right, the equations of equilibrium are

$$\sum F_x = 400\cos(30°) + A_X = 0,$$

$$\sum F_y = A_Y + B_Y - 400\sin(30°) = 0,$$

and $\sum M_A = (0.5)B_Y - (0.22)(400)\cos 30° = 0.$

Solving these three equations in the three unknowns, we get

$A_X = -346.4$ N,

$A_Y = 47.6$ N,

and $B_Y = 152.4$ N.

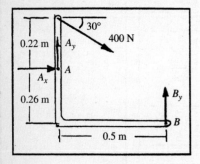

Problem 5.141 Paleontologists speculate that the stegosaur could stand on its hind limbs for short periods to feed. Based on the free-body diagram shown and assuming that $m = 2000$ kg, determine the magnitudes of the forces B and C exerted by the ligament—muscle brace and vertical column, and determine the angle α.

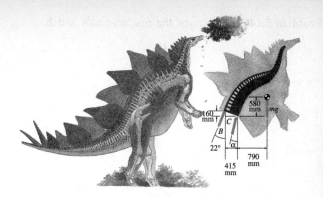

Solution: Take the origin to be at the point of application of the force C. The position vectors of the points of application of the forces B and W are:

$$\mathbf{r}_B = -415\mathbf{i} + 160\mathbf{j} \text{ (mm)},$$

$$\mathbf{r}_W = 790\mathbf{i} + 580\mathbf{j} \text{ (mm)}.$$

The forces are

$$\mathbf{C} = C(\mathbf{i}\cos(90° - \alpha) + \mathbf{j}\sin(90° - \alpha))$$

$$= C(\mathbf{i}\sin\alpha + \mathbf{j}\cos\alpha).$$

$$\mathbf{B} = B(\mathbf{i}\cos(270° - 22°) + \mathbf{j}\sin(270° - 22°))$$

$$= B(-0.3746\mathbf{i} - 0.9272\mathbf{j}).$$

$$\mathbf{W} = -2(9.81)\mathbf{j} = -19.62\mathbf{j} \text{ (kN)}.$$

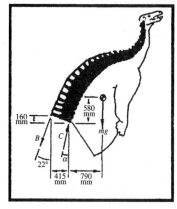

The moments about C,

$$\mathbf{M}_C = \begin{vmatrix} \mathbf{i} & \mathbf{j} & \mathbf{k} \\ -415 & 160 & 0 \\ -0.3746B & -0.9272B & 0 \end{vmatrix}$$

$$+ \begin{vmatrix} \mathbf{i} & \mathbf{j} & \mathbf{k} \\ 790 & 580 & 0 \\ 0 & -19.62 & 0 \end{vmatrix} = 0$$

$$= 444.72B - 15499.8 = 0,$$

from which

$$B = \frac{15499.8}{444.72} = 34.85 \text{ kN}.$$

The sums of the forces:

$$\sum \mathbf{F}_X = (C\sin\alpha - 0.3746B)\mathbf{i} = 0,$$

from which $C\sin\alpha = 13.06$ kN.

$$\sum \mathbf{F}_Y = (C\cos\alpha - 0.9272B - 19.62)\mathbf{j} = 0,$$

from which $C\cos\alpha = 51.93$ kN.

The angle α is

$$\alpha = \tan^{-1}\left(\frac{13.06}{51.93}\right) = 14.1°.$$

The magnitude of $\mathbf{C}$,

$$C = \sqrt{13.06^2 + 51.93^2} = 53.55 \text{ kN}$$

Problem 5.142 (a) Draw the free-body diagram of the 50-lb plate, and explain why it is statically indeterminate.

(b) Determine as many of the reactions at A and B as possible.

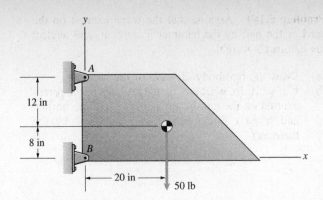

Solution:

(a) The pin supports at A and B are two-force supports, thus there are four unknown reactions A_X, A_Y, B_X, and B_Y, but only three equilibrium equations can be written, two for the forces, and one for the moment. Thus there are four unknowns and only three equations, so the system is indeterminate.

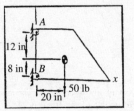

(b) Sums the forces:

$$\sum F_X = A_X + B_X = 0,$$

or $A_X = -B_X$, and

$$\sum F_Y = A_Y + B_Y - 50 = 0.$$

The sum of the moments about B

$$M_B = -20A_X - 50(20) = 0,$$

from which $A_X = -50$ lb,

and from the sum of forces $B_X = 50$ lb.

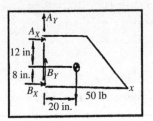

Problem 5.143 The mass of the truck is 4 Mg. Its wheels are locked, and the tension in its cable is $T = 10$ kN.

(a) Draw the free-body diagram of the truck.
(b) Determine the normal forces exerted on the truck's wheels by the road.

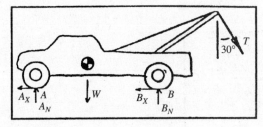

Solution: The weight is $4000(9.81) = 39.24$ kN. The sum of the moments about B

$$\sum M_B = -3T \sin 30° - 2.2T \cos 30° + 2.5W - 4.5A_N = 0$$

from which

$$A_N = \frac{2.5W - T(3 \sin 30° + 2.2 \cos 30°)}{4.5}$$

$$= \frac{64.047}{4.5} = 14.23 \text{ N}$$

The sum of the forces:

$$\sum F_Y = A_N - W + B_N - T \cos 30° = 0,$$

from which $B_N = T \cos 30° - A_N + W = 33.67$ N

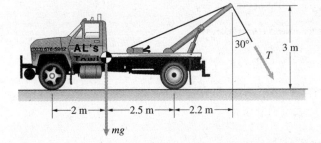

Problem 5.144 Assume that the force exerted on the head of the nail by the hammer is vertical, and neglect the hammer's weight.

(a) Draw the free-body diagram of the hammer.
(b) If $F = 10$ lb, what are the magnitudes of the forces exerted on the nail by the hammer and the normal and friction forces exerted on the floor by the hammer?

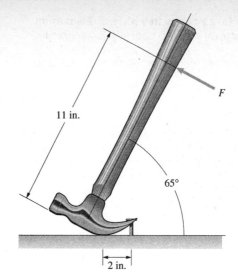

11 in.

65°

2 in.

Solution: Denote the point of contact with the floor by B. The perpendicular distance from B to the line of action of the force is 11 in. The sum of the moments about B is $M_B = 11F - 2F_N = 0$, from which the force exerted by the nail head is $F_N = \dfrac{11F}{2} = 5.5F$. The sum of the forces:

$$\sum F_X = -F \cos 25 + H_x = 0,$$

from which the friction force exerted on the hammer is $H_X = 0.9063F$.

$$\sum F_Y = N_H - F_N + F \sin 25° = 0,$$

from which the normal force exerted by the floor on the hammer is $N_H = 5.077F$

If the force on the handle is

$$F = 10 \text{ lb},$$

then $F_N = 55$ lb,

$$H_X = 9.063 \text{ lb},$$

and $N_H = 50.77$ lb

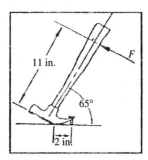

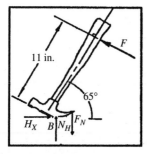

Problem 5.145 (a) Draw the free-body diagram of the beam.

(b) Determine the reactions at the supports.

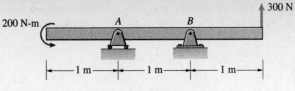

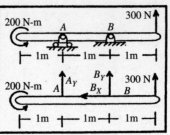

Solution:

(a) The free body diagram is shown.

(b) The sum of the moments about B

$$\sum M_B = +200 - (1)A_Y + (1)300 = 0,$$

from which $\boxed{A_Y = 200 + 300 = 500 \text{ N-m}}$. The sum of the forces:

$$\sum F_X = B_X = 0$$

and $\sum F_Y = A_Y + B_Y + 300 = 0,$

from which $\boxed{B_Y = -A_Y - 300 = -800 \text{ N}}$

Problem 5.146 Consider the beam shown in Problem 5.145. First represent the loads (the 300-N force and the 200-N-m couple) by a single equivalent force; and then determine the reactions at the supports.

Solution: The equivalent force is equal to the applied forces: $F = 300$ N. Measure the distance x from the point B. The moment about B due to the loads:

$$M_B = 300x + 200 + 1(300) = 0,$$

from which

$$x = -\frac{500}{300} = -1.6667 \text{ m},$$

or 1.6667 m to the left of B. The reactions: The sum of the moments about B

$$M_B = 300(1.6667) - (1)A_Y = 0$$

from which $A_Y = 500$ N. The sum of the forces

$$\sum F_X = B_X = 0,$$

$$\sum F_Y = A_Y + B_Y + 300 = 0,$$

from which $B_Y = -A_Y - 300 = -800$ N

Problem 5.147 The truss supports a 90-kg suspended object. What are the reactions at the supports A and B?

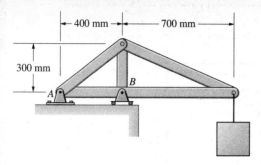

Solution: Treat the truss as a single element. The pin support at A is a two force reaction support; the roller support at B is a single force reaction. The sum of the moments about A is

$$M_A = B(400) - W(1100) = 0,$$

from which $B = \dfrac{1100W}{400} = 2.75W$

$$B = 2.75(90)(9.81) = 2427.975 = 2.43 \text{ kN.}$$

The sum of the forces:

$$\sum F_X = A_X = 0$$

$$\sum F_Y = A_Y + B - W = 0,$$

from which $A_Y = W - B = 882.9 - 2427.975 = -1.545$ kN

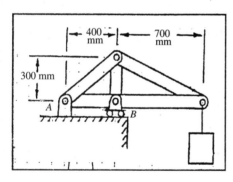

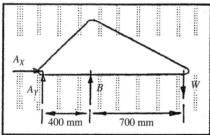

Problem 5.148 The trailer is parked on a 15° slope. Its wheels are free to turn. The hitch H behaves like a pin support. Determine the reactions at A and H.

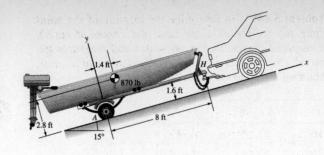

Solution: The coordinate system has the x-axis parallel to the road. The wheels are a one force reaction normal to the road, the pin H is a two force reaction. The position vectors of the points of the center of mass and H are:

$$\mathbf{r}_W = 1.4\mathbf{i} + 2.8\mathbf{j} \text{ ft and}$$

$$\mathbf{r}_H = 8\mathbf{i} + 1.6\mathbf{j}.$$

The angle of the weight vector realtive to the positive x-axis is

$$\alpha = 270° - 15° = 255°.$$

The weight has the components

$$\mathbf{W} = W(\mathbf{i}\cos 255° + \mathbf{j}\sin 255°) = 870(-0.2588\mathbf{i} - 0.9659\mathbf{j})$$

$$= -225.173\mathbf{i} - 840.355\mathbf{j} \text{ (lb)}.$$

The sum of the moments about H is

$$\mathbf{M}_H = (\mathbf{r}_W - \mathbf{r}_H) \times \mathbf{W} + (\mathbf{r}_A - \mathbf{r}_H) \times \mathbf{A},$$

$$\mathbf{M}_H = \begin{vmatrix} \mathbf{i} & \mathbf{j} & \mathbf{k} \\ -6.6 & 1.2 & 0 \\ -225.355 & -840.355 & 0 \end{vmatrix} + \begin{vmatrix} \mathbf{i} & \mathbf{j} & \mathbf{k} \\ -8 & -1.6 & 0 \\ 0 & A_Y & 0 \end{vmatrix} = 0$$

$$= 5816.55 - 8A_Y = 0,$$

from which $A_Y = \dfrac{5816.55}{8} = 727.1$ lb.

The sum of the forces is

$$\sum \mathbf{F}_X = (H_X - 225.173)\mathbf{i} = 0, \text{ from which } H_X = 225.2 \text{ lb},$$

$$\sum \mathbf{F}_Y = (A_Y + H_Y - 840.355)\mathbf{j} = 0, \text{ from which } H_Y = 113.3 \text{ lb}$$

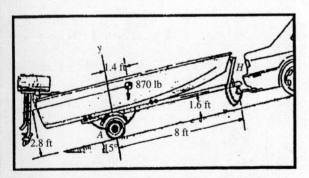

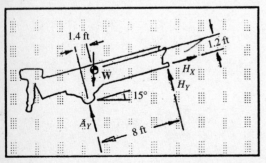

Problem 5.149 To determine the location of the point where the weight of a car acts (the *center of mass*), an engineer places the car on scales and measures the normal reactions at the wheels for two values of α, obtaining the following results:

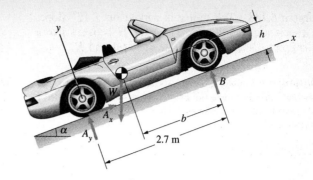

α	A_y (kN)	B (kN)
10°	10.134	4.357
20°	10.150	3.677

What are the distances b and h?

Solution: The position vectors of the cm and the point B are

$$\mathbf{r}_{CM} = (2.7 - b)\mathbf{i} + h\mathbf{j},$$

$$\mathbf{r}_B = 2.7\mathbf{i}.$$

The angle between the weight and the positive x-axis is $\beta = 270 - \alpha$. The weight vector at each of the two angles is

$$\mathbf{W}_{10} = W(\mathbf{i}\cos 260° + \mathbf{j}\sin 260°)$$

$$\mathbf{W}_{10} = W(-0.1736\mathbf{i} - 0.9848\mathbf{j})$$

$$\mathbf{W}_{20} = W(\mathbf{i}\cos 250° + \mathbf{j}\sin 250°) \text{ or}$$

$$\mathbf{W}_{20} = W(-0.3420\mathbf{i} - 0.9397\mathbf{j})$$

The weight W is found from the sum of forces:

$$\sum F_Y = A_Y + B_Y + W\sin\beta = 0,$$

from which $W_\beta = \dfrac{A_Y + B_Y}{\sin\beta}$.

Taking the values from the table of measurements:

$$W_{10} = -\frac{10.134 + 4.357}{\sin 260°} = 14.714 \text{ kN},$$

$$[\textit{check} : W_{20} = -\frac{10.150 + 3.677}{\sin 250°} = 14.714 \text{ kN } \textit{check}]$$

The moments about A are

$$\mathbf{M}_A = \mathbf{r}_{CM} \times \mathbf{W} + \mathbf{r}_B \times \mathbf{B} = 0.$$

Taking the values at the two angles:

$$\mathbf{M}_A^{10} = \begin{vmatrix} \mathbf{i} & \mathbf{j} & \mathbf{k} \\ 2.7 - b & h & 0 \\ -2.5551 & -14.4910 & 0 \end{vmatrix} + \begin{vmatrix} \mathbf{i} & \mathbf{j} & \mathbf{k} \\ 2.7 & 0 & 0 \\ 0 & 4.357 & 0 \end{vmatrix} = 0$$

$$= 14.4903b + 2.5551h - 27.3618 = 0$$

$$\mathbf{M}_A^{20} = \begin{vmatrix} \mathbf{i} & \mathbf{j} & \mathbf{k} \\ 2.7 - b & h & 0 \\ -5.0327 & -13.8272 & 0 \end{vmatrix} + \begin{vmatrix} \mathbf{i} & \mathbf{j} & \mathbf{k} \\ 2.7 & 0 & 0 \\ 0 & 3.677 & 0 \end{vmatrix}$$

$$= 013.8272b + 5.0327h - 27.4054 = 0$$

These two simultaneous equations in two unknowns were solved using the HP-28S hand held calculator.

$$b = 1.80 \text{ m},$$

$$h = 0.50 \text{ m}$$

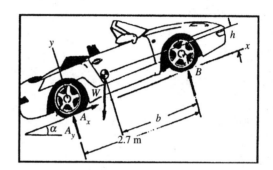

Problem 5.150 The bar is attached by pin supports to collars that slide on the two fixed bars. Its mass is 10 kg, it is 1 m in length, and its weight acts at its midpoint. Neglect friction and the masses of the collars. The spring is unstretched when the bar is vertical ($\alpha = 0$), and the spring constant is $k = 100$ N/m. Determine the values of α in the range $0 \leq \alpha \leq 60°$ at which the bar is in equilibrium.

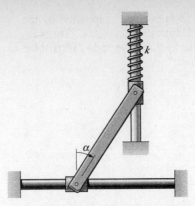

Solution: The force exerted by the spring is given by $F_S = k(L - L\cos\alpha)$. The equations of equilibrium, from the free body diagram, are

$$\sum F_x = N_B = 0,$$

$$\sum F_y = F_S + N_A - mg = 0,$$

and $\sum M_B = (-L\sin\alpha)N_A + \left(\dfrac{L}{2}\sin\alpha\right)mg = 0.$

These equations can be solved directly with most numerical solvers and the required plot can be developed. The plot over the given α range is shown at the left and a zoom-in is given at the right. The solution and the plot were developed with the **TK Solver Plus** commercial software package. From the plot, the required equilibrium value is $\alpha \cong 59.4°$.

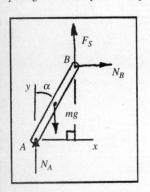

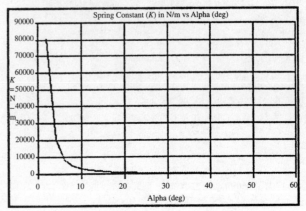

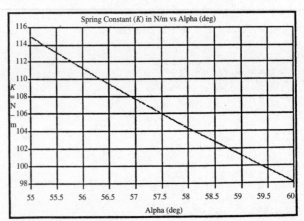

Problem 5.151 The 450-lb ladder is supported by the hydraulic cylinder AB and the pin support at C. The reaction at B is parallel to the hydraulic cylinder. Determine the reactions on the ladder.

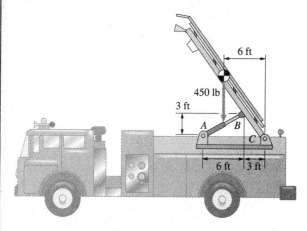

Solution: Setting the coordinate origin at C, point A is located at $(-9, 0)$ ft and point B is at $(-3, 3)$ ft. The angle $\alpha = 45°$ and point G is located at $(-6, 6)$ ft. The unit vector along the hydraulic cylinder, AC, is

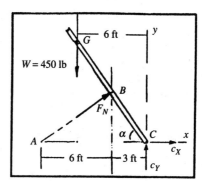

$$e_{AB} = 0.894\mathbf{i} + 0.447\mathbf{j}$$

and

$$F_{HX} = 0.894F_H,$$

$$F_{HY} = 0.447F_H.$$

The equations of equilibrium are:

$$\sum F_x = C_X + F_{HX} = 0,$$

$$\sum F_y = C_Y + F_{HY} - 450 = 0,$$

and $\sum M_C = (-6)(-450) - (3)F_{HX} - (3)F_{HY} = 0.$

All distances are in ft, forces are in lb, and moments in ft-lb. Solving the equations for the unknown support reactions yields

$$C_X = -600 \text{ lb},$$

$$C_Y = 150 \text{ lb},$$

and $F_H = 671$ lb.

Problem 5.152 Consider the crane shown in Problem 5.138. The hydraulic actuator BC exerts a force at C that points along the line from B to C. Treat A as a pin support. The mass of the suspended load is 6000 kg. If the angle $\alpha = 35°$, what are the reactions at A?

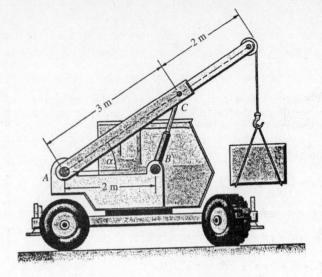

Solution:

$$BC^2 = 3^2 + 2^2 - 2(2)(3)\cos 35°$$

$$BC = 1.78 \text{ m}$$

$$\frac{\sin 35°}{BC} = \frac{\sin \gamma}{3}\, \gamma > 90°$$

$$\gamma = 104.9°$$

$$(180° - \gamma) = 75.1°$$

$$\sum F_X = A_X + F_{BC}\cos(180° - \gamma)$$

$$\sum F_Y = A_Y + F_{BC}\sin(180° - \gamma) - W = 0$$

$$\sum M_A = \mathbf{r}_{AC} \times \mathbf{F}_{BC}$$

$$+ \mathbf{r}_{AD} \times \mathbf{W} = 0$$

where

$$\mathbf{r}_{AC} = 3\cos(35°)\mathbf{i} + 3\sin(35°)\mathbf{j}$$

$$\mathbf{r}_{AD} = 5\cos(35°)\mathbf{i} + 5\sin(35°)\mathbf{j}$$

$$\mathbf{F}_{BC} = F_{BC}\cos(75.11°)\mathbf{i}$$

$$+ F_{BC}\sin(75.11°)\mathbf{j}$$

$$\mathbf{W} = -(6000)(9.81)\mathbf{j} \text{ N}$$

Solving for the unknowns, we get

$$A_X = -32.04 \text{ kN}$$

$$A_Y = -61.68 \text{ kN}$$

$$F_{BC} = 124.73 \text{ kN}$$

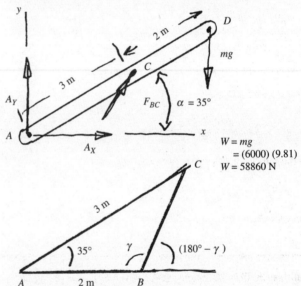

Problem 5.153 The horizontal rectangular plate weighs 800 N and is suspended by three vertical cables. The weight of the plate acts at its midpoint. What are the tensions in the cables?

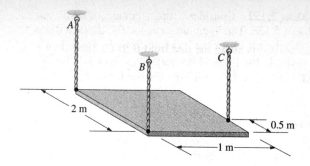

Solution: Choose an origin at A, with the x-axis coincident with the line AB, and the y-axis normal to the plate, positive upward. The position vectors of the points B, C, and the cm are

$$\mathbf{r}_B = 2\mathbf{i},$$

$$\mathbf{r}_C = 1.5\mathbf{i} - 1\mathbf{k},$$

$$\mathbf{r}_{CM} = 1\mathbf{i} - 0.5\mathbf{k}.$$

The sum of the moments about the point A is

$$\mathbf{M}_A = \mathbf{r}_B \times \mathbf{T}_B + \mathbf{r}_C \times \mathbf{T}_C + \mathbf{r}_{CM} \times \mathbf{W} = 0$$

$$\mathbf{M}_A = \begin{vmatrix} \mathbf{i} & \mathbf{j} & \mathbf{k} \\ 2 & 0 & 0 \\ 0 & T_B & 0 \end{vmatrix} + \begin{vmatrix} \mathbf{i} & \mathbf{j} & \mathbf{k} \\ 1.5 & 0 & -1 \\ 0 & T_C & 0 \end{vmatrix} + \begin{vmatrix} \mathbf{i} & \mathbf{j} & \mathbf{k} \\ 1 & 0 & -0.5 \\ 0 & -800 & 0 \end{vmatrix} = 0$$

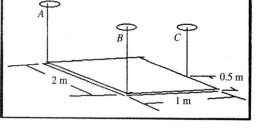

$$\mathbf{M}_A = (T_C - 0.5(800))\mathbf{i} + (2T_B + 1.5T_C - 800)\mathbf{k} = 0$$

From which $T_C = 400$ N,

$$T_B = \frac{800 - 1.5T_C}{2} = 100 \text{ N}.$$

The reaction at A is found from the sum of forces:

$$\sum F_Y = T_A + T_B + T_C - 800 = 0,$$

from which $T_A = 800 - T_B - T_C = 300$ N

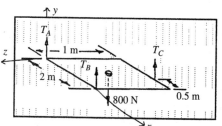

Problem 5.154 Consider the suspended 800-N plate in Problem 5.153. The weight of the plate acts at its midpoint. If you represent the reactions exerted on the plate by the three cables by a single equivalent force, what is the force, and where does its line of action intersect the plate?

Solution: The equivalent force must equal the sum of the reactions: $F_{EQ} = T_A + T_B + T_C$ From the solution to Problem 5.127, $F_{EQ} = 300 + 100 + 400 = 800$ N. The moment due to the action of the equivalent force must equal the moment due to the reactions: The moment about A is

$$\mathbf{M}_A = \begin{vmatrix} \mathbf{i} & \mathbf{j} & \mathbf{k} \\ 2 & 0 & 0 \\ 0 & 100 & 0 \end{vmatrix} + \begin{vmatrix} \mathbf{i} & \mathbf{j} & \mathbf{k} \\ 1.5 & 0 & -1 \\ 0 & 400 & 0 \end{vmatrix} = \begin{vmatrix} \mathbf{i} & \mathbf{j} & \mathbf{k} \\ x & 0 & z \\ 0 & 800 & 0 \end{vmatrix}$$

$$\mathbf{M}_A = 400\mathbf{i} + 800\mathbf{k} = -(800z)\mathbf{i} + (800x)\mathbf{k},$$

from which $z = -0.5$ m, and $x = 1$ m, which corresponds to the midpoint of the plate. *Thus the equivalent force acts upward at the midpoint of the plate.*

Problem 5.155 The 20-kg mass is suspended by cables attached to three vertical 2-m posts. Point A is at (1, 1.2, 0) m. Determine the reactions at the built-in support at E.

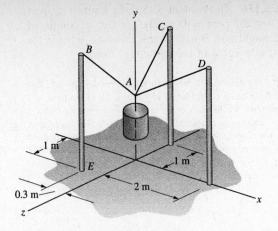

Solution: All distances will be in meters, all forces in Newtons, and all moments in Newton-meters. To solve the three dimensional point equilibrium problem at A, we will need unit vectors $\mathbf{e}_{AB}$, $\mathbf{e}_{AC}$, and $\mathbf{e}_{AD}$. To determine these, we need the coordinates of points A, B, C, and D. The rest of the problem will require knowing where points E, G (under C), and H(under D) are located. From the diagram, the required point locations are A (0, 1.2, 0), B (−0.3, 2, 1), C (0, 2, −1), D (2, 2, 0), E (−0.3, 0, 1), $G(0, 0, −1)$, and $H(2, 0, 0)$. The required unit vectors are calculated from the coordinates of the points of the ends of the lines defining the vector. These are

$$\mathbf{e}_{AB} = -0.228\mathbf{i} + 0.608\mathbf{j} + 0.760\mathbf{k},$$

$$\mathbf{e}_{AC} = 0\mathbf{i} + 0.625\mathbf{j} - 0.781\mathbf{k},$$

and $\mathbf{e}_{AD} = 0.928\mathbf{i} + 0.371\mathbf{j} + 0\mathbf{k}.$

The force $\mathbf{T}_{AB}$ in cable AB can be written as

$$\mathbf{T}_{AB} = T_{ABX}\mathbf{i} + T_{ABY}\mathbf{j} + T_{ABZ}\mathbf{k},$$

where $T_{ABX} = |\mathbf{T}_{AB}|e_{ABX}$, etc. Similar equations can be written for the forces in AC and AD. The free body diagram of point A yields the following three equations of equilibrium.

$$\sum F_x = T_{ABX} + T_{ACX} + T_{ADX} = 0,$$

$$\sum F_y = T_{ABY} + T_{ACY} + T_{ADY} - W = 0,$$

and $\sum F_z = T_{ABZ} + T_{ACZ} + T_{ADZ} = 0,$

where $W = mg = (20)(9.81) = 196.2$ N. Solving the equations above after making the substitutions related to the force components yields the tensions in the cables. They are

$$|\mathbf{T}_{AB}| = 150 \text{ N},$$

$$|\mathbf{T}_{AC}| = 146 \text{ N, and}$$

$$|\mathbf{T}_{AD}| = 36.9 \text{ N}.$$

Now that we know the tensions in the cables, we are ready to tackle the reactions at E (also G and H). The first step is to draw the free body diagram of the post EB and to write the equations of equilibrium for the post. A key point is to note that the force on the post from cable AB is opposite in direction to the force found in the first part of the problem. The equations of equilibrium for post EB are

$$\sum F_x = E_X - T_{ABX} = 0,$$

$$\sum F_y = E_Y - T_{ABY} = 0,$$

$$\sum F_z = E_Z - T_{ABZ} = 0,$$

and, summing moments around the base point E,

$$\sum \mathbf{M} = \mathbf{M}_E + (2\mathbf{j}) \times (-\mathbf{T}_{AB}) = 0.$$

The couple $\mathbf{M}_E$ is the couple exerted on the post by the built in support. Solving these equations, we get

$$\mathbf{E} = -34.2\mathbf{i} + 91.3\mathbf{j} + 114.1\mathbf{k} \text{ N}$$

and $\mathbf{M}_E = 228.1\mathbf{i} + 0\mathbf{j} + 68.44\mathbf{k}$ N-m.

Also, $|\mathbf{M}_E| = 238.2$ N-m.

Using a procedure identical to that followed for post EB above, we can find the built-in support forces and moments for posts CG and DH. The results for CG are:

$$\mathbf{G} = 0\mathbf{i} + 91.3\mathbf{j} - 114.1\mathbf{k} \text{ N}$$

and $\mathbf{M}_G = -228.1\mathbf{i} + 0\mathbf{j} + 0\mathbf{k}$ N-m.

Also, $|\mathbf{M}_G| = 228.1$ N-m.

The results for DH are:

$$\mathbf{H} = 34.2\mathbf{i} + 13.7\mathbf{j} + 0 \text{ kN}$$

and $\mathbf{M}_H = 0\mathbf{i} + 0\mathbf{j} + 68.4\mathbf{k}$ N-m.

Also, $|\mathbf{M}_G| = 68.4$ N-m

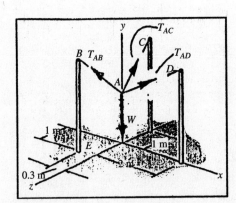

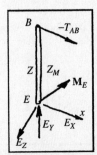
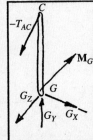
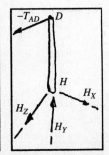

Problem 5.156 In Problem 5.155, the built-in support of each vertical post will safely support a couple of 800 N-m magnitude. Based on this criterion, what is the maximum safe value of the suspended mass?

Solution: We have all of the information necessary to solve this problem in the solution to Problem 5.155 above. All of the force and moment equations are linear and we know from the solution that a 20 kg mass produces a couple of magnitude 238.2 N-m at support E and that the magnitudes of the couples at the other two supports are smaller than this. All we need to do is scale the Problem. The scale factor is $f = 800/238.2 = 3.358$ and the maximum value for the suspended mass is $m_{max} = 20f = 67.16$ kg

Problem 5.157 The 80-lb bar is supported by a ball and socket support at A, the smooth wall it leans against, and the cable BC. The weight of the bar acts at its midpoint.

(a) Draw the free-body diagram of the bar.
(b) Determine the tension in cable BC and the reactions at A.

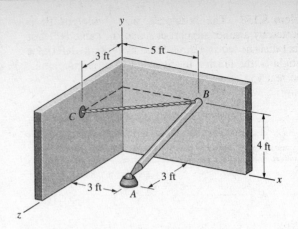

Solution: (a) The ball and socket is a three reaction force support; the cable and the smooth wall are each one force reaction supports.
(b) The coordinates of the points A, B and C are A (3, 0, 3), B (5, 4, 0), and C(0, 4, 3).

The vector parallel to the bar is

$$\mathbf{r}_{AB} = \mathbf{r}_B - \mathbf{r}_A = 2\mathbf{i} + 4\mathbf{j} - 3\mathbf{k}.$$

The length of the bar is

$$|\mathbf{r}_{AB}| = \sqrt{2^2 + 4^2 + 3^2} = 5.3852.$$

The unit vector parallel to the bar is

$$\mathbf{e}_{AB} = 0.3714\mathbf{i} + 0.7428\mathbf{j} - 0.5571\mathbf{k}.$$

The vector parallel to the cable is

$$\mathbf{r}_{BC} = \mathbf{r}_C - \mathbf{r}_B = -5\mathbf{i} + 3\mathbf{k}.$$

The unit vector parallel to the cable is

$$\mathbf{e}_{BC} = -0.8575\mathbf{i} + 0.5145\mathbf{k}.$$

The cable tension is $\mathbf{T} = |\mathbf{T}|\mathbf{e}_{BC}$. The point of application of the weight relative to A is

$$\mathbf{r}_{AW} = 2.6936\mathbf{e}_{AB}$$

$$\mathbf{r}_{AW} = 1.000\mathbf{i} + 2.000\mathbf{j} - 1.500\mathbf{k}.$$

The reaction at B is $\mathbf{B} = |\mathbf{B}|\mathbf{k}$, since it is normal to a wall in the y-z plane. The sum of the moments about A is

$$\mathbf{M}_A = \mathbf{r}_{AW} \times \mathbf{W} + \mathbf{r}_{AB} \times \mathbf{B} + \mathbf{r}_{AB} \times \mathbf{T} = 0$$

$$\mathbf{M}_A = \begin{vmatrix} \mathbf{i} & \mathbf{j} & \mathbf{k} \\ 1 & 2 & -1.5 \\ 0 & -80 & 0 \end{vmatrix} + \begin{vmatrix} \mathbf{i} & \mathbf{j} & \mathbf{k} \\ 2 & 4 & -3 \\ 0 & 0 & |\mathbf{B}| \end{vmatrix}$$

$$+ \begin{vmatrix} \mathbf{i} & \mathbf{j} & \mathbf{k} \\ 2 & 4 & -3 \\ -0.8575 & 0 & 0.5145 \end{vmatrix} |\mathbf{T}| = 0$$

$$\mathbf{M}_A = (-120 + 4|\mathbf{B}| + 2.058|\mathbf{T}|)\mathbf{i} - (2|\mathbf{B}| - 1.544|\mathbf{T}|)\mathbf{j}$$

$$+ (3.43|\mathbf{T}| - 80)\mathbf{k} = 0.$$

Solve:

$$|\mathbf{T}| = \frac{80}{3.43} = 23.32 \text{ lb}$$

$$|\mathbf{B}| = \frac{120 - 2.058|\mathbf{T}|}{4} = 18.00 \text{ lb}.$$

The reactions at A are found from the sums of forces:

$$\sum F_X = A_X - |\mathbf{T}|(0.8575) = 0 \text{ from which } A_X = 20 \text{ lb}$$

$$\sum F_Y = A_Y - 80 = 0, \text{ from which } A_Y = 80 \text{ lb}$$

$$\sum F_Z = A_Z + |\mathbf{T}|(0.5145) + |\mathbf{B}| = 0, \text{ from which } A_Z = -30 \text{ lb}$$

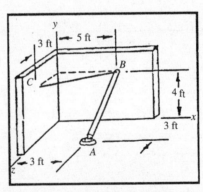

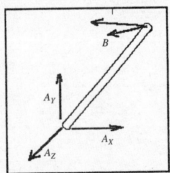

Problem 5.158 The horizontal bar of weight W is supported by a roller support at A and the cable BC. Use the fact that the bar is a three-force member to determine the angle α, the tension in the cable, and the magnitude of the reaction at A.

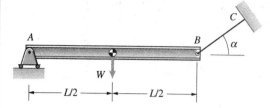

Solution: The sum of the moments about B is

$$M_B = -LA_Y + \left(\frac{L}{2}\right)W = 0,$$

from which $A_Y = \dfrac{W}{2}$. The sum of the forces:

$$\sum F_X = T\cos\alpha = 0,$$

from which $\mathbf{T} = 0$ or $\cos\alpha = 0$. The choice is made from the sum of forces in the y-direction:

$$\sum F_Y = A_Y - W + T\sin\alpha = 0,$$

from which $T\sin\alpha = W - A_Y = \dfrac{W}{2}$. This equation cannot be satisfied if $T = 0$, hence $\cos\alpha = 0$, or $\alpha = 90°$, and $T = \dfrac{W}{2}$

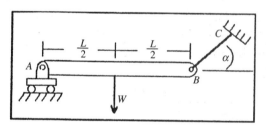

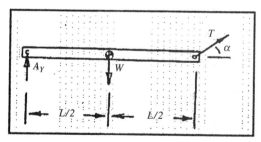

Problem 5.159 The bicycle brake on the right is pinned to the bicycle's frame at A. Determine the force exerted by the brake pad on the wheel rim at B in terms of the cable tension T.

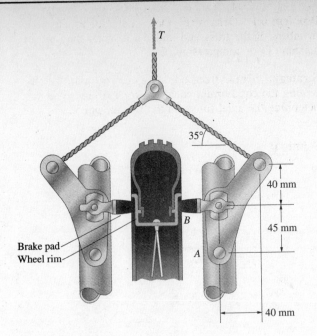

Brake pad
Wheel rim

35°

40 mm

45 mm

40 mm

B

A

T

Solution: From the force balance equation for the cables: the force on the brake mechanism T_B in terms of the cable tension T is

$$T - 2T_B \sin 35° = 0,$$

from which $T_B = \dfrac{T}{2 \sin 35°} = 0.8717T$.

Take the origin of the system to be at A. The position vector of the point of attachment of B is $\mathbf{r}_B = 45\mathbf{j}$ (mm). The position vector of the point of attachment of the cable is $\mathbf{r}_C = 40\mathbf{i} + 85\mathbf{j}$ (mm).

The force exerted by the brake pad is $\mathbf{B} = -B\mathbf{i}$. The force vector due the cable tension is

$$\mathbf{T}_B = T_B(\mathbf{i}\cos 145° + \mathbf{j}\sin 145°) = T_B(-0.8192\mathbf{i} + 0.5736\mathbf{j}).$$

The moment about A is

$$\mathbf{M}_A = \mathbf{r}_B \times \mathbf{B} + \mathbf{r}_C \times \mathbf{T}_B = 0$$

$$\mathbf{M}_A = \begin{vmatrix} \mathbf{i} & \mathbf{j} & \mathbf{k} \\ 0 & 45 & 45 \\ -B & 0 & 0 \end{vmatrix} + \begin{vmatrix} \mathbf{i} & \mathbf{j} & \mathbf{k} \\ 40 & 85 & 85 \\ -0.8192 & 0.5736 & 0 \end{vmatrix} T_B = 0$$

$$\mathbf{M}_A = (45B + 92.576T_B)\mathbf{k} = 0,$$

from which $B = \dfrac{92.576T_B}{45} = 2.057T_B$.

Substitute the expression for the cable tension:

$$B = (2.057)(0.8717)T = 1.793T$$

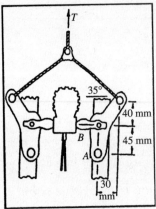

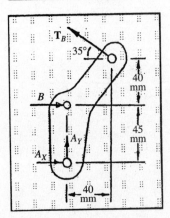

Problem 6.1 Determine the axial forces in the members of the truss and indicate whether they are in tension (T) or compression (C).

Strategy: Draw free-body diagram of joint A. By writing the equilibrium equations for the joint, you can determine the axial forces in the two members.

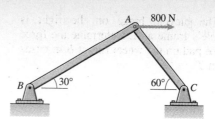

Solution:

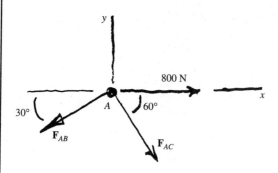

Assume the forces are in the directions shown (both in tension). If a force turns up negative, that force will be in compression.

Equilibrium Eqns.

$$\sum F_x : \quad -F_{AB}\cos 30° + F_{AC}\cos 60° + 800 = 0$$

$$\sum F_y : \quad -F_{AB}\sin 30° - F_{AC}\sin 60° = 0$$

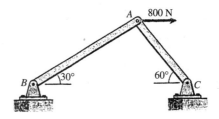

Solving: We get

$$F_{AB} = 693 \text{ N (tension)}$$

$$F_{AC} = -400 \text{ N (compression)}$$

Problem 6.2 The truss supports a 10-kN load at C.

(a) Draw the free-body diagram of the entire truss, and determine the reactions at its supports.
(b) Determine the axial forces in the members. Indicate whether they are in tension (T) or compression (C).

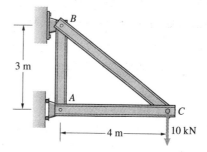

Solution: (a) The free-body diagram of the system is shown. The sum of the moments about B is: $M_B = 3A_x - 4(10) = 0$, from which $A_x = 13.33$ kN. The sums of the forces:

$$\sum F_x = A_x + B_x = 0,$$

from which $\boxed{B_x = -A_x = -13.33 \text{ kN}}$.

$$\sum F_y = B_y - 10 = 0,$$

from which $\boxed{B_y = 10 \text{ kN}}$. (b) The interior angle ACB is $\alpha = \tan^{-1}(0.75) = 36.87°$. (b) Assume that the unknown forces act away from the joint. Denote the axial force in the member I, K by IK. The axial forces are $\mathbf{F}_{CB} = BC(-\mathbf{i}\cos\alpha + \mathbf{j}\sin\alpha)$, and $\mathbf{F}_{CA} = -AC\mathbf{i}$. Summing the forces:

$$\sum F_y = BC\sin\alpha - 10 = 0,$$

from which $\boxed{BC = 16.67 \text{ kN } (T)}$.

$$\sum F_x = -BC\cos\alpha - AC = 0,$$

from which $\boxed{AC = -13.33 \text{ kN } (C)}$. For the joint A,

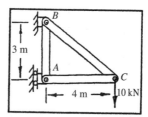

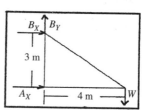

$$\sum F_y = AB = 0,$$

from which $\boxed{AB = 0}$

Problem 6.3 In Example 6.1, suppose that the 2-kN load is applied at D in the horizontal direction, pointing from D toward B. What are the axial forces in the members?

Solution: First, solve for the support forces and then use the method of joints at each joint to solve for the forces.

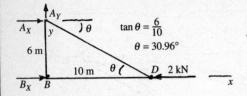

$$\tan \theta = \frac{6}{10}$$
$$\theta = 30.96°$$

$$\sum F_x : \quad B_x + A_x - 2 \text{ kN} = 0$$

$$\sum F_y : \quad A_y = 0$$

$$\sum M_B : \quad -6A_x = 0$$

Solving, we get

$$A_x = A_y = 0,$$

$$B_x = 2 \text{ kN}$$

Joint A:

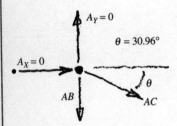

$$\theta = 30.96°$$

$$\sum F_x : \quad AC \cos \theta = 0$$

$$\sum F_y : \quad -AB - AC \sin \theta = 0$$

Solving, we get $AB = AC = 0$

Joint C:

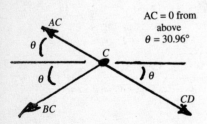

$AC = 0$ from above

$\theta = 30.96°$

$$\sum F_x : \quad \overset{0}{\cancel{AC}} \cos \theta - BC \cos \theta + CD \cos \theta = 0$$

$$-BC + CD = 0$$

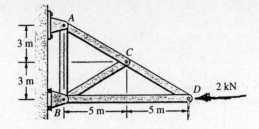

$$\sum F_y : \quad \overset{0}{\cancel{AC}} \sin \theta - BC \sin \theta - CD \sin \theta = 0$$

$$-BC - CD = 0$$

Solving, we get $BC = CD = 0$

Joint B:

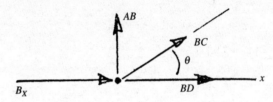

We already know $AB = BC = 0$ and $B_x = 2$ kN

$$\sum F_x : \quad \overset{0}{\cancel{BC}} \cos \theta + BD + B_x = 0$$

$$BD + 2 \text{ kN} = 0$$

$$BD = -2 \text{ kN (compression)}$$

$$\sum F_y : \text{(all forces zero)} = 0$$

we have $AB = AC = BC = CD = 0$

$$BD = -2 \text{ kN } (c)$$

Note that we did not have to use joint D as we had already solved for the forces there. The FBD at D is BD, with the $(-)$ sign, is opposite the direction shown.

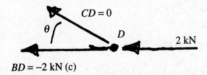

$CD = 0$

$BD = -2$ kN (c)

Problem 6.4 Determine the axial forces in the members of the truss.

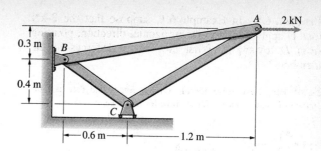

Solution: First, solve for the support reactions at B and C, and then use the method of joints to solve for the forces in the members.

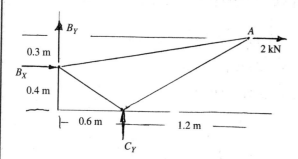

$$\sum F_x: \quad B_x + 2 \text{ kN} = 0$$

$$\sum F_y: \quad B_y + C_y = 0$$

$$\curvearrowleft + \sum M_B: \quad 0,6 C_y - (0,3)(2 \text{ kN}) = 0$$

Solving, $B_x = -2$ kN $\quad C_y = 1$ kN $\quad B_y = -1$ kN

Joint B:

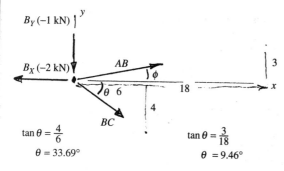

$$\tan \theta = \frac{4}{6}$$
$$\theta = 33.69°$$

$$\tan \theta = \frac{3}{18}$$
$$\theta = 9.46°$$

$$\sum F_x: \quad AB \cos \phi + BC \cos \theta - 2 = 0$$

$$\sum F_y: \quad AB \sin \phi - BC \sin \theta - 1 = 0$$

Solving, we get $AB = 2.839$ kN, $BC = -0.961$ kN

Joint C:

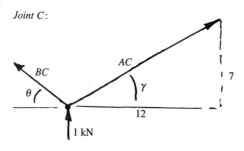

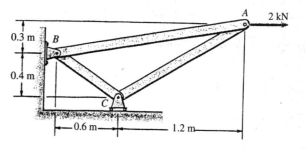

$$\tan \gamma = \frac{7}{12}$$

$$(BC = -0.961 \text{ kN})$$

$$\gamma = 30.26°$$

$$\sum F_x = -BC \cos \theta + AC \cos \gamma = 0$$

$$\sum F_y = BC \sin \theta + AC \sin \gamma + 1 = 0$$

Solving, we get $AC = -0.926$ kN

We have $AB = 2.839$ kN (T)

$$BC = -0.961 \text{ kN } (C)$$

$$AC = -0.926 \text{ kN } (C)$$

Check: Look at Joint A

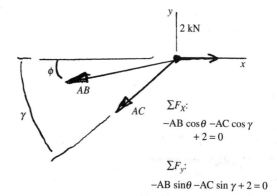

$$\sum F_x:$$
$$-AB \cos \theta - AC \cos \gamma + 2 = 0$$

$$\sum F_y:$$
$$-AB \sin \theta - AC \sin \gamma + 2 = 0$$

$$\sum F_x: \quad -AB \cos \phi - AC \cos \gamma + 2 = 0$$

$$\sum F_y: \quad -AB \sin \phi - AC \sin \gamma = 0$$

Substituting in the known values, the equations are satisfied: $\therefore$ *Check!*

Problem 6.5 (a) Let the dimension $h = 0.1$ m. Determine the axial forces in the members, and show that in this case this truss is equivalent to the one in Problem 6.4.

(b) Let the dimension $h = 0.5$ m. Determine the axial forces in the members. Compare the results to (a), and observe the dramatic effect of this simple change in design on the maximum tensile and compressive forces to which the members are subjected.

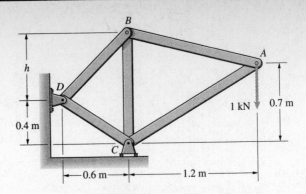

Solution: To get the force components we use equations of the form $\mathbf{T}_{PQ} = T_{PQ}\mathbf{e}_{PQ} = T_{PQX}\mathbf{i} + T_{PQY}\mathbf{j}$ where P and Q take on the designations A, B, C, and D as needed.

Equilibrium yields

At joint A:

$$\sum F_x = T_{ABX} + T_{ACX} = 0,$$

and $\sum F_y = T_{ABY} + T_{ACY} - 1 \text{ kN} = 0.$

At joint B:

$$\sum F_x = -T_{ABX} + T_{BCX} + T_{BDX} = 0,$$

and $\sum F_y = -T_{ABY} + T_{BCY} + T_{BDY} = 0.$

At joint C:

$$\sum F_x = -T_{BCX} - T_{ACX} + T_{CDX} = 0,$$

and $\sum F_y = -T_{BCY} - T_{ACY} + T_{CDY} + C_Y = 0.$

At joint D:

$$\sum F_x = -T_{CDX} - T_{BDX} + D_X = 0,$$

and $\sum F_y = -T_{CDY} - T_{BDY} + D_Y = 0.$

Solve simultaneously to get

$$T_{AB} = T_{BD} = 2.43 \text{ kN},$$

$$T_{AC} = -2.78 \text{ kN},$$

$$T_{BC} = 0, \quad T_{CD} = -2.88 \text{ kN}.$$

Note that with appropriate changes in the designation of points, the forces here are the same as those in Problem 6.4. This can be explained by noting from the unit vectors that AB and BC are parallel. Also note that in this configuration, BC carries no load. This geometry is the same as in Problem 6.4 except for the joint at B and member BC which carries no load. Remember member BC in this geometry—we will encounter things like it again, will give it a special name, and will learn to recognize it on sight.

(b) For this part of the problem, we set $h = 0.5$ m. The unit vectors change because h is involved in the coordinates of point B. The new unit vectors are

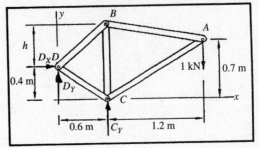

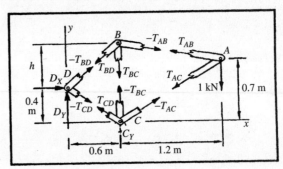

$$\mathbf{e}_{AB} = -0.986\mathbf{i} + 0.164\mathbf{j},$$

$$\mathbf{e}_{AC} = -0.864\mathbf{i} - 0.504\mathbf{j},$$

$$\mathbf{e}_{BC} = 0\mathbf{i} - 1\mathbf{j},$$

$$\mathbf{e}_{BD} = -0.768\mathbf{i} - 0.640\mathbf{j},$$

and $\mathbf{e}_{CD} = -0.832\mathbf{i} + 0.555\mathbf{j}.$

We get the force components as above, and the equilibrium forces at the joints remain the same. Solving the equilibrium equations simultaneously for this situation yields

$$T_{AB} = 1.35 \text{ kN},$$

$$T_{AC} = -1.54 \text{ kN},$$

$$T_{BC} = -1.33,$$

$$T_{BD} = 1.74 \text{ kN},$$

and $T_{CD} = -1.60 \text{ kN}.$

These numbers differ significantly from (a). Most significantly, member BD is now carrying a compressive load and this has reduced the loads in all members except member BD. "Sharing the load" among more members seems to have worked in this case.

Problem 6.6 The load $F = 10$ kN. Determine the axial forces in the members.

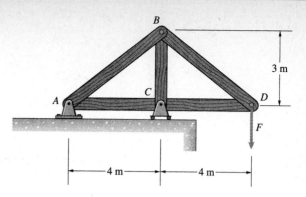

Solution: The free-body diagram of joint D is

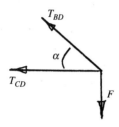

where $\alpha = \arctan(3/4) = 36.9°$. From the equations

$$\sum F_x = -T_{CD} - T_{BD} \cos \alpha = 0,$$

$$\sum F_y = T_{BD} \sin \alpha - F = 0,$$

we obtain

$$T_{BD} = 1.67F = 16.7 \text{ kN},$$

$$T_{CD} = -1.33F = -13.3 \text{ kN}.$$

Joint B

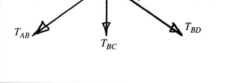

From the equations

$$\sum F_x = -T_{AB} \cos \alpha + T_{BD} \cos \alpha = 0,$$

$$\sum F_y = -T_{BC} - T_{AB} \sin \alpha - T_{BD} \sin \alpha = 0,$$

we obtain

$$T_{AB} = 1.67F = 16.7 \text{ kN},$$

$$T_{BC} = -2F = -20 \text{ kN}.$$

Joint C

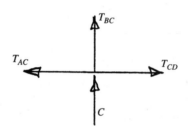

we see that

$$T_{AC} = T_{CD} = -1.33F = -13.3 \text{ kN}.$$

Problem 6.7 Consider the truss in Problem 6.6. Each member will safely support a tensile force of 150 kN and a compressive force of 30 kN. What is the largest downward load F that the truss will safely support at D?

Solution: See the solution of Problem 6.6. The largest tensile load is $1.67F$ in members BD and AB. Setting

$$1.67F = 150 \text{ kN}$$

gives $F = 90$ kN. The largest compressive load is $2F$ in member BC. Setting

$$2F = 30 \text{ kN}$$

gives $F = 15$ kN. The largest load is $F = 15$ kN.

Problem 6.8 The Howe and Pratt bridge trusses are subjected to identical loads.

(a) In which truss does the largest tensile force occur? In what member(s) does it occur, and what is its value?

(b) In which truss does the largest compressive force occur? In what member(s) does it occur, and what is its value?

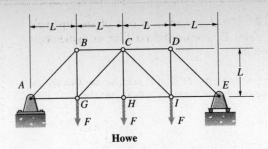

Howe

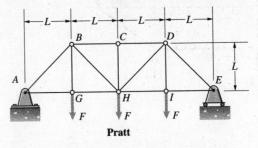

Pratt

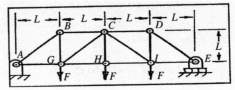

Solution: (a) **Howe Bridge:** The moment about A is $M_A = -6F + 4E = 0$, from which $E = \frac{3}{2}F$. Denote the axial force in the member I, K by IK.

(1) *Joint E:* $DE = -\dfrac{E}{\sin 45°} = -\dfrac{3\sqrt{2}}{2}F \ (C)$

$EI = DE\cos 45° = \dfrac{3}{2}F\,(T)$

(2) *Joint D:* $CD = DE\cos 45° = -\dfrac{3}{2}F \ (C)$,

$DI = -DE\sin 45° = \dfrac{3}{2}F(T)$

(3) *Joint I:* $CI = \dfrac{F - |DI|}{\sin 45°} = -\dfrac{\sqrt{2}}{2}F(C)$,

$HI = EI - CI\sin 45° = 2F(T)$

(4) *Joint H:* $CH = F(T)$, $GH = HI = 2F(T)$.

By symmetry (the reaction at A has no x-component) the axial forces in the other members are $HG = HI$, $CG = CI$, $BG = DI$, $CD = BC$, $AG = EI$, and $AB = DE$. In the Howe truss, the members HI and GH have the highest tensile force $\boxed{GH = HI = 2F(T)}$ and the members DE and AB have the highest compressive force

$$\boxed{AB = DE = -\dfrac{3\sqrt{2}}{2}F(C)}$$

(b) **Pratt Bridge:** The moment about A is $M_A = -6F + 4E = 0$, from which $E = \dfrac{3}{2}F$.

(1) *Joint E:* $DE = -\dfrac{3\sqrt{2}}{2}F(C)$, $EI = \dfrac{-DE}{\sqrt{2}} = \dfrac{3}{2}F(T)$

(2) *Joint I:* $DI = F(T)$, $HI = EI = \dfrac{3}{2}F(T)$

(3) *Joint D:* $DH = -\sqrt{2}DI - DE = \dfrac{\sqrt{2}}{2}F(T)$, $DC = \dfrac{DE}{\sqrt{2}} - \dfrac{DH}{\sqrt{2}}$
$= -2F(C)$

(4) *Joint C:* $BC = DC = -2F(C)$, $CH = 0$

(5) *Joint H:* $GH = HI = \dfrac{3}{2}F(T)$. The axial forces in the remaining members are determined from symmetry. In the Pratt Bridge, the highest tensile force occurs in members EI, HI, GH, and

$AG \boxed{= \dfrac{3}{2}F(T)}$, and the highest compressive force occurs in

members DE and AB $\boxed{= -\dfrac{3\sqrt{2}}{2}F(C)}$. Thus (a) the Howe

bridge has the highest tensile force in a member, and (b) the value of the compressive force is the same in members DE and

$AB = \dfrac{3\sqrt{2}}{2}F(C)$ for both bridges.

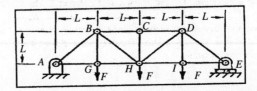

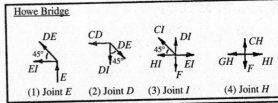

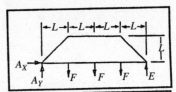

Howe Bridge

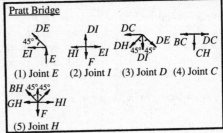

(1) Joint E   (2) Joint D   (3) Joint I   (4) Joint H

Pratt Bridge

(1) Joint E   (2) Joint I   (3) Joint D   (4) Joint C

(5) Joint H

Problem 6.9 The truss shown is part of an airplane's internal structure. Determine the axial forces in members BC, BD, and BE.

Solution: First, solve for the support reactions and then use the method of joints to solve for the reactions in the members.

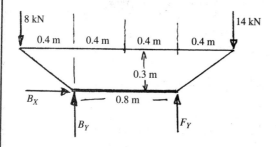

$$\sum F_x: \quad B_x = 0$$

$$\sum F_y: \quad B_y + F_y - 8 - 14 = 0 \text{ (kN)}$$

$$\curvearrowleft + \sum M_B: \quad (0.4)(8) + 0.8F_y - 1.2(14) = 0$$

Solving, we get $B_x = 0$, $B_y = 5.00$ kN $F_y = 17.00$ kN.

The forces we are seeking are involved at joints B, C, D, and E. The method of joints allows us to solve for two unknowns at a joint. We need a joint with only two unknowns. Joints A and H qualify. Joint A is nearest to the members we want to know about, so let us choose it. Assume tension in all members.

Joint A:

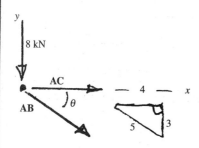

$$\sin \theta = 0.6 \quad \cos \theta = 0.8 \quad \theta = 36.87°$$

$$\sum F_x = AC + AB \cos \theta = 0$$

$$\sum F_y = -8 - AB \sin \theta = 0$$

Solving, we get $AC = 10.67$ kN (T)

$$AB = -13.33 \text{ kN } (C)$$

Joint C: (Again, assume all forces are in tension)

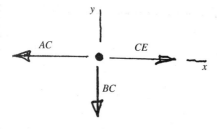

$[AC = 10.67 \text{ kN } (T)]$

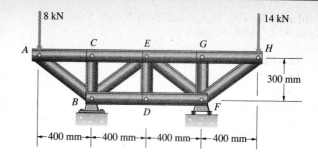

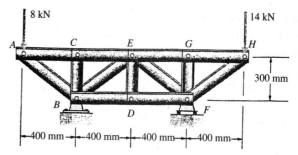

$$\sum F_x: \quad -BC = 0$$

$$\sum F_y: \quad -AC + CE = 0$$

Solving, we get $BC = 0$,

$$CE = 10.67 \text{ kN } (T)$$

Joint B:

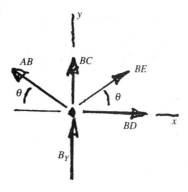

We know $AB = -13.33$ kN $BC = 0$ $B_y = 5.00$ kN.

We know 3 of the 5 forces at B Hence, we can solve for the other two.

$$\sum F_x: \quad BD + BE \cos \theta - AB \cos \theta = 0$$

$$\sum F_y: \quad BC + B_y + BE \sin \theta + AB \sin \theta = 0$$

Solving, we get $BD = -14.67$ kN (C)

$$BE = 5.00 \text{ kN } (T)$$

From Joint C, we had $BC = 0$

Thus $\boxed{\begin{array}{l} BC = 0, \quad BD = -14.67 \text{ kN } (C) \\ BE = 5.00 \text{ kN } (T) \end{array}}$

Problem 6.10 For the truss in Problem 6.9, determine the axial forces in members DF, EF, and FG.

Solution: First, solve for the support reactions and then use the method of joints to solve for the reactions in the members.

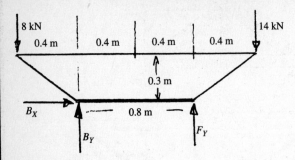

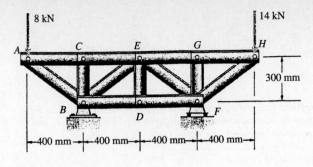

$$\sum F_x: \quad B_x = 0$$

$$\sum F_y: \quad B_y + F_y - 8 - 14 = 0 \text{ (kN)}$$

$$\curvearrowleft + \sum M_B: \quad (0.4)(8) + 0.8F_y - 1.2(14) = 0$$

Solving, we get $B_x = 0$,

$$B_y = 5.00 \text{ kN}$$

$$F_y = 17.00 \text{ kN}$$

The forces we are seeking are involved with joints D, E, F, and G The method of joints allows us to solve for two unknown forces at a joint. We need to start with a joint with only two unknowns. Joints A and H qualify. Joint H is nearest to the members we want to know about, so let us start there. Assume all unknown forces are tensions. If we get a negative force in a solution, this will then imply compression in that member.

Joint G:

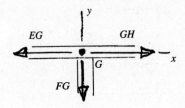

$[GH = 18.67 \text{ kN } (T)]$

$$\sum F_x: \quad GH - EG = 0$$

$$\sum F_y: \quad FG = 0$$

Solving $EG = 18.67 \text{ kN } (T)$

$$FG = 0$$

Joint F:

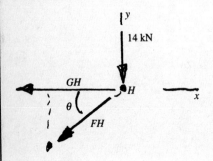

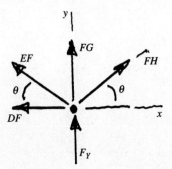

Joint H

$$\sin \theta = \frac{3}{5} = 0.6$$

$$\cos \theta = \frac{4}{5} = 0.8$$

$$\sum F_x: \quad -GH - FH \cos \theta = 0$$

$$\sum F_y: \quad -14 - FH \sin \theta = 0$$

Solving $GH = 18.67 \text{ kN } (T)$,

$$FH = -23.33 \text{ kN } (C)$$

We know $FH = -23.33 \text{ kN } (C)$

$$FG = 0$$

$$F_y = 17.00 \text{ kN}$$

$$\sum F_x: \quad FH \cos \theta - EF \cos \theta - DF = 0$$

$$\sum F_y: \quad FG + F_y + FH \sin \theta + EF \sin \theta = 0$$

Solving, we get

$$\boxed{\begin{array}{l} EF = -5.00 \text{ kN } (C) \\ DF = -14.67 \text{ kN } (C) \\ \text{and from above } FG = 0 \end{array}}$$

446

Problem 6.11   The loads $F_1 = F_2 = 8$ kN. Determine the axial forces in members BD, BE, and BG.

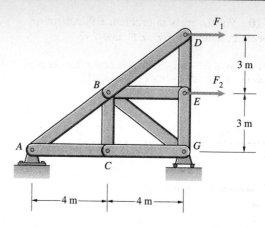

Solution: First find the external support loads and then use the method of joints to solve for the required unknown forces. (Assume all unknown forces in members are tensions).

External loads:

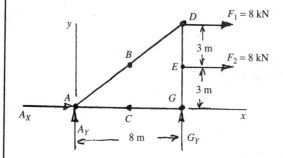

$$\sum F_x: \quad A_x + F_1 + F_2 = 0 \ (\text{kN})$$

$$\sum F_y: \quad A_y + G_y = 0$$

$$\curvearrowleft + \sum M_A: \quad 8G_y - 3F_2 - 6F_1 = 0$$

Solving for the external loads, we get

$A_x = -16$ kN (to the left)

$A_y = -9$ kN (downward)

$G_y = 9$ kN (upward)

Now use the method of joints to determine BD, BE, and BG.

Start with joint D.

Joint D:

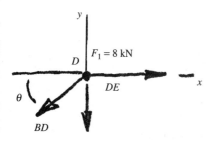

$\cos \theta = 0.8$

$\sin \theta = 0.6$

$\theta = 36.87°$

$$\sum F_x: \quad F_1 - BD \cos \theta = 0$$

$$\sum F_y: \quad -BD \sin \theta - DE = 0$$

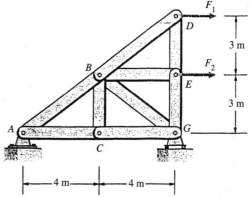

Solving, $BD = 10$ kN (T)

$DE = -6$ kN (C)

Joint E:

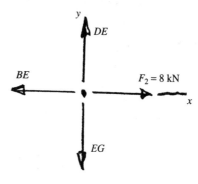

$DE = -6$ kN

$$\sum F_x = DE - EG = 0$$

$$\sum F_y = -BE + F_2 = 0$$

Solving: $EG = -6$ kN (C)

$BE = 8$ kN (T)

6.11 *Contd.*

Joint G:

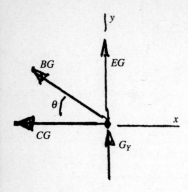

$(EG = -6$ kN $(C))$

$G_y = 9$ kN

$\sum F_x: \quad -CG - BG\cos\theta = 0$

$\sum F_y: \quad BG\sin\theta + EG + G_y = 0$

Solving, we get

$BG = -5$ kN (C)

$CG = 4$ kN (T)

Thus, we have

$$\boxed{\begin{aligned} BD &= 10 \text{ kN } (T) \\ BE &= 8 \text{ kN } (T) \\ BG &= -5 \text{ kN } (C) \end{aligned}}$$

Problem 6.12 If the loads on the truss shown in Problem 6.11 are $F_1 = 6$ kN and $F_2 = 10$ kN, what are the axial forces in members AB, BC, and BD?

Solution: Find the external support loads and then use the method of joints to determine loads in members. (Assume all loads in members to be tensions).

External Loads:

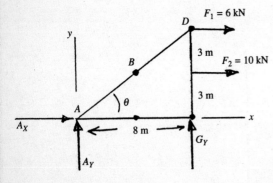

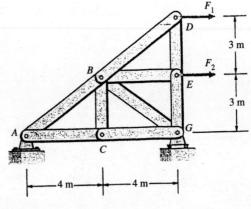

$\sin\theta = 0.6 \quad \cos\theta = 0.8 \quad \theta = 36.87°$

$\sum F_x: \quad A_x + F_1 + F_2 = 0$

$\sum F_y: \quad A_y + G_y = 0$

$\curvearrowleft + \sum M_A: \quad 8G_y - 3F_2 - 6F_1 = 0$

Solving, the external loads are

$A_x = -16$ kN,

$A_y = -8.25$ kN,

$G_y = 8.25$ kN.

Now use the method of joints to determine AB, BC, and BD.

Start with Joint A:

Joint A:

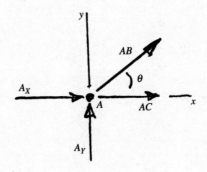

$A_y = -8.25$ kN

$A_x = -16$ kN

$\sum F_x: \quad AC + A_x + AB\cos\theta = 0$

$\sum F_y: \quad A_y + AB\sin\theta = 0$

448

Solving, $AC = 5$ kN (T)

           $AB = 13.75$ kN (T)

Joint C:

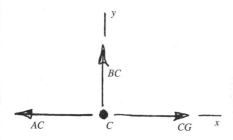

$(AC = 5$ kN$)$

$\sum F_x:$ $CG - AC = 0$

$\sum F_y:$ $BC = 0$

Solving,

$BC = 0,$

$CG = 5$ kN (T)

Joint D:

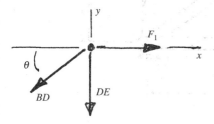

$F_1 = 6$ kN

$\sum F_x:$ $F_1 - BD \cos \theta = 0$

$\sum F_y:$ $- BD \sin \theta - DE = 0$

Solving, we get

     $DE = -4.5$ kN (C)

and $BD = 7.5$ kN (T)

Thus, we have

$AB = 13.75$ kN (T)

$BC = 0$

$BD = 7.5$ kN (T)

Problem 6.13 The truss supports loads at C and E. If $F = 3$ kN, what are the axial forces in members BC and BE?

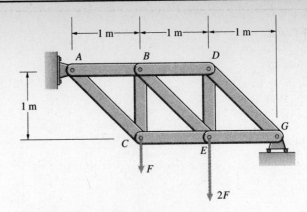

Solution: The moment about A is

$$\sum M_A = -1F - 4F + 3G = 0,$$

from which $G = \dfrac{5}{3}F = 5$ kN. The sums of forces:

$$\sum F_Y = A_Y - 3F + G = 0,$$

from which $A_Y = \dfrac{4}{3}F = 4$ kN.

$$\sum F_X = A_X = 0,$$

from which $A_X = 0$. The interior angles GDE, EBC are $45°$,

from which $\sin\alpha = \cos\alpha = \dfrac{1}{\sqrt{2}}$.

Denote the axial force in a member joining I, K by IK.

(1) *Joint G*:

$$\sum F_y = \frac{DG}{\sqrt{2}} + G = 0,$$

from which

$$DG = -\sqrt{2}G = -\frac{5\sqrt{2}}{3}F = -5\sqrt{2} \text{ kN } (C).$$

$$\sum F_x = -\frac{DG}{\sqrt{2}} - EG = 0,$$

from which

$$EG = -\frac{DG}{\sqrt{2}} = \frac{5}{3}F = 5\text{kN } (T).$$

(2) *Joint D*:

$$\sum F_y = -DE - \frac{DG}{\sqrt{2}} = 0,$$

from which

$$DE = \frac{5}{3}F = 5 \text{ kN } (T).$$

$$\sum F_x = -BD + \frac{DG}{\sqrt{2}} = 0,$$

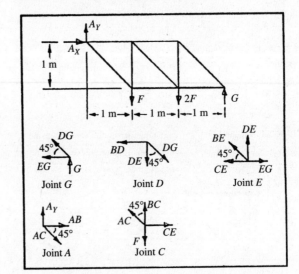

from which

$$BD = -\frac{5}{3}F = -5 \text{ kN } (C).$$

(3) *Joint E*:

$$\sum F_y = \frac{BE}{\sqrt{2}} - 2F + DE = 0,$$

from which $\boxed{BE = 2\sqrt{2}F - \sqrt{2}DE = \dfrac{\sqrt{2}}{3}F = \sqrt{2} \text{ kN } (T).}$

$$\sum F_x = -CE - \frac{BE}{\sqrt{2}} + EG = 0,$$

from which

$$CE = EG - \frac{BE}{\sqrt{2}} = \frac{4}{3}F = 4 \text{ kN } (T).$$

6.13 *Contd.*

(4)   *Joint A:*

$$\sum F_y = A_y - \frac{AC}{\sqrt{2}} = 0,$$

from which $AC = \frac{4\sqrt{2}}{3}F = 4\sqrt{2}$ kN (T).

$$\sum F_x = AB + \frac{AC}{\sqrt{2}} = 0,$$

from which $AB = -\frac{4}{3}F = -4$ kN (C).

(5)   *Joint C:*

$$\sum F_y = BC + \frac{AC}{\sqrt{2}} - F = 0,$$

from which $\boxed{BC = F - \frac{AC}{\sqrt{2}} = -\frac{1}{3}F = -1 \text{ kN } (C).}$

Problem 6.14   Consider the truss in Problem 6.13. Each member will safely support a tensile force of 28 kN and a compressive force of 12 kN. Taking this criterion into account, what is the largest safe (positive) value of F?

Solution: From the solution to Problem 6.14, the member with the largest tensile force is $EG = \frac{5}{3}F$, from which $F = \frac{3}{5}EG = 16.8$ kN. The member with the largest compressive force is DG, $DG = \frac{-5\sqrt{2}}{3}F$, from which $\boxed{F = \frac{3}{5\sqrt{2}}DG = \frac{36}{5\sqrt{2}} = 5.09 \text{ kN}}$ is the largest safe value.

Problem 6.15 The truss is a preliminary design for a structure to attach one end of a stretcher to a rescue helicopter. Based on dynamic simulations, the design engineer estimates that the downward forces the stretcher will exert will be no greater than 360 lb at A and at B. What are the resulting axial forces in members CF, DF, and FG?

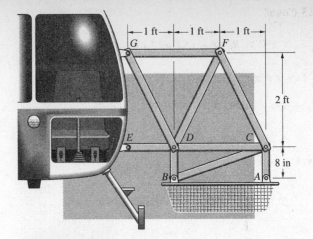

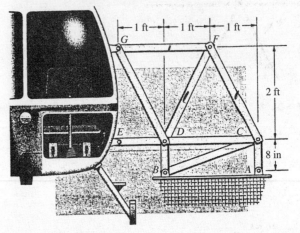

Solution: Assume loads of 360 lbs at A and at B. Use the method of joints, starting with A and B, to work through the structure.

Joint A:

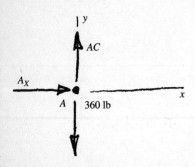

$$\sum F_y: \quad AC - 360 \text{ lb} = 0$$

$$AC = 360 \text{ lb}$$

$$\sum F_x: \quad A_x = 0$$

If $A_x = 0$, then $B_x = 0$ because the stretcher must be in equilibrium

Joint B:

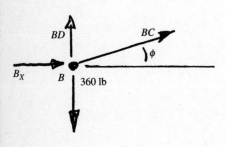

$$\tan \phi = \frac{8}{24}$$

$$\phi = 18.43°$$

$$B_x = 0$$

$$\sum F_x: \quad B_x + BC \cos \phi = 0$$

$$\sum F_y: \quad BC \sin \phi + BD - 360 = 0$$

Solving, $BD = 360$ lb, $BC = 0$

Joint C:

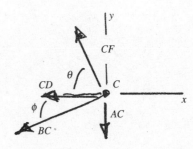

$$\tan \theta = \frac{2}{1}$$

$$\theta = 63.43°$$

$$BC = 0,$$

$$AC = 360 \text{ lb}$$

$\sum F_x:\quad -CD - BC\cos\phi - CF\cos\theta = 0$

$\sum F_y:\quad CF\sin\theta - BC\sin\phi - AC = 0$

Solving, $CD = -180$ lb (C)

$\qquad CF = 402$ lb (T)

Joint F:

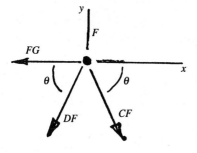

$\theta = 63.43°$

$(CF = 402\ \text{lbs}\ (T))$

$\sum F_x:\quad CF\cos\theta - DF\cos\theta - FG = 0$

$\sum F_y:\quad -CF\sin\theta - DF\sin\theta = 0$

Solving; we get

$\boxed{\begin{array}{l} DF = -402\ \text{lb}\ (C) \\ FG = 360\ \text{lb}\ (T) \\ \text{and from earlier} \\ CF = 402\ \text{lb}\ (T) \end{array}}$

Problem 6.16   Upon learning of an upgrade in the helicopter's engine, the engineer designing the truss shown in Problem 6.15 does new simulations and concludes that the downward forces the stretcher will exert at A and at B may be as large as 400 lb. What are the resulting axial forces in members DE, DF, and DG?

Solution: Assume loads of 400 lb at A and B. Use the method of Joints, starting with A and B, and work through the structure.

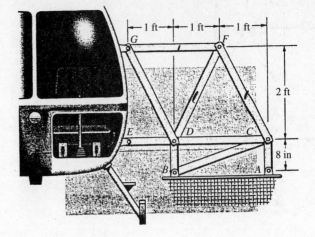

Joint A:

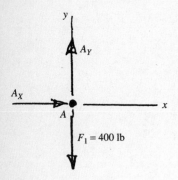

$$\sum F_x: \quad A_x = 0$$

$$\sum F_y: \quad A_y - F_1 = 0$$

$$F_1 = 400 \text{ lb}$$

Solving, $A_y = 400$ lb.

$$A_x = 0$$

If $A_x = 0$, then $B_x = 0$ for the stretcher not to move horizontally. $(A_x + B_x = 0)$

Joint B:

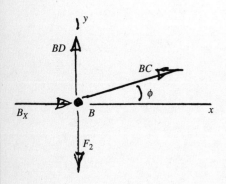

$$B_x = 0$$

$$F_2 = 400 \text{ lb}$$

$$\tan \phi = \frac{8}{24}$$

$$\phi = 18.43°$$

$$\sum F_x: \quad B_x + BC \cos \phi = 0$$

$$\sum F_y: \quad BC \sin \phi + BD - F_2 = 0$$

Solving, $BC = 0$, $BD = 400$ lb(T)

Joint C:

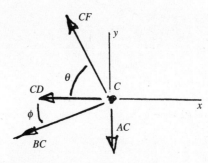

$$\tan \theta = \frac{2}{1}$$

$$\theta = 63.43°$$

$$BC = 0, \quad AC = 400 \text{ lb}.$$

$$\sum F_x: \quad -CD - BC \cos \phi - CF \cos \theta = 0$$

$$\sum F_y: \quad CF \sin \theta - BC \sin \phi - AC = 0$$

Solving, $CD = -200$ lb (C)

6.16 *Contd.*

Joint F:

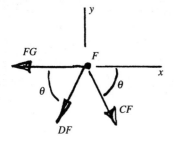

$\theta = 63.43°$

$CF = 44.7$ lb (T)

$\sum F_x: \quad CF\cos\theta - DF\cos\theta - FG = 0$

$\sum F_y: \quad -CF\sin\theta - DF\sin\theta = 0$

Solving, we get

$CF = 447$ lb (T)

$DF = -447$ lb (C)

$FG = 400$

Joint D:

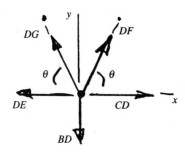

$CD = -200$ lb (C)

$BD = 400$ lb (T)

$DF = -447$ lb (C)

$\sum F_x: \quad CD - DE + DF\cos\theta - DG\cos\theta = 0$

$\sum F_y: \quad DF\sin\theta + DG\sin\theta - BD = 0$

Solving $\quad DE = -968$ lb (C)

$\quad\quad\quad\quad DG = 894$ lb (T)

Thus, $\quad DE = -800$ lb (C)
$\quad\quad\quad DF = -447$ lb (C)
$\quad\quad\quad DG = 894$ lb (T)

Problem 6.17 Determine the axial forces in the members in terms of the weight W.

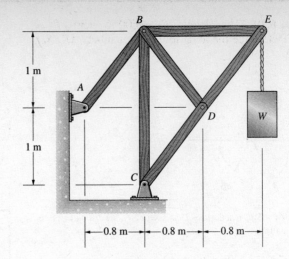

Solution: Denote the axial force in a member joining two points I, K by IK. The angle between member DE and the positive x axis is $\alpha = \tan^{-1} 0.8 = 38.66°$. The angle formed by member DB with the positive x axis is $90° + \alpha$. The angle formed by member AB with the positive x-axis is α.

Joint E:

$$\sum F_y = -DE \cos \alpha - W = 0,$$

from which $\boxed{DE = -1.28W \ (C)}$.

$$\sum F_y = -BE - DE \sin \alpha = 0,$$

from which $\boxed{BE = 0.8W \ (T)}$

Joint D:

$$\sum F_x = DE \cos \alpha + BD \cos \alpha - CD \cos \alpha = 0,$$

from which $BD - CD = -DE$.

$$\sum F_y = -BD \sin \alpha + DE \sin \alpha - CD \sin \alpha = 0,$$

from which $BD + CD = DE$.

Solving these two equations in two unknowns:

$$\boxed{CD = DE = -1.28W \ (C)}, \quad \boxed{BD = 0}$$

Joint B:

$$\sum F_x = BE - AB \sin \alpha - BD \sin \alpha = 0,$$

from which $\boxed{AB = \dfrac{BE}{\sin \alpha} = 1.28W(T)}$

$$\sum F_y = -AB \cos \alpha - BC = 0,$$

from which $\boxed{BC = -AB \cos \alpha = -W(C)}$

Problem 6.18 Consider the truss in Problem 6.17. Each member will safely support a tensile force of 6 kN and a compressive force of 2 kN. Use this criterion to determine the largest weight W the truss will safely support.

Solution: From the solution to Problem 6.17, the largest tensile force is in member AB, $AB = 1.28W(T)$, from which $W = \dfrac{6}{1.28} = 4.69$ kN is the maximum safe load for tension. The largest compressive forces occur in members DE and CD, $DE = CD = 1.28W(C)$, from which $\boxed{W = \dfrac{2}{1.28} = 1.56 \text{ kN}}$ is the largest safe load for compression.

Problem 6.19 The loads $F_1 = 600$ lb and $F_2 = 300$ lb. Determine the axial forces in members AE, BD, and CD.

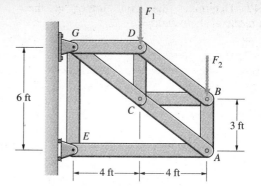

Solution: The reaction at E is determined by the sum of the moments about G:

$$M_G = +6E - 4F_1 - 8F_2 = 0,$$

from which

$$E = \frac{4F_1 + 8F_2}{6} = 800 \text{ lb}.$$

The interior angle EAG is

$$\alpha = \tan^{-1}\left(\frac{6}{8}\right) = 36.87°.$$

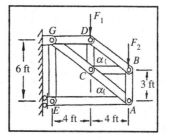

From similar triangles this is also the value of the interior angles ACB, CBD, and CGD. *Method of joints:* Denote the axial force in a member joining two points I, K by IK.

Joint E:

$$\sum F_y = E + AE = 0,$$

from which $\boxed{AE = -E = -800 \text{ lb } (C)}$.

$$\sum F_y = EG = 0,$$

from which $EG = 0$.

Joint A:

$$\sum F_y = -AE - AC \cos\alpha = 0,$$

from which $AC = -\dfrac{AE}{0.8} = 1000$ lb(T).

$$\sum F_y = AC \sin\alpha + AB = 0,$$

from which $AB = -AC(0.6) = -600$ lb(C).

Joint B:

$$\sum F_y = BD \sin\alpha - AB - F_1 = 0,$$

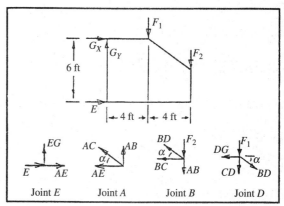

from which $\boxed{BD = \dfrac{F_2 + AB}{0.6} = \dfrac{-300}{0.6} = -500 \text{ lb}(C)}$.

$$\sum F_x = -BC - BD \cos\alpha = 0,$$

from which $BC = -BD(0.8) = 400$ lb(T).

Joint D:

$$\sum F_y = -BD \sin\alpha - CD - F_1 = 0,$$

from which $\boxed{CD = -F_1 - BD(0.6) = -300 \text{ lb}(C)}$

Problem 6.20 Consider the truss in Problem 6.19. The loads $F_1 = 450$ lb and $F_2 = 150$ lb. Determine the axial forces in members AB, AC, and BC.

Solution: From the solution to Problem 6.19 the angle $\alpha = 36.87°$ and the reaction at E is $E = \dfrac{4F_1 + 8F_2}{6} = 500$ lb. Denote the axial force in a member joining two points I, K by IK.

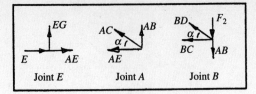

Joint E   Joint A   Joint B

Joint E:

$$\sum F_y = EG = 0.$$

$$\sum F_x = AE + E = 0,$$

from which $AE = -E = -500$ lb(C).

Joint A:

$$\sum F_x = -AE - AC \cos \alpha = 0,$$

from which $\boxed{AC = -\dfrac{AE}{0.8} = 625 \text{ lb}(T)}$.

$$\sum F_y = AC \sin \alpha + AB = 0,$$

from which $\boxed{AB = -AC(0.6) = -375 \text{ lb}(C)}$

Joint B:

$$\sum F_y = BD \sin \alpha - F_2 - AB = 0,$$

from which $BD = \dfrac{F_2 + AB}{0.6} = -375$ lb(C)

$$\sum F_x = -BC - BD \cos \alpha = 0,$$

from which $\boxed{BC = -BD(0.8) = 300 \text{ lb}(T)}$

Problem 6.21 Each member of the truss will safely support a tensile force of 4 kN and a compressive force of 1 kN. Determine the largest mass m that can safely be suspended.

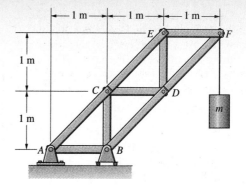

Solution: The common interior angle $BAC = DCE = EFD = CDB$ is $\alpha = \tan^{-1}(1) = 45°$.

Note $\cos\alpha = \sin\alpha = \dfrac{1}{\sqrt{2}}$. Denote the axial force in a member joining two points I, K by IK.

Joint F:

$$\sum F_y = -\frac{DF}{\sqrt{2}} - W = 0,$$

from which $DF = -\sqrt{2}W\,(C)$.

$$\sum F_x = -EF - \frac{DF}{\sqrt{2}} = 0,$$

from which $EF = W\,(T)$.

Joint E:

$$\sum F_x = -\frac{CE}{\sqrt{2}} + EF = 0$$

from which $CE = \sqrt{2}W\,(T)$.

$$\sum F_y = -ED - \frac{CE}{\sqrt{2}} = 0,$$

from which $ED = -W\,(C)$.

Joint D:

$$\sum F_Y = ED + \frac{DF}{\sqrt{2}} - \frac{BD}{\sqrt{2}} = 0,$$

from which $BD = -2\sqrt{2}W\,(C)$.

$$\sum F_X = \frac{DF}{\sqrt{2}} - \frac{BD}{\sqrt{2}} - CD = 0,$$

from which $CD = W\,(T)$

Joint C:

$$\sum F_x = -\frac{AC}{\sqrt{2}} + \frac{CE}{\sqrt{2}} + CD = 0,$$

from which $AC = 2\sqrt{2}W\,(T)$

$$\sum F_y = -\frac{AC}{\sqrt{2}} + \frac{CE}{\sqrt{2}} - BC = 0,$$

from which $BC = -W\,(C)$

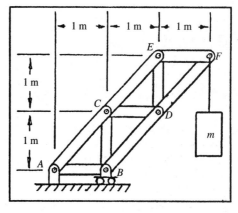

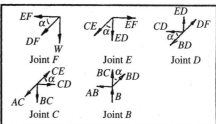

Joint B:

$$\sum F_x = -AB + \frac{BD}{\sqrt{2}} = 0,$$

from which $AB = -2W\,(C)$

This completes the determination of the axial forces in all nine members. The maximum tensile force occurs in member AC, $AC = 2\sqrt{2}W\,(T)$, from which the safe load is $W = \dfrac{4}{2\sqrt{2}} = \sqrt{2} = 1.414$ kN. The maximum compression occurs in member BD, $BD = -2\sqrt{2}W\,(C)$, from which the maximum safe load is $W = \dfrac{1}{2\sqrt{2}} = 0.3536$ kN. The largest mass m that can be safely supported is

$$\boxed{m = \frac{353.6}{9.81} = 36.0 \text{ kg}}$$

Problem 6.22 The Warren truss supporting the walkway is designed to support vertical 50-kN loads at B, D, F, and H. If the truss is subjected to these loads, what are the resulting axial forces in members BC, CD, and CE?

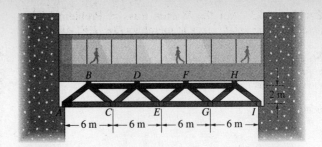

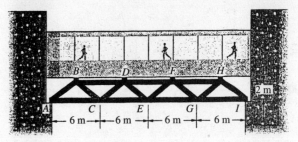

Solution: Assume vertical loads at A and I Find the external loads at A and I, then use the method of joints to work through the structure to the members needed.

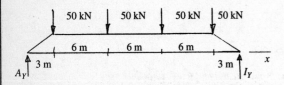

$$\sum F_y: \quad A_y + I_y - 4(50) = 0 \text{ (kN)}$$

$$\sum M_A: \quad -3(50) - 9(50) - 15(50) - 21(50) + 24I_y = 0$$

Solving $A_y = 100$ kN

$$I_y = 100 \text{ kN}$$

Joint A:

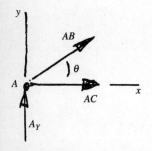

$\tan \theta = \frac{2}{3}$

$\theta = 33.69°$

$$\sum F_x: \quad AB \cos\theta + AC = 0$$

$$\sum F_y: \quad AB \sin\theta + A_y = 0$$

Solving, $AB = -180.3$ kN (C)

$AC = 150$ kN (T)

Joint B:

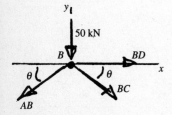

$AB = -180.3$ kN

$\theta = 33.69°$

$$\sum F_x: \quad BC \cos\theta + BD - AB \cos\theta = 0$$

$$\sum F_y: \quad -50 - AB \sin\theta - BC \sin\theta = 0$$

Solving, $BC = 90.1$ kN (T)

$BD = -225$ kN (C)

Joint C:

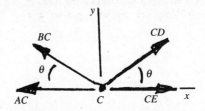

$\theta = 33.69°$

$AC = 150$ kN (T)

$BC = 90.1$ kN (T)

$$\sum F_x: \quad CE - AC + CD \cos\theta - BC \cos\theta = 0$$

$$\sum F_y: \quad CD \sin\theta + BC \sin\theta = 0$$

Solving,

$CE = 300$ kN (T)

$CD = -90.1$ kN (C)

Hence $BC = 90.1$ kN (T)
$CD = -90.1$ kN (C)
$CE = 300$ kN (T)

Problem 6.23 For the Warren truss in Problem 6.22, determine the axial forces in members DF, EF, and FG.

Solution: In the solution to Problem 6.22, we solved for the forces in AB, AC, BC, BD, CD, and CE. Let us continue the process. We ended with Joint C. Let us continue with Joint D.

Joint D:

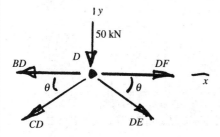

$\theta = 33.69°$

$BD = -225$ kN (C)

$CD = -90.1$ kN (C)

$\sum F_x:\quad DF - BD + DE\cos\theta - CD\cos\theta = 0$

$\sum F_y:\quad -50 - CD\sin\theta - DE\sin\theta = 0$

Solving, $DF = -300$ kN (C)

$\qquad\qquad DE = 0$

At this point, we have solved half of a symmetric truss with a symmetric load. We could use symmetry to determine the loads in the remaining members. We will continue, and use symmetry as a check.

Joint E:

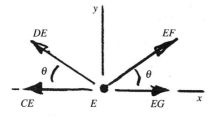

$\theta = 33.69°$

$CE = 300$ kN (T)

$DE = 0$

$\sum F_x:\quad EG - CE + EF\cos\theta - DE\cos\theta = 0$

$\sum F_y:\quad DE\sin\theta + EF\sin\theta = 0$

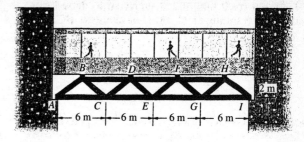

Solving, we get

$EF = 0$

$EG = 300$ kN (T)

Note: The results are symmetric to this point!

Joint F:

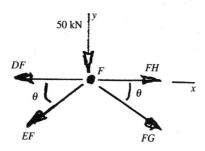

$\theta = 33.69°$

$DF = -300$ kN (C)

$EF = 0$

$\sum F_x:\quad FH - DF + FG\cos\theta - EF\cos\theta = 0$

$\sum F_y:\quad -50 - EF\sin\theta - FG\sin\theta = 0$

Solving: $FH = -225$ kN (C)

$\qquad\qquad FG = -90.1$ kN (C)

> Thus, we have
> $DF = -300$ kN (C)
> $EF = 0$
> $FG = -90.1$ kN (C)

Note-symmetry holds!

Problem 6.24 The Pratt bridge truss supports five forces ($F = 300$ kN). The dimension $L = 8$ m. Determine the axial forces in members BC, BI, and BJ.

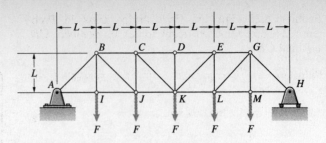

Solution: Find support reactions at A and H. From the free body diagram,

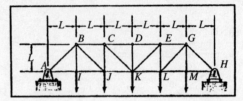

$$\sum F_x = A_X = 0,$$

$$\sum F_y = A_Y + H_Y - 5(300) = 0,$$

and $\sum M_A = 6(8)H_Y - 300(8 + 16 + 24 + 32 + 40) = 0.$

From these equations, $A_Y = H_Y = 750$ kN.

From the geometry, the angle $\theta = 45°$

Joint A: From the free body diagram,

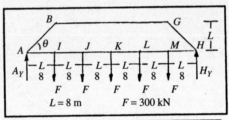

$$\sum F_x = A_X + T_{AB} \cos\theta + T_{AI} = 0,$$

$$\sum F_y = T_{AB} \sin\theta + A_Y = 0.$$

From these equations,

$T_{AB} = -1061$ kN

and $T_{AI} = 750$ kN.

Joint I: From the free body diagram,

$$\sum F_x = T_{IJ} - T_{AI} = 0,$$

$$\sum F_y = T_{BI} - 300 = 0.$$

From these equations,

$T_{BI} = 300$ kN

and $T_{IJ} = 750$ kN.

Joint B: From the free body diagram,

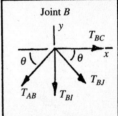

$$\sum F_x = T_{BC} + T_{BJ} \cos\theta - T_{AB} \cos\theta = 0,$$

$$\sum F_y = -T_{BI} - T_{BJ} \sin\theta - T_{AB} \sin\theta = 0.$$

From these equations,

$T_{BC} = -1200$ kN

and $T_{BJ} = 636$ kN.

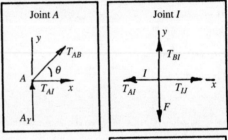

Problem 6.25 For the Pratt bridge truss in Problem 6.24, determine the axial forces in members CD, CJ, and CK.

Solution: Use all of the known values from Problem 6.24, and start with Joint J.

Joint J: From the free body diagram,

$$\sum F_x = T_{JK} - T_{BJ}\cos\theta - T_{IJ} = 0,$$

$$\sum F_y = T_{CJ} + T_{BJ}\sin\theta - 300 = 0.$$

From these equations,

$$T_{JK} = 1200 \text{ kN}$$

and $T_{CJ} = -150$ kN.

Joint C: From the free body diagram,

$$\sum F_x = T_{CD} + T_{CK}\cos\theta - T_{BC} = 0,$$

$$\sum F_y = -T_{CJ} - T_{CK}\sin\theta = 0.$$

From these equations,

$$T_{CD} = -1350 \text{ kN}$$

and $T_{CK} = 212$ kN.

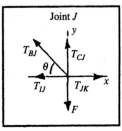

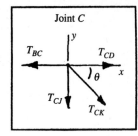

Problem 6.26 The Howe truss helps support a roof. Model the supports at A and G as roller supports. Determine the axial forces in members AB, BC, and CD.

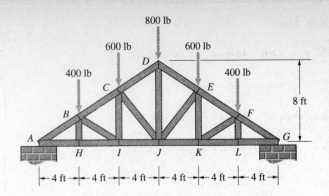

Solution: The strategy is to proceed from end A, choosing joints with only one unknown axial force in the x- and/or y-direction, if possible, and if not, establish simultaneous conditions in the unknowns.

The interior angles HIB and HJC differ. The pitch angle is

$$\alpha_{\text{Pitch}} = \tan^{-1}\left(\frac{8}{12}\right) = 33.7°.$$

The length of the vertical members:

$$\overline{BH} = 4\left(\frac{8}{12}\right) = 2.6667 \text{ ft},$$

from which the angle

$$\alpha_{HIB} = \tan^{-1}\left(\frac{2.6667}{4}\right) = 33.7°.$$

$$\overline{CI} = 8\frac{8}{12} = 5.3333 \text{ ft},$$

from which the angle

$$\alpha_{IJC} = \tan^{-1}\left(\frac{5.333}{4}\right) = 53.1°.$$

The moment about G:

$$M_G = (4+20)(400) + (8+16)(600) + (12)(800) - 24A = 0,$$

from which $A = \dfrac{33600}{24} = 1400$ lb. *Check*: The total load is 2800 lb. From left-right symmetry each support A, G supports half the total load. *check*.

The method of joints: Denote the axial force in a member joining two points I, K by IK.

Joint A:

$$\sum F_y = AB \sin \alpha_P + 1400 = 0,$$

from which $\boxed{AB = -\dfrac{1400}{\sin \alpha_p} = -2523.9 \text{ lb } (C)}$

$$\sum F_x = AB \cos \alpha_{\text{Pitch}} + AH = 0,$$

from which $AH = (2523.9)(0.8321) = 2100$ lb (T)

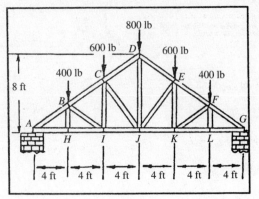

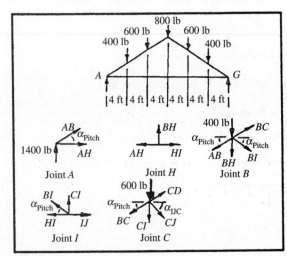

Joint H:

$$\sum F_y = BH = 0, \text{ or, } BH = 0.$$

$$\sum F_x = -AH + HI = 0,$$

from which $HI = 2100$ lb (T)

Joint B:

$$\sum F_x = -AB \cos \alpha_{\text{Pitch}} + BC \cos \alpha_{\text{Pitch}}$$
$$+ BI \cos \alpha_{\text{Pitch}} = 0,$$

from which $BC + BI = AB$

6.26 *Contd.*

$$\sum F_y = -400 - AB \sin \alpha_{\text{Pitch}} + BC \sin \alpha_{\text{Pitch}}$$

$$- BI \sin \alpha_{\text{Pitch}} = 0,$$

from which $BC - BI = AB + \dfrac{400}{\sin \alpha_{\text{Pitch}}}$.

Solve the two simultaneous equations in unknowns BC, BI:

$$BI = -\frac{400}{2 \sin \alpha_{\text{Pitch}}} = -360.56 \text{ lb } (C),$$

and $\boxed{BC = AB - BI = -2163.3 \text{ lb } (C)}$

Joint I:

$$\sum F_x = -BI \cos \alpha_{\text{Pitch}} - HI + IJ = 0,$$

from which $IJ = 1800$ lb (T)

$$\sum F_y = +BI \sin \alpha_{\text{Pitch}} + CI = 0,$$

from which $CI = 200$ lb (T)

Joint C:

$$\sum F_x = -BC \cos \alpha_{\text{Pitch}} + CD \cos \alpha_{\text{Pitch}} + CJ \cos \alpha_{IJC} = 0,$$

from which $CD(0.8321) + CJ(0.6) = -1800$

$$\sum F_y = -600 - CI - BC \sin \alpha_{\text{Pitch}} + CD \sin \alpha_{\text{Pitch}}$$

$$- CJ \sin \alpha_{IJC} = 0,$$

from which $CD(0.5547) - CJ(0.8) = -400$

Solve the two simultaneous equations to obtain $CJ = -666.67$ lb (C),

and $\boxed{CD = -1682.57 \text{ lb } (C)}$

Problem 6.27 The plane truss forms part of the supports of a crane on an offshore oil platform. The crane exerts vertical 75-kN forces on the truss at B, C, and D. You can model the support at A as a pin support and model the support at E as a roller support that can exert a force normal to the dashed line but cannot exert a force parallel to it. The angle $\alpha = 45°$. Determine the axial forces in the members of the truss.

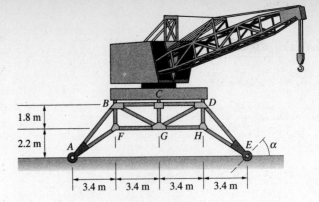

Solution: The included angles

$$\gamma = \tan^{-1}\left(\frac{4}{3.4}\right) = 49.64°,$$

$$\beta = \tan^{-1}\left(\frac{2.2}{3.4}\right) = 32.91°,$$

$$\theta = \tan^{-1}\left(\frac{1.8}{3.4}\right) = 27.9°.$$

The complete structure as a free body: The sum of the moments about A is

$$M_A = -(75)(3.4)(1 + 2 + 3) + (4)(3.4)E_y = 0.$$

with this relation and the fact that $E_x \cos 45° + E_y \cos 45° = 0$, we obtain $E_x = -112.5$ kN and $E_y = 112.5$ kN. From

$$\sum F_x^A = A_x + E_x = 0, \quad A_X = -E_X = 112.5 \ kN.$$

$$\sum F_y^A = A_y - 3(75) + E_y = 0,$$

from which $A_y = 112.5$ kN. Thus the reactions at A and E are symmetrical about the truss center, which suggests that symmetrical truss members have equal axial forces.

The method of joints: Denote the axial force in a member joining two points I, K by IK.

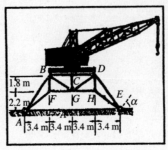

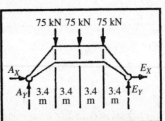

Joint A:

$$\sum F_x = AB \cos \gamma + A_x + AF \cos \beta = 0,$$

$$\sum F_y = AB \sin \gamma + A_y + AF \sin \beta = 0,$$

from which two simultaneous equations are obtained.

Solve: $\boxed{AF = -44.67 \text{ kN } (C)}$,

and $\boxed{AB = -115.8 \text{ kN } (C)}$

Joint E:

$$\sum F_y = -DE \cos \gamma + E_x - EH \cos \beta = 0.$$

$$\sum F_y = DE \sin \gamma + E_y + EH \sin \beta = 0,$$

from which two simultaneous equations are obtained.

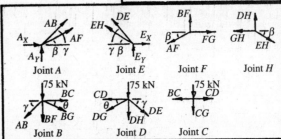

Solve: $\boxed{EH = -44.67 \text{ kN}(C)}$,

and $\boxed{DE = -115.8 \text{ kN}(C)}$

Joint F:

$$\sum F_x = -AF \cos \beta + FG = 0,$$

from which $\boxed{FG = -37.5 \text{ kN } (C)}$

$$\sum F_y = -AF \sin \beta + BF = 0,$$

from which $\boxed{BF = -24.26 \text{ kN } (C)}$

Joint H:

$$\sum F_x = EH \cos \beta - GH = 0,$$

from which $\boxed{GH = -37.5 \text{ kN } (C)}$

$\sum F_y = -EH \sin \beta + DH = 0,$

from which $\boxed{DH = -24.26 \text{ kN } (C)}$

Joint B:

$\sum F_y = -AB \sin \gamma - BF + BG \sin \theta - 75 = 0,$

from which $\boxed{BG = 80.1 \text{ kN } (T)}$

$\sum F_x = -AB \cos \gamma + BC + BG \cos \theta = 0,$

from which $\boxed{BC = -145.8 \text{ kN } (C)}$

Joint D:

$\sum F_y = -DE \sin \gamma - DH - DG \sin \theta - 75 = 0,$

from which $\boxed{DG = 80.1 \text{ kN } (T)}$

$\sum F_x = DE \cos \gamma - CD - DG \cos \theta = 0,$

from which $\boxed{CD = -145.8 \text{ kN } (C)}$

Joint C:

$\sum F_x = CD - BC = 0,$

from which $\boxed{CD = BC}$ *Check.*

$\sum F_y = -CG - 75 = 0,$

from which $\boxed{CG = -75 \text{ kN } (C)}$

Problem 6.28 (a) Design a truss attached to the supports A and B that supports the loads applied at points C and D.

(b) Determine the axial forces in the members of the truss you designed in (a)

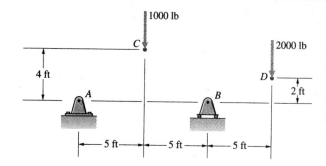

Solution: Problem 6.28 don't have unique solution

Problem 6.29 (a) Design a truss attached to the supports A and B that supports the loads applied at points C and D.
(b) Determine the axial forces in the members of the truss you designed in (a).

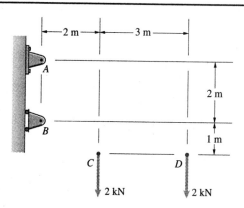

Solution: Problem 6.29 don't have unique solution

Problem 6.30 Suppose that you want to design a truss supported at A and B (Fig. a) to support a 3-kN downward load at C. The simplest design (Fig. b) subjects member AC to 5-kN tensile force. Redesign the truss so that the largest force is less than 3 kN.

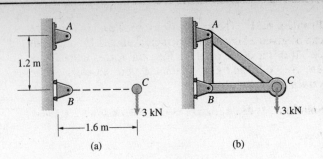

(a)   (b)

Solution: There are many possible designs. To better understand the problem, let us calculate the support forces in A and B and the forces in the members in Fig. (b).

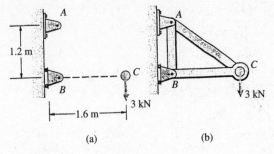

(a)   (b)

$\theta = 36.87°$

$$\sum F_x: \quad -BC - AC\cos\theta = 0$$

$$\sum F_y: \quad AC\sin\theta - 3\text{ kN} = 0$$

Solving: $BC = -4$ kN (C) $AC = 5$ kN (C)

Thus, AC is beyond the limit, but BC (in compression) is not,

Joint B:

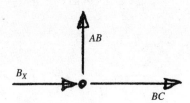

$$\sum F_x: \quad B_x + BC = 0$$

$$\sum F_y: \quad AB = 0$$

Solving, BC and B_x are both already known. We get $AB = 0$

Thus, we need to reduce the load in AC. Consider designs like that shown below where D is inside triangle ABC. Move D around to adjust the load.

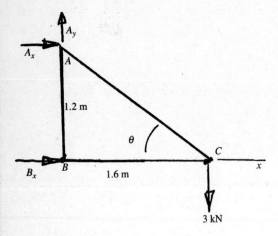

$\tan\theta = \dfrac{1.2}{1.6}$

$\theta = 36.87°$

$\sin\theta = 0.6$

$\cos\theta = 0.8$

$$\sum F_x: \quad A_x + B_x = 0$$

$$\sum F_y: \quad A_y - 3\text{ kN} = 0$$

$$\curvearrowright + \sum M_A: \quad 1.2B_x - 1.6(3) = 0$$

Solving, we get $A_x = -4$ kN

$B_x = 4$ kN

$A_y = 3$ kN

Note: These will be the external reactions for *every* design that we produce (the supports and load do not change).

Reference Solution (Fig. (b))

Joint C:

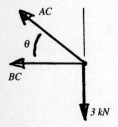

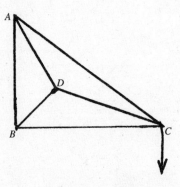

However, the simplest solution is to place a second member parallel to AC, reducing the load by half.

Problem 6.31 The bridge structure shown in Fig. 6.14 can be given a higher arch by increasing the 15° angles to 20°. If this is done, what are the axial forces in members *AB*, *BC*, *CD*, and *DE*? Compare your answers to the values in Table 6.1.

Solution: Follow the solution method in Example 6.3. *F* is known

Joint B:

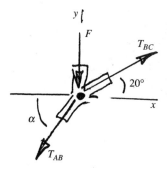

Joint C:

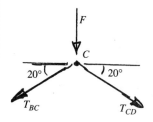

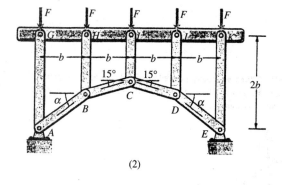

(2)

For joint *C*,

$$\sum F_x: \quad -T_{BC}\cos 20° + T_{CD}\cos 20° = 0$$

$$\sum F_y: \quad -F - T_{BC}\sin 20° - T_{CD}\sin 20° = 0$$

$$T_{BC} = T_{CD} = -1.46F \quad (C)$$

For joint *B*.

$$\sum F_x: \quad T_{BC}\cos 20 - T_{AB}\cos\alpha = 0$$

$$\sum F_y: \quad T_{BC}\sin 20° - F - T_{AB}\sin\alpha = 0$$

Solving, we get $\alpha = 47.5°$ and $T_{AB} = -2.03F$ (C)

For the new truss (using symmetry)

Members	Forces
AG, BH, CI, *DJ, EK*	*F*
AB, DE	2.03*F* (*C*)
BC, CD	1.46*F* (*C*)

469

Problem 6.32 Determine the axial forces in the Pratt truss in Fig. 6.16 and confirm the values in Table 6.2

Solution: The common angle is $\alpha = \tan^{-1}\dfrac{b}{b} = 45°$

The complete structure as a free body: The moment about A is $M_A = -bF(1+2+3+4) + 4bE = 0$, from which $E = 2.5F$. The reaction at A:

$$\sum F_Y = A - 5F + E = 0,$$

from which $A = 2.5F$.

The method of joints:

Joint E:

$$\sum F_y = E + EI\sin\alpha - F = 0,$$

from which $\boxed{EI = -2.12F}$.

$$\sum F_x = -DE - EI\cos\alpha = 0,$$

from which $\boxed{DE = 1.5F}$.

Joint A:

$$\sum F_y = AG\sin\alpha - F + A = 0,$$

from which $\boxed{AG = 2.12F}$.

$$\sum F_x = AG\cos\alpha + AB = 0,$$

from which $\boxed{AB = 1.5F}$.

Joint D:

$$\sum F_y = DI - F = 0,$$

from which $\boxed{DI = F}$.

$$\sum F_x = DE - CD = 0,$$

from which $\boxed{CD = 1.5F}$.

Joint I:

$$\sum F_y = -DI - CI\sin\alpha - EI\sin\alpha = 0,$$

from which $\boxed{CI = 0.707F}$.

$$\sum F_x = -HI - CI\cos\alpha + EI\cos\alpha = 0,$$

from which $\boxed{HI = -2F}$.

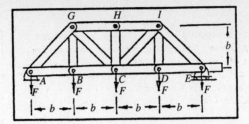

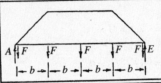

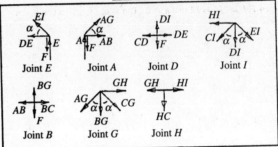

Joint E Joint A Joint D Joint I

Joint B Joint G Joint H

Joint B:

$$\sum F_y = BG - F = 0,$$

from which $\boxed{BG = F}$.

$$\sum F_x = -AB + BC = 0,$$

from which $\boxed{BC = 1.5F}$

Joint G:

$$\sum F_y = -AG\cos\alpha - CG\cos\alpha - BG = 0,$$

from which $\boxed{CG = 0.707F}$

$$\sum F_x = -AG\sin\alpha + GH + CG\sin\alpha = 0,$$

from which $\boxed{GH = -2F}$

Joint H:

$$\boxed{\sum F_y = HC = 0}.$$

A term by term comparison confirms Table 6.2.

Problem 6.33 Determine the axial forces in the suspension bridge structure in Fig. 6.18, including the reactions exerted on the towers, and confirm the values in Table 6.3

Solution: The roadway has pinned joints at H, I, and J, and at the towers. The strategy is to use the method of joints to show that the axial forces in members BH, CI and DF are each equal to F. An analysis of the joints at B and D yields the reaction at the towers. *Method of joints:* Denote the axial force in a member joining two points I, K, by IK. *Joints H, I, K.* The sum of forces in the x direction,

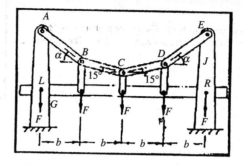

$$\sum F_x^H = -HL + HI = 0,$$

$$\sum F_x^I = -HI + IJ = 0,$$

$$\sum F_x^J = -IJ + JR = 0,$$

from which $HL = HI = IJ = JR = 0$. The sum of the forces in the y-direction

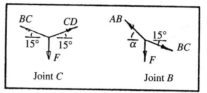

$$\sum F_y^H = BH - F = 0,$$

$$\sum F_y^I = CI - F = 0,$$

$$\sum F_y^J = DJ - F = 0,$$

from which $\boxed{BH = F(T)}$, $\boxed{CI = F(T)}$, $\boxed{DJ = F(T)}$.

Joint C:

$$\sum F_x = -BC \cos 15° + CD \cos 15° = 0,$$

from which $\boxed{CD = BC}$

$$\sum F_y = CD \sin 15° + BC \sin 15° - F = 0,$$

from which $\boxed{CD = BC = 1.93F(T)}$

Joint B: The sum of forces:

$$\sum F_x = BC \cos 15° - AB \cos \alpha = 0,$$

and $\sum F_y = AB \sin \alpha - BC \sin 15° - F = 0$,

from which.

$$\boxed{\alpha = \tan^{-1} \left(\frac{BC \sin 15° + F}{BC \cos 15°} \right) = 38.79°}$$

and

$$\boxed{AB = BC \left(\frac{\cos 15°}{\cos \alpha} \right) = 2.39F(T)}.$$

By symmetry, $\boxed{DE = AB}$

Problem 6.34 The truss supports a 100-kN load at J. The horizontal members are each 1 m in length.

(a) Use the method of joints to determine the axial force in member DG.

(b) Use the method of sections to determine the axial force in member DG.

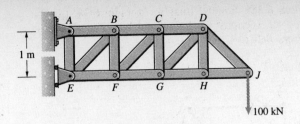

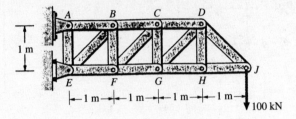

Solution: (a) Start with Joint J

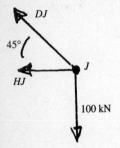

$\sum F_x$: $\quad -HJ - DJ\cos 45° = 0$

$\sum F_y$: $\quad DJ\sin 45° - 100 = 0$

Solving $\quad DJ = 141.4$ kN (T)

$\qquad HJ = -100$ kN (C)

Joint H:

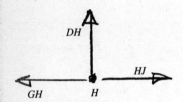

$\sum F_x$: $\quad HJ - GH = 0$

$\sum F_y$: $\quad DH = 0$

$\qquad DH = 0,$

$\qquad GH = -100$ kN (C)

Joint D

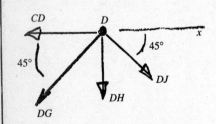

$\sum F_x$: $\quad -CD - DG\cos 45° + DJ\cos 45° = 0$

$\sum F_y$: $\quad -DG\sin 45° - DJ\sin 45° - DH = 0$

Solving, $\quad CD = 200$ kN

$\qquad DG = -141.4$ kN (C)

(b) Method of Sections

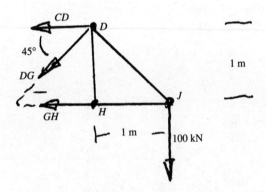

$\sum F_x$: $\quad -CD - DG\cos 45° - GH = 0$

$\sum F_y$: $\quad -DG\sin 45° - 100 = 0$

$\sum M_D$: $\quad -(1)GH - (1)(100) = 0$

Solving, $\quad GH = -100$ kN (C)

$\qquad CD = 200$ kN (T)

$\qquad DG = -141.4$ kN (C)

Problem 6.35 For the truss in Problem 6.34, use the method of sections to determine the axial forces in members BC, CF, and FG.

Solution:

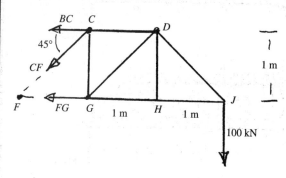

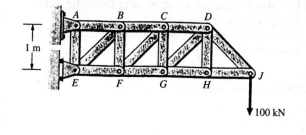

$$\sum F_x: \quad -BC - CF\cos 45 - FG = 0$$

$$\sum F_y: \quad -CF\sin 45° - 100 = 0$$

$$\sum M_C: \quad -(1)FG - 2(100) = 0$$

Solving $BC = 300$ kN (T)

$CF = -141.4$ kN (C)

$FG = -200$ kN (C)

Problem 6.36 Use the method of sections to determine the axial forces in members AB, BC, and CE.

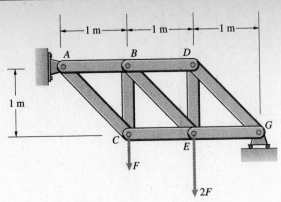

Solution: First, determine the forces at the supports

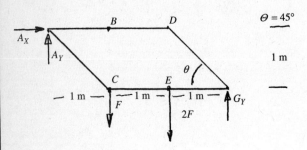

$\Theta = 45°$

$$\sum F_x: \quad A_x = 0$$

$$\sum F_y: \quad A_y + G_y - 3F = 0$$

$$\left.\begin{array}{c}\curvearrowleft\end{array}\right. + \sum M_A: \quad -1(F) - 2(2F) + 3G_y = 0$$

Solving $A_x = 0$ $G_y = 1.67F$

$$A_y = 1.33F$$

Method of Sections:

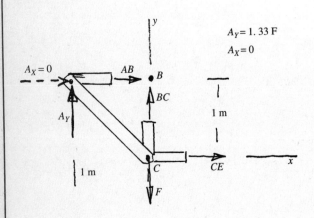

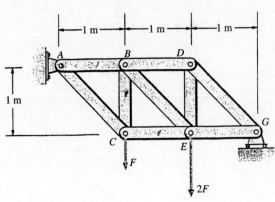

$$\sum F_x: \quad CE + AB = 0$$

$$\sum F_y: \quad BC + A_y - F = 0$$

$$\left.\begin{array}{c}\curvearrowleft\end{array}\right. + \sum M_B: \quad (-1)A_y + (1)CE = 0$$

Solving, we get

$$\boxed{\begin{array}{l} AB = -1.33F \ (C) \\ CE = 1.33F \ (T) \\ BC = -0.33F \ (C) \end{array}}$$

Problem 6.37 The truss supports loads at A and H. Use the method of sections to determine the axial forces in members CE, BE, and BD.

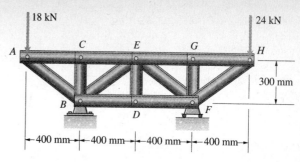

Solution: First find the external support loads on the truss

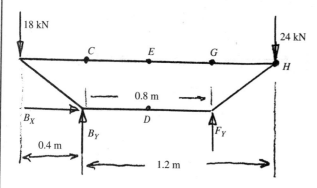

$\sum F_x$: $B_x = 0$

$\sum F_y$: $B_y + F_y - 18 - 24 = 0$ (kN)

$\sum M_B$: $0.8F_y - (1.2)(24) + (0.4)18 = 0$

Solving: $B_x = 0$

$B_y = 15$ kN

$F_y = 27$ kN

Method of sections:

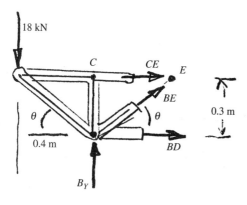

$\tan \theta = \dfrac{3}{4}$

$\theta = 36.87°$

$B_y = 15$ kN

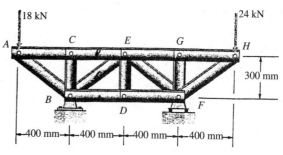

$\sum F_x$: $CE + BE \cos\theta + BD = 0$

$\sum F_y$: $B_y - 18 + BE \sin\theta = 0$

$\curvearrowleft + \sum M_B$: $+ (0.4)(18) - (0.3)(CE) = 0$

Solving,

$$\boxed{\begin{array}{l} CE = 24 \text{ kN } (T) \\ BE = 5 \text{ kN } (T) \\ BD = -28 \text{ kN } (C) \end{array}}$$

Problem 6.38 For the truss in Problem 6.37, use the method of sections to determine the axial forces in members EG, EF, and DF.

Solution: From the solution to Problem 6.37, the external forces at B and F are

$B_x = 0$,

$B_y = 15$ kN,

$F_y = 27$ kN.

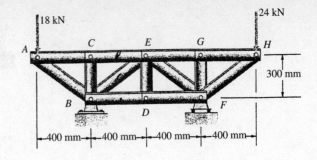

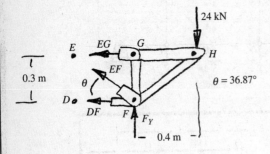

$\theta = 36.87°$

$\sum F_x$: $\quad -EG - EF \cos\theta - DF = 0$

$\sum F_y$: $\quad -24 + F_y + EF \sin\theta = 0$

$\sum M_F$: $\quad -(0.4)(24) + (0.3)EG$

Solving:

$$EG = 32 \text{ kN } (T)$$
$$EF = -5 \text{ kN } (C)$$
$$DF = -28 \text{ kN } (C)$$

Problem 6.39 For the Howe and Pratt trusses, use the method of sections to determine the axial force in member BC.

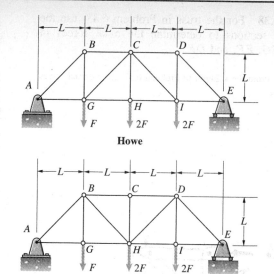

Howe

Pratt

Solution: From the free body diagram of the whole truss, the equations of equilibrium are

$$\sum F_x = A_X = 0,$$

$$\sum F_y = A_Y + E_Y - 5F = 0,$$

and $\sum M_A = 4LE_Y - LF - (2L)2F - (3L)2F = 0.$

From these equations, we get $A_X = 0$, $A_Y = 2.25F$, and $E_Y = 2.75F$. Note that the support forces are the same for the Howe and Pratt trusses.

Howe Section: From the Howe truss section, we see that if we sum moments about G, we get one equation in one unknown, i.e.,

$$\sum M_G = -LA_Y - LT_{BCHowe} = 0,$$

or $T_{BCHowe} = -2.25F$ (compression).

Pratt Section: From the Pratt truss section we see that summing moments about H is advantageous. Hence,

$$\sum M_H = -2LA_Y + LF - LT_{BCPratt} = 0,$$

or $T_{BCPratt} = -3.5F$ (compression).

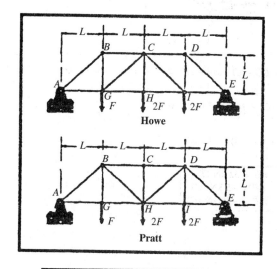

Howe

Pratt

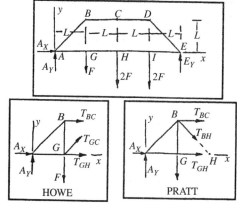

HOWE   PRATT

Problem 6.40 For the Howe and Pratt trusses in Problem 6.39, determine the axial force in member HI.

Solution: *Howe Section:* From the Howe truss section, we see that if we sum moments about C, we get one equation in one unknown, i.e.,

$$\sum M_C = 2LE_Y - 2LF - LT_{HIHowe} = 0,$$

or $T_{HIHowe} = 3.5F$ (tension).

Pratt Section: From the Pratt truss section we see that summing moments about D is advantageous. Hence,

$$\sum M_D = LE_Y - LT_{HIPratt} = 0$$

or $T_{HIPratt} = 2.75F$ (tension).

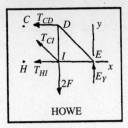

HOWE

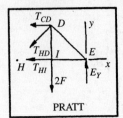

PRATT

Problem 6.41 The Pratt bridge truss supports five forces $F = 340$ kN. The dimension $L = 8$ m. Use the method of sections to determine the axial force in member JK.

Solution: First determine the external support forces.

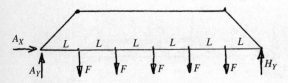

$F = 340$ kN, $L = 8$ M

$$\sum F_x: \quad A_x = 0$$

$$\sum F_y: \quad A_y - 5F + H_y = 0$$

$$\curvearrowleft + \sum M_A: \quad 6LH_y - LF - 2LF - 3LF - 4LF - 5LF = 0$$

Solving: $A_x = 0$,

$$A_y = 850 \text{ kN}$$

$$H_y = 850 \text{ kN}$$

Note the symmetry:

Method of sections to find axial force in member JK.

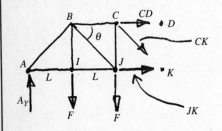

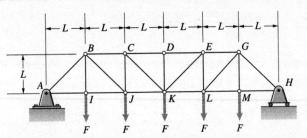

$\theta = 45°$

$L = 8M$

$F = 340$ kN

$A_y = 850$ kN

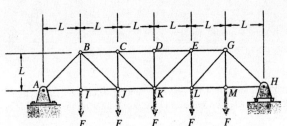

$$\sum F_x: \quad CD + JK + CK \cos\theta = 0$$

$$\sum F_y: \quad A_y - 2F - CK \sin\theta = 0$$

$$\curvearrowleft + \sum M_C: \quad L(JK) + L(F) - 2L(A_y) = 0$$

Solving, $JK = 1360$ kN (T)

Also, $CK = 240.4$ kN (T)

$$CD = -1530 \text{ kN } (C)$$

Problem 6.42 For the Pratt bridge truss in Problem 6.41, use the method of sections to determine the axial force in member EK.

Solution: From the solution to Problem 6.41, the support forces are $A_x = 0$, $A_y = H_y = 850$ kN.

Method of Sections to find axial force in EK.

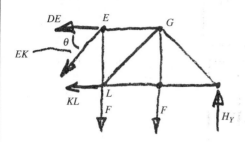

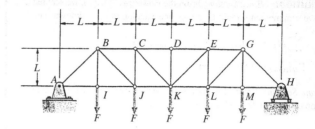

Solution: $EK = 240.4$ kN (T)

Also, $KL = 1360$ kN (T)

$DE = -1530$ kN (C)

$\sum F_x: \quad -DE - EK \cos\theta - KL = 0$

$\sum F_y: \quad H_y - 2F - EK \sin\theta = 0$

$\sum M_E: \quad -(L)(KL) - (L)(F) + (2L)H_y = 0$

Problem 6.43 The walkway exerts vertical 50-kN loads on the Warren truss at B, D, F, and H. Use the method of sections to determine the axial force in member CE.

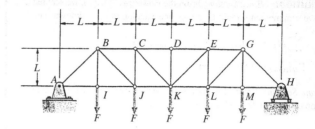

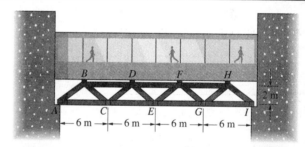

Solution: First, find the external support forces. By symmetry, $A_y = I_y = 100$ kN (we solved this problem earlier by the method of joints).

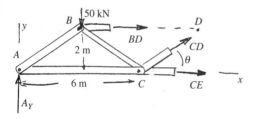

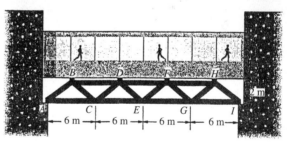

Solving: $CE = 300$ kN (T)

Also, $BD = -225$ kN (C)

$CD = -90.1$ kN (C)

$\tan\theta = \dfrac{2}{3}$

$\theta = 33.69°$

$\sum F_x: \quad BD + CD \cos\theta + CE = 0$

$\sum F_y: \quad A_y - 50 + CD \sin\theta = 0$

$\sum M_C: \quad -6A_y + 3(50) - 2BD = 0$

Problem 6.44 The walkway in Problem 6.43 exerts equal vertical loads on the Warren truss at B, D, F, and H. Use the method of sections to determine the maximum allowable value of each vertical load if the magnitude of the axial force in member FG is not to exceed 100 kN.

Solution: Let the loads at B, D, F, and H be denoted by W. By summetry $A_y = I_y = 2W$.

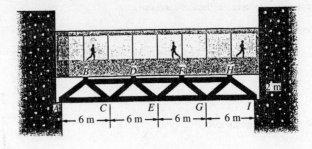

Method of Sections

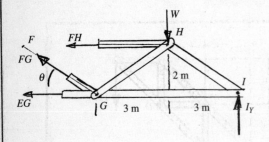

$$\tan\theta = \frac{2}{3}$$

$$\theta = 33.69°$$

$$\sum F_x: \quad -EG - FH - FG\cos\theta = 0$$

$$\sum F_y: \quad I_y - W + FG\sin\theta = 0$$

$$\sum M_G: \quad 2FH + 6I_y - 3W = 0$$

We set $FG = \pm100$ kN and solve:

For $FG = +100$ kN, $W = -55.5$ kN (this implies an upward load on the bridge)

For $FG = -100$ kN (in compression)

$W = 55.5$ kN.

This is the load limit on the bridge based on the load in member FG.

Problem 6.45 The mass $m = 120$ kg. Use the method of sections to determine the axial forces in members BD, CD, and CE.

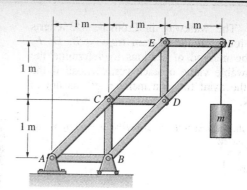

Solution: First, find the support reactions using the first free body diagram. Then use the section shown in the second free body diagram to determine the forces in the three members.

Support Reactions: Equilibrium equations are

$$\sum F_x = A_X = 0,$$

$$\sum F_y = A_Y + B_Y - mg = 0,$$

and summing moments around A,

$$\sum M_A = -3mg + (1)B_Y = 0.$$

Thus, $A_X = 0$, $A_Y = -2.35$kN, and $B_Y = 3.53$ kN

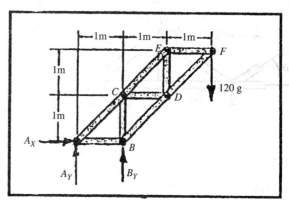

Section: From the second free body diagram, the equilibrium equations for the section are

$$\sum F_x = A_X + T_{CD} + T_{CE}\cos(45°) + T_{BD}\cos(45°) = 0,$$

$$\sum F_y = A_Y + B_Y + T_{CE}\sin(45°) + T_{BD}\sin(45°) = 0,$$

and, summing moments around C,

$$\sum M_C = (1)T_{BD}\cos(45°) - (1)A_Y + (1)A_X = 0.$$

Solving, we get $T_{BD} = -3.30$ kN,

$$T_{CD} = 1.18 \text{ kN},$$

$$T_{CE} = 1.66 \text{ kN}.$$

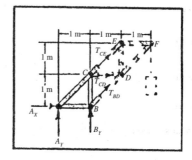

Problem 6.46 For the truss in Problem 6.45, use the method of sections to determine the axial forces in members AC, BC, and BD.

Solution: Use the support reactions found in Problem 6.45. The free body diagram for the section necessary to find the three unknowns is shown at right. The equations of equilibrium are

$$\sum F_x = A_X + T_{AC}\cos(45°) + T_{BD}\cos(45°) = 0,$$

$$\sum F_y = A_Y + B_Y + T_{BC} + T_{AC}\sin(45°) + T_{BD}\sin(45°) = 0,$$

and, summing moments around B,

$$\sum M_B = (-1)A_Y - (1)T_{AC}\sin(45°) = 0.$$

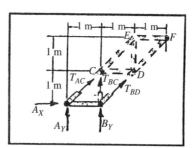

The results are

$$T_{AC} = 3.30 \text{ kN},$$

$$T_{BC} = -1.18 \text{ kN},$$

and $T_{BD} = -3.30$ kN.

Problem 6.47 The Howe truss helps support a roof. Model the supports at A and G as roller supports.

(a) Use the method of joints to determine the axial force in member BI.
(b) Use the method of sections to determine the axial force in member BI.

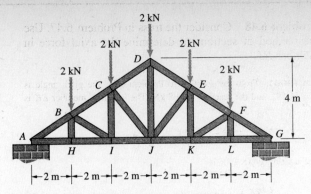

Solution: The pitch of the roof is

$$\alpha = \tan^{-1}\left(\frac{4}{6}\right) = 33.69°.$$

This is also the value of interior angles HAB and HIB. *The complete structure as a free body:* The sum of the moments about A is

$$M_A = -2(2)(1+2+3+4+5) + 6(2)G = 0,$$

from which $G = \dfrac{30}{6} = 5$ kN. The sum of the forces:

$$\sum F_Y = A - 5(2) + G = 0,$$

from which $A = 10 - 5 = 5$ kN.

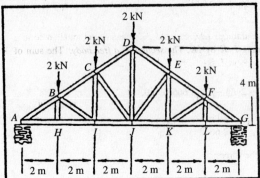

The method of joints: Denote the axial force in a member joining I, K by IK.

(a) *Joint A:*

$$\sum F_y = A + AB\sin\alpha = 0,$$

from which $AB = \dfrac{-A}{\sin\alpha} = \dfrac{-5}{0.5547} = -9.01$ kN (C).

$$\sum F_x = AB\cos\alpha + AH = 0,$$

from which $AH = -AB\cos\alpha = 7.5$ kN (T).

Joint H:

$$\sum F_y = BH = 0.$$

Joint B:

$$\sum F_x = -AB\cos\alpha + BI\cos\alpha + BC\cos\alpha = 0,$$

$$\sum F_y = -2 - AB\sin\alpha - BI\sin\alpha + BC\sin\alpha = 0.$$

Solve: $\boxed{BI = -1.803 \text{ kN } (C)}$, $BC = -7.195$ kN (C)

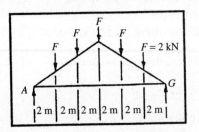

(b) Make the cut through BC, BI and HI. *The section as a free body:* The sum of the moments about B:

$$M_B = -A(2) + HI(2\tan\alpha) = 0,$$

from which $HI = \dfrac{3}{2}A = 7.5$ kN(T). The sum of the forces:

$$\sum F_x = BC\cos\alpha + BI\cos\alpha + HI = 0,$$

$$\sum F_y = A - F + BC\sin\alpha - BI\sin\alpha = 0.$$

Solve: $\boxed{BI = -1.803 \text{ kN } (C)}$.

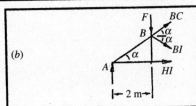

Problem 6.48 Consider the truss in Problem 6.47. Use the method of sections to determine the axial force in member EJ.

Solution: From the solution to Problem 6.47, the pitch angle is $\alpha = 36.69°$, and the reaction $G = 5$ kN. The length of member EK is

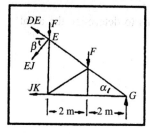

$$L_{EK} = 4\tan\alpha = \frac{16}{6} = 2.6667 \text{ m}.$$

The interior angle KJE is

$$\beta = \tan^{-1}\left(\frac{L_{EK}}{2}\right) = 53.13°.$$

Make the cut through ED, EJ, and JK. Denote the axial force in a member joining I, K by IK. *The section as a free body:* The sum of the moments about E is

$$M_E = +4G - 2(F) - JK(2.6667) = 0,$$

from which $JK = \dfrac{20 - 4}{2.6667} = 6$ kN (T).

The sum of the forces:

$$\sum F_x = -DE\cos\alpha - EJ\cos\beta - JK = 0.$$

$$\sum F_y = DE\sin\alpha - EJ\sin\beta - 2F + G = 0,$$

from which the two simultaneous equations:

$$0.8321DE + 0.6EJ = -6,$$

$$0.5547DE - 0.8EJ = -1.$$

Solve: $\boxed{EJ = -2.5 \text{ kN } (C)}$.

Problem 6.49 Use the method of sections to determine the axial force in member *EF*.

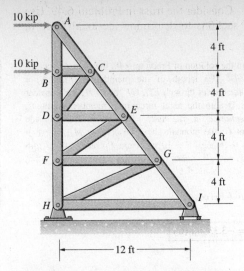

Solution: The included angle at the apex *BAC* is

$$\alpha = \tan^{-1}\left(\frac{12}{16}\right) = 36.87°.$$

The interior angles *BCA, DEC, FGE, HIG* are $\gamma = 90° - \alpha = 53.13°$. The length of the member *ED* is $L_{ED} = 8\tan\alpha = 6$ ft. The interior angle *DEF* is

$$\beta = \tan^{-1}\left(\frac{4}{L_{ED}}\right) = 33.69°.$$

The complete structure as a free body: The moment about *H* is $M_H = -10(12) - 10(16) + I(12) = 0$, from which $I = \dfrac{280}{12} = 23.33$ kip.

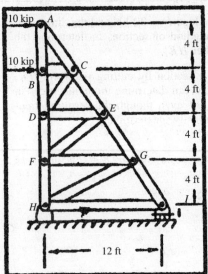

The sum of forces:

$$\sum F_y = H_y + I = 0,$$

from which $H_y = -I = -23.33$ kip.

$$\sum F_x = H_x + 20 = 0,$$

from which $H_x = -20$ kip. Make the cut through *EG, EF,* and *DE*. Consider the upper section only. Denote the axial force in a member joining *I, K* by *IK*. *The section as a free body:* The sum of the moments about *E* is $M_E = -10(4) - 10(8) + DF(L_{ED}) = 0$, from which $DF = \dfrac{120}{6} = 20$ kip.

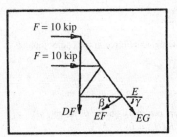

The sum of forces:

$$\sum F_y = -EF\sin\beta - EG\sin\gamma - DF = 0,$$

$$\sum F_x = -EF\cos\beta + EG\cos\gamma + 20 = 0,$$

from which the two simultaneous equations: $0.5547EF + 0.8EG = -20$, and $0.8320EF - 0.6EG = 20$. Solve: $EF = 4.0$ kip (*T*).

Problem 6.50   Consider the truss in Problem 6.49. Use the method of sections to determine the axial force in member FG.

Solution: From the solution of Problem 6.49, the apex A included angle is $\alpha = 36.87°$. The length of the member FG is $L_{FG} = 12 \tan \alpha = 9$ ft. Make the cut through EG, GF, and FH, and consider the upper section. Denote the axial force in a member joining I, K by IK. *The section as a free body:* The cut in EG is made very near the point G; the moment about this cut by $M_G = -(8 + 12)F + L_{FG}FH = 0$ (where $F = 10$ kip from Problem 6.49), from which $FH = 22.22$ kip (T). The sum of the forces, from which $EG = -27.78$ kip(C).

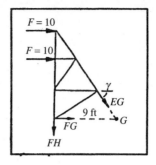

$$\sum F_x = FG + 2F + EG \cos \beta = 0,$$

from which $\boxed{FG = -3.33 \text{ kip } (C)}$.

Problem 6.51   The load $F = 20$ kN and the dimension $L = 2$ m. Use the method of sections to determine the axial force in member HK.

Strategy: Obtain a section by cutting members HK, HI, IJ, and JM. You can determine the axial forces in members HK and JM even though the resulting free-body diagram is statically indeterminate.

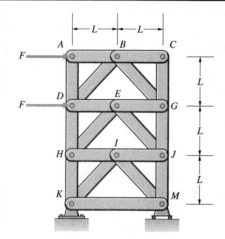

Solution: *The complete structure as a free body:* The sum of the moments about K is $M_K = -FL(2+3) + ML(2) = 0$, from which $M = \dfrac{5F}{2} = 50$ kN. The sum of forces:

$$\sum F_Y = K_Y + M = 0,$$

from which $K_Y = -M = -50$ kN.

$$\sum F_X = K_X + 2F = 0,$$

from which $K_X = -2F = -40$ kN.

The section as a free body: Denote the axial force in a member joining I, K by IK. The sum of the forces:

$$\sum F_x = K_x - HI + IJ = 0,$$

from which $HI - IJ = K_x$. Sum moments about K to get $M_K = M(L)(2) + JM(L)(2) - IJ(L) + HI(L) = 0$.

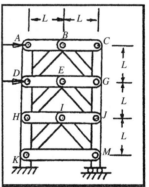

Substitute $HI - IJ = K_x$, to obtain $JM = -M - \dfrac{K_x}{2} = -30$ kN (C).

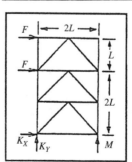

$$\sum F_y = K_y + M + JM + HK = 0,$$

from which $\boxed{HK = -JM = 30 \text{ kN}(T)}$

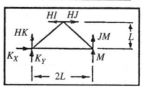

485

Problem 6.52 The weight of the bucket is $W = 1000$ lb. The cable passes over pulleys at A and D.

(a) Determine the axial forces in member FG and HI.
(b) By drawing free-body diagrams of sections, explain why the axial forces in members FG and HI are equal.

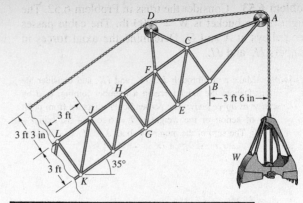

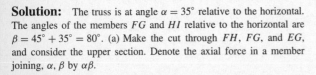

Solution: The truss is at angle $\alpha = 35°$ relative to the horizontal. The angles of the members FG and HI relative to the horizontal are $\beta = 45° + 35° = 80°$. (a) Make the cut through FH, FG, and EG, and consider the upper section. Denote the axial force in a member joining, α, β by $\alpha\beta$.

The section as a free body: The perpendicular distance from point F is $L_{FW} = 3\sqrt{2}\sin\beta + 3.5 = 7.678$ ft.

The sum of the moments about F is $M_F = -WL_{FW} + W(3.25) - |EG|(3) = 0$, from which $EG = -1476.1$ lb (C).

The sum of the forces:

$$\sum F_Y = -FG\sin\beta - FH\sin\alpha - EG\sin\alpha - W\sin\alpha - W = 0,$$

$$\sum F_X = -FG\cos\beta - FH\cos\alpha - EG\cos\alpha - W\cos\alpha = 0,$$

from which the two simultaneous equations:

$-0.9848FG - 0.5736FH = 726.9$, and $-0.1736FG - 0.8192FH = -389.97$.

Solve: $\boxed{FG = -1158.5 \text{ lb } (C)}$, and $FH = 721.64$ lb (T). Make the cut through JH, HI, and GI, and consider the upper section.

The section as a free body: The perpendicular distance from point H to the line of action of the weight is $L_{HW} = 3\cos\alpha + 3\sqrt{2}\sin\beta + 3.5 = 10.135$ ft. The sum of the moments about H is $M_H = -W(L) - |GI|(3) + W(3.25) = 0$, from which $|GI| = -2295$ lb (C).

$$\sum F_Y = -HI\sin\beta - JH\sin\alpha - GI\sin\alpha - W\sin\alpha - W = 0,$$

$$\sum F_X = -HI\cos\beta - JH\cos\alpha - GI\cos\alpha - W\cos\alpha = 0,$$

from which the two simultaneous equations:

$$-0.9848HI - 0.5736JH = 257.22,$$

and $-0.1736HI - 0.8192JH = -1060.8$.

Solve: $\boxed{HI = -1158.5 \text{ lb}(C)}$,

and $\boxed{JH = 1540.6 \text{ lb}(T)}$.

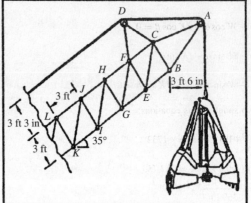

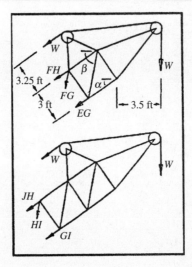

(b) Choose a coordinate system with the y-axis parallel to JH. Isolate a section by making cuts through FH, FG, and EG, and through HJ, HI, and GI. The free section of the truss is shown. The sum of the forces in the x- and y-direction are each zero; since the only external x-components of axial force are those contributed by FG and HI, the two axial forces must be equal:

$$\sum F_x = HI\cos 45° - FG\cos 45° = 0,$$

from which $HI = FG$

Problem 6.53   Consider the truss in Problem 6.52. The weight of the bucket is $W = 1000$ lb. The cable passes over pulleys at A and D. Determine the axial forces in members IK and JL.

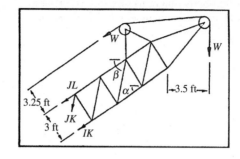

Solution: Make a cut through JL, JK, and IK, and consider the upper section. Denote the axial force in a member joining, α, β by $\alpha\beta$. *The section as a free body:* The perpendicular distance from point J to the line of action of the weight is $L = 6\cos\alpha + 3\sqrt{2}\sin\beta + 3.5 = 12.593$ ft. The sum of the moments about J is $M_J = -W(L) + W(3.25) - IK(3) = 0$, from which $IK = -3114.4$ lb(C).

The sum of the forces:

$$\sum F_x = JL\cos\alpha - IK\cos\alpha$$

$$- W\cos\alpha - JK\cos\beta = 0,$$

and $\sum F_y = -JL\sin\alpha - IK\sin\alpha$

$$- W\sin\alpha - W - JK\sin\beta = 0,$$

from which two simultaneous equations:

$$0.8192JL + 0.1736JK = -1732$$

and $0.5736JL + 0.9848JK = 212.75.$

Solve: $\boxed{JL = 2360 \text{ lb}(T)}$,

and $\boxed{JK = -1158.5 \text{ lb}(C)}$.

487

Problem 6.54   The truss supports loads at N, P, and R.
Determine the axial forces in members IL and KM.

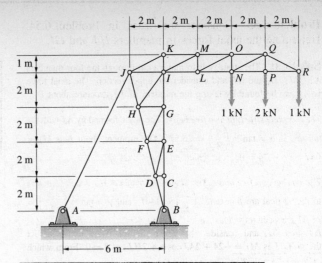

Solution: The strategy is to make a cut through KM, IM, and
IL, and consider only the outer section. Denote the axial force in a
member joining, α, β by $\alpha\beta$.

The section as a free body: The moment about M is

$$M_M = -IL - 2(1) - 4(2) - 6(1) = 0,$$

from which $\boxed{IL = -16 \text{ kN } (C)}$.

The angle of member IM is $\alpha = \tan^{-1}(0.5) = 26.57°$.

The sums of the forces:

$$\sum F_y = -IM \sin\alpha - 4 = 0,$$

from which $IM = -\dfrac{4}{\sin\alpha} = -8.944$ kN (C).

$$\sum F_x = -KM - IM\cos\alpha - IL = 0,$$

from which $\boxed{KM = 24 \text{ kN}(T)}$

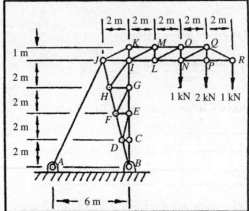

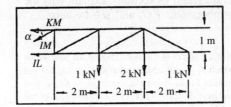

Problem 6.55 Consider the truss in Problem 6.54. Determine the axial forces in members HJ and GI.

Solution: The strategy is to make a cut through the four members AJ, HJ, HI, and GI, and consider the upper section. The axial force in AJ can be found by taking the moment of the structure about B.

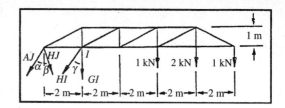

The complete structure as a free body: The angle formed by AJ with the vertical is $\alpha = \tan^{-1}\left(\dfrac{4}{8}\right) = 26.57°$. The moment about B is $M_B = 6AJ \cos \alpha - 24 = 0$, from which $AJ = 4.47$ kN (T).

The section as a free body: The angles of members HJ and HI relative to the vertical are $\beta = \tan^{-1}\left(\dfrac{2}{8}\right) = 14.0°$, and $\gamma = \tan^{-1}\left(\dfrac{1.5}{2}\right) = 36.87°$ respectively. Make a cut through the four members AJ, HJ, HI, and GI, and consider the upper section. The moment about the point I is $M_I = -24 + 2AJ \cos \alpha + 2HJ \cos \beta = 0$. From which $\boxed{HJ = 8.25 \text{ kN } (T)}$. The sums of the forces:

$$\sum F_x = -AJ \sin \alpha + HJ \sin \beta - HI \sin \gamma = 0,$$

from which $HI = \dfrac{AJ \sin \alpha - HJ \sin \beta}{\sin \gamma} = \dfrac{2-2}{\sin \gamma} = 0.$

$$\sum F_Y = -AJ \cos \alpha - HJ \cos \beta - HI \cos \gamma - GI - 4 = 0,$$

from which $\boxed{GI = -16 \text{ kN } (C)}$

Problem 6.56 Consider the truss in Problem 6.54. By drawing free-body diagrams of sections, explain why the axial forces in members DE, FG, and HI are zero.

Solution: Define α, β to be the interior angles BAJ and ABJ respectively. The sum of the forces in the x-direction at the base yields $A_X + B_X = 0$, from which $A_x = -B_x$. Make a cut through AJ, BD and BC, from which the sum of forces in the x-direction, $A_x - BD \sin \beta = 0$. Since $A_x = AJ \sin \alpha$, then $AJ \sin \alpha - BD \sin \beta = 0$. A repeat of the solution to Problem 6.55 shows that this result holds for each section, where BD is to be replaced by the member parallel to BD. For example: make a cut through AJ, FD, DE, and CE. Eliminate the axial force in member AJ as an unknown by taking the moment about A. Repeat the solution process in Problem 6.55, obtaining the result that

$$DE = \frac{AJ \sin \alpha - DF \sin \beta}{\cos \theta_{DE}} = 0$$

where θ_{DE} is the angle of the member DE with the vertical. Similarly, a cut through AJ, FH, FG, and EG leads to

$$FG = \frac{AJ \sin \alpha - FH \sin \beta}{\cos \theta_{FG}} = 0,$$

and so on. Thus the explanation is that each member BD, DF, FH and HJ has equal tension, and that this tension balances the x-component in member AJ

489

Problem 6.57 The mass of the suspended object is 900 kg. Determine the axial forces in the bars AB and AC.

Strategy: Draw the free-body diagram of joint A.

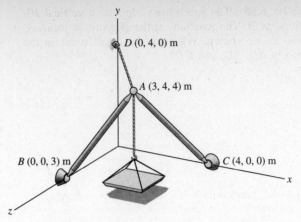

Solution: The free-body diagram of joint A is.

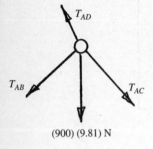

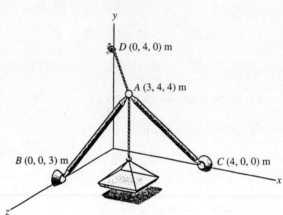

The position vectors from pt A to pts B, C, and D are

$$\mathbf{r}_{AB} = -3\mathbf{i} - 4\mathbf{j} - \mathbf{k} \text{ (m)},$$

$$\mathbf{r}_{AC} = \mathbf{i} - 4\mathbf{j} - 4\mathbf{k} \text{ (m)},$$

$$\mathbf{r}_{AD} = -3\mathbf{i} - 4\mathbf{k} \text{ (m)}.$$

Dividing these vectors by their magnitudes, we obtain the unit vectors

$$\mathbf{e}_{AB} = -0.588\mathbf{i} - 0.784\mathbf{j} - 0.196\mathbf{k},$$

$$\mathbf{e}_{AC} = 0.174\mathbf{i} - 0.696\mathbf{j} - 0.696\mathbf{k},$$

$$\mathbf{e}_{AD} = -0.6\mathbf{i} - 0.8\mathbf{k}.$$

From the equilibrium equation

$$T_{AB}\mathbf{e}_{AB} + T_{AC}\mathbf{e}_{AC} + T_{AD}\mathbf{e}_{AD} - (900)(9.81)\mathbf{j} = \mathbf{O},$$

We obtain the equations

$$-0.588T_{AB} + 0.174T_{AC} - 0.6T_{AD} = 0,$$

$$-0.784T_{AB} - 0.696T_{AC} - (900)(9.81) = 0,$$

$$-0.196T_{AB} - 0.696T_{AC} - 0.8T_{AD} = 0.$$

Solving, we obtain

$$T_{AB} = -7200 \text{ N},$$

$$T_{AC} = -4560 \text{ N},$$

$$T_{AD} = 5740 \text{ N}.$$

Problem 6.58 The space truss supports a vertical 10-kN load at D. The reactions at the supports at joints A, B, and C are shown. What are the axial forces in the members AD, BD, and CD?

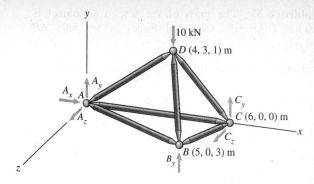

Solution: Consider the joint D only. The position vectors parallel to the members from D are

$$\mathbf{r}_{DA} = -4\mathbf{i} - 3\mathbf{j} - \mathbf{k},$$

$$\mathbf{r}_{DB} = \mathbf{i} - 3\mathbf{j} + 2\mathbf{k},$$

$$\mathbf{r}_{DC} = 2\mathbf{i} - 3\mathbf{j} - \mathbf{k}.$$

The unit vectors parallel to the members from D are:

$$\mathbf{e}_{DA} = \frac{\mathbf{r}_{DA}}{|\mathbf{r}_{DA}|} = -0.7845\mathbf{i} - 0.5883\mathbf{j} - 0.1961\mathbf{k}$$

$$\mathbf{e}_{DB} = \frac{\mathbf{r}_{DB}}{|\mathbf{r}_{DB}|} = 0.2673\mathbf{i} - 0.8018\mathbf{j} + 0.5345\mathbf{k}$$

$$\mathbf{e}_{DC} = \frac{\mathbf{r}_{DC}}{|\mathbf{r}_{DC}|} = 0.5345\mathbf{i} - 0.8018\mathbf{j} - 0.2673\mathbf{k}$$

The equilibrium conditions for the joint D are

$$\sum \mathbf{F} = T_{DA}\mathbf{e}_{DA} + T_{DB}\mathbf{e}_{DB} + T_{DC}\mathbf{e}_{DC} - \mathbf{F}_D = 0,$$

from which

$$\sum F_x = -0.7845 T_{DA} + 0.2673 T_{DB} + 0.5345 T_{DC} = 0$$

$$\sum F_y = -0.5883 T_{DA} - 0.8018 T_{DB} - 0.8108 T_{DC} - 10 = 0$$

$$\sum F_z = -0.1961 T_{DA} + 0.5345 T_{DB} - 0.2673 T_{DC} = 0.$$

Solve: $\boxed{T_{DA} = -4.721 \text{ kN } (C)}$, $\boxed{T_{DB} = -4.157 \text{ kN } (C)}$

$\boxed{T_{DC} = -4.850 \text{ kN } (C)}$

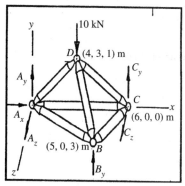

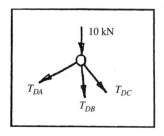

Problem 6.59 Consider the space truss in Problem 6.58. The reactions at the supports at joints A, B, and C are shown. What are the axial forces in members AB, AC, and AD?

Solution: The reactions at A are required for a determination of the equilibrium conditions at A.

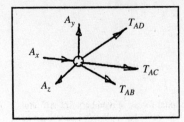

The complete structure as a free body: The position vectors are $\mathbf{r}_{AB} = 5\mathbf{i} + 3\mathbf{k}$, $\mathbf{r}_{AC} = 6\mathbf{i}$, $\mathbf{r}_{AD} = 4\mathbf{i} + 3\mathbf{j} + \mathbf{k}$. The sum of the forces:

$$\sum F_x = A_x = 0,$$

$$\sum F_y = A_y + C_y + B_y - 10 = 0,$$

and $\sum F_z = A_z + C_z = 0.$

The moments due to the reactions:

$$\mathbf{M} = \mathbf{r}_{AB} \times \mathbf{F}_B + \mathbf{r}_{AC} \times \mathbf{F}_C + \mathbf{r}_{AD} \times \mathbf{F}_D = 0$$

$$\mathbf{M} = \begin{vmatrix} \mathbf{i} & \mathbf{j} & \mathbf{k} \\ 5 & 0 & 3 \\ 0 & B_y & 0 \end{vmatrix} + \begin{vmatrix} \mathbf{i} & \mathbf{j} & \mathbf{k} \\ 6 & 0 & 0 \\ 0 & C_y & C_z \end{vmatrix} + \begin{vmatrix} \mathbf{i} & \mathbf{j} & \mathbf{k} \\ 4 & 3 & 1 \\ 0 & -10 & 0 \end{vmatrix} = 0$$

$$= (-3B_y + 10)\mathbf{i} - (6C_z)\mathbf{j} + (5B_y + 6C_y - 40)\mathbf{k} = 0.$$

These equations for the forces and moments are to be solved for the unknown reactions. The solution:

$$A_x = A_y = C_z = 0,$$

$$A_y = 2.778 \text{ kN},$$

$$B_y = 3.333 \text{ kN},$$

and $C_y = 3.889$ kN

The method of joints: Joint A: The position vectors are given above. The unit vectors are:

$$\mathbf{e}_{AB} = 0.8575\mathbf{i} + 0.5145\mathbf{k},$$

$$\mathbf{e}_{AC} = \mathbf{i},$$

$$\mathbf{e}_{AD} = 0.7845\mathbf{i} + 0.5883\mathbf{j} + 0.1961\mathbf{k}.$$

The equilibrium conditions are:

$$\sum \mathbf{F} = T_{AB}\mathbf{e}_{AB} + T_{AC} + \mathbf{e}_{AC} + T_{AD}\mathbf{e}_{AD} + \mathbf{A} = 0,$$

from which

$$\sum F_x = 0.8575T_{AB} + T_{AC} + 0.7845T_{AD} = 0$$

$$\sum F_y = 0T_{AB} + 0T_{AC} + 0.5883T_{AD} + 2.778 = 0$$

$$\sum F_z = 0.5145|T_{AB}| + 0|T_{AC}| + 0.1961|T_{AD}| = 0.$$

Solve: $\boxed{T_{AB} = 1.8 \text{ kN } (T)}$, $\boxed{T_{AC} = 2.16 \text{ kN } (T)}$

$$\boxed{T_{AD} = -4.72 \text{ kN } (C)}$$

Problem 6.60 The space truss supports a vertical load F at A. Each member is of length L, and the truss rests on the horizontal surface on roller supports at B, C, and D. Determine the axial forces in members AB, AC, and AD.

Solution: By symmetry, the axial forces in members AB, AC, and AD are equal. We just need to determine the angle θ between each of these members and the vertical:

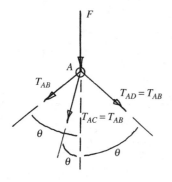

$$F + 3T_{AB}\cos\theta = 0,$$

so $\quad T_{AB} = T_{AC} = T_{AD} = -\dfrac{F}{3\cos\theta}.$

From the top view,

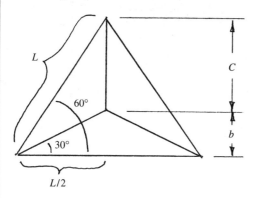

we see that

$$\frac{b}{\left(\dfrac{L}{2}\right)} = \tan 30°$$

and $\quad \dfrac{b+c}{\left(\dfrac{L}{2}\right)} = \tan 60°,$

from which we obtain

$$c = \frac{1}{2}L(\tan 60° - \tan 30°).$$

Then $\quad \theta = \arcsin\left(\dfrac{c}{L}\right)$

$$= 35.26°$$

and $\quad T_{AB} = T_{AC} = T_{AD} = -\dfrac{F}{3\cos 35.26°}$

$$= -0.408F.$$

493

Problem 6.61 For the truss in Problem 6.60, determine the axial forces in members AB, BC, and BD.

Solution: See the solution of Problem 6.60. The axial force in member AB is $T_{AB} = -0.408F$, and the angle between AB and the vertical is $\theta = 35.26°$. The free-body diagram of joint B is

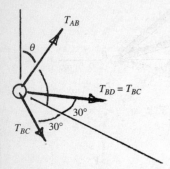

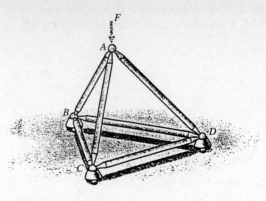

we obtain

$$T_{BC} = T_{BD} = 0.136F.$$

From the equilibrium equation

$$T_{AB} \sin\theta + 2T_{BC}\cos 30° = 0,$$

Problem 6.62 The space truss has roller supports at B, C, and D and supports a vertical 800-lb load at A. What are the axial forces in members AB, AC, and AD?

Solution: The position vectors of the points A, B, C, and D are

$$\mathbf{r}_A = 4\mathbf{i} + 3\mathbf{j} + 4\mathbf{k},$$

$$\mathbf{r}_C = 5\mathbf{i} + 6\mathbf{k},$$

$$\mathbf{r}_D = 6\mathbf{i}.$$

The position vectors from joint A to the vertices are:

$$\mathbf{r}_{AB} = \mathbf{r}_B - \mathbf{r}_A = -4\mathbf{i} - 3\mathbf{j} - 4\mathbf{k},$$

$$\mathbf{r}_{AC} = \mathbf{r}_C - \mathbf{r}_A = 1\mathbf{i} - 3\mathbf{j} + 2\mathbf{k},$$

$$\mathbf{r}_{AD} = \mathbf{r}_D - \mathbf{r}_A = 2\mathbf{i} - 3\mathbf{j} - 4\mathbf{k}$$

Joint A: The unit vectors parallel to members AB, AC, and AD are

$$\mathbf{e}_{AB} = \frac{\mathbf{r}_{AB}}{|\mathbf{r}_{AB}|} = -0.6247\mathbf{i} - 0.4685\mathbf{j} - 0.6247\mathbf{k},$$

$$\mathbf{e}_{AC} = \frac{\mathbf{r}_{AC}}{|\mathbf{r}_{AC}|} = 0.2673\mathbf{i} - 0.8018\mathbf{j} + 0.5345\mathbf{k},$$

and $$\mathbf{e}_{AD} = \frac{\mathbf{r}_{AD}}{|\mathbf{r}_{AD}|} = 0.3714\mathbf{i} - 0.5570\mathbf{j} - 0.7428\mathbf{k}.$$

The equilibrium conditions at point A:

$$\sum F_x = -0.6247T_{AB} + 0.2673T_{AC} + 0.3714T_{AD} = 0$$

$$\sum F_y = -0.4685T_{AB} - 0.8018T_{AB} - 0.5570T_{AD} - 800 = 0$$

$$\sum F_z = -0.6247T_{AB} + 0.5345T_{AC} - 0.7428T_{AD} = 0.$$

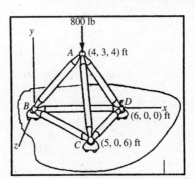

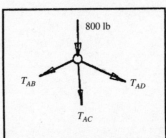

Solve: $\boxed{T_{AB} = -379.4 \text{ lb } (C)}$, $\boxed{T_{AC} = -665.2 \text{ lb } (C)}$,

and $\boxed{T_{AD} = -159.6 \text{ lb } (C)}$

Problem 6.63 The space truss shown models an airplane's landing gear. It has ball and socket supports at C, D, and E. If the force exerted at A by the wheel is $\mathbf{F} = 40\mathbf{j}$ (kN), what are the axial forces in members AB, AC, and AD?

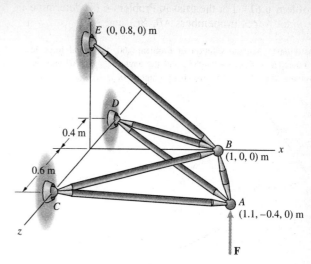

Solution: The important points in this problem are A (1.1, -0.4, 0), B (1, 0, 0), C (0, 0, 6), and D (0, 0, -0.4). We do not need point E as all of the needed unknowns converge at A and none involve the location of point E. The unit vectors along AB, AC, and AD are

$$\mathbf{u}_{AB} = -0.243\mathbf{i} + 0.970\mathbf{j} + 0\mathbf{k},$$

$$\mathbf{u}_{AC} = -0.836\mathbf{i} + 0.304\mathbf{j} + 0.456\mathbf{k},$$

and $\mathbf{u}_{AD} = -0.889\mathbf{i} + 0.323\mathbf{j} - 0.323\mathbf{k}.$

The forces can be written as

$$\mathbf{T}_{RS} = T_{RS}\mathbf{u}_{RS} = T_{RSX}\mathbf{i} + T_{RSY}\mathbf{j} + T_{RSZ}\mathbf{k},$$

where RS takes on the values AB, AC, and AD. We now have three forces written in terms of unknown magnitudes and known directions. The equations of equilibrium for point A are

$$\sum F_x = T_{AB}u_{ABX} + T_{AC}u_{ACX} + T_{AD}u_{ADX} + F_X = 0,$$

$$\sum F_y = T_{AB}u_{ABY} + T_{AC}u_{ACY} + T_{AD}u_{ADY} + F_Y = 0,$$

and $\sum F_z = T_{AB}u_{ABZ} + T_{AC}u_{ACZ} + T_{AD}u_{ADZ} + F_Z = 0,$

where $\mathbf{F} = F_X\mathbf{i} + F_Y\mathbf{j} + F_Z\mathbf{k} = 40\mathbf{j}$ kN. Solving these equations for the three unknowns, we obtain $T_{AB} = -45.4$ kN (compression), $T_{AC} = 5.26$ kN (tension), and $T_{AD} = 7.42$ kN (tension).

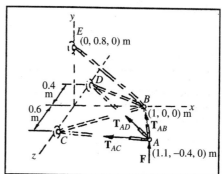

Problem 6.64 If the force exerted at point A of the truss in Problem 6.63 is $\mathbf{F} = 10\mathbf{i} + 60\mathbf{j} + 20\mathbf{k}$ (kN), what are the axial forces in members BC, BD and BE?

Solution: The important points in this problem are A (1.1, −0.4, 0), B (1, 0, 0), C (0, 0, 0.6), D (0, 0, −0.4), and E (0, 0.8, 0). The unit vectors along AB, AC, AD, BC, BD, and BE are

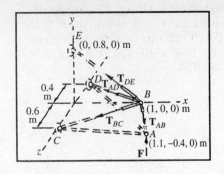

$$\mathbf{u}_{AB} = -0.243\mathbf{i} + 0.970\mathbf{j} + 0\mathbf{k},$$

$$\mathbf{u}_{AC} = -0.836\mathbf{i} + 0.304\mathbf{j} + 0.456\mathbf{k},$$

$$\mathbf{u}_{AD} = -0.889\mathbf{i} + 0.323\mathbf{j} - 0.323\mathbf{k},$$

$$\mathbf{u}_{BC} = -0.857\mathbf{i} + 0\mathbf{j} + 0.514\mathbf{k},$$

$$\mathbf{u}_{BD} = -0.928\mathbf{i} + 0\mathbf{j} - 0.371\mathbf{k},$$

and $\mathbf{u}_{BE} = -0.781\mathbf{i} + 0.625\mathbf{j} + 0\mathbf{k}.$

The forces can be written as $\mathbf{T}_{RS} = T_{RS}\mathbf{u}_{RS} = T_{RSX}\mathbf{i} + T_{RSY}\mathbf{j} + T_{RSZ}\mathbf{k}$, where RS takes on the values AB, AC, and AD when dealing with joint A and AB, BC, BD, and BD when dealing with joint B. We now have three forces written in terms of unknown magnitudes and known directions.

Joint A: The equations of equilibrium for point A are,

$$\sum F_x = T_{AB}u_{ABX} + T_{AC}u_{ACX} + T_{AD}u_{ADX} + F_X = 0,$$

$$\sum F_y = T_{AB}u_{ABY} + T_{AC}u_{ACY} + T_{AD}u_{ADY} + F_Y = 0,$$

and $\sum F_z = T_{AB}u_{ABZ} + T_{AC}u_{ACZ} + T_{AD}u_{ADZ} + F_Z = 0,$

where $\mathbf{F} = F_X\mathbf{i} + F_Y\mathbf{j} + F_Z\mathbf{k} = 10\mathbf{i} + 60\mathbf{j} + 20\mathbf{k}$ kN. Solving these equations for the three unknowns at A, we obtain $T_{AB} = -72.2$ kN (compression), $T_{AC} = -13.2$ kN (compression), and $T_{AD} = 43.3$ kN (tension).

Joint B: The equations of equilibrium at B are

$$\sum F_x = -T_{AB}u_{ABX} + T_{BC}u_{BCX} + T_{BD}u_{BDX} + T_{BE}u_{BEX} = 0,$$

$$\sum F_y = -T_{AB}u_{ABY} + T_{BC}u_{BCY} + T_{BD}u_{BDY} + T_{BE}u_{BEY} = 0,$$

and $\sum F_z = -T_{AB}u_{ABZ} + T_{BC}u_{BCZ} + T_{BD}u_{BDZ} + T_{BE}u_{BEZ} = 0.$

Since we know the axial force in AB, we have three equations in the three axial forces in BC, BD, and BE. Solving these, we get $T_{BC} = 32.7$ kN (tension), $T_{BD} = 45.2$ kN (tension), and $T_{BE} = -112.1$ kN (compression).

Problem 6.65 The space truss is supported by roller supports on the horizontal surface at C and D and a ball and socket support at E. The y axis points upward. The mass of the suspended object is 120 kg. The coordinates of the joints of the truss are A: (1.6, 0.4, 0) m, B: (1.0, 1.0, −0.2) m, C: (0.9, 0, 0.9) m, D: (0.9, 0, −0.6) m, and E: (0, 0.8, 0) m. Determine the axial forces in members AB, AC, and AD.

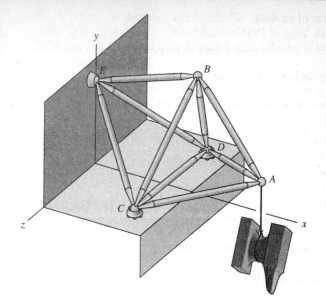

Solution: The important points in this problem are A: (1.6, 0.4, 0) m, B: (1, 1, −0.2) m, C: (0.9, 0, 0.9) m, and D: (0.9, 0, −0.6) m. We do not need point E as all of the needed unknowns converge at A and none involve the location of point E. The unit vectors along AB, AC, and AD are

$$\mathbf{u}_{AB} = -0.688\mathbf{i} + 0.688\mathbf{j} - 0.229\mathbf{k},$$

$$\mathbf{u}_{AC} = -0.579\mathbf{i} - 0.331\mathbf{j} + 0.745\mathbf{k},$$

and $\mathbf{u}_{AD} = -0.697\mathbf{i} - 0.398\mathbf{j} - 0.597\mathbf{k}.$

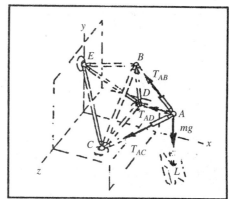

The forces can be written as $\mathbf{T}_{RS} = T_{RS}\mathbf{u}_{RS} = T_{RSX}\mathbf{i} + T_{RSY}\mathbf{j} + T_{RSZ}\mathbf{k}$, where **RS** takes on the values AB, AC, and AD. We now have three forces written in terms of unknown magnitudes and known directions. The equations of equilibrium for point A are

$$\sum F_x = T_{AB}u_{ABX} + T_{AC}u_{ACX} + T_{AD}u_{ADX} + F_X = 0,$$

$$\sum F_y = T_{AB}u_{ABY} + T_{AC}u_{ACY} + T_{AD}u_{ADY} + F_Y = 0,$$

and $\sum F_z = T_{AB}u_{ABZ} + T_{AC}u_{ACZ} + T_{AD}u_{ADZ} + F_Z = 0,$

where $F = F_X\mathbf{i} + F_Y\mathbf{j} + F_Z\mathbf{k} = -mg\mathbf{j} = -1177\mathbf{j}$ N. Solving these equations for the three unknowns, we obtain $T_{AB} = 1088$ N (tension), $T_{AC} = -316$ N (compression), and $T_{AD} = -813$ N (compression).

497

Problem 6.66 The free-body diagram of the part of the construction crane to the left of the plane is shown. The coordinates (in meters) of the joints A, B, and C are (1.5, 1.5, 0), (0, 0, 1), and (0, 0, −1), respectively. The axial forces P_1, P_2, and P_3 are parallel to the x axis. The axial forces P_4, P_5, and P_6 point in the directions of the unit vectors

$$e_4 = 0.640i - 0.640j - 0.426k,$$

$$e_5 = 0.640i - 0.640j - 0.426k,$$

$$e_6 = 0.832i - 0.555k.$$

The total force exerted on the free-body diagram by the weight of the crane and the load it supports is $-F\mathbf{j} = -44\mathbf{j}$ (kN) acting at the point (−20, 0, 0) m. What is the axial force P_3?

Strategy: Use the fact that the moment about the line that passes through joints A and B equals zero.

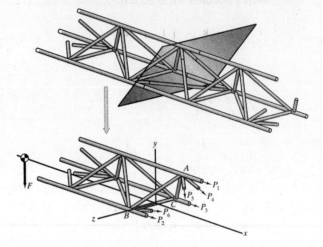

Solution: The axial force P_3 and F are the only forces that exert moments about the line through A and B. The moment they exert about pt B is

$$\mathbf{M}_B = \begin{bmatrix} \mathbf{i} & \mathbf{j} & \mathbf{k} \\ -20 & 0 & -1 \\ 0 & -44 & 0 \end{bmatrix} + \begin{bmatrix} \mathbf{i} & \mathbf{j} & \mathbf{k} \\ 0 & 0 & -2 \\ P_3 & 0 & 0 \end{bmatrix}$$

$$= -44\mathbf{i} - 2P_3\mathbf{j} + 880\mathbf{k} \text{ (kN-m)}.$$

The position vector from B to A is

$$\mathbf{r}_{BA} = 1.5\mathbf{i} + 1.5\mathbf{j} - \mathbf{k} \text{ (m)},$$

and the unit vector that points from B toward A is

$$\mathbf{e}_{BA} = \frac{\mathbf{r}_{BA}}{|\mathbf{r}_{BA}|} = 0.640\mathbf{i} + 0.640\mathbf{j} - 0.426\mathbf{k}.$$

From the condition that

$$\mathbf{e}_{BA} \cdot \mathbf{M}_B = 0.640(-44) + 0.640(-2P_3)$$

$$- 0.426(880) = 0,$$

we obtain $P_3 = -315$ kN.

Problem 6.67 In Problem 6.66, what are the axial forces P_1, P_4, and P_5?

Strategy: Write the equilibrium equations for the entire free-body diagram.

Solution: The equilibrium equations are

$$\sum F_x = P_1 + P_2 + P_3 + 0.64P_4 + 0.64P_5 + 0.832P_6 = 0,$$

$$\sum F_y = -0.64P_4 - 0.64P_5 - 44 = 0,$$

$$\sum F_z = -0.426P_4 + 0.426P_5 - 0.555P_6 = 0,$$

$$\sum \mathbf{M}_B = \begin{bmatrix} \mathbf{i} & \mathbf{j} & \mathbf{k} \\ -20 & 0 & -1 \\ 0 & -44 & 0 \end{bmatrix} + \begin{bmatrix} \mathbf{i} & \mathbf{j} & \mathbf{k} \\ 0 & 0 & -2 \\ P_3 & 0 & 0 \end{bmatrix}$$

$$+ \begin{bmatrix} \mathbf{i} & \mathbf{j} & \mathbf{k} \\ 1.5 & 1.5 & -1 \\ P_1 & 0 & 0 \end{bmatrix}$$

$$+ \begin{bmatrix} \mathbf{i} & \mathbf{j} & \mathbf{k} \\ 1.5 & 1.5 & -1 \\ 0.64P_4 & -0.64P_4 & -0.426P_4 \end{bmatrix}$$

$$+ \begin{bmatrix} \mathbf{i} & \mathbf{j} & \mathbf{k} \\ 1.5 & 1.5 & -1 \\ 0.64P_5 & -0.64P_5 & 0.426P_5 \end{bmatrix} = \mathbf{0}.$$

The components of the moment equation are

$$\sum M_{Bx} = -44 - 1.279P_4 - 0.001P_5 = 0,$$

$$\sum M_{By} = -2P_3 - P_1 - 0.001P_4 - 1.279P_5 = 0,$$

$$\sum M_{Bz} = 880 - 1.5P_1 - 1.92P_4 - 1.92P_5 = 0.$$

Solving these equations, we obtain

$$P_1 = 674.7 \text{ kN},$$

$$P_2 = P_3 = -315.3 \text{ kN},$$

$$P_4 = P_5 = -34.4 \text{ kN},$$

and $P_6 = 0$.

Problem 6.68 The mirror housing of the telescope is supported by a 6-bar space truss. The mass of the housing is 3 Mg (megagrams), and its weight acts at G. The distance from the axis of the telescope to points A, B, and C is 1 m, and the distance from the axis to points D, E, and F is 2.5 m. If the telescope axis is vertical ($\alpha = 90°$), what are the axial forces in the members of the truss?

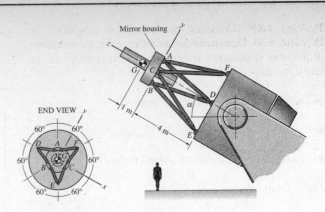

Solution: A cut through the 6-bar space truss leads to six equations in the unknowns (see Problem 6.59). However for this problem an alternate strategy based on reasonable assumptions about the equality of the tensions is used to get the reactions. Assume that each support carries one-third of the weight, which is equally divided between the two bars at the support.

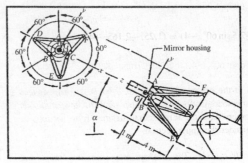

The coordinate system has its origin in the upper platform, with the x-axis passing though the point C. The coordinates of the points are:

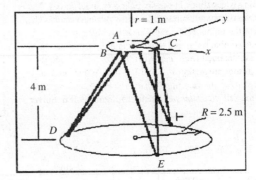

$A(-\cos 60°, \sin 60°, 0) = (-0.5, 0.866, 0)$,

$B(-\cos 60°, -\sin 60°, 0) = (-0.5, -0.866, 0)$,

$C(1, 0, 0)$,

$D(-2.5, 0, -4)$,

$E(2.5 \cos 60°, -2.5 \sin 60°, -4) = (1.25, -2.165, -4)$,

$F(2.5 \cos 60°, 2.5 \sin 60°, -4) = (1.25, 2.165, -4)$.

Consider joint B in the upper housing. The position vectors of the points E and D relative to B are

$\mathbf{r}_{BD} = -2\mathbf{i} + 0.866\mathbf{j} - 4\mathbf{k}$,

$\mathbf{r}_{BE} = 1.75\mathbf{i} - 1.299\mathbf{j} - 4\mathbf{k}$.

The unit vectors are

$\mathbf{e}_{BD} = -0.4391\mathbf{i} + 0.1901\mathbf{j} - 0.8781\mathbf{k}$,

and $\mathbf{e}_{BE} = 0.3842\mathbf{i} - 0.2852\mathbf{j} - 0.8781\mathbf{k}$.

The weight is balanced by the z components:

$$\sum F_z = -\frac{W}{3} - (0.8781)T_{BD} - (0.8781)T_{BE} = 0.$$

Assume that the magnitude of the axial force is the same in both members BD and BE, $T_{BE} = T_{BD}$. The weight is $W = 3(9.81) = 29.43$ kN. Thus the result: $\boxed{T_{BE} = T_{BD} = -5.5858 \text{ kN } (C)}$. From symmetry (and the assumptions made above) the axial force is the same in all members.

Problem 6.69 Consider the telescope described in Problem 6.68. Determine the axial forces in the members of the truss if the angle α between the horizontal and the telescope axis is 20°.

Solution: The coordinates of the points are,

$A(-\cos 60°, \sin 60°, 0) = (-0.5, 0.866, 0)$ (m),

$B(-\cos 60°, -\sin 60°, 0) = (-0.5, -0.866, 0)$ (m),

$C(1, 0, 0)$ (m),

$D(-2.5, 0, -4)$ (m),

$E(2.5\cos 60°, -2.5\sin 60°, -4) = (1.25, -2.165, -4)$ (m),

$F(2.5\cos 60°, 2.5\sin 60°, -4) = (1.25, 2.165, -4)$ (m).

The coordinates of the center of gravity are $G(0, 0, 1)$ (m). Make a cut through the members just below the upper platform supports, such that the cut members have the same radial distance from the axis as the supports. Consider the upper section.

The section as a free body: The strategy is to sum the forces and moments to obtain six equations in the six unknown axial forces. The axial forces and moments are expressed in terms of unit vectors. The position vectors of the points E, D, and F relative to the points A, B, and C are required to obtain the unit vectors parallel to the members. The unit vectors are obtained from these vectors. The vectors and their associated unit vectors are given in Table I. *Note:* While numerical values are shown below to four significant figures, the calculations were done with the full precision permitted (15 digits for **TK Solver Plus**.)

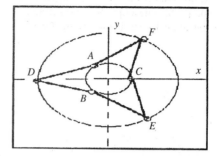

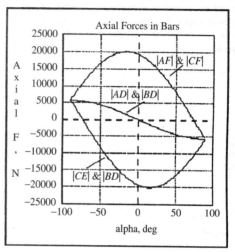

Axial Forces in Bars

Table I

Vector	x	y	z	Unit Vector	x	y	z
r_{AD}	-2	-0.866	-4	e_{AD}	-0.4391	-0.1901	-0.8781
r_{AF}	1.75	1.299	-4	e_{AF}	0.3842	0.2852	-0.8781
r_{BD}	-2	0.866	-4	e_{BD}	-0.4391	0.1901	-0.8781
r_{BE}	1.75	-1.299	-4	e_{BE}	0.3842	-0.2852	-0.8781
r_{CE}	0.25	-2.165	-4	e_{CE}	0.0549	-0.4753	-0.8781
r_{CF}	0.25	2.165	-4	e_{CF}	0.0549	-0.4753	-0.8781

The equilibrium condition for the forces is

$$|T_{AB}|e_{AD} + |T_{AF}|e_{AF} + |T_{BD}|e_{BD} + |T_{BE}|e_{BE} + |T_{CE}|e_{CE}$$

$$+ |T_{CF}|e_{CF} + W = 0.$$

This is three equations in six unknowns. The unit vectors are given in Table I. The weight vector is $W = |W|(-j\cos\alpha - k\sin\alpha)$, where α is the angle from the horizontal of the telescope housing. The remaining three equations in six unknowns are obtained from the moments:

$$r_A \times (T_{AD} + T_{AF}) + r_B \times (T_{BD} + T_{BE}) + r_C \times (T_{CE}$$

$$+ T_{CF}) + r_G \times W = 0.$$

501

Carry out the indicated operations on the moments to obtain the vectors defining the moments:

$$\mathbf{r}_A \times \mathbf{T}_{AD} = |\mathbf{T}_{AD}| \begin{vmatrix} \mathbf{i} & \mathbf{j} & \mathbf{k} \\ -0.5 & 0.866 & 0 \\ -0.4391 & -0.1901 & -0.8781 \end{vmatrix}$$

$$= |\mathbf{T}_{AD}|(-0.7605\mathbf{i} - 0.4391\mathbf{j} + 0.4753)$$

$$= |\mathbf{T}_{AD}|(\mathbf{i}u_{ADx} + \mathbf{j}u_{ADy} + \mathbf{j}u_{ADz})$$

$$\mathbf{r}_A \times \mathbf{T}_{AF} = |\mathbf{T}_{AF}| \begin{vmatrix} \mathbf{i} & \mathbf{j} & \mathbf{k} \\ -0.5 & 0.866 & 0 \\ 0.3842 & 0.2852 & -0.8781 \end{vmatrix}$$

$$= |\mathbf{T}_{AF}|(-0.7605\mathbf{i} - 0.4391\mathbf{j} - 0.4753\mathbf{k})$$

$$= |\mathbf{T}_{AF}|(\mathbf{i}u_{AFx} + \mathbf{j}u_{AFy} + \mathbf{k}u_{AFz})$$

$$\mathbf{r}_B \times \mathbf{T}_{BD} = |\mathbf{T}_{BD}| \begin{vmatrix} \mathbf{i} & \mathbf{j} & \mathbf{k} \\ -0.5 & -0.866 & 0 \\ -0.4391 & 0.1901 & -0.8781 \end{vmatrix}$$

$$= |\mathbf{T}_{BD}|(0.7605\mathbf{i} - 0.4391\mathbf{j} - 0.4753\mathbf{k})$$

$$= |\mathbf{T}_{BD}|(\mathbf{i}u_{BDx} + \mathbf{j}u_{BDy} + \mathbf{k}u_{BDz})$$

$$\mathbf{r}_B \times \mathbf{T}_{BE} = |\mathbf{T}_{BE}| \begin{vmatrix} \mathbf{i} & \mathbf{j} & \mathbf{k} \\ -0.5 & -0.866 & 0 \\ 0.3842 & -0.2852 & -0.8781 \end{vmatrix}$$

$$= |\mathbf{T}_{BE}|(0.7605\mathbf{i} - 0.4391\mathbf{j} - 0.4753\mathbf{k})$$

$$= |\mathbf{T}_{BE}|(\mathbf{i}u_{BEx} + \mathbf{j}u_{BEy} + \mathbf{k}u_{BEz})$$

$$\mathbf{r}_C \times \mathbf{T}_{CE} = |\mathbf{T}_{CE}| \begin{vmatrix} \mathbf{i} & \mathbf{j} & \mathbf{k} \\ 1 & 0 & 0 \\ 0.0549 & -0.4753 & -0.8781 \end{vmatrix}$$

$$= |\mathbf{T}_{CE}|(0\mathbf{i} + 0.8781\mathbf{j} - 0.4753\mathbf{k})$$

$$= |\mathbf{T}_{CE}|(\mathbf{i}u_{CEx} + \mathbf{j}u_{CEy} + \mathbf{k}u_{CEz})$$

$$\mathbf{r}_C \times \mathbf{T}_{CF} = |\mathbf{T}_{CF}| \begin{vmatrix} \mathbf{i} & \mathbf{j} & \mathbf{k} \\ 1 & 0 & 0 \\ 0.0549 & 0.4753 & -0.8781 \end{vmatrix}$$

$$= |\mathbf{T}_{CF}|(0\mathbf{i} + 0.8781\mathbf{j} + 0.4753\mathbf{k})$$

$$= |\mathbf{T}_{CF}|(\mathbf{i}u_{CFx} + \mathbf{j}u_{CFy} + \mathbf{k}u_{CFz})$$

$$\mathbf{r}_G \times \mathbf{W} = |\mathbf{W}| \begin{vmatrix} \mathbf{i} & \mathbf{j} & \mathbf{k} \\ 0 & 0 & 1 \\ -0 & -\cos\alpha & -\sin\alpha \end{vmatrix}$$

$$= |\mathbf{W}|(\mathbf{i}\cos\alpha - \mathbf{j}0 + \mathbf{k}0) = (\mathbf{i}M_{Wx})$$

The six equations in six unknowns are:

$$|\mathbf{T}_{AD}|e_{ADx} + |\mathbf{T}_{AF}|e_{AFx} + |\mathbf{T}_{BD}|e_{BDx} + |\mathbf{T}_{BE}|e_{BEx} + |\mathbf{T}_{CE}|e_{CEx}$$
$$+ |\mathbf{T}_{CF}|e_{CFx} + W_x = 0$$

$$|\mathbf{T}_{AD}|e_{ADy} + |\mathbf{T}_{AF}|e_{AFy} + |\mathbf{T}_{BD}|e_{BDy} + |\mathbf{T}_{BE}|e_{BEy} + |\mathbf{T}_{CE}|e_{CEy}$$
$$+ |\mathbf{T}_{CF}|e_{CFy} + W_y = 0$$

$$|\mathbf{T}_{AD}|e_{ADz} + |\mathbf{T}_{AF}|e_{AFz} + |\mathbf{T}_{BD}|e_{BDz} + |\mathbf{T}_{BE}|e_{BEz} + |\mathbf{T}_{CE}|e_{CEz}$$
$$+ |\mathbf{T}_{CF}|e_{CFz} + W_z = 0$$

$$|\mathbf{T}_{AD}|u_{ADx} + |\mathbf{T}_{AF}|u_{AFx} + |\mathbf{T}_{BD}|u_{BDx} + |\mathbf{T}_{BE}|u_{BEx} + |\mathbf{T}_{CE}|u_{CEx}$$
$$+ |\mathbf{T}_{CF}|u_{CFx} + M_{Wx} = 0$$

$$|\mathbf{T}_{AD}|u_{ADy} + |\mathbf{T}_{AF}|u_{AFy} + |\mathbf{T}_{BD}|u_{BDy} + |\mathbf{T}_{BE}|u_{BEy} + |\mathbf{T}_{CE}|u_{CEy}$$
$$+ |\mathbf{T}_{CF}|u_{CFy} = 0,$$

$$|\mathbf{T}_{AD}|u_{ADz} + |\mathbf{T}_{AF}|u_{AFz} + |\mathbf{T}_{BD}|u_{BDz} + |\mathbf{T}_{BE}|u_{BEz} + |\mathbf{T}_{CE}|u_{CEz}$$
$$+ |\mathbf{T}_{CF}|u_{CFz} = 0$$

This set of equations was solved by iteration using **TK Solver 2**. For $\alpha = 20°$ the results are:

$$\boxed{|\mathbf{T}_{AD}| = |\mathbf{T}_{BD}| = -1910.5 \text{ N } (C)},$$

$$\boxed{|\mathbf{T}_{AF}| = |\mathbf{T}_{CF}| = 16272.5 \text{ N } (T)},$$

$$\boxed{|\mathbf{T}_{BE}| = |\mathbf{T}_{CE}| = -19707 \text{ N } (C)}.$$

Check: For $\alpha = 90°$, the solution is $|\mathbf{T}_{AD}| = |\mathbf{T}_{AF}| = |\mathbf{T}_{BD}| = |\mathbf{T}_{BE}| = |\mathbf{T}_{CE}| = |\mathbf{T}_{CF}| = -5585.8$ N (C), which agrees with the solution to Problem 6.68, obtained by another method. *check.*

Check: The solution of a six-by-six system by iteration has risks, since the matrix of coefficients may be ill-conditioned. As a reasonableness test for the solution process, **TK Solver Plus** was used to graph the axial forces in the supporting bars over the range $-90° < \alpha < 90°$.

The graph is shown. The negative values are compression, and the positive values are tension. When $\alpha = -90°$, the telescope platform is pointing straight down, and the bars are in equal tension, as expected. When $\alpha = 90°$ the telescope mount is upright and the supporting bars are in equal compression, as expected. The values of compression and tension at the two extremes are equal and opposite in value, and the values agree with those obtained by another method (see Problem 6.58), as expected. Since the axial forces go from tension to compression over this range of angles, all axial forces must pass through zero in the interval. *check.*

Problem 6.70   Determine the reactions on member AB at A. (Notice that BC is a two-force member.)

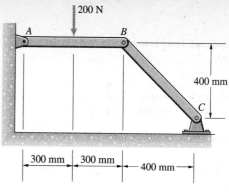

200 N

400 mm

300 mm | 300 mm | 400 mm

Solution: Since BC is a two force member, the force in BC must be a long the line between B and C.

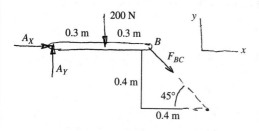

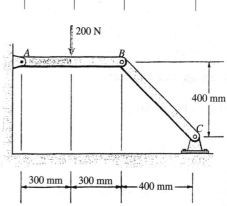

200 N

400 mm

300 mm | 300 mm | 400 mm

$$\sum F_x: \quad A_x + F_{BC}\cos 45° = 0$$

$$\sum F_y: \quad A_y - F_{BC}\sin 45° - 200 = 0$$

$$\sum M_A: \quad -(0.3)(200) - (0.6)CF_{BC}\sin 45° = 0$$

Solving: $A_x = 100$ N,

$\quad A_y = 100$ N

$\quad F_{BC} = 141.2$ N (compression)

Problem 6.71 (a) Determine the forces and couples on member AB for cases (1) and (2).
(b) You know that the moment of a couple is the same about any point. Explain why the answers are not the same in cases (1) and (2).

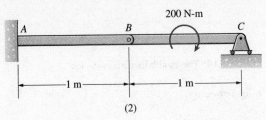

(1)

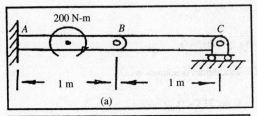

(2)

Solution: Case (a) *Element BC:* The moment about B is $M_B = (1)C_y = 0$, hence $\boxed{C_y = 0}$. The sum of the forces:

$$\sum F_y = B_y + C_y = 0,$$

from which $\boxed{B_y = 0}$.

$$\sum F_x = B_x = 0.$$

Element AB: The sum of the moments about A: $M = M_A - 200 = 0$, from which $\boxed{M_A = 200 \text{ N-m}}$. The sum of forces:

$$\sum F_y = B_y + A_y = 0,$$

from which $\boxed{A_y = 0}$,

$$\sum F_x = A_x = 0.$$

Case (b) *Element BC:* The sum of the moments about B:

$$\sum M_B = (1)C_y - 200 = 0,$$

from which $C_y = 200$ N. The sum of the forces:

$$\sum F_y = B_y^{BC} + C_y = 0,$$

from which $B_y^{BC} = -200$ N.

$$\sum F_x = B_x^{BC} = 0.$$

Element AB: The moments about A:

$$\sum M = M_A + (1)B_y^{AB} = 0,$$

from which, since the reactions across the joint are equal and opposite:

$\boxed{B_y^{AB} = -B_y^{BC} = 200 \text{ N}}$, $\boxed{M_A = -200 \text{ N-m}}$. The sum of the forces:

$$\sum F_y = A_y + B_y^{AB} = 0,$$

from which $\boxed{A_y = -200 \text{ N}}$.

$$\sum F_x = A_x + B_x^{AB} = 0,$$

from which $A_x = 0$.

Explanation of difference: The forces are equal and opposite across the joint B, so it matters on which side of B the couple is applied.

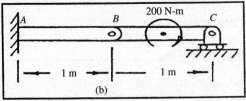

(a)

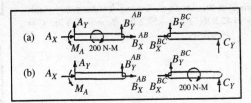

(b)

Problem 6.72 For the frame shown, determine the reactions at the built-in support A and the force exerted on member AB at B.

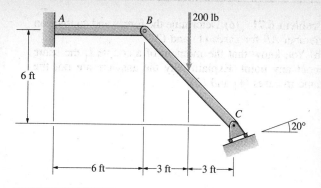

Solution: *Element AB:* The equilibrium equations are:

$$\sum F_X = A_X + B_X = 0,$$

$$\sum F_Y = A_Y + B_Y = 0,$$

and $\sum M_A = N_A + (6)B_Y = 0.$

Element BC: The equilibrium conditions are

$$\sum F_X = -B_X - C\sin(20°) = 0,$$

$$\sum F_Y = -B_Y - 200 + C\cos(20°) = 0,$$

and, summing moments around B,

$$\sum M_B = -(3)200 - (6)C\sin(20°) + (6)C\cos(20°) = 0.$$

We have six equations in six unknowns. Solving simultaneously yields $A_X = 57.2$ lb, $A_Y = 42.8$ lb, $B_X = -57.2$ lb, $B_Y = -42.8$ lb, $C = 167.3$ lb, and $N_A = 256.6$ ft-lb.

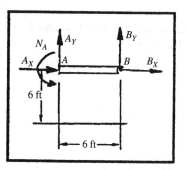

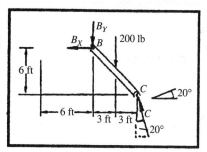

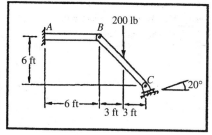

505

Problem 6.73 The force $F = 10$ kN. Determine the forces on member ABC, presenting your answers as shown in Fig. 6.35.

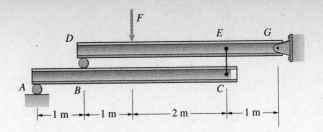

Solution: *The complete structure as a free body:* The sum of the moments about G:

$$\sum M_G = +3F - 5A = 0,$$

from which $A = \dfrac{3F}{5} = 6$ kN which is the reaction of the floor. The sum of the forces:

$$\sum F_y = G_y - F + A = 0,$$

from which $G_y = F - A = 10 - 6 = 4$ kN.

$$\sum F_x = G_x = 0.$$

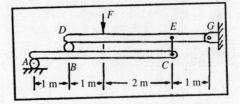

Element DEG: The sum of the moments about D

$$\sum M = -F + 3E + 4G_y = 0,$$

from which $E = \dfrac{F - 4G_y}{3} = \dfrac{10 - 16}{3} = -2$ kN.

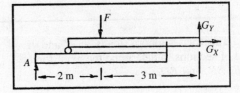

The sum of the forces:

$$\sum F_y = G_y - F + E + D = 0,$$

from which $D = F - E - G_y = 10 + 2 - 4 = 8$ kN.

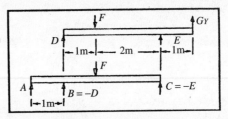

Element ABC: Noting that the reactions are equal and opposite:

$$\boxed{B = -D = -8 \text{ kN}},$$

and $\boxed{C = -E = 2 \text{ kN}}$.

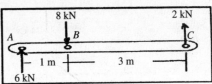

The sum of the forces:

$$\sum F_y = A + B + C = 0,$$

from which $A = 8 - 2 = 6$ kN. *Check*

Problem 6.74 Consider the frame in Problem 6.73. The cable CE will safely support a tension of 10 kN. Based on this criterion, what is the largest downward force F that can be applied to the frame?

Solution: From the solution to Problem 6.73: $E = \dfrac{F - 4G_y}{3}$, $G_y = F - A$, and $A = \dfrac{3}{5}F$. Back substituting, $E = -\dfrac{F}{5}$ or $F = -5E$, from which, for $E = 10$ kN, $F = -50$ kN

Problem 6.75 The hydraulic actuator BD exerts a 6-kN force on member ABC. The force is parallel to BD, and the actuator is in compression. Determine the forces on member ABC, presenting your answers as shown in Fig. 6.35.

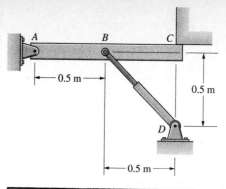

Solution: The surface at C is smooth.

Element ABC: The sum of the moments about A is

$$\sum M = (0.5)B\sin 45° + (1)C = 0,$$

from which $\boxed{C = -3(0.707) = -2.121 \text{ kN}}$.

The sum of the forces:

$$\sum F_y = A_y + B\sin 45° + C = 0,$$

from which $\boxed{A_y = -B\,(0.707) - C = -2.121 \text{ kN}}$.

$$\sum F_x = A_x - B\cos 45° = 0,$$

from which $\boxed{A_x = 4.24 \text{ kN}}$

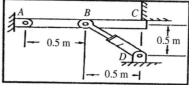

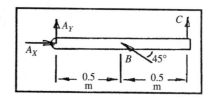

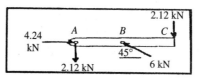

Problem 6.76 The simple hydraulic jack shown in Problem 6.75 is designed to exert a vertical force at point C. The hydraulic actuator BD exerts a force on the beam ABC that is parallel to BD. The largest lifting force the jack can exert is limited by the pin support A, which will safely support a force of magnitude 20 kN. What is the largest lifting force the jack can exert at C, and what is the resulting axial force in the hydraulic actuator?

Solution: From the solution to Problem 6.65

$$A_y = -\frac{B}{\sqrt{2}} - C, \quad A_x = \frac{B}{\sqrt{2}},$$

and $C = -\dfrac{B}{2\sqrt{2}}$.

Substituting, $A_y = -\dfrac{B}{2\sqrt{2}}$,

and $\quad |\mathbf{A}| = \sqrt{A_x^2 + A_y^2} = \dfrac{B}{\sqrt{2}}\sqrt{1^2 + \left(\dfrac{1}{2}\right)^2} = \dfrac{\sqrt{5}B}{2\sqrt{2}}$.

For $|\mathbf{A}| = 20$ kN,

$$\boxed{B = \frac{2\sqrt{2}(20)}{\sqrt{5}} = 25.3 \text{ kN}} \text{ is the largest axial force,}$$

and $\boxed{C = -\dfrac{B}{2\sqrt{2}} = -8.944 \text{ kN}}$ is the largest lifting force.

Problem 6.77 Determine the forces on member BC and the axial force in member AC.

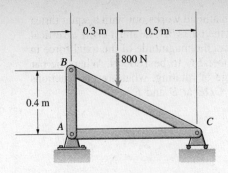

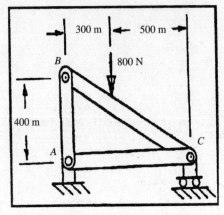

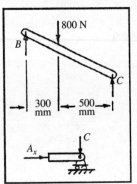

Solution: *Element BC:* The sum of the moments about B:

$$\sum M = -(0.3)800 + (0.8)C = 0,$$

from which $\boxed{C = 300 \text{ N}}$. The sum of the forces

$$\sum F_y = B - 800 + C = 0,$$

from which $\boxed{B = 500 \text{ N}}$.

$$\sum F_x = C_x = 0.$$

(The roller support prevents an x-direction reaction in C.) *Element AC:* The sum of the forces

$$\boxed{\sum F_x = A_x = 0}$$

Problem 6.78 An athlete works out with a squat thrust machine. To rotate the bar ABD, he must exert a vertical force at A that causes the magnitude of the axial force in the two-force member BC to be 1800 N. When the bar ABD is on the verge of rotating, what are the reactions on the vertical bar CDE at D and E?

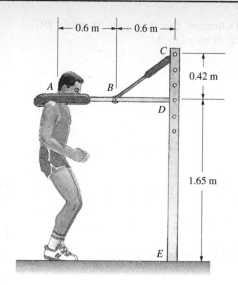

Solution: Member BC is a two force member. The force in BC is along the line from B to C.

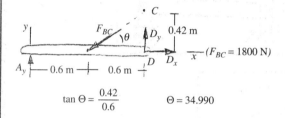

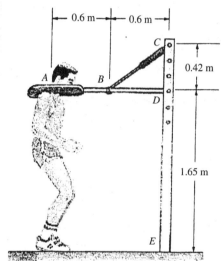

$$\tan \Theta = \frac{0.42}{0.6} \qquad \Theta = 34.990$$

$(F_{BC} = 1800 \text{ N})$

$$\tan \theta = \frac{0.42}{0.6} \quad \theta = 34.99°.$$

$$\sum F_x: \quad D_x - F_{BC} \cos \theta = 0$$

$$\sum F_y: \quad A_y - F_{BC} \sin \theta + D_y = 0$$

$$\curvearrowleft + \sum M_D: \quad -1.2A_y + 0.6F_{BC} \sin \theta = 0$$

Solving, we get $D_x = 1475$ N

$$D_y = 516 \text{ N}$$

$$A_y = 516 \text{ N}$$

Problem 6.79 The frame supports a 6-kN load at C. Determine the reactions on the frame at A and D.

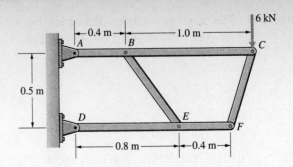

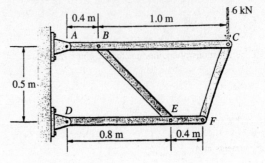

Solution: Note that members BE and CF are two force members. Consider the 6 kN load as being applied to member ABC.

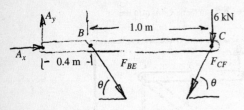

$$\tan\theta = \frac{0.5}{0.4} \quad \theta = 51.34°$$

$$\tan\phi = \frac{0.5}{0.2} \quad \phi = 68.20°$$

Member DEF

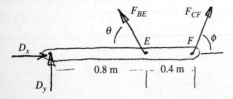

Equations of equilibrium:

Member ABC:

$$\sum F_x: \quad A_x + F_{BE}\cos\theta - F_{CF}\cos\phi = 0$$

$$\sum F_y: \quad A_y - F_{BE}\sin\theta - F_{CF}\sin\phi - 6 = 0$$

$$\curvearrowleft + \sum M_A: \quad -(0.4)F_{BE}\sin\theta - (1.4)F_{CF}\sin\phi - 1.4(6) = 0$$

Member DEF:

$$\sum F_x: \quad D_x - F_{BE}\cos\theta + F_{CF}\cos\phi = 0$$

$$\sum F_y: \quad D_y + F_{BE}\sin\theta + F_{CF}\sin\phi = 0$$

$$\curvearrowleft + \sum M_D: \quad (0.8)(F_{BE}\sin\theta) + 1.2F_{CF}\sin\phi = 0$$

Unknowns A_x, A_y, D_x, D_y, F_{BE}, F_{CF} we have 6 eqns in 6 unknowns.

Solving, we get

$A_x = -16.8$ kN
$A_y = 11.25$ kN
$D_x = 16.3$ kN
$D_y = -5.25$ kN

Also, $F_{BE} = 20.2$ kN (T)

$$F_{CF} = -11.3 \text{ kN } (C)$$

510

Problem 6.80 The mass $m = 120$ kg. Determine the forces on member ABC, presenting your answers as shown in Fig. 6.35.

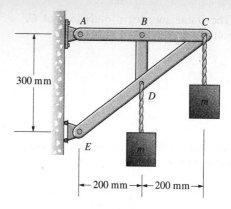

300 mm

200 mm — 200 mm

Solution: The equations of equilibrium for the entire frame are

$$\sum F_X = A_X + E_X = 0,$$

$$\sum F_Y = A_Y - 2mg = 0,$$

and summing moments at A,

$$\sum M_A = (0.3)E_X - (0.2)mg - (0.4)mg = 0.$$

Solving yields $A_X = -2354$ N, $A_Y = 2354$ N, and $E_X = 2354$ N.

Member ABC: The equilibrium equations are

$$\sum F_X = A_X + C_X = 0,$$

$$\sum F_Y = A_Y - B_Y + C_Y = 0,$$

and $\sum M_A = -(0.2)B_Y + (0.4)C_Y = 0.$

We have three equations in the three unknowns B_Y, C_X, and C_Y. Solving, we get $B_Y = 4708$ N, $C_X = 2354$ N, and $C_Y = 2354$ N. This gives all of the forces on member ABC. A similar analysis can be made for each of the other members in the frame. The results of solving for all of the forces in the frame is shown in the figure.

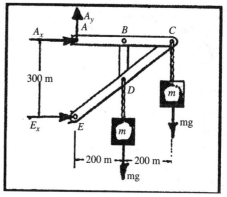

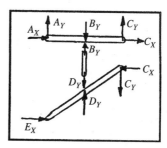

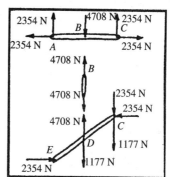

511

Problem 6.81 The tension in cable BD is 500 lb. Determine the reactions at A for cases (1) and (2).

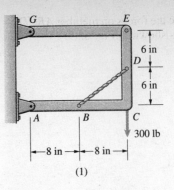

(1)

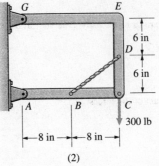

(2)

Solution: Case (a) *The complete structure as a free body:* The sum of the moments about G:

$$\sum M_G = -16(300) + 12A_x = 0,$$

from which $\boxed{A_x = 400\text{ lb}}$. The sum of the forces:

$$\sum F_x = A_x + G_x = 0,$$

from which $G_x = -400$ lb.

$$\sum F_y = A_y - 300 + G_y = 0,$$

from which $\boxed{A_y = 300 - G_y}$. *Element GE:* The sum of the moments about E:

$$\sum M_E = -16G_y = 0,$$

from which $G_y = 0$, and from above $A_y = 300$ lb.

Case (b) *The complete structure as a free body:* The free body diagram, except for the position of the internal pin, is the same as for case (a). The sum of the moments about G is

$$\sum M_C = -16(300) + 12A_x = 0,$$

from which $\boxed{A_x = 400\text{ lb}}$.

Element ABC: The tension at the lower end of the cable is up and to the right, so that the moment exerted by the cable tension about point C is negative. The sum of the moments about C:

$$\sum M_C = -8B \sin\alpha - 16A_y = 0,$$

noting that $B = 500$ lb and $\alpha = \tan^{-1}\left(\dfrac{6}{8}\right) = 36.87°$,

then $\boxed{A_y = -150\ lb.}$

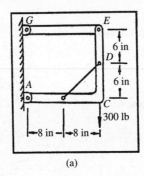

(a)

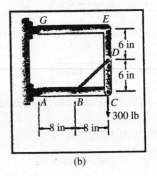

(b)

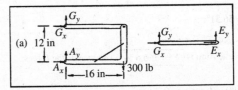

(a)

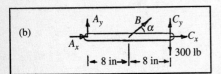

(b)

Problem 6.82 Determine the forces on member *ABCD*, presenting your answers as shown in Fig. 6.35.

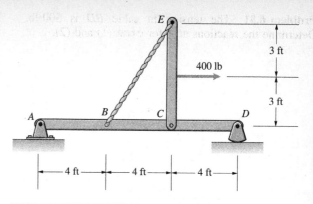

Solution: *The complete structure as a free body:* The sum of the moments about *A*:

$$\sum M_A = -400(3) + 12D_y = 0,$$

from which $\boxed{D_y = 100 \text{ lb}}$. The sum of the forces:

$$\sum F_x = A_x + 400 = 0,$$

from which $\boxed{A_x = -400 \text{ lb}}$.

$$\sum F_y = A_y + D_y = 0,$$

from which $\boxed{A_y = -100 \text{ lb}}$.

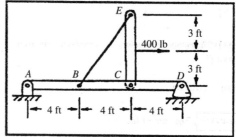

Element EC: The sum of the moments about *C*:

$$\sum M_C = 6E \cos\alpha - 3(400) = 0.$$

The angle of cable element *EB* is

$$\alpha = \tan^{-1}\left(\frac{6}{4}\right) = 56.31°,$$

from which the cable tension is $\boxed{E = 360.6 \text{ lb}}$. The sum of the forces:

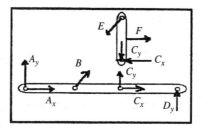

$$\sum F_x = -C_x + 400 - E\cos\alpha = 0,$$

from which $C_x = 200$ lb.

$$\sum F_y = -C_y - E\sin\alpha = 0,$$

from which $C_y = -300$ lb.

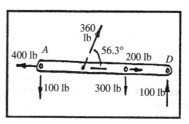

Element ABCD: The tension in the cable acts on element *ABCD* with equal and opposite tension to the reaction on element *EB*, up and to the right at an angle of 56.31°, $\boxed{C_x = 200 \text{ lb}}$ to the right, and $\boxed{C_y = -300 \text{ lb}}$ downward.

Problem 6.83 The mass $m = 50$ kg. Determine the forces on member $ABCD$, presenting your answers as shown in Fig. 6.35.

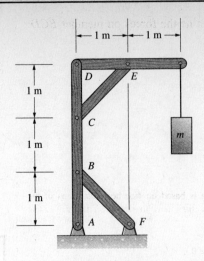

Solution: The weight of the mass hanging is $W = mg = 50(9.81) = 490.5$ N *The complete structure as a free body:* The sum of the moments about A:

$$\sum M_A = -2W + F_y = 0,$$

from which $F_y = 981$ N. The sum of the forces:

$$\sum F_y = A_y + F_y - W = 0,$$

from which $A_y = -490.5$ N,

$$\sum F_x = A_x + F_x = 0,$$

from which $A_x = -F_x$. *Element BF:* The sum of the moments about F:

$$\sum M_F = -B_x - B_y = 0,$$

from which $B_y = -B_x$. The sum of the forces:

$$\sum F_y = B_y + F_y = 0,$$

from which $B_y = -981$ N, and $B_x = 981$ N.

$$\sum F_x = B_x + F_x = 0,$$

from which $F_x = -981$ N, and from above, $\boxed{A_x = 981 \text{ N}}$,

Element DE: The sum of the moments about D:

$$\sum M_D = -E_y - 2W = 0,$$

from which $E_y = -981$ N. The sum of the forces:

$$\sum F_y = -D_y - E_y - W = 0,$$

from which $\boxed{D_y = 490.5 \text{ N}}$.

$$\sum F_x = -D_x - E_x = 0,$$

from which $D_x = -E_x$. *Element CE:* The sum of the moments about C:

$$\sum M_C = E_y - E_x = 0,$$

from which $E_x = -981$ N, and from above $\boxed{D_x = 981 \text{ N}}$.

$$\sum F_y = E_y + C_y = 0,$$

from which $C_y = 981$ N.

$$\sum F_x = E_x + C_x = 0,$$

from which $C_x = 981$ N, and

Element ABCD: All reactions on $ABCD$ have been determined above. The components at B and C have the magnitudes

$\boxed{B = C = \sqrt{981^2 + 981^2} = 1387 \text{ N}}$, at angles of $45°$.

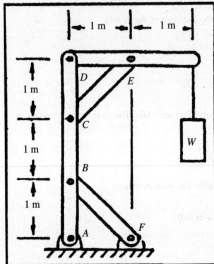

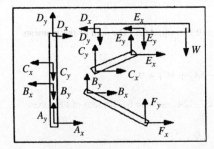

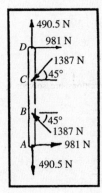

514

Problem 6.84 Determine the forces on member *BCD*.

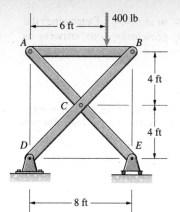

Solution: The following is based on free body diagrams of the elements: *The complete structure as a free body:* The sum of the moments about *D*:

$$\sum M_D = -(6)400 + 8E_y = 0,$$

from which $E_y = 300$ lb. The sum of the forces:

$$\sum F_x = D_x = 0.$$

$$\sum F_y = E_y + D_y - 400 = 0,$$

from which $D_y = 100$ lb. *Element AB:* The sum of the moments about *A*:

$$\sum M_A = -8B_y - (6)400 = 0,$$

from which $B_y = -300$ lb. The sum of forces:

$$\sum F_y = -B_y - A_y - 400 = 0,$$

from which $A_y = -100$ lb.

$$\sum F_x = -A_x - B_x = 0,$$

from which (1) $A_x + B_x = 0$ *Element ACE:* The sum of the moments about *E*:

$$\sum M_E = -8A_x + 4C_x - 8A_y + 4C_y = 0,$$

from which (2) $-2A_x + C_x - 2A_y + C_y = 0$. The sum of the forces:

$$\sum F_y = A_y + E_y - C_y = 0,$$

from which $\boxed{C_y = 200 \text{ lb}}$.

$$\sum F_x = A_x - C_x = 0,$$

from which (3) $A_x = C_x$. The three numbered equations are solved:
$A_x = -400$ lb, $\boxed{C_x = 400 \text{ lb}}$, and $\boxed{B_x = -400 \text{ lb}}$.

Element BCD:

The reactions are now known:

$\boxed{B_y = -300 \text{ lb}}$, $\boxed{B_x = -400 \text{ lb}}$, $\boxed{C_y = 200 \text{ lb}}$,

$\boxed{D_x = 0}$, $\boxed{D_y = 100 \text{ lb}}$,

where negative sign means that the force is reversed from the direction shown on the free body diagram.

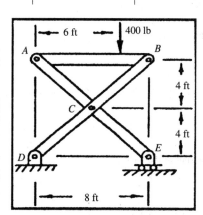

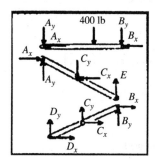

Problem 6.85 Determine the forces on member *ABC*.

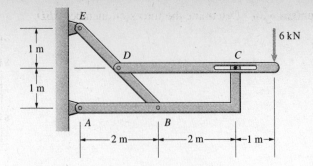

Solution: *The frame as a whole:* The equations of equilibrium are

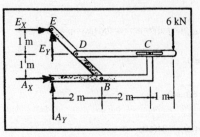

$$\sum F_X = A_X + E_X = 0,$$

$$\sum F_Y = A_Y + E_Y - 6000 \text{ N} = 0,$$

and, with moments about E,

$$\sum M_E = 2A_X - (5)6000 = 0.$$

Solving for the support reactions, we get $A_X = 15,000$ N and $E_X = -15,000$ N. We cannot yet solve for the forces in the y direction at A and E.

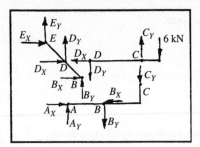

Member ABC: The equations of equilibrium are

$$\sum F_X = A_X - B_X = 0,$$

$$\sum F_Y = A_Y - B_Y - C_Y = 0,$$

and summing moments about A,

$$\sum M_A = -2B_Y - 4C_Y = 0.$$

Member BDE: The equations of equilibrium are

$$\sum F_X = E_X + D_X + B_X = 0,$$

$$\sum F_Y = E_Y + D_Y + B_Y = 0,$$

and, summing moments about E,

$$\sum M_E = (1)D_Y + (1)D_X + (2)B_Y + (2)B_X = 0.$$

Member CD: The equations of equilibrium are

$$\sum F_X = -D_X = 0,$$

$$\sum F_Y = -D_Y + C_Y - 6000 = 0,$$

and summing moments about D,

$$\sum M_D = -(4)6000 + 3C_Y = 0.$$

Solving these equations simultaneously gives values for all of the forces in the frame. The values are $A_X = 15,000$ N, $A_Y = -8,000$ N, $B_X = 15,000$ N, $B_Y = -16,000$ N, $C_Y = 8,000$ N, $D_X = 0$, and $D_Y = 2,000$ N.

Problem 6.86 Determine the forces on member *ABD*.

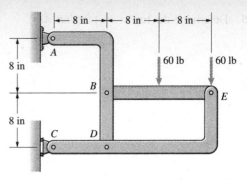

Solution: The equations of equilibrium for the truss as a whole are

$$\sum F_X = A_X + C_X = 0,$$

$$\sum F_Y = A_Y - 60 - 60 = 0,$$

and $\sum M_A = 16C_X - 16(60) - 24(60) = 0.$

Solving these three equations yields

$$A_X = -150 \text{ lb},$$

$$A_Y = 120 \text{ lb},$$

and $C_X = 150$ lb.

Member ABD: The equilibrium equations for this member are:

$$\sum F_X = A_X - B_X - D_X = 0,$$

$$\sum F_Y = A_Y - B_Y - D_Y = 0,$$

and $\sum M_A = -8B_Y - 8D_Y - 8B_X - 16D_X = 0.$

Member BE: The equilibrium equations for this member are:

$$\sum F_X = B_X + E_X = 0,$$

$$\sum F_Y = B_Y + E_Y - 60 - 60 = 0,$$

and $\sum M_B = -8(60) - 16(60) + 16E_Y = 0.$

Member CDE: The equilibrium equations for this member are:

$$\sum F_X = C_X + D_X - E_X = 0,$$

$$\sum F_Y = D_Y - E_Y = 0,$$

and $\sum M_D = 8E_X - 16E_Y = 0.$

Solving these equations, we get $B_X = -180$ lb, $B_Y = 30$ lb, $D_X = 30$ lb, $D_Y = 90$ lb, $E_X = 180$ lb, and $E_Y = 90$ lb. Note that we have 12 equations in 9 unknowns. The extra equations provide a check.

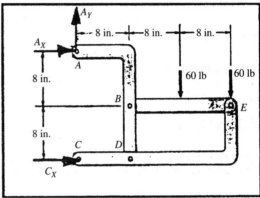

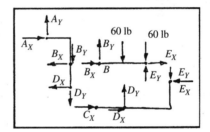

Problem 6.87 The mass $m = 12$ kg. Determine the forces on member CDE.

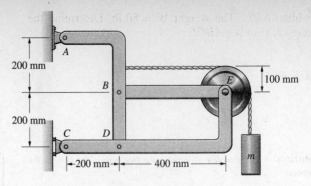

Solution: The equations of equilibrium for the entire truss are:

$$\sum F_X = A_X + C_X = 0,$$

$$\sum F_Y = A_Y - mg = 0,$$

and $\sum M_A = 0.4C_X - 0.7mg = 0.$

From these equations we get

$$A_X = -206.0 \text{ N}, \quad A_Y = 117.7 \text{ N},$$

and $C_X = 206.0$ N.

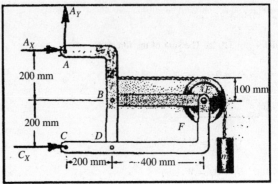

Member ABD: The equations are

$$\sum F_X = A_X + B_X + D_X + T = 0,$$

$$\sum F_Y = A_Y + B_Y + D_Y = 0,$$

and $\sum M_A = 0.2B_Y + 0.2B_X + 0.2D_Y + 0.4D_X + 0.1T = 0.$

Member CDE: The equations are

$$\sum F_X = C_X - D_X + E_X = 0,$$

$$\sum F_Y = -D_Y + E_Y = 0,$$

and $\sum M_D = 0.4E_Y - 0.2E_X = 0.$

Member BE: The equations are

$$\sum F_X = -B_X + P_X - E_X = 0,$$

$$\sum F_Y = -B_Y + P_Y - E_Y = 0,$$

and $\sum M_E = 0.4B_Y = 0.$

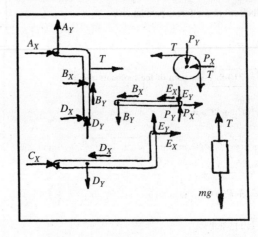

The Pulley: The equations are

$$\sum F_X = -T - P_X = 0,$$

and $\sum F_Y = -T - P_Y = 0.$

The Weight: The equation is

$$\sum F_Y = T - mg = 0.$$

Solving the equations simultaneously, we get

$$B_X = 117.7 \text{ N}, \quad B_Y = 0, D_X = -29.4 \text{ N}, \quad D_Y = -117.7 \text{ N},$$

$$E_X = -235.4 \text{ N}, \quad E_Y = -117.7 \text{ N}, \quad T = 117.7 \text{ N},$$

$$P_X = -117.7 \text{ N}, \quad P_Y = -117.7 \text{ N}$$

Problem 6.88 The weight $W = 80$ lb. Determine the forces on member $ABCD$.

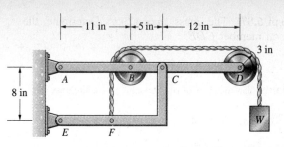

Solution: *The complete structure as a free body:* The sum of the moments about A:

$$\sum M_A = -31W + 8E_x = 0,$$

from which $E_x = 310$ lb. The sum of the forces:

$$\sum F_x = E_x + A_x = 0,$$

from which $\boxed{A_x = -310 \text{ lb}}$.

$$\sum F_y = E_y + A_y - W = 0,$$

from which (1) $E_y + A_y = W$.

Element CFE: The sum of the forces parallel to x:

$$\sum F_x = E_x - C_x = 0,$$

from which $\boxed{C_x = 310 \text{ lb}}$. The sum of the moments about E:

$$\sum M_E = 8F - 16C_y + 8C_x = 0.$$

For frictionless pulleys, $F = W$, and thus $\boxed{C_y = 195 \text{ lb}}$. The sum of forces parallel to y:

$$\sum F_y = E_y - C_y + F = 0,$$

from which $\boxed{E_y = 115 \text{ lb}}$.

Equation (1) above is now solvable: $\boxed{A_y = -35 \text{ lb}}$.

Element ABCD: The forces exerted by the pulleys on element $ABCD$ are, by inspection: $\boxed{B_x = W = 80 \text{ lb}}$, $\boxed{B_y = 80 \text{ lb}}$, $\boxed{D_x = 80 \text{ lb}}$, and $\boxed{D_y = -80 \text{ lb}}$, where the negative sign means that the force is reversed from the direction of the arrows shown on the free body diagram.

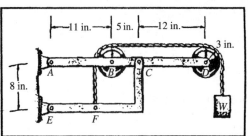

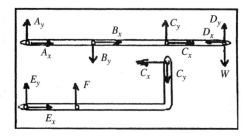

Problem 6.89 The man using the exercise machine is holding the 80-lb weight stationary in the position shown. What are the reactions at the built-in support E and the pin support F? (A and C are pinned connections.)

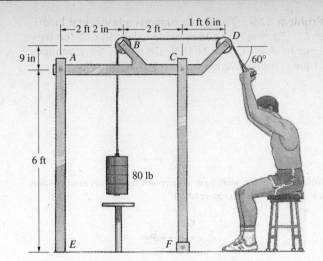

Solution: *The complete structure as a free body:* The sum of the moments about E:

$$\sum M = -26W - 68W \sin 60° + 50F_y - 81W \cos 60° + M_E = 0$$

from which (1) $50F_y + M_E = 10031$. The sum of the forces:

$$\sum F_x = F_x + W \cos 60° + E_x = 0,$$

from which (2) $F_x + E_x = -40$.

$$\sum F_y = -W - W \sin 60° + E_y + F_y = 0,$$

from which (3) $E_y + F_y = 149.28$

Element CF: The sum of the moments about F:

$$\sum M = -72C_x = 0,$$

from which $C_x = 0$. The sum of the forces:

$$\sum F_x = C_x + F_x = 0,$$

from which $\boxed{F_x = 0}$. From (2) above, $\boxed{E_x = -40 \text{ lb}}$
Element AE: The sum of the moments about E:

$$\sum M = M_E - 72A_x = 0, .$$

from which (4) $M_E = 72A_x$. The sum of the forces:

$$\sum F_y = E_y + A_y = 0,$$

from which (5) $E_y + A_y = 0$.

$$\sum F_x = A_x + E_x = 0;$$

from which $A_x = 40$ lb, and from (4) $\boxed{M_E = 2880 \text{ in lb} = 240 \text{ ft lb}}$.
From (1) $\boxed{F_y = 143.0 \text{ lb}}$, and from (2) $\boxed{E_y = 6.258 \text{ lb}}$. This completes the determination of the 5 reactions on E and F.

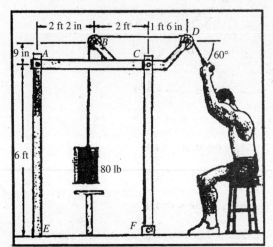

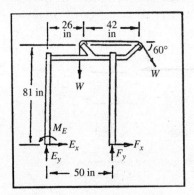

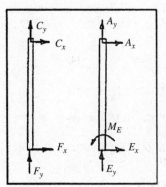

Problem 6.90 The frame supports a horizontal load F at C. The resulting compressive axial force in the two-force member CD is 2400 N. Determine the magnitude of the reaction exerted on member ABC at B.

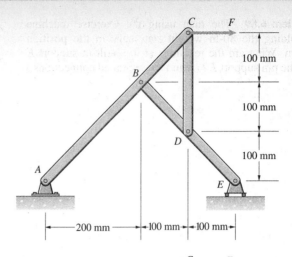

Solution: First, write eqns to determine the support reactions at A and E (CD is a two force member)

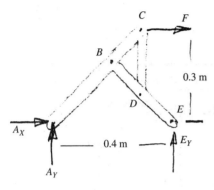

$$\sum F_x: \quad A_x + F = 0 \qquad (1)$$

$$\sum F_y: \quad A_y + E_y = 0 \qquad (2)$$

$$\curvearrowleft + \sum M_A: \quad 0.4E_y - 0.3F = 0 \quad (3)$$

We have these eqns in four Unknowns (A_x, A_y, E_y, and F) Now write eqns for member ABC

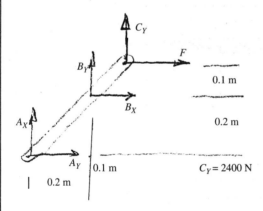

$$C_y = 2400 \text{ N}$$

$$\sum F_x: \quad A_x + B_x + F = 0 \qquad (4)$$

$$\sum F_y: \quad A_y + B_y + C_y = 0 \qquad (5)$$

$$\curvearrowleft + \sum M_A: \quad 0.2B_y - 0.2B_x + 0.3C_y - 0.3F = 0 \quad (6)$$

We now have 6 eqns in unknowns: (A_x, A_y, B_x, $B_y E_y$, F) Next, write the equations for member BDE.

Solving, we get $B_x = 0 \; B_y = -1200$ N

$$|\mathbf{B}| = 1200 \text{ N}$$

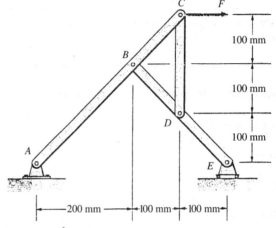

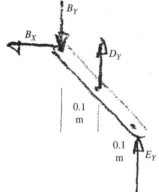

$$C_y = -D_y$$

(two force member)

$$\sum F_x: \quad -B_x = 0 \qquad (7)$$

$$\sum F_y: \quad -B_y + D_y + E_y = 0 \quad (8)$$

$$\sum M_B: \quad 0.1D_y + 0.2E_y = 0 \qquad (9)$$

We now have 9 equations in 8 unknowns. Obviously, if they are compatible, one is a linear combination of the others. We could also have more than one redundant equation and still need another equation.

Combining Eqs. (4) and (7) gives Eq. (1). Thus, one of these three equations is not need.

521

Problem 6.91 The two-force member CD of the frame shown in Problem 6.90 will safely support a compressive axial load of 3 kN. Based on this criterion, what is the largest safe magnitude of the horizontal load F?

Solution: In the solution to Problem 6.90, we derived the equation's listed below for the loads shown on the frame.

$$\left.\begin{array}{r} A_x + F = 0 \\ A_y + E_y = 0 \\ 0.4E_y - 0.3F = 0 \end{array}\right\} \text{Entire Frame}$$

$$\left.\begin{array}{r} A_x + B_x + F = 0 \\ A_y + B_y + C_y = 0 \\ 0.2B_y - 0.2B_x + 0.3C_y - 0.3F = 0 \end{array}\right\} \text{Member } ABC$$

$C_y = -D_y - 2$ force member

Set $C_y = 3000$ N and solve.

We get $F = 2000$ N $= 2$ kN

$A_x = -2$ kN

$A_y = -1.5$ kN

$E_y = 1.5$ kN

$B_x = 0$

$B_y = -1.5$ kN

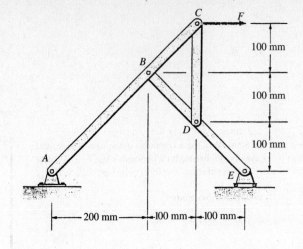

Problem 6.92   The unstretched length of the string is L_O. Show that when the system is in equilibrium the angle α satisfies the relation $\sin\alpha = 2(L_O - 2F/k)L$.

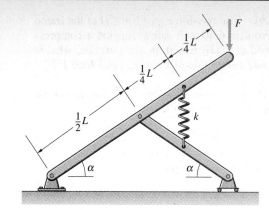

Solution: Since the action lines of the force F and the reaction E are co-parallel and coincident, the moment on the system is zero, and the system is always in equilibrium, for a non-zero force F. The object is to find an expression for the angle α for any non-zero force F.

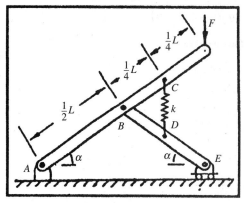

The complete structure as a free body:

The sum of the moments about A

$$\sum M_A = -FL\sin\alpha + EL\sin\alpha = 0,$$

from which $E = F$. The sum of forces:

$$\sum F_x = A_x = 0,$$

from which $A_x = 0$.

$$\sum F_y = A_y + E - F = 0,$$

from which $A_y = 0$, which completes a demonstration that F does not exert a moment on the system. *The spring C:* The elongation of the spring is $\Delta s = 2\dfrac{L}{4}\sin\alpha - L_O$, from which the force in the spring is

$$T = k\left(\frac{L}{2}\sin\alpha - L_O\right)$$

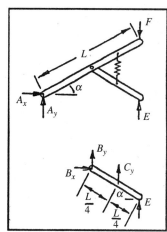

Element BE: The strategy is to determine C_y, which is the spring force on BE. The moment about E is

$$\sum M_E = -\frac{L}{4}C_y\cos\alpha - \frac{L}{2}B_y\cos\alpha - \frac{L}{2}B_x\cos\alpha = 0,$$

from which $\dfrac{C_y}{2} + B_y = -B_x$. The sum of forces:

$$\sum F_x = B_x = 0,$$

from which $B_x = 0$.

$$\sum F_y = C_y + B_y + E = 0,$$

from which $C_y + B_y = -E = -F$. The two simultaneous equations are solved: $C_y = -2F$, and $B_y = F$.

The solution for angle α: The spring force is

$$C_y = T = k\left(\frac{L}{2}\sin\alpha - L_O\right),$$

from which $k\left(\dfrac{L}{2}\sin\alpha - L_O\right) = -2F$.

Solve: $\sin\alpha = \dfrac{2\left(L_O - \dfrac{2F}{k}\right)}{L}$

523

Problem 6.93 The pin support B will safely support a force of 24-kN magnitude. Based on this criterion, what is the largest mass m that the frame will safely support?

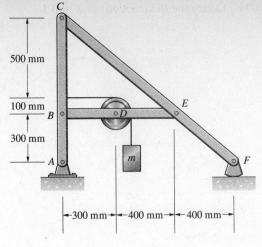

Solution: The weight is given by $W = mg = 9.81\ g$

The complete structure as a free body:

Sum the forces in the x-direction:

$$\sum F_x = A_x = 0,$$

from which $A_x = 0$
Element ABC: The sum of the moments about A:

$$\sum M_A = +0.3B_x + 0.9C_x - 0.4W = 0,$$

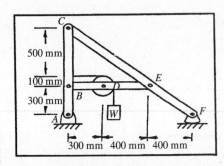

from which (1) $0.3B_x + 0.9C_x = 0.4W$. The sum of the forces:

$$\sum F_x = -B_x - C_x + W + A_x = 0,$$

from which (2) $B_x + C_x = W$. Solve the simultaneous equations (1) and (2) to obtain $B_x = \dfrac{5}{6}W$

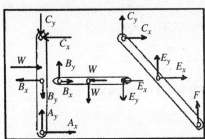

Element BE: The sum of the moments about E:

$$\sum M_E = 0.4W - 0.7B_y = 0,$$

from which $B_y = \dfrac{4}{7}W$. The magnitude of the reaction at B is

$$|\mathbf{B}| = W\sqrt{\left(\frac{5}{6}\right)^2 + \left(\frac{4}{7}\right)^2} = 1.0104W.$$

For a safe value of $|\mathbf{B}| = 24$ kN, $W = \dfrac{24}{1.0104} = 23.752$ kN is the maximum load that can be carried. Thus, the largest mass that can be supported is $m = W/g = 23752$ N$/9.81$ m/s$^2 = 2421$ kg.

Problem 6.94 Determine the reactions at A and C.

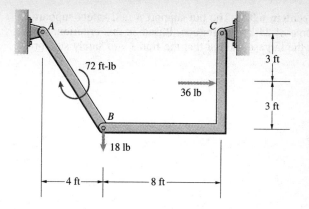

Solution: *The complete structure as a free body:*

The sum of the moments about A:

$$\sum M_A = -4(18) + 3(36) + 12C_y - 72 = 0,$$

from which $C_y = 3$ lb. The sum of the forces:

$$\sum F_y = A_y + C_y - 18 = 0,$$

from which $A_y = 15$ lb.

$$\sum F_x = A_x + C_x + 36 = 0,$$

from which (1) $C_x = -A_x - 36$

Element AB: The sum of the forces:

$$\sum F_y = A_y - B_y - 18 = 0,$$

from which $B_y = -3$ lb. The sum of the moments:

$$\sum M_A = 6B_x - 4(18) - 4B_y - 72 = 0,$$

from which $B_x = 22$ lb. The sum of the forces:

$$\sum F_x = A_x + B_x = 0,$$

from which $A_x = -22$ lb From equation (1) $C_x = -14$ lb

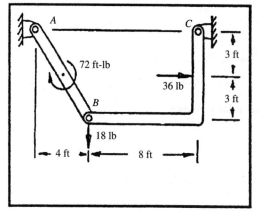

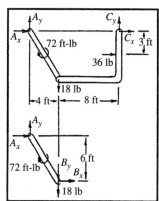

525

Problem 6.95 Determine the forces on member *AD*.

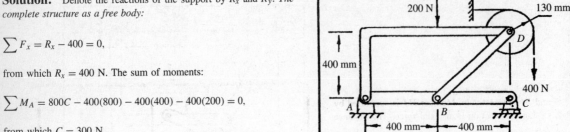

Solution: Denote the reactions of the support by R_x and R_y. The complete structure as a free body:

$$\sum F_x = R_x - 400 = 0,$$

from which $R_x = 400$ N. The sum of moments:

$$\sum M_A = 800C - 400(800) - 400(400) - 400(200) = 0,$$

from which $C = 300$ N.

$$\sum F_y = C + R_y - 400 - 200 = 0,$$

from which $R_y = 300$ N. *Element ABC*: The sum of the moments:

$$\sum M_A = -4B_y + 8C = 0,$$

from which $B_y = 600$ N. *Element BD*: The sum of the forces:

$$\sum F_y = B_y - D_y - 400 = 0,$$

from which $D_y = 200$ N.

Element AD: The sum of the forces:

$$\sum F_y = A_y + D_y - 200 = 0,$$

from which $A_y = 0$: *Element AD:* The sum of the forces:

$$\sum F_x = A_x + D_x = 0$$

and $\sum M_A = -400(200) + 800D_y - 400D_x = 0$

$A_x = -200$ N, and $D_x = 200$ N.

Element BD: The sum of forces:

$$\sum F_x = B_x - D_x - 400 = 0$$

from which $B_x = 600$ N. This completes the solution of the nine equations in nine unknowns, of which A_x, A_y, D_x, and D_y are the values required by the Problem.

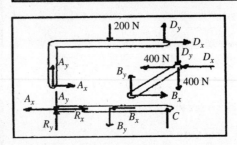

Problem 6.96 The frame shown is used to support high-tension wires. If $b = 3$ ft, $\alpha = 30°$, and $W = 200$ lb, what is the axial force in member HJ?

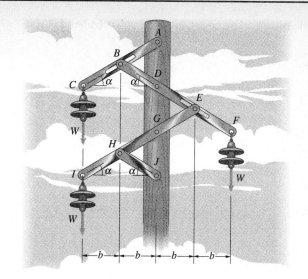

Solution: Joints B and E are sliding joints, so that the reactions are normal to AC and BF, respectively. Member HJ is supported by pins at each end, so that the reaction is an axial force. The distance $h = b \tan \alpha = 1.732$ ft

Member ABC. The sum of the forces:

$$\sum F_x = A_x + B \sin \alpha = 0,$$

$$\sum F_y = A_y - W - B \cos \alpha = 0.$$

The sum of the moments about B:

$$\sum M_B = bA_y - hA_x + bW = 0.$$

These three equations have the solution: $A_x = 173.21$ lb, $A_y = -100$ lb, and $B = -346.4$ lb.

Member BDEF: The sum of the forces:

$$\sum F_x = D_x - B \sin \alpha - E \sin \alpha = 0,$$

$$\sum F_y = D_y - W + B \cos \alpha - E \cos \alpha = 0.$$

The sum of the moments about D:

$$\sum M_D = -2bW - bE \cos \alpha - hE \sin \alpha - bB \cos \alpha + hB \sin \alpha = 0.$$

These three equations have the solution: $D_x = -259.8$ lb, $D_y = 350$ lb, $E = -173.2$ lb.

Member EGHI: The sum of the forces:

$$\sum F_x = G_x + E \sin \alpha - H \cos \alpha = 0,$$

$$\sum F_y = G_y - W + E \cos \alpha + H \sin \alpha = 0.$$

The sum of the moments about H:

$$\sum M_H = bG_y - hG_x + bW + 2bE \cos \alpha - 2hE \sin \alpha = 0.$$

These three equations have the solution: $G_x = 346.4$ lb, $G_y = 200$ lb, and $H = 300$ lb. This is the axial force in HJ.

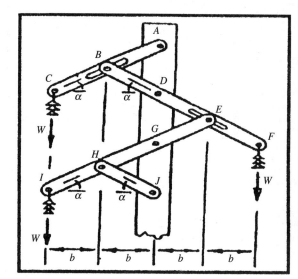

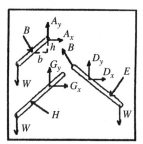

Problem 6.97 What are the magnitudes of the forces exerted by the pliers on the bolt at *A* when 30-lb forces are applied as shown? (*B* is a pinned connection.)

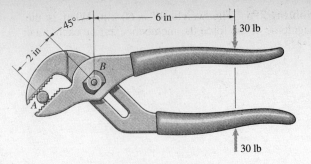

Solution: *Element AB:* The sum of the moments about *B*:

$$\sum M_B = 2F - (6)30 = 0,$$

from which $F = 90$ lb.

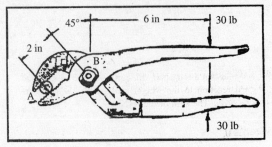

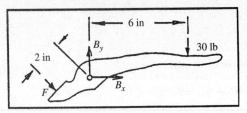

Problem 6.98 The weight $W = 60$ kip. What is the magnitude of the force the members exert on each other at D?

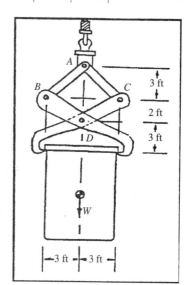

Solution: Assume that a tong half will carry half the weight, and denote the vertical reaction to the weight at A by R. *The complete structure as a free body:* The sum of the forces:

$$\sum F_y = R - W = 0,$$

from which $R = W$

Tong-Half ACD:

Element AC: The sum of the moments about A:

(1) $\quad \sum M_A = 3C_y + 3C_x = 0.$

The sum of the forces:

(2) $\quad \sum F_y = \dfrac{R}{2} + C_y + A_y = 0$, and

(3) $\quad \sum F_x = C_x + A_x = 0.$

Element CD: The sum of the forces:

(4) $\quad \sum F_x = D_x - P - C_x = 0$, and

(5) $\quad \sum F_y = D_y - C_y - \dfrac{W}{2} = 0.$

The sum of the moments:

(6) $\quad \sum M_D = 2C_x - 3C_y - 3P + \dfrac{3}{2}W = 0$

Element AB: The sum of the forces:

(7) $\quad \sum F_y = -A_y + \dfrac{R}{2} - B_y = 0$, and

(8) $\quad \sum F_x = -A_x - B_x = 0.$

Element BD: The sum of the forces:

(9) $\quad \sum F_y = B_y - D_y - \dfrac{W}{2} = 0$, and

(10) $\quad \sum F_x = B_x - D_x + P = 0.$

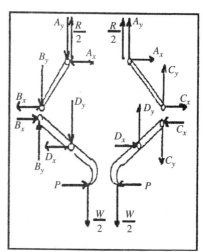

These are ten equations in ten unknowns. These have the solution $R = 60$ kip. *Check,* $A_x = -30$ kip, $A_y = 0$, $B_x = 30$ kip, $B_y = 30$ kip, $C_x = 30$ kip, $C_y = -30$ kip, $D_x = 110$ kip, $D_y = 0$, and $P = 80$ kip. The magnitude of the force the members exert on each other at D is $D = 110$ kip.

Problem 6.99 Figure a is a diagram of the bones and biceps muscle of a person's arm supporting a mass. Tension in the biceps muscle holds the forearm in the horizontal position, as illustrated in the simple mechanical model in Fig. b. The weight of the forearm is 9 N, and the mass $m = 2$ kg.

(a) Determine the tension in the biceps muscle AB.
(b) Determine the magnitude of the force exerted on the upper arm by the forearm at the elbow joint C.

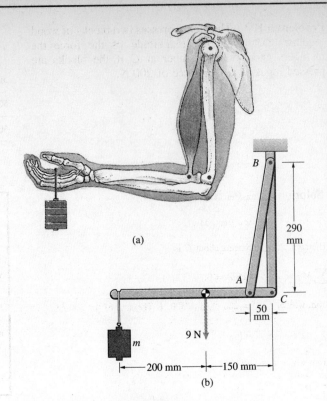

(a)

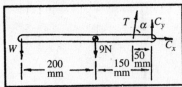

(b)

Solution: Make a cut through AB and BC just above the elbow joint C. The angle formed by the biceps muscle with respect to the forearm is $\alpha = \tan^{-1}\left(\dfrac{290}{50}\right) = 80.2°$. The weight of the mass is $W = 2(9.81) = 19.62$ N.

The section as a free body: The sum of the moments about C is

$$\sum M_C = -50T\sin\alpha + 150(9) + 350W = 0,$$

from which $T = 166.76$ N is the tension exerted by the biceps muscle AB. The sum of the forces on the section is

$$\sum F_X = C_x + T\cos\alpha = 0,$$

from which $C_x = -28.33$ N.

$$\sum F_Y = C_y + T\sin\alpha - 9 - W = 0,$$

from which $C_y = -135.72$. The magnitude of the force exerted by the forearm on the upper arm at joint C is

$$F = \sqrt{C_x^2 + C_y^2} = 138.65 \text{ N}$$

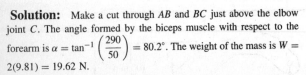

(a)

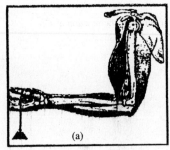

(b)

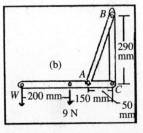

Problem 6.100 The clamp presses two blocks of wood together. Determine the magnitude of the force the members exert on each other at C if the blocks are pressed together with a force of 200 N.

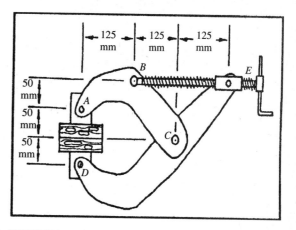

Solution: Consider the upper jaw only.

The section ABC as a free body:

The sum of the moments about C is

$$\sum M_C = 100B - 250A = 0,$$

from which, for $A = 200$ N, $B = 500$ N. The sum of the forces:

$$\sum F_x = C_x - B = 0,$$

from which $C_x = 500$ N,

$$\sum F_y = C_y + A = 0,$$

from which $C_y = -200$ N. The magnitude of the reaction at C:

$$C = \sqrt{C_x^2 + C_y^2} = 538.52 \text{ N}$$

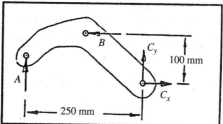

Problem 6.101 The pressure force exerted on the piston is 2 kN toward the left. Determine the couple M necessary to keep the system in equilibrium.

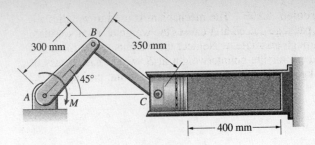

Solution: From the diagram, the coordinates of point B are (d, d) where $d = 0.3 \cos(45°)$. The distance b can be determined from the Pythagorean Theorem as $b = \sqrt{(0.35)^2 - d^2}$. From the diagram, the angle $\theta = 37.3°$. From these calculations, the coordinates of points B and C are B (0.212, 0.212), and C (0.491, 0) with all distances being measured in *meters*. All forces will be measured in *Newtons*.

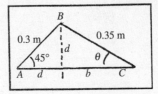

The unit vector from C toward B is $\mathbf{u}_{CB} = -0.795\mathbf{i} + 0.606\mathbf{j}$.

The equations of force equilibrium at C are

$$\sum F_X = F_{BC} \cos\theta - 2000 = 0,$$

and $\sum F_Y = N - F_{BC} \sin\theta = 0.$

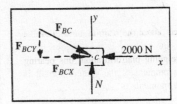

Solving these equations, we get $N = 1524$ *Newtons(N)*, and $F_{BC} = 2514$ N.

The force acting at B due to member BC is $F_{BC}\mathbf{u}_{BC} = -2000\mathbf{i} + 1524\mathbf{j}$ N.

The position vector from A to B is $\mathbf{r}_{AB} = 0.212\mathbf{i} + 0.212\mathbf{j}$ m, and the moment of the force acting at B about A, calculated from the cross product, is given by $\mathbf{M}_{FBC} = 747.6\mathbf{k}$ N-m (counter - clockwise). The moment $\mathbf{M}$ about A which is necessary to hold the system in equilibrium, is equal and opposite to the moment just calculated. Thus, $\mathbf{M} = -747.6\mathbf{k}$ N-m (clockwise).

Problem 6.102 In Problem 6.101, determine the forces on member AB at A and B.

Solution: In the solution of Problem 6.101, we found that the force acting at point B of member AB was $F_{BC}\mathbf{u}_{BC} = -2000\mathbf{i} + 1524\mathbf{j}$ N, and that the moment acting on member BC about point A was given by $\mathbf{M} = -747.6\mathbf{k}$ N-m (clockwise). Member AB must be in equilibrium, and we ensured moment equilibrium in solving Problem 6.101.

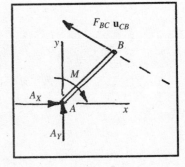

From the free body diagram, the equations for force equilibrium are

$$\sum F_X = A_X + F_{BC}u_{BCX} = A_X - 2000 \text{ N} = 0,$$

and $\sum F_Y = A_Y + F_{BC}u_{BCY} = A_Y + 1524 \text{ N} = 0.$

Thus, $A_X = 2000$ N, and $A_Y = -1524$ N.

Problem 6.103 The mechanism is used to weigh mail. A package placed at A causes the weighted point to rotate through an angle α. Neglect the weights of the members except for the counterweight at B, which has a mass of 4 kg. If $\alpha = 20°$, what is the mass of the package at A?

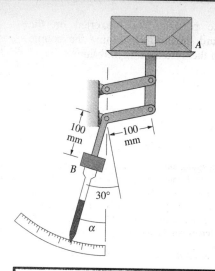

Solution: Consider the moment about the bearing connecting the motion of the counter weight to the motion of the weighing platform. The moment arm of the weighing platform about this bearing is $100\cos(30 - \alpha)$. The restoring moment of the counter weight is $100\,mg\sin\alpha$. Thus the sum of the moments is

$$\sum M = 100\,m_{B}g\sin\alpha - 100\,m_{A}g\cos(30 - \alpha) = 0.$$

Define the ratio of the masses of the counter weight to the mass of the package to be $R_M = \dfrac{m_B}{m_A}$. The sum of moments equation reduces to

$$\sum M = R_M\sin\alpha - \cos(30 - \alpha) = 0,$$

from which $R_M = \dfrac{\cos(30 - \alpha)}{\sin\alpha} = 2.8794$, and the mass of the package is $m_A = \dfrac{4}{R_M} = 1.3892 = 1.39$ kg

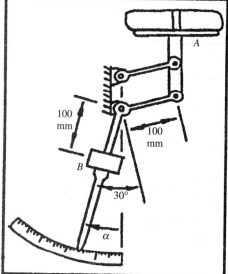

Problem 6.104 The scoop C of the front-end loader is supported by two identical arms, one on each side of the loader. One of the two arms (ABC) is visible in the figure. It is supported by a pin support at A and the hydraulic actuator BD. The sum of the other loads exerted on the arm, including its own weight, is $F = 1.6$ kN. Determine the axial force in the actuator BD and the magnitude of the reaction at A.

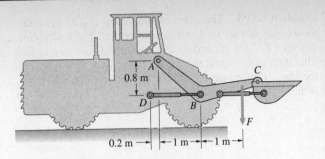

Solution: *The section ABC as a free body:* The sum of the moments about A:

$$\sum M_A = 0.8BD - 2F = 0,$$

from which $BD = 4$ kN.

The sum of the forces:

$$\sum F_x = A_x + BD = 0,$$

from which $A_x = -4$ kN.

$$\sum F_y = A_y - F = 0,$$

from which $A_y = 1.6$ kN. The magnitude of the reaction at A is

$$A = \sqrt{A_x^2 + A_y^2} = 4.308 \text{ kN}$$

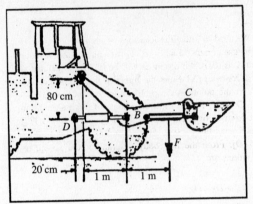

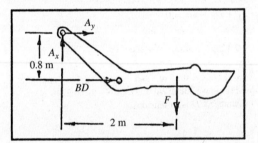

Problem 6.105 The mass of the scoop is 220 kg, and its weight acts at G. Both the scoop and the hydraulic actuator BC are pinned to the horizontal member at B. The hydraulic actuator can be treated as a two-force member. Determine the forces exerted on the scoop at B and D.

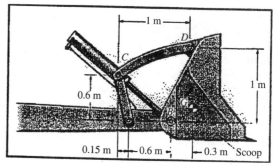

Solution: We need to know the locations of various points in the Problem . Let us use horizontal and vertical axes and define the coordinates of point A as $(0,0)$. All distances will be in *meters (m)* and all forces will be in *Newtons (N)*. From the figure in the text, the coordinates in meters of the points in the problem are A $(0, 0)$, B $(0.6, 0)$, C $(-0.15, 0.6)$, D $(0.85, 1)$, and the x coordinate of point G is 0.9 m. The unit vector from C toward D is given by $\mathbf{u}_{CD} = 0.928\mathbf{i} + 0.371\mathbf{j}$, and the force acting on the scoop at D is given by $\mathbf{D} = D_X\mathbf{i} + D_Y\mathbf{j} = 0.928D\mathbf{i} + 0.371D\mathbf{j}$. From the free body diagram of the scoop, the equilibrium equations are

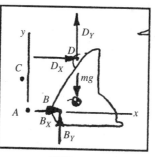

$$\sum F_X = B_X + D_X = 0,$$

$$\sum F_Y = B_Y + D_Y - mg = 0,$$

and $\sum M_B = -0.3\,mg + x_{BD}D_Y - y_{BD}D_X = 0.$

From the geometry, $x_{BD} = 0.25$ m, and $y_{BD} = 1$ m. Solving the equations of equilibrium, we obtain $B_X = 719.4$ N, $B_Y = 2246$ N, and $D = -774.8$ N (member CD is in tension).

Problem 6.106 In Problem 6.105, determine the axial force in the hydraulic actuator BC.

Solution: The unit vectors in the directions of the forces acting at C are $\mathbf{u}_{CD} = 0.928\mathbf{i} + 0.371\mathbf{j}$, $\mathbf{u}_{CA} = 0.243\mathbf{i} - 0.970\mathbf{j}$, and $\mathbf{u}_{CB} = 0.781\mathbf{i} - 0.625\mathbf{j}$. The force equilibrium equations at C are

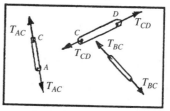

$$\sum F_X = T_{BC}u_{CBX} + T_{AC}u_{CAX} + T_{CD}u_{CDX} = 0,$$

and $\sum F_Y = T_{BC}u_{CBY} + T_{AC}u_{CAY} + T_{CD}u_{CDY} = 0.$

Solving these equations, we get $T_{BC} = -1267$ N(*compression*), and $T_{AC} = 1112$ N(*tension*).

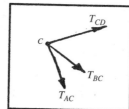

Problem 6.107 Determine the force exerted on the bolt by the bolt cutters.

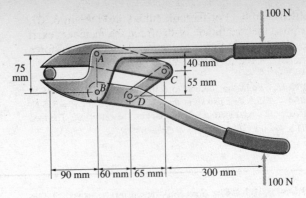

Solution: The equations of equilibrium for each of the members will be developed.

Member AB: The equations of equilibrium are:

$$\sum F_X = A_X + B_X = 0,$$

$$\sum F_Y = A_Y + B_Y = 0,$$

and $\sum M_B = 90F - 75A_X - 425(100) = 0$

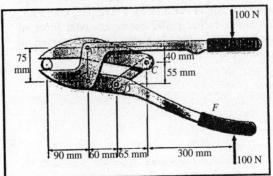

Member BD: The equations are

$$\sum F_X = -B_X + D_X = 0,$$

$$\sum F_Y = -B_Y + D_Y + 100 = 0,$$

and $\sum M_B = 15D_X + 60D_Y + 425(100) = 0.$

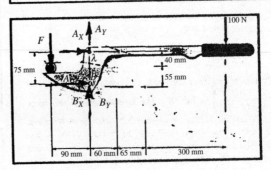

Member AC: The equations are

$$\sum F_X = -A_X + C_X = 0,$$

$$\sum F_Y = -A_Y + C_Y + F = 0,$$

and $\sum M_A = -90F + 125C_Y + 40C_X = 0.$

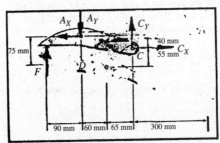

Member CD: The equations are:

$$\sum F_X = -C_X - D_X = 0,$$

$$\sum F_Y = -C_Y - D_Y = 0.$$

Solving the equations simultaneously (we have extra (but compatible) equations, we get $F = 1051$ N, $A_X = 695$ N, $A_Y = 1586$ N, $B_X = -695$ N, $B_Y = -435$ N, $C_X = 695$ N, $C_Y = 535$ N, $D_X = -695$ N, and $D_y = -535$ N

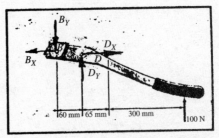

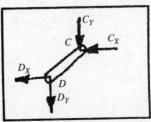

Problem 6.108 For the bolt cutters in Problem 6.107, determine the magnitude of the force the members exert on each other at the pin connection B and the axial force in the two-force member CD.

Solution: From the solution to 6.107, we know $B_X = -695$ N, and $B_Y = -435$ N. We also know that $C_X = 695$ N, and $C_Y = 535$ N, from which the axial load in <u>member CD</u> can be calculated. The load in CD is given by $T_{CD} = \sqrt{C_X^2 + C_Y^2} = 877$ N

Problem 6.109 The device is designed to exert a large force on the horizontal bar at A for a stamping operation. If the hydraulic cylinder DE exerts an axial force of 800 N and $\alpha = 80°$, what horizontal force is exerted on the horizontal bar at A?

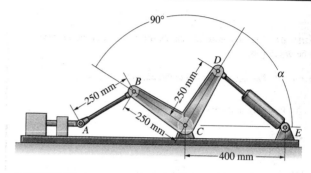

Solution: Define the x-y coordinate system with origin at C. The projection of the point D on the coordinate system is

$$R_y = 250 \sin \alpha = 246.2 \text{ mm},$$

and $R_x = 250 \cos \alpha = 43.4$ mm.

The angle formed by member DE with the positive x axis is $\theta = 180 - \tan^{-1}\left(\dfrac{R_y}{400 - R_x}\right) = 145.38°$. The components of the force produced by DE are $F_x = F \cos \theta = -658.3$ N, and $F_y = F \sin \theta = 454.5$ N. The angle of the element AB with the positive x axis is $\beta = 180 - 90 - \alpha = 10°$, and the components of the force for this member are $P_x = P \cos \beta$ and $P_y = P \sin \beta$, where P is to be determined. The angle of the arm BC with the positive x axis is $\gamma = 90 + \alpha = 170°$. The projection of point B is $L_x = 250 \cos \gamma = -246.2$ mm, and $L_y = 250 \sin \gamma = 43.4$ mm. Sum the moments about C:

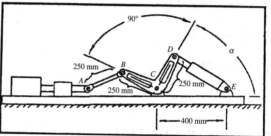

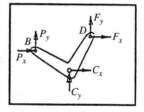

$$\sum M_C = R_x F_y - R_y F_x + L_x P_y - L_y P_x = 0.$$

Substitute and solve: $P = 2126.36$ N, and $P_x = P \cos \beta = 2094$ N is the horizontal force exerted at A.

Problem 6.110 This device raises a load W by extending the hydraulic actuator DE. The bars AD and BC are 4 ft long, and the distances $b = 2.5$ ft and $h = 1.5$ ft. If $W = 300$ lb, what force must the actuator exert to hold the load in equilibrium?

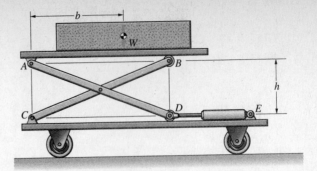

Solution: The angle ADC is $\alpha = \sin^{-1}\left(\dfrac{h}{4}\right) = 22.02°$. The distance CD is $d = 4\cos\alpha$.

The complete structure as a free body: The sum of the forces:

$$\sum F_y = -W + C_y + D_y = 0.$$

$$\sum F_x = C_x + D_x = 0.$$

The sum of the moments about C:

$$\sum M_C = -bW + dD_y = 0.$$

These have the solution:

$C_y = 97.7$ lb,

$D_y = 202.3$ lb,

and $C_x = -D_x$.

Divide the system into three elements: the platform carrying the weight, the member AB, and the member BC.

The Platform: (See Free body diagram) The moments about the point A:

$$\sum M_A = -bW - dB = 0.$$

The sum of the forces:

$$\sum F_y = A + B + W = 0.$$

These have the solution:

$B = -202.3$ lb,

and $A = -97.7$ lb.

Element BC: The sum of the moments about E is

$$\sum M_C = -\left(\frac{h}{2}\right)C_y + \left(\frac{d}{2}\right)C_x + \left(\frac{d}{2}\right)B = 0, \text{ from which}$$

(1) $dC_x - hC_y - dB = 0$. The sum of the forces:

$$\sum F_x = C_x - E_x = 0, \text{ from which}$$

(2) $E_x - C_x = 0,$

$$\sum F_y = C_y - E_y + B = 0,$$

from which

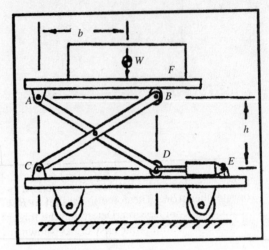

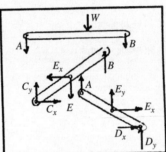

(3) $C_y - E_y + B = 0$

Element AD: The sum of the moments about E:

$$\sum M_E = \left(\frac{d}{2}\right)D_y + \left(\frac{h}{2}\right)D_x - \left(\frac{d}{2}\right)A = 0,$$

from which

(4) $dD_y + hD_x - dA = 0$.

These are four equations in the four unknowns: E_X, E_Y, D_x, C_X and D_X

Solving, we obtain $D_x = -742$ lb.

Problem 6.111 The linkage is in equilibrium under the action of the couples M_A and M_B. If $\alpha_A = 60°$ and $\alpha_B = 70°$, what is the ratio M_A/M_B?

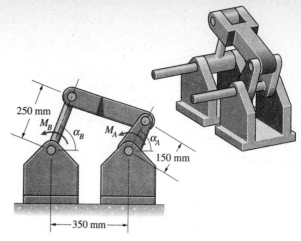

250 mm
M_B α_B M_A α_A
150 mm
—350 mm—

Solution: Make a cut through the linkage connecting the two cranks, and treat each system as a free body. The equilibrium condition occurs when the reaction forces in the linkage are equal and opposite.

The position vector of the end of the system B crank is

$$\mathbf{r}_B = R_B \; (\mathbf{i}\cos\alpha_B + \mathbf{i}\sin\alpha_B) = 85.51\mathbf{i} + 234.92\mathbf{j} \text{ (mm)}.$$

The position vector at the end of the system A crank is

$$\mathbf{r}_A = R_A(\mathbf{i}\cos\alpha_A + \mathbf{j}\sin\alpha_A) = 75\mathbf{i} + 129.9\mathbf{j} \text{ (mm)}.$$

The angle of the linkage from the end of the system B crank with respect to the horizontal is

$$\beta = \tan^{-1}\left(\frac{y_A - y_B}{x_A - x_B + 350}\right) = -17.19°.$$

The unit vector parallel to the linkage, originating at the B crank, is

$$\mathbf{e}_{BA} = \mathbf{i}\cos\beta + \mathbf{j}\sin\beta = 0.9553\mathbf{i} - 0.2955\mathbf{j}.$$

The unit vector originating at A crank is $\mathbf{e}_{AB} = -\mathbf{e}_{BA}$. The components of the forces in the linkage are $|\mathbf{F}|\mathbf{e}_{AB}$, and $|\mathbf{F}|\mathbf{e}_{BA}$.
System B: When the system is in equilibrium,

$$M_B + |\mathbf{F}| \begin{vmatrix} 0 & 0 & 1 \\ 85.5 & 234.9 & 0 \\ 0.9553 & -0.2955 & 0 \end{vmatrix} = 0,$$

from which $M_B = 249.7|\mathbf{F}|$.
System A: When the system is in equilibrium:

$$M_A + |\mathbf{F}| \begin{vmatrix} 0 & 0 & 1 \\ 75 & 129.9 & 0 \\ -0.9553 & 0.2955 & 0 \end{vmatrix} = 0,$$

from which $M_A = -146.27|\mathbf{F}|$.

Complete system: Both systems are in equilibrium for the value $|\mathbf{F}|$. Take the ratio of the two moments to eliminate $|\mathbf{F}|$.

$$\frac{M_A}{M_B} = -\frac{146.27}{249.7} = -0.5858$$

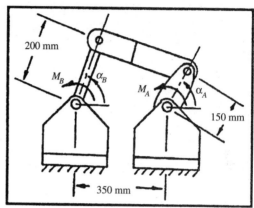

200 mm
M_B α_B M_A α_A
150 mm
350 mm

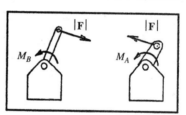

$|\mathbf{F}|$ $|\mathbf{F}|$
M_B M_A

Problem 6.112 A load $W = 2$ kN is supported by the members ACG and the hydraulic actuator BC. Determine the reactions at A and the compressive axial force in the actuator BC.

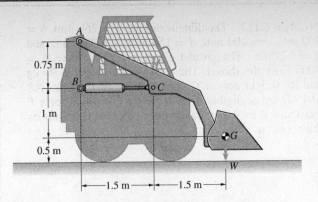

Solution: The sum of the moments about A is

$$\sum M_A = 0.75BC - 3(2) = 0,$$

from which $BC = 8$ kN is the axial force. The sum of the forces

$$\sum F_X = A_X + BC = 0,$$

from which $A_X = -8$ kN.

$$\sum F_Y = A_Y - 2 = 0,$$

from which $A_Y = 2$ kN.

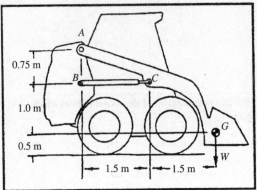

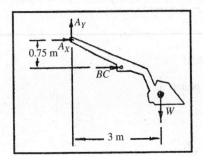

Problem 6.113 The dimensions are $a = 260$ mm, $b = 300$ mm, $c = 200$ mm, $d = 150$ mm, $e = 300$ mm, and $f = 520$ mm. The ground exerts a vertical force $F = 7000$ N on the shovel. The mass of the shovel is 90 kg and its weight acts at G. The weights of the links AB and AD are negligible. Determine the horizontal force P exerted at A by the hydraulic piston and the reactions on the shovel at C.

Solution: The free-body diagram of the shovel is from which we obtain the equations

$$\sum F_x = C_x - T \cos \beta = 0, \qquad (1)$$

$$\sum F_y = C_y + T \sin \beta + F - mg = 0, \qquad (2)$$

$$\sum M_{(ptC)} = fF - emg + (b - c)T \sin \beta$$

$$+ dT \cos \beta = 0. \qquad (3)$$

The angle $\beta = \arctan[(a - d)/b]$.

From the free-body diagram of joint A,

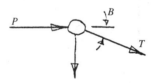

we obtain the equation

$$\sum F = P + T \cos \beta = 0. \qquad (4)$$

Substituting the given information into Eqs. (1)–(4) and solving, we obtain

$T = -19,260$ N,

$P = 18,080$ N,

$C_x = -18,080$ N,

and $C_y = 513$ N.

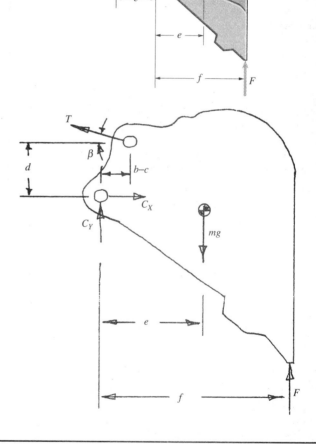

Problem 6.114 The dimensions of the mechanism in Problem 6.113 are $a = 10$ in., $b = 12$ in., $c = 8$ in., $d = 6$ in., $e = 12$ in., and $f = 20$ in. The 200-lb weight of the shovel acts at G. The weights of the links AB and AD are negligible. The horizontal force P exerted at A by the hydraulic piston is 4000 lb. Determine the vertical force F exerted on the ground by the shovel and the reactions on the shovel at C.

Solution: See the solution of Problem 6.113. Substituting the given information into Eqs. (1)–(4) and solving, we obtain

$T = -4216$ lb,

$F = 1587$ lb,

$C_x = -4000$ lb,

and $C_y = -53.3$ lb.

Problem 6.115 (a) For each member of the truss, obtain a graph of (axial force)/F as a function of x for $0 \le x \le 2$ m.
(b) If you were designing this truss, what value of x would you choose based on your results in (a)?

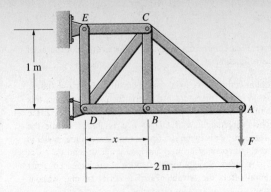

Solution: The angle of member CD with the positive x axis is $\beta = \tan^{-1}\left(\dfrac{1}{x}\right)$, which lies in the interval $90° > \beta > 26.6°$. The angle of member AC with the negative x axis is $\alpha = \tan^{-1}\left(\dfrac{1}{2-x}\right)$, which lies in the interval $26.57° \le \alpha < 90°$.

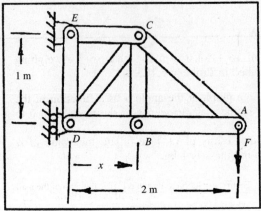

The complete structure as a free body: The sum of the moments about E is

$$\sum M_E = -2F + D = 0,$$

from which $D = 2F$. The sum of forces

$$\sum F_X = E_X + D = 0,$$

from which $E_X = -2F$.

$$\sum F_Y = E_Y - F = 0,$$

from which $E_Y = F$. These values are to be used as checks on the joint analysis.

The method of joints: Divide each axial force by the applied force F. (This is equivalent to adopting the value $F = 1$)

Joint A: The sums of forces:

$$\sum F_Y = AC \sin \alpha - 1 = 0,$$

and $\sum F_X = -AC \cos \alpha - AB = 0$

Joint B: The sums of forces:

$$\sum F_Y = BC = 0,$$

and $\sum F_X = -BD + AB = 0$

Joint C: The sums of forces:

$$\sum F_Y = -CD \sin \beta - AC \sin \alpha = 0,$$

and $\sum F_X = -CE + AC \cos \alpha - CD \cos \beta = 0.$

Joint E: The sums of forces:

$$\sum F_X = E_X + CE = 0$$

and $\sum F_Y = E_Y - DE = 0.$

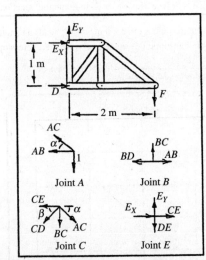

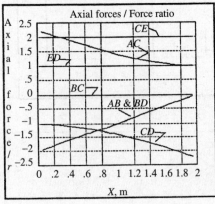

542

The **TK Solver Plus** commercial package was used to plot the axial force ratios as a function of x.

(b) The minimum compressive axial forces occur at about $x = 0.8$ m, so if compressive axial forces are a concern for safety reasons, this configuration offers advantages. However, note that as $\lim x \to 2$, the truss approaches a rectangle with CD as a cross brace. While the compressive force in CD is increased, the compressive force in BD is reduced (AB doesn't count, it no longer has any length) and the axial tension in AC is reduced. None of the axial tensions are increased. Thus this configuration offers the advantages of material saving, without safety penalties.

Problem 6.116   Consider the mechanism for weighing mail described in Problem 6.103.

(a)   Obtain a graph of the angle α as a function of the mass of the mail for values of the mass from 0 to 2 kg.

(b)   Use the results of (a) to estimate the value of α when the mass is 1 kg.

Solution: From the solution to Problem 6.103, the ratio of the mail mass to the pendulum bob mass is given as $\dfrac{M}{M_B} = \dfrac{\sin \alpha}{\cos(30° - \alpha)}$. The bob mass $M_B = 4$ kg. **TK Solver Plus** was used to graph this function.

(b) A close inspection of the values of near a mass of 1 yields an angle of $\boxed{\alpha = 13.9°}$. *Check:* Substitute this value back into the expression above: $M = M_B \left(\dfrac{\sin 13.9°}{\cos(30° - 13.9°)} \right) = 4(0.250035)$. *check.*

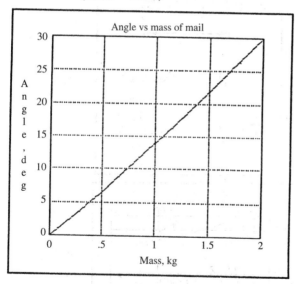

Problem 6.117 A preliminary design for a bridge structure is shown. The forces F are the loads the structure must support at G, H, I, J, and K. Plot the axial forces in members AB and BC as a function of the angle β. Use your graphs to estimate the value of β for which the maximum compressive load in any member of the bridge does not exceed $2F$. Draw a sketch of the resulting design.

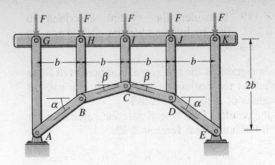

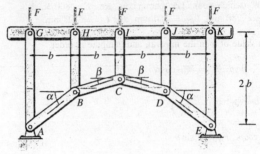

Solution: Follow Example 6.3. Draw a Freebody diagram of Joint B

Assume a unit load F.

$$\sum F_x: \quad -T_{AB}\cos\alpha + T_{BC}\cos\beta = 0 \quad \textbf{(1)}$$

$$\sum F_y: \quad F + T_{BC}\sin\beta - T_{AB}\sin\alpha = 0 \quad \textbf{(2)}$$

Joint C:

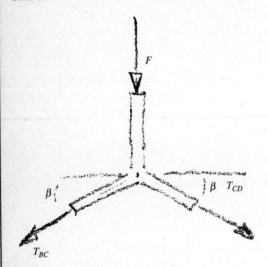

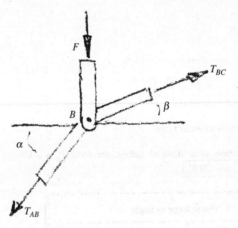

$$\sum F_x: \quad -T_{BC}\cos\beta + T_{CD}\cos\beta = 0$$

$$\therefore T_{BC} = T_{CD}$$

(obvious from summary)

$$\sum F_y: \quad -F - 2T_{BC}\sin\beta = 0 \quad \textbf{(3)}$$

Solving the three eqns in 3 unknown ($F = 1$), for $15° \leq \beta \leq 30°$ and plotting the results, we get

From the plot, $|T_{AB}| = 2F$ at $\beta \cong 20.5°$ (actually 20.7°). $A + \beta = 20.7°$, $\alpha = 48.6°$ and the loads are

MEMBER	LOAD
AG, BH, CI, DJ, EK,	F
AB, DE	ZF
BC, CD	1.414F

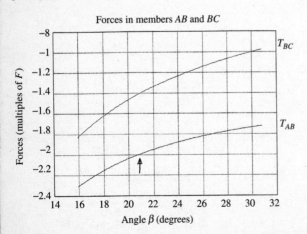

Forces in members AB and BC

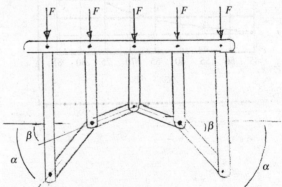

544

Problem 6.118 Consider the system described in Problem 6.109. The hydraulic cylinder DE exerts an axial force of 800 N.

(a) Obtain a graph of the horizontal component of force exerted on the horizontal bar at A by the rod AB for values of α from 45° to 85°.

(b) Use the results of (a) to estimate the value of α for which the horizontal force is 2 kN.

Solution: The algorithm is taken directly from the solution to Problem 6.109 (which see). The parameters are: $F = 800$ N, $b = 400$ mm, $L_{CD} = 250$ mm, $L_{BC} = 250$ mm, and $L_{AB} = 250$ mm.

(1) Adopt a value of α in the interval, and compute in order:

(2) $R_y = L_{CD} \sin \alpha, \ R_x = L_{CD} \cos \alpha$

(3) $\theta = 180° - \tan^{-1}\left(\dfrac{R_y}{b - R_x}\right)$

(4) $F_x = F \cos \theta, \ F_y = F \sin \theta$

(5) $\beta = 90° - \alpha$

(6) $\gamma = 90° + \alpha$

(7) $L_x = L \cos \gamma, \ L_y = L \sin \gamma$

(8) $P_x = \left(\dfrac{R_x F_y - R_y F_x}{L_y \cos \beta - L_x \sin \beta}\right) \cos \beta$

where P_x is the horizontal force.

(b) From an inspection of a Table of values, the force $P_x = 2$ kN occurs at an angle $\boxed{\alpha = 79.5°}$

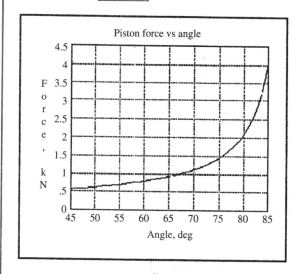

Piston force vs angle

545

Problem 6.119 The weight of the suspended object is 10 kN. The two members have equal cross-sectional areas A, and each will safely support an axial force of $40A$ MN, where A is in square meters. Determine the value of h that minimizes the total volume of material in the two members.

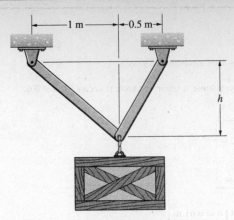

Solution: Assume that the maximum safe axial force is to be always imposed. The cross sectional area can always be modified to assure that this is true. However, one member will have a higher axial force than the other, and that member will determine the area for maximum safe axial force.

Make a cut near the pin supports.

The sum of the moments about C is

$$\sum M_C = -W + 1.5B_y = 0,$$

from which $B_y = \left(\dfrac{2}{3}\right)W$.

The sum of the forces

$$\sum F_y = C_y + B_y - W = 0,$$

from which $C_y = \left(\dfrac{1}{3}\right)W$.

The vertical components of the forces:

$$C_y - T_{CD}\sin\alpha = 0,$$

from which $T_{CD}\sin\alpha = \left(\dfrac{1}{3}\right)W$.

Similarly,

$$T_{BD}\sin\beta = \left(\dfrac{2}{3}\right)W$$

The angle is larger than the angle, and both are in the first quadrant, hence $\sin\beta > \sin\alpha$, so it is not obvious from the expressions for the axial force which will be the larger. A graph of the tensions in the two members demonstrates that T_{BD} is the larger. Thus, $T_{BD} = 40A$ MN, from which $A = \dfrac{T_{BD}}{40}$.

The algorithm for computing the volume:

(1) The angle $\beta = \tan^{-1}(2\,h)$.

(2) The tension $T_{BD} = \dfrac{2W}{3\sin\beta}$

(3) The lengths of the members:

$$L_{CD} = \sqrt{h^2 + 1}$$

and $L_{BD} = \sqrt{h^2 + 0.25}$

(4) The volume of the two members:

$$V = A(L_{CD} + L_{BD}) = \frac{T_{BD}}{40}(L_{CD} + L_{BD}).$$

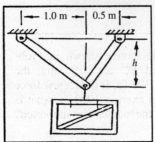

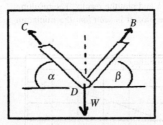

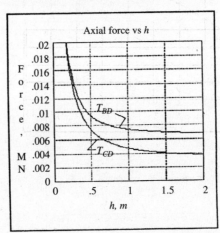

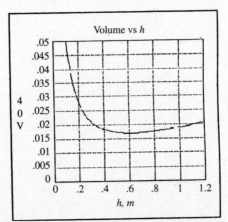

6.119 *Contd.*

TK Solver Plus was used to obtain the graphs.

From the graph of the volume, a minimum volume occurs for $h \cong 0.6$.
A Table of values:

h, m	40V
0.59	0.16904
0.60	0.16898
0.61	0.16896
0.62	0.16898

shows a minimum at $\boxed{h = 0.61 \text{ m}}$

Problem 6.120 Consider the device shown in Problem 6.110. The bars *AD* and *BC* are 4 ft long, the distance $b = 2.5$ ft, and $W = 300$ lb. If the largest force the hydraulic actuator *DE* can exert is 1000 lb, what is the smallest height h at which the load can be supported?

Solution: Follow the solution of Problem 6.110, solve the problem for the specified range of values for h and plot the results. The resulting plot is shown at the right. From the plot, it is seen that the minimum value for h is about $h = 1.15$ ft.

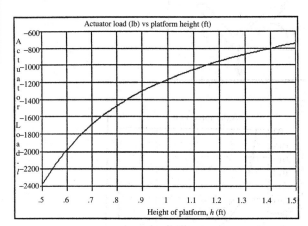

Problem 6.121 The linkage in Problem 6.111 is in equilibrium under the action of the couples M_A and M_B. When $\alpha_A = 60°$, $\alpha_B = 70°$. For the range of $0 \leq \alpha_A \leq 180°$, estimate the maximum positive and negative values of M_A/M_B and the values of α_A at which they occur.

Solution: The algorithm is taken from Problem 6.111, with the addition of the relationship between the angles. (See Figure with Problem 6.111 for dimensions.). The algorithm is:

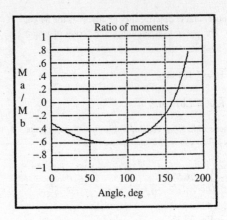

(a) For a value of α_A, $(0° \leq \alpha_A \leq 180°)$, solve for the angle α_B and the angle of the linkage connection β from the two simultaneous equations: (1) $R_A \cos \alpha_A - R_B \cos \alpha_B + 350 = L \cos \beta$, (2) $R_A \sin \alpha_A - R_B \sin \alpha_B = L \sin \beta$, where the length of the linkage connection L is

$$L = \sqrt{\begin{array}{c}(R_A \sin(60°) - R_B \sin(70°))^2 + (R_A \cos(60°) \\ - R_B \cos(70°) + 350)^2\end{array}}$$

$$= 355.367 \text{ mm}$$

(b) Compute the positions of the crank ends:

$$x_A = R_A \cos \alpha_A,$$

$$y_A = R_A \sin \alpha_A,$$

$$x_B = R_B \cos \alpha_B,$$

$$y_B = R_B \sin \alpha_B.$$

(d) Get the components of unit vector parallel to the linkage:

$$e_{BAX} = \cos \beta,$$

$$e_{BAY} = \sin \beta.$$

(e) Compute the moments:

$$M_B = -(x_B e_{ABY} - y_B e_{ABX}),$$

and $M_A = (x_A e_{ABY} - y_A e_{ABX})$

(f) Take the ratio: $R = \dfrac{M_A}{M_B}$. The graph is shown. The minimum occurs at $\boxed{\alpha_A = 78°}$, with a value of

$$\boxed{R = -0.60289 \cdots = -0.603}.$$

The maximum occurs at $\boxed{\alpha_A = 180°}$, with a value of $\boxed{R = 0.75}$

Problem 6.122 Consider the front-end loader in Problem 6.112. A load $W = 2$ kN is supported by the member ACG and the hydraulic actuator BC. If the actuator BC can exert a maximum axial force of 12 kN, what is the largest height above the ground at which the center of mass G can be supported?

Solution: The points G and C describe arcs of circles as the height above ground changes. The radii of these circles (see sketch of loader in Problem 6.112 for dimensions) are

$$R_{AG} = \sqrt{1.75^2 + 3^2} = 3.473 \text{ m},$$

and $R_{AC} = \sqrt{0.75^2 + 1.5^2} = 1.677$ m.

The angles made by these radii from the horizontal line through point A when the point G is 0.5 m above the ground are

$$\gamma_{AC} = \tan^{-1}\left(\frac{0.75}{1.5}\right) = 26.57°,$$

and $\beta_{AG} = \tan^{-1}\left(\frac{1.75}{3}\right) = 30.25°.$

The algorithm for computing height as a function of the hydraulic actuator force is developed from the geometry and the equilibrium conditions: (1) The vertical distance from A to C as the height is increased: $h = -R_{AC}\sin(\gamma_{AC} - \alpha)$, where α is the angle of the element AG, $(0 < \alpha)$, measured from the initial height of point G of 0.5 m, and a negative h means that h is below the point A. (2) The horizontal distance from A to C: $d = R_{AC}\cos(\gamma_{AC} - \alpha)$. (3) The height above the ground of point G: $H = 2.25 - R_{AG}\sin(\beta_{AG} - \alpha)$. (4) The angle of the hydraulic actuator BC with a horizontal line through B is $\theta = \tan^{-1}\left(\frac{0.75 + h}{d}\right)$. (5) The sum of the moments about point A is

$$\sum M_A = -hBC\cos\theta + dBC\sin\theta - WR_{AG}\cos(\beta_{AG} - \alpha) = 0.$$

Check: When $\alpha = 0$ these reduce to the algorithm used in the solution to Problem 6.112. *check*. The **TK Solver Plus** commercial package was used to graph the force against height. The hydraulic actuator reaches the limit of $BC = 12$ kN when the height is $\boxed{H = 3.54 \text{ m}}$

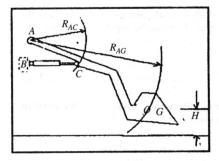

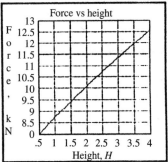

Force vs height

Height, H

Problem 6.123 Consider the truss in Problem 6.27. The crane exerts vertical 75-kN forces on the truss at B, C, and D. You can model the support at A as a pin support and model the support at E as a roller support that can exert a force normal to the dashed line but cannot exert a force parallel to it. Determine the value of the angle α for which the largest compressive force in any of the members is as small as possible. What are the resulting axial forces in the members?

Solution: The algorithm is taken directly from the solution to Problem 6.27, with the addition of a MAX function. The algorithm is as follows:

(1) Compute the angles of the members: AB and ED relative to the horizontal,

$$\gamma = \tan^{-1}\left(\frac{4}{3.4}\right) = 49.64°.$$

AF and EH relative to the horizontal:

$$\beta = \tan^{-1}\left(\frac{2.2}{3.4}\right) = 32.91°.$$

BG and DG relative to the horizontal:

$$\theta = \tan^{-1}\left(\frac{1.8}{3.4}\right) = 27.9°.$$

(See the sketch with Problem 6.27.)

(2) For a given value of α, get the unit vector components for the reaction angle at E:

$$\mathbf{e}_E = \mathbf{i}\cos(90+\alpha) + \mathbf{j}\sin(90+\alpha) = -\mathbf{i}\sin\alpha + \mathbf{j}\cos\alpha$$

(3) *The complete structure as a free body:* From the sum of moments: The x- and y-components:

$$E_x = -E\sin\alpha \text{ kN}$$

and $E_y = 112.5$ kN

(a constant). The reactions at A:

$$A_x = -E_x.$$

$$A_y = 3(75) - E_y = 112.5,$$

from which $A_y = 112.5$ kN. (a constant)
Two equations are developed for each joint:

(d) *Joint A:*

$$AB\cos\gamma + A_x + AF\cos\beta = 0,$$

and $AB\sin\gamma + A_y + AF\sin\beta = 0.$

(e) *Joint E:*

$$DE\cos\gamma - E_x + EH\cos\beta = 0$$

and $DE\sin\gamma + E_y + EH\sin\beta = 0$

(f) *Joint F:*

$$-AF\cos\beta + FG = 0,$$

and $-AF\sin\beta + BF = 0.$

(g) *Joint H:*

$$EH\cos\beta - GH = 0,$$

and $-EH\sin\beta + DH = 0$

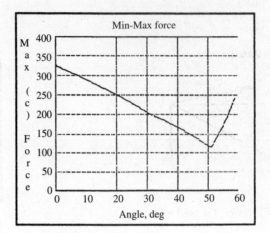

Min-Max force

(h) *Joint B:*

$$-AB\sin\gamma - BF - BG\sin\theta - 75 = 0,$$

and $-AB\cos\gamma + BC + BG\cos\theta = 0.$

(i) *Joint D:*

$$-DE\sin\gamma - DH - DG\sin\theta - 75 = 0,$$

and $DE\cos\gamma - CD - DG\cos\theta = 0$

(j) *Joint C: CD = BC Check. CG = -75 kN (C)*

(k) Use standard MAX function to get maximum compressive axial force:

$$F_{MAX} = MAX(-AB, -AF, -FG, -BF, -BC, -BG, -CG),$$

where it is necessary to test only one of a matching value pair. The maximum axial compressive force for all members is graphed against the angle. The min-max point occurs at about

$$\boxed{\alpha = 50.94\ldots° = 51°},$$

where $AF = EH = 113.9$ kN (C),

$$AB = DE = 66.5 \text{ kN } (C),$$

$$BF = DH = 61.9 \text{ kN } (C),$$

$$BG = DG = 80.2 \text{ kN } (T),$$

$$BC = CD = 113.9 \text{ kN } (C)$$

$$FG = GH = 95.6 \text{ kN } (C),$$

and $CG = 75$ kN (C).

Check. The minimum maximum compressive stress at $\alpha = 51°$ is $\boxed{R = 113.9 \text{ kN}}$ which occurs in elements AF, EH and BC, CD.

Problem 6.124 Draw graphs of the magnitudes of the axial forces in the members *BC* and *BD* as functions of the dimension *h* for 0.5 m ≤ *h* ≤ 1.5 m.

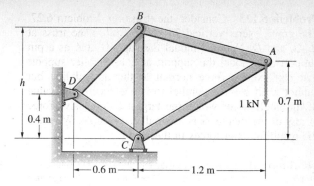

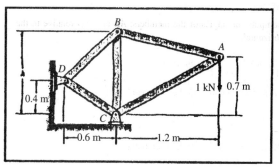

Solution: *Joint A*

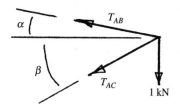

$$\sum F_x = -T_{AB}\cos\alpha - T_{AC}\cos\beta = 0,$$

$$\sum F_y = T_{AB}\sin\alpha - T_{AC}\sin\beta - 1 = 0.$$

The angles are

$$\alpha = \arctan\left(\frac{h-0.7}{1.2}\right),$$

$$\beta = \arctan\left(\frac{0.7}{1.2}\right).$$

Joint B

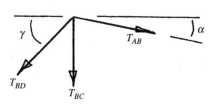

$$\sum F_x = T_{AB}\cos\alpha - T_{BD}\cos\gamma = 0,$$

$$\sum F_y = -T_{BC} - T_{AB}\sin\alpha - T_{BD}\sin\gamma = 0,$$

where

$$\gamma = \arctan\left(\frac{h-0.4}{0.6}\right).$$

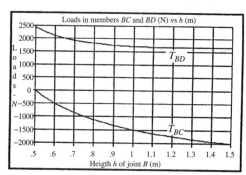

Loads in members *BC* and *BD* (N) vs *h* (m)

Joint C

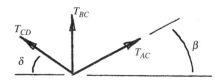

$$\sum F_x = T_{AC}\cos\beta - T_{CD}\cos\delta = 0,$$

where

$$\delta = \arctan\left(\frac{0.4}{0.6}\right).$$

These equations were solved for 0.5 m ≤ *h* ≤ 1.5 m. The graphs of the results are shown.

Problem 6.125 For the truss in Problem 6.124, determine the value of the dimension h in the range $0.5 \leq h \leq 1.5$ m so that the magnitude of the largest axial force in any of the members, tensile or compressive, is a minimum. What are the resulting axial forces in the members?

Solution: The plots obtained using this procedure are shown at the right. From the absolute value plot, we see that the minimum occurs where $h \cong 1.13$ m. Solving the original problem for this value of h gives the following values for the axial forces in the various members:

$T_{AB} = 1128$ N (tension),

$T_{AC} = -1230$ N (compression),

$T_{BC} = -1672$ N (compression),

$T_{BD} = 1672$ N (tension),

and $T_{CD} = -1276$ N (compression).

Note that the axial forces in BC and BD are the limiting factors in the loading of the truss. All other forces are smaller in magnitude.

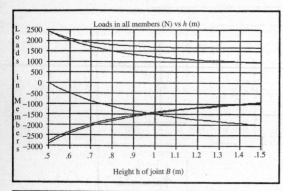

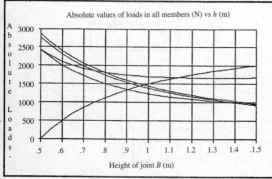

Problem 6.126   The loads $F_1 = 60$ N and $F_2 = 40$ N.

(a) Draw the free-body diagram of the entire truss, and determine the reactions at its supports.
(b) Determine the axial forces in its members. Indicate whether they are in tension (T) or compression (C).

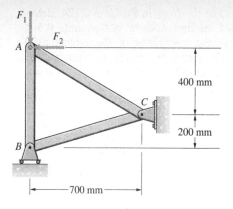

Solution: (a) The free-body diagram is shown. The sum of the moments about C is $M_C = -0.7B_y + 0.7F_1 + 0.4F_2 = 0$, from which

$$B_y = \frac{0.7(60) + 0.4(40)}{0.7}$$

$$\boxed{B_y = 82.857 \text{ N}}.$$

The sums of forces:

$$\sum F_x = C_x - F_2 = 0,$$

from which $\boxed{C_x = 40 \text{ N}}$.

$$\sum F_y = B_y + C_y - F_1 = 0,$$

from which

$$\boxed{C_y = F_1 - B_y = -22.857 = -22.9 \text{ N}}$$

(b) The included angle CBA is

$$\alpha = 90° - \tan^{-1}\left(\frac{200}{700}\right) = 74.05°.$$

Denote the axial force in the member I, K by IK. The axial forces at joint B are

$$\mathbf{F}_{BC} = BC(\mathbf{i}\sin\alpha + \mathbf{j}\cos\alpha) = BC(0.9615\mathbf{i} + 0.2747\mathbf{j}),$$

$$\mathbf{F}_{BA} = BA\mathbf{i},$$

and the external force is $\mathbf{B} = B_y\mathbf{j}$. The sums of the forces:

$$\sum F_x^B = 0.9615BC = 0,$$

from which $\boxed{BC = 0}$.

$$\sum F_y^B = B_y + BA = 0,$$

from which $\boxed{BA = -B_y = -82.9 \text{ N } (C)}$. The magnitude of the angle formed by member AC with respect to the x-axis is

$$\beta = \tan^{-1}\left(\frac{0.4}{0.7}\right) = 29.74°.$$

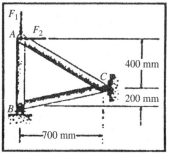

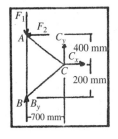

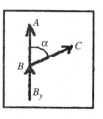

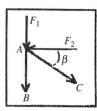

The sums of the axial forces:

$$\sum F_x^A = -F_2 + AC\cos\beta = 0,$$

from which $\boxed{AC = \dfrac{F_2}{\cos\beta} = 46.1 \text{ N } (T)}$

Problem 6.127 Consider the truss in Problem 6.126. The loads $F_1 = 440$ N and $F_2 = 160$ N. Determine the axial forces in the members. Indicate whether they are in tension (T) or compression (C).

Solution: From the solution to Problem 6.126, the sum of the moments about C is

$$M_C = -0.7B_Y + 0.7F_1 + 0.4F_2 = 0,$$

from which $\boxed{B_y = \dfrac{0.7F_1 + 0.4F_2}{0.7} = 531.43 \text{ N}}$.

Denote the axial force in the member I, K by IK. The axial loads at joint B are

$$\boxed{AB = -B_y = -531.4 \text{ N } (C)},$$

and $\boxed{BC = 0}$.

Similarly, the sum of the forces at the joint A is

$$\sum F_x^A = -F_2 + AC \cos \beta = 0,$$

from which

$$\boxed{AC = \dfrac{F_2}{\cos \beta} = 184.3 \text{ N } (T)}$$

Problem 6.128 The truss supports a load $F = 10$ kN. Determine the axial forces in the members AB, AC, and BC.

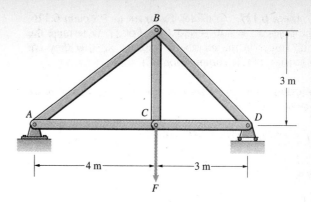

Solution: Find the support reactions at A and D.

$$\sum F_x: \quad A_x = 0$$

$$\sum F_y: \quad A_y + D_y - 10 = 0$$

$$\curvearrowleft + \sum M_A: \quad (-4)(10) + 7D_y = 0$$

Solving, $A_x = 0$,

$$A_y = 4.29 \text{ kN}$$

$$D_y = 5.71 \text{ kN}$$

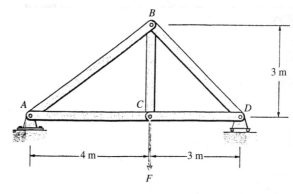

Joint A:

$$\tan \theta = \tfrac{3}{4}$$

$$\theta = 36.87°$$

$$(A_y = 4.29 \text{ kN})$$

$$\sum F_x: \quad F_{AB} \cos \theta + F_{AC} = 0$$

$$\sum F_y: \quad A_y + F_{AB} \sin \theta = 0$$

Solving, $F_{AB} = -7.14$ kN (C)

$$F_{AC} = 5.71 \text{ kN } (T)$$

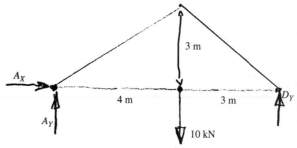

Joint C:

$$\sum F_x: \quad F_{CD} - F_{AC} = 0$$

$$\sum F_y: \quad F_{BC} - 10 \text{ kN} = 0$$

Solving $F_{BC} = 10$ kN (T)

$$F_{CD} = +5.71 \text{ kN } (T)$$

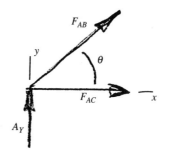

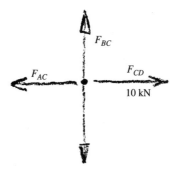

555

Problem 6.129 Each member of the truss shown in Problem 6.128 will safely support a tensile force of 40 kN and a compressive force of 32 kN. Based on this criterion, what is the largest downward load F that can safely be applied at C?

Solution: Assume a unit load F and find the magnitudes of the tensile and compressive loads in the truss. Then scale the load F up (along with the other loads) until either the tensile limit or the compressive limit is reached.

External Support Loads:

$$\sum F_x: \quad A_x = 0 \qquad \textbf{(1)}$$

$$\sum F_y: \quad A_y + D_y - F = 0 \quad \textbf{(2)}$$

$$\sum M_A: \quad -4F + 7D_y = 0 \quad \textbf{(3)}$$

Joint A:

$$\tan\theta = \frac{3}{2}$$

$$\theta = 36.87°$$

$$\sum F_x: \quad F_{AC} + F_{AB}\cos\theta = 0 \quad \textbf{(4)}$$

$$\sum F_y: \quad F_{AB}\sin\theta + A_y = 0 \quad \textbf{(5)}$$

Joint C

$$\sum F_x: \quad F_{CD} - F_{AC} = 0 \quad \textbf{(6)}$$

$$\sum F_y: \quad F_{BC} - F = 0 \qquad \textbf{(7)}$$

Joint D

$$\tan\phi = \frac{3}{3}$$

$$\phi = 45°$$

$$\sum F_x: \quad -F_{CD} - F_{BD}\cos\phi = 0 \quad \textbf{(8)}$$

$$\sum F_y: \quad F_{BD}\sin\phi + D_y = 0 \qquad \textbf{(9)}$$

Setting $F = 1$ and solving, we get the largest tensile load of 0.571 in AC and CD. The largest compressive load is 0.808 in member BD.

> Largest Tensile is in member BC. $BC = F = 1$

The compressive load will be the limit

$$\frac{F_{max}}{1} = \frac{32}{0.808}$$

$$F_{max} = 40 \text{ kN}$$

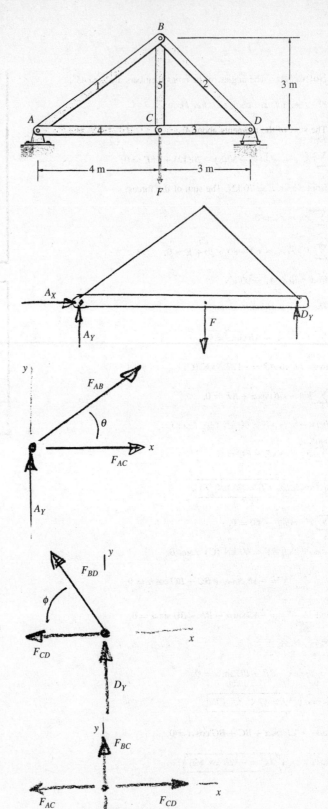

Problem 6.130 The Pratt bridge truss supports loads at F, G, and H. Determine the axial forces in members BC, BG, and FG.

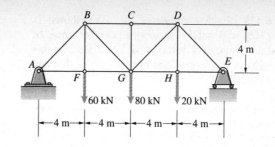

Solution: The angles of the cross-members are $\alpha = 45°$.

The complete structure as a free body:

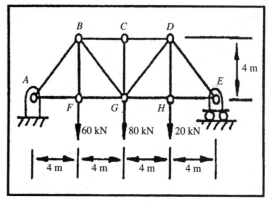

The sum of the moments about A:

$$\sum M_A = -60(4) - 80(8) - 20(12) + 16E = 0,$$

from which $E = 70$ kN. The sum of the forces:

$$\sum F_x = A_x = 0.$$

$$\sum F_y = A_y - 60 - 80 - 20 + E = 0,$$

from which $A_y = 90$ kN

The method of joints: Joint A:

$$\sum F_Y = A_y + AB \sin \alpha = 0,$$

from which $AB = -127.3$ kN (C),

$$\sum F_x = AB \cos \alpha + AF = 0,$$

from which $AF = 90$ kN (T). *Joint F:*

$$\sum F_x = -AF + FG = 0,$$

from which $\boxed{FG = 90 \text{ kN } (T)}$.

$$\sum F_y = BF - 60 = 0,$$

from which $BF = 60$ kN (C). *Joint B:*

$$\sum F_x = -AB \cos \alpha + BC + BG \cos \alpha = 0,$$

and $\sum F_y = -AB \sin \alpha - BF - BG \sin \alpha = 0,$

from which:

$$-AB \sin \alpha - BF - BG \sin \alpha = 0.$$

Solve: $\boxed{BG = 42.43 \text{ kN } (T)}$,

and $-AB \cos \alpha + BC + BG \cos \alpha = 0,$

from which $\boxed{BC = -120 \text{ kN } (C)}$

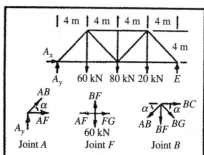

Problem 6.131 Consider the truss in Problem 6.130. Determine the axial forces in members CD, GD, and GH.

Solution: Use the results of the solution of Problem 6.130:

$BC = -120$ kN (C),

$BG = 42.43$ kN (T),

and $FG = 90$ kN (T).

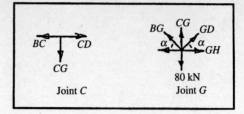

Joint C   Joint G

The angle of the cross-members with the horizontal is $\alpha = 45°$.

Joint C:

$$\sum F_x = -BC + CD = 0,$$

from which $\boxed{CD = -120 \text{ kN } (C)}$

$$\sum F_Y = -CG = 0,$$

from which $CG = 0$.

Joint G:

$$\sum F_y = BG \sin\alpha + GD \sin\alpha + CG - 80 = 0,$$

from which $\boxed{GD = 70.71 \text{ kN } (T)}$.

$$\sum F_y = -BG \cos\alpha + GD \cos\alpha - FG + GH = 0,$$

from which $\boxed{GH = 70 \text{ kN } (T)}$

Problem 6.132 The truss supports loads at F and H. Determine the axial forces in members AB, AC, BC, BD, CD, and CE.

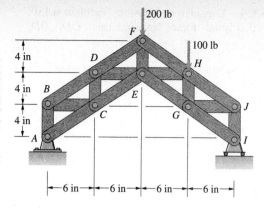

Solution: *The complete structure as a free body:* The sum of the moments about I:

$$\sum M_A = 100(6) + 200(12) - 24A_Y = 0,$$

from which $A_Y = 125$ lb. The sum of forces:

$$\sum F_x = A_x = 0.$$

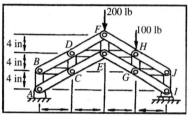

The method of joints: The angles of the inclined members with the horizontal are

$$\alpha = \tan^{-1}(0.6667) = 33.69°$$

Joint A:

$$\sum F_x = AC \cos \alpha = 0,$$

from which $AC = 0$.

$$\sum F_y = A_y + AB + AC \sin \alpha = 0,$$

from which $\boxed{AB = -125 \text{ lb } (C)}$

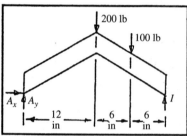

Joint B:

$$\sum F_{yt} = -AB + BD \sin \alpha = 0,$$

from which $\boxed{BD = -225.3 \text{ lb } (C)}$.

$$\sum F_x = BD \cos \alpha + BC = 0,$$

from which $\boxed{BC = 187.5 \text{ lb } (T)}$

Joint C:

$$\sum F_x = -BC - AC \cos \alpha + CE \cos \alpha = 0,$$

from which $\boxed{CE = 225.3 \text{ lb } (T)}$

$$\sum F_y = -AC \sin \alpha + CD + CE \sin \alpha = 0,$$

from which $\boxed{CD = -125 \text{ lb } (C)}$

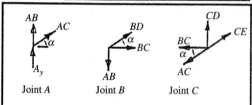

Problem 6.133 Consider the truss in Problem 6.132. Determine the axial forces in members EH and FH.

Solution: Use the results from the solution to Problem 6.112:

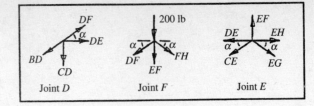

Joint D Joint F Joint E

$CE = 225.3$ lb (T),

$CD = -125$ lb (C),

$BD = -225.3$ lb (C).

The method of joints: The angle of inclined members with the horizontal is $\alpha = 33.69°$.

Joint D:

$$\sum F_y = -BD \sin\alpha - CD + DF \sin\alpha = 0,$$

from which $DF = -450.7$ lb (C).

$$\sum F_x = -DF \cos\alpha + DE - BD \cos\alpha = 0,$$

from which $DE = 187.5$ lb (T)

Joint F:

$$\sum F_x = -DF \cos\alpha + FH \cos\alpha = 0,$$

from which $\boxed{FH = -450.7 \text{ lb } (C)}$

$$\sum F_y = -200 - DF \sin\alpha - FH \sin\alpha - EF = 0,$$

from which $EF = 300$ lb (T)

Joint E:

$$\sum F_y = -CE \sin\alpha + EF - EG \sin\alpha = 0,$$

from which $EG = 315$ lb (T)

$$\sum F_x = -DE + EH - CE \cos\alpha + EG \cos\alpha = 0,$$

from which $\boxed{EH = 112.5 \text{ lb } (T)}$

Problem 6.134 Determine the axial forces in members *BD*, *CD*, and *CE*.

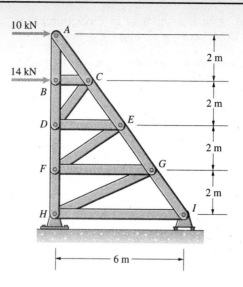

Solution: Use the method of sections

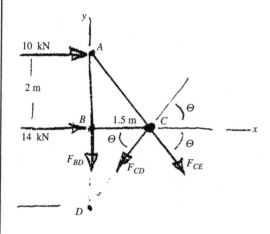

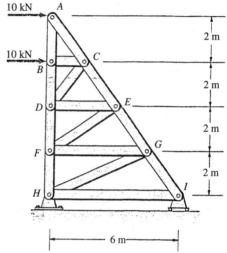

$$\tan\theta = \frac{2}{1.5}$$

$$\theta = 53.13°$$

$$\sum F_x: \quad F_{CE}\cos\theta - F_{CD}\cos\theta + 24 = 0$$

$$\sum F_y: \quad -F_{BD} - F_{CD}\sin\theta - F_{CE}\sin\theta = 0$$

$$\sum M_B: \quad -2(10) - 1.5F_{CD}\sin\theta - 1.5F_{CE}\sin\theta = 0$$

3 eqns-3 unknowns.

Solving $F_{BD} = 13.3$ kN,

$\qquad F_{CD} = 11.7$ kN,

$\qquad F_{CE} = -28.3$ kN

Problem 6.135 For the truss in Problem 6.134, determine the axial forces in members DF, EF, and EG.

Solution: Use method of sections

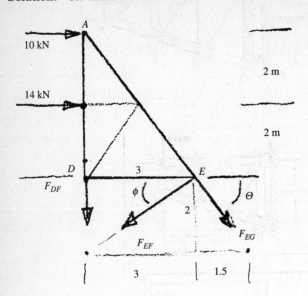

$$\tan\theta = \frac{2}{1.5}$$

$$\theta = 53.13°$$

$$\tan\phi = \frac{2}{3}$$

$$\phi = 33.69°$$

$$\sum F_x: \quad 24 + F_{EG}\cos\theta - F_{EF}\cos\phi = 0$$

$$\sum F_y: \quad -F_{DF} - F_{EF}\sin\phi - F_{EG}\sin\phi = 0$$

$$\sum M_E: \quad 3F_{DF} - 2(14) - 4(10) = 0$$

Solving, $\quad F_{EG} = -32.2$ kN (C)

$\qquad F_{DF} = 22.67$ kN (T)

$\qquad F_{EF} = 5.61$ kN (T)

Problem 6.136 The truss supports a 400-N load at G.
Determine the axial forces in members AC, CD, and CF

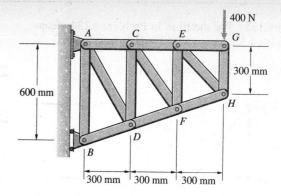

Solution: *The complete structure as a free body:* The sum of the moments about A:

$$\sum M_A = -900(400) + 600B = 0,$$

from which $B = 600$ N. The sum of forces:

$$\sum F_x = A_x + B = 0,$$

from which $A_x = -600$ N.

$$\sum F_y = A_y - 400 = 0,$$

from which $A_y = 400$ N.

The method of joints: The angle from the horizontal of element BD is

$$\theta = \tan^{-1}\left(\frac{300}{900}\right) = 18.43°.$$

The angle from the horizontal of element AD is

$$\alpha_{AD} = 90 - \tan^{-1}\left(\frac{300}{600 - 300\tan\theta}\right) = 59.04°.$$

The angle from the horizontal of element CF is

$$\alpha_{CF} = 90 - \tan^{-1}\left(\frac{300}{600(1 - \tan\theta)}\right) = 53.13°.$$

Joint B:

$$\sum F_x = B + BD\cos\theta = 0,$$

from which $BD = -632.5$ N (C)

$$\sum F_y = AB + BD\sin\theta = 0,$$

from which $AB = 200$ N (T)

Joint A:

$$\sum F_y = A_y - AD\sin\alpha_{AD} - AB = 0,$$

from which $AD = 233.2$ N (T)

$$\sum F_x = A_x + AC + AD\cos\alpha_{AD} = 0,$$

from which $\boxed{AC = 480 \text{ N } (T)}$

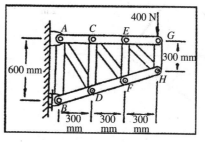

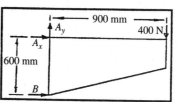

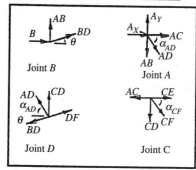

Joint D:

$$\sum F_x = -AD\cos\alpha_{AD} - BD\cos\theta + DF\cos\theta = 0,$$

from which $DF = -505.96$ N (C)

$$\sum F_y = AD\sin\alpha_{AD} + CD - BD\sin\theta + DF\sin\theta = 0,$$

from which $\boxed{CD = -240 \text{ N } (C)}$

Joint C:

$$\sum F_y = -CD - CF\sin\alpha_{CF} = 0,$$

from which $\boxed{CF = 300 \text{ N } (T)}$

Problem 6.137 Consider the truss in Problem 6.136. Determine the axial forces in members CE, EF, and EH.

Solution: Use the results of the solution of Problem 6.136:

$AC = 480$ N (T),

$CF = 300$ N (T),

$DF = -505.96$ N (C),

$\quad \theta = 18.4°$,

$\alpha_{CF} = 53.1°$.

The method of joints: The angle from the horizontal of element EH is

$$\alpha_{EH} = 90 - \tan^{-1}\left(\frac{300}{600 - 900\tan\theta}\right) = 45°$$

Joint C:

$$\sum F_x = -AC + CE + CF\cos\alpha_{CF} = 0,$$

from which $\boxed{CE = 300 \text{ N } (T)}$

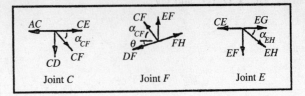

Joint C   Joint F   Joint E

Joint F:

$$\sum F_y = -CF\cos\alpha_{CF} - DF\cos\theta + FH\cos\theta = 0,$$

from which $FH = -316.2$ N (C)

$$\sum F_y = EF + CF\sin\alpha_{CF} - DF\sin\theta + FH\sin\theta = 0,$$

from which $\boxed{EF = -300 \text{ N } (C)}$

Joint E:

$$\sum F_y = -EH\sin\alpha_{EH} - EF = 0,$$

from which $\boxed{EH = 424.3 \text{ N } (T)}$

Problem 6.138 Consider the truss in Problem 6.136. Which members have the largest tensile and compressive forces, and what are their values?

Solution: The axial forces for all members have been obtained in Problems 6.136 and 6.137 except for members EG and GH. These are:

Joint E:

$$\sum F_x = -CE + EG + EH\cos\alpha_{EH} = 0,$$

from which $EG = 0$

Joint G:

$$\sum F_y = -GH - 400 = 0,$$

from which $GH = -400$ N (C).

This completes the determination for all members. A comparison of tensile forces shows that $\boxed{AC = 480 \text{ N } (T)}$ is the largest value, and a comparison of compressive forces shows that $\boxed{BD = -632.5 \text{ N } (C)}$ is the largest value.

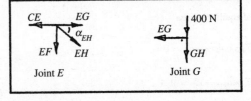

Joint E   Joint G

Problem 6.139 The Howe truss helps support a roof. Model the supports at A and G as roller supports. Use the method of joints to determine the axial forces in members BC, CD, CI, and CJ.

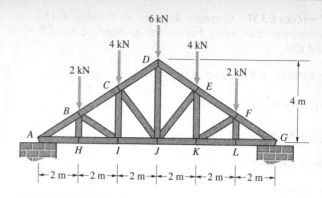

Solution: The free body diagrams for the entire truss and the required joints are shown.

The whole truss: The equations of equilibrium for the entire truss are:

$$\sum F_X = 0,$$

$$\sum F_Y = A_Y + G_Y - 18 \text{ kN} = 0.$$

Instead of using the moment equation here (it would work), we see that the loading is symmetric. Thus, $A_Y = G_Y = 9$ kN.

We need unit vectors along AB, BC, CD, (note that these are the same), and along BI, and CJ. We get

$$\mathbf{u}_{AB} = \mathbf{u}_{BC} = \mathbf{u}_{CD} = 0.832\mathbf{i} + 0.555\mathbf{j},$$

$$\mathbf{u}_{BI} = 0.832\mathbf{i} - 0.555\mathbf{j},$$

and $\mathbf{u}_{CJ} = 0.6\mathbf{i} - 0.8\mathbf{j}.$

Joint A:

The equations of equilibrium are

$$\sum F_X = T_{AB}u_{ABX} + T_{AH} = 0$$

and $\sum F_Y = T_{AB}u_{ABY} + A_Y = 0.$

Joint H: The equations of equilibrium are

$$\sum F_X = -T_{AH} + T_{HI} = 0,$$

and $\sum F_Y = T_{BH} = 0.$

Joint B:

$$\sum F_X = -T_{AB}u_{ABX} + T_{BC}u_{BCX} + T_{BI}u_{BIX} = 0,$$

$$\sum F_Y = -T_{AB}u_{ABY} + T_{BC}u_{BCY} + T_{BI}u_{BIY} - T_{BH} - 2 = 0,$$

Joint I:

$$\sum F_X = -T_{HI} + T_{IJ} - T_{BI}u_{BIX} = 0,$$

and $\sum F_Y = T_{CI} - T_{BI}u_{BIY} = 0,$

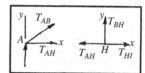

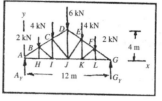

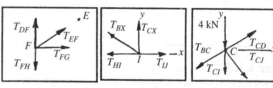

Joint C:

$$\sum F_X = -T_{BC}u_{BCX} + T_{CJ}u_{CJX} + T_{CD}u_{CDX} = 0,$$

$$\sum F_Y = -T_{BC}u_{BCY} + T_{CJ}u_{CJY} + T_{CD}u_{CDY} - T_{CI} - 4 = 0.$$

Solving these equations in sequence (we can solve at each joint before going to the next), we get

$$T_{AB} = -16.2 \text{ kN}, \quad T_{AH} = 13.5 \text{ kN}, \quad T_{BH} = 0 \text{ kN},$$

$$T_{HI} = 13.5 \text{ kN}, T_{BC} = -14.4 \text{ kN}, \quad T_{BI} = -1.80 \text{ kN},$$

$$T_{IJ} = 12.0 \text{ kN}, \quad T_{CI} = 1.00 \text{ kN}, \quad T_{CJ} = -4.17 \text{ kN},$$

and $T_{CD} = -11.4$ kN.

Problem 6.140 For the roof truss in Problem 6.139, use the method of sections to determine the axial forces in members CD, CJ, and IJ.

Solution: The free body diagram of the section is shown at the right. The support force at A is already known from the solution to Problem 6.139. The equations of equilibrium for the section are

$$\sum F_X = T_{CD}u_{CDX} + T_{CJ}u_{CJX} + T_{IJ} = 0,$$

$$\sum F_Y = T_{CD}u_{CDY} + T_{CJ}u_{CJY} + A_Y = 0,$$

and $\sum M_C = y_C T_{IJ} - 4A_Y = 0.$

Solving, we get

$$T_{IJ} = 12.0 \text{ kN},$$

$$T_{CJ} = -4.17 \text{ kN},$$

and $T_{CD} = -11.4$ kN.

Note that these values check with the values obtained in Problem 6.139.

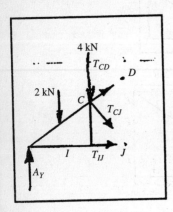

Problem 6.141 A speaker system is suspended from the truss by cables attached at D and E. The mass of the speaker system is 130 kg, and its weight acts at G. Determine the axial forces in members BC and CD.

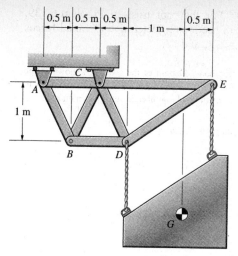

Solution: *The speaker as a free body:* The weight of the speaker is $W = 130(9.81) = 1275.3$ N. Make a cut through the suspension cables D, E, the sum of the moments about cable D is

$$\sum M_D = -(1)W + (1.5)E = 0,$$

from which $E = 850.2$ N. The sum of the forces:

$$\sum F_y = D + E - W = 0,$$

from which $D = 425.1$ N.

The structure as a free body: The sum of the moments about C is

$$\sum M_C = +(1)A - 0.5D - (2)E = 0,$$

from which $A = 1912.95$ N. The sum of the forces:

$$\sum F_y = -A + C_y - W = 0,$$

from which $C_y = -637.65$ N and

$$\sum F_x = C_x = 0.$$

The method of joints: The angle of member DE relative to the horizontal is $\alpha = \tan^{-1}\left(\dfrac{1}{1.5}\right) = 33.69°$. The angles of members AB, BC, and CD are $\beta = 90 - \tan^{-1}(0.5) = 63.43°$.

Joint E:

$$\sum F_y = -E - DE\sin\alpha = 0,$$

from which $DE = -1532.72$ N (C).

$$\sum F_x = -CE - DE\cos\alpha = 0,$$

from which $CE = 1275.3$ N (T)

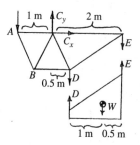

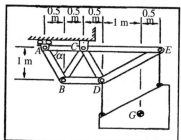

Joint E Joint D Joint C

Joint D:

$$\sum F_y = CD\sin\beta + DE\sin\alpha - D = 0,$$

from which $\boxed{CD = 1425.8 \text{ N } (T)}$

Joint C:

$$\sum F_y = -CD\sin\beta - BC\sin\beta + C_y = 0,$$

from which $\boxed{BC = 2138.7 \text{ N } (T)}$

Problem 6.142 Consider the system described in Problem 6.141. If each member of the truss will safely support a tensile force of 5 kN and a compressive force of 3 kN, what is the maximum safe value of the mass of the speaker system?

Solution: In the solution of Problem 6.141, the axial forces have been determined for four of the seven elements in the structure. The others are:

Joint D:

$$\sum F_x = -BD + DE\cos\alpha = 0$$

from which $BD = -1275.7$ N (C)

Joint C:

$$\sum F_x = -AC + CE - BC\cos\beta + CD\cos\beta = 0,$$

from which $AC = 956.5$ N (T)

Joint B:

$$\sum F_y = BC\sin\beta + AB\sin\beta = 0,$$

from which $AB = -2138.7$ N (C)

The values are tabulated:

Member	Axial F, kN	Type
DE	−1.533	(C)
CE	1.275	(T)
CD	1.425	(T)
BC	2.138	(T)
BD	−1.275	(C)
AC	0.956	(T)
AB	−2.138	(C)

The maximum tension occurs in element BC, and the maximum compression occurs in element AB. Since the system is linear, the ratio of the axial forces to two distinct mass loadings will be equal to the ratio of the masses: $\dfrac{T}{T_{SAFE}} = \dfrac{m}{m_T}$. Similarly, $\dfrac{C}{C_{SAFE}} = \dfrac{m}{m_C}$. The safe loading for max tensile forces

$$m_T = \left(\frac{T_{SAFE}}{T}\right)m = \left(\frac{5000}{BC}\right)130 = 303.9\ldots = 304 \text{ kg.}$$

Similarly for compressive forces,

$$m_T = \left(\frac{C_{SAFE}}{C}\right)m = \left(\frac{-3000}{AB}\right)130 = 182.35\ldots = 182.4 \text{ kg.}$$

The compressive force safety limit controls the loading, and the maximum safe mass is $\boxed{m = 182.4 \text{ kg}}$

Joint D   Joint C   Joint B

Problem 6.143 Determine the forces on member ABC, presenting your answers as shown in Fig. 6.35. Obtain the answer in two ways:

(a) When you draw the free-body diagrams of the individual members, place the 400-lb load on the free-body diagram of member ABC.

(b) When you draw the free-body diagrams of the individual members, place the 400-lb load on the free-body diagram of member CD.

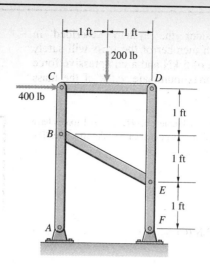

Solution: The angle of element BE relative to the horizontal is $\alpha = \tan^{-1}\left(\frac{1}{2}\right) = 26.57°$.

The complete structure as a free body: The sum of the moments about A:

$$\sum M_A = -3(400) - 1(200) + 2F_y = 0$$

from which $F_y = 700$ lb. The sum of forces:

$$\sum F_y = A_y + F_y - 200 = 0,$$

from which $\boxed{A_y = -500 \text{ lb}}$.

$$\sum F_x = A_x + F_x + 400 = 0.$$

(a) *Element CD:* The sum of the moments about D:

$$\sum M_D = 200 + 2C_y = 0,$$

from which $\boxed{C_y = -100 \text{ lb}}$.

$$\sum F_y = -D_y - C_y - 200 = 0,$$

from which $D_y = -100$.

$$\sum F_x = -C_x - D_x = 0,$$

from which $D_x = -C_x$.

Element DEF: The sum of the moments about F:

$$\sum M_F = -3D_x + B\cos\alpha = 0,$$

from which $D_x = B\left(\frac{\cos\alpha}{3}\right)$.

$$\sum F_y = F_y + B\sin\alpha + D_y = 0,$$

from which $\boxed{B = \dfrac{-700 + 100}{\sin\alpha} = -1341.6 \text{ lb}}$, and $D_x = -400$ lb

Element ABC:

$$\sum M_A = -2B\cos\alpha - 3(400) - 3C_x = 0.$$

The sum of the forces

$$\sum F_y = C_y - B\sin\alpha + A_y = 0,$$

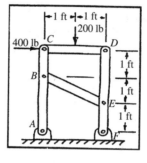

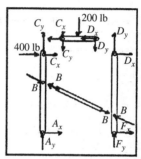

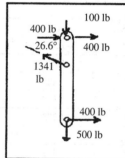

from which *Check:*

$$B = \frac{500 + 100}{\sin\alpha} = -1341.6 \text{ lb}.$$

check. From above: $\boxed{C_x = -D_x = 400 \text{ lb}}$.

$$\sum F_x = 400 + C_x + B\cos\alpha + A_x = 0,$$

from which $\boxed{A_x = 400 \text{ lb}}$.

(b) When the 400 lb load is applied to element CD instead, the following changes to the equilibrium equations occur: *Element CD:*

$$\sum F_x = -C_x - D_x + 400 = 0,$$

from which $C_x + D_x = 400$. *Element ABC:*

$$\sum F_x = C_x + A_x - B\cos\alpha = 0.$$

Element DEF: No changes. The changes in the solution for Element ABC $C_x = 800$ lb when the external load is removed, instead of $C_x = 400$ lb when the external load is applied, so that the total load applied to point C is the same in both cases.

Problem 6.144 The mass $m = 120$ kg. Determine the forces on member ABC.

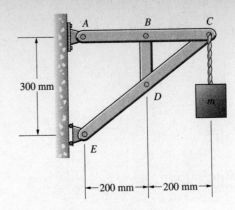

Solution: The weight of the hanging mass is given by

$$W = mg = 120 \text{ kg} \left(9.81 \frac{\text{m}}{\text{s}^2}\right) = 1177 \text{ N}.$$

The complete structure as a free body: The equilibrium equations are:

$$\sum F_X = A_X + E_X = 0,$$

$$\sum F_Y = A_Y - W = 0,$$

and $\sum M_A = 0.3E_X - 0.4W = 0.$

Solving, we get

$$A_X = -1570 \text{ N},$$

$$A_Y = 1177 \text{ N},$$

and $E_X = 1570$ N.

Element ABC: The equilibrium equations are

$$\sum F_X = A_x + C_X = 0,$$

$$\sum F_Y = A_Y + C_Y - B_Y - W = 0,$$

and: $\sum M_A = -0.2B_Y + 0.4c_Y - 0.4W = 0.$

Solution gives $B_Y = 2354$ N (member BD is in tension),

$$C_X = 1570 \text{ N},$$

and $C_Y = 2354$ N.

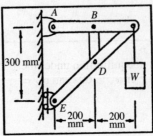

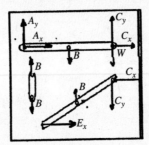

Problem 6.145 Determine the forces on member ABC, presenting your answers as shown in Fig. 6.35.

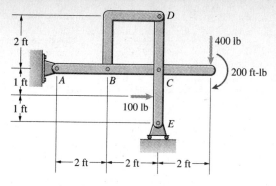

Solution: *The complete structure as a free body:* The sum of the moments:

$$\sum M_A = 100(1) - 400(6) - 200 + 4E = 0,$$

from which $E = 625$ lb. The sum of the forces:

$$\sum F_y = A_y + E - 400 = 0,$$

from which $A_y = -225$ lb.

$$\sum F_x = A_x + 100 = 0,$$

from which $A_x = -100$ lb. These results are used as a check on the solution below.

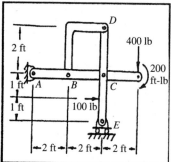

Element ECD: (See the free body diagram.) The sum of the moments about E:

$$\sum M_E = -4D_x - 2C_x - 100 = 0,$$

from which (1) $4D_x + 2C_x = -100$. The sum of the forces:

$$\sum F_x = D_x + C_x + 100 = 0,$$

from which (2) $D_x + C_x = -100$.

$$\sum F_y = E + C_y + D_y = 0,$$

thus (3) $D_y + C_y + E = 0$.

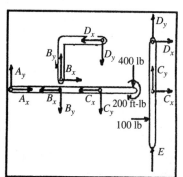

Element BD: The sum of the moments about B:

$$\sum M_B = 2D_x - 2D_y = 0,$$

from which (4) $D_x - D_y = 0$. The sum of the forces:

$$\sum F_x = B_x - D_x = 0,$$

from which (5) $B_x - D_x = 0$.

$$\sum F_y = B_y - D_y = 0,$$

from which (6) $B_y - D_y = 0$

Element ABC: The sum of the moments about A:

$$\sum M_A = -2B_y - 4C_y - 200 - 6(400) = 0,$$

from which (7) $B_y + 2C_y = -1300$.

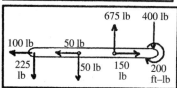

The sum of the forces:

$$\sum F_x = A_x - B_x - C_x = 0,$$

from which (8) $A_x - B_x - C_x = 0$.

$$\sum F_y = A_y - B_y - C_y - 400 = 0,$$

from which (9) $A_y - B_y - C_y = 400$. These nine equations are solved for the nine reactions The reactions are $D_X = 50$ lb, $D_Y = 50$ lb,:

$$C_X = -150 \text{ lb}, \quad C_Y = -675 \text{ lb}, \quad B_X = 50 \text{ lb},$$

$$B_Y = 50 \text{ lb}, \quad A_X = -100 \text{ lb}, \quad A_Y = -225 \text{ lb},$$

and $E = 625$ lb.

Problem 6.146 Determine the force exerted on the bolt by the bolt cutters and the magnitude of the force the members exert on each other at the pin connection A.

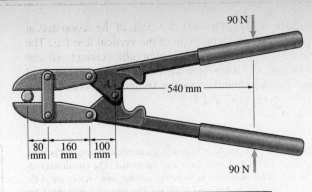

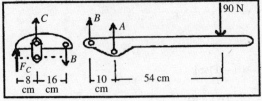

Solution: *Element AB:* The moment about A is

$$\sum M_A = -10B - 54F = 0,$$

where $F = 90$ N. From which $B = -486$ N. The sum of the forces:

$$\sum F_y = A + B - F = 0,$$

from which $\boxed{A = 576 \text{ N}}$

Element BC: The moment about C:

$$\sum M_C = -16B - 8F_C = 0,$$

from which the cutting force is $\boxed{F_C = 972 \text{ N}}$

Problem 6.147 The 600-lb weight of the scoop acts at a point 1 ft 6 in. to the right of the vertical line CE. The line ADE is horizontal. The hydraulic actuator AB can be treated as a two-force member. Determine the axial force in the hydraulic actuator AB and the forces exerted on the scoop at C and E.

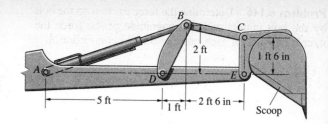

Solution: The free body diagrams are shown at the right. Place the coordinate origin at A with the x axis horizontal. The coordinates (in ft) of the points necessary to write the needed unit vectors are A (0, 0), B (6, 2), C (8.5, 1.5), and D (5, 0). The unit vectors needed for this problem are

$$\mathbf{u}_{BA} = -0.949\mathbf{i} - 0.316\mathbf{j},$$

$$\mathbf{u}_{BC} = 0.981\mathbf{i} - 0.196\mathbf{j},$$

and $\mathbf{u}_{BD} = -0.447\mathbf{i} - 0.894\mathbf{j}.$

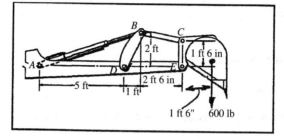

The scoop: The equilibrium equations for the scoop are

$$\sum F_X = -T_{CB}u_{BCX} + E_X = 0,$$

$$\sum F_Y = -T_{CB}u_{BCY} + E_Y - 600 = 0,$$

and $\sum M_C = 1.5E_X - 1.5(600 \text{ lb}) = 0.$

Solving, we get

$$E_X = 600 \text{ lb},$$

$$E_Y = 480 \text{ lb},$$

and $T_{CB} = 611.9$ lb.

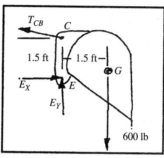

Joint B: The equilibrium equations for the scoop are

$$\sum F_X = T_{BA}u_{BAX} + T_{BD}u_{BDX} + T_{CB}u_{BCX} = 0,$$

and $\sum F_Y = T_{BA}u_{BAY} + T_{BD}u_{BDY} + T_{CB}u_{BCY} = 0.$

Solving, we get

$$T_{BA} = 835 \text{ lb},$$

and $T_{BD} = -429$ lb.

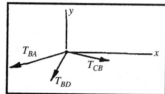

Problem 6.148 This structure supports a conveyor belt used in a lignite mining operation. The cables connected to the belt exert the force F at J. As a result of the counterweight $W = 8$ kip, the reaction at E and the vertical reaction at D are equal. Determine F and the axial forces in members BG and EF.

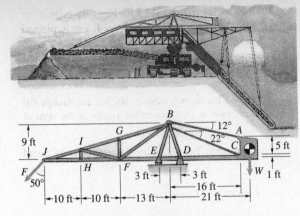

Solution: *The complete structure as a free body:* The moments about point J: using the fact that the vertical reactions at E and D are equal:

$$\sum M_J = -54W + 66D_y = 0$$

from which $E = D_y = 6.545$ kip. The sum of forces:

$$\sum F_y = -F\cos(50°) + 2D_y - W = 0,$$

from which $\boxed{F = 7.920 \text{ kip}}$.

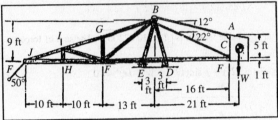

The method of sections: Make a cut through BG, BF, and EF. Consider the section to the left of the cut. The angle of member BG from the horizontal is

$$\alpha = \tan^{-1}\left(\frac{9}{33}\right) = 15.26°.$$

The angle of member BF from the horizontal is

$$\beta = \tan^{-1}\left(\frac{9}{13}\right) = 34.7°.$$

The length of member FG is $L_{FG} = 20\tan\alpha$.

The section as a free body: The sum of the moments about the point F:

$$\sum M_F = 20F\cos(50°) - L_{FG}BG\cos\alpha = 0,$$

from which $\boxed{BG = 19.35 \text{ kip } (T)}$.

The sum of the forces:

$$\sum F_y = BF\sin\beta + BG\sin\alpha - F\cos(50°) = 0,$$

from which $BF = 0$

$$\sum F_y = EF + BF\cos\beta + BG\cos\alpha - F\sin(50°) = 0,$$

from which $\boxed{EF = -12.6 \text{ kip } (C)}$.

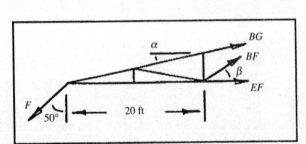

Problem 6.149 Consider the structure described in Problem 6.148. The counterweight $W = 8$ kip is pinned at D and is supported by the cable ABC, which passes over a pulley at A. What is the tension in the cable, and what forces are exerted on the counterweight at D?

Solution: Make a cut through cable at AB, BC, and through CD near to the pinned joint at D. Consider the section to the right of the cut.

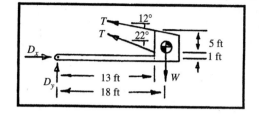

The section as a free body: The sum of the moments about the pinned joint at D is:

$$\sum M_D = 13T \sin(22°) + 1T \cos(22°)$$

$$+ 6T \cos(12°) + 13T \sin(12°) - 18W = 0,$$

from which the cable tension is $\boxed{T = 10.022 \text{ kip}}$. The sum of forces:

$$\sum F_y = T \sin(22°) + T \sin(12°) - W + D_y^{CD} = 0,$$

from which $\boxed{D_y^{CD} = 2.162 \text{ kip}}$

$$\sum F_x = T \cos(22°) + T \cos(12°) + D_x^{CD} = 0,$$

from which $\boxed{D_x^{CD} = -19.095 \text{ kip}}$. This is the force exerted on the pinned joint at D by member CD.

575

Problem 6.150 The weights $W_1 = 4$ kN and $W_2 = 10$ kN. Determine the forces on member $ACDE$ at points A and E.

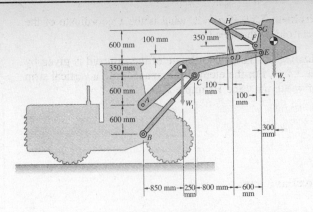

Solution: *The complete structure as a free body:* The horizontal distance from A to C is 1100 mm. The vertical distance is 600 mm. The horizontal distances to the action line of the weights W_1, W_2 are 850 mm and 2800 mm. The angle of the hydraulic lifter BC relative to the horizontal is

$$\alpha = \tan^{-1}\left(\frac{1200}{1100}\right) = 47.49°.$$

The sum of the moments about the point A is

$$\sum M_A = -850W_1 + 2800W_2 + 1100BC\sin\alpha - 600BC\cos\alpha = 0,$$

from which $BC = 77.45$ kN. The sum of the forces:

$$\sum F_x = A_x + BC\cos\alpha = 0,$$

from which $A_x = -52.33$ kN

$$\sum F_y = A_y + BC\sin\alpha - W_1 - W_2 = 0,$$

from which $A_Y = -43.09$ kN. These results are to be used as a check on the solution below.

The angle of member DH relative to the horizontal is

$$\beta = \tan^{-1}\left(\frac{600}{100}\right) = 80.54°.$$

The angle of the force F relative to the horizontal is

$$\phi = \tan^{-1}\left(\frac{350}{600}\right) = 30.25°.$$

The bucket as a free body: The sum of the moments about point E:

$$\sum M_E = 500G - 300W_2 - F(150\cos\phi - 100\sin\phi) = 0.$$

The sum of the forces on the bucket:

$$\sum F_x = E_x + F\cos\phi - G = 0,$$

and $\sum F_y = E_y - W_2 - F\sin\phi = 0.$

The linkage H as a free body: The sum of the forces:

$$\sum F_x = -F\cos\phi + G + D\cos\beta = 0,$$

and $\sum F_y = F\sin\phi - D\sin\beta = 0.$

The member ACDE as a free body: The sum of the moments about point A:

$$\sum M_A = -850W_1 - C\,(600\cos\alpha - 1100\sin\alpha)$$
$$+ D\,(1900\sin\beta + 950\cos\beta) + 2500E_y - 1050E_x = 0.$$

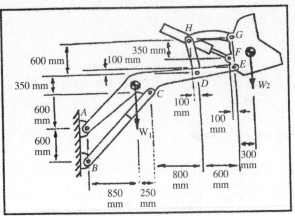

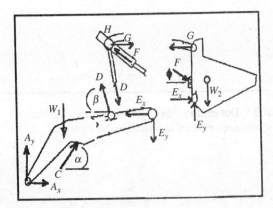

The sum of forces:

$$\sum F_x = A_x + C\cos\alpha - D\cos\beta + E_x = 0,$$

and $\sum F_y = A_y - W_1 + C\sin\alpha + D\sin\beta + E_y = 0.$

These equilibrium conditions lead to 8 equations in 8 unknowns, which are solved by iteration using **TK Solver Plus** The results:

$\boxed{G = 7.53 \text{ kN}}$, $\boxed{D = 4.93 \text{ kN}}$, $\boxed{F = 9.65 \text{ kN}}$,

$\boxed{E_x = 0.811 \text{ kN}}$, $\boxed{E_y = -14.9 \text{ kN}}$, $\boxed{A_x = -52.3 \text{ kN}}$,

$\boxed{A_y = -43.1 \text{ kN}}$, and $\boxed{C = 77.4 \text{ kN}}$:

The last three values check the results obtained from the solution for the complete structure as a free body.

Problem 7.1 If $a = 2$, what is the x coordinate of the centroid of the area?

Strategy: The x coordinate of the centroid is given by Eq. (7.6). For the element of area dA, use a vertical strip of width dx. (See Example 7.1).

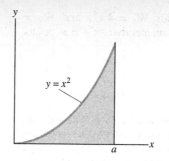

Solution:

$$\mathbf{x} = \frac{\int x\,dA}{\int dA}$$

$$\mathbf{x} = \frac{\int_0^a x(y\,dx)}{\int_0^a y\,dx}$$

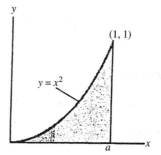

Substituting $y = x^2$, we get

$$\mathbf{x} = \frac{\int_0^a x^3\,dx}{\int_0^a x^2\,dx} = \frac{\left[\dfrac{x^4}{4}\right]\Big|^a}{\left[\dfrac{x^3}{3}\right]\Big|_0} = \frac{3a}{4}$$

For $a = 2$

$$\mathbf{x} = \frac{3}{2}$$

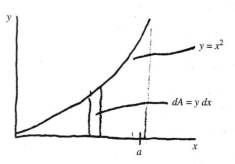

Problem 7.2 Determine the y coordinate of the centroid of the area shown in Problem 7.1 if $a = 3$.

Solution:

$$\mathbf{y} = \frac{\int y\,dA}{\int dA}$$

$$\mathbf{y} = \frac{\int_0^a \frac{1}{2}y(y\,dx)}{\int_0^a (y\,dx)}$$

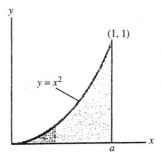

Substituting $y = x^2$, we get

$$\mathbf{y} = \frac{\int_0^a \frac{1}{2}x^4\,dx}{\int_0^a x^2\,dx} = \frac{\frac{1}{2}\left[\dfrac{x^5}{5}\right]_0^a}{\left[\dfrac{x^3}{3}\right]_0^a} = \frac{\dfrac{a^5}{2.5}}{\dfrac{a^3}{3}}$$

$$\mathbf{y} = \frac{3}{10}a^2$$

For $a = 3$, $\mathbf{y} = \dfrac{27}{10}$

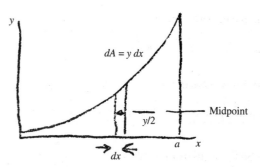

Problem 7.3 If the x coordinate of the centroid of the area is $\mathbf{x} = 2$, what is the value of a?

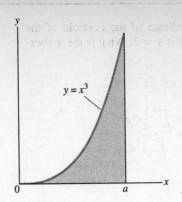

$y = x^3$

0   a

Solution:

$$\mathbf{x} = \frac{\displaystyle\int_A x\,dA}{\displaystyle\int_A dA}$$

$$\mathbf{x} = \frac{\displaystyle\int_0^a x(y\,dx)}{\displaystyle\int_0^a (y\,dx)}.$$

Substituting $y = x^3$,

$$\mathbf{x} = \frac{\displaystyle\int_0^a x^4\,dx}{\displaystyle\int_0^a x^3\,dx} = \frac{\left[\dfrac{x^5}{5}\right]_0^a}{\left[\dfrac{x^4}{4}\right]_0^a} = \frac{4a}{5}$$

If $\mathbf{x} = 2$, $2 = \dfrac{4a}{5}$ and $a = \dfrac{10}{4} = 2.5$

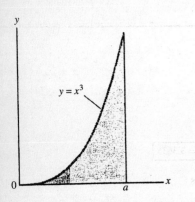

$y = x^3$

0   a

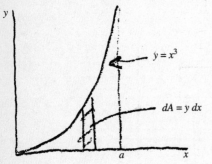

$y = x^3$

$dA = y\,dx$

a

Problem 7.4 The x coordinate of the centroid of the area shown in Problem 7.3 is $\mathbf{x} = 2$. What is the y coordinate of the centroid?

Solution: From Problem 7.4, $a = 2.5$

$$\mathbf{y} = \frac{\int y\,dA}{\int dA} = \frac{\int_0^{2.5} \frac{1}{2} y(y\,dx)}{\int_0^{2.5} y\,dx} = \frac{\int_0^{2.5} \frac{1}{2} x^6\,dx}{\int_0^{2.5} x^3\,dx}$$

$$\mathbf{y} = \frac{\left[\frac{x^7}{14}\right]\Big|_0^{2.5}}{\left[\frac{x^4}{4}\right]\Big|_0} = \frac{4x^3}{14}\Big|_0^{2.5} = 4.46$$

$\mathbf{y} = 4.46$

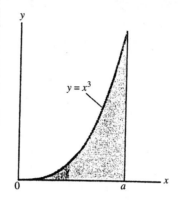

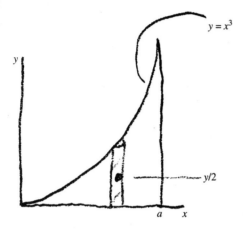

Problem 7.5 Consider the area in Problem 7.3. The "center of the area" is defined to be the point for which there is as much area to the right of the point as to the left of it and as much area above the point as below it. If $a = 4$, what are the x coordinate of the center of area and the x coordinate of the centroid?

Solution: *Center of Area:* Let X be the coordinate of the center of the area. The area to the left of X is

$$A_L = \int_0^X x^3\,dx = \frac{X^4}{4}.$$

The area to the right is

$$A_R = \int_X^a x^3\,dx = \frac{a^4}{4} - \frac{X^4}{4}.$$

Equating the two areas,

$$\frac{a^4}{4} - \frac{X^4}{4} = \frac{X^4}{4},$$

from which $a^4 = 2X^4$

or $X = a(2)^{-\frac{1}{4}}$.

For $a = 4$, $\boxed{X = 0.8408(4) = 3.3636}$

The centroid: The centroid is

$$\mathbf{x} = \frac{\int_0^a x^4\,dx}{\int_0^a x^3\,dx} = \frac{4a}{5}.$$

For $a = 4$, $\boxed{\mathbf{x} = \frac{16}{5} = 3.200}$

Problem 7.6 Determine the x coordinate of the centroid of the area and compare your answer to the value given in Appendix B.

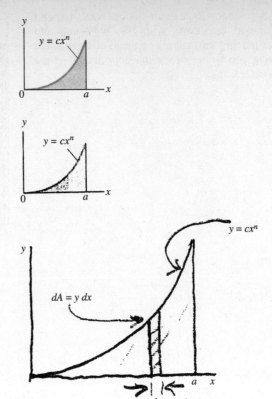

Solution:

$$x = \frac{\int x\, dA}{\int dA}$$

$$x = \frac{\int_0^a x(y\, dx)}{\int_0^a y\, dx} = \frac{\int_0^a x\mathcal{C}x^n\, dx}{\int_0^a \mathcal{C}x^n\, dx}$$

$$x = \frac{\left[\frac{x^{n+2}}{(n+2)}\right]_0^a}{\left[\frac{x^{n+1}}{(n+1)}\right]_0^a} = \frac{(n+1)}{(n+2)}a$$

$$x = a\frac{(n+1)}{(n+2)}$$

Checks with result in Appendix

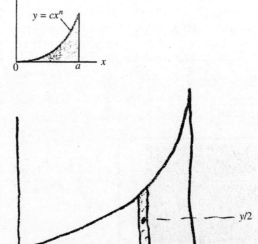

Problem 7.7 Determine the y coordinate of the centroid of the area and compare your answer to the value given in Appendix B.

Solution:

$$y = \frac{\int y\, dA}{\int dA}$$

$$y = \frac{\int_0^a y\left(\frac{1}{2}y\, dx\right)}{\int_0^a y\, dx} = \frac{1}{2}\frac{\int_0^a y^2\, dx}{\int_0^a y\, dx}$$

$$y = \frac{\int_0^a c^2 x^{2n}\, dx}{2\int_0^a cx^n\, dx} = \frac{c^2}{c}\frac{\left(\frac{x^{2n+1}}{(2n+1)}\right)\Big|_0^a}{\left(\frac{x^{n+1}}{(n+1)}\right)\Big|_0}$$

$$y = \frac{c}{2}\frac{(n+1)}{(2n+1)}a^n$$

Checks with Appendix

580

Problem 7.8 Suppose that an art student wants to paint a panel of wood as shown, with the horizontal and vertical lines passing through the centroid of the painted area, and asks you to determine the coordinates of the centroid. What are they?

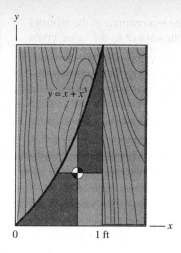

Solution: *The area:*

$$A = \int_0^1 (x + x^3)\,dx = \left[\frac{x^2}{2} + \frac{x^4}{4} \right]_0^1 = \frac{3}{4}.$$

The x-coordinate:

$$\int_0^1 x(x + x^3)\,dx = \left[\frac{x^3}{3} + \frac{x^5}{5} \right]_0^1 = \frac{8}{15}.$$

Divide by the area: $\boxed{\mathbf{x} = \dfrac{32}{45} = 0.711}$

The y-coordinate: The element of area is $dA = (1 - x)\,dy$. Note that $dy = (1 + 3x^2)\,dx$, hence $dA = (1 - x)(1 + 3x^2)\,dx$. Thus

$$\mathbf{y}A = \int_A y\,dA = \int_0^4 (x + x^3)(1 - x)(1 + 3x^2)\,dx,$$

from which

$$\int_0^1 (x - x^2 + 4x^3 - 4x^4 + 3x^5 - 3x^6)\,dx$$

$$= \frac{1}{2} - \frac{1}{3} + \frac{4}{4} - \frac{4}{5} + \frac{3}{6} - \frac{3}{7} = 0.4381.$$

Divide by A $\boxed{\mathbf{y} = 0.5841}$

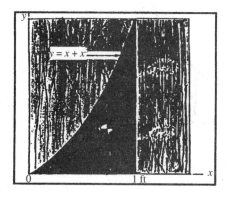

Problem 7.9 The y coordinate of the centroid of the area is $\mathbf{y} = 1.063$. Determine the value of the constant c and the x coordinate of the centroid.

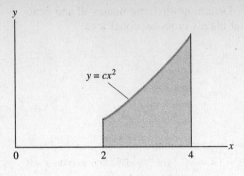

Solution:

$$\mathbf{y} = \frac{\int y\, dA}{\int dA}$$

$$dA = y\, dx$$

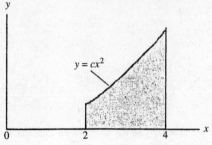

$$\mathbf{y} = \frac{\int_2^4 \frac{y}{2} y\, dx}{\int_2^4 y\, dx} = \frac{\frac{1}{2}\int_2^4 C^2 x^4\, dx}{\int_2^4 Cx^2\, dx}$$

$$\mathbf{y} = \frac{C^2\left(\frac{x^5}{5}\right)\Big|_2^4}{2C\left(\frac{x^3}{3}\right)\Big|_2^4} = \frac{C\left[\frac{1024}{5} - \frac{32}{5}\right]}{2\left[\frac{64}{3} - \frac{8}{3}\right]}$$

$$\mathbf{y} = 5.314C$$

But $\mathbf{y} = 1.063$ $\quad \therefore C = 0.200$

Now we have C known and $y = Cx^2$

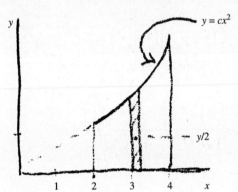

$$\mathbf{x} = \frac{\int x\, dA}{\int dA} = \frac{\int_2^4 Cx^3\, dx}{\int_2^4 Cx^2\, dx} = \frac{\left(\frac{x^4}{4}\right)\Big|_2^4}{\left(\frac{x^3}{3}\right)\Big|_2^4}$$

$$\mathbf{x} = \frac{\frac{(256 - 16)}{4}}{\frac{(64 - 8)}{3}} = 3.214$$

$$\mathbf{x} = 3.214$$

Problem 7.10 Determine the coordinates of the centroid of the metal plate's cross-sectional area.

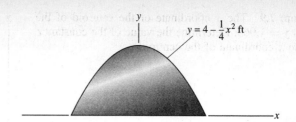

Solution: Let dA be a vertical strip:

The area $dA = y\, dx = \left(4 - \dfrac{1}{4}x^2\right) dx$. The curve intersects the x axis

where $4 - \dfrac{1}{4}x^2 = 0$, or $x = \pm 4$.

Therefore

$$\mathbf{x} = \frac{\displaystyle\int_A x\, dA}{\displaystyle\int_A dA} = \frac{\displaystyle\int_{-4}^{4}\left(4x - \frac{1}{4}x^3\right) dx}{\displaystyle\int_{-4}^{4}\left(4 - \frac{1}{4}x^2\right) dx} = \frac{\left[2x^2 - \dfrac{x^4}{16}\right]_{-4}^{4}}{\left[4x - \dfrac{x^3}{12}\right]_{-4}^{4}} = 0.$$

To determine **y**, let y in equation (7.7) be the height of the midpoint of the vertical strip:

$$\mathbf{y} = \frac{\displaystyle\int_A y\, dA}{\displaystyle\int_A dA} = \frac{\displaystyle\int_{-4}^{4} \frac{1}{2}\left(4 - \frac{1}{4}x^2\right)\left[\left(4 - \frac{1}{4}x^2\right) dx\right]}{\displaystyle\int_{-4}^{4}\left(4 - \frac{1}{4}x^2\right) dx}$$

$$= \frac{\displaystyle\int_{-4}^{4}\left(8 - x^2 + \frac{1}{32}x^4\right) dx}{\displaystyle\int_{-4}^{4}\left(4 - \frac{x^2}{4}\right) dx} = \frac{\left[8x - \dfrac{x^3}{3} + \dfrac{x^5}{5(32)}\right]_{-4}^{4}}{\left[4x - \dfrac{x^3}{12}\right]_{-4}^{4}}$$

$$= \frac{34.1}{21.3} = 1.6 \text{ ft.}$$

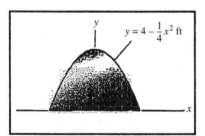

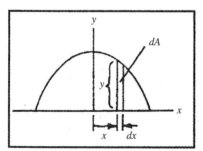

Problem 7.11 An architect wants to build a wall with the profile shown. To estimate the effects of wind loads, he must determine the wall's area and the coordinates of its centroid. What are they?

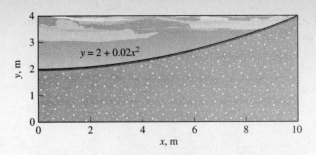

Solution:

$$\text{Area} = \int_0^{10} y\,dx = \int_0^{10} (2 + 0.02x^2)\,dx$$

$$\text{Area} = \left[2x + 0.02\frac{x^3}{3}\right]_0^{10} = 26.67 \text{ m}^2$$

$$dA = y\,dx = (2 + 0.02x^2)\,dx$$

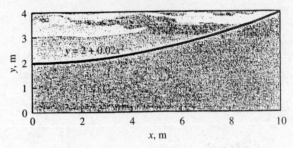

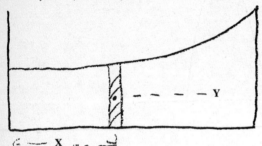

$$\overline{x} = \frac{\int_0^{10} x\,dA}{\int_0^{10} dA} = \frac{\int_0^{10}(2x + 0.02x^3)\,dx}{26.67}$$

$$\overline{x} = \frac{\left(2\frac{x^2}{2} + 0.02\frac{x^4}{4}\right)\Big|_0^{10}}{26.67} \text{ m}$$

$$\overline{x} = \frac{\left(100 + (0.02)\frac{10^4}{4}\right)}{26.67} = \frac{150}{26.67}$$

$$\overline{x} = 5.62 \text{ m}$$

$$\overline{y} = \frac{\int_0^{10}\left(\frac{y}{2}\right)y\,dx}{\int_0^{10} dA} = \frac{1}{(2)}\frac{\int_0^{10}(2 + 0.02x^2)^2\,dx}{(26.67)}$$

$$\overline{y} = \frac{1}{2(26.67)}\int_0^{10}(4 + 0.08x^2 + 0.0004x^4)\,dx$$

$$\overline{y} = \frac{\left(4x + 0.08\left(\frac{x^3}{3}\right) + 0.0004\left(\frac{x^5}{5}\right)\right)\Big|_0^{10}}{2(26.67)}$$

$$\overline{y} = \frac{74.67}{53.34}$$

$$\overline{y} = 1.40 \text{ m}$$

Problem 7.12 Determine the x coordinate of the centroid of the area.

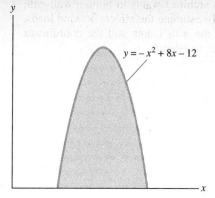

Solution: First, we must determine where the curve intersects the x-axis. These will be the limits of our integration.

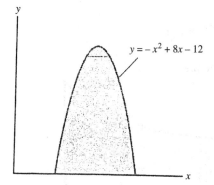

Set $y = 0$

$$0 = -x^2 + 8x - 12$$

or $x^2 - 8x + 12 = 0$

$$(x - 6)(x - 2) = 0$$

Thus, $y = 0$ at $x = 2$ and $x = 6$.

$$\mathbf{x} = \frac{\int_2^6 x\,dA}{\int_2^6 dA} = \frac{\int_2^6 x(y\,dx)}{\int_2^6 (y\,dx)}$$

$$\mathbf{x} = \frac{\int_2^6 (-x^3 + 8x^2 - 12x)\,dx}{\int_2^6 (-x^2 + 8x - 12)\,dx}$$

$$\mathbf{x} = \frac{\left[-\dfrac{x^4}{4} + 8\dfrac{x^3}{3} - 12\dfrac{x^2}{2}\right]_2^6}{\left[-\dfrac{x^3}{3} + 8\dfrac{x^2}{2} - 12x\right]_2^6} = \frac{42.67}{10.67} = 4$$

Note: Once we had the limits of integration, the result was apparent due to symmetry.

Problem 7.13   Determine the y coordinate of the centroid of the area shown in Problem 7.12.

Solution: From Problem 7.12, the limits of integration are $x = 2$ and $x = 6$. The area is 10.67 units.

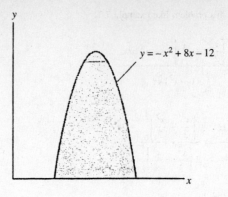

$y = -x^2 + 8x - 12$

$$\mathbf{y} = \frac{\int_2^6 \left(\frac{y}{2}\right) dA}{\text{Area}} = \frac{\frac{1}{2}\int_2^6 y^2\, dx}{\text{Area}}$$

$$\mathbf{y} = \left(\frac{1}{2}\right)\frac{\int_2^6 (-x^2 + 8x - 12)^2\, dx}{\text{Area}}$$

$$\mathbf{y} = \frac{1}{2}\frac{\int_2^6 (x^4 - 16x^3 + 88x^2 - 192x + 144)\, dx}{\text{Area}}$$

$$\mathbf{y} = \frac{1}{2}\frac{\left[\frac{x^5}{5} - 16\frac{x^4}{4} + 88\frac{x^3}{3} - 192\frac{x^2}{2} + 144x\right]\Big|_2^6}{(10.67)}$$

$$\mathbf{y} = \frac{34.13}{21.33} = 1.6$$

$$\mathbf{y} = 1.6$$

Problem 7.14   Determine the x coordinate of the centroid of the area.

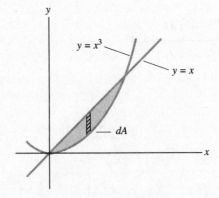

$y = x^3$

$y = x$

Solution: Work this problem like Example 7.2

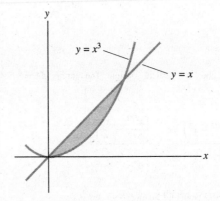

$y = x^3$

$y = x$

dA

$$\mathbf{x} = \frac{\int_0^1 x\, dA}{\int_0^1 dA} = \frac{\int_0^1 x(x - x^3)\, dx}{\int_0^1 (x - x^3)\, dx}$$

$$\mathbf{x} = \frac{\left[\frac{x^3}{3} - \frac{x^5}{5}\right]_0^1}{\left[\frac{x^2}{2} - \frac{x^4}{4}\right]_0^1} = \frac{\left(\frac{1}{3} - \frac{1}{5}\right)}{\left(\frac{1}{2} - \frac{1}{4}\right)} = \frac{\frac{2}{15}}{\frac{1}{4}} = 0.533$$

$$\mathbf{x} = 0.533$$

Problem 7.15 Determine the y coordinate of the centroid of the area shown in Problem 7.14.

Solution: Solve this problem like example 7.2.

$$\bar{y} = \frac{\int_A y\,dA}{\int_A dA} = \frac{\int_0^1 \left[\frac{1}{2}(x+x^3)\right](x-x^3)\,dx}{\int_0^1 (x-x^3)\,dx}$$

$$\bar{y} = \frac{1}{2}\frac{\int_0^1 (x^2 - x^6)\,dx}{\int_0^1 (x-x^3)\,dx} = \frac{\left[\frac{x^3}{3} - \frac{x^7}{7}\right]_0^1}{2\left[\frac{x^2}{2} - \frac{x^4}{4}\right]_0^1}$$

$$\bar{y} = \frac{\left[\frac{1}{3} - \frac{1}{7}\right]}{2\left[\frac{1}{2} - \frac{1}{4}\right]} = \frac{\left(\frac{4}{21}\right)}{2} = \frac{8}{21} = 0.381$$

$$\bar{y} = 0.381$$

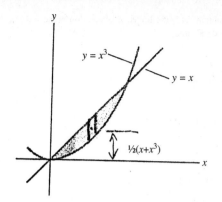

Problem 7.16 Determine the coordinates of the centroid of the area.

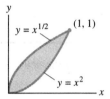

Solution: Let dA be a vertical strip: The area $dA = (x^{1/2} - x^2)\,dx$, so

$$\bar{x} = \frac{\int_A x\,dA}{\int_A dA} = \frac{\int_0^1 \left(x^{3/2} - x^3\right)\,dx}{\int_0^1 \left(x^{1/2} - x^2\right)\,dx} = \frac{\left[\frac{x^{5/2}}{5/2} - \frac{x^4}{4}\right]_0^1}{\left[\frac{x^{3/2}}{3/2} - \frac{x^3}{3}\right]_0^1} = 0.45.$$

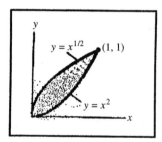

If we use a horizontal strip to obtain $\bar{y}$, we obtain

$$\bar{y} = \frac{\int_A y\,dA}{\int_A dA} = \frac{\int_0^1 \left(y^{3/2} - y^3\right)\,dy}{\int_0^1 \left(y^{1/2} - y^2\right)\,dy} = 0.45$$

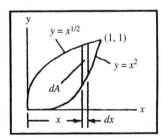

Problem 7.17 Determine the x coordinate of the centroid of the area.

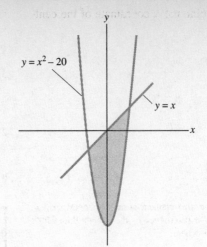

Solution: The intercept of the straight line with the parabola occurs at the roots of the simultaneous equations: $y = x$, and $y = x^2 - 20$. This is equivalent to the solution of the quadratic $x^2 - x - 20 = 0$, $x_1 = -4$, and $x_2 = 5$. These establish the limits on the integration. *The area:* Choose a vertical strip dx wide. The length of the strip is $(x - x^2 + 20)$, which is the distance between the straight line $y = x$ and the parabola $y = x^2 - 20$. Thus the element of area is $dA = (x - x^2 + 20)\,dx$ and

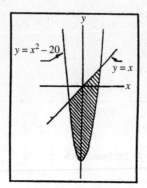

$$A = \int_{-4}^{+5} (x - x^2 + 20)\,dx = \left[\frac{x^2}{2} - \frac{x^3}{3} + 20x\right]_{-4}^{+5} = 121.5.$$

The x-coordinate:

$$\mathbf{x}A = \int_A x\,dA = \int_{-4}^{+5} (x^2 - x^3 + 20x)\,dx$$

$$= \left[\frac{x^3}{3} - \frac{x^4}{4} + 10x^2\right]_{-4}^{+5} = 60.75.$$

$$\boxed{\mathbf{x} = \frac{60.75}{121.5} = 0.5}$$

Problem 7.18 Determine the y coordinate of the centroid of the area in Problem 7.17.

Solution: Use the results of the solution to Problem 7.17 in the following.

The y-coordinate: The centroid of the area element occurs at the midpoint of the strip enclosed by the parabola and the straight line, and the y-coordinate is:

$$\mathbf{y} = x - \left(\frac{1}{2}\right)(x - x^2 + 20) = \left(\frac{1}{2}\right)(x + x^2 - 20).$$

$$\mathbf{y}A = \int_A y\,dA = \left(\frac{1}{2}\right)\int_{-4}^{5}(x + x^2 - 20)(x - x^2 + 20)\,dx$$

$$= \left(\frac{1}{2}\right)\int_{-4}^{+5}(-x^4 + 41x^2 - 400)\,dx$$

$$= \left(\frac{1}{2}\right)\left[-\frac{x^5}{5} + \frac{41x^3}{3} - 400x\right]_{-4}^{5} = -923.4.$$

$$\boxed{\mathbf{y} = -\frac{923.4}{121.5} = -7.6}$$

Problem 7.19 Determine the y coordinate of the centroid of the area.

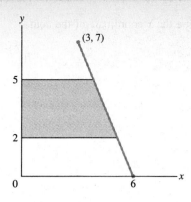

Solution: *The area:* The area element is the horizontal strip x-long and dy wide. The length is determined by the straight line, which has the equation $y = mx + b$, where

$$m = \frac{y_1 - y_2}{x_1 - x_2} = \frac{(7 - 0)}{(3 - 6)} = -2.3333,$$

and $b = y_1 - mx_1 = 7 - (2.3333)3 = 14$.

The length of the strip is

$$x = \left(\frac{1}{m}\right)(y - b).$$

The element of area is $dA = \left(\frac{1}{m}\right)(y - b)\,dy$, from which

$$A = \left(\frac{1}{m}\right)\int_2^5 (y - b)\,dy = \left(\frac{1}{m}\right)\left[\frac{y^2}{2} - by\right]_2^5 = 13.5.$$

The y-coordinate:

$$yA = \int_A y\,dA = \left(\frac{1}{m}\right)\int_2^5 y(y - b)\,dy$$

$$= \left(\frac{1}{m}\right)\left[\frac{y^3}{3} - b\frac{y^2}{2}\right]_2^5 = 46.2857.$$

$$\boxed{y = 3.4286}$$

Problem 7.20 Determine the x coordinate of the centroid of the area in Problem 7.19.

Solution: From the solution to Problem 7.19, the area $A = 13.5$ is bounded by the straight line $y = mx + b$, where $m = -2.3333$, and $b = 14$. The horizontal strip is x-wide and dy high, where

$$x = \left(\frac{1}{m}\right)(y - b).$$

The centroid of x is one half this strip, hence

$$xA = \left(\frac{1}{2m^2}\right)\int (y - b)^2\,dy = \left(\frac{1}{6m^2}\right)[(y - b)^3]_2^5 = 30.583,$$

from which $\boxed{x = \dfrac{30.583}{13.5} = 2.265}$

Problem 7.21 An agronomist wants to measure the rainfall at the centroid of a plowed field between two roads. What are the coordinates of the point where the rain gauge should be placed?

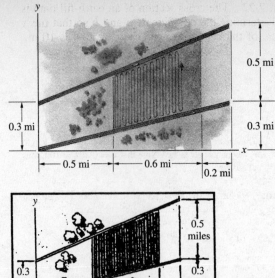

Solution: *The area:* The element of area is the vertical strip $(y_t - y_b)$ long and dx wide, where $y_t = m_t x + b_t$ and $y_b = m_b x + b_b$ are the two straight lines bounding the area, where

$$m_t = \frac{(0.8 - 0.3)}{(1.3 - 0)} = 0.3846,$$

and $b_t = 0.8 - 1.3\, m_t = 0.3$.

Similarly:

$$m_b = \frac{(0.3 - 0)}{(1.3 - 0)} = 0.2308,$$

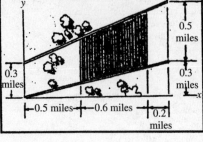

and $b_b = 0$.

The element of area is

$$dA = (y_t - y_b)\,dx = ((m_t - m_b)x + b_t - b_b)\,dx$$

$$= (0.1538x + 0.3)\,dx,$$

from which

$$A = \int_{0.5}^{1.1} (0.1538x + 0.3)\,dx$$

$$= \left[0.1538\frac{x^2}{2} + 0.3x\right]_{0.5}^{1.1} = 0.2538 \text{ sq mile.}$$

The x-coordinate:

$$\int_A x\,dA = \int_{0.5}^{1.1} (0.1538x + 0.3)x\,dx$$

$$= \left[0.1538\frac{x^3}{3} + 0.3\frac{x^2}{2}\right]_{0.5}^{1.1} = 0.2058.$$

$$\boxed{\mathbf{x} = 0.8109 \text{ mi}}$$

The y-coordinate: The y-coordinate of the centroid of the elemental area is

$$\mathbf{y} = y_b + (\tfrac{1}{2})(y_t - y_b) = (\tfrac{1}{2})(y_t + y_b) = 0.3077x + 0.15.$$

Thus, $\quad \mathbf{y}A = \int_A y\,dA$

$$= \int_{0.5}^{1.1} (0.3077x + 0.15)(0.1538x + 0.3)\,dx$$

$$= \int_{0.5}^{1.1} (0.0473x^2 + 0.1154x + 0.045)\,dx$$

$$= \left[0.0471\frac{x^3}{3} + 0.1153\frac{x^2}{2} + 0.045x\right]_{0.5}^{1.1} = 0.1014.$$

Divide by the area: $\quad \boxed{\mathbf{y} = \dfrac{0.1014}{0.2538} = 0.3995 \text{ mi}}$

Problem 7.22 The cross section of an earth-fill dam is shown. Determine the coefficients a and b so that the y coordinate of the centroid of the cross section is 10 m.

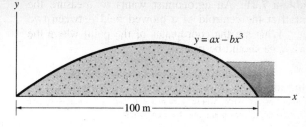

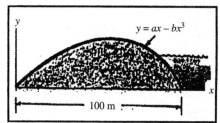

Solution: *The area:* The elemental area is a vertical strip of length y and width dx, where $y = ax - bx^3$. Note that $y = 0$ at $x = 100$, thus $b = a \times 10^{-4}$. Thus

$$A = \int_A dA = a \int_0^{100} (x - (10^{-4})x^3)\, dx$$

$$= (0.5a)[x^2 - (0.5 \times 10^{-4})x^4]_0^{100}$$

$$= 0.5a \times 10^4 - 0.25b \times 10^8,$$

and the area is $A = 0.25a \times 10^4$. *The y-coordinate:* The y-coordinate of the centroid of the elemental area is

$$y = (0.5)(ax - bx^3) = (0.5a)(x - (10^{-4})x^3),$$

from which

$$yA = \int_A y\, dA$$

$$= (0.5)a^2 \int_0^{100} (x - (10^{-4})x^3)^2\, dx$$

$$= (0.5)a^2 \int_0^{100} (x^2 - 2(10^{-4})x^4 + (10^{-8})x^6)\, dx$$

$$= (0.5a^2)\left[\frac{x^3}{3} - (10^{-4})\frac{2x^5}{5} + (10^{-8})\frac{x^7}{7}\right]_0^{100}$$

$$= 3.81a^2 \times 10^4.$$

Divide by the area:

$$y = \frac{3.810a^2 \times 10^4}{0.25a \times 10^4} = 15.2381a.$$

For $y = 10$, $\boxed{a = 0.6562}$, and $\boxed{b = 6.562 \times 10^{-5}\,\text{m}^{-2}}$

Problem 7.23 The Supermarine Spitfire used by Great Britain in World War II had a wing with an elliptical profile. Determine the coordinates of its centroid.

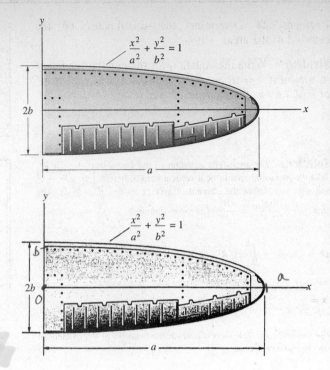

Solution:

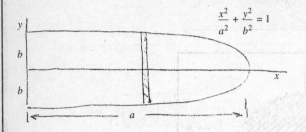

$$\frac{x^2}{a^2} + \frac{y^2}{b^2} = 1$$

By symmetry, $\mathbf{y} = 0$.

From the equation of the ellipse,

$$y = \frac{b}{a}\sqrt{a^2 - x^2}$$

By symmetry, the **x** centroid of the wing is the same as the **x** centroid of the upper half of the wing. Thus, we can avoid dealing with ± values for y.

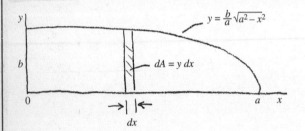

$y = \frac{b}{a}\sqrt{a^2-x^2}$

$dA = y\,dx$

$$\mathbf{x} = \frac{\displaystyle\int x\,dA}{\displaystyle\int dA} = \frac{\dfrac{b}{a}\displaystyle\int_0^a x\sqrt{a^2 - x^2}\,dx}{\dfrac{b}{a}\displaystyle\int_0^a \sqrt{a^2 - x^2}\,dx}$$

$A = \pi\, ab$

half of ellipse: $A = \dfrac{\pi\, ab}{2}$

Using integral tables

$$\int x\sqrt{a^2 - x^2}\,dx = -\frac{(a^2 - x^2)^{3/2}}{3}$$

$$\int \sqrt{a^2 - x^2}\,dx = \frac{x\sqrt{a^2 - x^2}}{2} + \frac{a^2}{2}\sin^{-1}\left(\frac{x}{a}\right)$$

Substituting, we get

$$\mathbf{x} = \frac{\left[-(a^2 - x^2)^{3/2}/3\right]_0^a}{\left[\dfrac{x\sqrt{a^2 - x^2}}{2} + \dfrac{a^2}{2}\sin^{-1}\left(\dfrac{x}{a}\right)\right]_0^a}$$

$$\mathbf{x} = \frac{[-0 + a^3/3]}{\left[0 + \dfrac{a^2}{2}\left(\dfrac{\pi}{2}\right) - 0 - 0\right]} = \frac{a^3/3}{a^2\pi/4}$$

$$\mathbf{x} = \frac{4a}{3\pi}$$

Problem 7.24 Determine the coordinates of the centroid of the area.

Strategy: Write the equation for the circular boundary in the form $y = (R^2 - x^2)^{1/2}$ and use a vertical "strip" of width dx as the element of area dA.

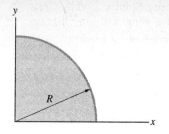

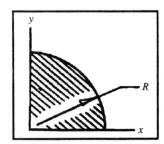

Solution: *The area:* The equation of the circle is $x^2 + y^2 = R^2$. Take the elemental area to be a vertical strip of height $y = \sqrt{R^2 - x^2}$ and width dx, hence the element of area is $dA = \sqrt{R^2 - x^2}\, dx$. The area is $A = \dfrac{A_{circle}}{4} = \dfrac{\pi R^2}{4}$. *The x-coordinate:*

$$\mathbf{x}A = \int_A x\, dA = \int_0^R x\sqrt{R^2 - x^2}\, dx = \left[-\frac{(R^2 - x^2)^{3/2}}{3} \right]_0^R = \frac{R^3}{3} :$$

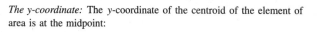

$$\boxed{\mathbf{x} = \frac{4R}{3\pi}}$$

The y-coordinate: The y-coordinate of the centroid of the element of area is at the midpoint:

$$\mathbf{y} = (\tfrac{1}{2})\sqrt{R^2 - x^2},$$

hence $\mathbf{y}A = \displaystyle\int_A y\, dA = \left(\frac{1}{2}\right) \int_0^R (R^2 - x^2)\, dx$

$$= \left(\frac{1}{2}\right) \left[R^2 x - \frac{x^3}{3} \right]_0^R = \frac{R^3}{3}$$

$$\boxed{\mathbf{y} = \frac{4R}{3\pi}}$$

Problem 7.25 Determine the x coordinate of the centroid of the area. By setting $h = 0$, confirm the answer to Problem 7.24.

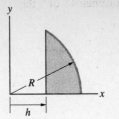

Solution: Use a vertical strip:

$$x = \frac{\int_A x\,dA}{\int_A dA} = \frac{\int_h^R x(R^2 - x^2)^{1/2}\,dx}{\int_h^R (R^2 - x^2)^{1/2}\,dx}.$$

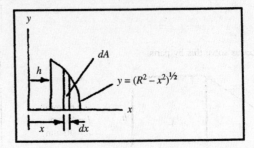

The upper integral is

$$\int_h^R x(R^2 - x^2)^{1/2}\,dx = R\int_h^R x\left(1 - \frac{x^2}{R^2}\right)^{1/2}\,dx$$

$$= R\left[-\frac{1}{3R}(R^2 - x^2)^{3/2}\right]_h^R = \frac{1}{3}(R^2 - h^2)^{3/2}.$$

The area is

$$A = \int_A dA = \int_h^R (R^2 - x^2)^{1/2}\,dx = R\int_h^R (1^2 - x^2)^{1/2}\,dx$$

$$= R\int_h^R \left(1 - \frac{x^2}{R^2}\right)^{1/2}\,dx$$

$$= \frac{R}{2}\left[x\left(1 - \frac{x^2}{R^2}\right)^{1/2} + R\arcsin\left(\frac{x}{R}\right)\right]_h^R$$

$$= \frac{R}{2}\left[\frac{\pi R}{2} - h\left(1 - \frac{h^2}{R^2}\right)^{1/2} - R\arcsin\left(\frac{h}{R}\right)\right].$$

The centroid is $\mathbf{x} = (R^2 - h^2)^{3/2}/(3A)$.

If $h = 0$, $\mathbf{x} = \dfrac{R^3}{3\left(\dfrac{R}{2}\right)\left(\dfrac{\pi R}{2}\right)} = \dfrac{4R}{3\pi}$

Problem 7.26 Determine the y coordinate of the centroid of the area in Problem 7.25.

Solution: Let y in Equation (7.7) be the height of the midpoint of a vertical strip:

$$y = \frac{\int_A y\,dA}{\int_A dA} = \frac{\int_h^R \frac{1}{2}(R^2 - x^2)^{1/2}\left[(R^2 - x^2)^{1/2}\,dx\right]}{\int_A dA}.$$

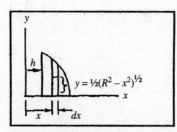

The upper integral is

$$\int_h^R \frac{1}{2}(R^2 - x^2)\,dx = \frac{1}{2}\left[R^2 x - \frac{x^3}{3}\right]_h^R$$

$$= \frac{1}{2}\left(\frac{2R^3}{3} - R^2 h + \frac{h^3}{3}\right).$$

From the solution of Problem 7.25,

$$A = \int_A dA = \frac{R}{2}\left[\frac{\pi R}{2} - h\left(1 - \frac{h^2}{R^2}\right)^{1/2} - R\arcsin\left(\frac{h}{R}\right)\right].$$

The centroid is $\mathbf{y} = \dfrac{1}{2A}\left(\dfrac{2R^3}{3} - R^2 h + \dfrac{h^3}{3}\right)$

Problem 7.27 Determine the coordinates of the centroids.

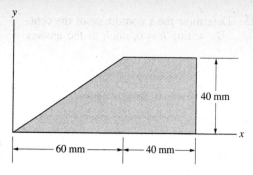

Solution: Let us solve this by parts.

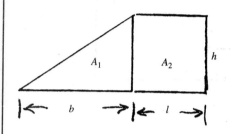

$b = 60$ mm
$l = 40$ mm
$h = 40$ mm

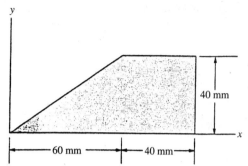

$b = 60$ mm

$l = 40$ mm

$h = 40$ mm

$A_1 = \frac{1}{2}bh = \frac{1}{2}(60)(40) = 1200$ mm^2

$A_2 = lh = (40)(40) = 1600$ mm^2

$A_1 + A_2 = 2800$ mm^2

From the tables and inspection

$\mathbf{x}_1 = \frac{2}{3}b \quad \mathbf{x}_2 = b + l/z$

$\mathbf{y}_1 = \frac{1}{3}h \quad \mathbf{y}_2 = \frac{1}{2}h$

$\mathbf{x}_1 = 40$ mm $\qquad \mathbf{x}_2 = 80$ mm

$\mathbf{y}_1 = 13.33$ mm $\qquad \mathbf{y}_2 = 20$ mm

For the composite, substituting,

$\mathbf{x} = \dfrac{\mathbf{x}_1 A_1 + \mathbf{x}_2 A_2}{A_1 + A_2} = 62.9$ mm

$\mathbf{y} = \dfrac{\mathbf{y}_1 A_1 + \mathbf{y}_2 A_2}{A_1 + A_2} = 17.1$ mm

Problem 7.28 Determine the coordinates of the centroids.

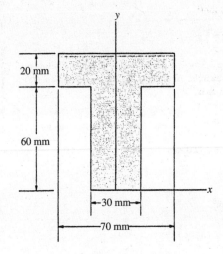

Solution: Let us solve this problem by using symmetry and by breaking the composite shape into parts.

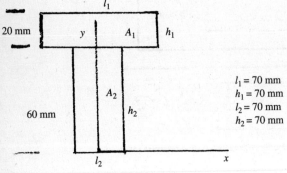

$l_1 = 70$ mm
$h_1 = 70$ mm
$l_2 = 70$ mm
$h_2 = 70$ mm

$l_1 = 70$ mm

$h_1 = 20$ mm

$l_2 = 30$ mm

$h_2 = 60$ mm

$A_1 = l_1 h_1 = 1400$ mm^2

$A_2 = l_2 h_2 = 1800$ mm^2

By symmetry,

$x_1 = 0$ $\qquad$ $x_2 = 0$

$y_1 = 70$ mm $\qquad$ $y_2 = 30$ mm

For the composite,

$$x = \frac{x_1 A_1 + x_2 A_2}{A_1 + A_2} = \frac{0 + 0}{320 \text{ mm}^2} = 0$$

$$y = \frac{y_1 A_1 + y_2 A_2}{A_1 + A_2}$$

$$y = \frac{(70)(1400) + (30)(1800)}{3200} = \frac{152000}{3200}$$

$y = 47.5$ mm

$x = 0$

Problem 7.29 Determine the coordinates of the centroids.

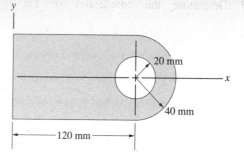

Solution: Divide the shape up into a rectangle, a semicircle, and a circular cutout as shown. Note that the y coordinates of the centroids of all three component areas lie on the x axis. Thus, $\mathbf{y} = 0$ for the combined area.

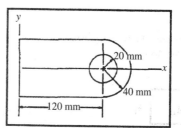

Rectangle:

$$\text{Area}_1 = a(2R) = 9600 \text{ mm}^2,$$

and $\mathbf{x}_1 = a/2 = 60$ mm.

Semicircle: See example 7.3 or 7.4 for the value of the x coordinate of the centroid of a semicircle. Also note the x displacement of the centroid relative to the y axis.

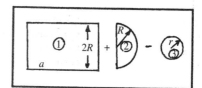

$$\text{Area}_2 = \pi R^2/2 = 2513 \text{ mm}^2,$$

$$\mathbf{x}_2 = a + (4R)/(3\pi) = 137.0 \text{ mm}.$$

Cutout:

$$\text{Area}_3 = \pi r^2 = 1257 \text{ mm}^2,$$

$$\mathbf{x}_3 = 120 \text{ mm}.$$

Combined Area:

$$\mathbf{x} = (\mathbf{x}_1\text{Area}_1 + \mathbf{x}_2\text{Area}_2 - \mathbf{x}_3\text{Area}_3)/(\text{Area}_1 + \text{Area}_2 - \text{Area}_3)$$

$$= 70.9 \text{ mm}$$

Problem 7.30 Determine the coordinates of the centroids.

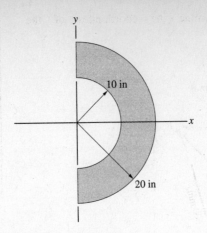

Solution: The strategy is to find the centroid for the half circle area, and use the result in the composite algorithm. *The area:* The element of area is a vertical strip y high and dx wide. From the equation of the circle, $y = \pm\sqrt{R^2 - x^2}$. The height of the strip will be twice the positive value, so that $dA = 2\sqrt{R^2 - x^2}\,dx$, from which

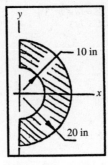

$$A = \int_A dA = 2\int_0^R (R^2 - x^2)^{1/2}\,dx$$

$$= 2\left[\frac{x\sqrt{R^2 - x^2}}{2} + \frac{R^2}{2}\sin^{-1}\left(\frac{x}{R}\right)\right]_0^R = \frac{\pi R^2}{2}$$

The x-coordinate:

$$\int_A x\,dA = 2\int_0^R x\sqrt{R^2 - x^2}\,dx$$

$$= 2\left[-\frac{(R^2 - x^2)^{3/2}}{3}\right]_0^R = \frac{2R^3}{3}.$$

Divide by A: $x = \dfrac{4R}{3\pi}$

The y-coordinate: From symmetry, the y-coordinate is zero.

The composite: For a complete half circle $x_1 = \dfrac{4(20)}{3\pi} = 8.488$ in..
For the inner half circle $x_2 = 4.244$ in. The areas are

$$A_1 = 628.32 \text{ in.}^2$$

and $A_2 = 157.08$ in^2.

Problem 7.31 Determine the coordinates of the centroids.

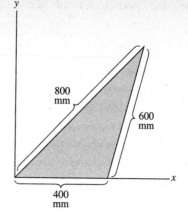

Solution: Use Appendix B:

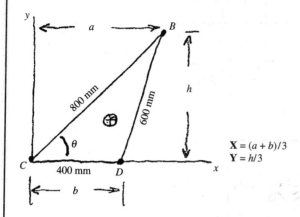

$$X = (a + b)/3$$
$$Y = h/3$$

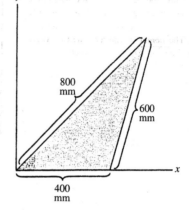

We need to know h and a. This is equivalent to knowing the coordinates of point B.

We can use the law of cosines to find the angle θ and then use θ to find (x_B, y_B).

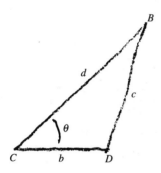

$b = 400$ mm

$c = 600$ mm

$d = 800$ mm

From the law of cosines

$c^2 = b^2 + d^2 - 2\,bd\cos\theta$

Substituting, $\theta = 46.57°$

$x_B = d\cos\theta = 550.0$ mm

$y_B = d\sin\theta = 580.9$ mm

$\therefore h = 580.9$ mm

$a = 550.0$ mm $b = 400$ mm

$\mathbf{x} = (a + b)/3 = 316.67$ mm

$\mathbf{y} = h/3 = 193.6$ mm

Problem 7.32 Determine the coordinates of the centroids.

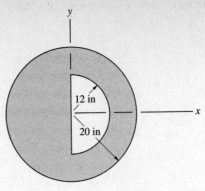

Solution: The results for a half-circle of radius R:

$$A_1 = \frac{\pi R^2}{2}, \quad x_1 = \frac{4R}{3\pi}, \quad y_1 = 0.$$

Consider three figures: The complete circle, (1) the half circle cut out, and (2) the composite figure. The centroid of the complete circle is at the origin; $x = 0$ and $y = 0$. The product of its centroid coordinates and its area is zero. From the composite algorithm, it follows that

$$0 = A_1 x_1 + A_2 x_2,$$

from which

$$x_2 = -\left(\frac{A_1}{A_2}\right) x_1,$$

and $y_2 = -\left(\frac{A_1}{A_2}\right) y_1.$

The areas:

$$A_1 = \frac{\pi R_1^2}{2},$$

$$A_2 = \pi R_2^2 - \frac{\pi R_1^2}{2}.$$

For $R_1 = 12$ in. and $R_2 = 20$ in., $A_1 = 226.2$ in.^{2}, and $A_2 = 1030.4$ in.^{2}, and $x_1 = 5.093$ in.. Thus

$$\boxed{x_2 = -\left(\frac{226.2}{1030.4}\right)(5.093) = -1.18 \text{ in.,}}$$

and $\boxed{y_2 = 0}$, since $\boxed{y_1 = 0}$.

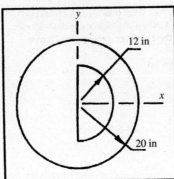

Problem 7.33 Determine the coordinates of the centroids.

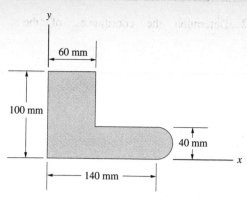

Solution: Divide the object into three areas: (1) A rectangle on the left, 100 mm by 60 mm. (2) A rectangle at the lower right, 80 mm by 40 mm. (3) A semi circle to the far lower right, radius 20 mm.

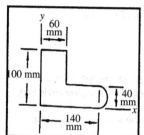

The areas and centroid coordinates are

(1) $A_1 = 6 \times 10^3$ mm^2,

  $x_1 = 30$ mm,

  $y_1 = 50$ mm

(2) $A_2 = 3.2 \times 10^3$ mm^2,

  $x_2 = 100$ mm,

  $y_2 = 20$ mm, and

(3) $A_3 = 628.32$ mm^2,

  $x_3 = 148.49$ mm,

  $y_3 = 20$ mm.

(1) The composite area is

$$A = \sum_1^3 A_i = 9.828 \times 10^3.$$

The centroid coordinates for the composite are

$$\boxed{x = \frac{\sum_1^3 A_i x_i}{A} = 60.37 \text{ mm}},$$

and $\boxed{y = \dfrac{\sum_1^3 A_i y_i}{A} = 38.31 \text{ mm}}$

Problem 7.34 Determine the coordinates of the centroids.

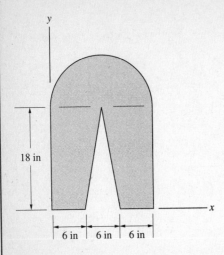

Solution: Divide the object into four areas: (1) The rectangle 18 in by 18 in, (2) The triangle of altitude 18 in and base 6 in, and (3) the semi circle with radius 9 in and (4) The object itself.

The areas and their centroids are determined by inspection:

(1) $A_1 = 18^2 = 324$ in.^{2}, $x_1 = 9$ in., $y_1 = 9$ in.

(2) $A_2 = (\frac{1}{2})(18)(6) = 54$ in.^{2}, $x_2 = 9$ in., $y_2 = 6$ in.

(3) $A_3 = \dfrac{\pi 9^2}{2} = 127.2$ in.^{2}, $x_3 = 9$ in., $y_3 = 18 + \dfrac{4(9)}{3\pi} = 21.8$ in.

The composite area: $A = A_1 - A_2 + A_3 = 397.2$ in.^{2}.

The composite centroid:

$$\mathbf{x} = \frac{A_1 x_1 - A_2 x_2 + A_3 x_3}{A} = 9 \text{ in.}$$

$$\mathbf{y} = \frac{A_1 y_1 - A_2 y_2 + A_3 y_3}{A} = 13.51 \text{ in.}$$

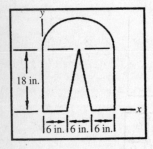

Problem 7.35 Determine the coordinates of the centroids.

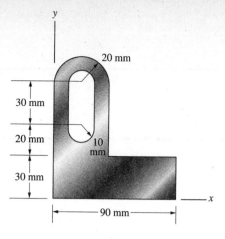

Solution: Determine this result by breaking the compound object into parts

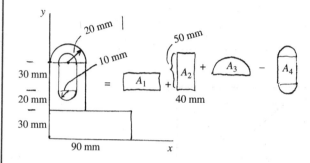

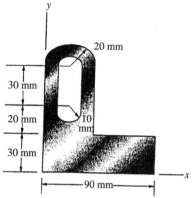

A_1 : $A_1 = (30)(90) = 2700 \text{ mm}^2$

$x_1 = 45 \text{ mm}$

$y_1 = 15 \text{ mm}$

A_2 : (sits on top of A_1)

$A_2 = (40)(50) = 2000 \text{ mm}^2$

$x_2 = 20 \text{ mm}$

$y_2 = 30 + 25 = 55 \text{ mm}$

A_3 : $A_3 = \dfrac{1}{2}\pi r_0^2 = \dfrac{\pi}{2}(20)^2 = 628.3 \text{ mm}^2$

$x_3 = 20 \text{ mm}$

$y_3 = 80 \text{ mm} + \dfrac{4r_0}{3\pi} = 88.49 \text{ mm}$

A_4 : $A_4 = (30)(20) + \pi r_i^2$

$A_4 = 600 + \pi(10)^2 = 914.2 \text{ mm}^2$

$x_4 = 20 \text{ mm}$

$y_4 = 50 + 15 = 65 \text{ mm}$

Area (composite)

$= A_1 + A_2 + A_3 - A_4$

$= 4414.2 \text{ mm}^2$

For the composite:

$$\mathbf{x} = \frac{\mathbf{x}_1 A_1 + \mathbf{x}_2 A_2 + \mathbf{x}_3 A_3 - \mathbf{x}_4 A_4}{(A_1 + A_2 + A_3 - A_4)}$$

$$\mathbf{x} = \frac{155782}{4414.2} = 35.3 \text{ mm}$$

$$\mathbf{y} = \frac{\mathbf{y}_1 A_1 + \mathbf{y}_2 A_2 + \mathbf{y}_3 A_3 - \mathbf{y}_4 A_4}{A_1 + A_2 + A_3 - A_4}$$

$$\mathbf{y} = \frac{146675}{4414.2} = 33.2 \text{ mm}$$

The value for **y** is not the same as in the new problem statement. This value seems correct. (The **x** value checks).

Problem 7.36 Determine the coordinates of the centroids.

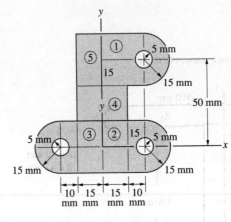

Solution: Comparison of the solution to Problem 7.29 and our areas 1, 2, and 3, we see that in order to use the solution of Problem 7.29, we must set $a = 25$ mm, $R = 15$ mm, and $r = 5$ mm. If we do this, we find that for this shape, measuring from the y axis, $\mathbf{x} = 18.04$ mm. The corresponding areas for regions 1, 2, and 3 is 1025 mm^2. The centroids of the rectangular areas are at their geometric centers. By inspection, we how have the following information for the five areas

Area 1: Area$_1 = 1025$ mm^2, $\mathbf{x}_1 = 18.04$ mm, and $\mathbf{y}_1 = 50$ mm.

Area 2: Area$_2 = 1025$ mm^2, $\mathbf{x}_2 = 18.04$ mm, and $\mathbf{y}_2 = 0$ mm.

Area 3: Area$_3 = 1025$ mm^2, $\mathbf{x}_3 = -18.04$ mm, and $\mathbf{y}_3 = 0$ mm.

Area 4: Area$_4 = 600$ mm^2, $\mathbf{x}_4 = 0$ mm, and $\mathbf{y}_4 = 25$ mm.

Area 5: Area$_5 = 450$ mm^2, $\mathbf{x}_5 = -7.5$ mm, and $\mathbf{y}_5 = 50$ mm.

Combining the properties of the five areas, we can calculate the centroid of the composite area made up of the five regions shown.

$$\text{Area}_{\text{TOTAL}} = \text{Area}_1 + \text{Area}_2 + \text{Area}_3 + \text{Area}_4 + \text{Area}_5$$

$$= 4125 \text{ mm}^2.$$

Then, $\mathbf{x} = (\mathbf{x}_1\text{Area}_1 + \mathbf{x}_2\text{Area}_2 + \mathbf{x}_3\text{Area}_3 + \mathbf{x}_4\text{Area}_4$

$$+ \mathbf{x}_5\text{Area}_5)/\text{Area}_{\text{TOTAL}} = 3.67 \text{ mm},$$

and $\mathbf{y} = (\mathbf{y}_1\text{Area}_1 + \mathbf{y}_2\text{Area}_2 + \mathbf{y}_3\text{Area}_3 + \mathbf{y}_4\text{Area}_4$

$$+ \mathbf{y}_5\text{Area}_5)/\text{Area}_{\text{TOTAL}} = 21.52 \text{ mm}.$$

Problem 7.37 The dimensions $b = 42$ mm and $h = 22$ mm. Determine the y coordinate of the centroid of the beam's cross section.

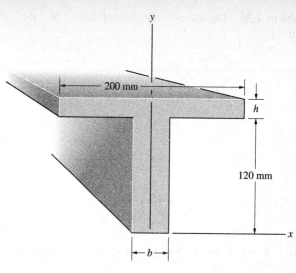

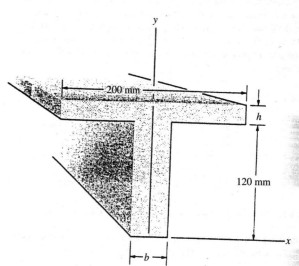

Solution: Work as a composite shape

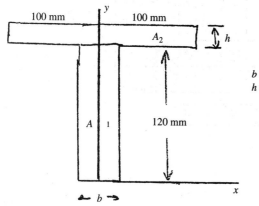

$b = 42$ mm
$h = 42$ mm

$b = 42$ mm

$h = 22$ mm

$A_1 = 120\ b$ mm$^2 = 5040$ mm^2

$\left.\begin{array}{l} \mathbf{x}_1 = 0 \\ \mathbf{y}_1 = 60 \text{ mm} \end{array}\right\}$ by symmetry

$A_2 = 200\ h = 4400$ mm^2

$\mathbf{x}_2 = 0$

$\mathbf{y}_2 = 120 + \dfrac{h}{2} = 131$ mm

$\mathbf{x} = \dfrac{A_1\mathbf{x}_1 + A_2\mathbf{x}_2}{A_1 + A_2} = \dfrac{0 + 0}{9440}$

$\mathbf{x} = 0$

$\mathbf{y} = \dfrac{A_1\mathbf{y}_1 + A_2\mathbf{y}_2}{A_1 + A_2} = 93.1$ mm

Problem 7.38 If the cross-sectional area of the beam shown in Problem 7.37 is 8400 mm² and the y coordinate of the centroid of the area is $y = 90$ mm, what are the dimensions b and h?

Solution: From the solution to Problem 7.37

$$A_1 = 120\ b,\ \ A_2 = 200\ h$$

and $$y = \frac{y_1A_1 + y_2A_2}{A_1 + A_2}$$

$$y = \frac{(60)(120\ b) + \left(120 + \dfrac{h}{2}\right)(200\ h)}{120\ b + 200\ h}$$

where $y_1 = 60$ mm

$$y = 90 \text{ mm}$$

$$A_1 + A_2 = 8400 \text{ mm}^2$$

Also, $y_2 = 120 + h/2$

Solving these equations simultaneously we get

$h = 18.2$ mm

$b = 39.7$ mm

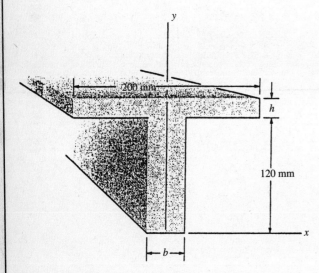

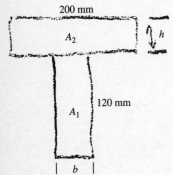

Problem 7.39 Determine the x coordinate of the centroid of the Boeing 747's vertical stabilizer.

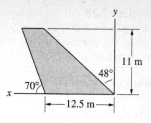

Solution: We can treat the stabilizer as a rectangular area (1) with two triangular cutouts (2 and 3): The dimensions a and b are

$$a = 11 \tan 48° = 12.22 \text{ m}$$

and $b = \dfrac{11}{\tan 70°} = 4.00$ m.

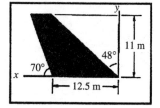

The areas are

$$A_1 = (11)(12.5 + b) = 181.5,$$

$$A_2 = \tfrac{1}{2}(11)a = 67.2 \text{ m},$$

$$A_3 = \tfrac{1}{2}(11)b = 22.0 \text{ m}.$$

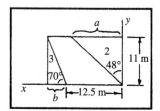

The x coordinate of the centroid is

$$\mathbf{x} = \frac{A_1 \mathbf{x}_1 - A_2 \mathbf{x}_2 - A_3 \mathbf{x}_3}{A_1 - A_2 - A_3}$$

$$= \frac{A_1 \left[\dfrac{12.5 + b}{2}\right] - A_2 \left(\dfrac{a}{3}\right) - A_3(12.5 + 2b/3)}{A_1 - A_2 - A_3} = 9.64 \text{ m}$$

Problem 7.40 Determine the y coordinate of the centroid of the vertical stabilizer in Problem 7.39.

Solution: Treating the stabilizer as a rectangular area (1) with triangular cutouts (2 and 3) as shown in the sol of Problem 7.39, the y coordinate of the centroid is

$$\mathbf{y} = \frac{A_1 \mathbf{y}_1 - A_2 \mathbf{y}_2 - A_3 \mathbf{y}_3}{A_1 - A_2 - A_3}$$

$$= \frac{A_1(11/2) - A_2[2(11/3)] - A_3(11/3)}{A_1 - A_2 - A_3}.$$

From the solution of Problem 7.39,

$$A_1 = 181.5 \text{ m},$$

$$A_2 = 67.2 \text{ m},$$

and $A_3 = 22.0$ m,

giving the result $\mathbf{y} = 4.60$ m.

Problem 7.41 The area has elliptical boundaries. If $a = 30$ mm, $b = 15$ mm, and $\varepsilon = 6$ mm, what is the x coordinate of the centroid of the area?

Solution: The equation of the outer ellipse is

$$\frac{x^2}{(a+\varepsilon)^2} + \frac{y^2}{(b+\varepsilon)^2} = 1$$

and for the inner ellipse

$$\frac{x^2}{a^2} + \frac{y^2}{b^2} = 1$$

We will handle the problem by considering two solid ellipses

For any ellipse

$$\mathbf{x} = \frac{\int x\,dA}{\int dA} = \frac{\frac{\beta}{\alpha} \int_0^\alpha x\sqrt{\alpha^2 - x^2}\,dx}{\frac{\beta}{\alpha} \int \sqrt{\alpha^2 - x^2}\,dx}$$

From integral tables

$$\int x\sqrt{\alpha^2 - x^2}\,dx = -\frac{(\alpha^2 - x^2)^{3/2}}{3}$$

$$\int \sqrt{\alpha^2 - x^2}\,dx = \frac{x\sqrt{\alpha^2 - x^2}}{2} + \frac{\alpha^2}{2}\sin^{-1}\left(\frac{x}{\alpha}\right)$$

Substituting $\mathbf{x} = \dfrac{\left[-(\alpha^2 - x^2)^{3/2}\right]_0^\alpha}{\left[\dfrac{x\sqrt{\alpha^2 - x^2}}{3} + \dfrac{\alpha^2}{2}\sin\left(\dfrac{x}{\alpha}\right)\right]_0^\alpha}$

$$\mathbf{x} = \frac{[-0 + \alpha^3/3]}{\left[0 + \frac{\alpha^2}{2}\left(\frac{\pi}{2}\right) - 0 - 0\right]} = \frac{\alpha^3/3}{\alpha^2\pi/4}$$

$$\mathbf{x} = \frac{4\alpha}{3\pi}$$

Also Area $= \displaystyle\int dA = \frac{\beta}{\alpha}\int_0^\alpha \sqrt{\alpha^2 + x^2}\,dx$

$$= \frac{\beta}{\alpha}\left[\frac{x\sqrt{\alpha^2 - x^2}}{2} + \frac{\alpha^2}{2}\sin^{-1}\left(\frac{x}{\alpha}\right)\right]_0^\alpha$$

$$\text{Area} = \frac{\beta}{\alpha}\left(\frac{\alpha^2}{2}\right)\left(\frac{\pi}{2}\right) = \pi\alpha\beta/4$$

(The area of a full ellipse is $\pi\alpha\beta$ so this checks.)

Now for the composite area.

For the outer ellipse, $\alpha = a + \varepsilon$ $\beta = b + \varepsilon$ and for the inner ellipse $\alpha = a$ $\beta = b$

Outer ellipse

$$\mathbf{x}_1 = \frac{4(a+\varepsilon)}{3\pi}$$

$$A_1 = \frac{\pi(a+\varepsilon)(b+\varepsilon)}{4}$$

Inner Ellipse

$$\mathbf{x}_2 = \frac{4a}{3\pi}$$

$$A_2 = \frac{\pi ab}{4}$$

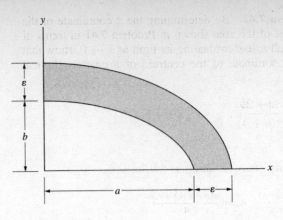

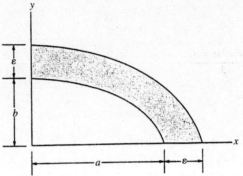

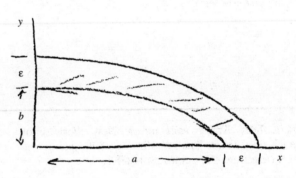

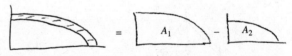

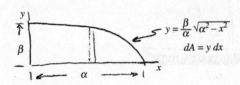

For the composite

$$\mathbf{x} = \frac{\mathbf{x}_1 A_1 - \mathbf{x}_2 A_2}{A_1 - A_2}$$

Substituting, we get

$\mathbf{x}_1 = 15.28$ mm $\mathbf{x}_2 = 12.73$ mm

$A_1 = 2375$ mm^2 $A_2 = 1414$ mm^2

and $\mathbf{x} = 19.0$ mm

Problem 7.42 By determining the x coordinate of the centroid of the area shown in Problem 7.41 in terms of a, b, and ε, and evaluating its limit as $\varepsilon \to 0$, show that the x coordinate of the centroid of a quarter-elliptical line is

$$\mathbf{x} = \frac{4a(a+2b)}{3\pi(a+b)}.$$

Solution: From the solution to 7.41, we have

$$\mathbf{x}_1 = \frac{4(a+\varepsilon)}{3\pi} \quad A_1 = \frac{\pi(a+\varepsilon)(b+\varepsilon)}{4}$$

$$\mathbf{x}_2 = \frac{4a}{3\pi} \quad A_2 = \frac{\pi ab}{4}$$

so $\mathbf{x}_1 A_1 = \dfrac{(a+\varepsilon)^2(b+\varepsilon)}{3}$

$$\mathbf{x}_2 A_2 = \frac{a^2 b}{3}$$

$$A_1 - A_2 = \frac{\pi}{4}(ab + a\varepsilon + b\varepsilon + \varepsilon^2 - ab)$$

$$A_1 - A_2 = \frac{\pi}{4}(a\varepsilon + b\varepsilon + \varepsilon^2)$$

$$(\mathbf{x}_1 A_1 - \mathbf{x}_2 A_2) = \tfrac{1}{3}(a^2 b + 2ab\varepsilon + b\varepsilon^2$$

$$+ a^2\varepsilon + 2a\varepsilon^2 + \varepsilon^3 - a^2 b)$$

$$(\mathbf{x}_1 A_1 - \mathbf{x}_2 A_2) = \tfrac{1}{3}((2ab + a^2)\varepsilon$$

$$+ (2a+b)\varepsilon^2 + \varepsilon^3)$$

Finally $\mathbf{x} = \dfrac{\mathbf{x}_1 A_1 - \mathbf{x}_2 A_2}{A_1 - A_2}$

$$\mathbf{x} = \frac{\dfrac{1}{3}\left[(2ab + a^2) + (2a+b)\varepsilon + \varepsilon^2\right]\varepsilon}{\dfrac{\pi}{4}\left[(a+b) + \varepsilon\right]\varepsilon}$$

$$\mathbf{x} = \frac{4a(a+2b)}{3\pi(a+b)} + \frac{4(2a+b)\varepsilon}{3\pi} + \frac{4}{3\pi}\varepsilon^2$$

Taking the limit as $\varepsilon \to 0$

$$\mathbf{x} = \frac{4a(a+2b)}{3\pi(a+b)}$$

Problem 7.43 Three sails of a New York pilot schooner are shown. The coordinates of the points are in feet. Determine the centroid of sail 1.

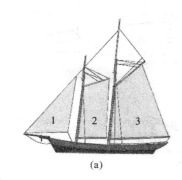

(a)

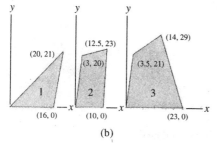

(b)

Solution: Divide the object into three areas: (1) The triangle with altitude 21 ft and base 20 ft. (2) The triangle with altitude 21 ft and base $(20 - 16) = 4$ft, and (3) the composite sail. The areas and coordinates are:

(1) $A_1 = 210$ ft^2,

$$\mathbf{x}_1 = \left(\frac{2}{3}\right) 20 = 13.33 \text{ ft},$$

$$\mathbf{y}_1 = \left(\frac{1}{3}\right) 21 = 7 \text{ ft}.$$

(2) $A_2 = 42$ ft^2,

$$\mathbf{x}_2 = 16 + \left(\frac{2}{3}\right) 4 = 18.67 \text{ ft},$$

$$\mathbf{y}_2 = 7 \text{ ft}.$$

(3) The composite area: $A = A_1 - A_2 = 168$ ft^2. The composite centroid:

$$\boxed{\mathbf{x} = \frac{A_1\mathbf{x}_1 - A_2\mathbf{x}_2}{A} = 12 \text{ ft}},$$

$$\boxed{\mathbf{y} = \frac{A_1\mathbf{y}_1 - A_2\mathbf{y}_2}{A} = 7 \text{ ft}}$$

Problem 7.44 Determine the centroid of sail 2 in Problem 7.43.

Solution: Divide the object into five areas: (1) a triangle on the left with altitude 20 ft and base 3 ft, (2) a rectangle in the middle 23 ft by 9.5 ft, (3) a triangle at the top with base of 9.5 ft and altitude of 3 ft. (4) a triangle on the right with altitude of 23 ft and base of 2.5 ft. (5) the composite sail. The areas and centroids are:

(1) $A_1 = \dfrac{3(20)}{2} = 30 \text{ ft}^2$,

$x_1 = \left(\dfrac{2}{3}\right) 3 = 2 \text{ ft}$,

$y_1 = \left(\dfrac{1}{3}\right) 20 = 6.67 \text{ ft}$.

(2) $A_2 = (23)(9.5) = 218.5 \text{ ft}^2$,

$x_2 = 3 + \left(\dfrac{9.5}{2}\right) = 7.75 \text{ ft}$,

$y_2 = \dfrac{23}{2} = 11.5 \text{ ft}$

(3) $A_3 = \left(\dfrac{1}{2}\right)(3)(9.5) = 14.25 \text{ ft}^2$,

$x_3 = 3 + \left(\dfrac{1}{3}\right) 9.5 = 6.167 \text{ ft}$,

$y_3 = 20 + \left(\dfrac{2}{3}\right) 3 = 22 \text{ ft}$

(4) $A_4 = \left(\dfrac{1}{2}\right)(2.5)(23) = 28.75 \text{ ft}^2$,

$x_4 = 10 + \left(\dfrac{2}{3}\right)(2.5) = 11.67 \text{ ft}$,

$y_4 = \left(\dfrac{1}{3}\right) 23 = 7.66 \text{ ft}$

(5) The composite area: $A = A_1 + A_2 - A_3 - A_4 = 205.5 \text{ ft}^2$. The composite centroid:

$$\boxed{x = \frac{A_1 x_1 + A_2 x_2 - A_3 x_3 - A_4 x_4}{A} = 6.472 \text{ ft}}$$,

$$\boxed{y = \frac{A_1 y_1 + A_2 y_2 - A_3 y_3 - A_4 y_4}{A} = 10.603 \text{ ft}}$$

Problem 7.45 Determine the centroid of sail 3 in Problem 7.43.

Solution: Divide the object into six areas: (1) The triangle Oef, with base 3.5 ft and altitude 21 ft. (2) The rectangle Oabc, 14 ft by 29 ft. (3) The triangle beg, with base 10.5 ft and altitude 8 ft. (4) The triangle bcd, with base 9 ft and altitude 29 ft. (5) The rectangle agef 3.5 ft by 8 ft. (6) The composite, Oebd. The areas and centroids are:

(1) $A_1 = 36.75 \text{ ft}^2$,

$x_1 = 1.167 \text{ ft}$,

$y_1 = 14 \text{ ft}$.

(2) $A_2 = 406 \text{ ft}^2$,

$x_2 = 7 \text{ ft}$,

$y_2 = 14.5 \text{ ft}$.

(3) $A_3 = 42 \text{ ft}^2$,

$x_3 = 7 \text{ ft}$,

$y_3 = 26.33 \text{ ft}$

(4) $A_4 = 130.5 \text{ ft}^2$,

$x_4 = 17 \text{ ft}$,

$y_4 = 9.67 \text{ ft}$.

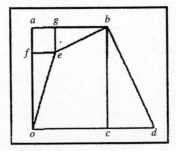

(5) $A_5 = 28 \text{ ft}^2$,

$x_5 = 1.75 \text{ ft}$,

$y_5 = 25 \text{ ft}$.

(6) The composite area:

$$A = -A_1 + A_2 - A_3 + A_4 - A_5 = 429.75 \text{ ft}^2.$$

The composite centroid:

$$\boxed{x = \frac{-A_1 x_1 + A_2 x_2 - A_3 x_3 + A_4 x_4 - A_5 x_5}{A} = 10.877 \text{ ft}}$$

$$\boxed{y = \frac{-A_1 y_1 + A_2 y_2 - A_3 y_3 + A_4 y_4 - A_5 y_5}{A} = 11.23 \text{ ft}}$$

Problem 7.46 The value of the distributed load w at $x = 6$ m is 240 N/m.

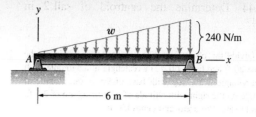

(a) The equation for the loading curve is $w = 40x$ N/m. Use Eq. (7.10) to determine the magnitude of the total force exerted on the beam by the distributed load.

(b) If you use the area analogy to represent the distributed load by an equivalent force, what is the magnitude of the force and where does it act?

(c) Determine the reactions at A and B.

Solution:

(a) $\omega(x) = 40x$ N/m

$$F = \int_0^6 \omega(x)\,dx = \int_0^6 40x\,dx = 40\frac{x^2}{2}\Big|_0^6$$

$$F = 720 \text{ N}$$

(b) Using the area analogy

$$\mathbf{x} = \frac{\int_0^6 \omega(x)x\,dx}{\int_0^6 \omega(x)\,dx} = \frac{\int_0^6 40x^2\,dx}{720}$$

$$\mathbf{x} = \frac{\left[40\frac{x^3}{3}\right]_0^6}{720} = 4.00 \text{ m}$$

$$\mathbf{x} = 4.00 \text{ m (720 N force)}$$

(c) $\sum F_x : \quad A_x = 0$

$\sum F_y : \quad A_y + B_y - 720 = 0$

$\sum M_A : \quad (-4)(720) + (6)B_y = 0$

Solving,

$$\boxed{\begin{array}{l} B_y = 480 \text{ N} \\ A_y = 240 \text{ N} \\ A_x = 0 \end{array}}$$

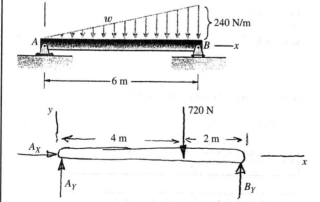

Problem 7.47 In a preliminary design study for a pedestrian bridge, an engineer models the combined weight of the bridge and maximum expected load due to traffic by the distributed load shown.

(a) Use Eq. (7.10) to determine the magnitude of the total force exerted on the bridge by the distributed load.
(b) If you use the area analogy to represent the distributed load by an equivalent force, what is the magnitude of the force and where does it act?
(c) Determine the reactions at A and B.

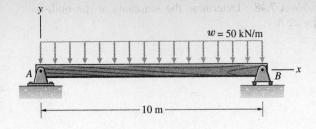

Solution:

(a) $F = \int_0^{10} \omega(x)\, dx = \int_0^{10} 50\, dx = 50x \Big|_0^{10}$ kN

$F = 500$ kN

(b) Area analogy

$$x = \frac{\int_0^{10} x\omega(x)\, dx}{\int_0^{10} \omega(x)\, dx} = \frac{\int_0^{10} 50x\, dx}{500 \text{ kN}}$$

$$x = \frac{25x^2 \big|_0^{10}}{500 \text{ kN}} = \frac{2500 \text{ kN} \cdot \text{m}}{500} \frac{}{\text{kN}}$$

$x = 5$ m (500 kN force)

(c) $\sum F_x: \quad A_x = 0$

$\sum F_y: \quad A_y + B_y - 500 = 0$

$\sum M_A: \quad (-5)(500) + 10B_y = 0$

$$\boxed{\begin{array}{l} B_y = 250 \text{ kN} \\ A_x = 0 \\ A_y = 250 \text{ kN} \end{array}}$$

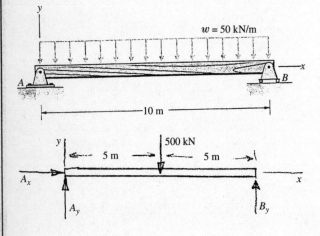

Problem 7.48 Determine the reactions at the built-in support A.

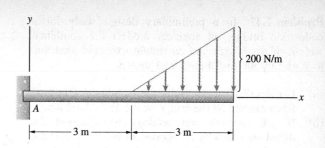

Solution: Total distributed force acting on the beam $\omega(x) = \dfrac{200}{3}(x-3)$ for $3 \le x \le 6$. The total force acting on the beam due to the distributed load is

$$F = \int_3^6 \frac{200}{3}(x-3)\,dx = \frac{200}{3}\left[\frac{x^2}{2} - 3x\right]_3^6$$

$$F = \frac{200}{3}\left[\frac{36}{2} - 18 - \frac{9}{2} + 9\right] = \frac{200}{3} \cdot \frac{9}{2}$$

$F = 300$ N.

Using the area analogy and the fact that the load is triangular, $\mathbf{x} = 5$ m.

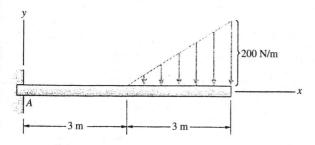

$$\sum F_x: \quad A_x = 0$$

$$\sum F_y: \quad A_y - 300 \text{ N} = 0$$

$$\sum M_A: \quad M_A - (5)(300) = 0$$

$$\boxed{\begin{aligned} A_x &= 0 \\ A_y &= 300 \text{ N} \\ M_A &= 1500 \text{ N-m} \end{aligned}}$$

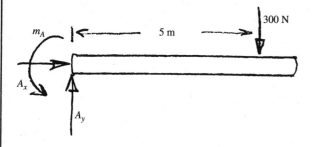

Problem 7.49 Determine the reactions at A and B.

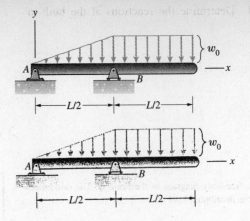

Solution: Let us break the load into two parts and use the area analogy.

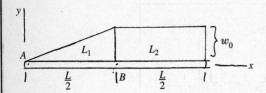

For Load L_1

$$\omega(x) = \frac{2\omega_0}{L}x \text{ for } (0 \leq x \leq L/2)$$

For Load L_2

$$\omega(x) = \omega_0 \text{ for } \left(\frac{L}{2} \leq x \leq L\right)$$

Load 1

$$L_1 = \int_0^{L/2} \frac{2\omega_0}{L}x\,dx = \frac{2\omega_0}{L}\frac{x^2}{2}\bigg|_0^{L/2}$$

$$L_1 = \frac{\omega_0}{L}\frac{L^2}{4} = \frac{L\omega_0}{4}$$

using the area analogy, load L_1 acts 2/3 of the distance from the origin to L/2. Thus

$$\mathbf{x}_1 = L/3$$

Load 2

$$L_2 = \int_{L/2}^{L} \omega_0\,dx = \omega_0 x\bigg|_{L/2}^{L} = \frac{\omega_0 L}{2}$$

And from the area analogy, L_2 acts half way between L/2 and L.

$$\mathbf{x}_2 = \frac{3L}{4}.$$

Now we can find the support reactions

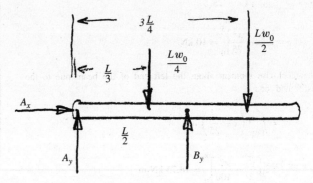

$$\sum F_x: \quad A_x = 0$$

$$\sum F_y: \quad A_y + B_y - \frac{L\omega_0}{4} - \frac{L\omega_0}{2} = 0$$

$$\sum M_A: \quad B_y\left(\frac{L}{2}\right) - \left(\frac{L\omega_0}{4}\right)\left(\frac{L}{3}\right) - \left(\frac{L\omega_0}{2}\right)\left(\frac{3L}{4}\right) = 0$$

Solving the third eqn.

$$B_y = \frac{L\omega_0}{6} + \frac{3L\omega_0}{4} = \frac{11}{12}L\omega_0$$

From the second eqn,

$$A_y + B_y = \frac{3}{4}L\omega_0$$

Hence $A_y = \frac{3}{4}l\omega_0 - B_y = -\frac{L\omega_0}{6}$

$$\boxed{\begin{array}{l} A_x = 0 \ A_y = -L\omega_0/6 \\ B_y = 11\,L\omega_0/12 \end{array}}$$

Problem 7.50 Determine the reactions at the built-in support A.

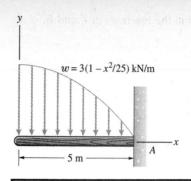

Solution: The free-body diagram of the beam is: The downward force exerted by the distributed load is

$$\int_L w\,dx = \int_0^5 3\left(1 - \frac{x^2}{25}\right) dx$$

$$= 3\left[x - \frac{x^3}{75}\right]_0^5 = 10 \text{ kN.}$$

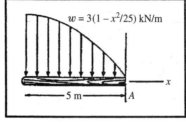

The clockwise moment about the left end of the beam due to the distributed load is

$$\int_L xw\,dx = \int_0^5 3\left(x - \frac{x^3}{25}\right) dx$$

$$= 3\left[\frac{x^2}{2} - \frac{x^4}{100}\right]_0^5 = 18.75 \text{ kN-m.}$$

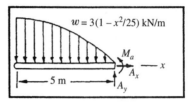

From the equilibrium equations

$$\sum F_x = A_x = 0,$$

$$\sum F_y = A_y - 10 = 0,$$

$$\sum m_{\text{(leftend)}} = M_a + 5A_y - 18.75 = 0,$$

we obtain

$$A_x = 0,$$

$$A_y = 10 \text{ kN,}$$

and $M_a = -31.25$ kN-m.

Problem 7.51 An engineer measures the forces exerted by the soil on a 10-m section of a building foundation and finds that they are described by the distributed load $w = -10x - x^2 + 0.2x^3$ kN[/]m.

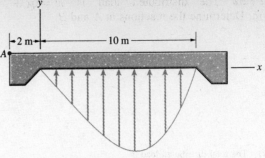

(a) Determine the magnitude of the total force exerted on the foundation by the distributed load.
(b) Determine the magnitude of the moment about A due to the distributed load.

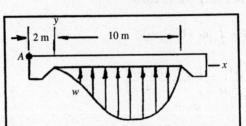

Solution:

(a) The total force is

$$F = -\int_0^{12} (10x + x^2 - 0.2x^3)\, dx$$

$$= \left[-5x^2 - \frac{x^3}{3} + \frac{0.2}{4}x^4 \right]_0^{10} \checkmark$$

$$|F| = 333.3 \text{ kN}$$

(b) The moment about the origin is

$$M = -\int_0^{10} (10x + x^2 - 0.2x^3)x\, dx$$

$$= \left[-\frac{10}{3}x^3 - \frac{1}{4}x^4 + \frac{0.2}{5}x^5 \right]_0^{10},$$

$$|M| = 1833.33 \text{ kN}.$$

The distance from the origin to the equivalent force is

$$d = \frac{|M|}{F} = 5.5 \text{ m},$$

from which

$$|M_A| = (d + 2)F = 2500 \text{ kN m}.$$

Problem 7.52 The distributed load is $w = 6x + 0.4x^2$ N/m. Determine the reactions at A and B.

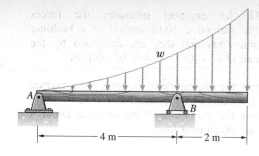

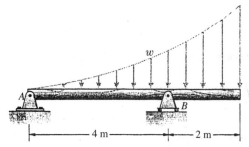

Solution: The total distributed load is

$$F = \int_0^6 w(x)\,dx = \int_0^6 (6x + 0.4x^3)\,dx$$

$$F = \left[6\frac{x^2}{2} + 0.4\frac{x^4}{4} \right]_0^6 = \left[3.36 + \frac{0.4(36)^2}{4} \right]$$

$$F = 237.6 \text{ N}$$

Using the area analogy, the point of application of the equivalent concentrated force F is

$$\mathbf{x} = \frac{\int_0^6 xw(x)\,dx}{\int_0^6 w(x)\,dx} = \frac{\int_0^6 (6x^2 + 0.4x^4)\,dx}{237.6}$$

$$\mathbf{x} = \frac{\left[6\frac{x^3}{3} + 0.4\frac{x^5}{5} \right]_0^6}{237.6} = 4.436 \text{ m}$$

Now to determine the support reactions

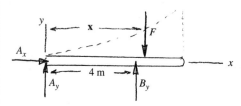

$$\sum F_x: \quad A_x = 0$$

$$\sum F_y: \quad A_y + B_y - F = 0$$

$$\sum M_A: \quad 4B_y - \mathbf{x}F = 0$$

Solving, we get

$$\boxed{\begin{aligned} A_x &= 0 \\ A_y &= -25.9 \text{ N} \\ B_y &= 263.5 \text{ N} \end{aligned}}$$

Problem 7.53 The aerodynamic lift of the wing is described by the distributed load

$$w = -300\sqrt{1 - 0.04x^2} \text{ N/m.}$$

The mass of the wing is 27 kg, and its center of mass is located 2 m from the wing root R.

(a) Determine the magnitudes of the force and the moment about R exerted by the lift of the wing.
(b) Determine the reactions on the wing at R.

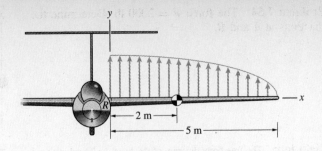

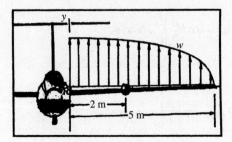

Solution:

(a) The force due to the lift is

$$F = -w = \int_0^5 300(1 - 0.04x^2)^{1/2} \, dx,$$

$$F = \frac{300}{5} \int_0^5 (25 - x^2)^{1/2} \, dx$$

$$F = 60 \left[\frac{x\sqrt{25 - x^2}}{2} + \frac{25}{2} \sin^{-1}\left(\frac{x}{5}\right) \right]_0^5 = 375\pi \text{ N,}$$

$$|F| = 1178.1 \text{ N.}$$

The moment about the root due to the lift is

$$M = 300 \int_0^5 (1 - 0.04x^2)^{1/2} x \, dx,$$

$$M = -60 \left[\frac{(25 - x^2)^{3/2}}{3} \right]_0^5 = \frac{60(25)^{3/2}}{3} = 2500$$

$$|M| = 2500 \text{ Nm.}$$

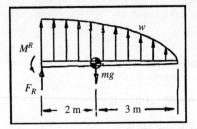

(b) The sum of the moments about the root:

$$\sum M = M^R + 2500 - 27g(2) = 0,$$

from which $M^R = -1970$ N-m. The sum of forces

$$\sum F_y = F_R + 1178.1 - 27g = 0,$$

from which $F_R = -1178.1 + 27g = -913.2$ N

Problem 7.54 The force $F = 2000$ lb. Determine the reactions at A and B.

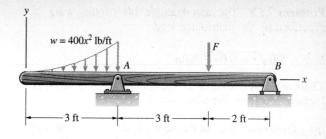

Solution: The free-body diagram of the beam is: The downward force exerted by the distributed load is

$$\int_L w \, dx = \int_0^3 400x^2 \, dx = 400 \left[\frac{x^3}{3} \right]_0^3 = 3600 \text{ lb}.$$

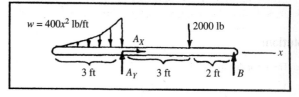

The clockwise moment about the left end of the beam due to the distributed load is

$$\int_L xw \, dx = \int_0^3 400x^3 \, dx = 400 \left[\frac{x^4}{4} \right]_0^3 = 8100 \text{ ft-lb}.$$

From the equilibrium equations

$$\sum F_x = A_x = 0,$$

$$\sum F_y = A_y + B - 3600 - 2000 = 0,$$

$$\sum m_{\text{(leftend)}} = 3A_y - 6(2000) + 8B - 8100 = 0,$$

we obtain $A_x = 0$, $A_y = 4940$ lb, $B = 660$ lb.

Problem 7.55 Determine the reactions at A and B.

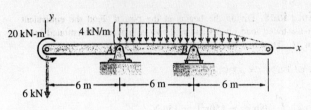

Solution: Break the load into two parts and find the equivalent concentrated load for each part. Then find the reactions at A and B

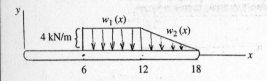

$w_1(x) = 4$ kN/m $\quad(6\text{ m} \le x \le 12\text{ m})$

$w_2(x) = \left(-\dfrac{2}{3}x + 12\right)$ kN/m $\quad(12\text{ m} \le x \le 18\text{ m})$

$F_1 = \displaystyle\int_6^{12} w_1(x)\,dx = \int_6^{12} 4\,dx$

$F_1 = 4x\Big|_6^{12} = 24$ kN

By symmetry, F_1 is applied at $x = 9$ m

$F_2 = \displaystyle\int_{12}^{18} w_2(x)\,dx = \int_{12}^{18} \left(-\dfrac{2}{3}x + 12\right) dx$

$F_2 = \left[-\dfrac{x^2}{3} + 12x\right]_{12}^{18} = 108 - 96$ kN

$F_2 = 12$ kN

By the area analogy, this load is applied at $x = 14$ m ($\frac{1}{3}$ of the way from 12 to 18).

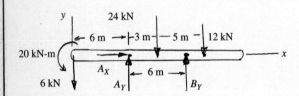

$\sum F_x:\quad A_x = 0$

$\sum F_y:\quad A_y + B_y - 24 - 12 - 6 = 0$

$\sum M_A:\quad (6)(6) + 20 - 3(24) + 6B_y - 8(12) = 0$

Solving $A_x = 0,\ A_y = 23.3$ kN, $B_y = 18.7$ kN

Problem 7.56 Determine the reactions on member AB at A and B.

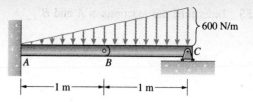

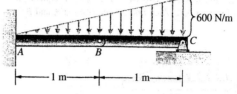

Solution: Divide the beams at the pin, B. Find the equivalent concentrated load on AB and find two equivalent concentrated loads on BC. Then find the support reactions

Load 1 $w_1(x) = 300x$ N/m

$$F_1 = \int_0^1 300x \, dx = 150x^2 \Big|_0^1 = 150 \text{ N}$$

Similarly,

$$F_2 = 150 \text{ N}$$

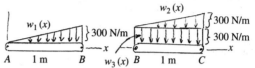

$$F_3 = \int_1^2 300 \, dx = 300x \Big|_1^2 = 300 \text{ N}$$

using the area analogy,

$$F_1 = 150 \text{ N applied at } x = \frac{2}{3} \text{ m}$$

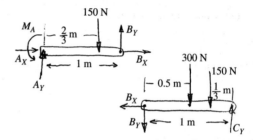

$$F_2 = 150 \text{ N applied at } x = \frac{5}{3} \text{ m}$$

$$F_3 = 300 \text{ N applied at } x = \frac{3}{2} \text{ m}$$

we now need to write the equilibrium equations.

For AB

$$\sum F_x: \quad A_x + B_x = 0$$

$$\sum F_y: \quad A_y + B_y - 150 = 0$$

$$\sum M_A: \quad (1)B_y - \left(\frac{2}{3}\right)(150) + M_A = 0$$

For BC

$$\sum F_x: \quad -B_x = 0$$

$$\sum F_y: \quad -B_y - 300 - 150 + C_y = 0$$

$$\sum M_B: \quad (1)C_y - (0.5)(300) - \left(\frac{2}{3}\right)(150) = 0$$

Solving, we get, acting on AB

$$
\begin{array}{l}
A_x = 0 \\
A_y = 350 \text{ N} \\
M_A = 300 \text{ N-m} \\
B_y = -200 \text{ N} \\
B_x = 0
\end{array}
$$

also $C_y = 250$ N

Problem 7.57 Determine the reactions on member *ABCD* at *A* and *D*.

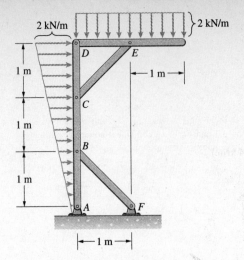

Solution: First, replace the distributed forces with equivalent concentrated forces, then solve for the loads. Note that *BF* and *CE* are two force members.

Distributed Load on *ABCD*, F_1

By area analogy, concentrated load is applied at $y = \pm m$. The load is $\frac{1}{2}(2)(3)$ kN

$F_1 = 3$ kN

By the area analogy,

$F_2 = 4$ kN applied at $x = 1$ m

Assume F_{CE} and F_{BF} are tensions

For *ABCD*:

$\sum F_x$: $A_x + F_{BF}\cos 45° + F_{CE}\cos 45° + D_x + 3$ kN $= 0$

$\sum F_y$: $A_y + D_y - F_{BF}\sin 45° + F_{CE}\sin 45° = 0$

$\sum M_A$: $-1(F_{BF}\cos 45°) - 2(F_{CE}\cos 45°) - 2(3) - 3D_x = 0$

For *DE*:

$\sum F_x$: $-D_x - F_{CE}\cos 45° = 0$

$\sum F_y$: $-D_y - F_{CE}\sin 45° - 4 = 0$

$\sum M_E$: $(1)D_y = 0$

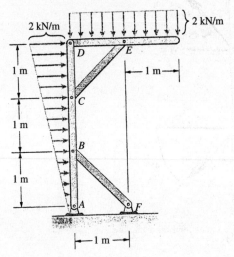

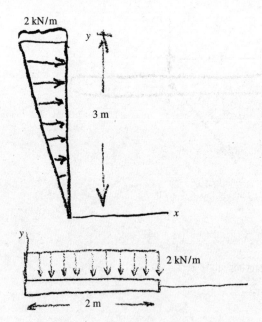

Solving, we get

$$
\begin{array}{l}
A_x = 7 \text{ kN} \\
A_y = -6 \text{ kN} \\
D_x = 4 \text{ kN} \\
D_y = 0
\end{array}
$$

also $F_{BF} = -14.14$ kN(c)

$F_{CE} = -5.66$ kN(c)

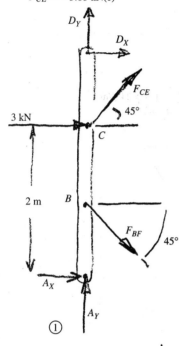

①

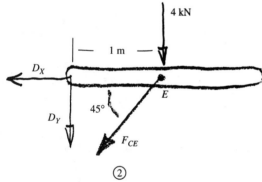

②

Problem 7.58 Determine the forces on member ABC of the frame.

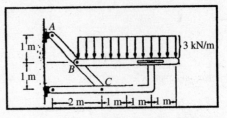

Solution: The free body diagram of the member on which the distributed load acts is

From the equilibrium equations

$$\sum F_x = B_x = 0,$$

$$\sum F_y = B_y + E - 12 = 0,$$

$$\sum m_{(leftend)} = 3E - (2)(12) = 0,$$

we find that $B_x = 0$, $B_y = 4$ kN, and $E = 8$ kN. From the lower fbd, writing the equilibrium equation

$$\sum m_{(leftend)} = -2C_y - (4)(8) = 0,$$

we obtain $C_y = -16$ kN. Then from the middle free body diagram, we write the equilibrium equations

$$\sum F_x = A_x + C_x = 0,$$

$$\sum F_y = A_y - 4 - 16 = 0,$$

$$\sum m_{(rightend)} = -2A_x - 2A_y + (1)(4) = 0$$

obtaining $A_x = -18$ kN, $A_y = 20$ kN, $C_x = 18$ kN.

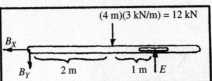

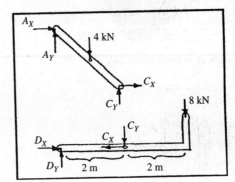

Problem 7.59 Determine the coordinates of the centroid of the truncated conical volume.

Strategy: Use the method described in Example 7.8.

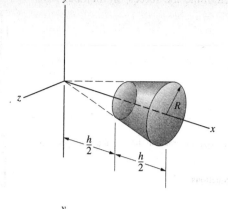

Solution: Refer to Example 7.8.

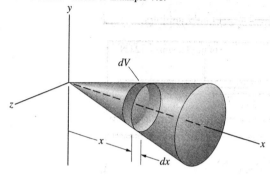

(a) An element dV in the form of a disk.

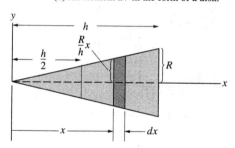

(b) The radius of the element is $(R/h)x$.

$$\mathbf{x} = \frac{\int_V x\,dV}{\int_V dV} = \frac{\int_{h/2}^{h} \pi \frac{R^2}{h^2} x^3 \, dx}{\int_{h/2}^{h} \pi \frac{R^2}{h^2} x^2 \, dx}$$

$$\mathbf{x} = \frac{\left[x^4/4\right]_{h/2}^{h}}{\left[x^3/3\right]_{h/2}^{h}} = \frac{\left[h^4/4 - h^4/64\right]}{\left[h^3/3 - h^3/24\right]}$$

$$\mathbf{x} = \frac{45}{56}h$$

Problem 7.60 A grain storage tank has the form of a surface of revolution with the profile shown. The height of the tank is 7 m and its diameter at ground level is 10 m. Determine the volume of the tank and the height *above ground level* of the centroid of its volume.

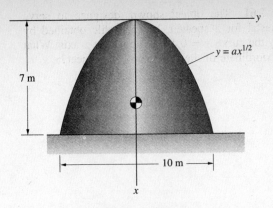

Solution:

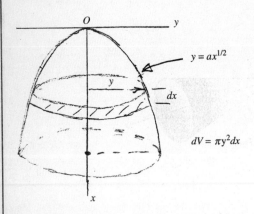

$dV = \pi y^2\, dx$

$dV = \pi y^2\, dx$

$$\mathbf{x} = \dfrac{\displaystyle\int_0^7 x\pi y^2\, dx}{\displaystyle\int_0^7 \pi y^2\, dx} = \dfrac{\displaystyle\int_0^7 x\pi a^2 x\, dx}{\displaystyle\int_0^7 \pi a^2 x\, dx}$$

$$\mathbf{x} = \dfrac{[x^3/3]_0^7}{[x^2/2]_0^7} = 4.67 \text{ m}$$

The height of the centroid above the ground is $7\text{ m} - \mathbf{x}$

$h = 2.33$ m

The volume is

$$V = \int_0^7 \pi a^2 x\, dx = \pi a^2 \left(\frac{49}{2}\right) \text{ m}^3$$

To determine a,

$y = 5$, m when $x = 7$ m.

$y = ax^{1/2}$, $5 = a\sqrt{7}$

$a = 5/\sqrt{7}a^2 = 25/7$

$$V = \pi \left(\frac{25}{7}\right)\left(\frac{49}{2}\right) = 275 \text{ m}^3$$

$V = 275$ m^3

Problem 7.61 The object shown, designed to serve as a pedestal for a speaker, has a profile obtained by revolving the curve $y = 0.167x^2$ about the x axis. What is the x coordinate of the centroid of the object?

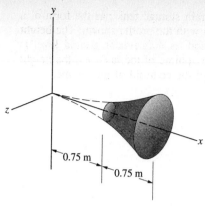

0.75 m

0.75 m

Solution:

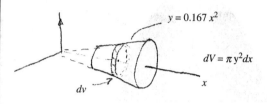

$y = 0.167\,x^2$

$dV = \pi\,y^2\,dx$

dv

x

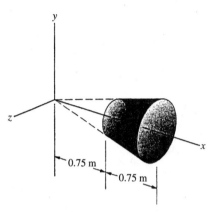

0.75 m

0.75 m

$$\mathbf{x} = \frac{\displaystyle\int_V x\,dV}{\displaystyle\int_V dV} = \frac{\displaystyle\int_{0.75}^{1.50} x\pi(0.167x^2)^2\,dx}{\displaystyle\int_{0.75}^{1.50} \pi(0.167x^2)^2\,dx}$$

$$\mathbf{x} = \frac{\pi(0.167)^2}{\pi(0.167)^2} \cdot \frac{\displaystyle\int_{0.75}^{1.5} x^5\,dx}{\displaystyle\int_{0.75}^{1.5} x^4\,dx} = \frac{\left[x^6/6\right]_{0.75}^{1.5}}{\left[x^5/5\right]_{0.75}^{1.5}}$$

$\mathbf{x} = 1.27$ m

Problem 7.62 Determine the volume and centroid of the pyramid.

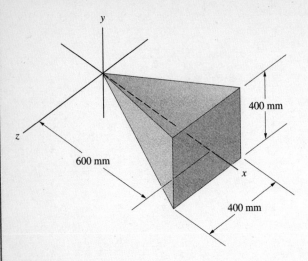

Solution: *The volume:* The element of volume is a square of thickness dx. The length of a side is a linear function of the height of the pyramid. Thus $L = Ax + B$. For $x = 0$, $L = 0$, and therefore $B = 0$. For $x = 600$, $L = 400$, therefore $A = \frac{2}{3}$. The area is $L^2 = \frac{4}{9}x^2$. The volume element is $dV = \frac{4}{9}x^2\,dx$, from which

$$V = \int_V dV = \left(\frac{4}{9}\right)\int_0^{600} x^2\,dx$$

$$= \left(\frac{4}{27}\right)[x^3]_0^{600} = 3.2 \times 10^7\ mm^3 = 0.032\ m^3$$

The x-coordinate:

$$\int_V x\,dV = \left(\frac{4}{9}\right)\int_0^{600} x^3\,dx$$

$$= \left(\frac{1}{9}\right)[x^4]_0^{600} = 1.44 \times 10^{10}.$$

Divide by V: $\mathbf{x} = 0.45$ m.

By symmetry, the y- and z-coordinates of the centroid are zero.

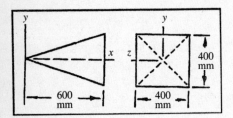

Problem 7.63 Determine the centroid of the hemi-spherical volume.

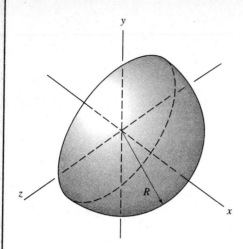

Solution: The equation of the surface of a sphere is $x^2 + y^2 + z^2 = R^2$.

The volume: The element of volume is a disk of radius ρ and thickness dx. The radius of the disk at any point within the hemisphere is $\rho^2 = y^2 + z^2$. From the equation of the surface of the sphere, $\rho^2 = (R^2 - x^2)$. The area is $\pi\rho^2$, and the element of volume is $dV = \pi(R^2 - x^2)\,dx$, from which

$$V = \frac{V_{\text{sphere}}}{2} = \frac{2\pi}{3}R^3.$$

The x-coordinate is:

$$\int_V x\,dV = \pi \int_0^R (R^2 - x^2)x\,dx$$

$$= \pi \left[\frac{R^2 x^2}{2} - \frac{x^4}{4} \right]_0^R$$

$$= \frac{\pi}{4}R^4.$$

Divide by the volume:

$$\mathbf{x} = \left(\frac{\pi R^4}{4} \right) \left(\frac{3}{2\pi R^3} \right) = \frac{3}{8}R.$$

By symmetry, the y- and z-coordinates of the centroid are zero.

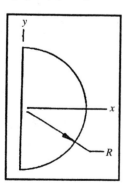

Problem 7.64 The volume consists of a segment of a sphere of radius R. Determine its centroid.

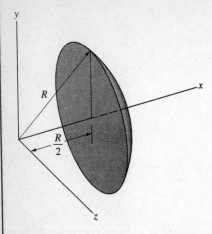

Solution: *The volume:* The element of volume is a disk of radius ρ and thickness dx. The area of the disk is $\pi\rho^2$, and the element of volume is $\pi\rho^2\,dx$. From the equation of the surface of a sphere (see solution to Problem 7.63) $\rho^2 = R^2 - x^2$, from which the element of volume is $dV = \pi(R^2 - x^2)\,dx$. Thus

$$V = \int_V dV = \pi \int_{R/2}^{R} (R^2 - x^2)\,dx$$

$$= \pi \left[R^2 x - \frac{x^3}{3} \right]_{R/2}^{R} = \left(\frac{5\pi}{24} \right) R^3.$$

The x-coordinate:

$$\int_V x\,dV = \pi \int_{R/2}^{R} (R^2 - x^2) x\,dx$$

$$= \pi \left[\frac{R^2 x^2}{2} - \frac{x^4}{4} \right]_{R/2}^{R} = \frac{9\pi}{64} R^4.$$

Divide by the volume:

$$\mathbf{x} = \left(\frac{9\pi R^4}{64} \right) \left(\frac{24}{5\pi R^3} \right) = \frac{27}{40} R = 0.675R.$$

By symmetry the y- and z-coordinates are zero.

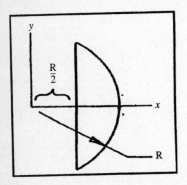

Problem 7.65 A volume of revolution is obtained by revolving the curve $\dfrac{x^2}{a^2} + \dfrac{y^2}{b^2} = 1$ about the x axis. Determine its centroid.

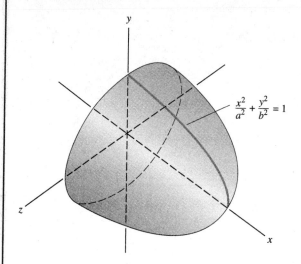

Solution: *The volume:* The element of volume is a disk of radius y and thickness dx. The area of the disk is πy^2. From the equation for the surface of the ellipse,

$$\pi y^2 = \pi b^2 \left(1 - \frac{x^2}{a^2}\right)$$

and $dV = \pi y^2\, dx = \pi b^2 \left(1 - \dfrac{x^2}{a^2}\right) dx$,

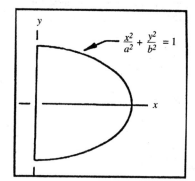

from which

$$V = \int_V dV = \pi b^2 \int_0^a \left(1 - \frac{x^2}{a^2}\right) dx$$

$$= \pi b^2 \left[x - \frac{x^3}{3a^2}\right]_0^a = \frac{2\pi b^2 a}{3}.$$

The x-coordinate:

$$\int_V x\, dV = \pi b^2 \int_0^a \left(1 - \frac{x^2}{a^2}\right) x\, dx$$

$$= \pi b^2 \left[\frac{x^2}{2} - \frac{x^4}{4a^2}\right]_0^a = \frac{\pi b^2 a^2}{4}.$$

Divide by volume:

$$\mathbf{x} = \left(\frac{\pi b^2 a^2}{4}\right)\left(\frac{3}{2\pi b^2 a}\right) = \left(\frac{3}{8}\right) a.$$

By symmetry, the y- and z-coordinates of the centroid are zero.

Problem 7.66 The volume of revolution has a cylindrical hole of radius R. Determine its centroid.

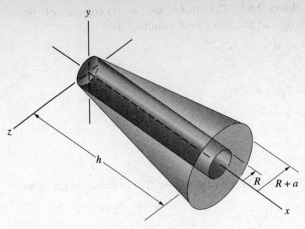

Solution: *The volume:* The element of volume is a disk of radius y and thickness dx. The area of the disk is $\pi(y^2 - R^2)$. The radius is $y = \left(\dfrac{a}{h}\right)x + R$. The volume element is

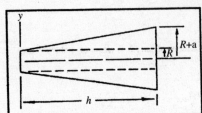

$$dV = \pi \left(\frac{a}{h}x + R\right)^2 dx - \pi R^2\, dx.$$

Denote

$$m = \left(\frac{a}{h}\right), \quad dV = \pi(m^2 x^2 + 2mRx)\,dx,$$

from which

$$V = \int_V dV = \pi m \int_0^h (mx^2 + 2Rx)\,dx$$

$$= \pi m \left[m\frac{x^3}{3} + Rx^2\right]_0^h = \pi m h^2 \left(\frac{mh}{3} + R\right).$$

The x-coordinate:

$$\int_V x\,dV = \pi m \int_0^h (mx^3 + 2Rx^2)\,dx$$

$$= \pi m \left[m\frac{x^4}{4} + \frac{2Rx^3}{3}\right]_0^h$$

$$= \pi m h^3 \left(m\frac{h}{4} + \frac{2R}{3}\right).$$

Divide by the volume:

$$\mathbf{x} = h\frac{\left(m\dfrac{h}{4} + \dfrac{2R}{3}\right)}{\left(m\dfrac{h}{3} + R\right)} = h\frac{\left(\dfrac{a}{4} + \dfrac{2R}{3}\right)}{\left(\dfrac{a}{3} + R\right)}.$$

By symmetry, the y- and z-coordinates of the centroid are zero.

Problem 7.67 Determine the y coordinate of the centroid of the line (see Example 7.9).

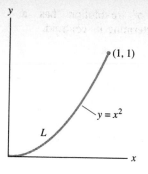

Solution: *The length of the line:* The elementary length of the line is

$$dL = \sqrt{1 + \left(\frac{dy}{dx}\right)^2}\, dx.$$

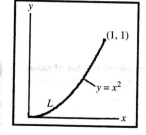

Noting that $\dfrac{dy}{dx} = 2x$, the element of length is $dL = (1 + 4x^2)^{1/2}\, dx$, from which

$$L = \int_L dL = \int_0^1 (1 + 4x^2)^{1/2}\, dx$$

$$= \frac{1}{2}\left[(1 + 4x^2)^{1/2}x + \frac{1}{2}\log_e(2x + (1 + 4x^2)^{1/2})\right]_0^1$$

$$= \frac{\sqrt{5}}{2} + \frac{1}{4}\log_e(2 + \sqrt{5}) = 1.4789.$$

The y-coordinate: The coordinate of the centroid of the length element is $y = y = x^2$, from which

$$y = \int_0^1 (1 + 4x^2)^{1/2}x^2\, dx = \left[\frac{x(1 + 4x^2)^{3/2}}{16} - \frac{x(1 + 4x^2)^{1/2}}{32}\right.$$

$$\left. - \frac{1}{64}\log_e(2x + (1 + 4x^2)^{1/2})\right]_0^1$$

$$= \frac{1}{16}(5)^{3/2} - \frac{1}{32}(5)^{1/2} - \frac{1}{64}\log_e(2 + \sqrt{5}) = 0.6063.$$

Divide by the length: $y = \dfrac{0.6063}{1.4789} = 0.410$

Problem 7.68 Determine the x coordinate of the centroid of the line.

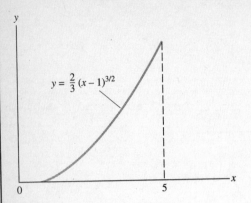

$y = \frac{2}{3}(x-1)^{3/2}$

Solution: *The length:* Noting that $\frac{dy}{dx} = (x-1)^{1/2}$, the element of length is

$$dL = \sqrt{1 + \left(\frac{dy}{dx}\right)^2}\, dx = \sqrt{x}\, dx$$

from which

$$L = \int_L dL = \int_1^5 (x)^{1/2}\, dx = \left[\frac{2}{3}(x)^{3/2}\right]_1^5 = 6.7869.$$

The x-coordinate:

$$\int_L x\, dL = \int_0^5 x^{3/2}\, dx = \left[\frac{2}{5}x^{5/2}\right]_1^5 = 21.961.$$

Divide by the length: $\mathbf{x} = \dfrac{21.961}{6.7869} = 3.2357$

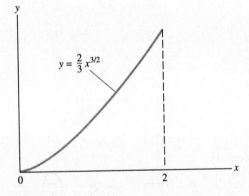

$y = \frac{2}{3}(x-1)^{3/2}$

Problem 7.69 Determine the x coordinate of the centroid of the line.

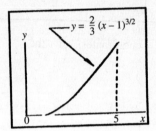

$y = \frac{2}{3}x^{3/2}$

Solution: *The length:* Noting that $\frac{dy}{dx} = x^{1/2}$ the element of length is

$$dL = \sqrt{1 + \left(\frac{dy}{dx}\right)^2}\, dx = \sqrt{1+x}\, dx$$

from which

$$L = \int_L dL = \int_0^2 (1+x)^{1/2}\, dx = \left[\frac{2}{3}(1+x)^{3/2}\right]_0^2 = 2.7974$$

The x-coordinate:

$$\int_L x\, dL = \int_0^2 x(1+x)^{1/2}\, dx = 2\left[\frac{(1+x)^{5/2}}{5} - \frac{(1+x)^{3/2}}{3}\right]_0^2$$

$$= 2\left[\frac{3^{5/2}}{5} - \frac{3^{3/2}}{3} - \left(\frac{1}{5}\right) + \left(\frac{1}{3}\right)\right] = 3.0379.$$

Divide by the length: $\mathbf{x} = 1.086$

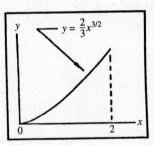

$y = \frac{2}{3}x^{3/2}$

Problem 7.70 Determine the centroid of the circular arc.

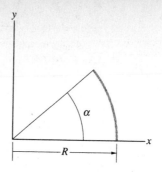

Solution: *The length:* From the equation for the circle,

$$y = \sqrt{R^2 - x^2} \text{ and } \frac{dy}{dx} = -(R^2 - x^2)^{-1/2}x.$$

The element of length

$$dL = \sqrt{1 + \left(\frac{dy}{dx}\right)^2}\, dx = R(R^2 - x^2)^{-1/2}\, dx,$$

from which

$$L = \int_L dL = \int_{R\cos\alpha}^{R} R(R^2 - x^2)^{-1/2}\, dx$$

$$= \left[R\sin^{-1}\left(\frac{x}{R}\right)\right]_{R\cos\alpha}^{R}$$

$$= R\left(\frac{\pi}{2} - \sin^{-1}(\cos\alpha)\right)$$

$$= R\left(\frac{\pi}{2} - \sin^{-1}\left(\sin\left(\frac{\pi}{2} - \alpha\right)\right)\right) = R\alpha$$

Check: $L = R\alpha$ from the definition of α. *check.*

The x-coordinate:

$$\int_L x\, dL = R\int_{R\cos\alpha}^{R} x(R^2 - x^2)^{-1/2}\, dx$$

$$= R\left[-(R^2 - x^2)^{1/2}\right]_{R\cos\alpha}^{R} = R^2\sin\alpha$$

Divide by the length: $\mathbf{x} = \left(\dfrac{R}{\alpha}\right)\sin\alpha.$

The y-coordinate: The y-coordinate of the centroid of each element is
$y = y = \sqrt{R^2 - x^2}$. Hence

$$\int_L y\, dL = R\int_{R\cos\alpha}^{R} (R^2 - x^2)^{1/2}(R^2 - x^2)^{-1/2}\, dx$$

$$= R\int_{R\cos\alpha}^{Rc} dx$$

$$= R^2(1 - \cos\alpha).$$

Divide by the length:

$$\mathbf{y} = \left(\frac{R}{\alpha}\right)(1 - \cos\alpha)$$

Problem 7.71 Determine the centroids of the volumes.

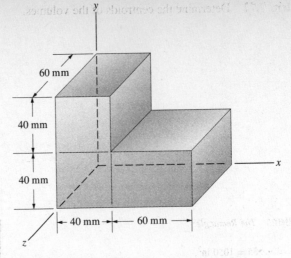

Solution: Divide the object into two volumes: (1) The left-most volume with dimensions 40 by 80 by 60 mm. (2) The right-most volume with dimensions 60 by 60 by 40 mm. The volumes and centroids are:

(1) $V_1 = 1.92 \times 10^5$ mm^3,

  $x_1 = 20$ mm,

  $y_1 = 40$ mm,

  $z_1 = 30$ mm.

(2) $V_2 = 1.44 \times 10^5$ mm^3,

  $x_2 = 70$ mm,

  $y_2 = 20$ mm,

  $z_2 = 30$ mm.

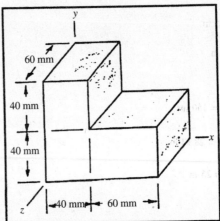

(3) The composite volume: $V = V_1 + V_2 = 3.36 \times 10^5$ mm^3. The composite centroid:

  $x = \dfrac{V_1 x_1 + V_2 x_2}{V} = 41.43$ mm.

  $y = \dfrac{V_1 y_1 + V_2 y_2}{V} = 31.43$ mm.

  $z = \dfrac{V_1 z_1 + V_2 z_2}{V} = 30$ mm.

Problem 7.72 Determine the centroids of the volumes.

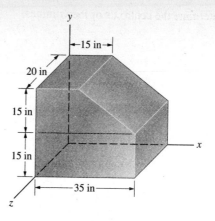

Solution: *The Rectangle:*

$\text{Area}_R = 30 \times 35 = 1050 \text{ in}^2$,

$\quad \mathbf{x}_R = 35/2 = 17.5 \text{ in}$,

$\quad \mathbf{y}_R = 30/2 = 15 \text{ in}$

The Triangle:

$\text{Area}_T = (20)(15)/2 = 150 \text{ in}^2$,

$\quad \mathbf{x}_T = 15 + \dfrac{2}{3}(20) = 28.33 \text{ in}$,

$\quad \mathbf{y}_T = 30 - 15/3 = 25 \text{ in}$

The Solid:

$\mathbf{x} = (\mathbf{x}_R \text{Area}_R - \mathbf{x}_T \text{Area}_T)/(\text{Area}_R - \text{Area}_T) = 15.7 \text{ in}$,

$\mathbf{y} = \mathbf{y} = (\mathbf{y}_R \text{Area}_R - \mathbf{y}_T \text{Area}_T)/(\text{Area}_R - \text{Area}_T) = 13.3 \text{ in}$,

and from symmetry, $\mathbf{z} = 0$.

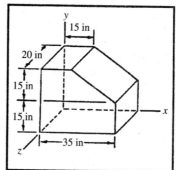

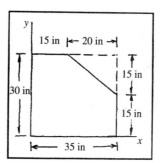

Problem 7.73   Determine the centroids of the volumes.

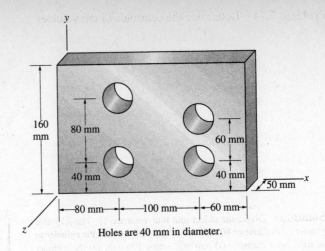

Holes are 40 mm in diameter.

Solution: For the block $L = 240$ mm, $H = 160$ mm, and $D = 50$ mm. For each hole, $r = 20$ mm. Centroids of parts are at the geometric centers.

Component Properties

Component	V	V (mm³)	x (mm)	y (mm)	z (mm)
Block	LHD	2×10^6	120	80	25
Hole 1	πr^2	62832	80	40	25
Hole 2	πr^2	62832	80	120	25
Hole 3	πr^2	62832	180	100	25
Hole 4	πr^2	62832	180	40	25

$$x = \frac{x_1 V_1 - x_2 V_2 - x_3 V_3 - x_4 V_4 - x_5 V_5}{V_1 - V_2 - V_3 - V_4 - V_5}$$

$$x = \frac{2.073 \times 10^8 \text{ mm}^4}{1.748 \times 10^6 \text{ mm}^3} = 118.56 \text{ mm}$$

$y = $ SIMILAR Eqn $= 80.72$ mm

$z = 25$ mm

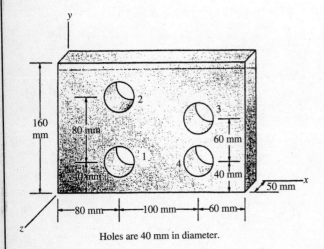

Holes are 40 mm in diameter.

Problem 7.74 Determine the centroids of the volumes.

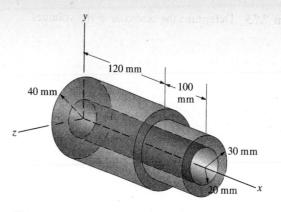

Solution: Divide the object into four volumes: (1) The left-most cylinder, with diameter 80 mm and length 120 mm, (2) the cylinder to the right, with diameter 60 mm and length 100 mm, (3) the cylinder bored through the center, with diameter 40 mm and length 220 mm, and (4) the composite cylinder. The volumes and centroids are:

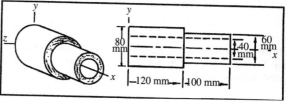

(1) $V_1 = 6.032 \times 10^5$ mm^3,

$\mathbf{x}_1 = 60$ mm,

$\mathbf{y}_1 = \mathbf{z}_1 = 0$,

(2) $V_2 = 2.83 \times 10^5$ mm^3,

$\mathbf{x}_2 = 170$ mm,

$\mathbf{y}_2 = \mathbf{z}_2 = 0$,

(3) $V_3 = 2.76 \times 10^5$ mm^3,

$\mathbf{x}_3 = 110$ mm,

$\mathbf{y}_3 = \mathbf{z}_3 = 0$.

(4) The composite volume: $V = V_1 + V_2 - V_3 = 6.095 \times 10^5$ mm^3.
The composite centroid:

$$\mathbf{x} = \frac{V_1\mathbf{x}_1 + V_2\mathbf{x}_2 - V_3\mathbf{x}_3}{V} = 88.4 \text{ mm},$$

$\mathbf{y} = \mathbf{z} = 0$

Problem 7.75 Determine the centroids of the volumes.

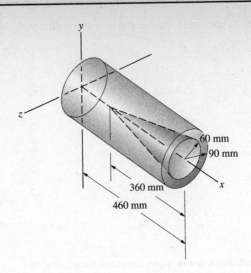

Solution: This is a composite shape. Let us consider a solid cylinder and then subtract the cone. Use information from the appendix

	Volume	Volume (mm³)	x	x (mm)
Cylinder	$\pi R^2 L$	1.1706×10^7	$L/2$	230
Cone	$\frac{1}{3}\pi r^2 h$	1.3572×10^6	$L-h/4$	370

$R = 90$ mm

$L = 460$ mm

$r = 60$ mm

$h = 360$ mm

$$x = \frac{X_{CyL}V_{CyL} - X_{CONE}V_{CONE}}{V_{CyL} - V_{CONE}}$$

$x = 211.6$ mm
$y = z = 0$ mm

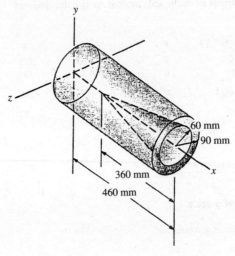

Problem 7.76   Determine the centroids of the volumes.

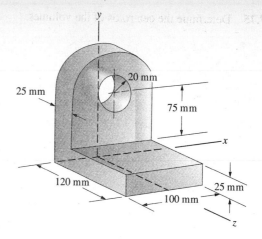

Solution: Break the composite object into simple shapes, find the volumes and centroids of each, and combine to find the required centroid.

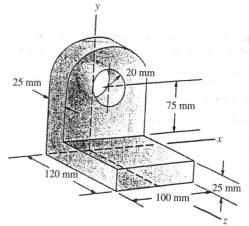

Object	Volume (V)	x	y	z
1	LWH	0	$H/2$	$L/2$
2	hWD	0	$(H + h/2)$	$D/2$
3	$\pi R^2 D/2$	0	$\left(H + h + \dfrac{4R}{3\pi}\right)$	$D/2$
4	$\pi r^2 D$	0	$(H + h)$	$D/2$

where $R = W/2$. For the composite,

$$\mathbf{x} = \frac{\mathbf{x}_1 V_1 + \mathbf{x}_2 V_2 + \mathbf{x}_3 V_3 - \mathbf{x}_4 V_4}{V_1 + V_2 + V_3 - V_4}$$

with similar eqns for **y** and **z**

The dimensions, from the figure, are

$L = 120$ mm

$W = 100$ mm

$H = 25$ mm

$r = 20$ mm

$h = 75$ mm

$D = 25$ mm

$R = 50$ mm

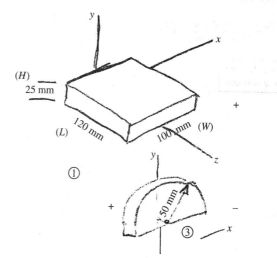

Object	V mm^3	x (mm)	y (mm)	z (mm)
+1	300000	0	12.5	60
+2	187500	0	62.5	12.5
+3	98175	0	121.2	12.5
−4	31416	0	100	12.5

7.76 *Contd.*

Substituting into the formulas for the composite, we get

$\mathbf{x} = 0$

$\mathbf{y} = 43.7$ mm

$\mathbf{z} = 38.2$ mm

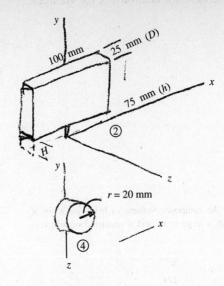

Problem 7.77   Determine the centroids of the volumes.

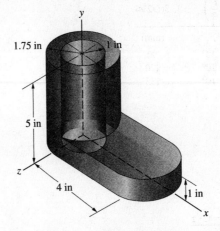

Solution: Divide the object into six volumes: (1) A cylinder 5 in. long of radius 1.75 in., (2) a cylinder 5 in. long of radius 1 in., (3) a block 4 in. long, 1 in. thick, and 2(1.75) = 3.5 in. wide. (4) Semi-cylinder 1 in long with a radius of 1.75 in., (5) a semi-cylinder 1 in long with a radius of 1.75 in. (6) The composite object. The volumes and centroids are:

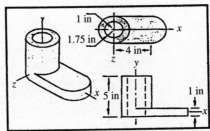

Volume	Vol, cu in	x, in.	y, in.	z, in.
V1	48.1	0	2.5	0
V2	15.7	0	2.5	0
V3	14	2	0.5	0
V4	4.81	0.743	0.5	0
V5	4.81	0	4.743	0

The composite volume is $V = V_1 - V_2 + V_3 - V_4 + V_5 = 46.4$ in^3. The composite centroid:

$$\mathbf{x} = \frac{V_1 \mathbf{x}_1 - V_2 \mathbf{x}_2 + V_3 \mathbf{x}_3 - V_4 \mathbf{x}_4 + V_5 \mathbf{x}_5}{V} = 1.02 \text{ in.,}$$

$$\mathbf{y} = \frac{V_1 y_1 - V_2 y_2 + V_3 y_3 - V_4 \mathbf{y}_4 + V_5 \mathbf{y}_5}{V} = 1.9 \text{ in.,}$$

$\mathbf{z} = 0$

Problem 7.78 Determine the centroids of the volumes.

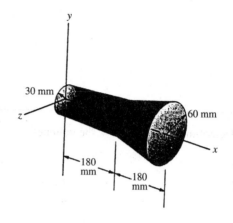

Solution: Consider the composite volume as being made up of three volumes, a cylinder, a large cone, and a smaller cone which is removed

Object	V	$\mathbf{x}$
Cylinder	$\pi r^2 L/2$	$L/4$
Cone 1	$\dfrac{1}{3}\pi R^2 L$	$3L/4$
Cone 2	$\dfrac{1}{3}\pi r^2 \left(\dfrac{L}{2}\right)$	$3(L/2)/4$

	(mm^3)	(mm)
Cylinder	5.089×10^5	90
Cone 1	1.357×10^6	270
Cone 2	1.696×10^5	135

$L = 360$ mm

$r = 30$ mm

$R = 60$ mm

For the composite shape

$$\mathbf{x} = \frac{\mathbf{x}_{Cyl} V_{CyL} + \mathbf{x}_1 V_1 - \mathbf{x}_2 V_2}{V_{CyL} + V_1 - V_2}$$

$\mathbf{x} = 229.5$ mm

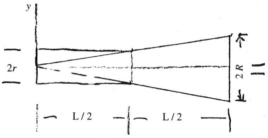

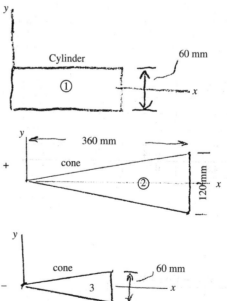

643

Problem 7.79 The dimensions of the *Gemini* space-craft (in meters) are $a = 0.70$, $b = 0.88$, $c = 0.74$, $d = 0.98$, $e = 1.82$, $f = 2.20$, $g = 2.24$, and $h = 2.98$. Determine the centroid of its volume.

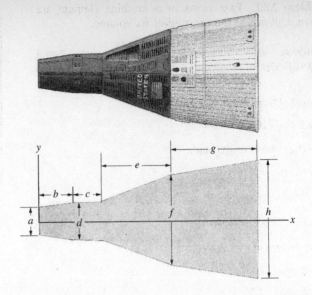

Solution: The spacecraft volume consists of three truncated cones and a cylinder. Consider the truncated cone of length L with radii at the ends R_1 and R_2, where $R_2 > R_1$. Choose the origin of the x-y coordinate system at smaller end. The radius of the cone is a linear function of the length; from geometry, the length of the cone before truncations was

(1) $\quad H = \dfrac{R_2 L}{(R_2 - R_1)}$ with volume

(2) $\quad \dfrac{\pi R_2^2 H}{3}$. The length of the truncated portion is

(3) $\quad \eta = \dfrac{R_1 L}{(R_2 - R_1)}$ with volume

(4) $\quad \dfrac{\pi R_1^2 \eta}{3}$. The volume of the truncated cone is the difference of the two volumes,

(5) $\quad V = \dfrac{\pi L}{3}\left(\dfrac{R_2^3 - R_1^3}{R_2 - R_1}\right)$. The centroid of the removed part of the cone is

(6) $\quad \mathbf{x}_\eta = \left(\dfrac{3}{4}\right)\eta$, and the centroid of the complete cone is

(7) $\quad \mathbf{x}_h = \left(\dfrac{3}{4}\right)H$, measured from the pointed end. From the composite theorem, the centroid of the truncated cone is

(8) $\quad \mathbf{x} = \dfrac{V_h \mathbf{x}_h - V_\eta \mathbf{x}_\eta}{V} - \eta + x$, where x is the x-coordinate of the left hand edge of the truncated cone in the specific coordinate system. These eight equations are the algorithm for the determination of the volumes and centroids of the truncated cones forming the spacecraft.

Beginning from the left, the volumes are (1) a truncated cone, (2) a cylinder, (3) a truncated cone, and (4) a truncated cone. The algorithm and the data for these volumes were entered into **TK Solver Plus** and the volumes and centroids determined. The volumes and x-coordinates of the centroids are:

Volume	Vol, cu m	x, m
V1	0.4922	0.4884
V2	0.5582	1.25
V3	3.7910	2.752
V4	11.8907	4.8716
Composite	16.732	3.999

The last row is the composite volume and x-coordinate of the centroid of the composite volume.

The total length of the spacecraft is 5.68 m, so the centroid of the volume lies at about 69% of the length as measured from the left end of the spacecraft. *Discussion:* The algorithm for determining the centroid of a system of truncated cones may be readily understood if it is implemented for a cone of known dimensions divided into sections, and the results compared with the known answer. Alternate algorithms (e.g. a Pappus-Guldinus algorithm) are useful for checking but arguably do not simplify the computations *End discussion.*

Problem 7.80 Two views of a machine element are shown. Determine the centroid of its volume.

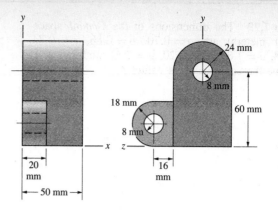

Solution: We divide the volume into six parts as shown. Parts 3 and 6 are the "holes", which each have a radius of 8 mm. The volumes are

$V_1 = (60)(48)(50) = 144,000 \text{ mm}^3$,

$V_2 = \frac{1}{2}\Pi(24)^2(50) = 45,239 \text{ mm}^3$,

$V_3 = \Pi(8)^2(50) = 10,053 \text{ mm}^3$,

$V_4 = (16)(36)(20) = 11,520 \text{ mm}^3$,

$V_5 = \frac{1}{2}\Pi(18)^2(20) = 10,179 \text{ mm}^3$,

$V_6 = \Pi(8)^2(20) = 4021 \text{ mm}^3$.

The coordinates of the centroids are

$x_1 = 25$ mm,

$y_1 = 30$ mm,

$z_1 = 0$,

$x_2 = 25$ mm,

$y_2 = 60 + \dfrac{4(24)}{3\Pi} = 70.2$ mm,

$z_2 = 0$,

$x_3 = 25$ mm,

$y_3 = 60$ mm,

$z_3 = 0$,

$x_4 = 10$ mm,

$y_4 = 18$ mm,

$z_4 = 24 + 8 = 32$ mm,

$x_5 = 10$ mm,

$y_5 = 18$ mm,

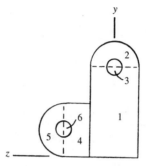

$z_5 = 24 + 16 + \dfrac{4(18)}{3\Pi} = 47.6$ mm,

$x_6 = 10$ mm,

$y_6 = 18$ mm,

$z_6 = 24 + 16 = 40$ mm.

The x coordinate of the centroid is

$$x = \frac{x_1 V_1 + x_2 V_2 - x_3 V_3 + x_4 V_4 + x_5 V_5 - x_6 V_6}{V_1 + V_2 - V_3 + V_4 + V_5 - V_6} = 23.65 \text{ mm}.$$

Calculating the y and z coordinates in the same way, we obtain $y = 36.63$ mm and $z = 3.52$ mm

---

Problem 7.81 Determine the centroids of the lines.

Solution: Break the line into two parts

	x_i	y_i	L_i
Part 1	4	2	$\sqrt{80} = 8.94$ m
Part 2	11	2	$\sqrt{52} = 7.21$ m

$x = \dfrac{x_1 L_1 + x_2 L_2}{L_1 + L_2} = 7.12$ m

By inspection, since $y_1 = y_2 = 2$ m we get

$y = 2$ m.

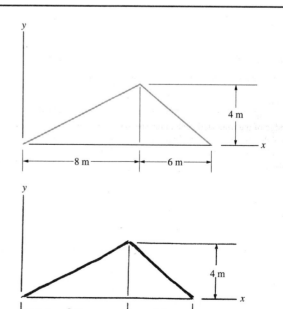

Problem 7.82 Determine the centroids of the lines.

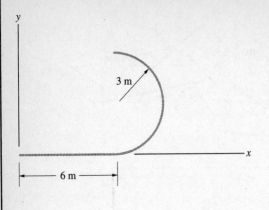

Solution: The object is divided into two lines and a composite.

(1) $L_1 = 6$ m, $x_1 = 3$ m, $y_1 = 0$.

(2) $L_2 = 3\pi$ m, $x_2 = 6 + \dfrac{6}{\pi}$ m (*Note*: See Example 7.13) $y_2 = 3$.

(3) The composite length: $L = 6 + 3\pi$ m. The composite centroid:

$$x = \frac{L_1 x_1 + L_2 x_2}{L} = 6 \text{ m},$$

$$y = \frac{3\pi}{2 + \pi} = 1.83 \text{ m}$$

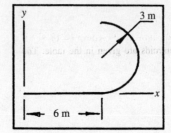

Problem 7.83 Determine the centroids of the lines.

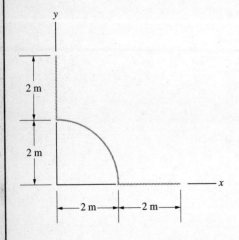

Solution: Break the composite line into two parts (the quarter circle and the straight line segment). (see Appendix B)

x_i	y_i	L_i	
Part 1	$2R/\pi$	$2R/\pi$	$\pi R/2$	$(R = 2$ m$)$
Part 2	3 m	0	2 m	

$$\frac{2R}{\pi} = 1.273 \quad \pi R/2 = 3.14 \text{ m}$$

$$x = \frac{x_1 L_1 + x_2 L_2}{L_1 + L_2} = 1.94 \text{ m}$$

$$y = \frac{y_1 L_1 + y_2 L_2}{L_1 + L_2} = 0.778 \text{ m}$$

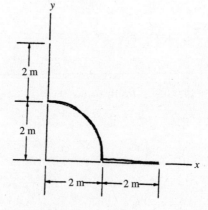

Problem 7.84 The semicircular part of the line lies in the $x - z$ plane. Determine the centroid of the line.

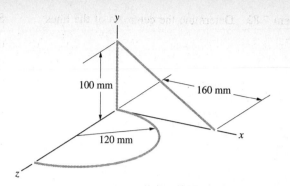

Solution: The bar is divided into three segments plus the composite. The lengths and the centroids are given in the table: The composite length is:

$$L = \sum_{i=1}^{3} L_i.$$

The composite coordinates are:

$$\mathbf{x} = \frac{\sum_{i=1}^{3} L_i x_i}{L},$$

and $\mathbf{y} = \dfrac{\sum_{i=1}^{3} L_i y_i}{L}$

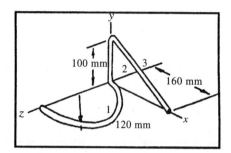

Segment	Length, mm	x, mm	y, mm	z, mm
L1	120π	$\dfrac{240}{\pi}$	0	120
L2	100	0	50	0
L3	188.7	80	50	0
Composite	665.7	65.9	21.7	68.0

Problem 7.85 The following theorem is *not true*: "The centroid of any area is coincident with the centroid of the line forming its boundary." Disprove it by finding a counterexample. That is, find an example for which it is not true.

Solution: Consider the 3, 4, 5 triangle. The centroid of the area is $\left(x = \dfrac{4}{3}, y = 1\right)$ *Proof:* Consider only the x-coordinate. Choose a vertical strip of area $y\,dx$. The boundary is $y = -\dfrac{3}{4}x + 3$.

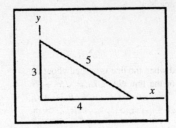

The area:

$$A = \int_0^4 \left(-\frac{3}{4}x + 3\right) dx = \left[-\frac{3}{8}x^2 + 3x\right]_0^4 = 6.$$

Check $A = \left(\dfrac{1}{2}\right)(3)(4) = 6$ *check.*

The x-coordinate:

$$\int_A x\,dA = \int_0^4 \left(-\frac{3}{4}x + 3\right) x\,dx = \left[-\frac{3}{12}x^3 + \frac{3}{2}x^2\right]_0^4 = 8.$$

Divide by the area: $\mathbf{x} = \dfrac{4}{3}$.

The Line: Divide the line into three segments, each corresponding to a side.

(1) $L_1 = 3$, $\mathbf{x}_1 = 0$, $\mathbf{y}_1 = \dfrac{3}{2}$.

(2) $L_2 = 4$, $\mathbf{x}_2 = 2$, $\mathbf{y}_2 = 0$.

(3) $L_3 = 5$, $\mathbf{x}_3 = 2$, $\mathbf{y}_3 = \dfrac{3}{2}$. The composite length is $L = 3 + 4 + 5 = 12$.

The centroid: $\mathbf{x} = \dfrac{(3)0 + (4)2 + (5)2}{12} = \dfrac{18}{12} = \dfrac{3}{2}$. *The theorem fails for the x-coordinate.* It is unnecessary to go further.

Problem 7.86 Revolving the area of the triangle ABC about the x axis generates a conical volume. Use the second Pappus–Guldinus theorem to calculate the volume and compare your answers to the value given in Appendix C.

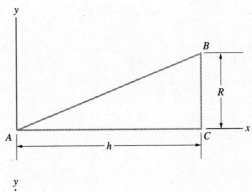

Solution: The centroid of the triangular area is located at ($2h/3$, $R/3$). Rotating the triangle about the x axis, the centroid moves through a distance $d = 2\pi(R/3)$. The area of the triangle is $A = 1/2Rh$ The second theorem of Pappas–Goldinus states that the volume generated by rotating the triangle about the x axis will be $v = Ad$

$$V = Ad = \frac{Rh}{2}(2\pi R/3)$$

$$V = \pi R^2 h/3$$

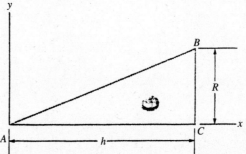

Problem 7.87 Revolving the line ABC shown in Problem 7.86 about the x axis generates a conical surface. Use the first Pappus–Guldinus theorem to calculate the area of the conical surface.

Solution: The centroid of the area is at

$$\left(\frac{2h}{3}, R/3\right)$$

The distance traveled by the centroid when the line is rotated about the x-axis is $d_1 = 2\pi R/3$. The length of the line OA is $L_1 = \sqrt{h^2 + R^2}$. The length of line AB is $L_2 = R$. The centroid of line AB is at $(h, R/2)$ and this centroid moves through a distance $d_2 = 2\pi(R/2)$ as the rotation occurs.

The total area of the conical surface, including the base, is

$$A = (2\pi R/3)\sqrt{h^2 + R^2} + (2\pi R/2)R$$

$$A = 2\pi R\sqrt{h^2 + R^2}/3 + \pi R^2$$

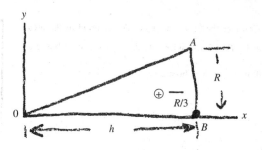

Problem 7.88 Use the second Pappus–Guldinus theorem to determine the volume generated by revolving the curve about the x axis.

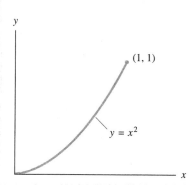

Solution: *The area:* The element of area is the vertical strip of height y and width dx. Thus

$$A = \int_0^1 y\,dx = \int_0^1 x^2\,dx.$$

Integrating,

$$A = \left[\frac{x^3}{3}\right]_0^1 = \frac{1}{3}.$$

The y-coordinate:

$$\int_A y\,dA = \int_0^1 y(1 - x)\,dy$$

$$= \int_0^1 (y - y^{3/2})\,dy = \left[\frac{y^2}{2} - \frac{2y^{5/2}}{5}\right]_0^1 = \frac{1}{10}.$$

Divide by the area: $\mathbf{y} = \dfrac{3}{10}$. *The Volume:* $V = 2\pi \mathbf{y} A = \dfrac{\pi}{5}$

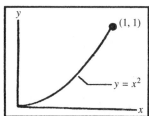

Problem 7.89 Use the second Pappus–Guldinus theorem to determine the volume generated by revolving the curve about the y axis.

Solution: *The x coordinate of the centroid:.* The element of area is the vertical strip of height $(1 - y)$ and width dx. Thus

$$A = \int_0^1 (1 - y)\, dx = \int_0^1 (1 - x^2)\, dx.$$

Integrating,

$$A = \left[x - \frac{x^3}{3} \right]_0^1 = \frac{2}{3}.$$

$$\int_A x\, dA = \int_0^1 (x - x^3)\, dx = \left[\frac{x^2}{2} - \frac{x^4}{4} \right]_0^1 = \frac{1}{4},$$

divide by the area: $\mathbf{x} = \dfrac{3}{8}$. The volume is $V = 2\pi \mathbf{x} A = \dfrac{\pi}{2}$

Problem 7.90 The length of the curve is $L = 1.479$, and the area generated by rotating it about the x axis is $A = 3.810$. Use the first Pappus–Guldinus theorem to determine the y coordinate of the centroid of the curve.

Solution: The surface area is $A = 2\pi \mathbf{y} L$, from which

$$\mathbf{y} = \frac{A}{2\pi L} = 0.41$$

Problem 7.91 Use the first Pappus–Guldinus theorem to determine the area of the surface generated by revolving the curve about the y axis.

Solution: The length of the line is given in Problem 7.88. $L = 1.479$. The elementary length of the curve is

$$dL = \sqrt{1 + \left(\frac{dy}{dx} \right)^2}\, dx.$$

Noting $\dfrac{dy}{dx} = 2x$, the element of line is $dL = (1 + 4x^2)^{1/2}$.

The x-coordinate:

$$\int_L x\, dL = \int_0^1 x(1 + 4x^2)^{1/2}\, dx$$

$$= \frac{1}{12} \left[(1 + 4x^2)^{3/2} \right]_0^1 = \frac{5^{3/2} - 1}{12} = 0.8484.$$

Divide by the length to obtain $\mathbf{x} = 0.5736$. The surface area is $A = 2\pi \mathbf{x} L = 5.33$

Problem 7.92 A nozzle for a large rocket engine is designed by revolving the function $y = \frac{2}{3}(x-1)^{3/2}$ about the y axis. Use the first Pappus–Guldinus theorem to determine the surface area of the nozzle.

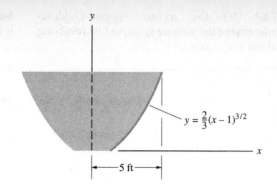

$y = \frac{2}{3}(x-1)^{3/2}$

5 ft

Solution: *The length:* Noting that $\dfrac{dy}{dx} = (x-1)^{1/2}$, the element of length is

$$dL = \sqrt{1 + \left(\frac{dy}{dx}\right)^2}\, dx = \sqrt{x}\, dx$$

from which

$$L = \int_L dL = \int_1^5 (x)^{1/2}\, dx = \left[\frac{2}{3}(x)^{3/2}\right]_1^5 = 6.7869 \text{ ft}$$

The x-coordinate:

$$\int_L x\, dL = \int_1^5 x^{3/2}\, dx = \left[\frac{2}{5}x^{5/2}\right]_1^5 = 21.961.$$

Divide by the length: $\mathbf{x} = 3.2357$. The area

$$A = 2\pi \mathbf{x} L = 138 \text{ ft}^2$$

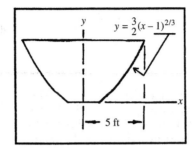

$y = \frac{3}{2}(x-1)^{2/3}$

5 ft

Problem 7.93 A volume of revolution is obtained by revolving the area between the function $y = \frac{2}{3}x^{3/2}$ about the y axis. Use the second Pappus–Guldinus theorem to determine its volume.

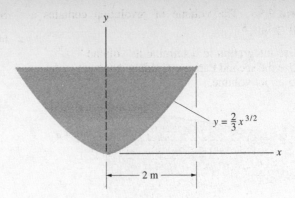

Solution: The element of area is the vertical strip between

$$y_1 = \left(\frac{2}{3}\right)\left[x^{3/2}\right]_{x=2} = 1.8856 \text{ and } y.$$

$$dA = (y_1 - y)\,dx = \left(y_1 - \left(\frac{2}{3}\right)x^{3/2}\right)dx.$$

The area is

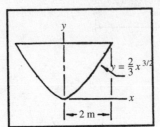

$$\int_0^2 \left(y_1 - \left(\frac{2}{3}\right)x^{3/2}\right)dx = \left[xy_1 - \left(\frac{2}{3}\right)\left(\frac{2}{5}\right)x^{5/2}\right]_0^2$$

$$= 2.2627.$$

The x-coordinate of the centroid:

$$\int_0^2 \left(y_1 - \left(\frac{2}{3}\right)x^{3/2}\right)x\,dx = \left[y_1\frac{x^2}{2} - \left(\frac{2}{3}\right)\left(\frac{2}{7}\right)x^{7/2}\right]_0^2$$

$$= 1.6162.$$

Divide by the area to obtain $\mathbf{x} = 0.714$ m. The volume is $V = 2\pi\mathbf{x}A = 10.155$ m^3

Problem 7.94 Use the first Pappus–Guldinus theorem to determine the area of the curved surface of the volume of revolution in Problem 7.93.

Solution: *The length:* Noting that $\dfrac{dy}{dx} = x^{1/2}$ the element of length is

$$dL = \sqrt{1 + \left(\frac{dy}{dx}\right)^2}\,dx = \sqrt{1 + x}\,dx$$

from which

$$L = \int_L dL = \int_0^2 (1+x)^{1/2}\,dx = \left[\frac{2}{3}(1+x)^{3/2}\right]_0^2 = 2.7974 \text{ m}.$$

The x-coordinate:

$$\int_L x\,dL = \int_0^2 x(1+x)^{1/2}\,dx$$

$$= 2\left[\frac{(1+x)^{5/2}}{5} - \frac{(1+x)^{3/2}}{3}\right]_0^2 = 3.0379.$$

Divide by the length: $\mathbf{x} = 1.086$. The area of the surface $A = 2\pi\mathbf{x}L = 19.09$ m^2

Problem 7.95 The volume of revolution contains a hole of radius R.

(a) Use integration to determine its volume.
(b) Use the second Pappus–Guldinus theorem to determine its volume.

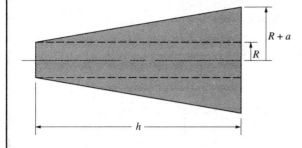

Solution:

(a) The element of volume is a disk of radius y and thickness dx. The area of the disk is $\pi(y^2 - R^2)$. The radius is

$$y = \left(\frac{a}{h}\right)x + R,$$

from which $dV = \pi\left(\frac{a}{h}x + R\right)^2 dx - \pi R^2\, dx.$

Denote $m = \left(\frac{a}{h}\right)$, $dV = \pi(m^2 x^2 + 2mRx)\,dx,$

from which

$$V = \int_V dV = \pi m \int_0^h (mx^2 + 2Rx)\,dx$$

$$= \pi m \left[m\frac{x^3}{3} + Rx^2\right]_0^h = \pi m h^2 \left(\frac{mh}{3} + R\right)$$

$$= \pi a h \left(\frac{a}{3} + R\right).$$

(b) The area of the triangle is $A = (\frac{1}{2})ah$. The y-coordinate of the centroid is $\mathbf{y} = R + (\frac{1}{3})a$. The volume is

$$\boxed{V = 2\pi\mathbf{y}A = \pi a h (R + (\tfrac{1}{3})a)}$$

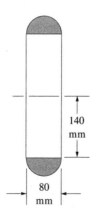

Problem 7.96 Determine the volume of the volume of revolution.

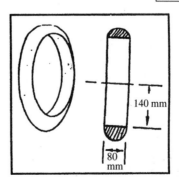

Solution: The area of the semicircle is $A = \dfrac{\pi r^2}{2}$. The centroid is $y = R + \dfrac{4r}{3\pi}$. The volume is

$$V = 2\pi \left(\frac{\pi r^2}{2}\right)\left(R + \frac{4r}{3\pi}\right) = \pi^2 r^2 \left(R + \frac{4r}{3\pi}\right).$$

For $r = 40$ mm and $R = 140$ mm, $\boxed{V = 2.48 \times 10^{-3}\ \text{m}^3}$

Problem 7.97 Determine the surface area of the volume of revolution in Problem 7.96.

Solution: The length and centroid of the semicircle is $L_o = \pi r$, $y = R + \dfrac{2r}{\pi}$. The length and centroid of the inner line is $L_i = 2r$, and $y = R$.

$$A = 2\pi(\pi r)\left(R + \frac{2r}{\pi}\right) + 2\pi(2r)(R) = 2\pi r(\pi R + 2r + 2R).$$

For $r = 40$ mm and $R = 140$ mm, $A = 0.201$ m^2

Problem 7.98 The volume of revolution has an elliptical cross section. Determine its volume.

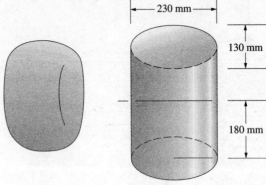

Solution: Use the second theorem of Pappus-Guldinus. The centroid of the ellipse is 180 mm from the axis of rotation. The area of the ellipse is πab where $a = 115$ mm, $b = 65$ mm.

The centroid moves through a distance $|d| = 2\pi R = 2\pi$ (180 mm) as the ellipse is rotated about the axis.

$$V = Ad = \pi abd = 2.66 \times 10^7 \text{ mm}^3$$

$$v = 0.0266 \text{ m}^3$$

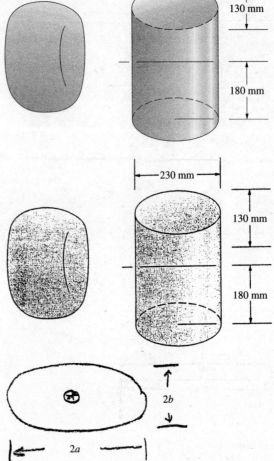

Problem 7.99 The mass of the homogeneous flat plate is 450 kg. What are the reactions at A and B?

Strategy: The center of mass of the plate is coincident with the centroid of its area. Determine the horizontal coordinate of the centroid and assume that the plate's weight acts there.

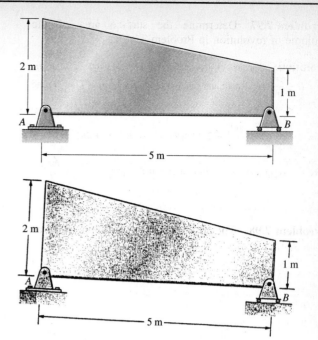

Solution: To find the location of the center of mass, find the centroid by breaking the plate into a triangle and a rectangle.

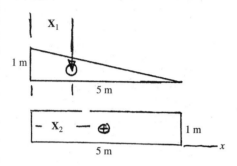

$\text{Area}_1 = 5/2 \text{ m}^2$

$\mathbf{x}_1 = 5/3 \text{ m}$

$\text{Area}_2 = 5 \text{ m}^2$

$\mathbf{x}_2 = \dfrac{5}{2} \text{ m}$

$\mathbf{x} = \dfrac{\mathbf{x}_1 A_1 + \mathbf{x}_2 A_2}{A_1 + A_2} = 2.22 \text{ m}$

$m = 450 \text{ kg}$

$\mathbf{x} = 2.22 \text{ m}$

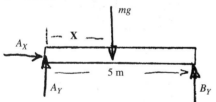

$\displaystyle\sum F_x: \quad A_x = 0$

$\displaystyle\sum F_y: \quad A_y + B_y - mg = 0$

$\displaystyle\sum M_A: \quad -\mathbf{x}\, mg + 5B_y = 0$

Solving:

$A_x = 0, \quad A_y = 2.45 \text{ kN}$
$B_y = 1.96 \text{ kN}$

Problem 7.100 The mass of the homogeneous flat plate is 50 kg. Determine the reactions at the supports A and B.

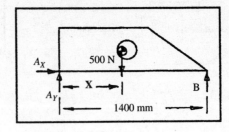

Solution: Divide the object into three areas and the composite. Since the distance to the action line of the weight is the only item of importance, and since there is no horizontal component of the weight, it is unnecessary to determine any centroid coordinate other than the x-coordinate. The areas and the x-coordinate of the centroid are tabulated. The last row is the composite area and x-coordinate of the centroid.

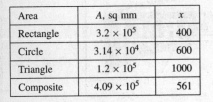

Area	A, sq mm	x
Rectangle	3.2×10^5	400
Circle	3.14×10^4	600
Triangle	1.2×10^5	1000
Composite	4.09×10^5	561

The composite area is $A = A_{rect} - A_{circ} + A_{triang}$. The composite x-coordinate of the centroid is

$$x = \frac{A_{rect}x_{rect} - A_{circ}x_{circ} + A_{triang}x_{triang}}{A}.$$

The sum of the moments about A:

$$\sum M_A = -500(561) + 1400B = 0,$$

from which $B = 200$ N. The sum of the forces:

$$\sum F_y = A_y + B - 500 = 0,$$

from which $A_y = 300$ N.

$$\sum F_x = A_x = 0$$

656

Problem 7.101   The suspended sign is a homogeneous flat plate that has a mass of 130 kg. Determine the axial forces in members AD and CE. (Notice that the y axis is positive downward.)

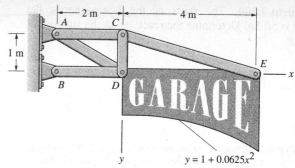

Solution: The strategy is to determine the distance to the action line of the weight (x-coordinate of the centroid) from which to apply the equilibrium conditions to the method of sections.

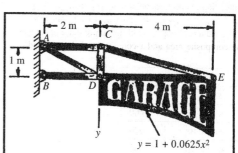

The area: The element of area is the vertical strip of length y and width dx. The element of area $dA = y\,dx = (1 + ax^2)\,dx$, where $a = 0.0625$. Thus

$$A = \int_A dA = \int_0^4 (1 + ax^2)\,dx = \left[x + \frac{ax^3}{3}\right]_0^4 = 5.3333 \text{ sq ft.}$$

The x-coordinate:

$$\int_A x\,dA = \int_0^4 x(1 + ax^2)\,dx = \left[\frac{x^2}{2} + \frac{ax^4}{4}\right]_0^4 = 12.$$

Divide A: $\mathbf{x} = \dfrac{12}{5.3333} = 2.25$ ft.

The equilibrium conditions: The angle of the member CE is

$$\alpha = \tan^{-1}\left(\tfrac{1}{4}\right) = 14.04^\circ.$$

The weight of the sign is $W = 130(9.81) = 1275.3$ N. The sum of the moments about D is

$$\sum M_D = -2.25W + 4CE\sin\alpha = 0,$$

from which $\boxed{CE = 2957.7 \text{ N } (T)}$.

Method of sections: Make a cut through members AC, AD and BD and consider the section to the right. The angle of member AD is

$$\beta = \tan^{-1}\left(\tfrac{1}{2}\right) = 26.57^\circ.$$

The section as a free body: The sum of the vertical forces:

$$\sum F_Y = AD\sin\beta - W = 0$$

from which $\boxed{AD = 2851.7 \text{ N } (T)}$.

Problem 7.102 The bar has a mass of 80 kg. What are the reactions at A and B?

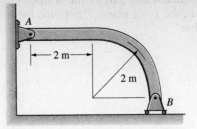

Solution: Break the bar into two parts and find the masses and centers of masses of the two parts. The length of the bar is

$$L = L_1 + L_2 = 2 \text{ m} + 2\pi R/4 (R = 2 \text{ m})$$

$$L = 2 + \pi \text{ m}$$

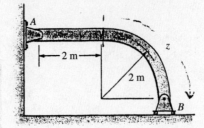

Part	Length$_i$ (m)	Mass$_i$ (kg)	$\mathbf{x}_i$ (m)
1	2	$\left(\dfrac{2}{2+\pi}\right) 80$	1
2	π	$\left(\dfrac{\pi}{2+\pi}\right) 80$	$\left(2 + \dfrac{2R}{\pi}\right)$

$m_1 = 31.12$ kg $\mathbf{x}_1 = 1$ m

$m_2 = 48.88$ kg $\mathbf{x}_2 = 3.27$ m

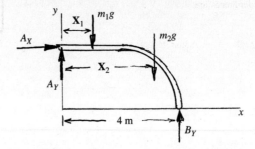

$$\sum F_x: \quad A_x = 0$$

$$\sum F_y: \quad A_y + B_y - m_1 g - m_2 g = 0$$

$$\sum M_A: \quad -\mathbf{x}_1 m_1 g - \mathbf{x}_2 m_2 g + 4B_y = 0$$

Solving

$$A_x = 0, \quad A_y = 316 \text{ N}, \quad B = 469 \text{ N}$$

Problem 7.103 The semicircular part of the homogeneous slender bar lies in the $x - z$ plane. Determine the center of mass of the bar.

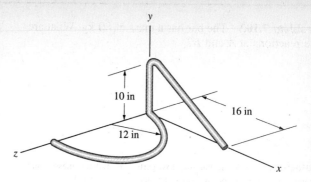

Solution: The bar is divided into three segments plus the composite. The lengths and the centroids are given in the table: The composite length is:

$$L = \sum_{i=1}^{3} L_i.$$

The composite coordinates are:

$$\mathbf{x} = \frac{\sum_{i=1}^{3} L_i \mathbf{x}_i}{L},$$

$$\text{and } \mathbf{y} = \frac{\sum_{i=1}^{3} L_i \mathbf{y}_i}{L}$$

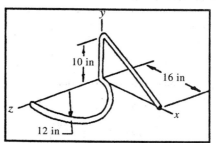

Segment	Length, in.	x, in.	y, in.	z, in.
L1	12π	$\dfrac{24}{\pi}$	0	12
L2	10	0	5	0
L3	18.868	8	5	0
Composite	66.567	6.594	2.168	6.796

659

Problem 7.104 When the truck is unloaded, the total reactions at the front and rear wheels are $A = 54$ kN and $B = 36$ kN. The density of the load of gravel is $\rho = 1600$ kg/m^3. The dimension of the load in the z direction is 3 m, and its surface profile, given by the function shown, does not depend on z. What are the total reactions at the front and rear wheels of the loaded truck?

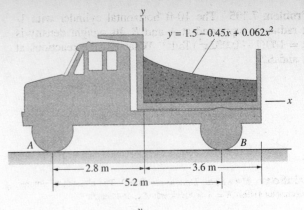

Solution: First, find the location of the center of mass of the unloaded truck (and its mass). Then find the center of mass and mass of the load. Combine to find the wheel loads on the loaded truck.

Unloaded Truck

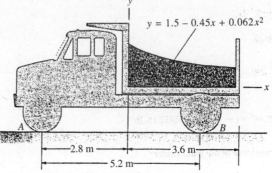

$$\sum F_x: \quad \text{no forces}$$

$$\sum F_y: \quad 54000 + 36000 - m_T g = 0(N)$$

$$\sum M_A: \quad -x_T m_T g + 5.2(36) = 0$$

Solving $x_T = 2.08$ m, $m_T = 9174$ kg

Next, find x_L and m_L (for the load)

$$x_L = \frac{\int_{m_L} x\,dm}{\int_{m_L} dm} = \frac{\text{Num}}{m_L}$$

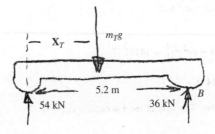

where $m_L = \int_{m_L} dm$, $\text{Num} = \int_{m_L} x\,dm$

$$m_L = \int_0^{3.6} 3\rho y\,dx = 3\rho \int_0^{3.6} (1.5 - 0.45x + 0.062x^2)\,dx$$

$$m_L = 3\rho \left[1.5x - 0.45\left(\frac{x^2}{2}\right) + 0.062\left(\frac{x^3}{3}\right) \right]_0^{3.6}$$

$$m_L = 16551 \text{ kg}$$

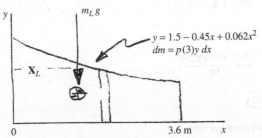

$$\text{Num} = 3\rho \int_0^{3.6} (1.5x - 0.45x^2 + 0.062x^3)\,dx$$

$$\text{Num} = 3\rho \left[1.5\left(\frac{x^2}{2}\right) - 0.45\left(\frac{x^3}{3}\right) + 0.062\left(\frac{x^4}{4}\right) \right]_0^{3.6}$$

$$\text{Num} = 25560 \text{ kg} \cdot \text{m}$$

$$x_L = \frac{\text{Num}}{m_L} = 1.544 \text{ m}$$

measured from the front of the load

The horizontal distance from A to the center of mass of the load is
$d_L = x_L + 2.8 \text{ m} = 4.344 \text{ m}$

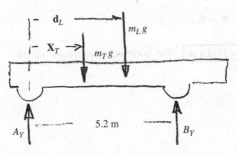

Now we can find the wheel loads on the loaded truck

$$\sum F_x: \quad \text{no forces}$$

$$\sum F_y: \quad A_y + B_y - m_T g - m_L g = 0$$

$$\sum M_A: \quad 5.2 B_y - x_T m_T g - d_L m_L g = 0$$

Solving $A_y = 80.7$ kN, $B_y = 171.6$ kN

Problem 7.105 The 10-ft horizontal cylinder with 1-ft radius is supported at A and B. Its weight density is $\gamma = 100(1 - 0.002x^2)$ lb/ft³. What are the reactions at A and B?

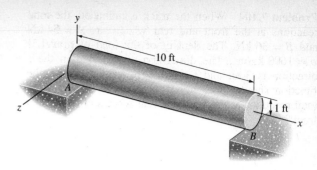

Solution: *The weight:* Denote $a = 0.002$. The element of volume is a disk of radius $R = 1$ ft, thickness dx, and weight

$$dW = \gamma \pi R^2 \, dx,$$

from which

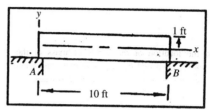

$$W = \int dW = 100\pi R^2 \int_0^L (1 - ax^2) \, dx$$

$$= 100\pi R^2 \left[x - \frac{ax^3}{3} \right]_0^L = 2932.15 \text{ lb}$$

The x-coordinate of the mass center:

$$\int_W x \, dW = 100\pi R^2 \int_0^L (1 - ax^2)x \, dx$$

$$= -\frac{25\pi R^2}{a} \left[(1 - ax^2)^2 \right]_0^L = 14137.17.$$

Divide by W: $\mathbf{x} = 4.8214$ ft.

The equilibrium conditions: The sum of the moments about A is

$$\sum M_A = -W\mathbf{x} + 10B = 0,$$

from which

$$B = \frac{W\mathbf{x}}{L} = \frac{(2932.15)(4.8214)}{10}$$

$$\boxed{= 1413.7 \text{ lb}}.$$

The sum of the vertical forces:

$$\sum F_Y = A + B - W = 0,$$

from which $\boxed{A = 1518.4 \text{ lb}}$. The horizontal components of the reactions are zero:

$$\sum F_X = 0$$

Problem 7.106 A horizontal cone with 800-mm length and 200-mm radius has a built-in support at A. Its mass density is $\rho = 6000(1 + 0.4x^2)$ kg/m^3, where x is in meters. What are the reactions at A?

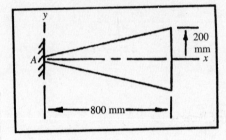

Solution: The strategy is to determine the distance to the line of action of the weight, from which to apply the equilibrium conditions.

The mass: The element of volume is a disk of radius y and thickness dx. y varies linearly with x: $y = 0.25x$. Denote $a = 0.4$. The mass of the disk is

$$dm = \rho \pi y^2 \, dx = 6000\pi(1 + ax^2)(0.25x)^2 \, dx$$

$$= 375\pi(1 + ax^2)x^2 \, dx,$$

from which

$$m = 375\pi \int_0^{0.8} (1 + ax^2)x^2 \, dx = 375\pi \left[\frac{x^3}{3} + a\frac{x^5}{5} \right]_0^{0.8}$$

$$= 231.95 \text{ kg}$$

The x-coordinate of the mass center:

$$\int_m x \, dm = 375\pi \int_0^{0.8} (1 + ax^2)x^3 \, dx = 375\pi \left[\frac{x^4}{4} + a\frac{x^6}{6} \right]_0^{0.8}$$

$$= 141.23.$$

Divide by the mass: $\mathbf{x} = 0.6089$ m
The equilibrium conditions: The sum of the moments about A:

$$\sum M = M_A - mg\mathbf{x} = 0,$$

from which

$$M_A = mg\mathbf{x} = 231.94(9.81)(0.6089)$$

$$\boxed{= 1385.4 \text{ N-m}}.$$

The sum of the vertical forces:

$$\sum F_Y = A_Y - mg = 0$$

from which $\boxed{A_Y = 2275.4 \text{ N}}$. The horizontal component of the reaction is zero,

$$\sum F_X = 0.$$

Problem 7.107 The circular cylinder is made of aluminum (Al) with mass density 2700 kg/m³ and iron (Fe) with mass density 7860 kg/m³.

(a) Determine the centroid of the volume of the cylinder.
(b) Determine the center of mass of the cylinder.

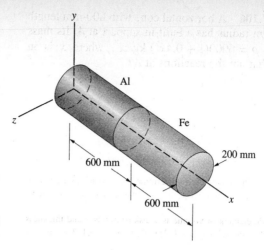

Solution:

(a) The volume of the cylinder is

$$V = \pi(0.1)^2(1.2) = 0.0377 \text{ m}^3.$$

The volume of the parts:

$$V_{Al} = V_{Fe} = \frac{V}{2} = 0.0188 \text{ m}^3.$$

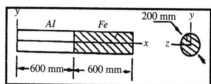

The centroid of the first part is $x_{Al} = 0.3$ m, $y_{Al} = z_{Al} = 0$. The centroid of the iron part is

$$x_{Fe} = 0.6 + 0.3 = 0.9 \text{ m},$$

$$y_{Fe} = z_{Fe} = 0.$$

The composite centroid

$$x = \frac{V_{Al}(0.3) + V_{Fe}(0.9)}{V} = \frac{1.2}{2} = 0.6 \text{ m},$$

$$y = z = 0.$$

(b) *The mass center:* The mass of the aluminum part is $m_{Al} = V_{Al}(2700) = 50.89$ kg. The mass of the iron part is $m_{Fe} = V_{Fe}(7860) = 148.16$ kg. The composite mass is $m = m_{Al} + m_{Fe} = 199.05$ kg. The composite center of mass is

$$x_m = \frac{(50.89)(0.3) + (148.16)(0.9)}{199.05} = 0.7466 \text{ m}$$

$$y_m = z_m = 0$$

Problem 7.108 The cylindrical tube is made of aluminum with mass density 2700 kg/m³. The cylindrical plug is made of steel with mass density 7800 kg/m³. Determine the coordinates of the center of mass of the composite object.

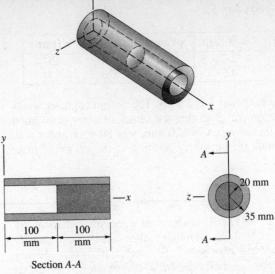

Section A-A

Solution: The volume of the aluminum tube is

$$V_{Al} = \pi(0.035^2 - 0.02^2)(0.2) = 5.18 \times 10^{-4} \text{ m}^3.$$

The mass of the aluminum tube is $m_{Al} = (2700)V_{Al} = 1.4$ kg. The centroid of the aluminum tube is $x_{AL} = 0.1$ m, $y_{Al} = z_{Al} = 0$.

The volume of the steel plug is $V_{Fe} = \pi(0.02)^2(0.1) = 1.26 \times 10^{-4}$ m³. The mass of the steel plug is $m_{Fe} = (7800)V_{Fe} = 0.9802$ kg. The centroid of the steel plug is $x_{Fe} = 0.15$ m, $y_{Fe} = z_{Fe} = 0$.

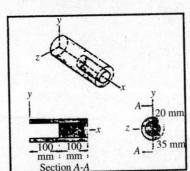

Section A-A

The composite mass is $m = 2.38$ kg. The composite centroid is

$$x = \frac{m_{Al}(0.1) + m_{Fe}(0.15)}{m} = 0.121 \text{ m}$$

$$y = z = 0$$

Problem 7.109 A machine consists of three parts. The masses and the locations of the centers of mass of the parts are:

Part	Mass (kg)	x (mm)	y (mm)	z (mm)
1	2.0	100	50	−20
2	4.5	150	70	0
3	2.5	180	30	0

Determine the coordinates of the center of mass of the machine.

Solution: The composite mass is 9 kg.

$$x = \frac{2(100) + 4.5(150) + 2.5(180)}{9} = 147 \text{ mm}$$

$$y = \frac{2(50) + 4.5(70) + 2.5(30)}{9} = 54.4 \text{ mm}$$

$$z = \frac{2(-20)}{9} = -4.4 \text{ mm}$$

Problem 7.110 A machine consists of three parts. The masses and the locations of the centers of mass of two of the parts are:

Part	Mass (kg)	x (mm)	y (mm)	z (mm)
1	2.0	100	50	−20
2	4.5	150	70	0

The mass of part 3 is 2.5 kg. The design engineer wants to position part 3 so that the center of mass of location of the machine is $x = 120$ mm, $y = 80$ mm, and $z = 0$. Determine the necessary position of the center of mass of part 3.

Solution: The composite mass is $m = 2.0 + 4.5 + 2.5 = 9$ kg. The location of the third part is

$$x_3 = \frac{120(9) - 2(100) - 4.5(150)}{2.5} = 82 \text{ mm}$$

$$y_3 = \frac{80(9) - 2(50) - 4.5(70)}{2.5} = 122 \text{ mm}$$

$$z_3 = \frac{2(20)}{2.5} = 16 \text{ mm}$$

Problem 7.111 Two views of a machine element are shown. Part 1 is aluminum alloy with mass density 2800 kg/m³, and part 2 is steel with mass density 7800 kg/m³. Determine the x coordinate of its center of mass.

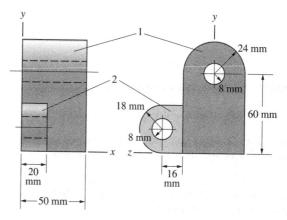

Solution: The volumes of the parts are

$$V_1 = \left[(60)(48) + \tfrac{1}{2}\pi(24)^2 - \pi(8)^2\right](50)$$

$$= 179,186 \text{ mm}^3 = 17.92 \times 10^{-5} \text{ m}^3,$$

$$V_2 = \left[(16)(36) + \tfrac{1}{2}\pi(18)^2 - \pi(8)^2\right](20) = 17,678 \text{ mm}^3$$

$$= 1.77 \times 10^{-5} \text{ m}^3,$$

so their masses are

$$m_1 = S_1 V_1 = (2800)(17.92 \times 10^{-5}) = 0.502 \text{ kg},$$

$$m_2 = S_2 V_2 = (7800)(1.77 \times 10^{-5}) = 0.138 \text{ kg}.$$

The x coordinates of the centers of mass of the parts are $x_1 = 25$ mm, $x_2 = 10$ mm, so

$$x = \frac{x_1 m_1 + x_2 m_2}{m_1 + m_2} = 21.8 \text{ mm}$$

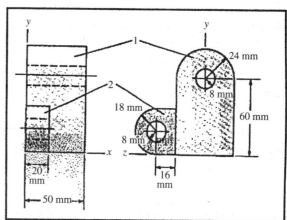

Problem 7.112 Determine the y and z coordinates of the center of mass of the machine element in Problem 7.111.

Solution: The z coordinate of the center of mass of part 1 is $z_1 = 0$. To determine the y coordinate, we divide it into three parts a, b, and c. (Part c is the "hole" with radius 8 mm). The volumes are

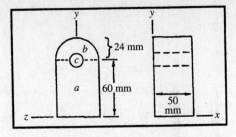

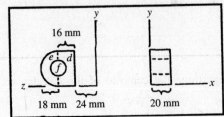

$$V_a = (60)(48)(50) = 144,000 \text{ mm}^3,$$

$$V_b = \tfrac{1}{2}\pi(24)^2(50) = 45,239 \text{ mm}^3,$$

$$V_c = \pi(8)^2(50) = 10,053 \text{ mm}^3$$

so $\quad y_1 = \dfrac{y_a V_a + y_b V_b - y_c V_c}{V_a + V_b - V_c}$

$$= \dfrac{(30)V_a + \left[60 + \dfrac{4(24)}{3\pi}\right]V_b - (60)V_c}{V_a + V_b - V_c}$$

$$= 38.5 \text{ mm}.$$

The y coordinate of the center of mass of part 2 is $y_2 = 18$ mm. To determine the z coordinate, we divide it into three parts d, e, and f. The volumes are

$$V_d = (16)(36)(20) = 11,520 \text{ mm}^3,$$

$$V_e = \tfrac{1}{2}\pi(18)^2(20) = 10,179 \text{ mm}^3,$$

$$V_f = \pi(8)^2(20) = 4021 \text{ mm}^3$$

so $\quad z_2 = \dfrac{z_d V_d + z_e V_e - z_f V_f}{V_d + V_e - V_f}$

$$= \dfrac{(24 + 8)V_d + \left[24 + 16 + \dfrac{4(18)}{3\pi}\right]V_e - (24 + 16)V_f}{V_d + V_e + V_f}$$

$$= 39.2 \text{ mm}.$$

From the solution of Problem 7.111, the masses are $m_1 = 0.502$ kg, $m_2 = 0.138$ kg, Therefore,

$$y = \dfrac{y_1 m_1 + y_2 m_2}{m_1 + m_2} = 34.05 \text{ mm},$$

$$z = \dfrac{z_1 m_1 + z_2 m_2}{m_1 + m_2} = 8.45 \text{ mm}.$$

Problem 7.113 With its engine removed, the mass of the car is 1100 kg and its center of mass is at C. The mass of the engine is 220 kg.

(a) Suppose that you want to place the center of mass E of the engine so that the center of mass of the car is midway between the front wheels A and the rear wheels B. What is the distance b?

(b) If the car is parked on a $15°$ slope facing up the slope, what total normal force is exerted by the road on the rear wheels B?

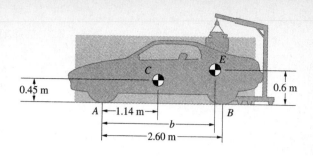

Solution:

(a) The composite mass is $m = m_C + m_E = 1320$ kg. The x-coordinate of the composite center of mass is given:

$$x = \frac{2.6}{2} = 1.3 \text{ m},$$

from which the x-coordinate of the center of mass of the engine is

$$x_E = b = \frac{(1.3 \text{ m} - 1.14 \, m_C)}{m_E} = 2.1 \text{ m}.$$

The y-coordinate of the composite center of mass is

$$y = \frac{0.45 \, m_C + 0.6 \, m_E}{m} = 0.475 \text{ m}.$$

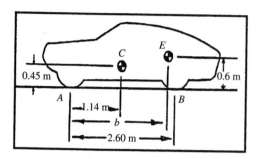

(b) Assume that the engine has been placed in the new position, as given in Part (a). The sum of the moments about B is

$$\sum M_A = 2.6A + ymg \sin(15°)$$

$$- (2.6 - x)mg \cos(15°) = 0,$$

from which $A = 5641.7$ N. This is the normal force exerted by the road on A. The normal force exerted on B is obtained from;

$$\sum F_N = A - mg \cos(15°) + B = 0,$$

from which $B = 6866$ N

Problem 7.114 The airplane is parked with its landing gear resting on scales. The weights measured at A, B, and C are 30 kN, 140 kN, and 146 kN, respectively. After a crate is loaded onto the plane, the weights measured at A, B, and C are 31 kN, 142 kN, and 147 kN, respectively. Determine the mass and the x and y coordinates of the center of mass of the crate.

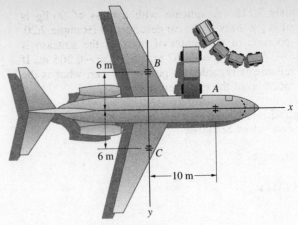

Solution: The weight of the airplane is $W_A = 30 + 140 + 146 = 316$ kN. The center of mass of the airplane:

$$\sum M_{y-axis} = 30(10) - x_A W_A = 0,$$

from which $x_A = 0.949$ m.

$$\sum M_{x-axis} = (140 - 146)(6) + y_A W_A = 0,$$

from which $y_A = 0.114$ m. The weight of the loaded plane:

$$W = 31 + 142 + 147 = 320 \text{ kN.}$$

The center of mass of the loaded plane:

$$\sum M_{y-axis} = (31)10 - xW = 0,$$

from which $x = 0.969$ m.

$$\sum M_{x-axis} = (142 - 147)(6) + yW = 0,$$

from which $y = 0.0938$ m. The weight of the crate is $W_c = W - W_A = 4$ kN. The center of mass of the crate:

$$x_c = \frac{Wx - W_A x_A}{W_c} = 2.5 \text{ m,}$$

$$y_c = \frac{Wy - W_A y_A}{W_c} = -1.5 \text{ m.}$$

The mass of the crate:

$$m_c = \frac{W_c \times 10^3}{9.81} = 407.75 \text{ kg}$$

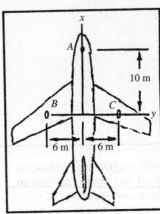

Problem 7.115 A suitcase with a mass of 90 kg is placed in the trunk of the car described in Example 7.20. The position of the center of mass of the suitcase is $x_s = -0.533$ m, $y_s = 0.762$ m, and $z_s = -0.305$ m. If the suitcase is regarded as part of the car, what is the new position of the car's center of mass?

Solution: In Example 7.20, the following results were obtained for the car without the suitcase

$$W_c = 17303 \text{ N}$$

$$x_c = 1.651 \text{ m}$$

$$y_c = 0.584 \text{ m}$$

$$z_c = 0.769 \text{ m}$$

For the suitcase

$$W_s = (90) \text{ g}, \quad x_s = -0.533 \text{ m},$$

$$y = 0.762 \text{ m}, \quad z = -0.305 \text{ m}.$$

The new center of mass is at

$$x_N = \frac{x_c W_c + x_s W_s}{(W_c + W_s)}$$

with similar eqns for y_N and z_N

Solving, we get

$$x_N = 1.545 \text{ m}, \quad y_N = 0.593 \text{ m}, \quad z_N = 0.717 \text{ m}$$

Problem 7.116 A group of engineering students constructs a miniature device of the kind described in Example 7.20 and uses it to determine the center of mass of a miniature vehicle. The data they obtain are shown in the following table:

Wheelbase = 36 in.		
Track = 30 in.	**Measured Loads (lb)**	
	$\alpha = 0$	$\alpha = 10°$
Left front wheel, N_{LF}	35	32
Right front wheel, N_{RF}	36	33
Left rear wheel, N_{LR}	27	34
Right rear wheel, N_{RR}	29	30

Determine the center of mass of the vehicle. Use the same coordinate system as in Example 7.20.

Solution: The weight of the go-cart: $W = 35 + 36 + 27 + 29 = 127$ lb. The sum of the moments about the z-axis

$$\sum M_{z-\text{axis}} = (Wheelbase)(N_{LF} + N_{RF}) - xW = 0,$$

from which

$$x = \frac{36(35 + 36)}{W} = 20.125 \text{ in.}$$

The sum of the moments about the x-axis:

$$\sum M_{x-\text{axis}} = zW - (Track)(N_{RF} + N_{RR}) = 0,$$

from which

$$z = \frac{(30)(36 + 29)}{W} = 15.354 \text{ in.}$$

With the go-cart in the tilted position, the sum of the moments about the z-axis

$$\sum M_{z-\text{axis}} = (Wheelbase)(N_{LF} + N_{RF})$$
$$+ yW \sin(10°) - xW \cos(10°) = 0,$$

from which

$$y = \frac{xW \cos(10°) - (36)(32 + 33)}{W \sin(10°)}$$

$$= 8.034 \text{ in.}$$

Problem 7.117 Determine the centroid of the area by letting dA be a vertical strip of width dx.

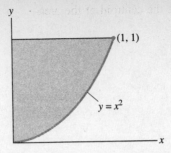

Solution: *The area:* The length of the vertical strip is $(1 - y)$, so that the elemental area is $dA = (1 - y)\,dx = (1 - x^2)\,dx$. The area:

$$\int_A dA = \int_0^1 (1 - x^2)\,dx = \left[x - \frac{x^3}{3}\right]_0^1 = 1 - \frac{1}{3} = \frac{2}{3}.$$

The x-coordinate:

$$\mathbf{x}A = \int_A x\,dA = \int_0^1 x(1 - x^2)\,dx = \left[\frac{x^2}{2} - \frac{x^4}{4}\right]_0^1 = \frac{1}{4} : \ \mathbf{x} = \frac{3}{8}$$

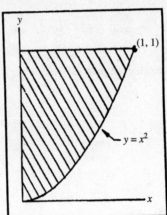

The y-coordinate: The y-coordinate of the centroid of each element of area is located at the midpoint of the vertical dimension of the area element.

$$\mathbf{y} = y + \tfrac{1}{2}(1 - x^2).$$

Thus

$$\int_A \mathbf{y}\,dA = \int_0^1 \left(x^2 + \left(\frac{1}{2}\right)(1 - x^2)(1 - x^2)\right)\,dx$$

$$= \left(\frac{1}{2}\right)\left[x - \frac{x^5}{5}\right]_0^1 = \frac{2}{5}.$$

$$\mathbf{y} = \frac{3}{5}$$

Problem 7.118 Determine the centroid of the area in Problem 7.117 by letting dA be a horizontal strip of height dy.

Solution: *The area:* The length of the horizontal strip is x, hence the element of area is

$$dA = x\,dy = y^{1/2}\,dy.$$

Thus

$$A = \int_0^1 y^{1/2}\,dy = \left[\frac{2y^{3/2}}{3}\right]_0^1 = \frac{2}{3}$$

Check:

The x-coordinate: The x-coordinate of the centroid of each element of area is $\mathbf{x} = \frac{1}{2}x = \frac{1}{2}y^{1/2}$. Thus

$$\int_A \left(\frac{1}{2}\right)y^{1/2}\,dA = \left(\frac{1}{2}\right)\int_0^1 y\,dy = \left(\frac{1}{2}\right)\left[\frac{y^2}{2}\right]_0^1 = \frac{1}{4}.$$

Divide by the area: $\mathbf{x} = \dfrac{3}{8}$

The y-coordinate:

$$\mathbf{y}A = \int_A y\,dA = \int_0^1 y\left(y^{1/2}\,dy\right)$$

$$= \int_0^1 y^{3/2}\,dy = \left[\frac{2y^{5/2}}{5}\right]_0^1 = \frac{2}{5}.$$

Divide by the area: $\mathbf{y} = \dfrac{3}{5}$

Problem 7.119   Determine the centroid of the area.

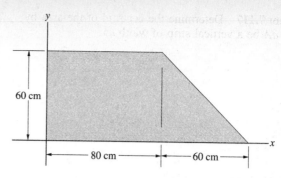

Solution: The strategy is to develop useful general results for the triangle and the rectangle.

The rectangle: The area of the rectangle of height h and width w is

$$A = \int_0^w h\,dx = hw = 4800 \text{ cm}^2.$$

The x-coordinate:

$$\int_0^w hx\,dx = h\left[\frac{x^2}{2}\right]_0^w = \left(\frac{1}{2}\right)hw^2.$$

Divide by the area: $\mathbf{x} = \dfrac{w}{2} = 40$ cm

The y-coordinate:

$$\left(\frac{1}{2}\right)\int_0^w h^2\,dx = \left(\frac{1}{2}\right)h^2 w.$$

Divide by the area: $\mathbf{y} = \left(\dfrac{1}{2}\right)h = 30$ cm

The triangle: The area of the triangle of altitude a and base b is (assuming that the two sides a and b meet at the origin)

$$A = \int_0^b y(x)\,dx = \int_0^b \left(-\frac{a}{b}x + a\right)dx = \left[-\frac{ax^2}{2b} - ax\right]_0^b$$

$$= \left[-\frac{ab}{2} + ab\right] = \frac{ab}{2} = 1800 \text{ cm}^2$$

Check: This is the familiar result. *check.*

The x-coordinate:

$$\int_0^b \left(-\frac{a}{b}x + a\right)x\,dx = \left[-\frac{ax^3}{3b} + \frac{ax^2}{2}\right]_0^b = \frac{ab^2}{6}.$$

Divide by the area: $\mathbf{x} = \dfrac{b}{3} = 20$ cm

The y-coordinate:

$$\int_A y\,dA = \left(\frac{1}{2}\right)\int_0^b \left(-\frac{a}{b}x + a\right)^2 dx$$

$$= -\frac{b}{6a}\left[\left(-\frac{a}{b}x + a\right)^3\right]_0^b = \frac{ba^2}{6}.$$

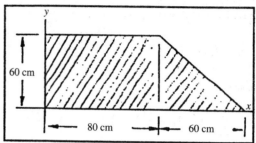

Divide by the area: $\mathbf{y} = \dfrac{a}{3}20$ cm. *The composite:*

$$\mathbf{x} = \frac{x_R A_R + x_T A_T}{A_R + A_T} = \frac{40(4800) + 100(1800)}{4800 + 1800}$$

$$\boxed{= 56.36 \text{ cm}}$$

$$\mathbf{y} = \frac{(30)(4800) + (20)(1800)}{4800 + 1800}$$

$$\boxed{= 27.27 \text{ cm}}$$

Problem 7.120 Determine the centroid of the area.

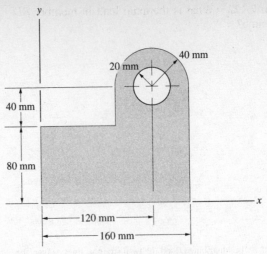

Solution: Divide the object into five areas:

(1) The rectangle 80 mm by 80 mm,
(2) The rectangle 120 mm by 80 mm,
(3) the semicircle of radius 40 mm,
(4) The circle of 20 mm radius, and
(5) the composite object. The areas and centroids:

(1) $A_1 = 6400$ mm^2,
   $x_1 = 40$ mm, $y_1 = 40$ mm,

(2) $A_2 = 9600$ mm^2,
   $x_2 = 120$ mm, $y_2 = 60$ mm,

(3) $A_3 = 2513.3$ mm^2,
   $x_3 = 120$ mm, $y_3 = 136.98$ mm,

(4) $A_4 = 1256.6$ mm^2,
   $x_4 = 120$ mm, $y_4 = 120$ mm.

(5) The composite area: $A = A_1 + A_2 + A_3 - A_4 = 17256.6$ mm^2.
The composite centroid:

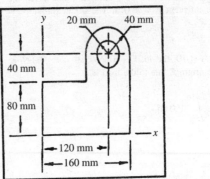

$$x = \frac{A_1 x_1 + A_2 x_2 + A_3 x_3 - A_4 x_4}{A} = 90.3 \text{ mm}$$

$$y = \frac{A_1 y_1 + A_2 y_2 + A_3 y_3 - A_4 y_4}{A} = 59.4 \text{ mm}$$

Problem 7.121 The cantilever beam is subjected to a triangular distributed load. What are the reactions at A?

Solution: The load distribution is a straight line with intercept $w = 200$ N/m at $x = 0$, and slope $-\left(\dfrac{200}{10}\right) = -20$ N/m^2. The sum of the moments is

$$\sum M = M_A - \int_0^{10} (-20x + 200) x \, dx = 0,$$

from which

$$M_A = \left[-\frac{20}{3}x^3 + 100x^2\right]_0^{10} = 3333.3 \text{ Nm}.$$

The sum of the forces:

$$\sum F_y = A_y - \int_0^{10} (-20x + 200) \, dx = 0,$$

from which

$$A_y = \left[-10x^2 + 200x\right]_0^{10} = 1000 \text{ N},$$

and $\sum F_x = A_x = 0$

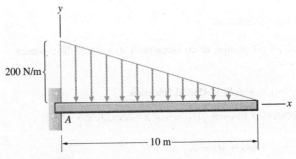

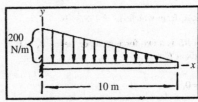

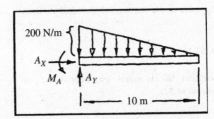

Problem 7.122 What is the axial load in member *BD* of the frame?

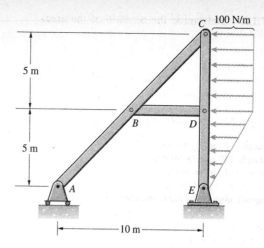

Solution: The distributed load is two straight lines: Over the interval $0 \le y \le 5$ the intercept is $w = 0$ at $y = 0$ and the slope is $+\dfrac{100}{5} = 20$.

Over the interval $5 \le y \le 10$, the load is a constant $w = 100$ N/m. The moment about the origin E due to the load is

$$M_E = \int_0^5 (20y)y\,dy + \int_5^{10} 100y\,dy,$$

from which

$$M_E = \left[\frac{20}{3}y^3\right]_0^5 + \left[\frac{100}{2}y^2\right]_5^{10} = 4583.33 \text{ N-m}.$$

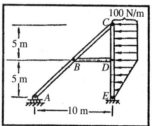

Check: The area of the triangle is

$$F_1 = (\tfrac{1}{2})(5)(100) = 250 \text{ N}.$$

The area of the rectangle: $F_2 = 500$ N. The centroid distance for the triangle is

$$d_1 = (\tfrac{2}{3})5 = 3.333 \text{ m}.$$

The centroid distance of the rectangle is $d_2 = 7.5$ m. The moment about E is

$$M_E = d_1F_1 + d_2F_2 = 4583.33 \text{ Nm } check.$$

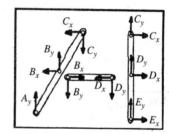

The Complete Structure: The sum of the moments about E is

$$\sum M = -10A_R + M_E = 0,$$

where A_R is the reaction at A, from which $A_R = 458.33$ N.

The element ABC: Element *BD* is a two force member, hence $B_y = 0$. The sum of the moments about C:

$$\sum M_C = -5B_x - 10A_y = 0,$$

where A_y is equal and opposite to the reaction of the support, from which

$$B_x = -2A_y = 2A_R = 916.67 \text{ N}.$$

Since the reaction in element *BD* is equal and opposite, $B_x = -916.67$ N, *which is a tension in BD.*

Problem 7.123 An engineer estimates that the maximum wind load on the 40-m tower in Fig. a is described by the distributed load in Fig. b. The tower is supported by three cables A, B, and C from the top of the tower to equally spaced points 15 m from the bottom of the tower (Fig. c). If the wind blows from the west and cables B and C are slack, what is the tension in cable A? (Model the base of the tower as a ball and socket support.)

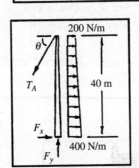

(a)   (b)   (c)

Solution: The load distribution is a straight line with the intercept $w = 400$ N/m, and slope -5. The moment about the base of the tower due to the wind load is

$$M_W = \int_0^{40} (-5y + 400)\, y\, dy,$$

$$M_W = \left[-\frac{5}{3} y^3 + 200 y^2 \right]_0^{40} = 213.33 \text{ kN-m},$$

clockwise about the base, looking North. The angle formed by the cable with the horizontal at the top of the tower is

$$\theta = 90° - \tan^{-1} \left(\frac{15}{40} \right) = 69.44°.$$

The sum of the moments about the base of the tower is

$$\sum M = -M_W + 40 T_A \cos \theta = 0,$$

from which

$$T_A = \left(\frac{1}{40 \cos \theta} \right) M_W = 15.19 \text{ kN}$$

Problem 7.124 If the wind in Problem 7.123 blows from the east and cable A is slack, what are the tensions in cables B and C?

Solution: From Problem 7.123, the moment about the base of the tower is $M_W = 213.33$ kN-m, counterclockwise if the wind is from the east and the observer is looking North. The angle in the horizontal plane between the cables and the east is $60°$. The sum of the moments about the base is

$$\sum M = M_W - 40 T_B \cos \theta \cos 60° - 40 T_C \cos \theta \cos 60° = 0.$$

From symmetry, the tensions in the two cables are equal, from which

$$T_B = T_C = \left(\frac{1}{80 \cos \theta \cos 60°} \right) M_W = 15.19 \text{ kN}$$

Problem 7.125 Estimate the centroid of the volume of the *Apollo* lunar return configuration (not including its rocket nozzle) by treating it as a cone and a cylinder.

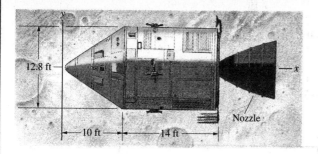

Solution: The volume of the cone is

$$V_1 = \frac{\pi R^2 h}{3} = 428.93 \text{ ft}^3.$$

The x-coordinate of the centroid from the nose of the cone is $x_1 = \frac{3h}{4} = 7.5$ ft. The volume of the cylinder is $V_2 = \pi R^2 L = 1801.5$ ft^3. The x-coordinate of the centroid from the nose of the cone is $x_2 = h + \frac{L}{2} = 17$ ft. The composite volume is $V = V_1 + V_2 = 2230.4$ ft^3. The x-coordinate of the composite centroid is

$$\mathbf{x} = \frac{V_1 x_1 + V_2 x_2}{V} = 15.2 \text{ ft}.$$

The y- and z-coordinates are zero, from symmetry.

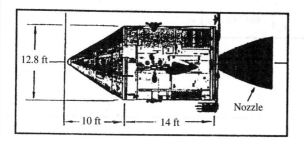

Problem 7.126 The shape of the rocket nozzle of the *Apollo* lunar return configuration is approximated by revolving the curve shown around the x axis. In terms of the coordinate system shown, determine the centroid of the volume of the nozzle.

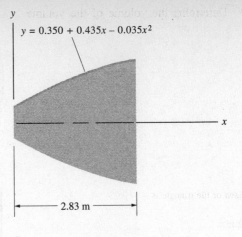

$y = 0.350 + 0.435x - 0.035x^2$

2.83 m

Solution:

$$\mathbf{x} = \frac{\int x\,dV}{\int dV}.$$

Let dV be a disk of radius y and thickness dx

Thus, $dV = \pi y^2\,dx$, where

$$y^2 = (0.350 + 0.435x - 0.035x^2)^2$$

$$y^2 = (a + bx + cx^2)^2$$

$$y^2 = a^2 + 2abx + (2ac + b^2)x^2 + 2bcx^3 + c^2x^4$$

$$a = 0.350$$

$$b = 0.435$$

$$c = -0.035$$

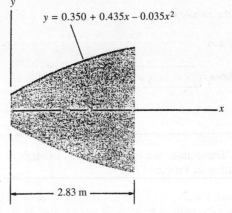

$y = 0.350 + 0.435x - 0.035x^2$

2.83 m

$$\mathbf{x} = \frac{\int_0^{2.83}(a^2x + 2abx^2 + (2ac + b^2)x^3 + 2bcx^4 + c^2x^5)\,dx}{\int_0^{2.83}(a^2 + 2abx + (2ac + b^2)x^2 + 2bcx^3 + c^2x^4)\,dx}$$

$$\mathbf{x} = \frac{\left[a^2\left(\frac{x^2}{2}\right) + 2ab\left(\frac{x^3}{3}\right) + (2ac + b^2)\left(\frac{x^4}{4}\right) + 2bc\left(\frac{x^5}{5}\right) + c^2\left(\frac{x^6}{6}\right)\right]_0^{2.83}}{\left[a^2x + 2ab\left(\frac{x^2}{2}\right) + (2ac + b^2)\left(\frac{x^3}{3}\right) + 2bc\left(\frac{x^4}{4}\right) + c^2\left(\frac{x^5}{5}\right)\right]_0^{2.83}}$$

Evaluating,

$$\mathbf{x} = \frac{4.43}{3.37} = 1.87 \text{ m}$$

Problem 7.127 Determine the volume of the volume of revolution.

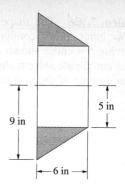

Solution: The area of the triangle is

$A = (\frac{1}{2})(4)(6) = 12$ in.^{2}.

The y-coordinate of the centroid is

$\mathbf{y} = 5 + (\frac{1}{3})4 = 6.3333$ in.

The volume of revolution is $\boxed{V = 2\pi A\mathbf{y} = 477.52 \text{ in.}^3}$

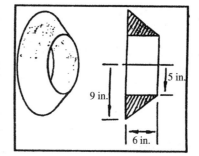

Problem 7.128 Determine the surface area of the volume of revolution in Problem 7.127.

Solution: *The outer surface:* The length of the line is $L_1 = \sqrt{4^2 + 6^2} = 7.2111$ in. The y-coordinate of the centroid is $y = 5 + 2 = 7$ in. The surface area is $A_1 = 2\pi L_1\mathbf{y}_1 = 317.16$ in.^{2}.

The side surface: The length of the line is $L_2 = 4$ in. The y-coordinate of the centroid is $\mathbf{y}_2 = 5 + 2 = 7$ in. The surface area is $A_2 = 2\pi L_2\mathbf{y}_2 = 87.96$ in.^{2}.

The inner surface: The length of the line is $L_3 = 6$ in. The y-coordinate is $\mathbf{y}_3 = 5$ in. The surface area is $A_3 = 2\pi L_3\mathbf{y}_3 = 188.5$ in^2. The total surface: $\boxed{A = A_1 + A_2 + A_3 = 681.6 \text{ in}^2}$

Problem 7.129 Determine the y coordinate of the center of mass of the homogeneous steel plate.

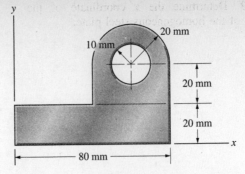

Solution: Divide the object into five areas: (1) The lower rectangle 20 by 80 mm, (2) an upper rectangle, 20 by 40 mm, (3) the semicircle of radius 20 mm, (4) the circle of radius 10 mm, and (5) the composite part. The areas and the centroids are tabulated. The last row is the composite and the centroid of the composite. The composite area is

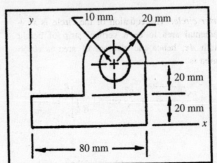

$$A = \sum_1^3 A_i - A_4.$$

The centroid:

$$x = \frac{\sum_1^3 A_i x_i - A_4 x_4}{A},$$

and $y = \dfrac{\sum_1^3 A_i y_i - A_4 y_4}{A}.$

The following relationships were used for the centroids: For a rectangle: the centroid is at half the side and half the base. For a semicircle, the centroid is on the centerline and at $\dfrac{4R}{3\pi}$ from the base. For a circle, the centroid is at the center.

Area	A, sq mm	x, mm	y, mm
A1	1600	40	10
A2	800	60	30
A3	628.3	60	48.5
A4	314.2	60	40
Composite	2714	48.2	21.3

Problem 7.130 Determine the x coordinate of the center of mass of the homogeneous steel plate.

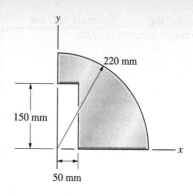

Solution: *The quarter circle:* The equation of the circle is $x^2 + y^2 = R^2$. Take the elemental area to be a vertical strip of height $y = \sqrt{R^2 - x^2}$ and width dx, hence the element of area is $dA = \sqrt{R^2 - x^2}\,dx$, and the area is

$$A = \int_0^R \sqrt{R^2 - x^2}\,dx = \left[\frac{x\sqrt{R^2 - x^2}}{2} + \frac{R^2}{2}\sin^{-1}\left(\frac{x}{R}\right)\right]_0^R = \frac{\pi R^2}{4}$$

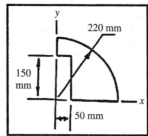

The x-coordinate:

$$\mathbf{x}_C A = \int_A x\,dA = \int_0^R x\sqrt{R^2 - x^2}\,dx = \left[-\frac{(R^2 - x^2)^{3/2}}{3}\right]_0^R = \frac{R^3}{3}$$

$$\mathbf{x}_C = \frac{4R}{3\pi}$$

The rectangle: The area is $A = 50(150) = 7500$ mm^2. The x-coordinate of the centroid is $\mathbf{x}_R = 25$ mm.

The composite: The area of the quarter circle is

$$A_C = \frac{\pi(220)^2}{4} = 3.8013 \times 10^4 \text{ mm.}$$

The area of the rectangle is $A_R = 50(150) = 0.75 \times 10^4$ mm^2. The composite area is $A = A_C - A_R = 3.0513 \times 10^4$ mm^2. The centroid:

$$\boxed{\mathbf{x} = \frac{A_C \mathbf{x}_C - A_R \mathbf{x}_R}{A} = 110 \text{ mm}}$$

Problem 7.131 The area of the homogeneous plate is 10 ft^2. The vertical reactions on the plate at A and B are 80 lb and 84 lb, respectively. Suppose that you want to equalize the reactions at A and B by drilling a 1-ft-diameter hole in the plate. What horizontal distance from A should the center of the hole be? What are the resulting reactions at A and B?

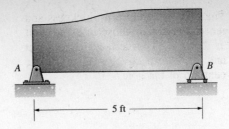

Solution: The weight of the plate is $W = 80 + 84 = 164$ lb. From the sum of moments about A, the centroid is

$$x = \frac{84(5)}{W} = 2.56 \text{ ft.}$$

The weight density is

$$w = \frac{W}{10} = 16.4 \text{ lb/ft}^2.$$

The weight of the cutout is $W_C = \pi (0.5^2)w = 12.88$ lb. The new weight of the plate is $W_2 = W - W_C = 151.12$ lb. The new centroid must be at

$$x_2 = \frac{5}{2} = 2.5 \text{ ft for the reactions to be equal.}$$

Therefore the x-coordinate of the center of the circle will be

$$x_C = \frac{Wx - W_2 x_2}{W_C} = 3.26 \text{ ft.}$$

The reactions at A and B will be

$$A = B = \frac{W_2}{2} = 75.56 \text{ lb}$$

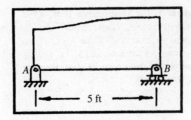

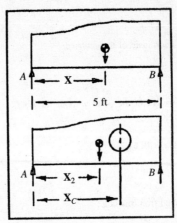

Problem 7.132 The plate is of uniform thickness and is made of homogeneous material whose mass per unit area of the plate is 2 kg/m². The vertical reactions at A and B are 6 N and 10 N, respectively. What is the x coordinate of the centroid of the hole?

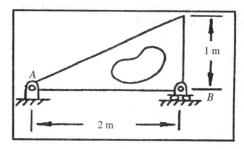

Solution: Choose an origin at A. The basic relation is $W_C \mathbf{x}_C = W\mathbf{x} - W_H \mathbf{x}_H$, where W_C is the weight of the composite plate (the one with the hole), W is the weight of the plate without the hole, W_H is the weight of the material removed from the hole, and $\mathbf{x}_C$, $\mathbf{x}$, and $\mathbf{x}_H$ are the x-coordinates of the centroids of the composite plate, the plate without the hole, and the hole, respectively.

The composite weight:

$$\sum F_Y = A + B - W_C = 0,$$

from which $W_C = 16$ N. The x-coordinate of the centroid:

$$\sum M_A = -W_C \mathbf{x}_C + 2B = 0,$$

from which $\mathbf{x}_C = 1.25$ m. The weight of the plate without the hole and the x-coordinate of the centroid:

$$W = \rho A g = (\tfrac{1}{2})(2)(1)(2)(9.81) = 19.62 \text{ N},$$

and $\mathbf{x} = (\tfrac{2}{3})2 = 1.3333$ m.

The weight of the material removed from the hole:

$$W_H = W - W_C = 3.62 \text{ N}.$$

Solve: $\mathbf{x}_H = \dfrac{W\mathbf{x} - W_C \mathbf{x}_C}{W_H} = 1.702$ m

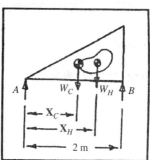

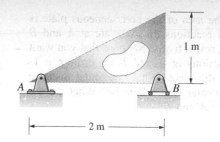

Problem 7.133 Determine the center of mass of the homogeneous sheet of metal.

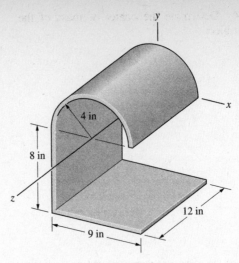

Solution: Divide the object into four parts: (1) The lower plate, (2) the left hand plate, (3) the semicircular plate, and (4) the composite plate. The areas and centroids are found by inspection:

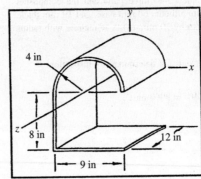

(1) Area: $A_1 = 9(12) = 108$ in.^{2},
$\mathbf{x}_1 = 0.5$ in., $\mathbf{y}_1 = -8$ in., $\mathbf{z}_1 = 6$ in.

(2) $A_2 = 8(12) = 96$ in.^{2},
$\mathbf{x}_2 = -4$ in.,
$\mathbf{y}_2 = -4$ in., $\mathbf{z}_2 = 6$ in.

(3) $A_3 = \pi 4(12) = 150.8$ in.^{2},
$\mathbf{x}_3 = 0$, $\mathbf{y} = \dfrac{2(4)}{\pi} = 2.546$ in., $z = 6$ in.

The composite area is

$$A = \sum_1^3 A_i = 354.796 \text{ in.}^2.$$

The centroid for the composite:

$$\mathbf{x} = \frac{\sum\limits_1^3 A_i \mathbf{x}_i}{A} = -0.930 \text{ in.}$$

$$\mathbf{y} = \frac{\sum\limits_1^3 A_i \mathbf{y}_i}{A} = -2.435 \text{ in.}$$

$$\mathbf{z} = \frac{\sum\limits_1^3 A_i \mathbf{z}_i}{A} = 6 \text{ in.}$$

Problem 7.134 Determine the center of mass of the homogeneous object.

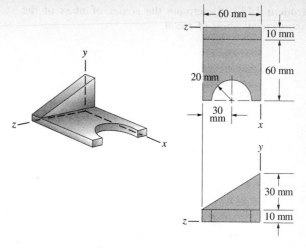

Solution: Divide the object into three parts and the composite:
(1) A triangular solid 30 mm altitude, 60 mm base, and 10 mm thick.
(2) A rectangle 60 by 70 mm by 10 mm. (3) A semicircle with radius 20 mm and 10 mm thick.

The volumes and their centroids are determined by inspection:

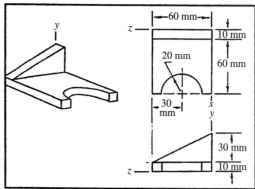

(1) $V_1 = \left(\dfrac{1}{2}\right)(30)(60)(10) = 9000 \text{ mm}^3$,

$\mathbf{x}_1 = 5 \text{ mm}$,

$\mathbf{y}_1 = 10 + \dfrac{30}{3} = 20 \text{ mm}$,

$\mathbf{z}_1 = \dfrac{60}{3} = 20 \text{ mm}$

(2) $V_2 = 60(70)(10) = 42000 \text{ mm}^3$,

$\mathbf{x}_2 = 35 \text{ mm}$,

$\mathbf{y}_2 = 5 \text{ mm}$,

$\mathbf{z}_2 = 30 \text{ mm}$

(3) $V_3 = \dfrac{\pi 20^2}{2}(10) = 6283.2 \text{ mm}^3$,

$\mathbf{x}_3 = 70 - \dfrac{4(20)}{3\pi} = 61.51 \text{ mm}$,

$\mathbf{y}_3 = 5 \text{ mm}$,

$\mathbf{z}_3 = 30 \text{ mm}$.

The composite volume is $V = V_1 + V_2 - V_3 = 44716.8 \text{ mm}^3$. The centroid is

$\mathbf{x} = \dfrac{V_1\mathbf{x}_1 + V_2\mathbf{x}_2 - V_3\mathbf{x}_3}{V} = 25.237 \text{ mm}$

$\mathbf{y} = \dfrac{V_1\mathbf{y}_1 + V_2\mathbf{y}_2 - V_3\mathbf{y}_3}{V} = 8.019 \text{ mm}$

$\mathbf{z} = \dfrac{V_1\mathbf{z}_1 + V_2\mathbf{z}_2 - V_3\mathbf{z}_3}{V} = 27.99 \text{ mm}$

Problem 7.135   Determine the center of mass of the homogeneous object.

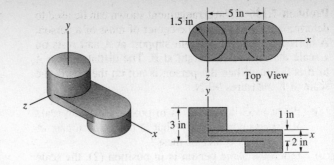

Solution: Divide the object into five parts plus the composite. (1) A solid cylinder with 1.5 in. radius, 3 in. long. (2) A rectangle 3 by 5 by 1 in. (3) A solid cylinder with radius 1.5 in., 2 in. long. (4) A semicircle with radius 1.5 in., 1 inch thick, (5) a semicircle with radius 1.5 in., 1 inch thick. The volumes and centroids are determined by inspection. These are tabulated:

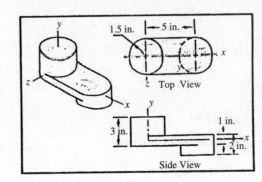

Part No	Vol, cu in.	x, in.	y, in.	z, in.
V1	21.205	0	1	0
V2	15	2.5	0	0
V3	14.137	5	−0.5	0
V4	3.534	0.6366	0	0
V5	3.534	4.363	0	0
Composite	43.27	2.09	0.3267	0

The composite is

$$V = \sum_1^3 V_i - \sum_4^5 V_i.$$

The centroid:

$$\mathbf{x} = \frac{\sum_1^3 V_i \mathbf{x}_i - \sum_4^5 V_i \mathbf{x}_i}{V},$$

with a corresponding expression for **y**. The z-coordinate is zero because of symmetry.

Problem 7.136 The arrangement shown can be used to determine the location of the center of mass of a person. A horizontal board has a pin support at A and rests on a scale that measures weight at B. The distance from A to B is 2.3 m. When the person is not on the board, the scale at B measures 90 N.

(a) When a 63-kg person is in position (1), the scale at B measures 496 N. What is the x coordinate of the person's center of mass?

(b) When the same person is in position (2), the scale measures 523 N. What is the x coordinate of his center of mass?

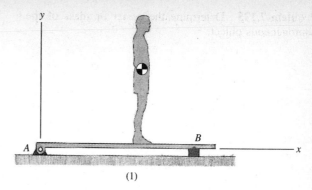

(1)

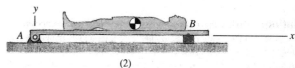

(2)

Solution:

$W = mg = 63 \, g = 618$ N

(a) Unloaded Beam (assume uniform beam)

$$\sum F_y: \quad A_y + B_y - W_B = 0$$

$$\sum M_A: \quad (-1.15)W_B + 2.3B_y = 0$$

Solving, $A_y = 90$ N, $W_B = 180$ N

(b)

$$\sum F_y: \quad A_y + B_y - W_B - W = 0$$

$$\sum M_A: \quad 2.3B_y - 1.15W_B - \mathbf{x}W = 0$$

$W = 618$ N, $W_B = 180$ N

For (a), $B_y = 496$ N. Solving the equations for this case yields
$\mathbf{x} = 1.511$ m

For (b), $B_y = 523$ N. Solving the equations for this case yields
$\mathbf{x} = 1.611$ m

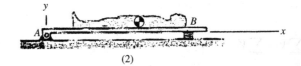

(1)

(2)

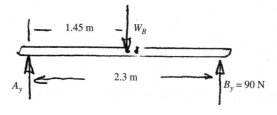

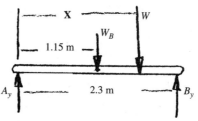

Problem 7.137 If a string is tied to the slender bar at *A* and the bar is allowed to hang freely, what will be the angle between *AB* and the vertical?

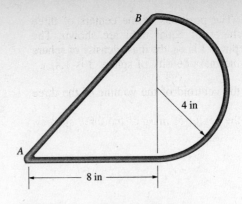

Solution: When the bar hangs freely, the action line of the weight will pass through the mass center. With a homogenous, slender bar, the mass center corresponds to the centroid of the lines making up the bar. Choose the origin at *A*, with the *x*-axis parallel to the lower bar. Divide the bar into three segments plus the composite: (1) The segment from *A* to the semi circle, (2) the segment *AB*, and (3) the semicircle.

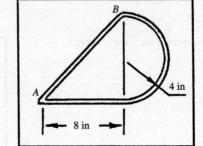

(1) $L_1 = 8$ in., $x_1 = 4$ in., $y_1 = 0$.

(2) $L_2 = \sqrt{8^2 + 8^2} = 11.314$ in., $x_2 = 4$, $y_2 = 4$

(3) $L_3 = 4\pi = 12.566$ in., $x_3 = 8 + \dfrac{2(4)}{\pi} = 10.546$ in., $y_3 = 4$.

The composite length

$$L = \sum_1^3 L_i = 31.88 \text{ in.}$$

The composite centroid:

$$x = \frac{L_1 x_1 + L_2 x_2 + L_3 x_3}{L} = 6.58 \text{ in.,}$$

$$y = \frac{L_1 y_1 + L_2 y_2 + L_3 y_3}{L} = 2.996 \text{ in.}$$

The angle from the point *A* to the centroid relative to the lower bar is

$$\alpha = \tan^{-1}\left(\frac{y}{x}\right) = 24.48°.$$

The angle between *AB* and the lower bar is 45°, hence the angle between the line from *A* to the centroid and *AB* is

$$\beta = 45 - \alpha = 20.52°$$

Since the line from *A* to the centroid will be vertical, this is the angle between *AB* and the vertical.

Problem 7.138 The positions of the centers of three homogeneous spheres of equal radii are shown. The mass density of sphere 1 is ρ_0, the mass density of sphere 2 is 1.2 ρ_0, and the mass density of sphere 3 is 1.4ρ_0.

(a) Determine the centroid of the volume of the three spheres.
(b) Determine the center of mass of the three spheres.

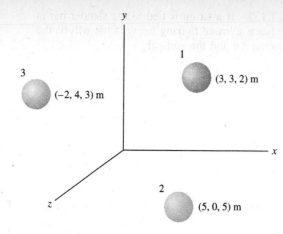

Solution: Assume that the spheres have equal volumes.

(a) *The volume centroid is*

$$\mathbf{x} = \frac{-2V + 3V + 5V}{3V} = 2 \text{ ft},$$

$$\mathbf{y} = \frac{4V + 3V + 0V}{3V} = 2.33 \text{ ft}$$

$$\mathbf{z} = \frac{3V + 2V + 5V}{3V} = 3.33 \text{ ft}$$

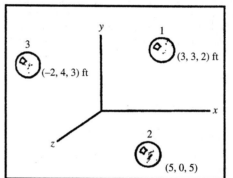

(b) *The mass centroid:*

$$\mathbf{x}_m = \frac{-2(1.4\rho_0 V) + 3(\rho_0 V) + 5(1.2\rho_0 V)}{(1.4 + 1 + 1.2)\rho_0 V} = \frac{6.2}{3.6} = 1.722 \text{ ft}$$

$$\mathbf{y}_m = \frac{4(1.4\rho_0 V) + 3(\rho_0 V) + 0(1.2\rho_0 V)}{(1.4 + 1 + 1.2)\rho_0 V} = \frac{8.6}{3.6} = 2.39 \text{ ft}$$

$$\mathbf{z}_m = \frac{3(1.4\rho_0 V) + 2(\rho_0 V) + 5(1.2\rho_0 V)}{(1.4 + 1 + 1.2)\rho_0 V} = \frac{12.2}{3.6} = 3.39 \text{ ft}$$

Problem 7.139 The mass of the moon is 0.0123 times the mass of the earth. If the moon's center of mass is 383,000 km form the center of mass of the earth, what is the distance from the center of mass of the earth to the center of mass of the earth–moon system?

Solution:

$\mathbf{x}(m_E + m_M) = 383,000 \, m_M)$

so $\mathbf{x} = \dfrac{m_M}{m_E + m_M}(383,000)$

$\quad = \dfrac{m_M/m_E}{1 + m_M/m_E}(383,000)$

$\quad = \dfrac{0.0123}{1 + 0.0123}(383,000)$

$\quad = 4650 \text{ km}.$

(The earth's radius is 6370 km, so the center of mass of the earth-moon system is within the earth.)

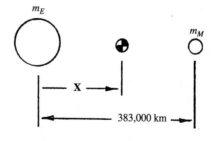

Problem 8.1 Determine the I_y and k_y.

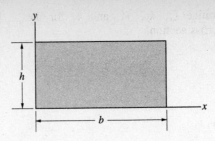

Solution: Let $dA = x\,dy = b\,dy$. $A = \int_0^h b\,dy = hb$.

$$I_y = \int_A x^2\,dA = h\int_0^b x^2\,dx = h\left[\frac{x^3}{3}\right]_0^b = \frac{b^3 h}{3}\quad k_y = \sqrt{\frac{I_y}{A}} = \frac{b}{\sqrt{3}}$$

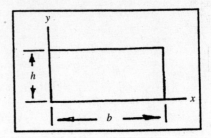

Problem 8.2 Determine I_x and k_x by letting dA be (a) a horizontal strip of height dy; (b) a vertical strip of width dx.

Solution: (See figure in Problem 8.1.)

(a) $A = \int_0^h b\,dy = hb$.

$$I_x = \int_A y^2\,dA = b\int_0^h y^2\,dy = \frac{bh^3}{3},$$

$$k_x = \sqrt{\frac{I_x}{A}} = \frac{h}{\sqrt{3}}$$

(b) $A = \int_0^b h\,dx = hb$.

$$I_x = h\int_0^b y^2\,dx = h\int_0^h y^2\left(\frac{b}{h}\right)dy = \frac{bh^3}{3},$$

$$k_x = \sqrt{\frac{I_x}{A}} = \frac{h}{\sqrt{3}}$$

Problem 8.3 Determine I_{xy}.

Solution: (See figure in Problem 8.1.)

$$A = \int_A dA = \int_0^b \int_0^h dx\,dy = hb.$$

$$I_{xy} = \int_A xy\,dA = \int_0^b \int_0^h xy\,dx\,dy = \left[\frac{y^2}{2}\right]_0^h \left[\frac{x^2}{2}\right]_0^b = \frac{h^2 b^2}{4}$$

Problem 8.4 Determine I_x, k_x, I_y, and k_y for the beam's rectangular cross section.

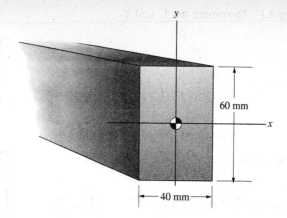

Solution:

$$I_x = \int_A y^2 \, dA$$

Let $dA = 40 \, dy = 60$ mm

$$I_x = \int_{-30}^{30} 40 y^2 \, dy = 40 \frac{y^3}{3} \bigg]_{-30}^{30}$$

$$= 40 \left[\frac{27000}{3} + \frac{27000}{3} \right]$$

$$= 40[18000] \text{ mm}^4$$

$$I_x = 7.2 \times 10^5 \text{ mm}^4$$

$$A = 2400 \text{ mm}^2$$

$$k_x = \sqrt{\frac{I_x}{A}} = \sqrt{\frac{7.2 \times 10^5}{2.4 \times 10^3}} \text{ mm}$$

$$k_x = 17.3 \text{ mm}$$

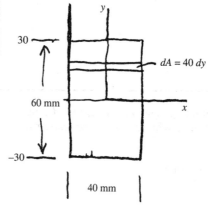

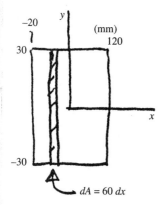

$$I_y = \int_A x^2 \, dA$$

$$I_y = \int_{-20}^{20} x^2 (60) \, dx = \int_{-20}^{20} 60 x^2 \, dx$$

$$I_y = 60 \left[\frac{x^3}{3} \right]_{-20}^{20} = 60 \left[\frac{8000}{3} + \frac{8000}{3} \right] \text{ mm}^4$$

$$I_y = 3.2 \times 10^5 \text{ mm}^4$$

$$k_y = \sqrt{\frac{I_y}{A}} = \sqrt{\frac{3.2 \times 10^5}{2.4 \times 10^3}}$$

$$k_y = \sqrt{133.3} = 11.5 \text{ mm}$$

Problem 8.5 Determine I_{xy} and J_O for the beam's rectangular cross section.

Solution:

$$I_{xy} = \int_A xy\, dA$$

$$I_{xy} = \int_{-30}^{30} \int_{-20}^{20} xy\, dx\, dy$$

$$I_{xy} = \int_{-30}^{30} \left[\frac{x^2}{2} y \right]_{-20}^{+20} dy = \int_{-30}^{30} 0\, dy = 0$$

$$I_{xy} = 0$$

$$J_O = \int_A r^2\, dA = \int_{-30}^{30} \int_{-20}^{20} (x^2 + y^2)\, dx\, dy$$

$$= \int_{-30}^{30} \left[\frac{x^3}{3} + y^2 x \right]_{-20}^{20} dy$$

$$= \int_{-30}^{30} \left[\frac{8000}{3} + 20y^2 + \frac{8000}{3} + 20y^2 \right] dy$$

$$J_O = \int_{-30}^{30} \left[\frac{16000}{3} + 40y^2 \right] dy$$

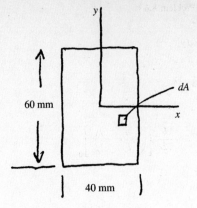

$$J_O = \left[\frac{16000}{3} y + 40 \frac{y^3}{3} \right]_{-30}^{30}$$

$$J_O = \left[\frac{(16000)}{3}(60) + 80 \left(\frac{30^3}{3} \right) \right] \text{mm}^4$$

$$J_O = 10.4 \times 10^5 \text{ mm}^4$$

Problem 8.6 Determine I_y and k_y.

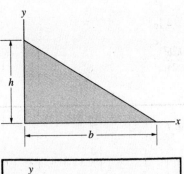

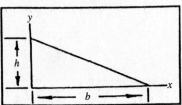

Solution: $y = -\left(\dfrac{h}{b} \right) x + h$, $dA = dy\, dx$, therefore

$$A = \int_0^b dx \int_0^{-\frac{h}{b}x+h} dy$$

$$= \int_0^b \left(-\frac{h}{b}x + h \right) dx = \left[-\frac{hx^2}{2b} + hx \right]_0^b = \frac{hb}{2}$$

$$I_y = \int_A x^2\, dA = \int_0^b x^2\, dx \int_0^{-\frac{h}{b}x+h} dy$$

$$= \int_0^b \left(-\frac{h}{b}x^3 + hx^2 \right) dx = \left[-\frac{hx^4}{4b} + \frac{hx^3}{3} \right]_0^b = \frac{hb^3}{12}$$

$$k_y = \sqrt{\frac{I_y}{A}} = \frac{b}{\sqrt{6}}$$

Problem 8.7   Determine J_O and k_O.

Solution: (See figure in Problem 8.6.)

$$y = -\left(\frac{h}{b}\right)x + h, \quad dA = dx\,dy$$

$$I_x = \int_A y^2\,dA = \int_0^b dx \int^{-\frac{h}{b}x+h} y^2\,dy$$

$$= \frac{1}{3}\int_0^b \left(-\frac{h}{b}x + h\right)^3 dx = -\frac{b}{12h}\left[\left(-\frac{h}{b}x + h\right)^4\right]_0^b$$

$$= \frac{bh^3}{12}$$

$$k_x = \sqrt{\frac{I_x}{A}} = \frac{h}{\sqrt{6}}$$

$$J_O = I_x + I_y = \left(\frac{bh}{12}\right)(b^2 + h^2)$$

$$k_O = \sqrt{k_x^2 + k_y^2} = \sqrt{\frac{(b^2 + h^2)}{6}}$$

Problem 8.8   Determine I_{xy}.

Solution: (See figure for Problem 8.6.)

$$I_{xy} = \int_A xy\,dA = \int_0^b x\,dx \int_0^{-\frac{h}{b}x+h} y\,dy$$

$$= \frac{1}{2}\int_0^b x\left(-\frac{h}{b}x + h\right)^2 dx$$

$$= \frac{1}{2}\left[\frac{h^2}{b^2}\frac{x^4}{4} - 2\frac{h^2}{b}\frac{x^3}{3} + h^2\frac{x^2}{2}\right]_0^b$$

$$= \frac{h^2 b^2}{2}\left[\frac{1}{4} - \frac{2}{3} + \frac{1}{2}\right] = \frac{h^2 b^2}{24}$$

Problem 8.9   Determine I_y.

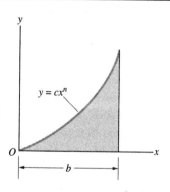

Solution:

$$I_y = \int_A x^2\,dA$$

$$I_y = \int_0^b x^2 (cx^n)\,dx$$

$$I_y = \int_0^b cx^{(n+2)}\,dx = \frac{cx^{n+3}}{(n+3)}\Big]_0^b$$

$$I_y = \frac{cb^{(n+3)}}{(n+3)}$$

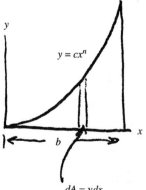

$$dA = y\,dx$$
$$= cx^n\,dx$$

Problem 8.10   Determine I_x.

Solution:

$$I_x = \int_A y^2 \, dA = \int_0^b \int_0^{cx^n} y^2 \, dy \, dx$$

$$I_x = \int_0^b \left[\frac{y^3}{3} \right]_0^{cx^n} dx$$

$$I_x = \int_0^b \left[\frac{c^3 x^{3n}}{3} \right] dx = \frac{c^3}{3} \int_0^b x^{3n} \, dx$$

$$I_x = \frac{c^3}{3} \left[\frac{x^{3n+1}}{(3n+1)} \right]_0^b = \frac{c^3 b^{3n+1}}{3(3n+1)}$$

$$I_x = c^3 b^{3n+1}/(9n+3)$$

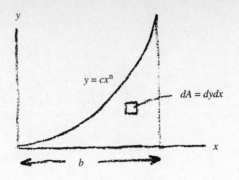

Problem 8.11   Determine J_O.

Solution:

$$J_O = \int_A r^2 \, dA = \int_0^b \int_0^{cx^n} (x^2 + y^2) \, dy \, dx$$

$$J_O = \int_0^b \left[x^2 y + \frac{y^3}{3} \right]_0^{cx^n} dx$$

$$J_O = \int_0^b \left[cx^{n+2} + \frac{c^3 x^{3n}}{3} \right] dx$$

$$J_O = \left[\frac{cx^{n+3}}{(n+3)} + \frac{c^3}{3} \frac{x^{3n+1}}{(3n+1)} \right]_0^b$$

$$J_O = \frac{cb^{(n+3)}}{(n+3)} + \frac{c^3 b^{(3n+1)}}{(9n+3)}$$

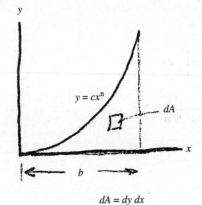

$dA = dy\,dx$

Problem 8.12   Determine I_{xy}.

Solution:

$$I_{xy} = \int_A xy \, dA = \int_0^b \int_0^{cx^n} xy \, dy \, dx$$

$$I_{xy} = \int_0^b \left[\frac{xy^2}{2} \right]_0^{cx^n} dx$$

$$I_{xy} = \int_0^b \frac{xc^2 x^{2n}}{2} \, dx = \int_0^b \frac{c^2}{2} x^{(2n+1)} \, dx$$

$$I_{xy} = \frac{c^2}{2} \frac{x^{2n+2}}{(2n+2)} \Big|_0^b$$

$$I_{xy} = c^2 b^{(2n+2)}/(4n+4)$$

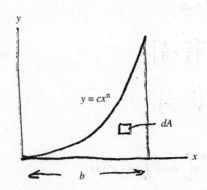

692

Problem 8.13 Determine I_y and k_y.

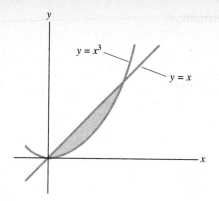

Solution:

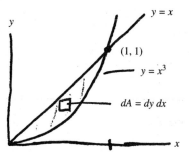

$$I_y = \int_A x^2 \, dA = \int_0^1 \int_{x^3}^x x^2 \, dy \, dx$$

$$I_y = \int_0^1 [x^2 y]_{x^3}^x \, dx = \int_0^1 (x^3 - x^5) \, dx$$

$$I_y = \left[\frac{x^4}{4} - \frac{x^6}{6}\right]\Big|_0^1 = \frac{1}{4} - \frac{1}{6}$$

$$I_y = 0.0833$$

$$\text{Area} = \int_0^1 \int_{x^3}^x dy \, dx = \int_0^1 y\Big]_{x^3}^x \, dx$$

$$\text{Area} = \int_0^1 (x - x^3) \, dx = \frac{x^2}{2} - \frac{x^4}{4}\Big|_0^1 = 0.25$$

$$k_y = \sqrt{\frac{I_y}{\text{Area}}} = \sqrt{\frac{0.0833}{0.25}}$$

$$k_y = 0.577$$

Problem 8.14 Determine I_x and k_x.

Solution:

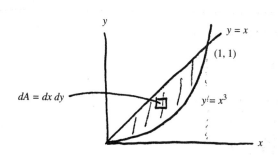

$$I_x = \int_A y^2 \, dA = \int_0^1 \int_{x^3}^x y^2 \, dy \, dx$$

$$I_x = \int_0^1 \left[\frac{y^3}{3}\right]\Big|_{x^3}^x \, dx = \int_0^1 \left[\frac{x^3}{3} - \frac{x^9}{3}\right] dx$$

$$I_x = \frac{1}{3}\left[\frac{x^4}{4} - \frac{x^{10}}{10}\right]\Big|_0^1 = \frac{1}{3}\left[\frac{1}{4} - \frac{1}{10}\right]$$

$$I_x = 0.0500$$

$$\text{Area} = \int_0^1 \int_{x^3}^x dy \, dx = \int_0^1 y\Big|_{x^3}^x \, dx = \int_0^1 (x - x^3) \, dx$$

$$\text{Area} = \left[\frac{x^2}{2} - \frac{x^4}{4}\right]_0^1 = 0.25$$

$$k_y = \sqrt{\frac{I_x}{A}} = \sqrt{\frac{0.050}{0.25}} = 0.447$$

Problem 8.15 Determine J_O and k_O.

Solution:

$$J_O = \int_A r^2\, dA = \int_0^1 \int_{x^3}^x (x^2 + y^2)\, dy\, dx$$

$$J_O = \int_0^1 \left[x^2 y + \frac{y^3}{3} \right]_{x^3}^x dx$$

$$J_O = \int_0^1 \left[x^3 + \frac{x^3}{3} - x^5 - \frac{x^9}{3} \right] dx$$

$$J_O = \int_0^1 \left[\frac{4}{3}x^3 - x^5 - \frac{x^9}{3} \right] dx$$

$$J_O = \left[\frac{4}{3}\left(\frac{x^4}{4} \right) - \frac{x^6}{6} - \frac{x^{10}}{30} \right]_0^1$$

$$J_O = \frac{1}{3} - \frac{1}{6} - \frac{1}{30}$$

$$J_O = 0.133$$

$$\text{Area} = \int_0^1 \int_{x^3}^x dy\, dx = \int_0^1 [y] \Big|_{x^3}^x dx$$

$$= \int_0^1 (x - x^3)\, dx = \left[\frac{x^2}{2} - \frac{x^4}{4} \right]_0^1$$

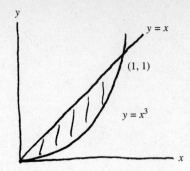

Area = 0.25

$$k_O = \sqrt{\frac{J_O}{\text{Area}}} = \sqrt{\frac{0.133}{0.25}} = 0.730$$

$$k_O = 0.730$$

Problem 8.16 Determine I_{xy}.

Solution:

$$I_{xy} = \int_0^1 \int_{x^3}^x xy\, dy\, dx$$

$$I_{xy} = \int_0^1 \left[x\frac{y^2}{2} \right]_{x^3}^x dx = \int_0^1 \left[\frac{x^3}{2} - \frac{x^7}{2} \right] dx$$

$$I_{xy} = \left[\frac{x^4}{8} - \frac{x^8}{16} \right] \Big|_0^1 = \left(\frac{1}{8} - \frac{1}{16} \right)$$

$$I_{xy} = 0.0625$$

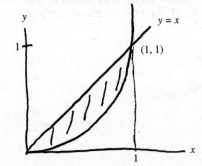

Problem 8.17 Determine the moment of inertia I_y of the metal plate's cross-sectional area.

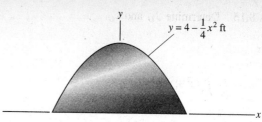

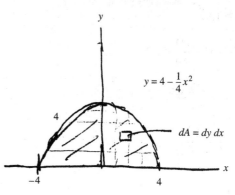

Solution:

$$I_y = \int_A x^2 \, dA = \int_{-4}^{4} \int_{0}^{(4-\frac{1}{4}x^2)} x^2 \, dy \, dx$$

$$I_y = \int_{-4}^{4} [x^2 y]_0^{(4-\frac{1}{4}x^2)} \, dx$$

$$I_y = \int_{-4}^{4} \left[4x^2 - \frac{1}{4}x^4 \right] dx$$

$$I_y = \left[4\frac{x^3}{3} - \frac{1}{4}\frac{x^5}{5} \right]_{-4}^{4}$$

$$I_y = \left[4\frac{4^3}{3} - \frac{4^5}{20} - \frac{4(-4^3)}{3} + \frac{(-4)^5}{20} \right]$$

$$I_y = 8\frac{4^3}{3} - \frac{2(4^5)}{20} = 170.67 - 102.4$$

$$I_y = 68.3 \text{ ft}^4$$

Problem 8.18 Determine the moment of inertia I_x and the radius of gyration k_x of the cross-sectional area of the metal plate.

Solution:

$$I_x = \int_A y^2 \, dA = \int_{-4}^{4} \int_{0}^{(4-\frac{1}{4}x^2)} y^2 \, dy \, dx$$

$$I_x = \int_{-4}^{4} \left[\frac{y^3}{3} \right]\Big|_0^{(4-\frac{1}{4}x^2)} \, dx$$

$$= \frac{1}{3} \int_{-4}^{4} \left(-4 - \frac{1}{4}x^2 \right)^3 dx$$

$$= \frac{1}{3} \int_{-4}^{4} \left(64 - 12x^2 + \frac{3}{4}x^4 - \frac{1}{64}x^6 \right) dx$$

$$= \frac{1}{3} \left[64x - \frac{12x^3}{3} + \frac{3}{4}\frac{x^5}{5} - \frac{1}{64}\frac{x^7}{7} \right]\Big|_{-4}^{4}$$

$$I_x = 78.0 \text{ ft}^4$$

$$\text{Area} = \int_A dA = \int_{-4}^{4} \int_{0}^{(4-\frac{1}{4}x^2)} dy \, dx$$

$$\text{Area} = \int_{-4}^{4} [y]\Big|_0^{4-\frac{1}{4}x^2} \, dx$$

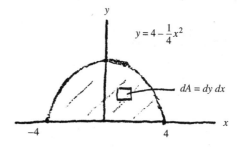

$$\text{Area} = \int_{-4}^{4} \left[4 - \frac{1}{4}x^2 \right] dx = \left[4x - \frac{1}{4}\frac{x^3}{3} \right]_{-4}^{4}$$

$$\text{Area} = \left[16 - \frac{16}{3} + 16 - \frac{16}{3} \right] = 21.33 \text{ ft}^2$$

$$k_x = \sqrt{\frac{I_x}{\text{Area}}} = \sqrt{\frac{78.02}{21.33}} \text{ ft}$$

$$k_x = 1.91 \text{ ft}$$

Problem 8.19 (a) Determine I_y and k_y by letting dA be a vertical strip of width dx.
(b) The polar moment of inertia of a circular area with its center at the origin is $J_O = \frac{1}{2}\pi R^4$. Explain how you can use this information to confirm your answer to (a).

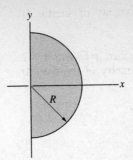

Solution: The equation of the circle is $x^2 + y^2 = R^2$, from which $y = \pm\sqrt{R^2 - x^2}$. The strip dx wide and y long has the elemental area $dA = 2\sqrt{R^2 - x^2}\, dx$. The area of the semicircle is

$$A = \frac{\pi R^2}{2} \qquad I_y = \int_A x^2\, dA = 2\int_0^R x^2\sqrt{R^2 - x^2}\, dx$$

$$= 2\left[-\frac{x(R^2 - x^2)^{3/2}}{4} + \frac{R^2 x(R^2 - x^2)^{1/2}}{8} + \frac{R^4}{8}\sin^{-1}\left(\frac{x}{R}\right)\right]_0^R$$

$$= \frac{\pi R^4}{8}$$

$$k_y = \sqrt{\frac{I_y}{A}} = \frac{R}{2}$$

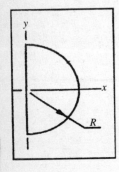

(b) If the integration were done for a circular area with the center at the origin, the limits of integration for the variable x would be from $-R$ to R, doubling the result. Hence, doubling the answer above,

$$I_y = \frac{\pi R^4}{4}.$$

By symmetry, $I_x = I_y$, and the polar moment would be

$$J_O = 2I_y = \frac{\pi R^4}{2},$$

which is indeed the case. Also, since $k_x = k_y$ by symmetry for the full circular area,

$$k_O = \sqrt{\frac{I_x}{A} + \frac{I_y}{A}} = \sqrt{2\frac{I_y}{A}} = \sqrt{\frac{J_O}{A}}$$

as required by the definition. Thus the result checks.

Problem 8.20 (a) Determine I_x and k_x for the area in Problem 8.19 by letting dA be a horizontal strip of height dy.
(b) The polar moment of inertia of a circular area with its center at the origin is $J_O = \frac{1}{2}\pi R^4$. Explain how you can use this information to confirm your answer to (a).

Solution: Use the results of the solution to Problem 8.19, $A = \frac{\pi R^2}{2}$. The equation for the circle is $x^2 + y^2 = R^2$, from which $x = \pm\sqrt{R^2 - y^2}$. The horizontal strip is from 0 to R, hence the element of area is

$$dA = \sqrt{R^2 - y^2}\, dy.$$

$$I_x = \int_A y^2\, dA = \int_{-R}^{+R} y^2\sqrt{R^2 - y^2}\, dy$$

$$= \left[-\frac{y(R^2 - y^2)^{3/2}}{4} + \frac{R^2 y(R^2 - y^2)^{1/2}}{8} + \frac{R^4}{8}\sin^{-1}\left(\frac{y}{R}\right)\right]_{-R}^{R}$$

$$= \left[\frac{R^4}{8}\frac{\pi}{2} + \frac{R^4}{8}\frac{\pi}{2}\right] = \frac{\pi R^4}{8}$$

$$k_x = \sqrt{\frac{I_x}{A}} = \frac{R}{2}.$$

(b) If the area were circular, the strip would be twice as long, and the moment of inertia would be doubled:

$$I_x = \frac{\pi R^4}{4}.$$

By symmetry $I_y = I_x$,

$$\text{and } J_O = 2I_x = \frac{\pi R^4}{2},$$

which is indeed the result. Since $k_x = k_y$ by symmetry for the full circular area, the

$$k_O = \sqrt{\frac{I_x}{A} + \frac{I_y}{A}} = \sqrt{2\frac{I_x}{A}} = \sqrt{\frac{J_O}{A}}$$

as required by the definition. This checks the answer.

Problem 8.21 Determine the moments of inertia I_x and I_y.

Strategy: Use the procedure described in Example 8.2 to determine J_O, then use the symmetry of the area to determine I_x and I_y.

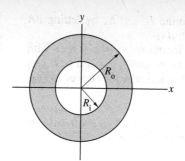

Solution: Let $dA = 2\pi r \, dr$

$$J_O = \int_{R_i}^{R_o} r^2 \, dA = 2\pi \int_{R_i}^{R_o} r^2 r \, dr$$

$$J_O = 2\pi \left[\frac{r^4}{4} \right]_{R_i}^{R_o} = 2\pi \left[\frac{R_o^4}{4} - \frac{R_i^4}{4} \right]$$

From symmetry $I_x = I_y$

Also $\quad J_O = I_x + I_y$

$$\therefore \; I_x = I_y = \frac{\pi}{4}(R_0^4 - R_i^4)$$

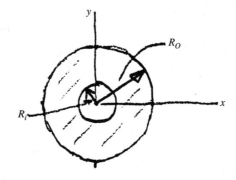

Problem 8.22 If $a = 5$ m and $b = 1$ m, what are the values of I_y and k_y for the elliptical area of the airplane's wing?

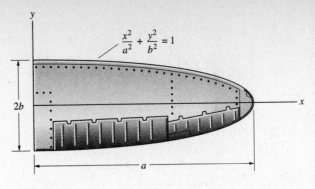

Solution:

$$I_y = \int_A x^2 \, dA = \int_{-0}^{a} \int_{-y}^{y} x^2 \, dy \, dx$$

$$I_y = 2 \int_0^a \int_0^y x^2 \, dy \, dx$$

$$I_y = 2 \int_0^a [x^2 y]_0^{b(1-\frac{x^2}{a^2})^{1/2}} dx$$

$$I_y = 2 \int_0^a x^2 b \left(1 - \frac{x^2}{a^2}\right)^{1/2} dx$$

$$I_y = 2b \int_0^a x^2 \sqrt{1 - \frac{x^2}{a^2}} \, dx$$

Rewriting

$$I_y = \frac{2b}{a} \int_0^a x^2 \sqrt{a^2 - x^2} \, dx$$

$$I_y = \frac{2b}{a} \left[-\frac{x(a^2 - x^2)^{3/2}}{4} + \frac{a^2 x \sqrt{a^2 - x^2}}{8} \right.$$

$$\left. + \frac{a^4}{8} \sin^{-1}\left(\frac{x}{a}\right) \right]_0^a$$

(from the integral tables)

$$I_y = \frac{2b}{a} \left\{ \left[-\frac{a(a^2 - a^2)^{3/2}}{4} + \frac{a^3 \sqrt{a^2 - a^2}}{8} \right. \right.$$

$$\left. + \frac{a^4}{8} \sin^{-1}\left(\frac{a}{a}\right) \right] - \left[\frac{0(a^2)^{3/2}}{4} \right.$$

$$\left. \left. + \frac{a^2 \cdot 0\sqrt{a^2}}{8} + \frac{a^4}{8} \sin^{-1}\left(\frac{0}{a}\right) \right] \right\}$$

$$I_y = \frac{2b}{a} \frac{a^4}{8} \frac{\pi}{2}$$

$$I_y = \frac{2a^3 b\pi}{8}$$

Evaluating, we get

$$I_y = 49.09 \text{ m}^4$$

The area of the ellipse (half ellipse) is

$$A = 2 \int_0^a \int_0^{b\left(1-\frac{x^2}{a}\right)^{1/2}} dy \, dx$$

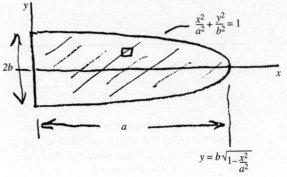

$$A = 2 \int_0^a b \left(1 - \frac{x^2}{a}\right) dx$$

$$= \frac{2b}{a} \int_0^a (a^2 - x^2)^{1/2} dx$$

$$= \frac{2b}{a} \left[\frac{x\sqrt{a^2 - x^2}}{2} + \frac{a^2}{2} \sin^{-1}\left(\frac{x}{a}\right) \right]_0^a$$

$$= \frac{2b}{a} \left[\left(\frac{a\sqrt{0}}{2} + \frac{a^2}{2} \sin^{-1}\left(\frac{a}{a}\right) \right) \right.$$

$$\left. - \left(\frac{0\sqrt{a}}{2} + \frac{a^2}{2} \sin^{-1}\left(\frac{0}{a}\right) \right) \right]$$

$$A = \frac{2b}{a} \frac{a^2}{2} \frac{\pi}{2} = \frac{\pi ab}{2}$$

Evaluating, we get

$$A = 7.85 \text{ m}^2$$

Finally

$$k_y = \sqrt{\frac{I_y}{A}} = \sqrt{\frac{49.09}{7.85}}$$

$$k_y = 2.5 \text{ m}$$

Problem 8.23 What are the values of I_x and k_x for the elliptical area of the airplane's wing in Problem 8.22?

Solution:

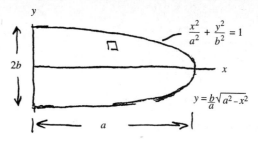

$$I_x = \int_A y^2 \, dA = 2 \int_0^a \int_0^{y=\frac{b}{a}\sqrt{a^2-x^2}} y^2 \, dy \, dx$$

$$I_x = 2 \int_0^a \left[\frac{y^3}{3} \right]_0^{\frac{b}{a}\sqrt{a^2-x^2}} dx$$

$$I_x = 2 \int_0^a \frac{b^3}{3a^3}(a^2 - x^2)^{3/2} \, dx$$

$$I_x = \frac{2b^3}{3a^3} \left[\frac{x(a^2-x^2)^{3/2}}{4} + \frac{3a^2 x\sqrt{a^2-x^2}}{8} \right.$$

$$\left. + \frac{3}{8}a^4 \sin^{-1}\left(\frac{x}{a}\right) \right]\Big|_0^a$$

$$I_x = \frac{2b^3}{3a^3} \left[\frac{a(0)}{4} + \frac{3a^3\sqrt{0}}{8} + \frac{3}{8}a^4 \frac{\pi}{2} \right.$$

$$\left. - \frac{0(a^2)}{4} - \frac{3a^2 \cdot 0\sqrt{a^2}}{8} + 0 \right]$$

$$I_x = \frac{2b^3}{3a^3} \cdot \left(\frac{3}{8}\right) a^4 \left(\frac{\pi}{2}\right)$$

$$I_x = \frac{3ab^3\pi}{3.8} = \frac{ab^3\pi}{8}$$

Evaluating ($a = 5$, $b = 1$)

$$I_x = \frac{5\pi}{8} = 1.96 \text{ m}^4$$

From Problem 8.22, the area of the wing is $A = 7.85 \text{ m}^2$

$$k_x = \sqrt{\frac{I_x}{A}} = \sqrt{\frac{1.96}{7.85}} \quad k_x = 0.500 \text{ m}$$

Problem 8.24 Determine I_y and k_y.

Solution: The straight line and curve intersect where $x = x^2 - 20$. Solving this equation for x, we obtain

$$x = \frac{1 \pm \sqrt{1 + 80}}{2} = -4, 5.$$

If we use a vertical strip: the area

$$dA = [x - (x^2 - 20)] \, dx.$$

Therefore

$$I_y = \int_A x^2 \, dA = \int_{-4}^5 x^2(x - x^2 + 20) \, dx$$

$$= \left[\frac{x^4}{4} - \frac{x^5}{5} + \frac{20x^3}{3} \right]_{-4}^5 = 522.$$

The area is

$$A = \int_A dA = \int_{-4}^5 (x - x^2 + 20) \, dx$$

$$= \left[\frac{x^2}{2} - \frac{x^3}{3} + 20x \right]_{-4}^5 = 122.$$

So $k_y = \sqrt{\frac{I_y}{A}} = \sqrt{\frac{522}{122}} = 2.07.$

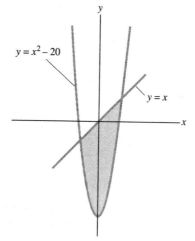

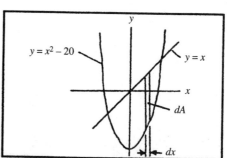

Problem 8.25 Determine I_x and k_x for the area in Problem 8.24.

Solution: Let us determine the moment of inertia about the x axis of a vertical strip holding x and dx fixed:

$$(I_x)_{(\text{strip})} = \int_{A_s} y^2\, dA_s = \int_{x^2-20}^{x} y^2 (dx\, dy) = dx \left[\frac{y^3}{3}\right]_{x^2-20}^{x}$$

$$= \frac{dx}{3}(-x^6 + 60x^4 + x^3 - 1200x^2 + 8000).$$

Integrating this value from $x = -4$ to $x = 5$ (see the solution to Problem 8.24), we obtain I_x for the entire area:

$$I_x = \int_{-4}^{5} \frac{1}{3}(-x^6 + 60x^4 + x^3 - 1200x^2 + 8000)\, dx$$

$$= \left[-\frac{x^7}{21} + 4x^5 + \frac{x^4}{12} - \frac{400x^3}{3} + \frac{8000x}{3}\right]_{-4}^{5} = 10{,}900.$$

From the solution to Problem 8.24, $A = 122$ so

$$k_x = \sqrt{\frac{I_x}{A}} = \sqrt{\frac{10{,}900}{122}} = 9.48.$$

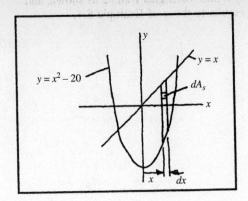

Problem 8.26 A vertical plate of area A is beneath the surface of a stationary body of water. The pressure of the water subjects each element dA of the surface of the plate to a force $(p_0 + \gamma y)\, dA$, where p_0 is the pressure at the surface of the water and γ is the weight density of the water. Show that the magnitude of the moment about the x axis due to the pressure on the front face of the plate is

$$M_{(x \text{ axis})} = p_0 \mathbf{y} A + \gamma I_x,$$

where $\mathbf{y}$ is the y coordinate of the centroid of A and I_x is the moment of inertia of A about the x axis.

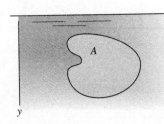

Solution: The moment about the x-axis is $dM = y(p_0 + \gamma y)\, dA$ integrating over the surface of the plate:

$$M = \int_A (p_0 + \gamma y) y\, dA.$$

Noting that p_0 and γ are constants over the area,

$$M = p_0 \int_A y\, dA + \gamma \int_A y^2\, dA.$$

By definition,

$$\mathbf{y} = \frac{\int_A y\, dA}{A}$$

and $I_x = \int_A y^2\, dA,$

then $M = p_0 \mathbf{y} A + \gamma I_x$, which demonstrates the result.

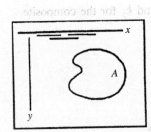

Problem 8.27 Determine I_x and k_x for the composite area by dividing it into rectangles 1 and 2 as shown, and compare your results to those of Example 8.4.

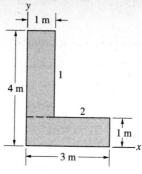

Solution:

$$I_x = \int_{A_1} y^2 \, dA_1 + \int_{A_2} y^2 \, dA_2$$

$$I_x = \int_0^1 \int_1^4 y^2 \, dy \, dx + \int_0^3 \int_0^1 y^2 \, dy \, dx$$

$$I_x = \int_0^1 \left[\frac{y^3}{3} \right]_1^4 dx + \int_0^3 \left[\frac{y^3}{3} \right]_0^1 dx$$

$$I_x = \int_0^1 \left[\frac{64}{3} - \frac{1}{3} \right] dx + \int_0^3 \frac{1}{3} dx$$

$$I_x = \frac{63}{3} x \Big]_0^1 + \frac{1}{3} x \Big]_0^3 = \frac{63}{3} + \frac{3}{3}$$

$$I_x = 21 + 1 = 22 \ \text{ft}^4$$

Area $= 3 + 3 = 6 \ \text{ft}^2$

$$k_x = \sqrt{\frac{I_x}{\text{Area}}} = \sqrt{\frac{22}{6}} = 1.91 \ \text{ft}$$

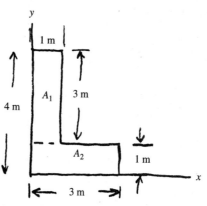

Problem 8.28 Determine I_y and k_y for the composite area.

Solution:

$$I_y = \int_{A_1} x^2 \, dA_1 + \int_{A_2} x^2 \, dA_2$$

$$I_y = \int_0^1 \int_1^4 x^2 \, dy \, dx + \int_0^3 \int_0^1 x^2 \, dy \, dx$$

$$I_y = \int_0^1 [x^2 y]_1^4 \, dx + \int_0^3 [x^2 y]_0^1 \, dx$$

$$I_y = \int_0^1 (4x^2 - x^2) \, dx + \int_0^3 x^2 \, dx$$

$$= \left[\frac{3x^3}{3} \right]_0^1 + \left[\frac{x^3}{3} \right]_0^3$$

$$I_y = 1 + 9 = 10.00 \ \text{m}^4$$

$$k_y = \sqrt{\frac{10}{6}} = 1.29 \ \text{m}$$

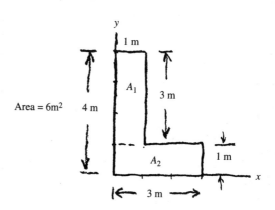

Problem 8.29 Determine I_x and k_x.

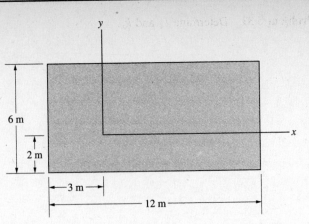

Solution:

$$I_x = \int_A y^2 \, dA = \int_{-3}^{9} \int_{-2}^{4} y^2 \, dy \, dx$$

$$I_x = \int_{-3}^{9} \left[\frac{y^3}{3} \right]_{-2}^{4} dx$$

$$I_x = \int_{-3}^{9} \left[\frac{(4)^3}{3} - \frac{(-2)^3}{3} \right] dx = \int_{-3}^{9} \left[\frac{64}{3} + \frac{8}{3} \right] dx$$

$$I_x = \int_{-3}^{9} \frac{72}{3} \, dx = 24 \int_{-3}^{9} dx = 24x \Big|_{-3}^{9}$$

$$I_x = 24[9 - (-3)] = (24)(12)$$

$$I_x = 288 \text{ m}^4$$

$$k_y = \sqrt{\frac{I_x}{\text{Area}}} = \sqrt{\frac{288}{72}} = \sqrt{4} = 2 \text{ m}$$

Area $= (6)(12)$ m^2
Area $= 72$ m^2

Problem 8.30 Determine I_y and k_y.

Solution:

$$I_y = \int_A x^2 \, dA = \int_{-3}^{9} \int_{-2}^{4} x^2 \, dy \, dx$$

$$I_y = \int_{-3}^{9} [x^2 y] \Big|_{-2}^{4} dx = \int_{-3}^{9} x^2 (4 - (-2)) \, dx$$

$$I_y = \int_{-3}^{9} 6x^2 \, dx = \left[6 \frac{x^3}{3} \right]_{-3}^{9} = [2x^3]_{-3}^{9}$$

$$I_y = 2[9^3 - (-3)^3]$$

$$I_y = 1512 \text{ m}^4$$

$$k_y = \sqrt{\frac{I_y}{\text{Area}}} = \sqrt{\frac{1512}{72}} = \sqrt{21}$$

$$k_y = 4.58 \text{ m}$$

Area $= (6)(12)$ m^2
Area $= 72$ m^2

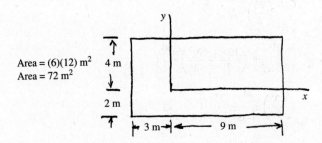

Problem 8.31 Determine I_x and k_x.

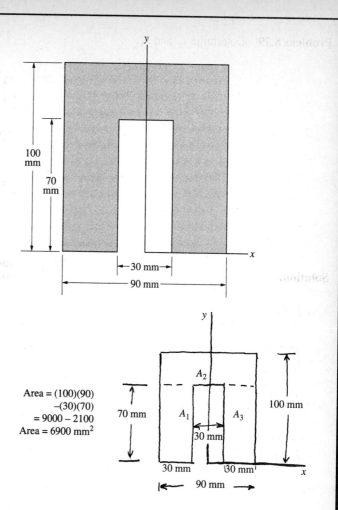

Solution:

$$I_x = \int_{A_1} y^2 \, dA_1 + \int_{A_2} y^2 \, dA_2 + \int_{A_3} y^2 \, dA_3$$

$$I_x = \int_{-45}^{-15} \int_0^{70} y^2 \, dy \, dx + \int_{-45}^{45} \int_{70}^{100} y^2 \, dy \, dx$$

$$+ \int_{15}^{45} \int_0^{70} y^2 \, dy \, dx$$

$$I_x = \int_{-45}^{-15} \left[\frac{y^3}{3} \right]_0^{70} dx + \int_{-45}^{45} \left[\frac{y^3}{3} \right]_{70}^{100} dx$$

$$+ \int_{15}^{45} \left[\frac{y^3}{3} \right]_0^{70} dx$$

$$I_x = \int_{-45}^{-15} \left(\frac{70^3}{3} \right) dx + \int_{-45}^{45} \left(\frac{100^3}{3} - \frac{70^3}{3} \right) dx$$

$$+ \int_{15}^{45} \left(\frac{70}{3} \right)^3 dx$$

$$I_x = \frac{70^3}{3} x \Big|_{-45}^{15} + \left(\frac{100^3}{3} - \frac{70^3}{3} \right) x \Big|_{-45}^{45}$$

$$+ \left(\frac{70^3}{3} \right) x \Big|_{-15}^{45}$$

$$I_x = \frac{70^3}{3}(30) + \left(\frac{100^3}{3} - \frac{70^3}{3} \right) 90 + \frac{70^3}{3}(30)$$

$$I_x = 2.66 \times 10^7 \text{ mm}^4$$

$$k_x = \sqrt{\frac{I_x}{\text{Area}}} = \sqrt{\frac{2.66 \times 10^7}{6900}} = 62.1 \text{ mm}$$

$$k_x = 62.1 \text{ mm}$$

Area = (100)(90)
−(30)(70)
= 9000 − 2100
Area = 6900 mm²

Problem 8.32 Determine I_y and k_y.

Solution:

$$I_y = \int_{A_1} x^2 \, dA_1 + \int_{A_2} x^2 \, dA_2 + \int_{A_3} x^2 \, dA_3$$

$$I_y = \int_{-45}^{-15} \int_0^{70} x^2 \, dy \, dx + \int_{-45}^{45} \int_{70}^{100} x^2 \, dy \, dx$$

$$+ \int_{15}^{45} \int_0^{70} x^2 \, dy \, dx$$

$$I_y = \int_{-45}^{-15} [x^2 y]_0^{70} \, dx + \int_{-45}^{45} (x^2 y) \Big|_{70}^{100} \, dx$$

$$+ \int_{15}^{45} (x^2 y) \Big|_0^{70} \, dx$$

$$I_y = \int_{-45}^{-15} 70 x^2 \, dx + \int_{-45}^{45} (100 - 70) x^2 \, dx + \int_{15}^{45} 70 x^2 \, dx$$

$$I_y = 70 \frac{x^3}{3} \Big|_{-45}^{-15} + 30 \frac{x^3}{3} \Big|_{-45}^{45} + 70 \frac{x^3}{3} \Big|_{15}^{45}$$

$$I_y = 70 \left(\frac{(-15)^3}{3} - \frac{(-45^3)}{3} \right) + 30 \left(\frac{45^3}{3} - \frac{(-45)^3}{3} \right)$$

$$+ 70 \left(\frac{(45)^3}{3} - \frac{(15)^3}{3} \right)$$

Area = 9000 mm^2
− 2100 mm^2
Area = 6900 mm^2

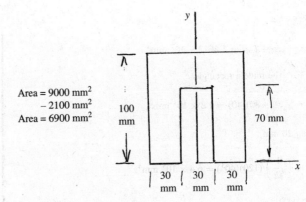

$$I_y = 140 \left(\frac{45^3}{3} - \frac{15^3}{3} \right) + 60 \left(\frac{45^3}{3} \right)$$

$$I_y = 5.92 \times 10^6 \text{ mm}^4$$

$$k_y = \sqrt{\frac{I_y}{\text{Area}}} = \sqrt{\frac{5.92 \times 10^6}{6900}} = 29.3 \text{ mm}$$

$$k_y = 29.3 \text{ mm}$$

Problem 8.33 Determine J_O and k_O.

Solution:

$$J_O = \int_A r^2 \, dA = \int_A (x^2 + y^2) \, dA$$

$$J_O = \int_A x^2 \, dA + \int_A y^2 \, dA = I_x + I_y$$

From the solutions to 8.31 and 8.32

$$I_x = 2.66 \times 10^7 \text{ mm}^4$$

and $I_y = 0.592 \times 10^7 \text{ mm}^4$

Hence,

$$J_O = 3.25 \times 10^7 \text{ mm}^4$$

$$k_O = \sqrt{\frac{J_O}{A}} = \sqrt{\frac{3.25 \times 10^7}{6900}}$$

$$k_O = 68.6 \text{ mm}$$

Area = 9000 mm^2
− 2100 mm^2
Area = 6900 mm^2

Problem 8.34 If you design the beam cross section so that $I_x = 6.4 \times 10^5$ mm^4, what are the resulting values of I_y and J_O?

Solution: The area moment of inertia for a triangle about the base is

$$I_x = \left(\frac{1}{12}\right) bh^3,$$

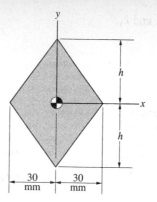

from which $I_x = 2\left(\frac{1}{12}\right)(60)h^3 = 10h^3$ mm^4,

$$I_x = 10h^3 = 6.4 \times 10^5 \text{ mm}^4,$$

from which $h = 40$ mm.

$$I_y = 2\left(\frac{1}{12}\right)(2h)(30^3) = \left(\frac{1}{3}\right) h(30^3)$$

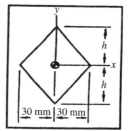

from which $I_y = \left(\frac{1}{3}\right)(40)(30^3) = 3.6 \times 10^5$ mm^4

$$\text{and } J_O = I_x + I_y = 3.6 \times 10^5 + 6.4 \times 10^5 = 1 \times 10^6 \text{ mm}^4$$

Problem 8.35 Determine I_y and k_y.

Solution: Divide the area into three parts:

Part (1): The top rectangle.

$$A_1 = 160(40) = 6.4 \times 10^3 \text{ mm}^2,$$

$$d_{x1} = \frac{160}{2} = 80 \text{ mm},$$

$$I_{yy1} = \left(\frac{1}{12}\right)(40)(160^3) = 1.3653 \times 10^7 \text{ mm}^4.$$

From which

$$I_{y1} = d_{x1}^2 A_1 + I_{yy1} = 5.4613 \times 10^7 \text{ mm}^4.$$

Part (2): The middle rectangle:

$$A_2 = (200 - 80)(40) = 4.8 \times 10^3 \text{ mm}^2,$$

$$d_{x2} = 20 \text{ mm},$$

$$I_{yy2} = \left(\frac{1}{12}\right)(120)(40^3) = 6.4 \times 10^5 \text{ mm}^4.$$

From which,

$$I_{y2} = d_{x2}^2 A_2 + I_{yy2} = 2.56 \times 10^6 \text{ mm}^4.$$

Part (3) The bottom rectangle:

$$A_3 = 120(40) = 4.8 \times 10^3 \text{ mm}^2,$$

$$d_{x3} = \frac{120}{2} = 60 \text{ mm},$$

$$I_{yy3} = \left(\frac{1}{12}\right) 40(120^3) = 5.76 \times 10^6 \text{ mm}^4$$

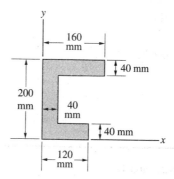

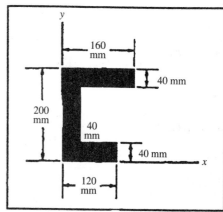

From which

$$I_{y3} = d_{X3}^2 A_3 + I_{yy3} = 2.304 \times 10^7 \text{ mm}^4$$

The composite:

$$I_y = I_{y1} + I_{y2} + I_{y3} = 8.0213 \times 10^7 \text{ mm}^4$$

$$k_y = \sqrt{\frac{I_y}{(A_1 + A_2 + A_3)}} = 70.8 \text{ mm}.$$

Problem 8.36 Determine I_x and k_x.

Solution: Use the solution to Problem 8.35. Divide the area into three parts:

Part (1): The top rectangle.

$$A_1 = 6.4 \times 10^3 \text{ mm}^2,$$

$$d_{y1} = 200 - 20 = 180 \text{ mm},$$

$$I_{xx1} = \left(\frac{1}{12}\right)(160)(40^3) = 8.533 \times 10^5 \text{ mm}^4.$$

From which

$$I_{x1} = d_{y1}^2 A_1 + I_{xx1} = 2.082 \times 10^8 \text{ mm}^4$$

Part (2): The middle rectangle:

$$A_2 = 4.8 \times 10^3 \text{ mm}^2,$$

$$d_{y2} = \frac{120}{2} + 40 = 100 \text{ mm},$$

$$I_{xx2} = \left(\frac{1}{12}\right)(40)(120^3) = 5.76 \times 10^6 \text{ mm}^4$$

from which

$$I_{x2} = d_{y2}^2 A_2 + I_{xx2} = 5.376 \times 10^7 \text{ mm}^4$$

Part (3) The bottom rectangle:

$$A_3 = 4.8 \times 10^3 \text{ mm}^2,$$

$$d_{y3} = 20 \text{ mm},$$

$$I_{xx3} = \left(\frac{1}{12}\right)120(40^3) = 6.4 \times 10^5 \text{ mm}^4$$

and $I_{x3} = d_{y3}^2 A_3 + I_{xx3} = 2.56 \times 10^6 \text{ mm}^4$.

The composite:

$$I_x = I_{x1} + I_{x2} + I_{x3} = 2.645 \times 10^8 \text{ mm}^4$$

$$k_x = \sqrt{\frac{I_x}{(A_1 + A_2 + A_3)}} = 128.6 \text{ mm}$$

Problem 8.37 Determine I_{xy}.

Solution: (See figure in Problem 8.35). Use the solutions in Problems 8.35 and 8.36. Divide the area into three parts:

Part (1): $A_1 = 160(40) = 6.4 \times 10^3 \text{ mm}^2$,

$$d_{x1} = \frac{160}{2} = 80 \text{ mm},$$

$$d_{y1} = 200 - 20 = 180 \text{ mm},$$

$$I_{xxyy1} = 0,$$

from which

$$I_{xy1} = d_{x1} d_{y1} A_1 + I_{xxyy1} = 9.216 \times 10^7 \text{ mm}^4.$$

Part (2) $A_2 = (200 - 80)(40) = 4.8 \times 10^3 \text{ mm}^2$,

$$d_{x2} = 20 \text{ mm},$$

$$d_{y2} = \frac{120}{2} + 40 = 100 \text{ mm},$$

from which

$$I_{xy2} = d_{x2} d_{y2} A_2 = 9.6 \times 10^6 \text{ mm}^4.$$

Part (3): $A_3 = 120(40) = 4.8 \times 10^3 \text{ mm}^2$,

$$d_{x3} = \frac{120}{2} = 60 \text{ mm},$$

$$d_{y3} = 20 \text{ mm},$$

from which

$$I_{xy3} = d_{x3} d_{y3} A_3 = 5.76 \times 10^6.$$

The composite:

$$I_{xy} = I_{xy1} + I_{xy2} + I_{xy3} = 1.0752 \times 10^8 \text{ mm}^4$$

Problem 8.38　Determine I_x and k_x.

Solution: The strategy is to use the relationship $I_x = d^2A + I_{xc}$, where I_{xc} is the area moment of inertia about the centroid. From this $I_{xc} = -d^2A + I_x$. Use the solutions to Problems 8.35, 8.36, and 8.37. Divide the area into three parts and locate the centroid relative to the coordinate system in the Problems 8.35, 8.36, and 8.37.

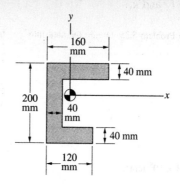

Part (1) $A_1 = 6.4 \times 10^3$ mm^2,

$d_{y1} = 200 - 20 = 180$ mm.

Part (2) $A_2 = (200 - 80)(40) = 4.8 \times 10^3$ mm^2,

$d_{x1} = \dfrac{160}{2} = 80$ mm,　$d_{x2} = 20$ mm,

$d_{y2} = \dfrac{120}{2} + 40 = 100$ mm,

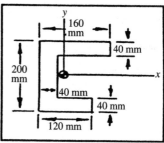

Part (3) $A_3 = 120(40) = 4.8 \times 10^3$ mm^2,

$d_{x3} = \dfrac{120}{2} = 60$ mm,　$d_{y3} = 20$ mm.

The total area is

$A = A_1 + A_2 + A_3 = 1.6 \times 10^4$ mm^2.

The centroid coordinates are

$\mathbf{x} = \dfrac{A_1 d_{x1} + A_2 d_{x2} + A_3 d_{x3}}{A} = 56$ mm,

$\mathbf{y} = \dfrac{A_1 d_{y1} + A_2 d_{y2} + A_3 d_{y3}}{A} = 108$ mm

from which

$I_{xc} = -\mathbf{y}^2A + I_x = -1.866 \times 10^8 + 2.645 \times 10^8$

$\qquad = 7.788 \times 10^7$ mm^4

$k_{xc} = \sqrt{\dfrac{I_{xc}}{A}} = 69.77$ mm

Problem 8.39　Determine I_y and k_y.

Solution: The strategy is to use the relationship $I_y = d^2A + I_{yc}$, where I_{yc} is the area moment of inertia about the centroid. From this $I_{yc} = -d^2A + I_y$. Use the solution to Problem 8.38. The centroid coordinates are $\mathbf{x} = 56$ mm, $\mathbf{y} = 108$ mm, from which

$I_{yc} = -\mathbf{x}^2A + I_y = -5.0176 \times 10^7 + 8.0213 \times 10^7$

$\qquad = 3.0 \times 10^7$ mm^4,

$k_{yc} = \sqrt{\dfrac{I_{yc}}{A}} = 43.33$ mm

Problem 8.40　Determine I_{xy}.

Solution: Use the solution to Problem 8.37. The centroid coordinates are

$\mathbf{x} = 56$ mm,　$\mathbf{y} = 108$ mm,

from which $I_{xyc} = -\mathbf{xy}A + I_{xy} = -9.6768 \times 10^7 + 1.0752 \times 10^8$

$\qquad\qquad = 1.0752 \times 10^7$ mm^4

Problem 8.41 Determine I_x and k_x.

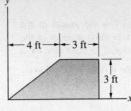

Solution: Divide the area into two parts:

Part (1): a triangle and Part (2): a rectangle. The area moment of inertia for a triangle about the base is

$$I_x = \left(\frac{1}{12}\right) bh^3.$$

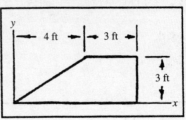

The area moment of inertia about the base for a rectangle is

$$I_x = \left(\frac{1}{3}\right) bh^3.$$

Part (1) $I_{x1} = \left(\frac{1}{12}\right) 4(3^3) = 9$ ft^2.

Part (2) $I_{x2} = \left(\frac{1}{3}\right) 3(3^3) = 27$.

The composite: $I_x = I_{x1} + I_{x2} = 36$ ft^4. The area:

$$A = \left(\frac{1}{2}\right) 4(3) + 3(3) = 15 \text{ ft}^2.$$

$$k_x = \sqrt{\frac{I_x}{A}} = 1.549 \text{ ft}.$$

Problem 8.42 Determine J_O and k_O.

Solution: (See Figure in Problem 8.41.) Use the solution to Problem 8.41.

Part (1): The area moment of inertia about the centroidal axis parallel to the base for a triangle is

$$I_{yc} = \left(\frac{1}{36}\right) bh^3 = \left(\frac{1}{36}\right) 3(4^3) = 5.3333 \text{ ft}^4,$$

from which

$$I_{y1} = \left(\frac{8}{3}\right)^2 A_1 + I_{yc} = 48 \text{ ft}^4.$$

where $A_1 = 6$ ft^2.

Part (2): The area moment of inertia about a centroid parallel to the base for a rectangle is

$$I_{yc} = \left(\frac{1}{12}\right) bh^3 = \left(\frac{1}{12}\right) 3(3^3) = 6.75 \text{ ft}^4,$$

from which

$$I_{y2} = (5.5)^2 A_2 + I_{yc} = 279 \text{ ft}^4,$$

where $A_2 = 9$ ft^2.

The composite: $I_y = I_{y1} + I_{y2} = 327$ ft^4, from which, using a result from Problem 8.41,

$$J_O = I_x + I_y = 327 + 36 = 363 \text{ ft}^4$$

and $k_O = \sqrt{\dfrac{J_O}{A}} = 4.92$ ft

Problem 8.43 Determine I_{xy}.

Solution: (See Figure in Problem 8.41.) Use the results of the solutions to Problems 8.41 and 8.42. The area cross product of the moment of inertia about centroidal axes parallel to the bases for a triangle is $I_{x'y'} = \frac{1}{72}b^2h^2$, and for a rectangle it is zero. Therefore:

$$I_{xy1} = \left(\frac{1}{72}\right)(4^2)(3^2) + \left(\frac{8}{3}\right)\left(\frac{3}{3}\right)A_1 = 18 \text{ ft}^4$$

and $I_{xy2} = (1.5)(5.5)A_2 = 74.25 \text{ ft}^4$,

$$I_{xy} = I_{x'y'1} + I_{xy2} = 92.25 \text{ ft}^4$$

Problem 8.44 Determine I_x and k_x.

Solution: Use the results of Problems 8.41, 8.42, and 8.43. The strategy is to use the parallel axis theorem and solve for the area moment of inertia about the centroidal axis. The centroidal coordinate

$$\mathbf{y} = \frac{A_1(1) + A_2(1.5)}{A} = 1.3 \text{ ft}.$$

From which

$$I_{xc} = -\mathbf{y}^2A + I_x = 10.65 \text{ ft}^4$$

and $k_{xc} = \sqrt{\dfrac{I_{xc}}{A}} = 0.843 \text{ ft}$

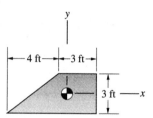
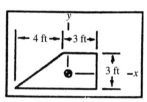

Problem 8.45 Determine J_O and k_O.

Solution: Use the results of Problems 8.41, 8.42, and 8.43. The strategy is to use the parallel axis theorem and solve for the area moment of inertia about the centroidal axis. The centroidal coordinate:

$$\mathbf{x} = \frac{A_1\left(\frac{8}{3}\right) + A_2(5.5)}{A} = 4.3667 \text{ ft},$$

from which

$$I_{YC} = -\mathbf{x}^2A + I_Y = 40.98 \text{ ft}^4.$$

Using a result from Problem 8.44,

$$J_O = I_{XC} + I_{YC} = 10.65 + 40.98 = 51.63 \text{ ft}^4$$

and $k_O = \sqrt{\dfrac{J_O}{A}} = 1.855 \text{ ft}$

Problem 8.46 Determine I_{XY}.

Solution: Use the results of Problems 8.41–8.45. The strategy is to use the parallel axis theorem and solve for the area moment of inertia about the centroidal axis. Using the centroidal coordinates determined in Problems 8.44 and 8.45,

$$I_{xyc} = -\mathbf{xy}A + I_{xy} = -85.15 + 92.25 = 7.1 \text{ ft}^4$$

Problem 8.47 Determine I_x and k_x.

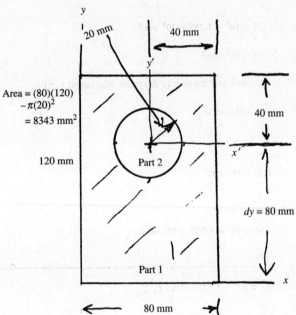

Solution: Let Part 1 be the entire rectangular solid without the hole and let part 2 be the hole.

$I_{x1} = \frac{1}{3}bh^3$ where $b = 80$ mm

$$h = 120 \text{ mm}$$

$I_{x1} = \frac{1}{3}(80)(120)^3 = 4.608 \times 10^7 \text{ mm}^4$

For Part 2,

$I_{x'2} = \frac{1}{4}\pi R^4 = \frac{1}{4}\pi(20)^4 \text{ mm}^4$

$I_{x'2} = 1.257 \times 10^5 \text{ mm}^4$

$I_{x2} = I_{x'2} + d_y^2 A$

where $A = \pi R^2 = 1257 \text{ mm}^2$

$\qquad d = 80$ mm

$I_{x2} = 1.257 \times 10^5 + \pi(20)^2(80)^2$

$I_{x2} = 0.126 \times 10^6 + 8.042 \times 10^6 \text{ mm}^4$

$\qquad = 8.168 \times 10^6 \text{ mm}^4 = 0.817 \times 10^7 \text{ mm}^4$

$I_x = I_{x1} - I_{x2} = 3.79 \times 10^7 \text{ mm}^4$

Area $= hb - \pi R^2 = (80)(120) - \pi R^2$

Area $= 8343 \text{ mm}^2$

$k_x = \sqrt{\dfrac{I_x}{\text{Area}}} = 67.4 \text{ mm}$

Problem 8.48 Determine J_O and k_O.

Solution: For the rectangle,

$$J_{O1} = I_{x1} + I_{y1} = \tfrac{1}{3}bh^3 + \tfrac{1}{3}hb^3$$

$$J_{O1} = 4.608 \times 10^7 + 2.048 \times 10^7 \text{ mm}^4$$

$$J_{O1} = 6.656 \times 10^7 \text{ mm}^4$$

$$A_1 = bh = 9600 \text{ mm}^2$$

For the circular cutout about $x'y'$

$$J'_{O2} = I_{x'2} + I_{y'_2} = \tfrac{1}{4}\pi R^4 + \tfrac{1}{4}\pi R^4$$

$$J'_{O2} = 1.257 \times 10^5 + 1.257 \times 10^5 \text{ mm}^4$$

$$J'_{O2} = 2.513 \times 10^5 \text{ mm}^2$$

Using the parallel axis theorem to determine J_{O2} (about x, y)

$$J_{O2} = J'_{0_2} + (d_x^2 + d_y^2)A_2$$

$$A_2 = \pi R^2 = 1257 \text{ mm}^2$$

$$J_{O2} = 1.030 \times 10^7 \text{ mm}^4$$

$$J_O = J_{O1} - J_{O2}$$

$$J_O = 6.656 \times 10^7 - 1.030 \times 10^7 \text{ mm}^4$$

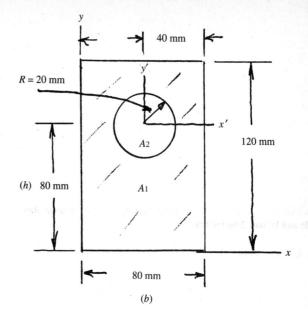

(b)

$$J_O = 5.63 \times 10^7 \text{ mm}^4$$

$$k_O = \sqrt{\frac{J_O}{\text{Area}}} = \sqrt{\frac{J_O}{A_1 - A_2}}$$

$$k_O = 82.1 \text{ mm}$$

Problem 8.49 Determine I_{xy}.

Solution:

$$A_1 = (80)(120) = 9600 \text{ mm}^2$$

$$A_2 = \pi R^2 = \pi(20)^2 = 1257 \text{ mm}^2$$

For the rectangle (A_1)

$$I_{xy_1} = \tfrac{1}{4}b^2h^2 = \tfrac{1}{4}(80)^2(120)^2$$

$$I_{xy_1} = 2.304 \times 10^7 \text{ mm}^2$$

For the cutout

$$I_{x'y'2} = 0$$

and by the parallel axis theorem

$$I_{xy2} = I_{x'y'2} + A_2(d_x)(d_y)$$

$$I_{xy2} = 0 + (1257)(40)(80)$$

$$I_{xy2} = 4.021 \times 10^6 \text{ mm}^4$$

$$I_{xy} = I_{xy1} - I_{xy2}$$

$$I_{xy} = 2.304 \times 10^7 - 0.402 \times 10^7 \text{ mm}^4$$

$$I_{xy} = 1.90 \times 10^7 \text{ mm}^4$$

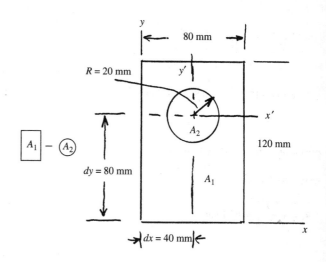

Problem 8.50 Determine I_x and k_x.

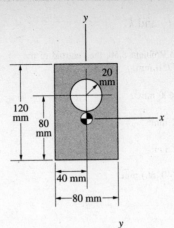

Solution: We must first find the location of the centroid of the total area. Let us use the coordinates XY to do this. Let A_1 be the rectangle and A_2 be the circular cutout. Note that by symmetry $X_c = 40$ mm

	Area	X_c	Y_c
Rectangle$_1$	9600 mm^2	40 mm	60 mm
Circle$_2$	1257 mm^2	40 mm	80 mm

$A_1 = 9600$ mm^2

$A_2 = 1257$ mm^2

For the composite,

$$X_c = \frac{A_1 X_{c1} - A_2 X_{c2}}{A_1 - A_2} = 40 \text{ mm}$$

$$Y_c = \frac{A_1 Y_{c1} - A_2 Y_{c2}}{A_1 - A_2} = 57.0 \text{ mm}$$

Now let us determine I_x and k_x about the centroid of the composite body.

Rectangle about its centroid (40, 60) mm

$$I_{x1} = \frac{1}{12} bh^3 = \frac{1}{12}(80)(120)^3$$

$I_{x1} = 1.152 \times 10^7$ mm^3,

Now to C

$$I_{xc1} = I_{x1} + (60 - Y_c)^2 A_1$$

$I_{xc1} = 1.161 \times 10^7$ mm^4

Circular cut out about its centroid

$A_2 = \pi R^2 = (20)^2 \pi = 1257$ mm^2

$I_{x2} = \frac{1}{4}\pi R^4 = \pi(20)^4/4$

$I_{x2} = 1.26 \times 10^5$ mm^4

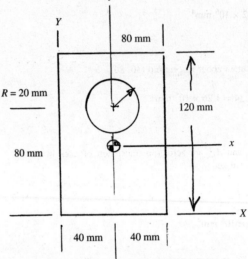

Now to $C \rightarrow d_{y2} = 80 - 57 = 23$ mm

$$I_{xc2} = I_{x2} + (d_{y2})^2 A_2$$

$I_{xc2} = 7.91 \times 10^5$ mm^4

For the composite about the centroid

$$I_x = I_{xc1} - I_{xc2}$$

$I_x = 1.08 \times 10^7$ mm^4

The composite Area $= 9600 - 1257$ mm^2

$$= 8343 \text{ mm}^2$$

$$k_x = \sqrt{\frac{I_x}{A}} = 36.0 \text{ mm}$$

Problem 8.51 Determine I_y and k_y.

Solution: From the solution to Problem 8.50, the centroid of the composite area is located at (40, 57.0) mm.

The area of the rectangle, A_1, is 9600 mm^2.

The area of the cutout, A_2, is 1257 mm^2.

The area of the composite is 8343 mm^2.

(1) Rectangle about its centroid (40, 60) mm.

$$I_{y1} = \frac{1}{12}hb^3 = \frac{1}{12}(120)(80)^3$$

$$I_{y1} = 5.12 \times 10^6 \text{ mm}^4$$

$$d_{x1} = 0$$

(2) Circular cutout about its centroid (40, 80)

$$I_{y2} = \pi R^4/4 = 1.26 \times 10^5 \text{ mm}^4$$

$$d_{x2} = 0$$

Since d_{x1} and d_{x2} are zero. (no translation of axes in the x-direction), we get

$$I_y = I_{y1} - I_{y2}$$

$$I_y = 4.99 \times 10^6 \text{ mm}^4$$

Finally,

$$k_y = \sqrt{\frac{I_y}{A_1 - A_2}} = \sqrt{\frac{4.99 \times 10^6}{8343}}$$

$$k_y = 24.5 \text{ mm}$$

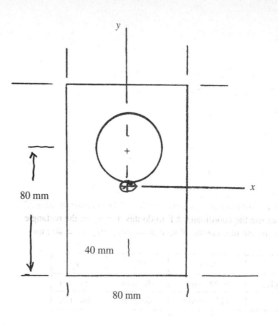

Problem 8.52 Determine J_O and k_O.

Solution: From the solutions to Problems 8.51 and 8.52,

$$I_x = 1.07 \times 10^7 \text{ mm}^4$$

$$I_y = 4.99 \times 10^6 \text{ mm}^4$$

and $A = 8343$ mm^2

$$J_O = I_x + I_y = 1.57 \times 10^7 \text{ mm}^4$$

$$k_O = \sqrt{\frac{J_O}{A}} = 43.4 \text{ mm}$$

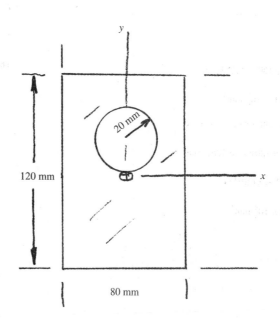

Problem 8.53 Determine I_y and k_y.

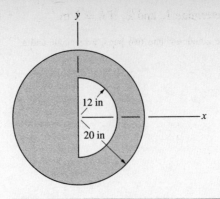

Solution: Treat the area as a circular area with a half-circular cutout: From Appendix B,

$$(I_y)_1 = \tfrac{1}{4}\pi(20)^4 \ \text{in}^4$$

and $(I_y)_2 = \tfrac{1}{8}\pi(12)^4 \ \text{in}^4$,

so $I_y = \tfrac{1}{4}\pi(20)^4 - \tfrac{1}{8}\pi(12)^4 = 1.18 \times 10^5 \ \text{in}^4$.

The area is $A = \pi(20)^2 - \tfrac{1}{2}\pi(12)^2 = 1030 \ \text{in}^2$

so, $k_y = \sqrt{\dfrac{I_y}{A}} = \sqrt{\dfrac{1.18 \times 10^5}{1.03 \times 10^3}}$

$= 10.7 \ \text{in}$

Problem 8.54 Determine J_O and k_O.

Solution: Treating the area as a circular area with a half-circular cutout as shown in the solution of Problem 8.53, from Appendix B,

$$(J_O)_1 = (I_x)_1 + (I_y)_1 = \tfrac{1}{2}\pi(20)^4 \ \text{in}^4$$

and $(J_O)_2 = (I_x)_2 + (I_y)_2 = \tfrac{1}{4}\pi(12)^4 \ \text{in}^4$.

Therefore $J_O = \tfrac{1}{2}\pi(20)^4 - \tfrac{1}{4}\pi(12)^4$

$= 2.35 \times 10^5 \ \text{in}^4$.

From the solution of Problem 8.53,

$A = 1030 \ \text{in}^2 \quad R_o = \sqrt{\dfrac{J_O}{A}}$

$= \sqrt{\dfrac{2.35 \times 10^5}{1.03 \times 10^3}} = 15.1 \ \text{in}$.

Problem 8.55   Determine I_y and k_y if $h = 3$ m.

Solution: Break the composite into two parts, a rectangle and a semi-circle.

For the semi-circle

$$I_{x'c} = \left(\frac{\pi}{8} - \frac{9}{8\pi} \right) R^4$$

$$I_{y'c} = \frac{1}{8}\pi R^4 \quad d = \frac{4R}{3\pi}$$

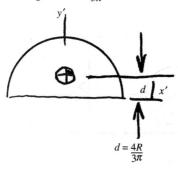

$$d = \frac{4R}{3\pi}$$

To get moments about the x and y axes, the (d_{xc}, d_{yc}) for the semi-circle are

$$d_{xc} = 0, \quad d_{yc} = 3 \text{ m} + \frac{4R}{3\pi}$$

and $A_c = \pi R^2 / 2 = 2.26 \text{ m}^2$

$$I_{y'c} = \frac{1}{8}\pi R^4$$

and $I_{yc} = I_{y'c} + d_{xc}^2 A \quad (d_x = 0)$

$$I_{yc} = I_{y'c} = \pi (1.2)^4 / 8$$

$$I_{yc} = 0.814 \text{ m}^4$$

For the Rectangle

$$I_{x'R} = \frac{1}{12} bh^3$$

$$I_{y'R} = \frac{1}{12} hb^3$$

$$A_R = bh$$

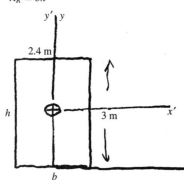

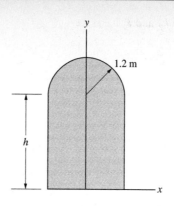

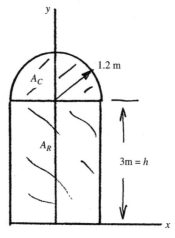

To get moments of area about the x, y axes, $d_{xR} = 0$, $d_{yR} = 1.5$ m

$$I_{yR} = I_{y'R} + (\overset{0}{\cancel{d_{xR}}})^2 (bh)$$

$$I_{yR} = I_{y'R} = \frac{1}{12}(3)(2,4)^3 \text{ m}^4$$

$$I_{yR} = 3.456 \text{ m}^2$$

$$A_R = bh = 7.2 \text{ m}^2$$

$$I_y = I_{yc} + I_{yR}$$

$$I_y = 4.27 \text{ m}^2$$

To find k_y, we need the total area, $A = A_R + A_c$

$$A = 7.20 + 2.26 \text{ m}^2$$

$$A = 9.46 \text{ m}^2$$

$$k_y = \sqrt{\frac{I_y}{A}} = 0.672 \text{ m}$$

Problem 8.56   Determine I_x and k_x if $h = 3$ m.

Solution: Break the composite into two parts, the semi-circle and the rectangle. From the solution to Problem 8.55,

$$I_{x'c} = \left(\frac{\pi}{8} - \frac{9}{8\pi}\right) R^4$$

$$d_{yc} = \left(3 + \frac{4R}{3\pi}\right) \text{ m}$$

$$A_c = 2.26 \text{ m}^2.$$

$$I_{xc} = I_{x'c} + A_c d_{yc}^2$$

Substituting in numbers, we get

$$I_{x'c} = 0.0717 \text{ m}^4$$

$$d_{yc} = 3.509 \text{ m}$$

and $I_{xc} = I_{x'c} + A_c d_y^2$

$$I_{xc} = 27.928 \text{ m}^2$$

For the Rectangle $h = 3$ m, $b = 2.4$ m

Area: $A_R = bh = 7.20 \text{ m}^2$

$$I_{x'R} = \frac{1}{12} bh^3, \quad d_{yR} = 1.5 \text{ m}$$

$$I_{xR} = I_{x'R} + d_{yR}^2 A_R$$

Substituting, we get

$$I_{x'R} = 5.40 \text{ m}^4$$

$$I_{xR} = 21.6 \text{ m}^4$$

For the composite,

$$I_x = I_{xR} + I_{xc}$$

$$I_x = 49.5 \text{ m}^4$$

Also $k_x = \sqrt{\dfrac{I_x}{A_R + A_c}} = 2.29$ m

$$k_x = 2.29 \text{ m}$$

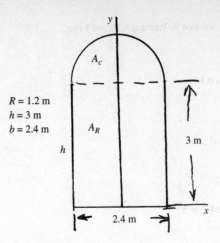

$R = 1.2$ m
$h = 3$ m
$b = 2.4$ m

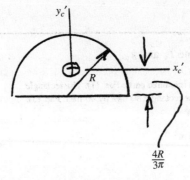

Problem 8.57 If $I_y = 5$ m^4, what is the dimension of h?

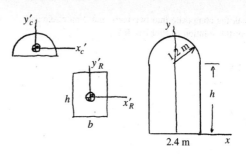

Solution: From the solution to Problem 8.55, we have:

For the semicircle

$$I_{y'c} = I_y = \pi(1.2)^4/8 = 0.814 \text{ m}^2$$

For the rectangle

$$I_{y'R} = I_{yR} = \frac{1}{12}(h)(2.4)^3 \text{ m}^4$$

Also, we know $I_{yR} + I_{yc} = 5$ m^4.

Hence $0.814 + \frac{1}{12}(h)(2.4)^3 = 5$

Solving, $h = 3.63$ m

Problem 8.58 Determine I_y and k_y.

Solution: Divide the object into three parts: Part (1): The rectangle 100 mm by 60 mm, Part (2) The rectangle 80 mm by 40 mm. Part (3): The semicircle of radius 20 mm.

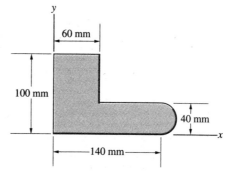

Part (1). $A_1 = 100(60) = 6000$ m^2,

$\mathbf{x}_1 = 30$ mm,

$\mathbf{y}_1 = 50$ mm,

$I_{xx1} = \left(\frac{1}{12}\right)(60)(100)^3 = 5 \times 10^6$ mm^4,

$I_{yy1} = \left(\frac{1}{12}\right)(100)(60)^3 = 1.8 \times 10^6$ mm^4.

Part (2) $A_2 = 80(40) = 3200$ mm^2,

$\mathbf{x}_2 = 100$ mm,

$\mathbf{y}_2 = 20$ mm.

$I_{xx2} = \left(\frac{1}{12}\right)80(40)^3 = 4.2667 \times 10^5$ mm^4,

$I_{yy2} = \left(\frac{1}{12}\right)40(80)^3 = 1.7067 \times 10^6$ mm^4.

Part (3): $A_3 = \frac{\pi(20)^2}{2} = 628.32$ mm^2,

$\mathbf{x}_3 = 140 + \frac{4(20)}{3\pi} = 148.49$ mm,

$\mathbf{y}_3 = 20$ mm.

$I_{xx3} = \left(\frac{1}{8}\right)\pi R^4 = 62831.8$ mm^4,

$I_{yy3} = \left(\frac{1}{8}\right)\pi R^4 = 62831.8$ mm^4.

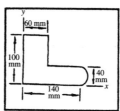

The area:

$$A = \sum_1^3 A_i = 9828.32 \text{ mm}^2.$$

$$I_y = \mathbf{x}_1^2 A_1 + I_{yy1} + \mathbf{x}_2^2 A_2 + I_{yy2} + \mathbf{x}_3^2 A_3 + I_{yy3}.$$

$$I_y = 5.482 \times 10^7 \text{ mm}^4$$

$$k_y = \sqrt{\frac{I_y}{A}} = 74.69 \text{ mm}$$

Problem 8.59   Determine I_x and k_x.

Solution: Use the results of the solution to Problem 8.58.

$$I_x = \mathbf{y}_1^2 A_1 + I_{xx1} + \mathbf{y}_2^2 A_2 + I_{xx2} + \mathbf{y}_3^2 A_3 + I_{xx3}$$

$$I_x = 2.202 \times 10^7 \text{ mm}^4.$$

$$k_x = \sqrt{\frac{I_x}{A}} = 47.33 \text{ mm}$$

Problem 8.60   Determine I_{xy}.

Solution: Use the solutions to Problems 8.58 and 8.59. The area cross product of inertia for each of the areas about their centroids is zero.

$$I_{xy} = \mathbf{x}_1 \mathbf{y}_1 A_1 + \mathbf{x}_2 \mathbf{y}_2 A_2 + \mathbf{x}_3 \mathbf{y}_3 A_3 = 1.727 \times 10^7 \text{ mm}^4$$

Problem 8.61   Determine I_y and k_y.

Solution: Use the solutions to Problems 8.56–8.58. The location of the centroid is

$$\mathbf{x} = \frac{A_1 \mathbf{x}_1 + A_2 \mathbf{x}_2 + A_3 x_3}{A}$$

$$= \frac{1.8(10^5) + 3.2(10^5) + 9.33(10^4)}{9.828(10^3)} = 60.37 \text{ mm}.$$

The area moment of inertia about the composite centroid:

$$I_{yc} = -\mathbf{x}^2 A + I_y = -3.58 \times 10^7 + 5.48 \times 10^7$$

$$= 1.9 \times 10^7 \text{ mm}^4$$

$$k_{yc} = \sqrt{\frac{I_{yc}}{A}} = 43.98 \text{ mm}$$

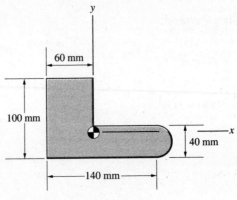

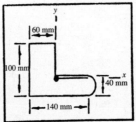

Problem 8.62   Determine I_x and k_x.

Solution: The location of the centroid is

$$\mathbf{y} = \frac{A_1 \mathbf{y}_1 + A_2 \mathbf{y}_2 + A_3 \mathbf{y}_3}{A} = \frac{3(10^5) + 6.4(10^4) + 1.26(10^4)}{9.828(10^3)}$$

$$= 38.3 \text{ mm}.$$

The area moment of inertia about the centroid is

$$I_{xc} = -\mathbf{y}^2 A + I_x = -1.443 \times 10^7 + 2.202 \times 10^7$$

$$= 7.593 \times 10^6 \text{ mm}^4$$

$$k_{xc} = \sqrt{\frac{I_{xc}}{A}} = 27.8 \text{ mm}$$

Problem 8.63 Determine I_{xy}.

Solution: Use the results of the solutions to Problems 8.61–8.62.

$$I_{xyc} = -\mathbf{xy}A + I_{xy} = -2.27 \times 10^7 + 1.726 \times 10^7$$

$$= -5.47 \times 10^6 \text{ mm}^4$$

Problem 8.64 Determine I_y and k_y.

Solution: Divide the area into three parts:

Part (1) The rectangle 18 by 18 inches; Part (2) The triangle with base 6 in and altitude 18 in; Part (3) The semicircle of 9 in radius.

Part (1): $A_1 = 18(18) = 324 \text{ in}^2$,

  $\mathbf{x}_1 = 9$ in,

  $\mathbf{y}_1 = 9$ in,

  $I_{xx1} = \left(\dfrac{1}{12}\right) 18(18^3) = 8748 \text{ in}^4$,

  $I_{yy1} = \left(\dfrac{1}{12}\right) 18(18^3) = 8748 \text{ in}^4$.

Part (2): $A_2 = \left(\dfrac{1}{2}\right) 18(6) = 54 \text{ in}^2$,

  $\mathbf{x}_2 = 9$ in,

  $\mathbf{y}_2 = \left(\dfrac{1}{3}\right) 18 = 6$ in,

  $I_{xx2} = \left(\dfrac{1}{36}\right) 6(18^3) = 972 \text{ in}^4$,

  $I_{yy2} = (1/18)18(3^3) = 27 \text{ in}^4$.

Part (3) $A_3 = \dfrac{\pi(9^2)}{2} = 127.23 \text{ in}^2$,

  $\mathbf{x}_3 = 9$ in,

  $\mathbf{y}_3 = 18 + \left(\dfrac{4(9)}{3\pi}\right) = 21.82$ in,

  $I_{xx3} = \left(\dfrac{1}{8}\right) \pi(9^4) - \left(\dfrac{4(9)}{3\pi}\right)^2 A_3 = 720.1 \text{ in}^4$,

  $I_{yy3} = \left(\dfrac{1}{8}\right) \pi(9^4) = 2576.5 \text{ in}^4$.

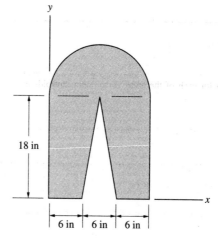

The composite area:

$$A = \sum_{1}^{3} A_i = 397.23 \text{ in}^2.$$

The area moment of inertia:

$$I_y = \mathbf{x}_1^2 A_1 + I_{yy1} - \mathbf{x}_2^2 A_2 - I_{yy2} + \mathbf{x}_3^2 A_3 + I_{yy3},$$

$$I_y = 4.347 \times 10^4 \text{ in}^4,$$

$$k_y = \sqrt{\dfrac{I_y}{A}} = 10.461 \text{ in}$$

Problem 8.65 Determine I_x and k_x.

Solution: Use the results of the solution to Problem 8.64.

$$I_X = \mathbf{y}_1^2 A_1 + I_{XX1} - \mathbf{y}_2^2 A_2 - I_{XX2} + \mathbf{y}_3^2 A_3 + I_{XX3},$$

$$I_x = 9.338 \times 10^4 \text{ in}^4,$$

$$k_x = \sqrt{\frac{I_x}{A}} = 15.33 \text{ in}$$

Problem 8.66 Determine I_{xy}.

Solution: Use the results of the solutions to Problems 8.63 and 8.64.

$$I_{xy} = \mathbf{x}_1 \mathbf{y}_1 A_1 - \mathbf{x}_2 \mathbf{y}_2 A_2 + \mathbf{x}_3 \mathbf{y}_3 A_3$$

$$I_{xy} = 4.8313 \times 10^4 \text{ in}^4$$

Problem 8.67 Determine I_y and k_y.

Solution: We divide the composite area into a triangle (1), rectangle (2), half-circle (3), and circular cutout (4):

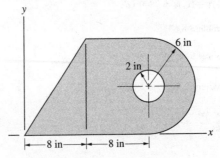

Triangle:

$$(I_y)_1 = \tfrac{1}{4}(12)(8)^3 = 1536 \text{ in}^4$$

Rectangle:

$$(I_y)_2 = \frac{1}{12}(12)(8)^3 + (12)^2(8)(12) = 14{,}336 \text{ in}^4.$$

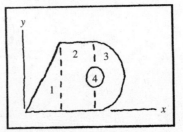

Half-Circle:

$$(I_y)_3 = \left(\frac{\pi}{8} - \frac{8}{9\pi}\right)(6)^4 + \left[16 + \frac{4(6)}{3\pi}\right]^2 \frac{1}{2}\pi(6)^2 = 19{,}593 \text{ in}^4$$

Circular cutout:

$$(I_y)_4 = \tfrac{1}{4}\pi(2)^4 + (16)^2\pi(2)^2 = 3230 \text{ in}^4.$$

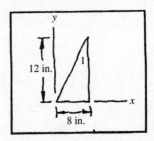

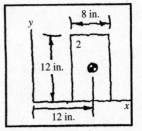

Therefore

$$I_y = (I_y)_1 + (I_y)_2 + (I_y)_3 - (I_y)_4 = 3.224 \times 10^4 \text{ in}^4.$$

The area is

$$A = A_1 + A_2 + A_3 - A_4$$

$$= \frac{1}{2}(12)(8) + (8)(12) + \frac{1}{2}\pi(6)^2 - \pi(2)^2 = 188 \text{ in}^2,$$

$$\text{so } k_y = \sqrt{\frac{I_y}{A}} = \sqrt{\frac{3.224 \times 10^4}{188}} = 13.1 \text{ in}.$$

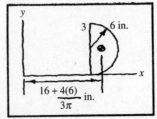

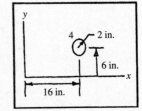

Problem 8.68 Determine J_O and k_O.

Solution: I_y is determined in the solution to Problem 8.67. We will determine I_x and use the relation $J_O = I_x + I_y$. Using the figures in the solution to Problem 8.67,

Triangle:

$$(I_x)_1 = \frac{1}{12}(8)(12)^3 = 1152 \text{ in}^4.$$

Rectangle:

$$(I_x)_2 = \tfrac{1}{3}(8)(12)^3 = 4608 \text{ in}^4.$$

Half Circle:

$$(I_x)_3 = \tfrac{1}{8}\pi(6)^4 + (6)^2\tfrac{1}{2}\pi(6)^2 = 2545 \text{ in}^4.$$

Circular Cutout:

$$(I_x)_4 = \tfrac{1}{4}\pi(2)^4 + (6)^2\pi(2)^2 = 465 \text{ in}^4.$$

Therefore

$$I_x = (I_x)_1 + (I_x)_2 + (I_x)_3 - (I_x)_4 = 7840 \text{ in}^4.$$

Using the solution of Problem 8.67,

$$J_O = I_x + I_y = 0.784 \times 10^4 + 3.224 \times 10^4 = 4.01 \times 10^4 \text{ in}^4.$$

From the solution of Problem 8.67, $A = 188 \text{ in}^2$, so

$$R_0 = \sqrt{\frac{J_O}{A}} = \sqrt{\frac{4.01 \times 10^4}{188}} = 14.6 \text{ in}.$$

Problem 8.69 Determine I_y and k_y.

Solution: Divide the area into four parts: Part (1) The rectangle 8 in by 16 in. Part (2): The rectangle 4 in by 8 in. Part (3) The semi-circle of radius 4 in, and Part (4) The circle of radius 2 in.

Part (1): $A_1 = 16(8) = 128$ in^2,

$x_1 = 8$ in,

$y_1 = 4$ in,

$I_{xx1} = \left(\dfrac{1}{12}\right) 16(8^3) = 682.67$ in^4,

$I_{yy1} = \left(\dfrac{1}{12}\right) 8(16^3) = 2730.7$ in^4.

Part (2): $A_2 = 4(8) = 32$ in^2,

$x_2 = 12$ in,

$y_2 = 10$ in,

$I_{xx2} = \left(\dfrac{1}{12}\right) 8(4^3) = 42.667$ in^4,

$I_{yy2} = \left(\dfrac{1}{12}\right) 4(8^3) = 170.667$ in^4.

Part (3): $A_3 = \dfrac{\pi(4^2)}{2} = 25.133$ in^2,

$x_3 = 12$ in.

$y_3 = 12 + \left(\dfrac{4(4)}{3\pi}\right) = 13.698$ in.

The area moments of inertia about the centroid of the semicircle are

$I_{yy3} = \left(\dfrac{1}{8}\right) \pi(4^4) = 100.53$ in^4,

$I_{xx3} = \left(\dfrac{1}{8}\right) \pi(4^4) - \left(\dfrac{4(4)}{3\pi}\right)^2 A_3 = 28.1$ in^4.

Check:

$I_{xx3} = 0.1098(R^4) = 28.1$ in^4.

check.

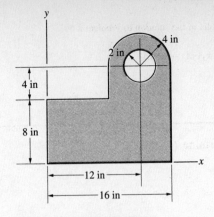

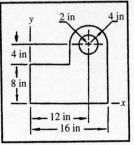

Part (4): $A_4 = \pi(2^2) = 12.566$ in^2,

$x_4 = 12$ in,

$y_4 = 12$ in,

$I_{xx4} = \left(\tfrac{1}{4}\right) \pi(2^4) = 12.566$ in^4,

$I_{yy4} = I_{xx4} = 12.566$ in^4.

The composite area:

$$A = \sum_1^3 A_i - A_4 = 172.566 \text{ in}^2.$$

The area moment of inertia:

$I_y = x_1^2 A_1 + I_{yy1} + x_2^2 A_2 + I_{yy2} + x_3^2 A_3 + I_{yy3} - x_4^2 A_4 - I_{yy4}$

$I_y = 1.76 \times 10^4$ in^4,

$k_y = \sqrt{\dfrac{I_y}{A}} = 10.1$ in

Problem 8.70 Determine I_x and k_x.

Solution: Use the results in the solution to Problem 8.69.

$I_x = y_1^2 A_1 + I_{xx1} + y_2^2 A_2 + I_{xx2} + y_3^2 A_3 + I_{xx3} - y_4^2 A_4 - I_{xx4}$

$I_x = 8.89 \times 10^3$ in^4

$k_x = \sqrt{\dfrac{I_x}{A}} = 7.18$ in

Problem 8.71 Determine I_{xy}.

Solution: Use the results in the solution to Problem 8.69.

$$I_{xy} = x_1 y_1 A_1 + x_2 y_2 A_2 + x_3 y_3 A_3 - x_4 y_4 A_4,$$

$$I_{xy} = 1.0257 \times 10^4 \text{ in}^4$$

Problem 8.72 Determine I_y and k_y.

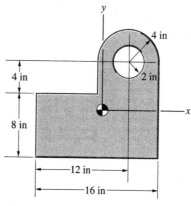

Solution: Use the results in the solutions to Problems 8.69 to 8.71. The centroid is

$$x = \frac{x_1 A_1 + x_2 A_2 + x_3 A_3 - x_4 A_4}{A}$$

$$= \frac{1024 + 384 + 301.6 - 150.8}{172.567} = 9.033 \text{ in},$$

from which

$$I_{yc} = -x^2 A + I_y = -1.408 \times 10^4 + 1.7598 \times 10^4 = 3518.2 \text{ in}^4$$

$$k_{yc} = \sqrt{\frac{I_{yc}}{A}} = 4.52 \text{ in}$$

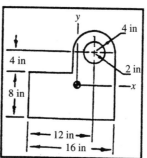

Problem 8.73 Determine I_x and k_x.

Solution: Use the results in the solutions to Problems 8.69 to 8.71. The centroid is

$$y = \frac{y_1 A_1 + y_2 A_2 + y_3 A_3 - y_4 A_4}{A} = 5.942 \text{ in},$$

from which

$$I_{xc} = -y^2 A + I_x = -6092.9 + 8894 = 2801 \text{ in}^4$$

$$k_{xc} = \sqrt{\frac{I_{xc}}{A}} = 4.03 \text{ in}$$

Problem 8.74 Determine I_{xy}.

Solution: Use the results in the solutions to Problems 8.69–8.71.

$$I_{xyc} = -xyA + I_{xy} = -9.263 \times 10^3 + 1.0257 \times 10^4 = 994.5 \text{ in}^4$$

Problem 8.75 Determine I_y and k_y.

Solution: We divide the area into parts as shown:

$$(I_y)_1 = \frac{1}{12}(50 + 15 + 15)(30)^3 = 180{,}000 \text{ mm}^4$$

$$(I_y)_2 = (I_y)_3 = (I_y)_4 = \frac{1}{12}(30)(10)^3 + (20)^2(10)(30)$$

$$= 122{,}500 \text{ mm}^4$$

$$(I_y)_5 = (I_y)_6 = (I_y)_7 = \left(\frac{\pi}{8} - \frac{8}{9\pi}\right)(15)^4$$

$$+ \left[25 + \frac{4(15)}{3\pi}\right]^2 \frac{1}{2}\pi(15)^2 = 353{,}274 \text{ mm}^4$$

$$(I_y)_8 = (I_y)_9 = (I_y)_{10} = \frac{1}{4}\pi(5)^4 + (25)^2\pi(5)^2 = 49{,}578 \text{ mm}^4.$$

Therefore,

$$I_y = (I_y)_1 + 3(I_y)_2 + 3(I_y)_5 - 3(I_y)_8 = 1.46 \times 10^6 \text{ mm}^4.$$

The area is

$$A = A_1 + 3A_2 + 3A_5 - 3A_8$$

$$= (30)(80) + 3(10)(30) + 3\left(\frac{1}{2}\right)\pi(15)^2 - 3\pi(5)^2$$

$$= 4125 \text{ mm}^2$$

$$\text{so } k_y = \sqrt{\frac{I_y}{A}} = \sqrt{\frac{1.46 \times 10^6}{4125}} = 18.8 \text{ mm}$$

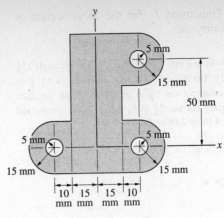

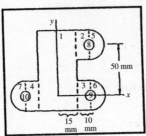

Problem 8.76 Determine J_O and k_O.

Solution: I_y is determined in the solution to Problem 8.75. We will determine I_x and use the relation $J_O = I_x + I_y$. Dividing the area as shown in the solution to Problem 8.75, we obtain

$$(I_x)_1 = \frac{1}{12}(30)(80)^3 + (25)^2(30)(80) = 2{,}780{,}000 \text{ mm}^4$$

$$(I_x)_2 = \frac{1}{12}(10)(30)^3 + (50)^2(10)(30) = 772{,}500 \text{ mm}^4$$

$$(I_x)_3 = (I_x)_4 = \frac{1}{12}(10)(30)^3 = 22{,}500 \text{ mm}^4$$

$$(I_x)_5 = \frac{1}{8}\pi(15)^4 + (50)^2\frac{1}{2}\pi(15)^2 = 903{,}453 \text{ mm}^4$$

$$(I_x)_6 = (I_x)_7 = \frac{1}{8}\pi(15)^4 = 19{,}880 \text{ mm}^4,$$

$$(I_x)_8 = \frac{1}{4}\pi(5)^4 + \pi(5)^2(50)^2,$$

$$(I_x)_9 = (I_x)_{10} = \frac{1}{4}\pi(5)^4 = 491 \text{ mm}^4.$$

Therefore

$$I_x = (I_x)_1 + (I_x)_2 + 2(I_x)_3 + (I_x)_5 + 2(I_x)_6 - (I_x)_8 - 2(I_x)_9$$

$$= 4.34 \times 10^6 \text{ mm}^4$$

and $J_O = I_x + I_y = 5.80 \times 10^6 \text{ mm}^4.$

From the solution to Problem 8.75, $A = 4125 \text{ mm}^2$

$$\text{so } k_O = \sqrt{\frac{J_O}{A}}$$

$$= \sqrt{\frac{5.80 \times 10^6}{4125}}$$

$$= 37.5 \text{ mm}.$$

Problem 8.77 Dimension I_y for the cross section of the concrete masonry unit.

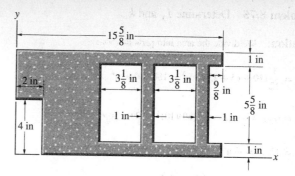

Solution: Divide the unit into 5 parts: Part (1): The rectangle $15\frac{5}{8}$ in by $7\frac{5}{8}$ in, Part (2): The cut-out to the far right, $5\frac{5}{8}$ in by $\frac{9}{8}$ in, Part (3). The rectangular cut out $5\frac{5}{8}$ in by $3\frac{1}{8}$ in to the far right, Part (4). The rectangular cut out $5\frac{5}{8}$ in by $3\frac{1}{8}$ in in the center, and Part (5). The cut out 4 in by 2 in on the lower left.

Part (1) $A_1 = (15.625)(7.625) = 119.14 \text{ in}^2$,

$$x_1 = \frac{15.625}{2} = 7.8125 \text{ in},$$

$$y_1 = \frac{7.625}{2} = 3.8125 \text{ in},$$

$$I_{xx1} = \left(\frac{1}{12}\right)(15.625)(7.625)^3 = 577.24 \text{ in}^4,$$

$$I_{yy1} = \left(\frac{1}{12}\right)(7.625)(15.625^3) = 2423.9 \text{ in}^4.$$

Part (2): $A_2 = (1.125)(5.625) = 6.328 \text{ in}^2$.

$$x_2 = 15.625 - \frac{1.125}{2} = 15.0625 \text{ in},$$

$$y_2 = 1 + \frac{5.625}{2} = 3.8125 \text{ in},$$

$$I_{xx2} = \left(\frac{1}{12}\right)(1.125)(5.625^3) = 16.685 \text{ in}^4,$$

$$I_{yy2} = \left(\frac{1}{12}\right)(5.625)(1.125^3) = 0.667 \text{ in}^4.$$

Part (3): $A_3 = (3.125)(5.625) = 17.578 \text{ in}^2$,

$$x_3 = 15.625 - 1.125 - 1 - \frac{3.125}{2} = 11.9375 \text{ in},$$

$$y_3 = 1 + \frac{5.625}{2} = 3.8125 \text{ in},$$

$$I_{xx3} = \left(\frac{1}{12}\right)(3.125)(5.625^3) = 46.3486 \text{ in}^4,$$

The results are tabulated:

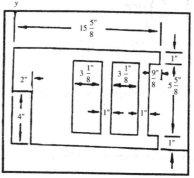

$$I_{yy3} = \left(\frac{1}{12}\right)(5.625)(3.125^3)$$

$$= 14.305 \text{ in}^4.$$

Part (4): $A_4 = A_3 = 17.578 \text{ in}^2$,

$$x_4 = 15.625 - 1.125 - 1 - 3.125 - 1 - \frac{3.125}{2} = 7.8125 \text{ in},$$

$$y_4 = y_3 = 3.8125 \text{ in},$$

$I_{xx4} = I_{xx3} = 46.3486 \text{ in}^4$, $I_{yy4} = I_{yy3} = 14.305 \text{ in}^4$.

Part (5): $A_5 = 2(4) = 8 \text{ in}^2$,

$$x_5 = 1 \text{ in}, \quad y_5 = 2 \text{ in},$$

$$I_{xx5} = \left(\frac{1}{12}\right)2(4^3) = 10.667 \text{ in}^4,$$

$$I_{yy5} = \left(\frac{1}{12}\right)4(2^3) = 2.667 \text{ in}^4.$$

Area	base, in	height, in	Area, in^2	x, in	y, in	I_{XX}, in^4	I_{YY} in^4
1	15.625	7.625	119.14	7.8125	3.8125	577.24	2423.9
2	1.125	5.625	6.3281	15.063	3.8125	16.685	0.6667
3	3.125	5.625	17.578	11.938	3.8125	46.349	14.305
4	3.125	5.625	17.578	7.8125	3.8125	46.349	14.305
5	2	4	8	1	2	10.667	2.6667

The area moment of inertia about the y-axis:

$$I_y = x_1^2 A_1 + I_{yy1} - x_2^2 A_2 - I_{yy2} - x_3^2 A_3 - I_{yy3}$$

$$- x_4^2 A_4 - I_{yy4} - x_5^2 A_5 - I_{yy5}$$

$$I_y = 4641.9 \text{ in}^4$$

Problem 8.78 Determine I_x for the cross section in Problem 8.77.

Solution: Use the results of the solution to Problem 8.77.

$$I_x = \mathbf{y}_1^2 A_1 + I_{xx1} - \mathbf{y}_2^2 A_2 - I_{xx2} - \mathbf{y}_3^2 A_3 - I_{xx3}$$

$$- \mathbf{y}_4^2 A_4 - I_{xx4} - \mathbf{y}_5^2 A_5 - I_{xx5},$$

$$I_x = 1553.94 \text{ in}^4$$

Problem 8.79 The area $A = 2 \times 10^4$ mm^2. Its moment of inertia about the y axis is $I_y = 3.2 \times 10^8$ mm^4. Determine its moment of inertia about the $\hat{y}$ axis.

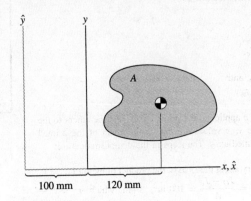

100 mm   120 mm

Solution: Use the parallel axis theorem. The moment of inertia about the centroid of the figure is

$$I_{yc} = -x^2 A + I_y = -(120^2)(2 \times 10^4) + 3.2 \times 10^8$$

$$= 3.20 \times 10^7 \text{ mm}^4.$$

The moment of inertia about the $\hat{y}$ axis is

$$I_{\hat{y}} = \mathbf{x}^2 A + I_{yc}$$

$$I_{\hat{y}} = (220^2)(2 \times 10^4) + 3.2 \times 10^7$$

$$= 1 \times 10^9 \text{ mm}^4$$

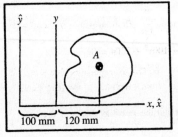

100 mm 120 mm

Problem 8.80 The area $A = 100$ in² and it is *symmetric* about the x' axis. The moments of inertia $I_{x'} = 420$ in⁴, $I_{y'} = 580$ in⁴, $J_O = 11000$ in⁴, and $I_{xy} = 4800$ in⁴. What are I_x and I_y?

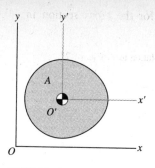

Solution: The basic relationships:

(1) $I_x = y^2 A + I_{xc}$,
(2) $I_y = x^2 A + I_{yc}$,
(3) $J_O = Ar^2 + J_c$,
(4) $J_O = I_x + I_y$,
(5) $J_c = I_{xc} + I_{yc}$, and
(6) $I_{xy} = Axy + I_{xyc}$,

where the subscript c applies to the primed axes, and the others to the unprimed axes. The x, y values are the displacement of the primed axes from the unprimed axes. The steps in the demonstration are:

(i) From symmetry about the x_c axis, the product of inertia $I_{xyc} = 0$.

(ii) From (3): $r^2 = \dfrac{J_O - J_c}{A} = 100$ in², from which $r^2 = x^2 + y^2 = 100$ in²

(iii) From (6) and $I_{xyc} = 0$, $y = \dfrac{I_{xy}}{Ax}$, from which $x^2 r^2 = x^4 + \left(\dfrac{I_{xy}}{A}\right)^2$. From which: $x^4 - 100x^2 + 2304 = 0$.

(iv) The roots: $x_1^2 = 64$, and $x_2^2 = 36$. The corresponding values of y are found from $y = \sqrt{r^2 - x^2}$ from which $(x_1, y_1) = (8, 6)$, and $(x_2, y_2) = (6, 8)$.

(v) Substitute these pairs to obtain the possible values of the area moments of inertia:

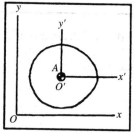

$I_{x1} = Ay_1^2 + I_{xc} = 4020$ in⁴,

$I_{y1} = Ax_1^2 + I_{yc} = 6980$ in⁴

$I_{x2} = Ay_2^2 + I_{xc} = 6820$ in⁴,

$I_{y2} = Ax_2^2 + I_{yc} = 4180$ in⁴

Problem 8.81 Derive the parallel-axis theorem for the product of inertia, Eq. (8.12) by using the same procedures we used to derive Eqs. (8.10) and (8.11).

Solution: By definition,

$$I_{xy} = \int_A xy\, dA.$$

Choose a coordinate system originating at the centroid, so that

$$\int_A x\, dA = \int_A y\, dA = 0.$$

Choose a new system (ξ, η) such that the distance to the centroid from the origin is $(\hat{x}, \hat{y})$. Thus $\xi = \hat{x} - x$, and $\eta = \hat{y} - y$. The area product of inertia in the new system is

$$I_{\xi\eta} = \int_A (\hat{x} - x)(\hat{y} - y)\, dA = \int_A \hat{x}\hat{y}\, dA$$

$$- \int_A \hat{y}x\, dA - \int_A \hat{x}y\, dA + \int_A xy\, dA.$$

Since the $(\hat{x}, \hat{y})$ are constant numbers, if the (x, y) system is at the centroid of the area, then the second and third integrals vanish, so that the product of inertia in the (ξ, η) coordinate system is

$$I_{\xi\eta} = \hat{x}\hat{y} \int_A dA + I_{XY}$$

$$= \hat{x}\hat{y}A + I_{XY},$$

which is the parallel axis theorem for the area product of inertia.

Problem 8.82 Derive the parallel-axis theorem for the polar moment of inertia, Eq. (8.13), (a) by using the same procedures we used to derive Eqs. (8.10) and (8.11); (b) by using Eqs. (8.10) and (8.11).

Solution:

(a) By definition

$$J_O = \int_A r^2 \, dA.$$

Define coordinates (ξ, η) such that $r^2 = \xi^2 + \eta^2$. Suppose that the polar moment of inertia is defined about the centroid of the area, such that

$$\int_A \xi \, dA = \int_A \eta \, dA = 0.$$

Choose a new system such that the origins are separated by a distance $(\hat{x}, \hat{y})$. In the new system:

$$\hat{J} = \int_A \rho^2 \, dA.$$

Note that

$$\rho^2 = (\hat{x} + \xi)^2 + (\hat{y} + \eta)^2,$$

$$\hat{J} = \int_A \rho^2 \, dA = \int_A (\hat{x} + \xi)^2 \, dA + \int_A (\hat{y} + \eta)^2 \, dA$$

$$\hat{J} = \int_A \hat{x}^2 \, dA + 2 \int_A \hat{x}\xi \, dA + \int_A \xi^2 \, dA$$

$$+ \int_A \hat{y}^2 \, dA + 2 \int \hat{y}\eta \, dA + \int_A \eta^2 \, dA.$$

The integrals of first powers of ξ and η vanish, from which

$$\hat{J} = \int_A (\hat{x}^2 + \hat{y}^2) \, dA + \int_A (\xi^2 + \eta^2) \, dA.$$

Since $\hat{x}$ and $\hat{y}$ are constant numbers,

$$\hat{J} = d^2 A + \int r^2 \, dA = d^2 A + J_O,$$

where d is the distance from the origin of the new system to the centroid of the area. This is the parallel axis theorem for the area polar moment of inertia.

(b) Eqs (8.10) and (8.11) are

$$I_x = I_{xc} + d_y^2 A$$

and

$$I_y = I_{yc} + d_x^2 A,$$

where $I_{xc} = \int_A x^2 \, dA$

and $I_{yc} = \int_A y^2 \, dA$

are area moments of inertia about axes passing through the area centroid, and parallel to the new axes located at a distance (d_X, d_Y) from the centroid. Define $\rho^2 = d_X^2 + d_Y^2$ and $r^2 = x^2 + y^2$. Add Eqs (8.10) and (8.11) and combine terms. The result,

$$J = \rho^2 A + \int_A r^2 \, dA,$$

which is the parallel axis theorem for the polar moment of inertia.

Problem 8.83 Determine the moment of inertia of the beam cross section about the x axis. Compare your result with the moment of inertia of a solid square cross section of equal area and confirm the ratio shown in Fig. 8.16.

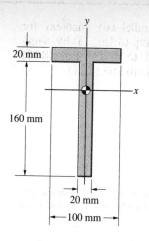

Solution: We first need to find the location of the centroid of the composite. Break the area into two parts. Use X, Y coords.

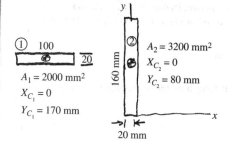

$A_2 = 3200$ mm^2

$X_{C_2} = 0$

$Y_{C_2} = 80$ mm

$A_1 = 2000$ mm^2

$X_{C_1} = 0$

$Y_{C_1} = 170$ mm

For the composite

$$X_c = \frac{X_{c1}A_1 + X_{c2}A_2}{A_1 + A_2} = 0$$

$$Y_c = \frac{Y_{c1}A_1 + Y_{c2}A_2}{A_1 + A_2}$$

Substituting, we get

$X_c = 0$ mm

$Y_c = 114.6$ mm

We now find I_x for each part about its center and use the parallel axis theorem to find I_x about C.

Part (1): $b_1 = 100$ mm, $h_1 = 20$ mm

$$I_{x'1} = \frac{1}{12}b_1h_1^3 = \frac{1}{12}(100)(20)^3 \text{ mm}^4$$

$I_{x'1} = 6.667 \times 10^4$ mm^4

$dy_1 = Y_{c1} - Y_c = 55.38$ mm

$I_{x1} = I_{x'1} + (dy_1)^2(A_1)$

$I_{x1} = 6.20 \times 10^6$ mm^4

Part (2) $b_2 = 20$ mm, $h_2 = 160$ mm

$$I_{x'2} = \frac{1}{12}(b_2)(h_2)^3 = \frac{1}{12}(20)(160)^3 \text{ mm}^4$$

$I_{x'2} = 6.827 \times 10^6$ mm^4

$dy_2 = Y_{c2} - Y_c = -34.61$ mm

$I_{x2} = I_{x'2} + (dy)^2A_2$

$I_{x2} = 1.066 \times 10^7$ mm^4

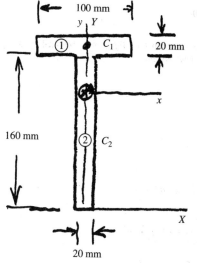

Finally, $I_x = I_{x1} + I_{x2}$

$I_x = 1.686 \times 10^7$ mm^4

for our composite shape.

Now for the comparison. For the solid square with the same total area $A_1 + A_2 = 5200$ mm^2, we get a side of length

$l^2 = 5200$: $l = 72.11$ mm

And for this solid section

$$I_{xSQ} = \frac{1}{12}bh^3 = \frac{1}{12}l^4$$

$I_{xSQ} = 2.253 \times 10^6$ mm^4

$$\text{Ratio} = I_x/I_{xSQ} = \frac{1.686 \times 10^7}{2.253 \times 10^6}$$

Ratio = 7.48

This matches the value in Figure 8.16.

Problem 8.84 The area of the beam cross section is 5200 mm². Determine the moment of inertia of the beam cross section about the x axis. Compare your result with the moment of inertia of a solid square cross section of equal area and confirm the ratio shown in Fig. 8.16.

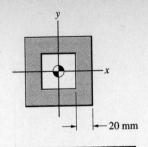

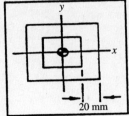

Solution: Let the outside dimension be b mm, then the inside dimension is $b - 40$ mm. The cross section is $A = b^2 - (b - 40)^2 = 5200$ mm². Solve: $b = 85$ mm. Divide the beam cross section into two parts: the inner and outer squares. Part (1)

$$A_1 = 85^2 = 7225 \text{ mm}^2,$$

$$I_{xx1} = \left(\frac{1}{12}\right) 85(85^3) = 4.35 \times 10^6.$$

Part (2)

$$A_2 = 45^2 = 2025 \text{ mm}^2.$$

$$I_{xx2} = \left(\frac{1}{12}\right) 45(45^3) = 3.417 \times 10^5.$$

The composite moment of inertia about the centroid is

$$I_x = I_{xx1} - I_{xx2} = 4.008 \times 10^6 \text{ mm}^4.$$

For a square cross section of the same area, $h = \sqrt{5200} = 72.111$ mm.

The area moment of inertia is

$$I_{xb} = \left(\frac{1}{12}\right) 72.111(72.111^3) = 2.253 \times 10^6 \text{ in}^4.$$

The ratio:

$$R = \frac{4.008 \times 10^6}{2.253 \times 10^6} = 1.7788 = 1.78$$

which confirms the value given in Figure 8.16.

Problem 8.85

(a) If I_x is expressed in m⁴, R is in meters, and M is in N-m, what are the *SI* units of the modulus of elasticity E?

(b) A beam with the cross section shown is subjected to couples $M = 180$ N-m as shown in Fig.8.15b. As a result, it bends into a circular arc with radius $R = 3$ m. What is the modulus of elasticity of the material?

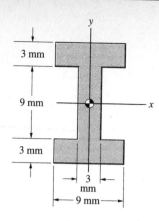

Solution:

(a) The equation relating R, I_x, M, and E is

$$R = EI_x/M$$

Solving for E, we get

$$E = RM/I_x$$

Writing units on the right hand side gives us the units of E. Hence

$$\text{units }(E) = \text{units}\left(\frac{RM}{I_x}\right) = \frac{m \cdot \text{N-m}}{m^4}$$

(a) Units $(E) = \text{N/m}^2$ or pascals (Pa)

(b) To find E, we must calculate the value for I_x for the I beam shown in the problem.

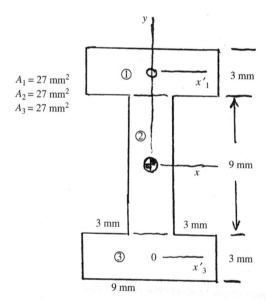

$A_1 = 27$ mm²
$A_2 = 27$ mm²
$A_3 = 27$ mm²

Part 1 ($b_1 = 9$ mm, $h_1 = 3$ mm)

$$I_{x'1} = \frac{1}{12}b_1h_1^3$$

$$= \frac{1}{12}(9)(3)^3 \text{ mm}^4$$

Part 3 ($b_3 = 9$ mm, $h_3 = 3$ mm)

$$I_{x'3} = \frac{1}{12}b_3h_3^2 = \frac{1}{12}(9)(3)^3 \text{ mm}^4$$

Part 2 $I_{x'2} = I_{x2} = \frac{1}{12}(3)(9)^3$ mm⁴

$$I_{x'1} = I_{x'3} = 20.25 \text{ mm}^4$$

$$I_{x2} = 182.25 \text{ mm}^4$$

Before we can add up the parts of I_x, we must use the parallel axis theorem.

Part 1, $dy_1 = 6$ mm

$$I_{x1} = I_{x'1} + (dy_1)^2A_1$$

$$I_{x1} = 992.25 \text{ mm}^4$$

Part 3, $dy_3 = 6$ mm

$$I_{x3} = I_{x'3} + (dy_3)^2A_3$$

$$I_{x3} = 992.25 \text{ mm}^4$$

$$I_x = I_{x1} + I_{x2} + I_{x3}$$

$$I_x = 2167 \text{ mm}^4$$

We now must get the units to meters

$$I_x = 2167 \text{ mm}^4 \left(\frac{1 \text{ m}}{1000 \text{ mm}}\right)^4$$

$$I_x = 2167 \text{ mm}^4 = 2.167 \times 10^{-9} \text{ m}^4$$

Now E can be calculated from

$$E = \frac{RM}{I_x} = \frac{(3)(180)}{(2.167 \times 10^{-9})} \text{ N/m}^2$$

$$E = 2.49 \times 10^{11} \text{ N/m}^2 = 2.49 \times 10^{11} \text{ Pa}$$

Problem 8.86 Suppose that you want to design a beam made of material whose density is 8000 kg/m^3. The beam is to be 4 m in length and have a mass of 320 kg. Design a cross section for the beam so that $I_x = 3 \times 10^{-5}$ m^4.

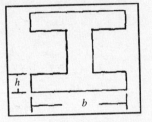

Solution: The strategy is to determine the cross sectional area, and then use the ratios given in Figure 8.16 to design a beam. The volume of the beam is $V = AL = 4A$ m^3. The mass of the beam is $m = V(8000) = 32000A = 320$ kg, from which $A = 0.01$ m^2. The moment of inertia for a beam of square cross section with this area is

$$I_{xxb} = \left(\frac{1}{12}\right)(0.1)(0.1^3) = 8.333 \times 10^{-6} \text{ m}^4.$$

The ratio is $R = \dfrac{3 \times 10^{-5}}{8.333 \times 10^{-6}} = 3.6$.

From Figure 8.16, this ratio suggests an *I*-beam of the form shown in the sketch. Choose an *I*-beam made up of three equal area rectangles, of dimensions b by hm in section. The moment of inertia about the centroid is $I_x = y_1^2 A_1 + I_{xx1} + y_2^2 A_2 + I_{xx2} + y_3^2 A_3 + I_{xx3}$.

Since all areas are equal, $A_1 = A_2 = A_3 = bh$, and $y_1 = \dfrac{b+h}{2}$, $y_2 = 0$, and $y_3 = -y_1$, this reduces to

$$I_x = \left(\frac{1}{6}\right)bh^3 + 2\left(\frac{b+h}{2}\right)^2 hb + \left(\frac{1}{12}\right)hb^3.$$

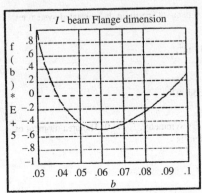

Note that $bh = \dfrac{A}{3}$, where A is the known total cross section area. These are two equations in two unknowns. Plot the function

$$f(b) = \left(\frac{1}{6}\right)bh^3 + 2\left(\frac{b+h}{2}\right)^2 bh + \left(\frac{1}{12}\right)hb^3 - I_x$$

subject to the condition that $hb = \dfrac{A}{3}$. The function was graphed using **TK Solver Plus.** The graph crosses the zero axis at approximately $b = 0.0395$ m. and $b = 0.09$ m. The lower value is an allowable value for h and the greater value corresponds to an allowable value of b. Thus the *I* beam design has the flange dimensions, $b = 90$ mm and $h = 39.5$ mm.

Problem 8.87 Determine $I_{x'}$, $I_{y'}$, and $I_{x'y'}$. (Do not use Mohr's circle.)

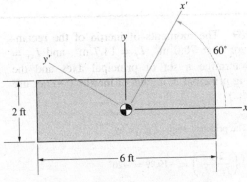

Solution: The area moments of inertia for the unrotated coordinates are

$$I_x = \left(\frac{1}{12}\right)6(2^3) = 4 \text{ ft}^4,$$

$$I_y = \left(\frac{1}{12}\right)2(6^3) = 36 \text{ ft}^4.$$

The rotation angle is 60°. The area moments in the rotated system are

$$I_{x'} = I_x \cos^2\theta - 2I_{xy}\sin\theta\cos\theta + I_y\sin^2\theta$$

$$I_{y'} = I_x \sin^2\theta + 2I_{xy}\sin\theta\cos\theta + I_y\cos^2\theta,$$

and $I_{x'y'} = (I_x - I_y)\sin\theta\cos\theta + (\cos^2\theta - \sin^2\theta)I_{xy}$.

By symmetry, $I_{xy} = 0$, so that

$$I_{x'} = 4\cos^2 60 + 36\sin^2 60 = 28 \text{ ft}^4,$$

$$I_{y'} = 4\sin^2 60 + 36\cos^2 60 = 12 \text{ ft}^4,$$

and $I_{x'y'} = (4 - 36)\sin 60\cos 60 = -13.856 \text{ ft}^4$

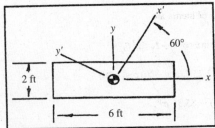

Problem 8.88 Determine $I_{x'}$, $I_{y'}$, and $I_{x'y'}$. (Do not use Mohr's circle.)

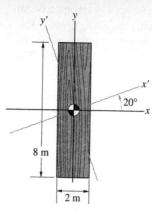

Solution: The area moments of inertia in the unrotated system are

$$I_x = \left(\frac{1}{12}\right) 2(8^3) = 85.33 \text{ m}^4,$$

$$I_y = \left(\frac{1}{12}\right) (2^3)(8) = 5.333 \text{ m}^4.$$

The rotation angle is $20°$. By symmetry, $I_{xy} = 0$. The area moment of inertia for the rotated system is

$$I_{x'} = I_x \cos^2 \theta + I_y \sin^2 \theta.$$

$$I_{x'} = 85.333 \cos^2(20°) + 5.333 \sin^2(20°) = 75.975 \text{ ft}^4$$

$$I_{y'} = I_x \sin^2 \theta + I_y \cos^2 \theta.$$

$$I_{y'} = 85.333 \sin^2(20°) + 5.333 \cos^2(20°) = 14.692 \text{ ft}^4.$$

$$I_{x'y'} = (I_x - I_y) \sin \theta \cos \theta.$$

$$I_{x'y'} = (85.333 - 5.333) \sin(20°) \cos(20°) = 25.712 \text{ ft}^4$$

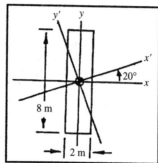

Problem 8.89 The moments of inertia of the rectangular area are $I_x = 76.0 \text{ m}^4$, $I_y = 14.7 \text{ m}^4$, and $I_{xy} = 25.7 \text{ m}^4$. Determine a set of principal axes and the corresponding principal moments of inertia. (Do not use Mohr's circle.)

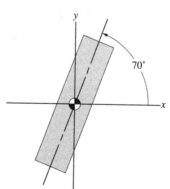

Solution: The principal angle is given by

$$\theta = \left(\frac{1}{2}\right) \tan^{-1} \left(\frac{2I_{xy}}{I_y - I_x}\right) = -19.99 = -20°.$$

The principal moments of inertia are

$$I_{xP} = I_x \cos^2 \theta - 2I_{xy} \sin \theta \cos \theta + I_y \sin^2 \theta,$$

$$I_{xP} = 76 \cos^2(-20) - 2(25.7) \sin(-20) \cos(-20)$$

$$+ 14.7 \sin^2(-20) = 85.35 \text{ m}^4,$$

$$I_{yP} = I_x \sin^2 \theta + 2I_{xy} \sin \theta \cos \theta + I_y \cos^2 \theta.$$

$$I_{yP} = (76) \sin^2(-20) + 2(25.7) \sin(-20) \cos(-20)$$

$$+ 14.7 \cos^2(-20) = 5.35 \text{ m}^4$$

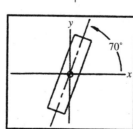

733

Problem 8.90 Determine the moments of inertia $I_{x'}$, $I_{y'}$ and $I_{x'y'}$ if $\theta = 50°$ (Do not use Mohr's circle.)

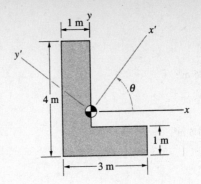

Solution:

(1) Break the L shaped member into two parts (1), an (2).
(2) Find the locations of the centroids and $I_{x'}$, $I_{y'}$, $I_{x'y'}$ for each part about its own centroid.
(3) Find the location of the centroid of the composite and use the parallel axis theorem to find I_x, I_y, and I_{xy} about the non-rotated centroid axes.
(4) Rotate the axes and find $I_{x'}$, $I_{y'}$, $I_{x'y'}$ about the rotated axes.

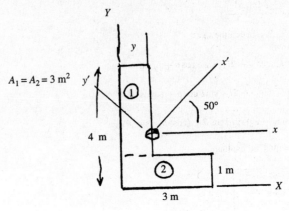

$$x_c = \frac{x_{c1}A_1 + x_{c2}A_2}{A_1 + A_2}$$

$$x_c = \frac{(0.5)(3) + (1.5)(3)}{6} = 1 \text{ m}$$

$$y_c = \frac{y_{c1}A_1 + y_{c2}A_2}{A_1 + A_2}$$

$$y_c = \frac{(2.5)(3) + (0.5)(3)}{6} = 1.5 \text{ m}$$

The overall centroid is at (1, 1.5) m.

For part (1), the distances for the parallel axis theorem are from (0.5, 2.5) to (1, 1.5) m $d_{x1} = 0.5$ $d_{y1} = -1$

For part (2), we get from (1.5, 0.5) to (1, 1.5) m $d_{x2} = -0.5$, $d_{y2} = 1$. Now, using the parallel axis theorem, we get

Part 1

Centroid at (0.5, 2.5) m

$$I_{xC1} = \frac{1}{12}(b_1)h_1^3 = \frac{1}{12}(1)(3)^3 \text{ m}^4$$

$$I_{yC1} = \frac{1}{12}(h_1)b_1^3 = \frac{1}{12}(3)(1)^3 \text{ m}^4$$

$$I_{xyC1} = 0$$

$$I_{xC1} = 2.25 \text{ m}^4, \quad I_{yC1} = 0.25 \text{ m}^4$$

$$I_{xyC1} = 0$$

Part 2

Centroid at (1.5, 0.5) m

$$I_{xC2} = \frac{1}{12}b_2h_2^3 = \frac{1}{12}(3)(1)^3 \text{ m}^4$$

$$I_{yC2} = \frac{1}{12}h_2b_2^3 = \frac{1}{12}(1)(3)^3 \text{ m}^4$$

$$I_{xyC2} = 0$$

$$I_{xC1} = 0.25 \text{ m}^4, \quad I_{yC2} = 2.25 \text{ m}^4 \quad I_{xyC2} = 0$$

Now we need to locate the centroid of the composite.

$$I_{x1} = I_{xC1} + (dy_1^2)A_1$$

$$I_{y1} = I_{yC1} + (dx^2)A_1$$

or $I_{x1} = 2.25 + (-1)^2(3)$ m^4

$$I_{x1} = 5.25 \text{ m}^4$$

$$I_{y1} = 0.25 + (0.5)^2(3)$$

$$I_{y1} = 1 \text{ m}^4$$

$$I_{x2} = I_{xC2} + (dy_2)^2(A_2)$$

$$I_{y2} = I_{yC2} + (dx_2)(A_2)$$

or $I_{x2} = 0.25 + (1)^2(3)$

$$I_{x2} = 3.25 \text{ m}^4$$

$$I_{y2} = 2.25 + (-0.5)^2(3)$$

$$I_{y2} = 3.00 \text{ m}^4$$

And for the Products of inertia

$$I_{xy1} = I_{xyC1} + dx_1\,dy_1A_1$$

$$= 0 + (0.5)(-1)(3)$$

$$I_{xy1} = -1.5 \text{ m}^4$$

$$I_{xy2} = I_{xyC2} + dx_2\,dy_2A_2$$

$$I_{xy2} = 0 + (-0.5)(1)(3)$$

$$I_{xy2} = -1.5 \text{ m}^4$$

8.90 *Contd.*

Combining, we get

$$I_x = I_{x1} + I_{x2} = 5.25 + 3.25 \text{ m}^4$$

$$I_y = I_{y1} + I_{y2} = 1 + 3 \text{ m}^4$$

$$I_{xy} = I_{xy1} + I_{xy2} = -1.5 - 1.5 \text{ m}^4$$

$$\boxed{\begin{aligned} I_x &= 8.50 \text{ m}^4 \\ I_y &= 4.00 \text{ m}^4 \\ I_{xy} &= -3.00 \text{ m}^4 \end{aligned}}$$

we now must rotate the axes.

$$I_{x'} = I_x \cos^2\theta - 2I_{xy} \sin\theta\cos\theta + I_y \sin^2\theta$$

$$I_{y'} = I_x \sin^2\theta + 2I_{xy} \sin\theta\cos\theta + I_y \cos^2\theta$$

$$I_{x'y'} = (I_x - I_y)\sin\theta\cos\theta + (\cos^2\theta - \sin^2\theta)I_{xy}$$

Set $\theta = 50°$ and evaluate

$$\boxed{\begin{aligned} I_{x'} &= 8.81 \text{ m}^4 \\ I_{y'} &= 3.69 \text{ m}^4 \\ I_{x'y'} &= 2.74 \text{ m}^4 \end{aligned}}$$

Problem 8.91 For the area in Problem 8.90, determine a set of principal axes and the corresponding principal moments of inertia. (Do not use Mohr's circle.)

Solution: We know, from the solution to Problem 8.90, the following

$$I_x = 8.50 \text{ m}^4$$

$$I_y = 4.00 \text{ m}^4$$

$$I_{xy} = -3.0 \text{ m}^4$$

For principal axes, we rotate through an angle θ_p, where

$$\tan(2\theta_p) = \frac{2I_{xy}}{I_y - I_x}$$

Solving, we get $\theta_p = 26.57°$

$$I_{xp} = I_x \cos^2\theta_p - 2I_{xy} \sin\theta_p \cos\theta_p + I_y \sin^2\theta_p$$

$$I_{yp} = I_x \sin^2\theta_p + 2I_{xy} \sin\theta_p \cos\theta_p + I_y \cos^2\theta_p$$

and $I_{xyp} = (I_x - I_y)\sin\theta_p \cos\theta_p$

$$+ (\cos^2\theta_p - \sin^2\theta_p)I_{xy}$$

Substituting, we get

$$\boxed{\begin{aligned} I_{xp} &= 10 \text{ m}^4 \\ I_{yp} &= 2.5 \text{ m}^4 \\ I_{xyp} &= 0 - \text{(checks)} \end{aligned}}$$

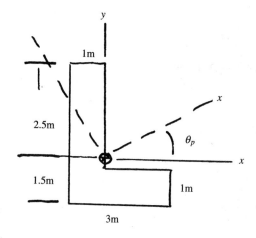

Problem 8.92 Determine a set of principal axes and the corresponding principal moments of inertia. (Do not use Mohr's circle).

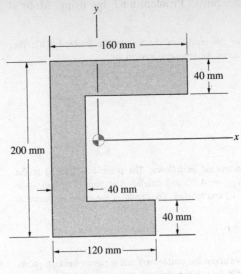

Solution: We divide the area into 3 rectangles as shown: In terms of the $\hat{x}$, $\hat{y}$ coordinate system, the position of the centroid is

$$\hat{x} = \frac{\hat{x}_1 A_1 + \hat{x}_2 A_1 + \hat{x}_3 A_3}{A_1 + A_2 + A_3}$$

$$= \frac{(20)(40)(200) + (100)(120)(40) + (80)(80)(40)}{(40)(200) + (120)(40) + (80)(40)} = 56 \text{ mm},$$

$$\hat{y} = \frac{\hat{y}_1 A_1 + \hat{y}_2 A_1 + \hat{y}_3 A_3}{A_1 + A_2 + A_3}$$

$$= \frac{(100)(40)(200) + (180)(120)(40) + (20)(80)(40)}{(40)(200) + (120)(40) + (80)(40)} = 108 \text{ mm}.$$

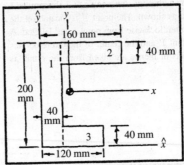

The moments and products of inertia in terms of the $\hat{x}$, $\hat{y}$ system are

$$\widehat{I}_x = (\widehat{I}_x)_1 + (\widehat{I}_x)_2 + (\widehat{I}_x)_3$$

$$= \frac{1}{3}(40)(200)^3 + \frac{1}{12}(120)(40)^3 + (180)^2(120)(40)$$

$$+ \frac{1}{3}(80)(40)^3 = 26.5 \times 10^7 \text{ mm}^4,$$

$$\widehat{I}_y = (\widehat{I}_y)_1 + (\widehat{I}_y)_2 + (\widehat{I}_y)_3$$

$$= \frac{1}{3}(200)(40)^3 + \frac{1}{12}(40)(120)^3 + (100)^2(120)(40)$$

$$+ \frac{1}{12}(40)(80)^3 + (80)^2(80)(40) = 8.02 \times 10^7 \text{ mm}^4,$$

$$\widehat{I}_{xy} = (\widehat{I}_{xy})_1 + (\widehat{I}_{xy})_2 + (\widehat{I}_{xy})_3$$

$$= (20)(100)(40)(200) + (100)(180)(40)(120)$$

$$+ (20)(80)(40)(80) = 10.75 \times 10^7 \text{ mm}.$$

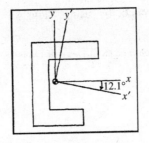

The moments and product of inertia in terms of the $\hat{x}$, $\hat{y}$ system are

$$I_x = \widehat{I}_x - (\hat{y})^2 A = 77.91 \times 10^6 \text{ mm}^4,$$

$$I_y = \widehat{I}_y - (\hat{x})^2 A = 30.04 \times 10^6 \text{ mm}^4,$$

$$I_{xy} = \widehat{I}_{xy} - \hat{x}\hat{y}A = 10.75 \times 10^6 \text{ mm}^4,$$

from Equation (8.26),

$$\tan 2\theta_p = \frac{2I_{xy}}{I_y - I_x} = \frac{2(10.75 \times 10^6)}{(30.04 \times 10^6) - (77.91 \times 10^6)},$$

we obtain $\theta p = -12.1°$. We can orient the principal axes as shown: Substituting the values of I_x, I_y and I_{xy} into Equations (8.23) and (8.24) and setting $\theta = -12.1°$, we obtain

$$I_{x^1} = 80.2 \times 10^6 \text{ mm}^4$$

$$I_{y^1} = 27.7 \times 10^6 \text{ mm}^4.$$

Problem 8.93 Solve Problem 8.87 by using Mohr's circle.

Solution: Use the results of the solution in Problem 8.87: the moments of inertia of the unrotated system are

$$I_x = 4 \text{ ft}^4,$$

$$I_y = 36 \text{ ft}^4,$$

and $I_{xy} = 0$.

The circle is constructed as follows: The point 1 is located at the coordinates $(I_x, I_{xy}) = (4, 0)$, and labeled. The point 2 is located at $(I_y, -I_{xy}) = (36, 0)$ and labeled. The center of the circle is located at

$$OC = \frac{I_x + I_y}{2} = 20.$$

The circle is drawn about the center such that it passes through points 1 and 2. A straight line drawn through the center and the points 1 and 2 coincides with the axis, as shown. The point $1'$ is located on the circle at an angle of 120° counterclockwise from point 1 and labeled. A straight line drawn though point $1'$ and the center of the circle defines the point $2'$. The new moments of inertia are taken from the graph as follows:

$$I'_x = \mathbf{OA} = 28 \text{ ft}^4.$$

$$I_{y'} = \mathbf{OB} = 12 \text{ ft}^4,$$

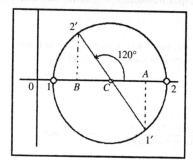

and the product of inertia is

$$I_{x'y'} = \mathbf{A1'} = -13.8 \text{ ft}^4.$$

It is negative because the point $1'$ has the coordinates

$$(I_{x'}, I_{x'y'}) = (28, -13.8).$$

Problem 8.94 Solve Problem 8.88 by using Mohr's circle.

Solution: From the solution to Problem 8.88, the area moments of inertia for the unrotated system are

$$I_x = 85.33 \text{ m}^4,$$

$$I_y = 5.333 \text{ m}^4,$$

and $I_{xy} = 0$.

The center of the circle is located on the x-axis at

$$OC = \frac{I_x + I_y}{2} = 45.3 \text{ m}^4.$$

The points 1 and 2 have the coordinates

$$(I_x, I_{xy}) = (85.3, 0)$$

and $(I_y, -I_{xy}) = (5.3, 0)$

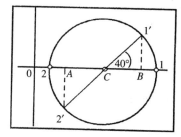

respectively. The circle is drawn through these two points about the center. The point $1'$ is located on the perimeter of the circle at an angle of 40° counterclockwise from point 1. Point $2'$ is located on the perimeter by drawing a straight line though $1'$ and the center. The new moments of inertia are taken from the graph as follows:

$$I_{x'} = \mathbf{OB} = 76 \text{ m}^4,$$

$$I_{y'} = \mathbf{OA} = 14.7 \text{ ft}^4,$$

and $I_{x'y'} = \mathbf{B1'} = 25.7 \text{ ft}^4$

737

Problem 8.95 Solve Problem 8.89 by using Mohr's circle.

Solution: The area moments of inertia are given:

$$I_x = 76 \text{ m}^4,$$

$$I_y = 14.7 \text{ m}^4,$$

and $I_{xy} = 25.7 \text{ m}^4.$

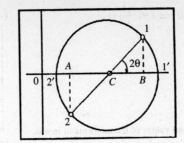

The objective is to determine the principal axes and the principal moments of inertia. The center of the circle lies on the x-axis at

$$OC = \frac{I_x + I_y}{2} = 45.4 \text{ m}^4.$$

The points 1 and 2 are located at the coordinates

$$(I_x, I_{xy}) = (76, 25.7),$$

and $(I_y, -I_{xy}) = (14.7, -25.7),$

respectively. The circle is drawn through these two points about the center. The point $1'$ lies on the periphery of the circle at the intersection with the x-axis. The point $2'$ is on the perimeter of the circle at the intersection of a straight line drawn through point $1'$ and the center of the circle. The angle of rotation is negative, and is half the measured angle on the circle, $\theta = -20°$. The moments of inertia are taken from the graph:

$$I_x = OB = 85.4 \text{ m}^4,$$

$$I_y = OA = 5.4 \text{ m}^4,$$

and $I_{xy} = 0.$

Problem 8.96 Solve Problem 8.90 by using Mohr's circle.

Solution: From Problem 8.90, we have

$$I_x = 8.50 \text{ m}^4$$

$$I_y = 4.00 \text{ m}^4$$

$$I_{xy} = -3.00 \text{ m}^4$$

and we want to find the values for $I_{x'}$, $I_{y'}$, and $I_{xy'}$ when the axes are rotated 50° counterclockwise.

From the circle:

$$I_x = 8.8 \text{ m}^4$$

$$I_y = 3.7 \text{ m}^4$$

$$I_{xy} = 2.7 \text{ m}^4$$

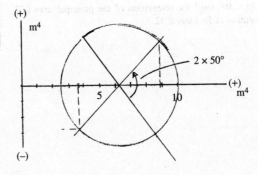

Problem 8.97 Solve Problem 8.91 by using Mohr's circle.

Solution: From Problems 8.90 and 8.91, we have

$I_x = 8.50 \text{ m}^4$

$I_y = 4.00 \text{ m}^4$

$I_{xy} = -3.00 \text{ m}^4$

We want to find θ_p and the principal values of the moments of inertia.

From the circle

$I_x = 10.0 \text{ m}^4$

$I_y = 2.5 \text{ m}^4$

By measurement,

$2\theta_p = 53.5°$

$\theta_p \cong 26.7°$

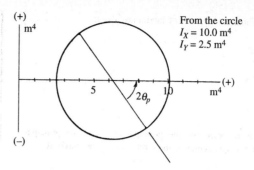

From the circle
$I_X = 10.0 \text{ m}^4$
$I_Y = 2.5 \text{ m}^4$

By measurement, $2\theta_p = 53.5°$
$\theta_p \cong 26.7°$

Problem 8.98 Solve Problem 8.92 by using Mohr's circle.

Solution: The moments and product of inertia are derived in terms of the xy coordinate system in the solution of Problem 8.92:

$I_x = 77.91 \times 10^6 \text{ mm}^4$

$I_y = 30.04 \times 10^6 \text{ mm}^4$

$I_{xy} = 10.75 \times 10^6 \text{ mm}^4$.

The Mohr's circle is: Measuring the $2\theta p$, angle we estimate that $\theta p = -12°$, and the principle moments of inertia are approximately $81 \times 10^6 \text{ mm}^4$ and $28 \times 10^6 \text{ mm}^4$ the orientation of the principal axes is shown in the solution of Problem 8.92.

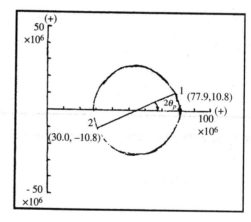

Problem 8.99 Derive Eq. (8.22) for the product of inertia by using the same procedure we used to derive Eqs. (8.20) and (8.21).

Solution: Suppose that the area moments of inertia of the area A are known in the coordinate system (x, y),

$$I_x = \int_A y^2 \, dA,$$

$$I_y = \int_A x^2 \, dA,$$

and $I_{xy} = \int_A xyA.$

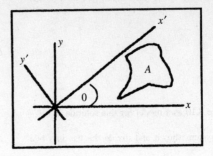

The objective is to find the product of inertia in the new coordinate system (x', y') in terms of the known moments of inertia. The new (x', y') system is formed from the old (x, y) system by rotation about the origin through a counterclockwise angle θ.

By definition,

$$I_{x'y'} = \int_A x'y' \, dA.$$

From geometry,

$$x' = x \cos\theta + y \sin\theta,$$

and $y' = -x \sin\theta + y \cos\theta.$

The product is

$$x'y' = xy \cos^2\theta - xy \sin^2\theta + y^2 \cos\theta \sin\theta - x^2 \cos\theta \sin\theta.$$

Substitute into the definition:

$$I_{x'y'} = (\cos^2\theta - \sin^2\theta) \int_A xy \, dA$$

$$+ (\cos\theta \sin\theta)\left(\int_A y^2 \, dA - \int_A x^2 \, dA\right),$$

from which

$$I_{x'y'} = (\cos^2\theta - \sin^2\theta)I_{xy} + (I_x - I_y)\sin\theta\cos\theta,$$

which is the expression required.

Problem 8.100 The axis L_O is perpendicular to both segments of the L-shaped slender bar. The mass of the bar is 6 kg and the material is homogeneous. Use integration to determine is mass moment of inertia about L_O.

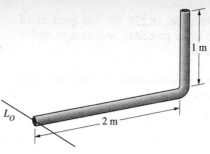

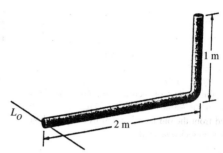

Solution: Use Example 8.10 as a model for this solution.

Introduce the coordinate system shown and divide the bar into two parts as shown

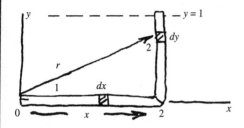

$$(I_0)_1 = \int r^2 \, dm = \int_0^2 \rho A x^2 \, dx = \rho A \frac{x^3}{3} \Big|_0^2$$

$$(I_0)_1 = \frac{8}{3}\rho A$$

However $m_1 = \rho A l_1 = (2\rho A)$.

Since part 1 is 2/3 of the length, its mass is $2/3(6 \text{ kg}) = 4$ kg. Part 2 has mass 2 kg.

For part 2, $dm = \rho A \, dy$ and

$$r = \sqrt{2^2 + y^2}$$

$$(I_0)_2 = \int_{m_2} r^2 \, dm = \int_0^1 \rho A (2^2 + y^2) \, dy$$

$$(I_0)_2 = \rho A (4y + \frac{y^3}{3}) \Big|_0^1 = \rho A \frac{13}{3}$$

$$I_{0\text{TOTAL}} = \frac{13}{3}\rho A + \frac{8}{3}\rho A = \frac{21}{3}\rho A$$

$$(I_0)_{\text{TOTAL}} = 7\rho A$$

The total mass $= 3\rho A = 6$ kg

$$I_{0\text{TOTAL}} = \frac{7}{6}(6 \text{ kg}) \cdot m^2 = 7 \text{ kg m}^2$$

Problem 8.101 Two homogenous slender bars, each of mass m and length l, are welded together to form the T-shaped object. Use integration to determine the mass moment of inertia of the object about the axis through point 0 that is perpendicular to the bars.

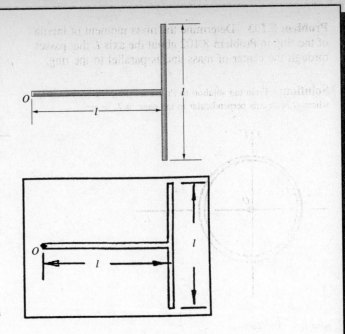

Solution: Divide the object into two pieces, each corresponding to a slender bar of mass m; the first parallel to the y-axis, the second to the x-axis. By definition

$$I = \int_0^l r^2\, dm + \int_m r^2\, dm.$$

For the first bar, the differential mass is $dm = \rho A\, dr$. Assume that the second bar is very slender, so that the mass is concentrated at a distance l from O. Thus $dm = \rho A\, dx$, where x lies between the limits

$$-\frac{l}{2} \le x \le \frac{l}{2}.$$

The distance to a differential dx is $r = \sqrt{l^2 + x^2}$. Thus the definition becomes

$$I = \rho A \int_0^l r^2\, dr + \rho A \int_{-\frac{l}{2}}^{\frac{l}{2}} (l^2 + x^2)\, dx\ I$$

$$= \rho A \left[\frac{r^3}{3} \right]_0^l + \rho A \left[l^2 x + \frac{x^3}{3} \right]_{-l/2}^{l/2}$$

$$= m l^2 \left(\frac{1}{3} + 1 + \frac{1}{12} \right) = \frac{17}{12} m l^2.$$

Problem 8.102 A homogeneous slender bar is bent into a circular ring of mass m and radius R. Determine the mass moment of inertia of the ring about the axis through its center of mass that is perpendicular to the right. (That is, the axis is perpendicular to the page.)

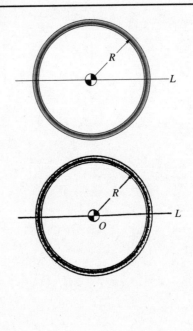

Solution: Let $dm = \rho A R\, d\theta$

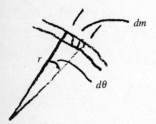

$$I_0 = \int_m r^2\, dm$$

$$I_0 = \int_0^{2\pi} r^2 (\rho A r\, d\theta) = \rho A r^3 \int_0^{2\pi} d\theta$$

$$I_0 = \rho A r^3 (2\pi)$$

However, $m = (2\pi r \rho A)$

$$I_0 = m r^2$$

Problem 8.103 Determine the mass moment of inertia of the ring in Problem 8.102 about the axis L that passes through the center of mass and is parallel to the ring.

Solution: From the solution to Problem 8.102, we know that I_o, where O is an axis perpendicular to the page, is $I_o = mr^2$

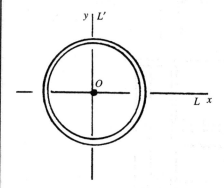

Also $I_o = \displaystyle\int r^2 \, dm$

$\qquad = \displaystyle\int (x^2 + y^2) \, dm$

$I_o = \displaystyle\int x^2 \, dm + \int y^2 \, dm$

$I_o = I_L + I'_L$

By symmetry, $I_L = I'_L$ and $I_L = \frac{1}{2} mr^2$

Problem 8.104 The homogeneous thin plate has mass $m = 12$ kg and dimensions $b = 1$ m and $h = 2$ m. Determine its mass moments of inertia about the x, y, and z axes.

Strategy: The mass moments of inertia of a thin plate of arbitrary shape are given by Eqs. (8.30)–(8.32) in terms of the moments of inertia of the cross-sectional area of the plate. You can obtain the moments of inertia of the triangular area from Appendix B.

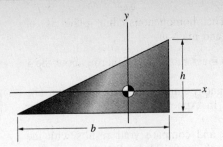

Solution: The center of mass of the homogeneous plate is located at $\left(-\dfrac{1}{3}b, \dfrac{1}{3h}\right)$ measured from the right angle corner. In the coordinates shown, A is at $\left(-\dfrac{2b}{3}, -\dfrac{h}{3}\right)$ and point b is located at $\left(\dfrac{b}{3}, \dfrac{2h}{3}\right)$. The equation of line AB is.

$$y = \frac{h}{b}x + \frac{h}{3} \text{ or } x = \frac{b}{h}y - \frac{b}{3}$$

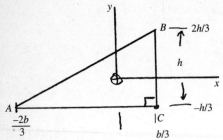

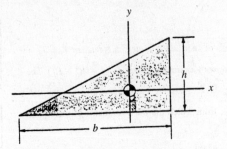

For I_y, let $dm = \rho A \left(y - \left(-\dfrac{h}{3}\right)\right) dx$

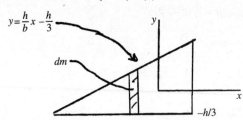

$$I_y = \int_m x^2 \, dm$$

$$= \int_{-2b/3}^{b/3} x^2 \rho A \left(y - \frac{h}{3}\right) dm$$

$$= \int_{-2b/3}^{b/3} \rho A \left[x^2 \left(\frac{h}{b}x - \frac{2h}{3}\right)\right] dx$$

$$= \rho A \left[\frac{h}{b}\left(\frac{x^4}{4}\right) - \frac{2h}{3}\left(\frac{x^3}{3}\right)\right]_{-2b/3}^{b/3}$$

$$I_y = \rho A \left[\frac{1}{36} hb^3\right]$$

Area $= \dfrac{1}{2}bh$

Mass $= \rho A$ Area

$$I_y = \frac{1}{18}mb^2$$

Finally I_z, about the axis perpendicular to the x, y plane, is given by

$$I_z = I_x + I_y$$

$$\boxed{I_z = \frac{1}{18}m(b^2 + h^2)}$$

Let ρA = mass per unit area

For I_x, let $dm = \rho A \left(\dfrac{b}{3} - x\right) dy$

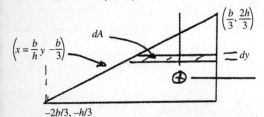

$$I_x = \int y^2 \, dm = \int_{-h/3}^{2h/3} y^2 \rho A \left(\frac{b}{3} - x\right) dy$$

$$= \int_{-h/3}^{2h/3} y^2 \rho A \left[\frac{2b}{3} - \frac{b}{h}y\right] dy$$

$$= \rho A \left[\frac{2by^3}{9} - \frac{b}{h}\frac{y^4}{4}\right]_{-h/3}^{2h/3}$$

$$I_x = \rho A \left[\frac{1}{36}bh^3\right]$$

Area $= \dfrac{1}{2} bh$

Mass $= \dfrac{\rho A}{2} bh$

$$\boxed{I_x = \frac{1}{18} mh^2}$$

Problem 8.105 The homogenous thin plate is of uniform thickness and mass m.

(a) Determine its mass moments of inertia about the x and z axes.
(b) Let $R_i = 0$, and compare your results with the values given in Appendix C for a thin circular plate.
(c) Let $R_i \rightarrow R_o$, and compare your results with the solutions of Problem 8.102 and 8.103.

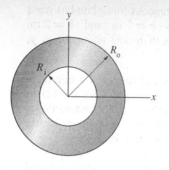

Solution:

(a) The area moments of inertia for a circular area are $I_x = I_y = \dfrac{\pi R^4}{4}$. For the plate with a circular cutout, $I_x = \dfrac{\pi}{4}(R_o^4 - R_i^4)$. The area mass density is $\dfrac{m}{A}$, thus for the plate with a circular cut, $\dfrac{m}{A} = \dfrac{m}{\pi(R_o^2 - R_i^2)}$, from which the mass moments of inertia

$$I_{(x\text{-axis})} = \frac{m(R_o^4 - R_i^4)}{4(R_o^2 - R_i^2)} = \frac{m}{4}(R_o^2 + R_i^2)$$

$$I_{(z\text{-axis})} = 2I_{(x\text{-axis})} = \frac{m}{2}(R_o^2 + R_i^2).$$

(b) Let $R_i = 0$, to obtain

$$I_{x\text{-axis}} = \frac{m}{4}R_o^2,$$

$$I_{(z\text{-axis})} = \frac{m}{2}R_o^2,$$

which agrees with table entries.

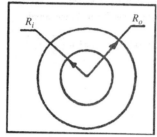

(c) Take the limit as $R_i \rightarrow R_o$,

$$I_{(x\text{-axis})} = \frac{m}{2}R_o^2,$$

$$I_{(z\text{-axis})} = mR_o^2,$$

which agrees with the solution of Problems 8.102 and 8.103.

Problem 8.106 The homogenous thin plate is of uniform thickness and weighs 20 lb. Determine its mass moment of inertia about the y axis.

Solution:

$y = 4 - \dfrac{1}{4}x^2$ ft

The plate's area is

$$A = \int_{-4}^{4} \left(4 - \frac{1}{4}x^2\right) dx = 21.3 \text{ ft}^2.$$

The plate's density *per unit area* is

$$\delta = (20/32.2)/21.3 = 0.0291 \text{ slug/ft}^2.$$

The mass moment of inertia about the y axis is

$$I_{(y \text{ axis})} = \int_{-4}^{4} x^2 \delta \left(4 - \frac{1}{4}x^2\right) dx$$

$$= 1.99 \text{ slug-ft}^2.$$

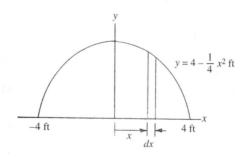

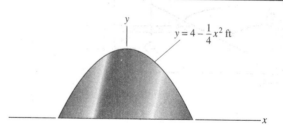

Problem 8.107 Determine the mass moment of inertia of the plate in Problem 8.106 about the x axis.

Solution: See the solution of Problem 8.106. The mass of the strip element is

$$m_{(strip)} = \delta \left(4 - \frac{1}{4}x^2 \right) dx.$$

The mass moment of inertia of the strip about the x axis is

$$I_{(strip)} = \frac{1}{3} m_{(strip)} \left(4 - \frac{1}{4}x^2 \right)^2$$

$$= \frac{1}{3} \delta \left(4 - \frac{1}{4}x^2 \right)^3 dx,$$

so the mass moment of inertia of the plate about the x axis is

$$I_{(x\ axis)} = \int_{-4}^{4} \frac{1}{3} \delta \left(4 - \frac{1}{4}x^2 \right)^3 dx = 2.27\ \text{slug-ft}^2.$$

Problem 8.108 The mass of the object is 10 kg. Its mass moment of inertia about L_1 is 10 kg-m^2. What is its mass moment of inertia about L_2? (The three axes lie in the same plane.)

Solution: The strategy is to use the data to find the mass moment of inertia about L, from which the mass moment of inertia about L_2 can be determined.

$$I_L = -(0.6)^2(10) + 10 = 6.4\ \text{m}^2,$$

from which $I_{L2} = (1.2)^2(10) + 6.4 = 20.8\ \text{m}^2$

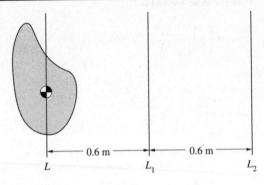

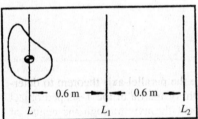

Problem 8.109 An engineer gathering data for the design of a maneuvering unit determines that the astronaut's center of mass is at $x = 1.01$ m, $y = 0.16$ m and that his mass moment of inertia about the z axis is 105.6 kg-m^2. His mass is 81.6 kg. What is his mass moment of inertia about the z' axis through his center of mass?

Solution: The distance d from the z axis to the z' axis is

$$d = \sqrt{(1.01)^2 + (0.16)^2}$$

$$= 1.0226\ \text{m}.$$

From the parallel-axis theorem,

$$I_{(z\ axis)} = I_{(z'\ axis)} + d^2\ m :$$

$$105.6 = I_{(z'\ axis)} + (1.0226)^2(81.6).$$

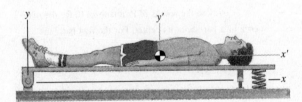

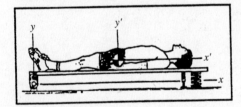

Solving, we obtain

$$I_{(z'\ axis)} = 20.27\ \text{kg-m}^2.$$

Problem 8.110   Two homogenous slender bars, each of mass m and length l, are welded together to form the T-shaped object. Use the parallel axis theorem to determine the mass moment of inertia of the object about the axis through point O that is perpendicular to the bars.

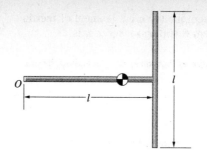

Solution: Divide the object into two pieces, each corresponding to a bar of mass m. By definition

$$I = \int_0^l r^2 \, dm.$$

For the first bar, the differential mass is $dm = \rho A \, dr$, from which the mass moment of inertia about one end is

$$I_1 = \rho A \int_0^l r^2 \, dr = \rho A \left[\frac{r^3}{3}\right]_0^l = \frac{ml^2}{3}.$$

For the second bar

$$I_2 = \rho A \int_{-\frac{l}{2}}^{\frac{l}{2}} r^2 \, dr = \rho A \left[\frac{r^3}{3}\right]_{-\frac{l}{2}}^{\frac{l}{2}} = \frac{ml^2}{12}$$

is the mass moment of inertia about the center of the bar. From the parallel axis theorem, the mass moment of inertia about O is

$$I_o = \frac{ml^2}{3} + l^2 m + \frac{ml^2}{12} = \frac{17}{12} ml^2.$$

Problem 8.111   Use the parallel-axis theorem to determine the mass moment of inertia of the T-shaped object in Problem 8.110 about the axis through the center of mass of the object that is perpendicular to the two bars.

Solution: The location of the center of mass of the object is
$$\mathbf{x} = \frac{m\left(\frac{l}{2}\right) + lm}{2m} = \frac{3}{4} l.$$ Use the results of Problem 8.110 for the mass moment of inertia of a bar about its center. For the first bar,

$$I_1 = \left(\frac{l}{4}\right)^2 m + \frac{ml^2}{12} = \frac{7}{48} ml^2.$$

For the second bar,

$$I_2 = \left(\frac{l}{4}\right)^2 m + \frac{ml^2}{12} = \frac{7}{48} ml^2.$$

The composite:

$$I_c = I_1 + I_2 = \frac{7}{24} ml^2$$

Problem 8.112
The mass of the homogenous slender bar is 20 kg. Determine its mass moment of inertia about the z axis.

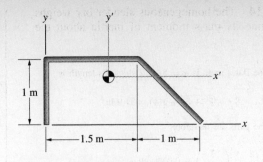

Solution: Divide the object into three segments. Part (1) is the 1 m bar on the left, Part (2) is the 1.5 m horizontal segment, and Part (3) is the segment on the far right. The mass density *per unit length* is

$$\rho = \frac{m}{L} = \frac{20}{(1 + 1.5 + \sqrt{2})} = 5.11 \text{ kg/m.}$$

The mass moments of inertia about the centers of mass and the distances to the centers of mass from the z-axis are:

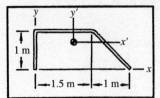

Part (1) $I_1 = \rho\left(\dfrac{l_1^3}{12}\right) = m_1\dfrac{l_1^2}{12} = 0.426 \text{ kg-m}^2,$

$m_1 = 5.11 \text{ kg,}$

$d_1 = 0.5 \text{ m,}$

Part (2), $I_2 = \rho\dfrac{l_2^3}{12} = m_2\dfrac{l_2^2}{12} = 1.437 \text{ kg- m}^2,$

$m_2 = 7.66 \text{ kg,}$

$d_2 = \sqrt{0.75^2 + 1^2} = 1.25 \text{ m}$

Part (3) $I_3 = \rho\dfrac{l_3^3}{12} = m_3\dfrac{(\sqrt{2})^2}{12} = 1.204 \text{ kg-m}^2,$

$m_3 = 7.23 \text{ kg,}$

$d_3 = \sqrt{2^2 + 0.5^2} = 2.062 \text{ m.}$

The composite:

$$I = d_1^2 m_1 + I_1 + d_2^2 m_2 + I_2 + d_3^2 m_3 + I_3 = 47.02 \text{ kg-m}^2$$

Problem 8.113
Determine the mass moment of inertia of the bar in Problem 8.112 about the z' axis through its center of mass.

Solution: The center of mass:

$$\mathbf{x} = \frac{x_1 m_1 + x_2 m_2 + x_3 m_3}{20}$$

$$= \frac{0 + 0.75(7.66) + 2(7.23)}{20} = 1.01 \text{ m.}$$

$$\mathbf{y} = \frac{0.5 m_1 + 1 m_2 + 0.5 m_3}{20}$$

$$= \frac{0.5(5.11) + 1(7.66) + 0.5(7.23)}{20} = 0.692 \text{ m.}$$

The distance from the z-axis to the center of mass is $d = \sqrt{\mathbf{x}^2 + \mathbf{y}^2} = 1.224$ m. The mass moment of inertia about the center o mass:

$$I_c = -d^2(20) + I_o$$

$$= 17.1 \text{ kg-m}^2$$

Problem 8.114 The homogeneous slender bar weighs 5 lb. Determine its mass moment of inertia about the z axis.

Solution: The Bar's mass is $m = 5/32.2$ slugs. Its length is

$$L = L_1 + L_2 + L_3 = 8 + \sqrt{8^2 + 8^2} + \pi(4) = 31.9 \text{ in.}$$

The masses of the parts are therefore,

$$m_1 = \frac{L_1}{L} m = \left(\frac{8}{31.9}\right)\left(\frac{5}{32.2}\right) = 0.0390 \text{ slugs,}$$

$$m_2 = \frac{L_2}{L} m = \left(\frac{\sqrt{2(64)}}{31.9}\right)\left(\frac{5}{32.2}\right) = 0.0551 \text{ slugs,}$$

$$m_3 = \frac{L_3}{L} m = \left(\frac{4\pi}{31.9}\right)\left(\frac{5}{32.2}\right) = 0.0612 \text{ slugs.}$$

The center of mass of part 3 is located to the right of its center C a distance $2R/\pi = 2(4)/\pi = 2.55$ in. The mass moment of inertia of part 3 about C is

$$\int_{m_3} r^2 \, dm = m_3 r^2 = (0.0612)(4)^2 = 0.979 \text{ slug-in}^2.$$

The mass moment of inertia of part 3 about the center of mass of part 3 is therefore

$$I_3 = 0.979 - m_3(2.55)^2 = 0.582 \text{ slug-in}^2.$$

The mass moment of inertia of the bar about the z axis is

$$I_{(z \text{ axis})} = \tfrac{1}{3} m_1 L_1^2 + \tfrac{1}{3} m_2 L_2^2 + I_3 + m_3[(8 + 2.55)^2 + (4)^2]$$

$$= 11.6 \text{ slug-in}^2 = 0.0802 \text{ slug-ft}^2.$$

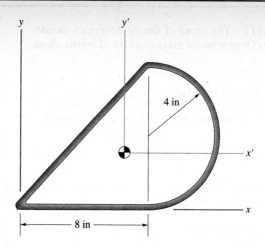

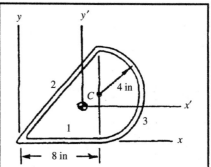

Problem 8.115 Determine the mass moment of inertia of the bar in Problem 8.114 about the z' axis through its center of mass.

Solution: In the solution of Problem 8.114, it is shown that the mass moment of inertia of the bar about the z axis is $I_{(z \text{ axis})} = 11.6$ slug-in². The x and y coordinates of the center of mass coincide with the centroid of the axis:

$$\mathbf{x} = \frac{\mathbf{x}_1 L_1 + \mathbf{x}_2 L_2 + \mathbf{x}_3 L_3}{L_1 + L_2 + L_3}$$

$$= \frac{(4)(8) + (4)\sqrt{8^2 + 8^2} + \left[8 + \frac{2(4)}{\pi}\right]\pi(4)}{8 + \sqrt{8^2 + 8^2} + \pi(4)} = 6.58 \text{ in,}$$

$$\mathbf{y} = \frac{\mathbf{y}_1 L_1 + \mathbf{y}_2 L_2 + \mathbf{y}_3 L_3}{L_1 + L_2 + L_3}$$

$$= \frac{0 + (4)\sqrt{8^2 + 8^2} + (4)\pi(4)}{8 + \sqrt{8^2 + 8^2} + \pi(4)} = 3.00 \text{ in.}$$

The mass moment of inertia about the z axis is

$$I_{(z' \text{ axis})} = I_{(z \text{ axis})} - (\mathbf{x}^2 + \mathbf{y}^2)\left(\frac{5}{32.2}\right) = 3.43 \text{ slug-in}^2.$$

Problem 8.116 The rocket is used for atmospheric research. Its weight and its mass moment of inertia about the z axis through its center of mass (including its fuel) are 10 kip and 10,200 slug-ft^2, respectively. The rocket's fuel weighs 6000 lb, its center of mass is located at $x = -3$ ft, $y = 0$, $z = 0$, and the mass moment of inertia of the fuel about the axis through the fuel's center of mass parallel to z is 2200 slug-ft^2. When the fuel is exhausted, what is the rocket's mass moment of inertia about the axis through its new center of mass parallel to z?

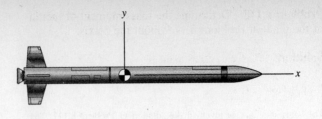

Solution: Denote the mass moment of inertia of the empty rocket as I_E about a center of mass x_E, and the mass moment of inertia of the fuel as I_F about a mass center x_F. Using the parallel axis theorem, the mass moment of inertia of the filled rocket is

$$I_R = I_E + x_E^2 m_E + I_F + x_F^2 m_F,$$

about a mass center at the origin ($x_R = 0$). Solve:

$$I_E = I_R - x_E^2 m_E - I_F - x_F^2 m_F.$$

The objective is to determine values for the terms on the right from the data given. Since the filled rocket has a mass center at the origin, the mass center of the empty rocket is found from $0 = m_E x_E + m_F x_F$, from which

$$x_E = -\left(\frac{m_F}{m_E}\right) x_F.$$

Using a value of $g = 32.2$ ft/s^2,

$$m_F = \frac{W_F}{g} = \frac{6000}{32.2} = 186.34 \text{ slug},$$

$$m_E = \frac{(W_R - W_F)}{g} = \frac{10000 - 6000}{32.2} = 124.23 \text{ slug}.$$

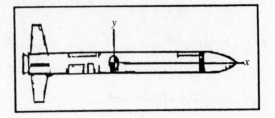

From which

$$x_E = -\left(\frac{186.335}{124.224}\right)(-3) = 4.5 \text{ ft}$$

is the new location of the center of mass. Substitute:

$$I_E = I_R - x_E^2 m_E - I_F - x_F^2 m_F$$

$$= 10200 - 2515.5 - 2200 - 1677.01$$

$$= 3807.5 \text{ slug-ft}^2$$

Problem 8.117 The mass of the homogenous thin plate is 36 kg. Determine its mass moment of inertia about the x axis.

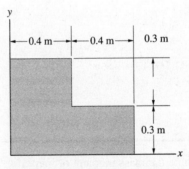

Solution: Divide the plate into two areas: the rectangle 0.4 m by 0.6 m on the left, and the rectangle 0.4 m by 0.3 m on the right. The mass density is $\rho = \dfrac{m}{A}$. The area is

$$A = (0.4)(0.6) + (0.4)(0.3) = 0.36 \text{ m}^2,$$

from which

$$\rho = \frac{36}{0.36} = 100 \text{ kg/m}^2.$$

The mass moment of inertia about the x-axis is

$$I_{x\text{-axis}} = \rho\left(\tfrac{1}{3}\right)(0.4)(0.6^3) + \rho\left(\tfrac{1}{3}\right)(0.4)(0.3)^3 = 3.24 \text{ kg-m}^2$$

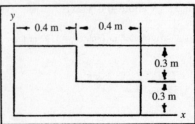

Problem 8.118 Determine the mass moment of inertia of the plate in Problem 8.117 about the z axis.

Solution: The basic relation to use is

$$I_{z\text{-axis}} = I_{x\text{-axis}} + I_{y\text{-axis}}.$$

The value of $I_{x\text{-axis}}$ is given in the solution of Problem 8.117. The mass moment of inertia about the y-axis using the same divisions as in Problem 8.117 and the parallel axis theorem is

$$I_{y\text{-axis}} = \rho\left(\frac{1}{3}\right)(0.6)(0.4)^3 + \rho\left(\frac{1}{12}\right)(0.3)(0.4)^3$$

$$+ (0.6)^2\rho(0.3)(0.4) = 5.76 \text{ kg-m}^2,$$

from which

$$I_{z\text{-axis}} = I_{x\text{-axis}} + I_{y\text{-axis}} = 3.24 + 5.76 = 9 \text{ kg-m}^2$$

Problem 8.119 The homogenous thin plate weighs 10 lb. Determine its mass moment of inertia about the x axis.

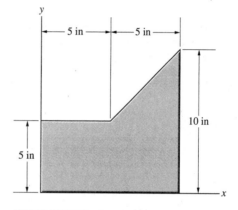

Solution: Divide the area into two parts: the lower rectangle 5 in by 10 in and the upper triangle 5 in base and 5 in altitude. The mass density is $\rho = \dfrac{W}{gA}$. The area is

$$A = 5(10) + \left(\tfrac{1}{2}\right)5(5) = 62.5 \text{ in}^2.$$

Using $g = 32 \text{ ft/s}^2$, the mass density is

$$\rho = \frac{W}{gA} = 0.005 \text{ slug/in}^2.$$

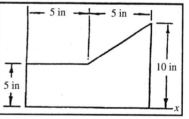

Using the parallel axis theorem, the mass moment of inertia about the x-axis is

$$I_{x\text{-axis}} = \rho\left(\frac{1}{3}\right)(10)(5)^3 + \rho\left(\frac{1}{36}\right)(5)(5^3)$$

$$+ \rho\left(5 + \frac{5}{3}\right)^2\left(\frac{1}{2}\right)(5)(5) = 4.948 \text{ slug-in}^2$$

$$I_{x\text{-axis}} = 0.03436 \text{ slug-ft}^2$$

Problem 8.120 Determine the mass moment of inertia of the plate in Problem 8.119 about the y axis.

Solution: Use the results of the solution in Problem 8.119 for the area and the mass density.

$$I_{y\text{-axis}} = \rho\left(\frac{1}{3}\right)5(10^3) + \rho\left(\frac{1}{36}\right)5(5^3)$$

$$+ \rho\left(5 + \frac{10}{3}\right)^2\left(\frac{1}{2}\right)5(5)$$

$$= 12.76 \text{ slug-in}^2 = 0.0886 \text{ slug-ft}^2$$

Problem 8.121 The thermal radiator (used to eliminate excess heat from a satellite) can modeled as a homogenous, thin rectangular plate. Its mass is 5 slugs. Determine its mass moment of inertia about the x, y, and z axes.

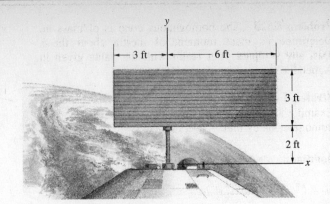

Solution: The area is $A = 9(3) = 27$ ft^2. The mass density is

$$\rho = \frac{m}{A} = \frac{5}{27} = 0.1852 \text{ slugs/ft}^2.$$

The mass moment of inertia about the centroid of the rectangle is

$$I_{xc} = \rho \left(\frac{1}{12}\right) 9(3^3) = 3.75 \text{ slug-ft}^2,$$

$$I_{yc} = \rho \left(\frac{1}{12}\right) 3(9^3) = 33.75 \text{ slug-ft}^2.$$

Use the parallel axis theorem:

$$I_{x\text{-axis}} = \rho A (2 + 1.5)^2 + I_{xc} = 65 \text{ slug-ft}^2,$$

$$I_{y\text{-axis}} = \rho A (4.5 - 3)^2 + I_{yc} = 45 \text{ slug-ft}^2.$$

$$I_{z\text{-axis}} = I_{x\text{-axis}} + I_{y\text{-axis}} = 110 \text{ slug-ft}^2$$

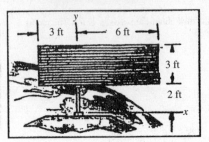

Problem 8.122 The mass of the homogenous thin plate is 2 kg. Determine its mass moment of inertia about the axis L_O through point O that is perpendicular to the plate.

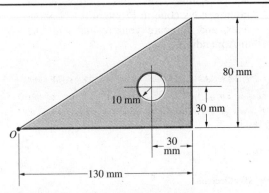

Solution: The strategy is to determine I_x and I_y about point O, from which to determine I_z. The area is

$$A_1 = \left(\tfrac{1}{2}\right) 80(130) = 5200 \text{ mm}^2,$$

$$A_2 = \pi(10^2) = 314.16 \text{ mm}^2,$$

$$A = A_1 - A_2 = 4885.84 \text{ mm}^2.$$

The mass density is

$$\rho = \frac{m}{A} = \frac{2}{A} = 0.0004093 \text{ kg/mm}^2.$$

The mass moments of inertia about the centroid of the circle are

$$I_{xc} = I_{yc} = \rho \left(\tfrac{1}{4}\right) \pi(10^4) = 3.215 \text{ kg-mm}^2.$$

Use the parallel axis theorem to determine the mass moments of inertia about the x- and y-axes.

$$I_{y\text{-axis}} = \rho \left(\frac{1}{36}\right) 80(130^3) + \rho A_1 \left(\frac{2}{3}130\right)^2 - \rho A_2 (100^2) - I_{yc}$$

$$= 16,697.5 \text{ kg-mm}^2$$

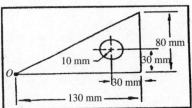

$$I_{x\text{-axis}} = \rho \left(\frac{1}{12}\right) 130(80^3) - \rho A_2 (30^2) - I_{xc}$$

$$= 2152 \text{ kg-mm}^2.$$

$$I_{z\text{-axis}} = I_{x\text{-axis}} + I_{y\text{-axis}} = 18,849 \text{ kg-mm}^2$$

$$= 0.0188 \text{ kg-m}^2$$

Problem 8.123 The homogenous cone is of mass m. Determine its mass moment of inertia about the z axis, and compare your result with the value given in Appendix C.

Strategy: Use the same approach we used in Example 8.14 to obtain the moments of inertia of a homogeneous cylinder.

Solution: The differential mass

$$dm = \left(\frac{m}{V}\right)\pi r^2\, dz = \frac{3m}{R^2 h} r^2\, dz.$$

The moment of inertia of this disk about the z-axis is $\frac{1}{2}mr^2$. The radius varies with z,

$$r = \left(\frac{R}{h}\right)z,$$

from which

$$I_{z\text{-axis}} = \frac{3mR^2}{2h^5}\int_0^h z^4\, dz = \frac{3mR^2}{2h^5}\left[\frac{z^5}{5}\right]_0^h = \frac{3mR^2}{10}$$

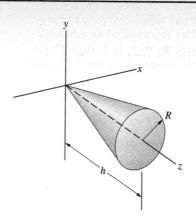

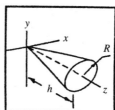

Problem 8.124 Determine the mass moments of inertia of the homogenous cone in Problem 8.123 about the x and y axes, and compare your results with the values given in Appendix C.

Solution: The mass density is $\rho = \dfrac{m}{V} = \dfrac{3m}{\pi R^2 h}$. The differential element of mass is $dm = \rho\pi r^2\, dz$. The moment of inertia of this elemental disk about an axis through its center of mass, parallel to the x- and y-axes, is

$$dI_x = \left(\tfrac{1}{4}\right)r^2\, dm.$$

Use the parallel axis theorem,

$$I_x = \int_m \left(\tfrac{1}{4}\right)r^2\, dm + \int_m z^2\, dm.$$

Noting that $r = \dfrac{R}{h}z$, then

$$r^2\, dm = \rho\left(\frac{\pi R^4}{h^4}\right)z^4\, dz,$$

and $z^2\, dm = \rho\left(\dfrac{\pi R^2}{h^2}\right)z^4\, dz.$

Substitute:

$$I_x = \rho\left(\frac{\pi R^4}{4h^4}\right)\int_0^h z^4\, dz + \rho\left(\frac{\pi R^2}{h^2}\right)\int_0^h z^4\, dz.$$

Integrating and collecting terms:

$$I_x = \left(\frac{3mR^2}{4h^5} + \frac{3m}{h^3}\right)\left[\frac{z^5}{5}\right]_0^h = m\left(\frac{3}{20}R^2 + \frac{3}{5}h^2\right).$$

By symmetry, $I_y = I_x$

Problem 8.125 The homogeneous object has the shape of a truncated cone and consists of bronze with a mass density $\rho = 8200 \text{ kg/m}^3$. Determine its mass moment of inertia about the z axis.

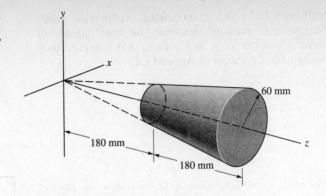

Solution: Consider an element of the cone consisting of a disk of thickness dz: We can express the radius as a linear function of z. $r = az + b$. Using the conditions that $r = 0$ at $z = 0$ and $r = 0.06$ m at $z = 0.36$ m to evaluate a and b we find that $r = 0.167\,z$. From appendix C, the mass moment of inertia of the element about the z axis is

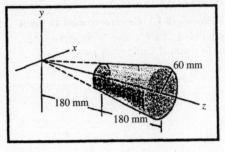

$$(I_z)_{\text{element}} = \tfrac{1}{2}mr^2 = \tfrac{1}{2}\left[s(\pi r^2)\,dz\right]r^2$$

$$= \tfrac{1}{2}s\pi(0.167z)^4\,dz.$$

We integrate this result to obtain the mass moment of inertia about the z axis for the cone:

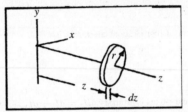

$$I_{(z\text{ axis})} = \int_{0.18}^{0.36}\tfrac{1}{2}s\pi(0.167)^4\left[\frac{z^5}{5}\right]_{0.18}^{0.36}$$

$$= \frac{1}{2}(8200)\pi(0.167)^4\left[\frac{z^5}{5}\right]_{0.18}^{0.36} = 0.0116 \text{ kg-m}^2.$$

Problem 8.126 Determine the mass moment of inertia of the object in Problem 8.125 about the x axis.

Solution: Consider the disk element described in the solution to Problem 8.125. The radius of the lament is $r = 0.167z$. Using Appendix C and the parallel axis theorem, the mass moment of inertia of the element about the x axis is

$$(I_x)_{\text{element}} = \tfrac{1}{4}mR^2 + mz^2 = \tfrac{1}{4}[s(\pi r^2)\,dz]r^2 + [s(\pi r^2)\,dz]z^2$$

$$= \tfrac{1}{4}s\pi(0.167z)^4\,dz + s\pi(0.167z)^2z^2\,dz.$$

Integrating the result,

$$I_{(x\text{ axis})} = \frac{1}{4}s\pi(0.167z)^4\int_{0.18}^{0.36}z^4\,dz + \rho\pi(0.167)^2\int_{0.18}^{0.36}z^4\,dz$$

$$= 0.844 \text{ kg-m}^2.$$

Problem 8.127 The homogenous rectangular parallelepiped is of mass m. Determine its mass moment of inertia about the x, y, and z axes, and compare your results with the values in Appendix C.

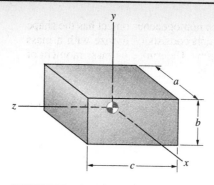

Solution: Consider a rectangular slice normal to the x-axis of dimensions b by c and mass dm. The area density of this slice is $\rho = \dfrac{dm}{bc}$. From Eqs (8.30) and (8.31), the mass moment of inertia about the y axis of the centroid of a thin plate is the product of the area density and the area moment of inertia of the plate:

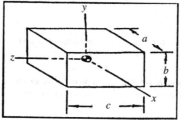

$$dI_y = \rho \left(\frac{1}{12}\right) bc^3,$$

from which

$$dI_y = \left(\frac{1}{12}\right) c^2 \, dm.$$

By symmetry, the mass moment of inertia about the z axis is

$$dI_z = \left(\frac{1}{12}\right) b^2 \, dm.$$

Since the labeling of the x- y- and z-axes is arbitrary, $dI_x = dI_z + dI_y$, where the x-axis is normal to the area of the plate. Thus

$$dI_x = \left(\frac{1}{12}\right)(b^2 + c^2) \, dm,$$

from which

$$I_x = \left(\frac{1}{12}\right)(b^2 + c^2) \int_m dm = \frac{m}{12}(b^2 + c^2).$$

By symmetry, the argument can be repeated for each coordinate, to obtain

$$I_y = \frac{m}{12}(a^2 + c^2) \quad I_z = \frac{m}{12}(b^2 + a^2)$$

Discussion: The parallel axis theorem does not apply above because the mass moment of inertia about the y and z axes are about *an origin at the centroid of the thin slice* and not at the origin of the coordinate system at the centroid of the block. Thus the mass moment of inertia about the x-axis of the slice $bc\,dx$ is independent of the location on the x-axis. *End of discussion.*

Problem 8.128 The L-shaped machine part is composed of two homogeneous bars. Bar 1 is tungsten alloy with mass density 14,000 kg/m³, and bar 2 is steel with mass density 7800 kg/m³. Determine its moment of inertia about the x axis.

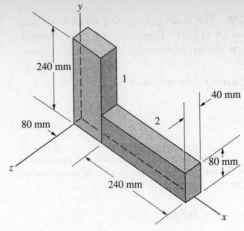

Solution: The masses of the bars are

$$m_1 = (14,000)(0.24)(0.08)(0.04) = 10.75 \text{ kg}$$

$$m_2 = (7800)(0.24)(0.08)(0.04) = 5.99 \text{ kg}.$$

Using Appendix C and the parallel axis theorem the mass moments of inertia of the parts about the x axis are

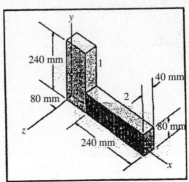

$$I_{(x \text{ axis})1} = \frac{1}{12} m_1[(0.04)^2 + (0.24)^2] + m_1(0.12)^2 = 0.2079 \text{ kg-m}^2,$$

$$I_{(x \text{ axis})2} = \frac{1}{12} m_2[(0.04)^2 + (0.08)^2] + m_2(0.04)^2 = 0.0136 \text{ kg-m}^2.$$

Therefore

$$I_{(x \text{ axis})} = I_{(x \text{ axis})1} + I_{(x \text{ axis})2} = 0.221 \text{ kg-m}^2$$

Problem 8.129 Determine the moment of inertia of the L-shaped machine part in Problem 8.128 about the z axis.

Solution: From the solution to Problem 8.128, the masses of the parts are $m_1 = 10.75$ kg, $m_2 = 5.99$ kg. Using Appendix C and the parallel axis theorem the mass moments of inertia of the parts about the z axis are

$$I_{(z \text{ axis})1} = \frac{1}{12} m_1[(0.08)^2 + (0.24)^2] + m_1[(0.04)^2 + (0.12)^2]$$

$$= 0.229 \text{ kg-m}^2,$$

$$I_{(x \text{ axis})2} = \frac{1}{12} m_2[(0.24)^2 + (0.08)^2]$$

$$+ m_2[(0.08 + 0.12)^2 + (0.04)^2]$$

$$= 0.281 \text{ kg-m}^2.$$

Therefore

$$I_{(z \text{ axis})} = I_{(z \text{ axis})1} + I_{(z \text{ axis})2}$$

$$= 0.511 \text{ kg-m}^2.$$

Problem 8.130 The homogenous ring consists of steel of density $\rho = 15$ slug/ft^3. Determine its mass moment of inertia about the axis L through its center of mass.

Solution: Consider a solid cylinder of radius R and height h. Its mass density is

$$\rho = \frac{m}{V} = \frac{m}{\pi R^2 h}.$$

Consider a thin slice normal to the axis L. The mass moment of inertia of this slice about the axis L is the product of the area density and the area moment of inertia:

$$dI_L = (\rho h)r^2\, dA = (\rho h)(2\pi)r^3\, dr,$$

from which

$$I_L = (2\rho h\pi)\int_0^R r^3\, dr = \left(\frac{1}{2}\right) mR^2.$$

From which, for the outer ring

$$I_{Lo} = \left(\frac{1}{2}\right) m_o R_o^2.$$

For the inner ring

$$I_{Li} = \left(\frac{1}{2}\right) m_i R_i^2,$$

from which

$$I_L = I_{Lo} - I_{Li} = \left(\frac{1}{2}\right)(m_o R_o^2 - m_i R_i^2).$$

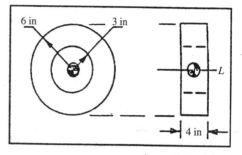

The mass of the outer cylinder is

$$m_o = \rho \pi R_o^2 h = 15\pi(0.5^2)(1/3) = 3.927 \text{ slugs}.$$

The mass of the inner cylinder is

$$m_i = \rho \pi R_i^2 h = 15\pi\ (0.25^2)(1/3) = 0.982 \text{ slugs},$$

from which

$$I_L = 0.46 \text{ slug-ft}^2$$

Problem 8.131 The homogenous half-cylinder is of mass m. Determine its mass moment of inertia about the axis L through its center of mass.

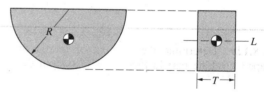

Solution: The centroid of the half cylinder is located a distance of $\left(\dfrac{4R}{3\pi}\right)$ from the edge diameter. The strategy is to use the parallel axis theorem to treat the mass moment of inertia of a complete cylinder as the sum of the mass moments of inertia for the two half cylinders. From Problem 8.118, the mass moment of inertia about the geometric axis for a cylinder is $I_{cL} = mR^2$, where m is one half the mass of the cylinder.

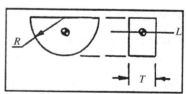

By the parallel axis theorem,

$$I_{cL} = 2\left(\left(\frac{4R}{3\pi}\right)^2 m + I_{hL}\right).$$

Solve

$$I_{hL} = \left(\frac{I_{cL}}{2} - \left(\frac{4R}{3\pi}\right)^2 m\right) = \left(\frac{mR^2}{2} - \left(\frac{16}{9\pi^2}\right) mR^2\right)$$

$$= mR^2\left(\frac{1}{2} - \frac{16}{9\pi^2}\right)$$

$$= mR^2\left(\frac{1}{2} - \frac{16}{9\pi^2}\right) = 0.31987\ mR^2 = 0.32\ mR^2$$

Problem 8.132 The homogeneous machine part is made of aluminum alloy with mass density $\rho = 2800$ kg/m^3. Determine its mass moment of inertia about the z axis.

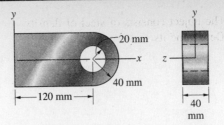

Solution: We divide the machine part into the 3 parts shown: (The dimension into the page is 0.04 m). The masses of the parts are

$$m_1 = (2800)(0.12)(0.08)(0.04) = 1.075 \text{ kg},$$

$$m_2 = (2800)\tfrac{1}{2}\pi(0.04)^2(0.04) = 0.281 \text{ kg},$$

$$m_3 = (2800)\pi(0.02)^2(0.04) = 0.141 \text{ kg}.$$

Using Appendix C and the parallel axis theorem the mass moment of inertia of part 1 about the z axis is

$$I_{(z \text{ axis})1} = \frac{1}{12}m_1[(0.08)^2 + (0.12)^2] + m_1(0.06)^2$$

$$= 0.00573 \text{ kg-m}^2.$$

The mass moment of inertia of part 2 about the axis through the center C that is parallel to the z axis is

$$\tfrac{1}{2}m_2R^2 = \tfrac{1}{2}m_2(0.04)^2.$$

The distance along the x axis from C to the center of mass of part 2 is

$$4(0.04)/(3\pi) = 0.0170 \text{ m}.$$

Therefore, the mass moment of inertia of part 2 about the z axis through its center of mass that is parallel to the axis is

$$\tfrac{1}{2}m_2(0.04)^2 - m_2(0.0170)^2 = 0.000144 \text{ kg-m}^2.$$

Using this result, the mass moment of inertia of part 2 about the z axis is

$$I_{(z \text{ axis})2} = 0.000144 + m_2(0.12 + 0.017)^2 = 0.00543 \text{ kg-m}^2.$$

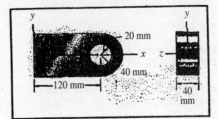

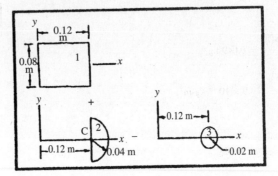

The mass moment of inertia of the material that would occupy the hole 3 about the z axis is

$$I_{(z \text{ axis})3} = \tfrac{1}{2}m_3(0.02)^2 + m_3(0.12)^2 = 0.00205 \text{ kg-m}^2.$$

Therefore $I_{(z \text{ axis})} = I_{(z \text{ axis})1} + I_{(z \text{ axis})2} - I_{(z \text{ axis})3}$

$$= 0.00911 \text{ kg-m}^2.$$

Problem 8.133 Determine the mass moment of inertia of the machine part in Problem 8.132 about the x axis.

Solution: We divide the machine part into the 3 parts shown in the solution to Problem 8.132. Using Appendix C and the parallel axis theorem, the mass moments of inertia of the parts about the x axis are:

$$I_{(x \text{ axis})1} = \frac{1}{12}m_1[(0.08)^2 + (0.04)^2] = 0.0007168 \text{ kg-m}^2$$

$$I_{(x \text{ axis})2} = m_2\left[\frac{1}{12}(0.04)^2 + \frac{1}{4}(0.04)^2\right]$$

$$= 0.0001501 \text{ kg-m}^2$$

$$I_{(x \text{ axis})3} = m_3\left[\frac{1}{12}(0.04)^2 + \frac{1}{4}(0.02)^2\right]$$

$$= 0.0000328 \text{ kg-m}^2.$$

Therefore, $I_{(x \text{ axis})} = I_{(x \text{ axis})1} + I_{(x \text{ axis})2} - I_{(x \text{ axis})3}$

$$= 0.000834 \text{ kg-m}^2.$$

Problem 8.134 The object consists of steel of density $\rho = 7800$ kg/m^3. Determine its mass moment of inertia about the axis L_O.

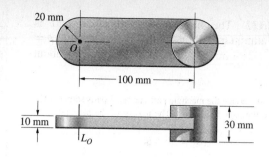

Solution: Divide the object into four parts: Part (1) The semi-cylinder of radius $R = 0.02$ m, height $h_1 = 0.01$ m.

Part (2): The rectangular solid $L = 0.1$ m by $h_2 = 0.01$ m by $w = 0.04$ m. Part (3): The semi-cylinder of radius $R = 0.02$ m, $h_1 = 0.01$ m Part (4) The cylinder of radius $R = 0.02$ m, height $h = 0.03$ m.

Part (1)

$$m_1 = \frac{\rho \pi R^2 h_1}{2} = 0.049 \text{ kg},$$

$$I_1 = \frac{m_1 R^2}{4} = 4.9 \times 10^{-6} \text{ kg-m}^2,$$

Part (2):

$$m_2 = \rho w L h_2 = 0.312 \text{ kg},$$

$$I_2 = \left(\frac{1}{12}\right) m_2 (L^2 + w^2) + m_2 \left(\frac{L}{2}\right)^2 = 0.00108 \text{ kg-m}^2.$$

Part (3)

$$m_3 = m_1 = 0.049 \text{ kg},$$

$$I_3 = -\left(\frac{4R}{3\pi}\right)^2 m_2 + I_1 + m_3 \left(L - \frac{4R}{3\pi}\right)^2 = 0.00041179 \text{ kg m}^2.$$

Part (4)

$$m_4 = \rho \pi R^2 h = 0.294 \text{ kg},$$

$$I_4 = \left(\frac{1}{2}\right) m_4 (R^2) + m_4 L^2 = 0.003 \text{ kg m}^2.$$

The composite:

$$I_{Lo} = I_1 + I_2 - I_3 + I_4 = 0.003674 \text{ kg m}^2$$

Problem 8.135 Determine the mass moment of inertia of the object in Problem 8.134 about the axis through the center of mass of the object parallel to L_O.

Solution: The center of mass is located relative to L_O

$$\mathbf{x} = \frac{m_1 \left(-\frac{4R}{3\pi}\right) + m_2(0.05) - m_3 \left(0.1 - \frac{4R}{3\pi}\right) + m_4(0.1)}{m_1 + m_2 - m_3 + m_4}$$

$$= 0.066 \text{ m},$$

$$I_c = -\mathbf{x}^2 m + I_{Lo} = -0.00265 + 0.00367 = 0.00102 \text{ kg m}^2$$

Problem 8.136 The thick plate consists of steel of density $\rho = 15$ slug/ft^3. Determine its mass moment of inertia about the z axis.

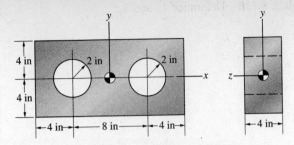

Solution: Divide the object into three parts: Part (1) the rectangle 8 in by 16 in, Parts (2) & (3) the cylindrical cut outs. Part (1):

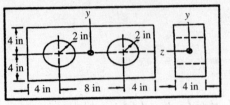

$$m_1 = \rho 8(16)(4) = 4.444 \text{ slugs.}$$

$$I_1 = \left(\frac{1}{12}\right) m_1 (16^2 + 8^2) = 118.52 \text{ slug in}^2.$$

Part (2):

$$m_2 = \rho \pi (2^2)(4) = 0.4363 \text{ slug,}$$

$$I_2 = \frac{m_2 (2^2)}{2} + m_2 (4^2) = 7.854 \text{ slug in}^2.$$

Part (3):

$$m_3 = m_2 = 0.4363 \text{ slugs,}$$

$$I_3 = I_2 = 7.854 \text{ slug-in}^2.$$

The composite:

$$I_{z\text{-axis}} = I_1 - 2I_2 = 102.81 \text{ slug-in}^2$$

$$I_{z\text{-axis}} = 0.714 \text{ slug-ft}^2$$

Problem 8.137 Determine the mass moment of inertia of the plate in Problem 8.136 about the x axis.

Solution: Use the same divisions of the object as in Problem 8.136.

Part (1):

$$I_{1x\text{-axis}} = \left(\frac{1}{12}\right) m_1 (8^2 + 4^2) = 29.63 \text{ slug-in}^2,$$

Part (2):

$$I_{2x\text{-axis}} = \left(\frac{1}{12}\right) m_2 (3(2^2) + 4^2) = 1.018 \text{ slug-in}^2.$$

The composite:

$$I_{x\text{-axis}} = I_{1x-\text{axis}} - 2I_{2x-\text{axis}} = 27.59 \text{ slug in}^2$$

$$= 0.1916 \text{ slug ft}^2$$

Problem 8.138 Determine I_y and k_y.

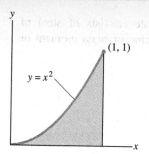

Solution:

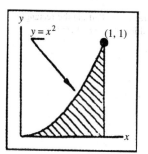

$$dA = dx\,dy \quad A = \int_0^1 dx \int_0^{x^2} dy = \int_0^1 x^2\,dx = \frac{1}{3}.$$

$$I_y = \int_A x^2\,dA = \int_0^1 x^2\,dx \int_0^{x^2} dy = \int_0^1 x^4\,dx = \left[\frac{x^5}{5}\right]_0^1 = \frac{1}{5}$$

$$k_y = \sqrt{\frac{I_y}{A}} = \sqrt{\frac{3}{5}}$$

Problem 8.139 Determine I_x and k_x.

Solution: (See figure in Problem 8.138.) $dA = dx\,dy$,

$$I_x = \int_A y^2\,dA = \int_0^1 dx \int_0^{x^2} y^2\,dy = \frac{1}{3}\int_0^1 x^6\,dx$$

$$= \left(\frac{1}{21}\right)[x^7]_0^1 = \frac{1}{21} \quad k_x = \sqrt{\frac{I_x}{A}} = \frac{1}{\sqrt{7}}$$

Problem 8.140 Determine J_O and k_O.

Solution: (See figure in Problem 8.138.)

$$J_O = I_x + I_y = \frac{1}{5} + \frac{1}{21} = \frac{26}{105},$$

$$k_O = \sqrt{k_x^2 + k_y^2} = \sqrt{\frac{3}{5} + \frac{1}{7}} = \sqrt{\frac{26}{35}}$$

Problem 8.141 Determine I_{xy}.

Solution: (See figure in Problem 8.38.) $dA = dx\,dy$

$$I_{xy} = \int_A xy\,dA = \int_0^1 x\,dx \int_0^{x^2} y\,dy$$

$$= \frac{1}{2}\int_0^1 x^5\,dx = \frac{1}{12}[x^6]_0^1 = \frac{1}{12}$$

Problem 8.142 Determine I_y and k_y.

Solution: By definition,

$$I_y = \int_A x^2 \, dA.$$

The element of area is $dA = dx \, dy$. The limits on the variable x are $0 \le x \le 4$. The area is

$$A = \int_0^4 dx \int_0^{X - X^2/4} dy = \left[\frac{x^2}{2} - \frac{x^3}{12} \right]_0^4 = 2.6667$$

$$I_y = \int_0^4 x^2 \, dx \int_0^{x - x^2/4} dy = \int_0^4 \left(x - \frac{x^2}{4} \right) x^2 \, dx$$

$$= \left[\frac{x^4}{4} - \frac{x^5}{20} \right]_0^4 = 12.8$$

from which

$$k_y = \sqrt{\frac{I_y}{A}} = 2.19$$

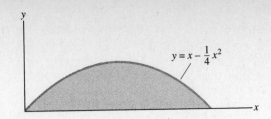

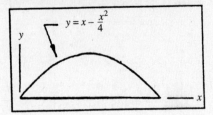

Problem 8.143 Determine I_x and k_x.

Solution: By definition,

$$I_x = \int_A y^2 \, dA,$$

from which

$$I_x = \int_0^4 dx \int_0^{x - x^2/4} y^2 \, dy = \left(\frac{1}{3} \right) \int_0^4 \left(x - \frac{x^2}{4} \right)^3 dx$$

$$I_x = \left(\frac{1}{3} \right) \left[\frac{x^4}{4} - \frac{3}{20} x^5 + \frac{3}{96} x^6 - \frac{x^7}{448} \right]_0^4 = 0.6095.$$

From Problem 8.142,

$$A = 2.667, \quad k_x = \sqrt{\frac{I_x}{A}} = 0.4781$$

Problem 8.144 Determine I_{xy}.

Solution:

$$I_{xy} = \int_A xy \, dA,$$

$$= \int_0^4 x \, dx \int_0^{x - x^2/4} y \, dy$$

$$= \left(\frac{1}{2} \right) \int_0^4 \left(x - \frac{x^2}{4} \right)^2 x \, dx$$

$$= \left(\frac{1}{2} \right) \left[\frac{x^4}{4} - \frac{x^5}{10} + \frac{x^6}{96} \right]_0^4 = 2.1333$$

Problem 8.145   Determine $I_{y'}$ and $k_{y'}$.

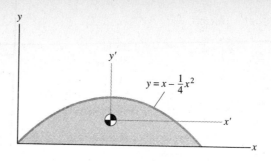

$$y = x - \frac{1}{4}x^2$$

Solution: The limits on the variable x are $0 \le x \le 4$. By definition,

$$A\mathbf{y} = \int_A y\, dA = \int_0^4 dx \int_0^{X-X^2/4} y\, dy$$

$$= \left(\frac{1}{2}\right) \int_0^4 \left(x - \frac{x^2}{4}\right)^2 dx$$

$$= \left(\frac{1}{2}\right) \left[\frac{x^3}{3} - \frac{x^4}{8} + \frac{x^5}{80}\right]_0^4 = 1.06667.$$

From Problem 8.142 the area is $A = 2.667$, from which $\mathbf{y} = 0.3999 = 0.4$. Similarly,

$$A\mathbf{x} = \int_0^4 x\, dx \int_0^{X-X^2/4} dy$$

$$= \int_0^4 x\left(x - \frac{x^2}{4}\right) dx = \left[\frac{x^3}{3} - \frac{x^4}{16}\right]_0^4 = 5.3333,$$

from which $\mathbf{x} = 1.9999 = 2$. The area moment of inertia is $I_{yy} = -\mathbf{x}^2 A + I_y$. Using the result of Problem 8.142, $I_y = 12.8$, from which the area mass moment of inertia about the centroid is

$$I_{y'} = -10.6666 + 12.8 = 2.133$$

and $k_{y'} = \sqrt{\dfrac{I_{y'}}{A}} = 0.8944$

Problem 8.146   Determine $I_{x'}$ and $k_{x'}$.

Solution: Using the results of Problems 8.143 and 8.145, $I_x = 0.6095$ and $\mathbf{y} = 0.4$. The area mass moment of inertia about the centroid is

$$I_{x'} = -\mathbf{y}^2 A + I_x = 0.1828$$

and $k_{x'} = \sqrt{\dfrac{I_{x'}}{A}} = 0.2618$

Problem 8.147   Determine $I_{x'y'}$.

Solution: From Problems 8.143 and 8.144, $I_{xy} = 2.133$ and $\mathbf{x} = 2$, $\mathbf{y} = 0.4$. The product of the moment of inertia about the centroid is

$$I_{x'y'} = -\mathbf{xy}A + I_{xy} = -2.133 + 2.133 = 0$$

Problem 8.148 Determine I_y and k_y.

Solution: Divide the section into two parts: Part (1) is the upper rectangle 40 mm by 200 mm, Part (2) is the lower rectangle, 160 mm by 40 mm.

Part (1) $A_1 = 0.040(0.200) = 0.008$ m^2,

$y_1 = 0.180$ m

$x_1 = 0$,

$I_{y1} = \left(\dfrac{1}{12}\right) 0.04(0.2)^3 = 2.6667 \times 10^{-5}$ m^4.

Part (2): $A_2 = (0.04)(0.16) = 0.0064$ m^2,

$y_2 = 0.08$ m,

$x_2 = 0$,

$I_{y2} = \left(\dfrac{1}{12}\right) (0.16)(0.04)^3 = 8.5 \times 10^{-7}$ m^4.

The composite:

$A = A_1 + A_2 = 0.0144$ m^2,

$I_y = I_{y1} + I_{y2}$,

$I_y = 2.752 \times 10^{-5}$ m$^4 = 2.752 \times 10^7$ mm^4,

and $k_y = \sqrt{\dfrac{I_y}{A}} = 0.0437$ m $= 43.7$ mm

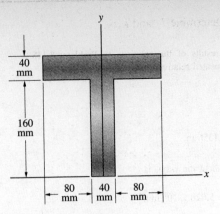

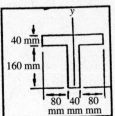

Problem 8.149 Determine I_x and k_x for the area in Problem 8.148.

Solution: Use the results in the solution to Problem 8.148. Part (1)

$A_1 = 0.040(0.200) = 0.008$ m^2,

$y_1 = 0.180$ m,

$I_{x1} = \left(\dfrac{1}{12}\right) 0.2(0.04^3) + (0.18)^2 A_1 = 2.603 \times 10^{-4}$ m^4.

Part (2):

$A_2 = (0.04)(0.16) = 0.0064$ m^2,

$y_2 = 0.08$ m,

$I_{x2} = \left(\dfrac{1}{12}\right) (0.04)(0.16)^3 + (0.08)^2 A_2 = 5.461 \times 10^{-5}$ m^4.

The composite: $A = A_1 + A_2 = 0.0144$ m^2, The area moment of inertia about the x axis is

$I_x = I_{x1} + I_{x2} = 3.15 \times 10^{-4}$ m$^4 = 3.15 \times 10^8$ mm^4,

and $k_x = \sqrt{\dfrac{I_x}{A}} = 0.1479$ m $= 147.9$ mm

Problem 8.150 Determine I_x and k_x.

Solution: Use the results of the solutions to Problems 8.148–8.149. The centroid is located relative to the base at

$$x_c = \frac{x_1 A_1 + x_2 A_2}{A} = 0,$$

$$y_c = \frac{y_1 A_1 + y_2 A_2}{A} = 0.1356 \text{ m}.$$

The moment of inertia about the x-axis is

$$I_{xc} = -y_C^2 A + I_X = 5.028 \times 10^7 \text{ mm}^4$$

and $k_{xc} = \sqrt{\frac{I_{xc}}{A}} = 59.1$ mm

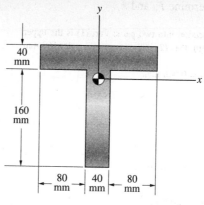

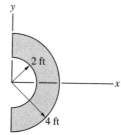

Problem 8.151 Determine J_O and k_O for the area in Problem 8.150.

Solution: Use the results of the solutions to Problems 8.148–8.149. The area moments of inertia about the centroid are

$$I_{xc} = 5.028 \times 10^{-5} \text{ m}^4$$

and $I_{yc} = I_y = 2.752 \times 10^{-5}$ m^4,

from which

$$J_O = I_{xc} + I_{yc} = 7.78 \times 10^{-5} \text{ m}^4 = 7.78 \times 10^7 \text{ mm}^4$$

and $k_O = \sqrt{\frac{J_O}{A}} = 0.0735$ m

$$= 73.5 \text{ mm}$$

Problem 8.152 Determine I_y and k_y.

Solution: For a semicircle about a diameter:

$$I_{yy} = I_{xx} = \left(\frac{1}{8}\right) \pi R^4,$$

$$I_y = \left(\frac{1}{8}\right) \pi (4)^4 - \left(\frac{1}{8}\right) \pi (2)^4 = \frac{\pi}{8}(4^4 - 2^4) = 94.25 \text{ ft}^4,$$

$$k_y = \sqrt{\frac{2I_y}{\pi(4^2 - 2^2)}} = 2.236 \text{ ft}$$

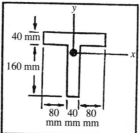

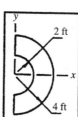

Problem 8.153   Determine J_O and k_O. for the area in Problem 8.152.

Solution: For a semicircle:

$$I_{yy} = I_{xx} = \left(\frac{1}{8}\right)\pi R^4.$$

$$I_x = \frac{\pi}{8}(4^4 - 2^4) = 94.248 \text{ ft}^4.$$

$$k_x = \sqrt{\frac{2I_x}{\pi(4^2 - 2^2)}} = 2.236 \text{ ft}.$$

Also use the solution to Problem 8.152.

$$J_O = I_x + I_y = 2(94.248) = 188.5 \text{ ft}^4$$

$$k_O = \sqrt{\frac{2J_O}{\pi(4^2 - 2^2)}} = 3.16 \text{ ft}$$

Problem 8.154   Determine I_x and k_x.

Solution: Break the area into three parts: Part (1) The rectangle with base $2a$ and altitude h; Part (2) The triangle on the right with base $(b-a)$ and altitude h, and Part (3) The triangle on the left with base $(b-a)$ and altitude h. Part (1) The area is

$$A_1 = 2ah = 24 \text{ ft}^2.$$

The centroid is

$$\mathbf{x}_1 = 0$$

and $\mathbf{y}_1 = \dfrac{h}{2} = 3$ ft.

The area moment of inertia about the centroid is

$$I_{xc1} = \left(\frac{1}{12}\right)(2a)h^3 = \left(\frac{1}{6}\right)ah^3 = 72 \text{ ft}^4.$$

Part (2): $A_2 = \left(\dfrac{1}{2}\right)h(b-a) = 3 \text{ ft}^2,$

$$\mathbf{x}_2 = a + \frac{b-a}{3} = 2.3333 \text{ ft},$$

$$\mathbf{y}_2 = \left(\frac{2}{3}\right)h = 4 \text{ ft},$$

$$I_{xc2} = \left(\frac{1}{36}\right)(b-a)h^3 = 6 \text{ ft}^4.$$

Part (3): $A_3 = A_2,$

$\mathbf{x}_3 = -\mathbf{x}_2, \ \mathbf{y}_3 = \mathbf{y}_2, \ I_{xc3} = I_{xc2}.$

The composite area is

$$A = A_1 + A_2 + A_2 = 30 \text{ ft}^2.$$

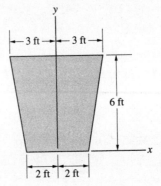

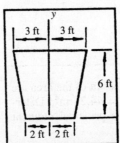
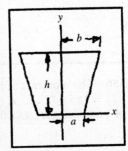

The composite moment of inertia

$$I_x = (\mathbf{y}_1)^2 A_1 + I_{xc1} + (\mathbf{y}_2)^2 A_2 + I_{xc2} + (\mathbf{y}_3)^2 A_3 + I_{xc3},$$

$$I_x = 396 \text{ ft}^4$$

$$k_x = \sqrt{\frac{I_x}{A}} = \sqrt{\frac{396}{30}} = 3.633 \text{ ft}$$

Problem 8.155   Determine I_y and k_y for the area in Problem 8.154.

Solution: Divide the area as in the solution to Problem 8.154.
Part (1) The area is $A_1 = 2ah = 24$ ft^2. The centroid is $\mathbf{x}_1 = 0$ and $\mathbf{y}_1 = \dfrac{h}{2} = 3$ ft. The area moment of inertia about the centroid is

$$I_{yc1} = \left(\frac{1}{12}\right) h(2a)^3 = \left(\frac{2}{3}\right) ha^3 = 32 \text{ ft}^4$$

Part (2): $A_2 = \left(\dfrac{1}{2}\right) h(b - a) = 3$ ft^2,

$$\mathbf{x}_2 = a + \frac{b - a}{3} = 2.3333 \text{ ft},$$

$$\mathbf{y}_2 = \left(\frac{2}{3}\right) h = 4 \text{ ft},$$

$$I_{yc2} = \left(\frac{1}{36}\right) h(b - a)^3 = 0.1667 \text{ ft}^4.$$

Part (3): $A_3 = A_2$,

$$\mathbf{x}_3 = -\mathbf{x}_2, \ \ \mathbf{y}_3 = \mathbf{y}_2, \ \ I_{yc3} = I_{yc2}.$$

The composite area is

$$A = A_1 + A_2 + A_2 = 30 \text{ ft}^2.$$

The composite moment of inertia,

$$I_y = \mathbf{x}_1^2 A_1 + I_{yc1} + \mathbf{x}_2^2 A_2 + I_{yc2} + \mathbf{x}_3^2 A_3 + I_{yc3},$$

$$I_y = 65 \text{ ft}^4$$

and $k_y = \sqrt{\dfrac{I_y}{A}} = 1.472$ ft

Problem 8.156   The moments of inertia of the area are $I_x = 36$ m^4, $I_y = 145$ m^4, and $I_{xy} = 44.25$ m^4. Determine a set of principal axes and the principal moment of inertia.

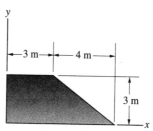

Solution: The principal angle is

$$\theta = \left(\frac{1}{2}\right) \tan^{-1} \left(\frac{2I_{xy}}{I_y - I_x}\right) = 19.54°.$$

The principal moments of inertia are

$$I_{xP} = I_x \cos^2 \theta - 2I_{xy} \sin \theta \cos \theta + I_y \sin^2 \theta = 20.298 = 20.3 \text{ m}^4$$

$$I_{yP} = I_x \sin^2 \theta + 2I_{xy} \sin \theta \cos \theta + I_y \cos^2 \theta = 160.70 \text{ m}^4$$

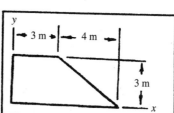

Problem 8.157 The mass moment of inertia of the 31-oz bat about a perpendicular axis through point B is 0.093 slug-ft^2. What is the bat's mass moment of inertia about a perpendicular axis through point A? (Point A is the bat's "instantaneous center", or center of rotation, at the instant shown.)

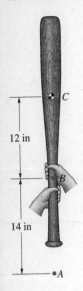

12 in

B

14 in

$\bullet A$

Solution: The mass of the bat is $m = \dfrac{31}{16(32.17)} = 0.06023$ slugs.

Use the parallel axis theorem to obtain the mass moment of inertia about the center of mass C, and then use the parallel axis theorem to translate to the point A.

$$I_C = -\left(\frac{12}{12}\right)^2 m + 0.093 = 0.0328 \text{ slug-ft}^2$$

$$I_A = \left(\frac{12+14}{12}\right)^2 m + 0.0328 = 0.3155 \text{ slug-ft}^2$$

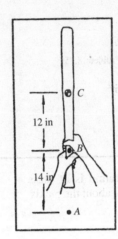

Problem 8.158 The mass of the thin homogenous plate is 4 kg. Determine its mass moment of inertia about the y axis.

Solution: Divide the object into two parts: Part (1) is the semicircle of radius 100 mm, and Part (2) is the rectangle 200 mm by 280 mm. The area of Part (1)

$$A_1 = \frac{\pi R^2}{2} = 15708 \text{ mm}^2.$$

The area of Part (2) is

$$A_2 = 280(200) = 56000 \text{ mm}^2.$$

The composite area is $A = A_2 - A_1 = 40292 \text{ mm}^2$. The area mass density is

$$\rho = \frac{4}{A} = 9.9275 \times 10^{-5} \text{ kg/mm}^2.$$

For Part (1) $x_1 = y_1 = 0$,

$$I_{y1} = \rho\left(\frac{1}{8}\right)\pi R^4 = 3898.5 \text{ kg-mm}^2.$$

For Part (2) $x_2 = 100$ mm.

$$I_{y2} = x_2^2 \rho A_2 + \rho\left(\frac{1}{12}\right)(280)(200^3) = 74125.5 \text{ kg-mm}^2.$$

The composite:

$$I_y = I_{y2} - I_{y1} = 70226 \text{ kg-mm}^2 = 0.070226 \text{ kg-m}^2$$

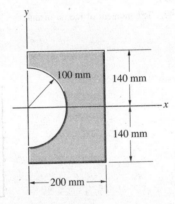

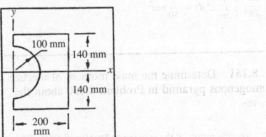

Problem 8.159   Determine the mass moment of inertia of the plate in Problem 8.158 about the z axis.

Solution: Use the same division of the parts and the results of the solution to Problem 8.158. For Part (1),

$$I_{x1} = \rho \left(\frac{1}{8}\right) \pi R^4 = 3898.5 \text{ kg-mm}^2.$$

For Part (2)

$$I_{x2} = \rho \left(\frac{1}{12}\right)(200)(280^3) = 36321.5 \text{ kg-mm}^2.$$

The composite: $I_x = I_{x2} - I_{x1} = 32423 \text{ kg-mm}^2$, from which, using the result of the solution to Problem 8.158

$$I_z = I_x + I_y = 32422 + 70226 = 102649 \text{ kg-mm}^2$$

$$= 0.10265 \text{ kg-m}^2$$

Problem 8.160   The homogenous pyramid is of mass m. Determine its mass moment of inertia about the z axis.

Solution: The mass density is

$$\rho = \frac{m}{V} = \frac{3m}{w^2 h}.$$

The differential mass is $dm = \rho \omega^2 \, dz$. The moment of inertia of this element about the z-axis is

$$dI_Z = \left(\frac{1}{6}\right) \omega^2 \, dm.$$

Noting that $\omega = \dfrac{wz}{h}$, then

$$dI_z = \rho \left(\frac{w^4}{6h^4}\right) z^4 \, dz = \frac{mw^2}{2h^5} z^4 \, dz.$$

Integrating:

$$I_{z\text{-axis}} = \left(\frac{mw^2}{2h^5}\right) \int_0^h z^4 \, dz = \frac{1}{10} mw^2$$

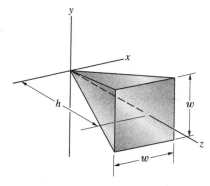

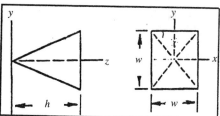

Problem 8.161   Determine the mass moment of inertia of the homogenous pyramid in Problem 8.160 about the x and y axes.

Solution: Use the results of the solution of Problem 8.160 for the mass density. The elemental disk is $dm = \rho \omega^2 \, dz$. The moment of inertia about an axis through its center of mass parallel to the x-axis is

$$dI_X = \left(\frac{1}{12}\right) \omega^2 \, dm.$$

Use the parallel axis theorem:

$$I_{x\text{-axis}} = \left(\frac{1}{12}\right) \int_m \omega^2 \, dm + \int_m z^2 \, dm.$$

Noting that $\omega = \dfrac{w}{h} z$, the integral is

$$I_{x\text{-axis}} = \frac{\rho w^4}{12h^4} \int_0^h z^4 \, dz + \frac{\rho w^2}{h^2} \int_0^h z^4 \, dz.$$

Integrating and collecting terms

$$I_{x\text{-axis}} = m \left(\frac{1}{20} w^2 + \frac{3}{5} h^2\right).$$

By symmetry, $I_{y\text{-axis}} = I_{x\text{-axis}}$

Problem 8.162 The homogenous object weighs 400 lb. Determine its mass moment of inertia about the x axis.

Solution: The volumes are

$$V_{cyl} = (46)\pi(9)^2 = 11{,}706 \text{ in}^3,$$

$$V_{cone} = \tfrac{1}{3}\pi(6)^2(36) = 1357 \text{ in}^3,$$

so $V = V_{cyl} - V_{cone} = 10{,}348 \text{ in}^3$.

The masses of the *solid* cylinder and the material that would occupy the conical hole are

$$m_{cyl} = \left(\frac{V_{cyl}}{V}\right)\left(\frac{400}{32.2}\right) = 14.052 \text{ slug},$$

$$m_{cone} = \left(\frac{V_{cone}}{V}\right)\left(\frac{400}{32.2}\right) = 1.629 \text{ slug}.$$

Using results from Appendix C,

$$I_{(x \text{ axis})} = \frac{1}{2}\, m_{cyl}(9)^2 - \frac{3}{10}\, m_{cone}(6)^2$$

$$= 551 \text{ slug-in}^2$$

$$= 3.83 \text{ slug-ft}^2$$

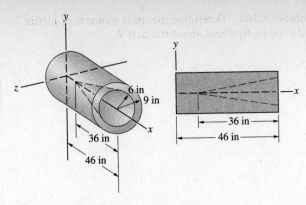

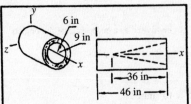

Problem 8.163 Determine the mass moments of inertia of the object in Problem 8.162 about the y and z axes.

Solution: See the solution of Problem 8.162. The position of the center of mass of the material that would occupy the conical hole is

$$x = (46 - 36) + \frac{3}{4}(36) = 37 \text{ in}.$$

From Appendix C,

$$I_{(y' \text{ axis})cone} = m_{cone}\left[\frac{3}{80}(36)^2 + \frac{3}{20}(6)^2\right]$$

$$= 87.97 \text{ slug-in}^2.$$

The moment of inertia about the y axis for the composite object is

$$I_{(y \text{ axis})} = m_{cyl}\left[\tfrac{1}{3}(46)^2 + \tfrac{1}{4}(9)^2\right]$$

$$- \left(I_{(y' \text{ axis})cone} + x^2 m_{cone}\right)$$

$$= 7877 \text{ slug-in}^2$$

$$= 54.7 \text{ slug-ft}^2.$$

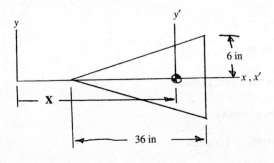

Problem 8.164 Determine the mass moment of inertia of the 14-kg flywheel about the axis L.

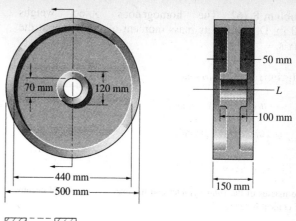

70 mm 120 mm

50 mm

L

100 mm

440 mm

500 mm

150 mm

Solution: The flywheel can be treated as a composite of the objects shown:

The volumes are

$V_1 = (150)\pi(250)^2 = 294.5 \times 10^5$ mm^3,

$V_2 = (150)\pi(220)^2 = 228.08 \times 10^5$ mm^3,

$V_3 = (50)\pi(220)^2 = 76.03 \times 10^5$ mm^3,

$V_4 = (50)\pi(60)^2 = 5.65 \times 10^5$ mm^3,

$V_5 = (100)\pi(60)^2 = 11.31 \times 10^5$ mm^3,

$V_6 = (100)\pi(35)^2 = 3.85 \times 10^5$ mm^3.

The volume

$V = V_1 - V_2 + V_3 - V_4 + V_5 - V_6$

$\quad = 144.3 \times 10^5$ mm^3,

so the density is

$\delta = \dfrac{14}{V} = 9.704 \times 10^{-7}$ kg/mm^3.

The moment of inertia is

$I_L = \frac{1}{2}\delta V_1(250)^2 - \frac{1}{2}\delta V_2(220)^2$

$\qquad + \frac{1}{2}\delta V_3(220)^2 - \frac{1}{2}\delta V_4(60)^2$

$\qquad + \frac{1}{2}\delta V_5(60)^2 - \frac{1}{2}\delta V_6(35)^2$

$\quad = 536,800$ kg-mm^2

$\quad = 0.5368$ kg-m^2.

Problem 9.1 The coefficients of static and kinetic friction between the 0.4-kg book and the table are $\mu_s = 0.30$ and $\mu_k = 0.28$. A person exerts a horizontal force on the book as shown.

(a) If the magnitude of the force is 1 N and the book remains stationary, what is the magnitude of the friction force exerted on the book by the table?

(b) What is the largest force the person can exert without causing the book to slip?

(c) If the person pushes the book across the table at a constant speed, what is the magnitude of the friction force?

Solution:

$$\sum F_x: \quad F - f = 0$$

$$\sum F_y: \quad N - W = 0$$

(a) $F = 1 \text{ N}$

Solving $f = 1 \text{ N}$

(b) $f_{max} = \mu_s N, \quad \mu_s = 0.3$

$N = 3.92 \text{ N}, \quad f_{max} = 1.18 \text{ N}$

$F_{max} = 1.18 \text{ N}$

(c) For constant speed,

$f = \mu_k N = (0.28)(3.92)$

$f = 1.10 \text{ N}$

Thus, since $F - f = 0$

$F = 1.10 \text{ N}$

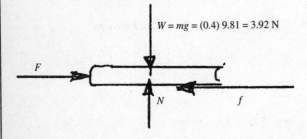

$W = mg = (0.4)\,9.81 = 3.92 \text{ N}$

Problem 9.2 The 10.5-kg Sojourner rover, placed on the surface of Mars by the Pathfinder Lander on July 4, 1997, was designed to negotiate a 45° slope without tipping over.

(a) What minimum static coefficient of friction between the wheels of the rover and the surface is necessary for it to rest on a 45° slope? The acceleration due to gravity at the surface of Mars is 3.69 m/s².

(b) Engineers testing the Sojourner on Earth want to confirm that it will negotiate a 45° slope without tipping over. What minimum static coefficient of friction between the wheels of the rover and the surface is necessary for it to rest on a 45° slope on Earth?

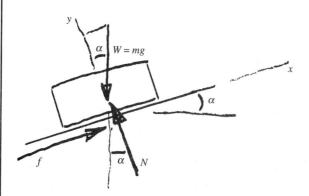

Solution: (a) Assume that slip is impending when the rover is on a 45° slope. The friction force $f = \mu_s N$, and the free-body diagram is: The equilibrium equations are:

$$\sum F_x = -\mu_s N + mg \sin 45° = 0,$$

$$\sum F_y = N - mg \cos 45° = 0.$$

Summing the two equations, we obtain $N - \mu_s N = 0$ so $\mu_s = 1$ is the minimum static coefficient of friction. (b) the solution in (a) is independent of the value of g so $\mu_s = 1$ is the minimum on earth also.

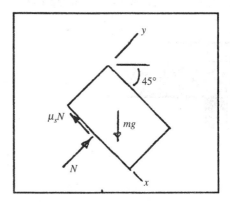

Problem 9.3 The coefficient of static friction between the tires of the 8000-kg truck and the road is $\mu_s = 0.6$.

(a) If the truck is stationary on the incline and $\alpha = 15°$, what is the magnitude of the total friction force exerted on the tires by the road?

(b) What is the largest value of α for which the truck will not slip?

Solution:

(b) Set $f = \mu_s N$ and solve for α in the basic eqns.

$$\sum F_x: \quad \mu_s N - mg \sin \alpha = 0$$

$$\sum F_y: \quad N - mg \cos \alpha = 0$$

$m = 8000$ kg, $g = 9.81$ m/s²

Solving, $\alpha = 30.96°$

(a) $\sum F_x: \quad f - mg \sin \alpha = 0$

$\sum F_y: \quad N - mg \cos \alpha = 0$

$g = 9.81$ m/s², $\alpha = 15°$, $m = 8000$ kg

Solving, $f = 20.3$ kN also $N = 75.8$ kN

Problem 9.4 The coefficient of static friction between the 5-kg box and the inclined surface is $\mu_s = 0.3$. The force F is horizontal and the box is stationary.

(a) If $F = 40$ N, what friction force is exerted on the box by the inclined surface?
(b) What is the largest value of F for which the box will not slip?

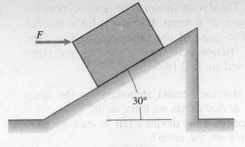

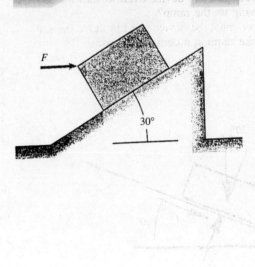

Solution:

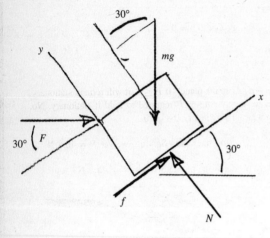

(a) $F = 40$ N

$$\sum F_x: \quad f + F\cos 30° - mg\sin 30° = 0$$

$$\sum F_y: \quad N - F\sin 30° - mg\cos 30° = 0$$

$f = -10.1$ N (down the plane)

(b) In the equilibrium eqns, set $f = -\mu_s N$ and treat F as unknown.
F is negative to resist F.
Solving, $F = 52.0$ N

Problem 9.5 In Problem 9.4, what is the smallest value of the force F for which the box will not slip?

Solution: For this problem, facts up the plane

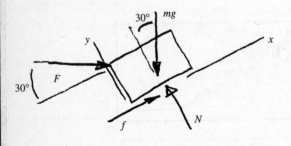

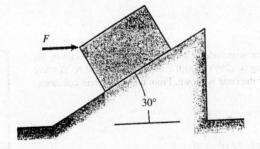

$$\sum F_x: \quad f + F\cos 30° - mg\sin 30° = 0$$

$$\sum F_y: \quad = N - mg\cos 30° - F\sin 30° = 0$$

Solving, $F = 11.6$ N

774

Problem 9.6 The device shown is designed to position pieces of luggage on a ramp. It exerts a force parallel to the ramp. The mass of the suitcase S is 9 kg. The coefficients of friction between the suitcase and ramp are $\mu_s = 0.20$ and $\mu_k = 0.18$.

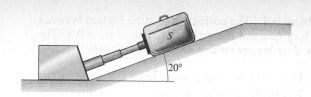

(a) Will the suitcase remain stationary on the ramp when the device exerts no force on it?
(b) What force must the device exert to start the suitcase moving up the ramp?
(c) What force must the device exert to move the suitcase up the ramp at a constant speed?

Solution:

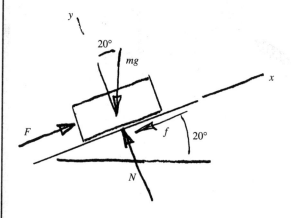

$$\sum F_x: \quad F - f - mg\sin(20°) = 0$$

$$\sum F_y: \quad N - mg\cos(20°) = 0$$

(a) Set $f = -\mu_s N$ (up the plane). If $F \le 0$, it will remain stationary. Solving, we get $F = 13.6$ N (required to hold it stationary. No, it will not remain stationary if $F = 0$.

(b) Set $f = \mu_s N$ (down the plane) Solving, we get $F = 46.8$ N

(c) Set $f = \mu_k N$ (down the plane) Solving, $F = 45.1$ N

$\mu_s = 0.20$

$\mu_k = 0.18$

$m = 9$ kg

Problem 9.7 The mass of the stationary crate is 40 kg. The length of the spring is 180 mm, its unstretched length is 200 mm, and the spring constant is $k = 2500$ N/m. The coefficient of static friction between the crate and the inclined surface is $\mu_s = 0.6$. Determine the magnitude of the friction force exerted on the crate.

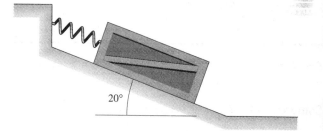

Solution: The magnitude of the force exerted on the crate by the compressed spring is. $(2500 \text{ N/m})(0.2 \text{ m} - 0.18 \text{ m}) = 50$ N. The free body diagram of the crate is shown. From the equilibrium equations

$$\sum F_x = 50 - f + (40)(9.81)\sin 20° = 0,$$

$$\sum F_y = N - (40)(9.81)\cos 20° = 0,$$

we obtain $N = 369$ N, $f = 184$ N.

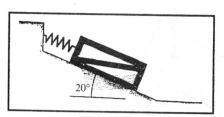

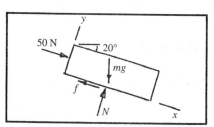

Problem 9.8 The coefficient of kinetic friction between the 40-kg crate and the floor is $\mu_k = 0.3$. If the angle $\alpha = 20°$, what tension must the person exert on the rope to move the crate at constant speed?

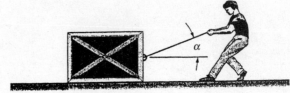

Solution:

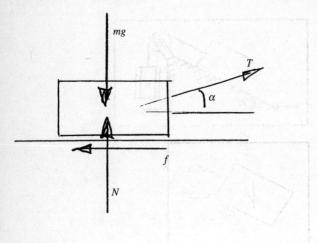

$m = 40$ kg

$\alpha = 20°$

$f = \mu_k N$

$\sum F_x: \quad T\cos 20° - f = 0$

$\sum F_y: \quad N + T\sin 20° - mg = 0$

Solving, $T = 112.94$ N

also $f = 106.13$ N

$\quad N = 353.77$ N

Problem 9.9 In Problem 9.8, for what angle α is the tension necessary to move the crate at constant speed a minimum? What is the necessary tension?

Solution: From the solution to Problem 9.8, we have

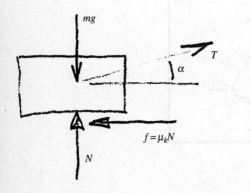

$f = \mu_k N$

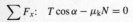

$\sum F_x: \quad T\cos\alpha - \mu_k N = 0$

$\sum F_y: \quad +T\sin\alpha + N - mg = 0$

Solving the second eqn. for N and substituting into the first, we get

$T\cos\alpha - \mu_k mg + T\mu_k \sin\alpha = 0$.

Differentiating with respect to α, we get

$$\frac{dT}{d\alpha} = \frac{T(\sin\alpha - \mu_k\cos\alpha)}{(\cos\alpha + \mu_k\sin\alpha)}$$

Setting $\dfrac{dT}{d\alpha} = 0$, we get $\tan\alpha = \mu_k$

Solving, $\alpha = 16.7°$. Substituting back into the equilibrium equations, we can now solve for N and T.

$T = 112.76$ N,

$N = 360$ N

$f = 108$ N

Problem 9.10   Box A weighs 100 lb, and box B weighs 30 lb. The coefficients of friction between box A and the ramp are $\mu_s = 0.30$ and $\mu_k = 0.28$. What is the magnitude of the friction force exerted on box A by the ramp?

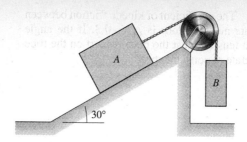

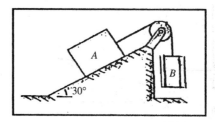

Solution: The sum of the forces parallel to the inclined surface is

$$\sum F = -A \sin \alpha + B + f = 0,$$

from which $f = A \sin \alpha - B = 100 \sin 30° - 30 = 20$ lb

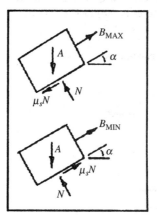

Problem 9.11   In Problem 9.10, box A weighs 100 lb, and the coefficients of friction between box A and the ramp are $\mu_s = 0.30$ and $\mu_k = 0.28$. For what range of the weights of the box B will the system remain stationary?

Solution: The upper and lower limits on the range are determined by the weight required to move the box up the ramp, and the weight that will allow the box to slip down the ramp. Assume impending slip. The friction force opposes the impending motion. For impending motion up the ramp the sum of forces parallel to the ramp are

$$\sum F = A \sin \alpha - B_{MAX} + \mu_s A \cos \alpha = 0,$$

from which

$$B_{MAX} = A(\sin \alpha + \mu_s \cos \alpha)$$

$$= 100(\sin 30° + 0.3 \cos 30°) = 75.98 \text{ lb}$$

For impending motion down the ramp:

$$\sum F = A \sin \alpha - B_{MIN} - \mu_s A \cos \alpha = 0,$$

from which

$$B = A(\sin \alpha - \mu_s \cos \alpha)$$

$$= 100(\sin 30° - 0.3 \cos 30°) = 24.02 \text{ lb}$$

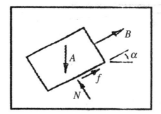

Problem 9.12 The mass of the box on the left is 30 kg, and the mass of the box on the right is 40 kg. The coefficient of static friction between each box and the inclined surface is $\mu_s = 0.2$. Determine the minimum angle α for with the boxes will remain stationary.

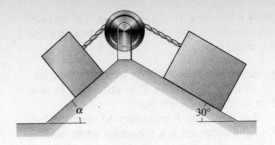

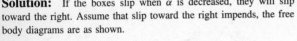

Solution: If the boxes slip when α is decreased, they will slip toward the right. Assume that slip toward the right impends, the free body diagrams are as shown.

The equilibrium equations are

$$\sum F_x = T - 0.2\,N_A - (30)(9.81)\sin\alpha = 0, \quad \textbf{(1)}$$

$$\sum F_y = N_A - (30)(9.81)\cos\alpha = 0, \quad \textbf{(2)}$$

$$\sum F_x = -T - 0.2\,N_B + (40)(9.81)\sin 30° = 0, \quad \textbf{(3)}$$

$$\sum F_y = N_B - (40)(9.81)\cos 30° = 0, \quad \textbf{(4)}$$

Summing Equations (1) and (3), we obtain $-0.2\,N_A - 0.2\,N_B - (30)(9.81)\sin\alpha + (40)(9.81)\sin 30° = 0$. Solving Equation (2) for N_A and Equation (4) for N_B and substituting the results into Equation (5) gives $15\sin\alpha + 3\cos\alpha = 10 - 4\cos 30°$. (6) Using the identity $\cos\alpha = \sqrt{1 - \sin^2\alpha}$ and solving Equation (6) for $\sin\alpha$, we obtain $\sin\alpha = 0.242$, so $\alpha = 14.0°$

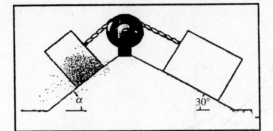

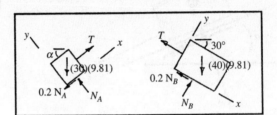

Problem 9.13 In Problem 9.12, determine the maximum angle α for with the boxes will remain stationary.

Solution: If the boxes slip when α is increased, they will slip toward the left. When slip toward the left impends, The free body diagrams are as shown.

The equilibrium equations are

$$\sum F_x = T + 0.2\,N_A - (30)(9.81)\sin\alpha = 0, \quad \textbf{(1)}$$

$$\sum F_y = N_A - (30)(9.81)\cos\alpha = 0, \quad \textbf{(2)}$$

$$\sum F_x = -T + 0.2\,N_B + (40)(9.81)\sin 30° = 0, \quad \textbf{(3)}$$

$$\sum F_y = N_B - (40)(9.81)\cos 30° = 0, \quad \textbf{(4)}$$

Summing Equations (1) and (3), we obtain

$$0.2 N_A + 0.2\,N_B - (30)(9.81)\sin\alpha + (40)(9.81)\sin 30° = 0. \quad \textbf{(5)}$$

Solving Equation (2) for N_A and Equation (4) for N_B and substituting the results into Equation (5) gives $15\sin\alpha - 3\cos\alpha = 10 + 4\cos 30°$. (6) Using the identity $\cos\alpha = \sqrt{1 - \sin^2\alpha}$ and solving Equation (6) for $\sin\alpha$, we obtain $\sin\alpha = 0.956$, so $\alpha = 73.0°$

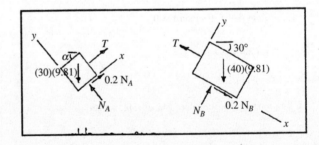

Problem 9.14 The box is stationary on the inclined surface. The coefficient of static friction between the box and the surface is μ_s.

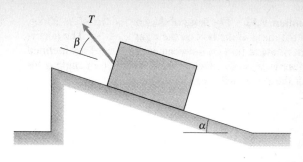

(a) If the mass of the box is 10 kg, $\alpha = 20°$, $\beta = 30°$, and $\mu_s = 0.24$, what force T is necessary to start the box sliding up the surface?

(b) Show that the force T necessary to start the box sliding up the surface is a minimum when $\tan \beta = \mu_s$.

Solution:

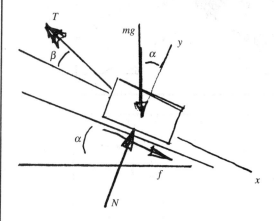

$\alpha = 20°$

$\mu_s = 0.24$

$m = 10$ kg

$g = 9.81$ m/s^2

$\sum F_x: \quad -T\cos\beta + f + mg\sin\alpha = 0$

$\sum F_y: \quad N + T\sin\beta - mg\cos\alpha = 0$

(a) $\beta = 30°, \quad f = \mu_s N$

   Substituting the known values and solving, we get

   $T = 56.5$ N,

   $N = 64.0$ N,

   $f = 15.3$ N

   Solving the 2nd equilibrium eqn for N and substituting for f ($f = \mu_s N$) in the first eqn, we get

   $-T\cos\beta + \mu_s mg\cos\alpha - \mu_s T\sin\beta + mg\sin\alpha = 0$

   Differentiating with respect to β, we get

   $\dfrac{dT}{d\beta} = \dfrac{T(\sin\beta - \mu_s\cos\beta)}{(\cos\beta + \mu_s\sin\beta)}$

   Setting $\dfrac{dT}{d\beta} = 0$, we get

   $\tan\beta = \mu_s$

Problem 9.15 To explain observations of ship launchings at the port of Rochefort in 1779, Coulomb analyzed the system shown in Problem 9.14 to determine the minimum force T necessary to hold the box stationary on the inclined surface. Show that the result is

$$T = \frac{(\sin\alpha - \mu_s\cos\alpha)mg}{\cos\beta - \mu_s\sin\beta}.$$

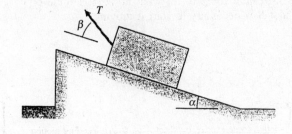

Solution:

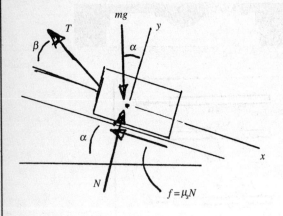

$$\sum F_x: \quad -T\cos\beta + mg\sin\alpha - \mu_s N = 0$$

$$\sum F_y: \quad N + T\sin\beta - mg\cos\alpha = 0$$

α is fixed, β is variable. Solve the second eqn for N and substitute into the first. We get

$$0 = T(\mu_s\sin\beta - \cos\beta) = mg(\sin\alpha - \mu_s\cos\alpha)$$

or $T = \dfrac{mg(\sin\alpha - \mu_s\cos\alpha)}{(\cos\beta - \mu_s\sin\beta)}$

To get the conditions for the minimum, set $\dfrac{dT}{d\beta} = 0$

$$\frac{dT}{d\beta} = \frac{T(\sin\beta + \mu_s\cos\beta)}{(\cos\beta - \mu_s\sin\beta)} = 0$$

For the min.

$$\tan\beta = -\mu_s.$$

Note β is negative!

Problem 9.16 Two sheets of plywood A and B lie on the bed of a truck. They have the same weight W, and the coefficient of static friction between the two sheets of wood and between sheet B and the truck bed is μ_s.

(a) If you apply a horizontal force to sheet A and apply no force to sheet B, can you slide sheet A off the truck without causing sheet B to move? What force is necessary to cause sheet A to start moving?

(b) If you prevent sheet A from moving by applying a horizontal force on it, what horizontal force on sheet B is necessary to start it moving?

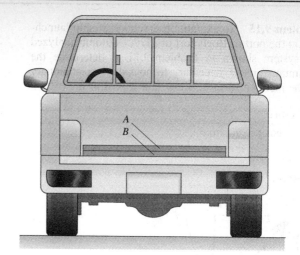

Solution:

(a) The friction force exerted by sheet A on B at impending motion is $f_{AB} = \mu_s W$. The friction force exerted by sheet B on the bed of the truck is $f_{BT} = \mu_s(2W)$, since the normal force is due to the weight of both sheets. Since $f_{BT} > f_{AB}$, the top sheet will begin moving before the bottom sheet. *Yes*

The force required to start sheet A to move is

$$F = f_{AB} = \mu_s W.$$

(b) The force on B is the friction between A and B and the friction between B and the truck bed. Thus the force required to start B in motion is

$$F_B = f_{AB} + f_{BT} = 3\mu_s W.$$

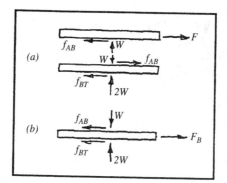

Problem 9.17 Suppose that the truck in Problem 9.16 is loaded with N sheets of plywood of the same weight W, labeled (from the top) sheets $1, 2, \ldots, N$. The coefficient of static friction between the sheets of wood and between the bottom sheet and the truck bed is μ_s. If you apply a horizontal force to the sheets above it to prevent them from moving, can you pull out the ith sheet, $1 \leq i \leq N$, without causing any of the sheets below it to move? What force must you apply to cause it to start moving?

Solution: The force holding the sheets below the ith sheet from moving is the friction force between the bed of the truck and the bottom sheet. The weight is NW, hence the force opposing motion of the sheets below the ith sheet is $F_N = \mu_s NW$. The force causing motion to start is the friction between the ith sheet and those below it, which is $F_B = \mu_s(iW)$. The resultant force is $F_R = \mu_s W(N-i)$. The bottom sheets will begin to move when the resultant is zero, which can only occur for the last sheet, $i = N$. Thus the ith sheet can be extracted without the sheets below it moving. *Yes* The force required to move the ith sheet is the force required to overcome the friction force due to sheet above it and the sheet below it. The weight of the sheets above is $(i-1)W$ and the weight on the sheet below it is iW. The maximum total friction force opposing motion is

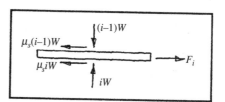

$$F_i = \mu_s(iW + (i-1)W) = \mu_s W(2i-1)$$

Problem 9.18 The masses of the two boxes are $m_1 = 45$ kg and $m_2 = 20$ kg. The coefficients of friction between the left box and the inclined surface are $\mu_s = 0.12$ and $\mu_k = 0.10$. Determine the tension the man must exert on the rope to pull the boxes upward at a constant rate.

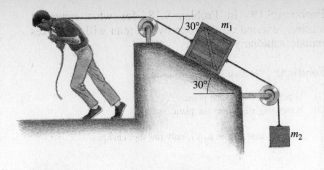

Solution:

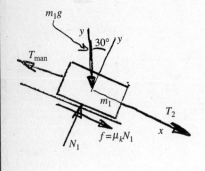

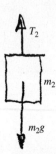

Equilibrium Eqns:

Mass 2:

$$\sum F: \quad T_2 - m_2 g = 0$$

Mass 1:

$$\sum F_x: \quad T_2 - T_{MAN} + \mu_k N_1 + m_1 g \sin 30° = 0$$

$$\sum F_y: \quad N_1 - m_1 g \cos 30° = 0$$

$m_1 = 45$ kg,

$m_2 = 20$ kg,

$g = 9.81$ m/s^2,

and $\mu_k = 0.1$.

Substituting these values into the eqns. and solving,

$T_{MAN} = 455$ N

Problem 9.19 In Problem 9.18, for what range of tensions exerted on the rope by the man will the boxes remain stationary?

Solution: We must look at two cases.

(1) Impending slip up the plane
(2) Impending slip down the plane.

In either case, $|f| = \mu_s N_1$, only the sign changes

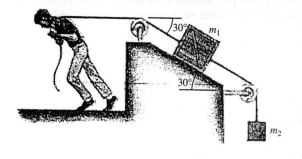

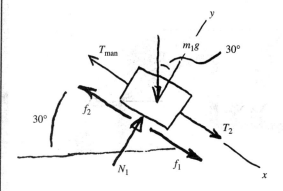

$T_2 = m_2 g$

f_1 is used in case 1

f_2 is used in case 2

Equilibrium Eqns:

$$\sum F_x: \quad T_2 - T_{man} \pm f + m_1 g \sin(30°) = 0$$

$$\sum F_y: \quad N_1 - m_1 g \cos(30°) = 0$$

$$f = \mu_s N_1 = 0.12 \, N_1.$$

The $(+)$ is used for case 1 and the $(-)$ is used for case 2

Solving case 1, we get

$T_{man} = 462.8$ N

Solving case 2, we get

$T_{man} = 371.0$ N

Thus, the boxes are stationary for

$371 \text{ N} \leq T_{man} \leq 463 \text{ N}$

Problem 9.20   The coefficient of static friction between the two boxes is $\mu_s = 0.2$, and between the lower box and the inclined surface it is $\mu_s = 0.32$. What is the largest angle α for which the lower box will not slip?

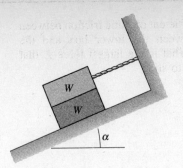

Solution: We need free body diagrams of both boxes

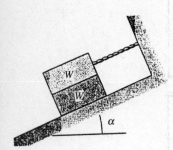

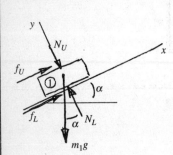   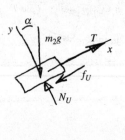

$$f_U = 0.2\, N_U$$

$$f_L = 0.32\, N_L$$

Lower Box $m_1 = m_2 = m$

$\sum F_x$: $f_L + f_U - mg\sin\alpha = 0$

$\sum F_y$: $N_L - N_U - mg\cos\alpha = 0$

Upper Box $m_1 = m_2 = m$

$\sum F_x$: $T - f_U - mg\sin\alpha = 0$

$\sum F_y$: $N_U - mg\cos\alpha = 0$

Substituting in known values and solving, we get

$\alpha = 40.0°$

Problem 9.21 The coefficient of static friction between the two boxes and between the lower box and the inclined surface is μ_s. What is the largest force F that will not cause the boxes to slip?

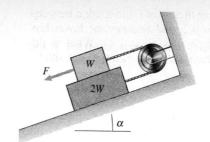

Solution: At impending motion, the sum of the forces parallel to the inclined surface for the upper box is

$$\sum F_P = F - \mu_s W \cos\alpha + W \sin\alpha - T = 0,$$

where T is the tension in the string, and the friction force opposes impending motion in the direction of F. For the lower box,

$$\sum F = 2W \sin\alpha + \mu_s(3W\cos\alpha) + \mu_s W \cos\alpha - T = 0,$$

where the friction force opposes impending motion in the direction of T. Combining:

$$F = \mu_s(5W\cos\alpha) + W\sin\alpha = W(5\mu_s\cos\alpha + \sin\alpha)$$

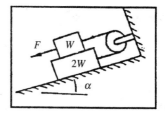

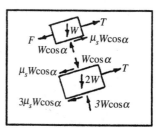

Problem 9.22 Consider the system shown in Problem 9.21. The coefficient of static friction between the two boxes and between the lower box and the inclined surface is μ_s. If $F = 0$, the lower box will slip down the inclined surface. What is the smallest force F for which the boxes will not slip?

Solution: The solution is obtained by the same procedure as in Problem 10.21, with the exception that the friction forces now oppose impending motion in the direction of T for the upper box, and impending motion down the surface, for the lower. The sums of forces parallel to the inclined surface for the two boxes are:

$$\sum F_P = F + \mu_s W \cos\alpha + W\sin\alpha - T = 0$$

and $\sum F = 2W \sin\alpha - \mu_s(3W\cos\alpha) - \mu_s W\cos\alpha - T = 0.$

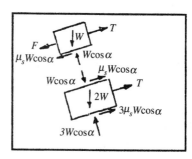

Combining:

$$F = -\mu_s W\cos\alpha + W\sin\alpha - 4\mu_s W\cos\alpha = W(\sin\alpha - 5\mu_s\cos\alpha)$$

Problem 9.23 A sander consists of a rotating disk with sandpaper bonded to the outer surface. The normal force exerted on the workpiece A by the sander is 30 lb. The workpiece A weighs 50 lb. The coefficients of friction between the sander and the workpiece A are $\mu_s = 0.65$ and $\mu_k = 0.60$. The coefficients of friction between the workpiece A and the table are $\mu_s = 0.35$ and $\mu_k = 0.30$. Will the workpiece remain stationary while it is being sanded?

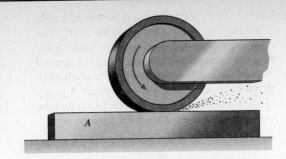

Solution: Two possible situations can cause impending motion:

(1) before the contact surface has begun slipping with respect to the workpiece (that is, as the sanding wheel is brought into contact with the work piece), so that the static coefficient of friction applies between the sanding wheel and the workpiece.

(2) After the sanding wheel has begun slipping relative to the workpiece, when the kinetic coefficient of friction applies between the sander and the workpiece. In the first situation, the force inducing motion of the workpiece is

$$F = \mu_s 30 = 19.5 \text{ lb.}$$

The force resisting motion is $F_A = \mu_s(30 + 50) = 28$ lb. *Thus the workpiece will not slip*. The second situation is less severe, since the force inducing motion is $F = 30\mu_k = 18$ lb, and the force opposing motion is the same. *The workpiece will remain stationary.*

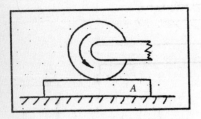

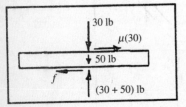

30 lb

$\mu(30)$

50 lb

f

$(30 + 50)$ lb

Problem 9.24 Suppose that you want the bar of length L to act as a simple brake that will allow the workpiece A to slide to the left but will not allow it to slide to the right no matter how large a horizontal force is applied to it. The weight of the bar is W, and the coefficient of static friction between it and the workpiece A is μ_s. You can neglect friction between the workpiece and the surface it rests on.

(a) What is the largest angle α for which the bar will prevent the workpiece from moving to the right?
(b) If α has the value determined in (a), what horizontal force is required to start the workpiece A toward the left at a constant rate?

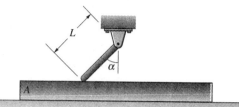

Solution:

(a) To resist motion to the right no matter how large the horizontal force requires a very large friction force. For impending motion to the right, the sum of the moments about the bar hinge is

$$\sum M = +\frac{W}{2}L\sin\alpha - F_N L\sin\alpha + fL\cos\alpha = 0,$$

where F_N is the normal force and f is the friction force resisting the impending motion.
Noting that $f = \mu_\text{s}F_N$, the sum of moments yields

$$F_N = \frac{W\sin\alpha}{2(\sin\alpha - \mu_\text{s}\cos\alpha)}.$$

If the denominator vanishes, the normal force and hence the friction force become as large as required. Thus $\sin\alpha - \mu_\text{s}\cos\alpha = 0$, from which $\mu_\text{s} = \tan\alpha$, or $\alpha = \tan^{-1}(\mu_\text{s})$

(b) For impending motion to the left, the sum of moments about the bar hinge is

$$\sum M = +W\left(\frac{L}{2}\right)\sin\alpha - F_N L\sin\alpha - fL\cos\alpha = 0,$$

where the friction force opposes the impending motion. Noting $F_N = \dfrac{f}{\mu_\text{s}}$, then

$$f = \frac{W\sin\alpha}{2\left(\dfrac{\sin\alpha}{\mu_\text{s}} + \cos\alpha\right)} = \frac{W\sin\alpha}{4\cos\alpha} = \frac{\mu_\text{s}W}{4}$$

is the force required to start motion to the left.

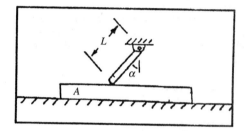

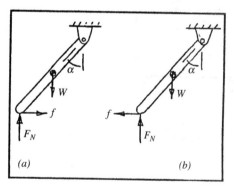

(a)   (b)

Problem 9.25 The coefficient of static friction between the 20-lb bar and the floor is $\mu_s = 0.3$. Neglect friction between the bar and the wall.

(a) If $\alpha = 20°$, what is the magnitude of the friction force exerted on the bar by the floor?

(b) What is the maximum value of α for which the bar will not slip?

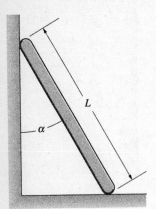

Solution: The sum of the moments about the upper end of the bar is

$$\sum M = -\frac{WL}{2}\sin\alpha + F_N L\sin\alpha - fL\cos\alpha = 0,$$

from which $f = \dfrac{\left(-\dfrac{W}{2} + F_N\right)\sin\alpha}{\cos\alpha}$.

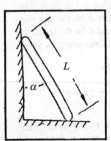

The sum of the forces in the vertical direction

$$\sum F_Y = -W + F_N = 0,$$

from which $F_N = W$.

Substitute:

$$f = \frac{W\sin\alpha}{2\cos\alpha} = 10\tan 20° = 3.64 \text{ lb}$$

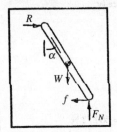

(b) At impending slip, $f = \mu_s F_N = \mu_s W$, from which, substituting above,

$$\mu_s = \left(\frac{1}{2}\right)\tan\alpha, \text{ or } \alpha = \tan^{-1}(2\mu_s) = \tan^{-1}(0.6) = 31°$$

Problem 9.26 The masses of the ladder and person are 18 kg and 90 kg, respectively. The center of mass of the 4-m ladder is at its midpoint. If $\alpha = 30°$, what is the minimum coefficient of static friction between the ladder and the floor necessary for the person to climb to the top of the ladder? Neglect friction between the ladder and the wall.

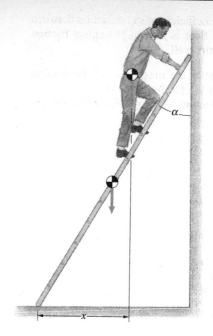

Solution: The weight of the ladder is $W = 18\,g = 176.58$ N. The weight of the person is $P = 90\,g = 882.9$ N. Let h be the distance along the ladder of the person's center of mass, and L be the length of the ladder. The horizontal distance is. The sum of the moments about the top of the ladder:

$$\sum M = P(L\sin\alpha - x) - F_N L\sin\alpha + W\frac{L}{2}\sin\alpha + fL\cos\alpha = 0.$$

From the sum of the forces, $\sum F_Y = F_N - W - P = 0$, from which the normal force at the foot of the ladder is $F_N = W + P$. Substitute, solve for the friction force, and reduce algebraically:

$$f = \left(\frac{h}{L}P + \frac{1}{2}W\right)\tan\alpha.$$

At the top of the ladder, $\dfrac{h}{L} = 1$, hence

$$f = \left(P + \frac{W}{2}\right)\tan\alpha = (883 + 88.3)(0.5774) = 560.72 \text{ N}$$

At impending slip, $f = \mu_s F_N = \mu_s(P + W)$, from which

$$\mu_s = \frac{f}{P + W} = \frac{560.72}{1059.48} = 0.5292$$

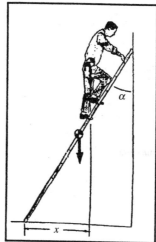

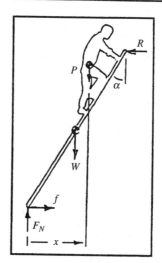

Problem 9.27 In Problem 9.26, the coefficient of static friction between the ladder and the floor is $\mu_s = 0.6$. The masses of the ladder and the person are 18 kg and 100 kg, respectively. The center of mass of the 4-m ladder is at its midpoint. What is the maximum value of α for which the person can climb to the top of the ladder? Neglect friction between the ladder and the wall.

Solution: The solution in Problem 9.26 for the friction force is

$$f = \left(\frac{h}{L}P + \frac{1}{2}W\right)\tan\alpha \text{ and } f = \mu_s(W + P).$$

At impending slip

$$\tan\alpha = \frac{\mu_s(W + P)}{\left(\frac{h}{L}P + \frac{1}{2}W\right)}.$$

At the top of the ladder

$$\frac{h}{L} = 1, \text{ and } \tan\alpha = 0.6495, \text{ or } \alpha = \tan^{-1}(0.6495) = 33°$$

Problem 9.28 In Problem 9.26, the coefficient of static friction between the ladder and the floor is $\mu_s = 0.6$, and $\alpha = 35°$. The center of mass of the 4-m ladder is at its midpoint, and its mass is 18 kg.

(a) If a football player with a mass of 140 kg attempts to climb the ladder, what maximum value of x will he reach? Neglect friction between the ladder and the wall.

(b) What minimum friction coefficient would be required for him to reach the top of the ladder?

Solution: The weight of the football player is $P = 140\,g = 1373.4$ N, and the weight of the ladder is $W = 176.58$ N. From the solution to Problem 9.26,

$$f = \left(\frac{h}{L}P + \frac{1}{2}W\right)\tan\alpha$$

and $f = \mu_s(W + P)$.

Substitute and solve for

$$\frac{h}{L} = \frac{\mu_s(W + P) - \frac{W}{2}\tan\alpha}{P\tan\alpha} = 0.90277.$$

From 9.26, we see that $x = h\sin\alpha$, from which

$$x = \left(\frac{h}{L}\right)L\sin\alpha = 2.07 \text{ m}$$

(b) Solve the above for the static friction coefficient:

$$\mu_s = \frac{\left(\frac{h}{L}P + \frac{1}{2}W\right)\tan\alpha}{(W + P)}.$$

At the top of the ladder, $\frac{h}{L} = 1$, and

$$\mu_s = \frac{\left(P + \frac{1}{2}W\right)\tan\alpha}{(P + W)},$$

$$\mu_s = 0.66$$

Problem 9.29 The disk weighs 50 lb. Neglect the weight of the bar. The coefficients of friction between the disk and the floor are $\mu_s = 0.6$ and $\mu_k = 0.4$.

(a) What is the largest couple M that can be applied to the stationary disk without causing it to start rotating?

(b) What couple M is necessary to rotate the disk at a constant rate?

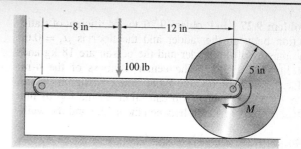

Solution: The normal force at the point of contact is found from the sum of moments about the pin support.

$$\sum M = -8(100) - 20(50) + 20F_N = 0,$$

from which $F_N = 90$ lb. The friction force is $f = \mu_s F_N$. The moment exerted by the friction force is

$$M_F = \mu_s R F_N = 0.6(5)(90) = 270 \text{ in lb}$$

This is the moment to be overcome at impending slip.

(b) The moment required to rotate the disk at a constant rate is

$$M_K = \mu_k R F_N = 0.4(5)(90) = 180 \text{ in lb}$$

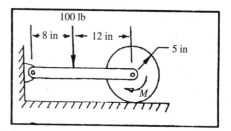

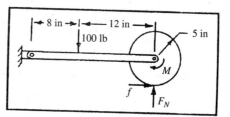

Problem 9.30 The cylinder has weight W. The coefficient of static friction between the cylinder and the floor and between the cylinder and the wall is μ_s. What is the largest couple M that can be applied to the stationary cylinder without causing it to rotate?

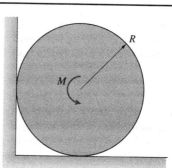

Solution: Assume impending slip. The force opposing rotation is the sum of the friction force at the wall and at the floor. Denote the normal force at the wall by F_{NW} and the normal force on the floor by F_{NF}. From the sum of forces:

$$\sum F_y = \mu_s F_{NW} + F_{NF} - W = 0,$$

and $\sum F_x = F_{NW} - \mu_s F_{NF} = 0.$

Solve these two simultaneous equations to obtain:

$$F_{NF} = \frac{W}{1 + \mu_s^2},$$

and $F_{NW} = \dfrac{\mu_s W}{1 + \mu_s^2}.$

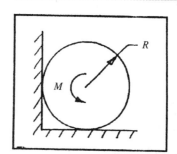

The sum of moments about the center of the cylinder is

$$\sum M_C = M_{app} - \mu_s R F_{NW} - \mu_s R F_{NF} = 0.$$

Substitute and solve:

$$M_{app} = \mu_s R W \left(\frac{1 + \mu_s}{1 + \mu_s^2} \right).$$

At impending slip, this is the maximum moment that can be applied to the cylinder.

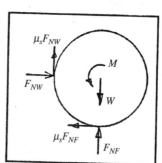

Problem 9.31 The cylinder has weight W. The coefficient of static friction between the cylinder and the floor and between the cylinder and the wall is μ_s. What is the largest couple M that can be applied to the stationary cylinder without causing it to rotate?

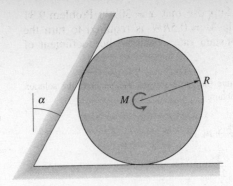

Solution: Assume impending slip. Denote the normal force at the wall by F_{NW} and the normal force at the floor by F_{NF}. The projection of the friction force at the wall on an x-y coordinate system is

$$\mathbf{f}_W = \mu_s |\mathbf{F}_{NW}|(\mathbf{i}\cos(90-\alpha) + \mathbf{j}\sin(90-\alpha))$$

$$= \mu_s|\mathbf{F}_{NW}|(\mathbf{i}\sin\alpha + \mathbf{j}\cos\alpha).$$

The projection of the normal force at the wall on an x-y coordinate system is

$$\mathbf{F}_{NW} = |\mathbf{F}_{NW}|(\mathbf{i}\cos\alpha - \mathbf{j}\sin\alpha).$$

The sum of the forces:

$$\sum F_y = |\mathbf{F}_{NW}|(\mu_s\cos\alpha - \sin\alpha) + |\mathbf{F}_{NF}| - |\mathbf{W}| = 0,$$

and $\sum F_x = |\mathbf{F}_{NW}|(\cos\alpha + \mu_s\sin\alpha) - \mu_s|\mathbf{F}_{NF}| = 0.$

Solve these simultaneous equations to obtain:

$$|\mathbf{F}_{NF}| = \frac{|\mathbf{W}|(\cos\alpha + \mu_s\sin\alpha)}{(1+\mu_s^2)\cos\alpha},$$

and $|\mathbf{F}_{NW}| = \dfrac{\mu_s|\mathbf{W}|}{(1+\mu_s^2)\cos\alpha}.$

The sum of the moments about the center of the cylinder is

$$\sum M_C = M_{app} - \mu_s R|\mathbf{F}_{NF}| - \mu_s R|\mathbf{F}_{NW}| = 0.$$

Substitute and reduce algebraically:

$$M_{app} = \frac{\mu_s RW(\cos\alpha + \mu_s\sin\alpha + \mu_s)}{(1+\mu_s^2)\cos\alpha}.$$

This is the maximum applied moment at impending slip. *Check:* This reduces to the solution of Problem 9.30 when $\alpha = 0$, as it should. *check.*

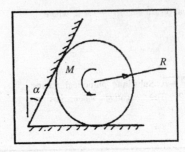

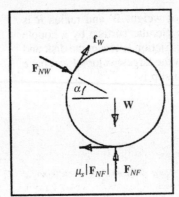

Problem 9.32 Suppose that $\alpha = 30°$ in Problem 9.31 and that a couple $M = 0.5RW$ is required to turn the cylinder at a constant rate. What is the coefficient of kinetic friction?

Solution: Substitute the angle and the moment into the solution of Problem 9.31 to obtain:

$$0.5 = \frac{\mu_k \left(\frac{\sqrt{3}}{2} + \frac{\mu_k}{2} + \mu_k \right)}{(1 + \mu_k^2)\frac{\sqrt{3}}{2}} = \frac{\mu_k(1 + \sqrt{3}\mu_k)}{(1 + \mu_k^2)}.$$

This reduces to the quadratic equation $\mu_k^2 + 2b\mu_k - c = 0$, where

$$b = c = \frac{1}{(2\sqrt{3} - 1)}.$$

The solution is $\mu_k = -b \pm \sqrt{b^2 + c}$. Substitute numerical values: $\mu_k = 0.3495$, or $\mu_k = -1.1612$. The negative value has no meaning here.

Problem 9.33 The disk of weight W and radius R is held in equilibrium on the circular surface by a couple M. The coefficient of static friction between the disk and the surface is μ_s. Show that the largest value M can have without causing the disk to slip is

$$M = \frac{\mu_s RW}{\sqrt{1 + \mu_s^2}}.$$

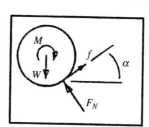

Solution: This is an inclined plane problem. Let α be the angle at the point of contact. From the sum of forces: the normal force is $F_N = W \cos\alpha$, and the friction force is $f = \mu_s F_N = W \sin\alpha$, from which $\mu_s = \tan\alpha$. The sum of moments about the center of the disk yields $M = fR = \mu_s RW \cos\alpha$. Noting that

$$\cos\alpha = \frac{1}{\sqrt{1 + \tan^2\alpha}},$$

then $M = \dfrac{\mu_s RW}{\sqrt{1 + \mu_s^2}}$,

which is the moment at impending slip.

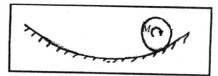

Problem 9.34 The coefficient of static friction between the jaws of the pliers and the gripped object is μ_s. What is the largest value of the angle α for which the gripped object will not slip? (Neglect the object's weight.)

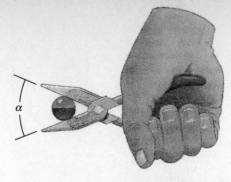

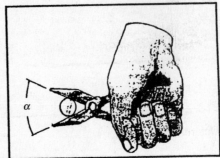

Solution: Choose an x-y coordinate system such that the x-axis bisects the angle α. Define

$$\beta = \frac{\alpha}{2}.$$

The projection of the normal forces on the x-y system is, for the top:

$$\mathbf{F}_{NT} = |\mathbf{F}_{NT}|(-\mathbf{i}\sin\beta - \mathbf{j}\cos\beta).$$

For the bottom:

$$\mathbf{F}_{NB} = |\mathbf{F}_{NB}|(-\mathbf{i}\sin\beta + \mathbf{j}\cos\beta).$$

The projection of the friction forces on the x-y system is, for the top:

$$\mathbf{f}_T = \mu_s|\mathbf{F}_{NT}|(\mathbf{i}\cos\beta - \mathbf{j}\sin\beta).$$

For the bottom:

$$\mathbf{f}_B = \mu_s|\mathbf{F}_{NB}|(\mathbf{i}\cos\beta + \mathbf{j}\sin\beta).$$

The forces tending to expel the gripped object are the components of the normal forces in the negative x direction, and the components tending to retain the gripped object are the friction forces in the positive x-direction. These must balance:

$$\sum F_x = -|\mathbf{F}_{NB}|\sin\beta - |\mathbf{F}_{NT}|\sin\beta + \mu_s|\mathbf{F}_{NT}|\cos\beta$$

$$+ \mu_s|\mathbf{F}_{NB}|\cos\beta = 0,$$

from which

$$|\mathbf{F}_{NB}|(-\sin\beta + \mu_s\cos\beta) + |\mathbf{F}_{NT}|(-\sin\beta + \mu_s\cos\beta) = 0.$$

From symmetry, $|\mathbf{F}_{NB}| = |\mathbf{F}_{Nt}|$, since the weight of the object is neglected. For non-trivial values of the normal forces, $-\sin\beta + \mu_s\cos\beta = 0$, from which $\mu_s = \tan\beta$, or $\beta = \tan^{-1}(\mu_s)$. Noting

$$\beta = \frac{\alpha}{2},$$

$$\alpha = 2\tan^{-1}(\mu_s)$$

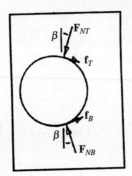

Problem 9.35 The stationary disk, of 300-mm radius, is attached to a pin support at D. The disk is held in place by the brake ABC in contact with the disk at C. The hydraulic actuator BE exerts a horizontal 400-N force on the brake at B. The coefficients of friction between the disk and the brake are $\mu_s = 0.6$ and $\mu_k = 0.5$. What couple must be applied to the stationary disk to cause it to slip in the counterclockwise direction?

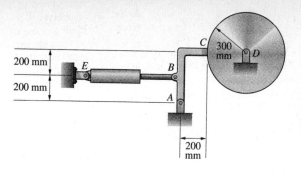

Solution: Assume impending slip. For counterclockwise motion the friction force $f = \mu_s F_N$ opposes the impending slip, so that it acts on the brake in a downward direction, producing a negative moment (clockwise) about A. The sum of the moments about A:

$$\sum M_A = -0.2(400) + (0.4 - 0.2\mu_s)F_N,$$

from which $F_N = 285.7$ N. The sum of the moments about the center of the disk:

$$\sum M_D = M - 0.3(\mu_s)F_N = 0,$$

from which $M = 51.43$ N m.

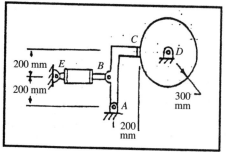

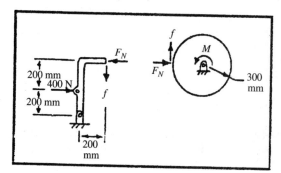

Problem 9.36 What couple must be applied to the stationary disk in Problem 9.35 to cause it to slip in a clockwise direction?

Solution: Assume impending slip. For clockwise motion the friction force $f = \mu_s F_N$ opposes the impending slip, so that it acts on the brake in an upward direction, producing a positive moment (counterclockwise) about A. The sum of the moments about A:

$$\sum M_A = -0.2(400) + (0.4 + 0.2\mu_s)F_N = 0,$$

from which $F_N = 153.85$ N. The sum of the moments about the center of the disk:

$$\sum M_D = M - 0.3\mu_s F_N = 0,$$

from which $M = 27.69$ N m

Problem 9.37 The mass of block B is 8 kg. The coefficient of static friction between the surfaces of the clamp and the block is $\mu_s = 0.2$. When the clamp is aligned as shown, what minimum force must the spring exert to prevent the block from slipping out?

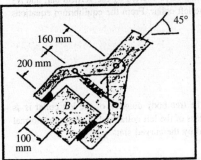

Solution: The free-body diagram of the block when slip is impending is shown. From the equilibrium equation

$$\mu_s F_T + \mu_s (F_T + W \cos \alpha) - W \cos \alpha = 0,$$

we obtain

$$F_T = \frac{w(1 - \mu_s) \cos \alpha}{2\mu_s}$$

$$= \frac{(8)(9.81)(1 - 0.2) \cos 45°}{2(0.2)}$$

$$= 111 \text{ N}.$$

The free-body diagram of the upper arm of the clamp is shown. Summing moments about the upper end,

$$0.16 F_s + 0.1 \mu_s F_T - 0.36 F_T = 0,$$

the force exerted by the spring is

$$F_s = \frac{0.36 F_T - 0.1 \mu_s F_T}{0.16}$$

$$= \frac{[0.36 - 0.1(0.2)]111}{0.16}$$

$$= 236 \text{ N}.$$

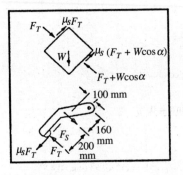

Problem 9.38 By altering its dimensions, redesign the clamp in Problem 9.37 so that the minimum force the spring must exert to prevent the block from slipping out is 180 N. Draw a sketch of your new design.

Solution: This problem does not have a unique solution.

Problem 9.39 The horizontal bar is attached to a collar that slides on the smooth vertical bar. The collar at P slides on the smooth horizontal bar. The total mass of the horizontal bar and the two collars is 12 kg. The system is held in place by the pin in the circular slot. The pin contacts only the lower surface of the slot, and the coefficient of static friction between the pin and the slot is 0.8. If the system is in equilibrium and $y = 260$ mm, what is the magnitude of the friction force exerted on the pin by the slot?

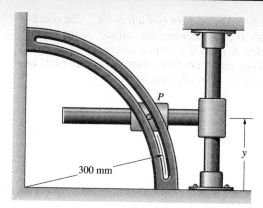

300 mm

Solution: The free body diagram of the horizontal bar and right collar is as shown, where m_1 is the mass of the horizontal bar and right collar, N_1 is the normal force exerted by the vertical bar, and N_2 is the force exerted by the left collar. From the equilibrium equations

$$\sum F_x = -N_1 = 0,$$

$$\sum F_x = N_2 - m_1 g = 0,$$

we see that $N_2 = m_1 g$. The free body diagram of the left collar is as shown, where m_2 is the mass of the left collar and N, f are the normal and friction forces exerted by the curved slot.

$y = 260$ mm $= (300$ mm$) \sin\theta$,

so the angle $\theta = 60.1°$.

From the equilibrium equations,

$$\sum F_x = -f + m_2 g \cos\theta + N_2 \cos\theta = 0,$$

$$\sum F_y = N - m_2 g \sin\theta - N_2 \sin\theta = 0,$$

we obtain

$$f = (m_2 g + N_2)\cos\theta = (m_2 + m_1)\cos\theta = (12)(9.81)\cos 60.1°$$

$$= 58.7 \text{ N}.$$

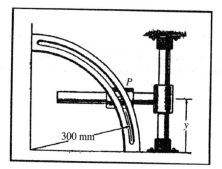

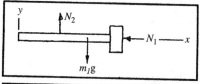

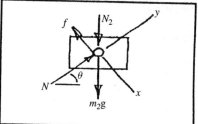

Problem 9.40 In Problem 9.39, what is the minimum height y at which the system can be in equilibrium?

Solution: From the solution of Problem 9.39, the friction and normal forces exerted on the pin by the circular slot are

$$f = (m_2 g + N_2)\cos\theta,$$

$$N = (m_2 g + N_2)\sin\theta,$$

so $\dfrac{f}{N} = \cot\theta$. When slip impends,

$$f = \mu_s N = 0.8 \text{ N},$$

so $0.8 = \cot\theta$ and $\theta = 51.3°$. The height $y = 300 \sin\theta = 234$ mm.

Problem 9.41 The rectangular 100-lb plate is supported by the pins A and B. If friction can be neglected at A and the coefficient of static friction between the pin at B and the slot is $\mu_s = 0.4$, what is the largest angle α for which the plate will not slip?

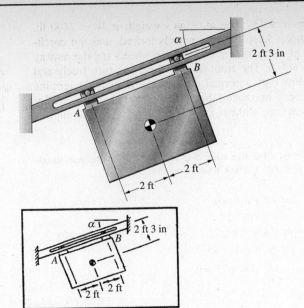

Solution: Choose a coordinate system with the x-axis parallel to the rail. The sum of the moments about A is

$$\sum M_A = -2W\cos\alpha - 2.25W\sin\alpha + 4B = 0,$$

from which

$$B = \frac{W}{4}(2\cos\alpha + 2.25\sin\alpha).$$

The component of weight causing the plate to slide is $F = W\sin\alpha$. This must be balanced by the friction force: $0 = -W\sin\alpha + \mu_s B$, from which

$$\frac{W\sin\alpha}{\mu_s} = \frac{W}{4}(2\cos\alpha + 2.25\sin\alpha).$$

Reduce algebraically to obtain

$$\alpha = \tan^{-1}\left(\frac{\mu_s}{2 - 1.125\mu_s}\right) = 14.47°.$$

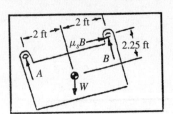

Problem 9.42 If you can neglect friction at B in Problem 9.41 and the coefficient of static friction between the pin at A and the slot is $\mu_s = 0.4$, what is the largest angle α for which the plate will not slide?

Solution: The normal force acts normally to the slots, and the friction force acts parallel to the slot. Choose a coordinate system with the x-axis parallel to the slots. The normal component of the reaction at A is found from the sum of the moments about B:

$$\sum M_B = -2.25W\sin\alpha + 2W\cos\alpha - 4A = 0,$$

from which

$$A_N = \frac{W}{4}(-2.25\sin\alpha + 2\cos\alpha).$$

The force tending to make the plate slide is $F = -W\sin\alpha$. This is balanced by the friction force at A,

$$0 = -W\sin\alpha + \mu_s A_N,$$

from which

$$\frac{W\sin\alpha}{\mu_s} = \frac{W}{4}(-2.25\sin\alpha + 2\cos\alpha).$$

Reduce algebraically to obtain

$$\alpha = \tan^{-1}\left(\frac{\mu_s}{2 - 1.125\mu_s}\right) = 9.27°.$$

Check: The normal reactions at A and B are unequal: as the slots are inclined from the horizontal, the parallel component of the gravity force reduces the normal force at A, and increases the normal force at B. *check.*

Check: The sum of the reactions at A and B are $A_N + B_N = W\cos\alpha$. *check.* The magnitude $\sqrt{(A_N + B_N)^2 + (\mu_s A_N)^2} = W$, hence the system is in equilibrium at impending slip. *check.*

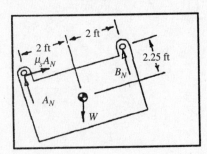

Problem 9.43 The airplane's weight is $W = 2400$ lb. Its brakes keep the rear wheels locked, and the coefficient of static friction between the wheels and the runway is $\mu_s = 0.6$. The front (nose) wheel can turn freely and so exerts only a normal force on the runway. Determine the largest horizontal thrust force T the plane's propeller can generate without causing the rear wheels to slip.

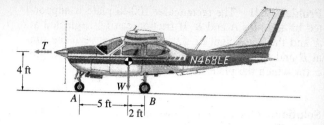

Solution: The free body diagram when slip of the rear wheels impends is shown. From the equilibrium equations

$$\sum f_x = -T + \mu_s B = 0,$$

$$\sum f_y = A + B - W = 0,$$

$$\sum M_{ptA} = 4T - 5W + 7B = 0,$$

we obtain

$A = 1120$ lb,

$B = 1280$ lb,

and $T = 766$ lb.

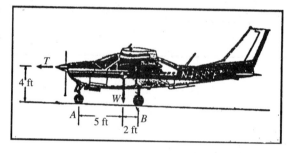

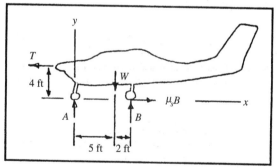

Problem 9.44 The refrigerator weighs 350 lb. The distances $h = 60$ in. and $b = 14$ in. The coefficient of static friction at A and B is $\mu_s = 0.24$.

(a) What force F is necessary for impending slip?
(b) Will the refrigerator tip over before it slips?

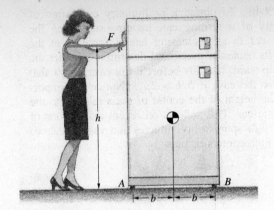

Solution: The normal forces on the right and left supports are found: The sum of moments about support A:

$$\sum M_A = -bW - hF + 2bB = 0,$$

from which

$$B = \frac{bW + hF}{2b}.$$

The sum of forces:

$$\sum F_Y = A + B - W = 0,$$

from which

$$A = W - B = \frac{bW - hF}{2b}.$$

(a) The friction forces must balance the applied force at impending slip:

$$0 = F - \mu_s A - \mu_s B = F - \mu_s \left(\frac{bW - hF}{2b} \right)$$

$$- \mu_s \left(\frac{bW + hF}{2b} \right),$$

from which $F = \mu_s W = 0.24(350) = 84$ lb.

(b) If the normal force at A approaches zero before motion occurs, the refrigerator will start to tip:

$$F_{\text{tip}} = \left(\frac{b}{h} \right) W = \left(\frac{14}{60} \right) 350 = 81.67 \text{ lb}.$$

Since $F_{\text{tip}} < F_{\text{move}}$, the refrigerator will tip.

Yes.

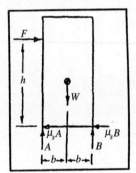

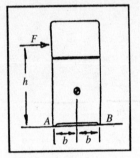

Problem 9.45 If you want the refrigerator in Problem 9.44 to slip before it tips over, what is the maximum height h at which you can push it?

Solution: From the solution to Problem 9.44, the tipping force must be equal to or greater than the moving force, $F_{\text{move}} = 84$ lb. Thus when the normal force at A approaches zero, the tipping force must equal or exceed 84 lb, from which

$$h \leq b \left(\frac{W}{F_{\text{move}}} \right) = 14 \left(\frac{350}{84} \right) \leq 58.33 \text{ in}$$

Problem 9.46 To obtain a preliminary evaluation of the stability of a turning car, imagine subjecting the stationary car to an increasing lateral force F at the height of its center of mass, and determine whether the car will slip (skid) laterally before it tips over. Show that this will be the case if $b/h > 2\mu_s$. (Notice the importance of the height of the center of mass relative to the width of the car. This reflects on recent discussions of the stability of sport utility vehicles and vans that have relatively high centers of mass.)

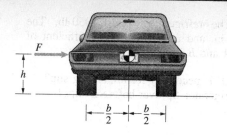

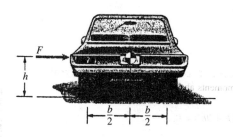

Solution:

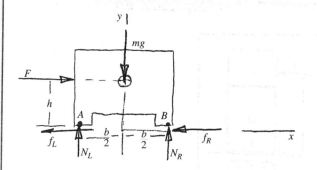

EQUILIBRIUM Eqns:

$$\sum F_x: \quad F - f_L - f_R = 0$$

$$\sum F_y: \quad N_L + N_R - mg = 0$$

$$\sum M_A: \quad -hF + bN_R - \frac{b}{2}mg = 0$$

Assume skid and tip simultaneously.

$$f_L = \mu_s N_L,$$

$$f_R = \mu_s N_R (skid)$$

and $N_L = 0$ (tip), $\therefore f_L = 0$.

$$f_R = \mu_s mg.$$

The equilibrium eqns become

$$F = f_R = \mu_s N_R = \mu_s mg$$

and the moment eqn. uses

$$-h(\mu_s mg) + b(mg) - \frac{b}{2}mg = 0$$

or $\dfrac{b}{h} = 2\mu_s$

For $\boxed{\dfrac{b}{h} > 2\mu_s}$, slip before tip

$\dfrac{b}{h} < 2\mu_s$, tip before slip

$\dfrac{b}{h}$ big N low cm, relative to track width

$\dfrac{b}{h}$ small N high cm, relative to track width

Problem 9.47 The man exerts a force P on the car at an angle $\alpha = 20°$. The 1760-kg car has front wheel drive. The driver spins the front wheels, and the coefficient of kinetic friction is $\mu_k = 0.02$. Snow behind the rear tires exerts a horizontal resisting force S. Getting the car to move requires overcoming a resisting force $S = 420$ N. What force P must the man exert?

Solution:

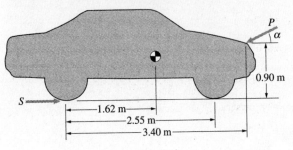

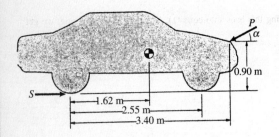

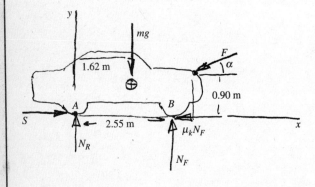

$$\sum F_x: \quad S - \mu_k N_F - P\cos\alpha = 0$$

$$\sum F_y: \quad N_R + N_F - mg - P\sin\alpha = 0$$

$$\sum M_A: \quad -(1.62)mg + 2.55\,N_F$$

$$+(0.90)P\cos\alpha - (3.40)P\sin\alpha = 0$$

$\alpha = 20°$,

$m = 1760$ kg,

$g = 9.81$ m/s^2

$S = 420$ N,

$\mu_k = 0.02$

3 eqns in 3 unknowns (N_R, N_F, and P)

Solving the equations, we get $P = 213$ N

$N_R = 6.34$ kN

$N_F = 11.00$ kN

Problem 9.48 In Problem 9.47, what value of the angle α minimizes the magnitude of the force P the man must exert to overcome the resisting force $S = 420$ N exerted on the rear tires by the snow? What force must he exert?

Solution: From the solution to Problem 9.47, we have

$$S - \mu_k N_F - P \cos\alpha = 0 \qquad \textbf{(1)}$$

$$N_R + N_F - mg - P \sin\alpha = 0 \qquad \textbf{(2)}$$

$$-1.62\,mg + 2.55\,N_F + 0.90P\cos\alpha - 3.40P\sin\alpha = 0 \quad \textbf{(3)}$$

where

$\mu_k = 0.02$,

$S = 420$ N,

$m = 1760$ kg,

and $g = 9.81$ m/s^2.

From Eqn (1),

$$N_F = \frac{1}{\mu_k}(S - P\cos\alpha) \quad \textbf{(a)}$$

From Eqn (2),

$$N_R = -N_F + mg + P\sin\alpha$$

or $N_R = -\dfrac{1}{\mu_k}(S - P\cos\alpha) + mg + P\sin\alpha$ **(b)**

Substitute (a) and (b) into (3)

We get

$$-1.62\,mg + 2.55\left(\frac{1}{\mu_k}\right)(S - P\cos\alpha)$$

$$+0.90\,P\cos\alpha - 3.40\,P\sin\alpha = 0$$

Use this eqn to find $\dfrac{dP}{d\alpha}$ and set it to zero.

$$\frac{2.55}{\mu_k}\left[-\frac{dP}{d\alpha}\cos\alpha + P\sin\alpha\right] + 0.90\frac{dP}{d\alpha}\cos\alpha - 0.90\,P\sin\alpha$$

$$-3.40\frac{dP}{d\alpha}\sin\alpha - 3.40\,P\cos\alpha = 0$$

or

$$\frac{dP}{d\alpha}\left[0.90\cos\alpha - 3.40\sin\alpha - \frac{2.55}{\mu_k}\cos\alpha\right]$$

$$+P\left[\frac{2.55}{\mu_k}\sin\alpha - 0.90\sin\alpha - 3.40\cos\alpha\right] = 0$$

$$\frac{dP}{d\alpha} = 0 = \frac{-P\left[\left(\dfrac{2.55}{\mu_k} - 0.90\right)\sin\alpha - 3.40\cos\alpha\right]}{\left[0.90\cos\alpha - 3.40\sin\alpha - \dfrac{2.55}{\mu_k}\cos\alpha\right]}$$

$$\tan\alpha = \frac{3.40}{\left(\dfrac{2.55}{\mu_k} - 0.90\right)}$$

Solving, $\alpha = 1.54°$

Substituting this back into eqns (1), (2), and (3), and solving, we get

$$P = 202 \text{ N}$$

Problem 9.49 The coefficient of static friction between the 3000-lb car's tires and the road is $\mu_s = 0.5$. Determine the steepest grade (the largest value of the angle α) the car can drive up at constant speed if the car has (a) rear-wheel drive; (b) front-wheel drive; (c) four-wheel drive.

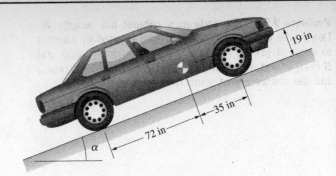

Solution: The friction force acts parallel to the incline, and the normal force is normal to the incline. Choose a coordinate system with the x-axis parallel to the incline. The component of the weight that acts parallel to the incline is $W \sin \alpha$, and the component acting normally to the incline is $W \cos \alpha$.

(a) *For rear wheel drive:* The moment about the point of contact of the front wheels:

$$\sum M_{FW} = 35W \cos \alpha + 19W \sin \alpha - 107R = 0,$$

from which the normal reaction of the two rear wheels is

$$R = \frac{W}{107} (35 \cos \alpha + 19 \sin \alpha).$$

The force causing impending slip is $W \sin \alpha$, which is balanced by the friction force: $0 = W \sin \alpha - \mu_s R$, from which

$$\frac{W \sin \alpha}{\mu_s} = \frac{W}{107} (35 \cos \alpha + 19 \sin \alpha).$$

Reduce and solve:

$$\alpha = \tan^{-1} \left(\frac{35}{\dfrac{107}{\mu_s} - 19} \right) = 10.18°$$

is the maximum angle at impending slip.

(b) *For front wheel drive:* The moments about the point of contact of the rear wheels is

$$\sum M_{RW} = -72W \cos \alpha + 19W \sin \alpha + 107F = 0,$$

from which the normal reaction of the two front wheels is

$$F = \frac{W}{107} (72 \cos \alpha - 19 \sin \alpha).$$

The friction force balances the component of gravity parallel to the incline: $0 = -W \sin \alpha + \mu_s F$, from which

$$\frac{W \sin \alpha}{\mu_s} = \frac{W}{107} (72 \cos \alpha - 19 \sin \alpha).$$

Reduce and solve:

$$\alpha = \tan^{-1} \left(\frac{72}{\dfrac{107}{\mu_s} + 19} \right) = 17.17°$$

(c) *For four wheel drive:* Use the reactions of the front and rear wheels obtained in Parts (a) and (b). The sum of the forces parallel to the incline is

$$\sum F_X = -W \sin \alpha + \mu_s R + \mu_s F = 0,$$

from which

$$\frac{W \sin \alpha}{\mu_s} = \frac{W}{107} (35 \cos \alpha + 19 \sin \alpha + 72 \cos \alpha - 19 \sin \alpha).$$

Reduce and solve: $\alpha = \tan^{-1}(\mu_s) = 26.57°$

Check: This result is the same as if the Mercedes with four wheel drive were a box on an incline, as it should be.

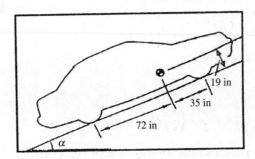

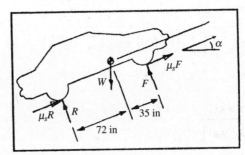

Problem 9.50 The stationary cabinet has weight W. Determine the force F that must be exerted to cause it to move if (a) the coefficient of static friction at A and B is μ_s; (b) if the coefficient of static friction at A is μ_{sA} and the coefficient of static friction at B is μ_{sB}.

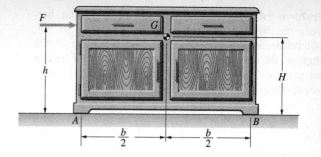

Solution: (a) The sum of the moments about B is

$$\sum M_B = -hF + \left(\frac{b}{2}\right)W - bA = 0,$$

from which

$$A = \frac{W}{2} - \left(\frac{h}{b}\right)F.$$

The sum of forces:

$$\sum F_y = -W + A + B = 0,$$

from which

$$B = W - A = \frac{W}{2} + \left(\frac{h}{b}\right)F.$$

$$\sum F_x = F - \mu_s A - \mu_s B = 0,$$

from which

$$F = \mu_s \left(\frac{W}{2} + \left(\frac{h}{b}\right)F + \frac{W}{2} - \left(\frac{h}{b}\right)F\right) = \mu_s W.$$

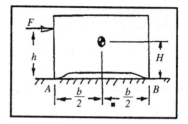

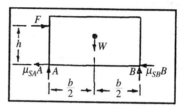

(b) Use the normal reactions found in Part (a). From the sum of forces parallel to the floor,

$$F = \mu_{sA}A + \mu_{sB}B = \mu_{sA}\left(\frac{W}{2} - \left(\frac{h}{b}\right)F\right) + \mu_{sB}\left(\frac{W}{2} + \left(\frac{h}{b}\right)\right).$$

Reduce and solve:

$$F = \frac{\dfrac{W}{2}(\mu_{sA} + \mu_{sB})}{\left(1 + \dfrac{h}{b}(\mu_{sA} - \mu_{sB})\right)}$$

Problem 9.51 The mass of the 3-m bar is 20 kg. It will slip if the angle α is larger than 15°. What is the coefficient of static friction between the ends of the bar and the circular surface?

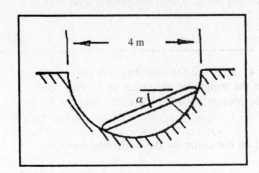

Solution: The free body diagram when slip impends is shown. From the geometry, $2m \sin \beta = 48.6°$, so the angle $\beta = 48.6°$. The equilibrium equations are:

$$\sum F_x = N_A \sin \beta + \mu_s N_A \cos \beta - N_B \sin \beta$$

$$+ \mu_s N_B \cos \beta - mg \sin \alpha = 0, \qquad (1)$$

$$\sum F_y = N_A \cos \beta - \mu_s N_A \sin \beta + N_B \cos \beta$$

$$+ \mu_s N_B \sin \beta - mg \cos \alpha = 0, \qquad (2)$$

$$\sum M_{(pto)} = 2\mu_s N_A + 2\mu_s N_B - (2\cos \beta)mg \sin \alpha = 0. \qquad (3)$$

Solving equation (3) for N_A substituting the result into equations (1) and (2), then eliminating N_B from the resulting equations results in a quadratic equation for μ_s:

$$\sin \alpha (1 - \cos^2 \beta)\mu_s^2 + \cos \alpha \mu_s - \sin \alpha \cos^2 \beta = 0.$$

Solving, we obtain $\mu_s = 0.115$

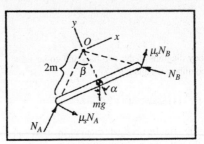

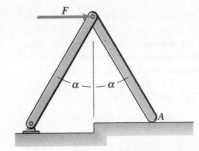

Problem 9.52 The coefficient of static friction between the right bar and the surface at A is $\mu_s = 0.6$. Neglect the weights of the bars. If $\alpha = 20°$, what is the magnitude of the friction force exerted at A?

Solution: Note that the condition of impending slip does not necessarily apply. The moments about the left pin support:

$$\sum M = -F \cos \alpha + 2A \sin \alpha = 0,$$

from which $A = \dfrac{F}{2 \tan \alpha}$.

Isolate the right bar and take moments about the upper pin joint:

$$\sum M = AL \sin \alpha - fL \cos \alpha = 0,$$

from which $f = A \tan \alpha$. Substitute for A:

$$f = A \tan \alpha = \frac{F \tan \alpha}{2 \tan \alpha} = \frac{F}{2}$$

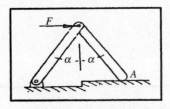

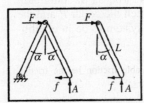

Problem 9.53 Consider the system shown in Problem 9.52. The coefficient of static friction between the right bar and the surface at A is $\mu_s = 0.6$. Neglect the weight of the bars. What is the largest angle α at which the truss will remain stationary without slipping?

Solution: From the solution to Problem 9.52, $f = A\tan\alpha$. Since $f = \mu_s A$ at impending slip, $\mu_s = \tan\alpha$, from which $\alpha = \tan^{-1}(0.6) = 30.96°$

Problem 9.54 Each of the uniform 2-ft bars weighs 4 lb. Neglect the weight of the collar at P. The coefficient of static friction between the collar and the horizontal bar is $\mu_s = 0.6$. If the system is in equilibrium and the angle $\theta = 45°$, what is the magnitude of the friction force exerted on the collar by the horizontal bar?

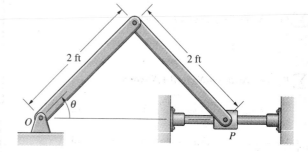

Solution: The free body diagram of the two bars and collar is as shown above. From the equilibrium equation

$$\sum M_{(ptA)} = -1\cos 45°(4) - (3)\cos 45°(4) + (4)\cos 45°N = 0,$$

The normal force is $N = 4$ lb. The free body diagram of the right bar and collar is as shown at the right. From the equilibrium equation

$$\sum M_{(ptB)} = (2)\cos 45°N - (2)\cos 45°f - (1)\cos 45°(4) = 0,$$

the friction force is $f = N - 2 = 2$ lb. The coefficient of static friction has not yet entered into the problem. The amount of friction force needed for equilibrium does not depend on the coefficient of static friction. However, the amount of friction available does depend on the coefficient. In this case, the amount of friction available is given by $f_{available} = \mu_s N = (0.6)4 = 2.4$ lb. Since only 2 lb of friction is needed, equilibrium is possible in the configuration.

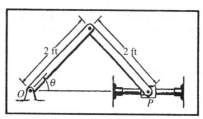

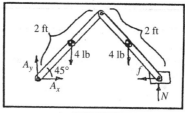

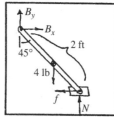

Problem 9.55 In Problem 9.54, what is the minimum coefficient of static friction between the collar P and the horizontal bar necessary for the system to be in equilibrium when $\theta = 45°$?

Solution: We require that the available friction be the friction needed for equilibrium. Hence,

$$f_{available} = f_{required} = 2 \text{ lb} = \mu_s N = \mu_s(4 \text{ lb}).$$

Hence, $\mu_s = 0.5$

Problem 9.56 The weight of the box is $W = 20$ lb and the coefficient of static friction between the box and the floor is $\mu_s = 0.65$. Neglect the weights of the bars. What is the largest value of the force F that will not cause the box to slip?

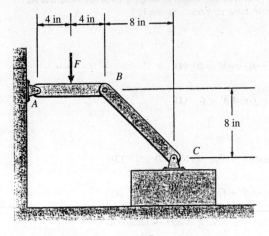

Solution: Note that BC is a two force member.

Member AB

$$\sum F_x: \quad A_x - F_{BC} \cos 45° = 0 \quad \textbf{(1)}$$

$$\sum F_y: \quad A_y - F + F_{BC} \sin 45° = 0 \quad \textbf{(2)}$$

$$\sum M_A: \quad -4F + 8F_{BC} \sin 45° = 0 \quad \textbf{(3)}$$

Unknowns A_x, A_y, F, F_{BC}

$W = 20$ lb

$\mu_s = 0.65$

$f = \mu_s N$ for impending slip.

$$\sum F_x: \quad -\mu_s N + F_{BC} \cos 45° = 0 \quad \textbf{(4)}$$

$$\sum F_y: \quad N - W - F_{BC} \sin 45° = 0 \quad \textbf{(5)}$$

Unknowns N, F_{BC}, A_x, A_y, F 5 eqns, 5 unknowns

Solving, we get

$F = 74.3$ lb.

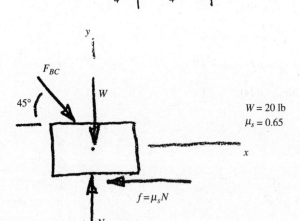

$W = 20$ lb
$\mu_s = 0.65$

Problem 9.57 The mass of the suspended object is 6 kg. The structure is supported at B by the normal and friction forces exerted on the plate by the wall. Neglect the weights of the bars.

(a) What is the magnitude of the friction force exerted on the plate at B ?
(b) What is the minimum coefficient of static friction at B necessary for the structure to remain in equilibrium?

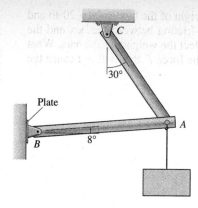

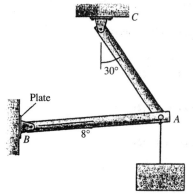

Solution: Consider the weight as hanging from AB. Note that AB and AC are two force members. ($m = 6$ kg)

Joint B:

$$\sum F_x: \quad N - f_{AB} \cos 8° = 0 \quad \textbf{(1)}$$

$$\sum F_y: \quad f - f_{AB} \sin 8° = 0 \quad \textbf{(2)}$$

Joint A:

$$\sum F_x: \quad f_{AB} \cos 8° - F_{AC} \cos 60° = 0 \quad \textbf{(3)}$$

$$\sum F_y: \quad f_{AB} \sin 8° + F_{AC} \sin 60° - mg = 0 \quad \textbf{(4)}$$

Unknowns: f_{AB}, F_{AC}, N, F 4 eqns–4 unknowns

Solving

(a) $f = 4.42$ N

$N = 31.43$ N

$f_{AB} = 31.74$ N

$F_{AC} = 62.86$ N

(b) $f = \mu_{MIN} N$

$\mu_{MIN} = 0.141$

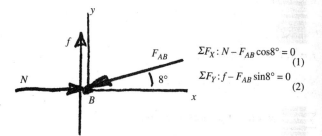

$$\sum F_X: N - F_{AB} \cos 8° = 0 \quad (1)$$

$$\sum F_Y: f - F_{AB} \sin 8° = 0 \quad (2)$$

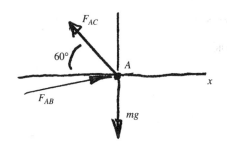

Problem 9.58 Suppose that the lengths of the bars in Problem 9.57 are $L_{AB} = 1.2$ m and $L_{AC} = 1.0$ m and their masses are $m_{AB} = 3.6$ kg and $m_{AC} = 3.0$ kg.

(a) What is the magnitude of the friction force exerted on the plate at B?

(b) What is the minimum coefficient of static friction at B necessary for the structure to remain in equilibrium?

Solution: This problem differs greatly from Problem 9.57. Neither bar is a two force member. We must draw free-body diagrams of each bar and use both force and moment equilibrium in our solutions. Assume that the weight hangs from bar AB and that the bars are uniform.

$m_L = 6$ kg

$m_{AB} = 3.6$ kg

$\sum F_x: \quad N + A_x = 0$ (1)

$\sum F_y: \quad f - m_{AB}g - m_L g + A_y = 0$ (2)

$\sum M_B: \quad -(0.6\cos 8°)m_{AB}g - (1.2\sin 8°)A_x$

         $+ (1.2\cos 8°)(A_y - m_L g) = 0$ (3)

$m_{AC} = 3.0$ kg

$\sum F_x: \quad -A_x + C_x = 0$ (4)

$\sum F_y: \quad C_y - A_y - m_{AC}g = 0$ (5)

$\sum M_A: \quad (0.5\cos 60°)m_{AC}g - (1\cos 60°)C_y$

         $- (1\sin 60°)C_x = 0$ (6)

Unknowns:

A_x, A_y, C_x, C_y, N, F

We have 6 eqns. in 6 unknowns.

Solving, we get

(a) $f = 24.5$ N, $N = 48.7$ N

Also,

$A_x = -48.7$ N, $A_y = 69.7$ N

$C_x = -48.7$ N, $C_y = 99.1$ N

(b) $\mu_{\text{MIN}} = \dfrac{f}{N} = 0.503$

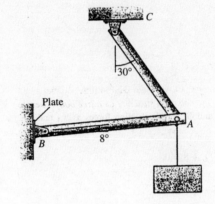

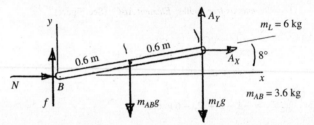

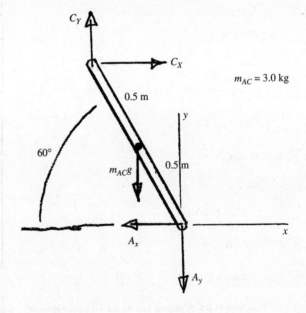

Problem 9.59 The frame is supported by the normal and friction forces exerted on the plates at A and G by the fixed surfaces. The coefficient of static friction at A is $\mu_s = 0.6$. Will the frame slip at A when it is subjected to the loads shown?

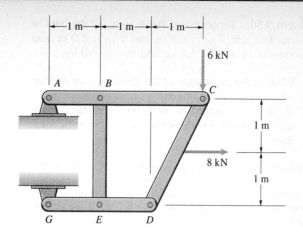

Solution: The strategy is to write the equilibrium equations and solve for the unknown. *The complete structure as a free body:* Denote the normal forces as A and G, and the friction forces as f_A and f_G. The sum of forces:

(1) $\displaystyle\sum F_x = -f_A + f_G + 8 = 0,$

(2) $\displaystyle\sum F_y = -A + G - 6 = 0.$

The elements as free bodies: Element ABC: (See Figure)

(3) $\displaystyle\sum M_B = +1A + 2C_y - 12 = 0.$

(4) $\displaystyle\sum F_x = -f_A + C_x = 0,$

(5) $\displaystyle\sum F_y = -A - B + C_y - 6 = 0.$

Element BE:

(6) $\displaystyle\sum F_y = B - E = 0.$

Element CD:

(7) $\displaystyle\sum M_C = +2D_x - D_y + 8 = 0,$

(8) $\displaystyle\sum F_x = -C_x + D_x + 8 = 0$

(9) $\displaystyle\sum F_y = D_y - C_y = 0.$

Element DEG:

(10) $\displaystyle\sum M_D = -2G - E = 0$

(11) $\displaystyle\sum F_x = f_G - D_x = 0$

(12) $\displaystyle\sum F_y = G - D_y + E = 0.$

These twelve equations in ten unknowns can be solved by iteration or by back substitution. The results in detail:

$A = -24$ kN,

$f_A = 13$ kN,

$C_y = 18$ kN,

$C_x = 13$ kN,

$B = 36$ kN,

$D_x = 5$ kN,

$D_y = 18$ kN,

$E = 36$ kN,

$G = -18$ kN,

$f_G = 5$ kN.

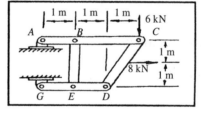

The assumed directions are shown in the Figure; a negative sign means that the result is opposite to the assumed direction. The magnitude of the coefficient of static friction for the reaction at A required to hold the frame in equilibrium is

$$\mu_{sA} = \frac{f_A}{A} = 0.5417.$$

Since this is less than the known value, $\mu_s = 0.6$, the frame will not slip at A.

Problem 9.60 The frame is supported by the normal and friction forces exerted on the plate at A by the wall.

(a) What is the magnitude of the friction force exerted on the plate at A?
(b) What is the minimum coefficient of static friction at A necessary for the structure to remain in equilibrium?

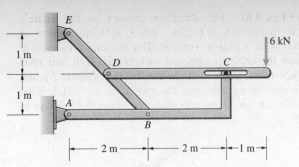

Solution: Draw a free body diagram of each member and write the corresponding equilibrium equations

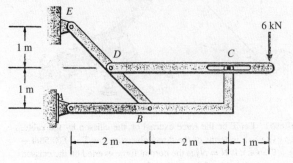

$$\sum F_x: \quad N + B_x = 0 \quad\quad (1)$$

$$\sum F_y: \quad f + B_y + C_y = 0 \quad\quad (2)$$

$$\sum M_A: \quad 2B_y + 4C_y = 0 \quad\quad (3)$$

$$\sum F_x: \quad E_x + D_x - B_x = 0 \quad\quad (4)$$

$$\sum F_y: \quad E_y + D_y - B_y = 0 \quad\quad (5)$$

$$\sum M_E: \quad 1D_y + 1D_x - 2B_y - 2B_x = 0 \quad (6)$$

$$\sum F_x: \quad -D_x = 0 \quad\quad (7)$$

$$\sum F_y: \quad -D_y - C_y - 6 = 0 \quad\quad (8)$$

$$\sum M_D: \quad -3C_y - 4(6) = 0 \quad\quad (9)$$

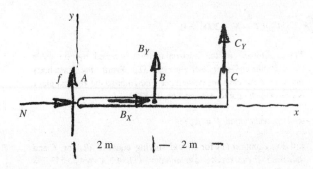

Unknowns:

$N, f, B_x, B_y, C_y, D_x, D_y, E_x, E_y.$

We have 9 eqns in 9 unknowns. Solving, we get

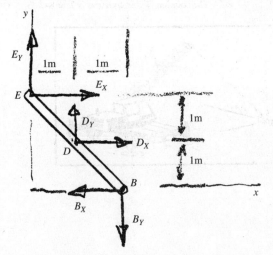

(a) $f = -8$ kN (friction acts down)

Also $N = 15$ kN

$B_x = -15$ kN, $B_y = 16$ kN

$C_y = -8$ kN (opposite the direction assumed)

$D_x = 0, \quad D_y = 2$ kN

$E_x = -15$ kN, $E_y = 14$ kN

(b) $\mu_{\text{MIN}} = \dfrac{|f|}{N} = 0.533$

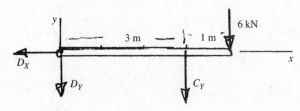

Problem 9.61 The direction cosines of the crane's cable are $\cos\theta_x = 0.558$, $\cos\theta_y = 0.766$, $\cos\theta_z = 0.260$. The y axis is vertical. The stationary caisson to which the cable is attached weights 2000 lb and rests on horizontal ground. If the coefficient of static friction between the caisson and the ground is $\mu_s = 0.4$, what tension in the cable necessary to cause the caisson to slip?

Solution: Let **T** be the force exerted on the caisson by the cable. We can express it in terms of the direction cosines as $\mathbf{T} = T(0.588\mathbf{i} + 0.766\mathbf{j} + 0.260\mathbf{k})$. If $\mathbf{N} = N\mathbf{j}$ is the normal force exerted on the caisson by the ground, the sum of the vertical forces on the caisson is

$$\sum F_y = 0.766T + N - 2000 = 0.$$

(1) The magnitude of the horizontal force exerted by the cable is $\sqrt{(0.588T)^2 + (0.260T)^2} = 0.643T$. From the free-body diagram of the caisson, viewed perpendicular to the vertical plane containing the cable, we see that $0.643T - f = 0$.

(2) slip impends when $f = \mu_s N$.

(3) Solving equation (1) for N and solving equation (2) for f and substituting the results into equation (3), we obtain $0.643T = \mu_s(2000 - 0.766T)$. The solution of this equation is $T = 843$ lb.

Problem 9.62 The 10-lb metal disk A is at the center of the inclined surface. The tension in the string AB is 5 lb. What minimum coefficient of static friction between the disk and the surface is necessary to keep the disk from slipping?

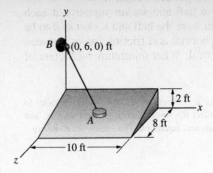

Solution: The coordinates of the disk A are $(5, 1, 4)$ ft, so the position vector of pt B relative to A is $\mathbf{r}_{AB} = (0 - 5)\mathbf{i} + (6 - 1)\mathbf{j} + (0 - 4)\mathbf{k}$ ft. We can express the force exerted on the disk by the string as

$$\mathbf{T} = (5\text{ lb})\frac{\mathbf{r}_{AB}}{|\mathbf{r}_{AB}|} = -3.08\mathbf{i} + 3.08\mathbf{j} - 2.46\mathbf{k} \text{ (lb)}.$$

The sum of the forces exerted on the disk by the string and the weight of the disk is

$$\mathbf{T} - 10\mathbf{j} = -3.08\mathbf{i} - 6.92\mathbf{j} - 2.46\mathbf{k} \text{ (lb)}.$$

The components of this force normal and parallel to the surface are balanced by the normal force and friction force, respectively. To determine these components, we need a unit vector $\mathbf{e}$ perpendicular to the surface: The angle $\beta = \arctan(2/8) = 14.0°$, so

$$\mathbf{e} = \cos\beta\mathbf{j} + \sin\beta\mathbf{k} = 0.970\mathbf{j} + 0.243\mathbf{k}.$$

The component of $\mathbf{T} - 10j$ normal to the surface is

$$[(\mathbf{T} - 10j) \cdot \mathbf{e}]\mathbf{e} = -7.09\mathbf{j} - 1.77\mathbf{k} \text{ (lb)}.$$

The magnitude of the normal force equals the magnitude of this vector:

$$N = |-7.09\mathbf{j} - 1.77\mathbf{k}| = 7.31 \text{ lb}.$$

The component of $\mathbf{T} - 10\mathbf{j}$ parallel to the surface is

$$(\mathbf{T} - 10\mathbf{j}) - [(\mathbf{T} - 10\mathbf{j}) \cdot \mathbf{e}]\mathbf{e} = -3.08\mathbf{i} + 0.17\mathbf{j} - 0.69\mathbf{k} \text{ (lb)}.$$

The magnitude of the friction force is

$$f = |-3.08\mathbf{i} + 0.17\mathbf{j} - 0.69\mathbf{k}| = 3.16 \text{ lb}.$$

Slip impends when $f = \mu_s N$ so the minimum friction coefficient is

$$\mu_s = \frac{f}{N} = \frac{3.16}{7.31} = 0.432.$$

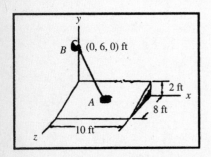

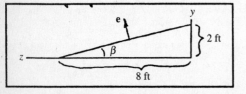

Problem 9.63 The suspended weight $W = 600$ lb. The bars AB and AC have ball and socket supports at each end. Suppose that you want the ball and socket at B to be held in place by the normal and friction forces between the support and the wall. What minimum coefficient of friction is required?

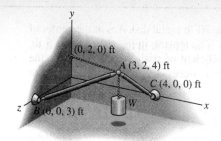

Solution: The strategy is to develop the unit vectors parallel to the bars and the rope, project the forces onto these unit vectors, and solve the associated equilibrium equations. The vector positions are

$$\mathbf{r}_A = 3\mathbf{i} + 2\mathbf{j} + 4\mathbf{k},$$

$$\mathbf{r}_B = 0\mathbf{i} + 0\mathbf{j} + 3\mathbf{k},$$

$$\mathbf{r}_C = 4\mathbf{i} + 0\mathbf{j} + 0\mathbf{k},$$

and $\mathbf{r}_O = 0\mathbf{i} + 2\mathbf{j} + 0\mathbf{k}.$

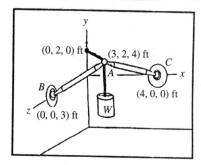

The unit vectors are defined:

$$\mathbf{e}_{AB} = \frac{\mathbf{r}_B - \mathbf{r}_A}{|\mathbf{r}_B - \mathbf{r}_A|}.$$

Apply this definition to obtain:

$$\mathbf{e}_{AB} = -0.8018\mathbf{i} - 0.5345\mathbf{j} - 0.2673\mathbf{k},$$

$$\mathbf{e}_{AC} = 0.2182\mathbf{i} - 0.4364\mathbf{j} - 0.8729\mathbf{k},$$

$$\mathbf{e}_{AO} = -0.6\mathbf{i} + 0\mathbf{j} - 0.8\mathbf{k}.$$

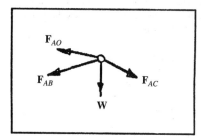

The weight vector is $\mathbf{W} = -600\mathbf{j}$. The equilibrium conditions:

$$\sum F_x = -0.2182|\mathbf{F}_{AC}| - 0.8018|\mathbf{F}_{AB}| - 0.6|\mathbf{F}_{AO}| = 0,$$

$$\sum F_y = -0.4364|\mathbf{F}_{AC}| - 0.5345|\mathbf{F}_{AB}| + 0|\mathbf{F}_{AO}| - |\mathbf{W}| = 0$$

$$\sum F_z = -0.8729|\mathbf{F}_{AC}| - 0.2673|\mathbf{F}_{AB}| - 0.8|\mathbf{F}_{AO}| = 0$$

Solve:

$$|\mathbf{F}_{AC}| = -494.92 \text{ lb } (C),$$

$$|\mathbf{F}_{AB}| = -718.4 \text{ lb } (C),$$

and $|\mathbf{F}_{AO}| = 780$ lb (T).

The projection of $|\mathbf{F}_{AB}|$ onto the unit vector is the force exerted on the wall at B:

$$\mathbf{F}_{AB} = |\mathbf{F}_{AB}|(-0.8018\mathbf{i} - 0.5345\mathbf{j} - 0.2673\mathbf{k})$$

$$= +576\mathbf{i} + 384\mathbf{j} + 192\mathbf{k}.$$

The magnitude of the x-component is the normal force, and the magnitude of the resultant of the y- and z-component is the friction force at impending slip. The resulting coefficient of static friction at impending slip is

$$\mu_s = \frac{\sqrt{384^2 + 192^2}}{576} = 0.7454.$$

This is the minimum coefficient of static friction required to prevent slip.

Problem 9.64 In Problem 9.63, what friction force is exerted on the support at B by the wall?

Solution: From the solution to Problem 9.63, the magnitude of the friction force is

$$f_B = \sqrt{384^2 + 192^2} = 429.3 \text{ lb}$$

Problem 9.65 A force $F = 200$ N is necessary to raise the block A at a constant rate. The mass of the wedge B is negligible. Between all of the contacting surfaces, $\mu_s = 0.28$ and $\mu_k = 0.26$. What is the mass of block A?

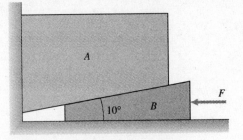

Solution: The friction at all surfaces is kinetic. Draw a free body diagram of each block and write the equilibrium equations.

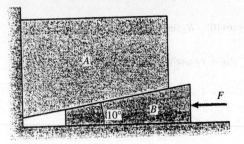

$f_1 = \mu_k N_1$ **(1)**

$f_2 = \mu_k N_2$ **(2)**

$f_3 = \mu_k N_3$ **(3)**

$F = 200$ N

$\mu_k = 0.26$

Block A:

$\sum F_x: \quad N_1 - f_2 \cos 10° - N_2 \sin 10° = 0$ **(4)**

$\sum F_y: \quad -f_1 - m_A g - f_2 \sin 10° + N_2 \cos 10° = 0$ **(5)**

Wedge B:

$\sum F_x: \quad f_3 - F + f_2 \cos 10° + N_2 \sin 10° = 0$ **(6)**

$\sum F_y: \quad N_3 + f_2 \sin 10° - N_2 \cos 10° = 0$ **(7)**

Unknowns:

$f_1, N_1, f_2, N_2, f_3, N_3, m_A$

We have 7 eqns. in 7 unknowns.

Solving, we get

$m_A = 25.0$ kg

Also,

$f_1 = 33.2$ N, $N_1 = 127.5$ N

$f_2 = 77.2$ N, $N_2 = 296.7$ N

$f_3 = 72.5$ N, $N_3 = 278.8$ N

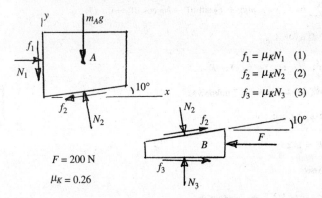

$f_1 = \mu_K N_1$ **(1)**

$f_2 = \mu_K N_2$ **(2)**

$f_3 = \mu_K N_3$ **(3)**

$F = 200$ N

$\mu_K = 0.26$

Problem 9.66 In Problem 9.65, suppose that the mass of block A is 30 kg and the mass of the wedge B is 5 kg. What force F is necessary to start the wedge B moving to the left?

Solution: The solution to this problem is very similar to that of Problem 9.65.

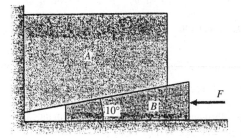

$m_A = 30$ kg

$f_1 = \mu_s N_1$ **(1)**

$f_2 = \mu_s N_2$ **(2)**

$f_3 = \mu_s N_3$ **(3)**

(impending slip)

$m_B = 5$ kg

Block A:

$\sum F_x$: $N_1 - f_2 \cos 10° - N_2 \sin 10° = 0$ **(4)**

$\sum F_y$: $-f_1 - m_A g - f_2 \sin 10° + N_2 \cos 10° = 0$ **(5)**

Wedge B:

$\sum F_x$: $f_3 - F + f_2 \cos 10° + N_2 \sin 10° = 0$ **(6)**

$\sum F_y$: $N_3 - m_B g + f_2 \sin 10° - N_2 \cos 10° = 0$ **(7)**

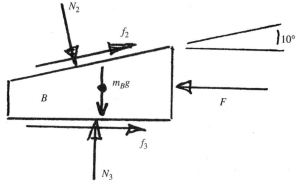

Unknowns:

$f_1, N_1, f_2, N_2, f_3, N_3, F$

We have 7 eqns. in 7 unknowns.

Solving, we get

$F = 272$ N

Also

$f_1 = 45.7$ N $N_1 = 163.2$ N

$f_2 = 101.7$ N $N_2 = 363.2$ N

$f_3 = 108.9$ N $N_3 = 389.0$ N

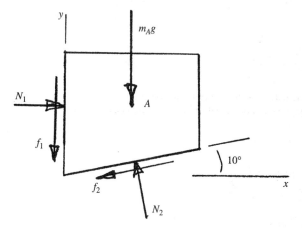

Problem 9.67 The wedge shown is being used to split the log. The wedge weighs 20 lb and the angle α equals 30°. The coefficient of kinetic friction between the faces of the wedge and the log is 0.28. If the normal force exerted by each face of the wedge must equal 150 lb to split the log, what vertical force F is necessary to drive the wedge into the log at a constant rate?

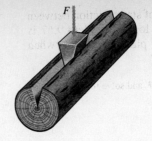

Solution:

$\mu_k = 0.28$

$f = 0.28 \, N$ **(1)**

$N = 150 \, \text{lb}$ **(2)**

$\sum F_x : (N - N) \cos 15° + (f - f) \sin 15° = 0$

(no information here)

$\sum F_y : \quad 2f \cos 15° + 2 \, N \sin 15° - F = 0 (3)$

Unknowns: N, f, F

We have 3 eqns. in 3 unknowns

Solving

$F = 159 \, \text{lb}, \quad f = 42 \, \text{lb}$

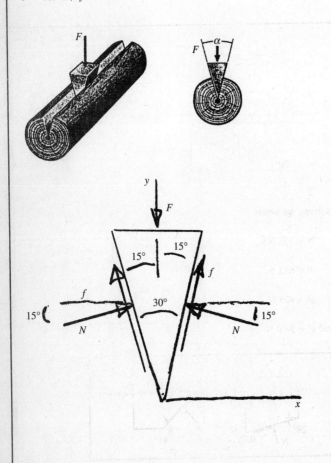

Problem 9.68 The coefficient of static friction between the faces of the wedge and the log in Problem 9.67 is 0.30. Will the wedge remain in place in the log when the vertical force F is removed?

Solution: For this problem, remove F and solve for the minimum μ_s necessary for equilibrium.

The required μ_s

$$f = \mu_s N$$

$$\mu_s = \left(\frac{f}{N}\right) \quad (1)$$

$$\sum F_y: \quad -2f \cos 15° + 2N \sin 15° = 0 \quad (2)$$

$$\frac{f}{N} = \mu_s = \tan 15° = 0.268 < 0.30.$$

Yes — the wedge will stay in place

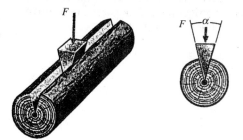

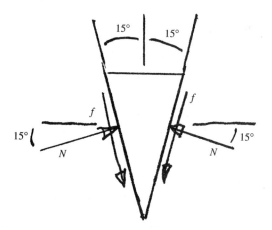

Problem 9.69 The masses of A and B are 42 kg and 50 kg, respectively. Between all contacting surfaces, $\mu_s = 0.05$. What force F is required to start A moving to the right?

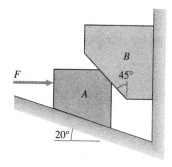

Solution: If F is decreased until slip of A to the left impends, the free body diagrams are as shown. The equilibrium equations are left block:

$$\sum F_x = F + N \sin 20° + 0.05\,N \cos 20° - P \cos 45°$$

$$+ 0.05P \cos 45° = 0,$$

$$\sum F_y = N \cos 20° - 0.05\,N \sin 20° - P \cos 45°$$

$$- 0.05P \cos 45° - (42)(9.81) = 0.$$

Right block:

$$\sum F_x = P \cos 45° - 0.05P \cos 45° - Q = 0,$$

$$\sum F_y = P \cos 45° + 0.05P \cos 45° + 0.05Q - (50)(9.81) = 0.$$

Solving, we obtain

$$N = 955 \text{ N},$$

$$P = 632 \text{ N},$$

$$Q = 425 \text{ N},$$

and $F = 53.0$ N.

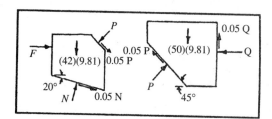

Problem 9.70 The stationary blocks A, B, and C each have a mass of 200 kg. Between all contacting surfaces, $\mu_s = 0.6$. What force F is necessary to start B moving downward?

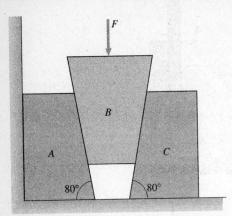

Solution: The wedge angle is 10° for each side. The block A cannot move, hence the friction contact surfaces are the wedge surfaces plus the bottom surface of block C. Assuming that downward slip of B impends, the free body diagrams of blocks B and C are as shown.

The equilibrium equations are Block B:

$$\sum F_x = N \sin 80° - \mu_s N \cos 80° - P \sin 80° + \mu_s P \cos 80°$$

$$= 0, \tag{1}$$

$$\sum F_y = N \cos 80° + \mu_s N \sin 80° + P \cos 80° + \mu_s P \sin 80°$$

$$- F - (200)(9.81) = 0. \tag{2}$$

Block C:

$$\sum F_x = P \sin 80° - \mu_s P \cos 80° - \mu_s Q = 0, \tag{3}$$

$$\sum F_y = Q - P \cos 80° - \mu_s P \sin 80° - (200)(9.81) = 0. \tag{4}$$

Solving them with $\mu_s = 0.6$, we obtain

$$N = 2790 \text{ N},$$

$$P = 2790 \text{ N},$$

$$Q = 4100 \text{ N},$$

and $F = 2300$ N

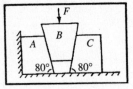

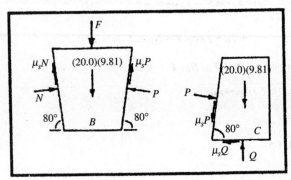

Problem 9.71 Small wedges called *shims* can be used to hold an object in place. The coefficient of kinetic friction between the contacting surfaces is 0.4. What force F is needed to push the shim downward until the horizontal force exerted on the object A is 200 N?

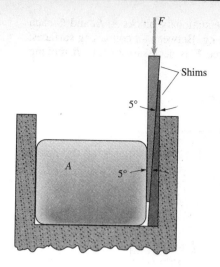

Solution:

$$f_L = \mu_k N_L \quad \textbf{(1)}$$

$$f_R = \mu_k N_R \quad \textbf{(2)}$$

$$N_L = 200 \text{ N} \quad \textbf{(3)}$$

$$\sum F_x: \quad N_L - N_R \cos 5° + f_R \sin 5° = 0 \quad \textbf{(4)}$$

$$\sum F_y: \quad -F + f_L + f_R \cos 5° + N_R \sin 5° = 0 \quad \textbf{(5)}$$

Unknowns: f_L, N_L, F_R, N_R, F

(5 eqns. in 5 unknowns)

Solving,

$$F = 181 \text{ N}$$

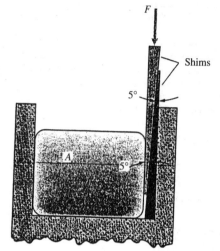

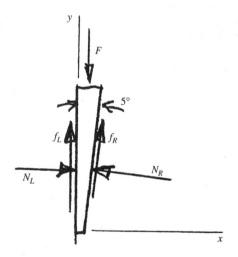

Problem 9.72 The coefficient of static friction between the contacting surfaces in Problem 9.71 is 0.44. If the shims are in place and exert a 200-N horizontal force on the object A, what upward force must be exerted on the left shim to loosen it?

Solution:

$F_L = \mu_s N_L$ (1)

$F_R = \mu_s N_R$ (2)

$\mu_s = 0.44$

$N_L = 200\ N$

$\sum F_x: \quad N_L - N_R \cos 5° - f_R \sin 5° = 0$ (3)

$\sum F_y: \quad F - f_L - f_R \cos 5° + N_R \sin 5° = 0$ (4)

Unknowns F, f_L, f_R, N_R

Solving, $F = 156\ N$

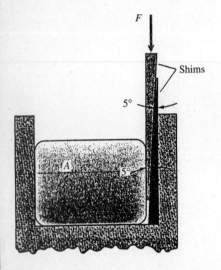

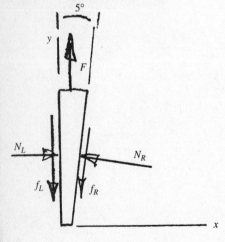

Problem 9.73 The crate A weighs 600 lb. Between all contacting surfaces, $\mu_s = 0.32$ and $\mu_k = 0.30$. Neglect the weights of the wedges. What force F is required to move A to the right at a constant rate?

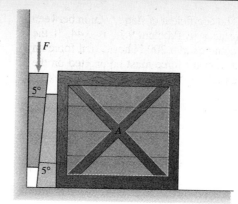

Solution: The active sliding contact surfaces are between the wall and the left wedge, between the wedges, between the floor and the bottom of the right wedge, and between the crate and the floor. *Leftmost wedge:* Denote the normal force exerted by the wall by Q, and the normal force between the wedges by N. The equilibrium conditions for the left wedge moving at a constant rate are:

$$\sum F_y = -F + \mu_k N \cos \alpha + N \sin \alpha + \mu_k Q = 0.$$

$$\sum F_x = Q - N \cos \alpha + \mu_k N \sin \alpha = 0.$$

For the right wedge: Denote the normal force exerted by the crate by A, and the normal force exerted by the floor by P.

$$\sum F_y = -N \sin \alpha - \mu_k N \cos \alpha + P = 0.$$

$$\sum F_x = N \cos \alpha - \mu_k N \sin \alpha - \mu_k P - A = 0.$$

For the crate: Denote the weight of the crate by W.

$$\sum F_x = A - \mu_k W = 0.$$

These five equations are solved for the five unknowns by iteration:

$Q = 204.4$ lb,

$N = 210.7$ lb

$P = 81.34$ lb,

$A = 180$ lb,

and $F = 142.66$ lb

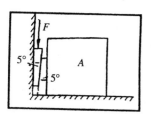

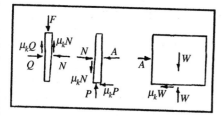

Problem 9.74 Suppose that between all contacting surfaces in Problem 9.73, $\mu_s = 0.32$ and $\mu_k = 0.30$. Neglect the weights of the 5° wedges. If a force $F = 800$ N is required to move A to the right at a constant rate, what is the mass of A?

Solution: The free body diagrams of the left wedge and the combined right wedge and crate are as shown. The equilibrium equations are

Wedge:

$$\sum F_x = N - P\cos 5° + 0.3P\sin 5° = 0,$$

$$\sum F_y = 0.3\,N + P\sin 5° + 0.3P\cos 5° - F = 0,$$

Wedge and box:

$$\sum F_x = P\cos 5° - 0.3P\sin 5° - 0.3Q = 0,$$

$$\sum F_y = Q - P\sin 5° - 0.3P\cos 5° - 9.81\,m = 0.$$

Solving them, we obtain

$P = 1180$ N,

$N = 1150$ N,

$Q = 3820$ N,

and $m = 343$ kg.

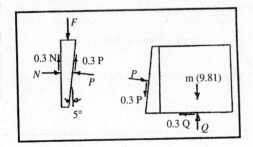

Problem 9.75 The box A has a mass of 80 kg, and the wedge B has a mass of 40 kg. Between all contacting surfaces, $\mu_s = 0.15$ and $\mu_k = 0.12$. What force F is required to raise A at a constant rate?

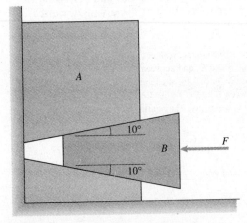

Solution: From the free-body diagrams shown, the equilibrium equations are

Box A:

$$Q - N\sin 10° - \mu_k N\cos 10° = 0,$$

$$N\cos 10° - \mu_k N\sin 10° - \mu_k Q - W = 0.$$

Wedge B:

$$P\sin 10° + \mu_k P\cos 10° + N\sin 10° + \mu_k N\cos 10° - F = 0$$

$$P\cos 10° - \mu_k P\sin 10° - N\cos 10° + \mu_k N\sin 10° - W_w = 0.$$

Solving with

$$W = (80)(9.81)\ \text{N},$$

$$W_w = (40)(9.81)\ \text{N},$$

and $\mu_k = 0.12$,

we obtain

$$N = 845\ \text{N},$$

$$Q = 247\ \text{N},$$

$$P = 1252\ \text{N},$$

and $F = 612$ N.

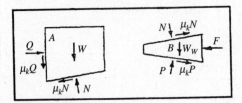

Problem 9.76   Suppose that in Problem 9.75, A weighs 800 lb and B weighs 400 lb. The coefficients of friction between all of the contacting surfaces are $\mu_s = 0.15$ and $\mu_k = 0.12$. Will B remain in place if the force F is removed?

Solution: The equilibrium conditions are: *For the box A*: Denote the normal force exerted by the wall by Q, and the normal force exerted by the wedge by N. The friction forces oppose motion.

$$\sum F_y = -W + N\cos\alpha + \mu_s N\sin\alpha + \mu_s Q = 0,$$

$$\sum F_x = +\mu_s N\cos\alpha - N\sin\alpha + Q = 0.$$

For the wedge B. Denote the normal force on the lower surface by P.

$$\sum F_x = -\mu_s N\cos\alpha - \mu_s P\cos\alpha + P\sin\alpha + N\sin\alpha = 0.$$

$$\sum F_y = -N\cos\alpha + P\cos\alpha - \mu_s N\sin\alpha + \mu_s P\sin\alpha - W_w = 0.$$

(A comparison with the equilibrium conditions for Problem 9.75 will show that the friction forces are reversed, since for slippage the box A will move downward, and the wedge B to the right.) The strategy is to solve these equations for the required μ_s to keep the wedge B in place when $F = 0$. The solution $Q = 0$, $N = 787.8$ lb, $P = 1181.8$ lb and $\mu_s = 0.1763$. Since the value of μ_s required to hold the wedge in place is greater than the value given, the wedge will slip out.

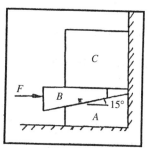

Problem 9.77   Between A and B, $\mu_s = 0.20$, and between B and C, $\mu_s = 0.18$. Between C and the wall, $\mu_s = 0.30$. The weights $W_B = 20$ lb and $W_C = 80$ lb. What force F is required to start C moving upward?

Solution: The active contact surfaces are between the wall and C, between the wedge B and C, and between the wedge B and A. *For the weight C*: Denote the normal force exerted by the wall by Q, and the normal force between B and C by N. Denote the several coefficients of static friction by subscripts. The equilibrium conditions are:

$$\sum F_y = -W_C + N - \mu_{CW}Q = 0,$$

$$\sum F_x = -Q + \mu_{BC}N = 0.$$

For the wedge B: Denote the normal force between A and B by P.

$$\sum F_y = -N + P\cos\alpha - \mu_{AB}P\sin\alpha - W_B = 0.$$

$$\sum F_x = F - \mu_{BC}N - \mu_{AB}P\cos\alpha - P\sin\alpha = 0.$$

These four equations in four unknowns are solved:

$Q = 15.2$ lb,

$N = 84.6$ lb,

$P = 114.4$ lb,

and $F = 66.9$ lb

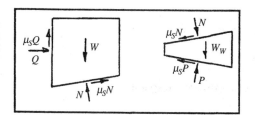

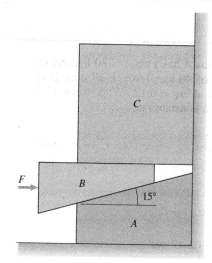

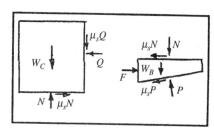

Problem 9.78 The masses of A, B, and C are 8 kg, 12 kg, and 80 kg, respectively. Between all contacting surfaces, $\mu_s = 0.4$. What force F is required to start C moving upward?

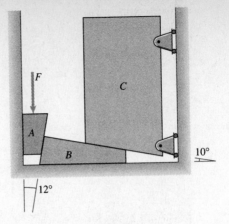

Solution: The active contact surfaces are between A and B, between A and the wall, between B and the floor, and between B and C. Assume that the roller supports between C and the wall exert no friction forces. *For the wedge A:* Denote the normal force exerted by the wall as Q and the normal force between A and B as N. The weight is $W_A = 8\,g = 78.48$ N. The equilibrium conditions:

$$\sum F_y = -F + \mu_s Q + \mu_s N \cos\alpha + N \sin\alpha - W_A = 0$$

$$\sum F_y = Q - N \cos\alpha + \mu_s N \sin\alpha = 0.$$

For wedge B: Denote the normal force exerted on B by the floor by P, and the normal exerted by the weight C as S. The weight of B is $W_B = 12\,g = 117.72$ N. The equilibrium conditions:

$$\sum F_y = -N \sin\alpha - S \cos\beta + P - \mu_s N \cos\alpha + \mu_s S \sin\beta - W_B$$

$$= 0.$$

$$\sum F_x = N \cos\alpha - \mu_s N \sin\alpha - \mu_s P - \mu_s S \cos\beta - S \sin\beta = 0.$$

For the weight C: The weight is $W_C = 80\,g = 784.8$ N. The equilibrium conditions:

$$\sum F_y = -W_C + S \cos\beta - \mu_s S \sin\beta = 0.$$

These five equations in five unknowns are solved:

$$Q = 1157.6 \text{ N},$$

$$N = 1293.5 \text{ N},$$

$$S = 857.4 \text{ N},$$

$$P = 1677.5,$$

and $F = 1160$ N

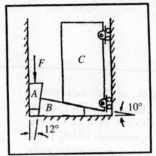

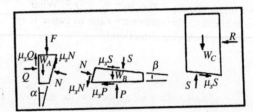

Problem 9.79 The vertical threaded shaft fits into a mating groove in the tube C. The pitch of the threaded shaft is $p = 0.1$ in., and the mean radius of the thread is $r = 0.5$ in. The coefficients of friction between the thread and the mating groove are $\mu_s = 0.15$ and $\mu_k = 0.10$. The weight $W = 200$ lb. Neglect the weight of the threaded shaft.

(a) Will the stationary threaded shaft support the weight if no couple is applied to the shaft?
(b) What couple must be applied to the threaded shaft to raise the weight at a constant rate?

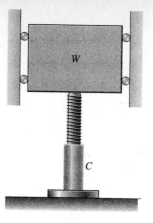

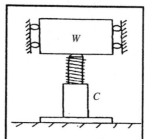

Solution: (a) The angle of static friction is $\theta_s = \tan^{-1}(0.15) = 8.53°$. The pitch angle is

$$\alpha = \tan^{-1}\left(\frac{p}{2\pi r}\right) = \tan^{-1}\left(\frac{0.1}{2\pi(0.5)}\right) = 1.82°.$$

From Eq. (10.14) the moment necessary for the shaft to be on the verge of rotating is $M = rF \tan(\theta_s - \alpha)$. For a zero moment, $\theta_s = \alpha$, which is not satisfied. Therefore the shaft will support the weight when no moment is applied. (b) The angle of kinetic friction is $\theta_k = \tan^{-1}(0.10) = 5.71°$. From Eq. (9.9) the moment required to raise the weight at a constant rate is

$$M = rW \tan(\theta_k + \alpha) = 0.5(200) \tan(7.533) = 13.2 \text{ in lb}.$$

Problem 9.80 Suppose that in Problem 9.79, the pitch of the threaded shaft is $p = 2$ mm and the mean radius of the thread is $r = 20$ mm. The coefficients of friction between the thread and the mating groove are $\mu_s = 0.22$, and $\mu_k = 0.20$. The weight $W = 500$ N. Neglect the weight of the threaded shaft. What couple must be applied to the threaded shaft to lower the weight at a constant rate?

Solution: The angle of kinetic friction is

$$\theta_k = \tan^{-1}(0.2) = 11.31°.$$

The angle of pitch is

$$\alpha = \tan^{-1}\left(\frac{p}{2\pi r}\right) = \tan^{-1}\left(\frac{2}{2\pi(20)}\right) = 0.9118°.$$

The moment required to lower the weight at a constant rate is

$$M = 0.02(500) \tan(11.31 - 0.9118) = 1.835 \text{ N-m}.$$

Problem 9.81 The position of the horizontal beam can be adjusted by turning the machine screw A. Neglect the weight of the beam. The pitch of the screw is $p = 1$ mm, and the mean radius of the thread is $r = 4$ mm. The coefficients of friction between the thread and the mating groove are $\mu_s = 0.20$ and $\mu_k = 0.18$. If the system is initially stationary, determine the couple that must be applied to the screw to cause the beam to start moving (a) upward; (b) downward.

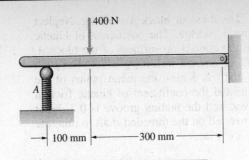

Solution: The sum of the moments about the pin support is

$$\sum M = -0.4F + (0.3)400 = 0,$$

from which the force exerted by the screw is $F = 300$ N. The pitch angle is

$$\alpha = \tan^{-1}\left(\frac{1}{2\pi(4)}\right) = 2.28°.$$

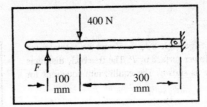

The static friction angle is $\theta_s = \tan^{-1}(0.2) = 11.31°$. (a) The moment required to start motion upward is

$$M = 0.004(300)\tan(11.31° + 2.28°) = 0.29 \text{ N-m}$$

(b) The moment required to start motion downward is

$$M = 0.004(300)\tan(11.31° - 2.28°) = 0.19 \text{ N-m}$$

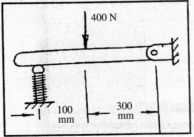

Problem 9.82 Suppose that in Problem 9.81, the pitch of the machine screw is $p = 1$ mm and the mean radius of the thread is $r = 4$ mm. What minimum value of the coefficient of static friction between the thread and the mating groove is necessary for the beam to remain in the position shown with no couple applied to the screw?

Solution: From the solution to Problem 9.81 the force applied to the screw is $F = 300$ N. The pitch angle is

$$\alpha = \tan^{-1}\left(\frac{1}{2\pi(4)}\right) = 2.28°.$$

The moment required to start motion downward is $M = 0.004(300)$ $\tan(\theta_s - \alpha)$. For $M = 0$, $\tan(\theta_s - \alpha) = 0$, from which

$$\theta_s = \alpha = 2.279°,$$

and $\mu_s = \tan(2.279°) = 0.0398$

Problem 9.83 The mass of block A is 60 kg. Neglect the weight of the 5° wedge. The coefficient of kinetic friction between the contacting surfaces of the block A, the wedge, the table, and the wall is $\mu_k = 0.4$. The pitch of the threaded shaft is 5 mm, the mean radius of the thread is 15 mm, and the coefficient of kinetic friction between the thread and the mating groove is 0.2. What couple must be exerted on the threaded shaft to raise the block A at a constant rate?

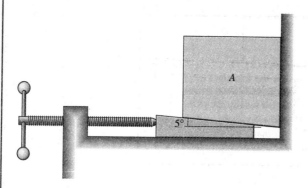

Solution: Denote the wedge angle by $\beta = 5°$ and the normal force on the top by N and on the lower surface by P. The free body diagrams of the wedge and block are as shown. The equilibrium equations for wedge:

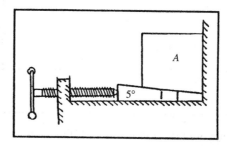

$$\sum F_x = F - \mu_k P - N \sin 5° - \mu_k N \cos 5° = 0,$$

$$\sum F_y = P - N \cos 5° + \mu_k N \sin 5° = 0.$$

For the Block:

$$\sum F_x = N \sin 5° + \mu_k N \cos 5° - Q = 0,$$

$$\sum F_y = N \cos 5° - \mu_k N \sin 5° - \mu_k Q - W = 0.$$

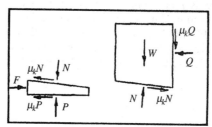

Solving them, we obtain $F = 668$ N. From Equation (9.9), the couple necessary to rotate the threaded shaft when it is subjected to the axial force F is $M = rF \tan(\theta_k + \alpha)$ r is the radius 15 mm $= 0.015$ m. θ_k is the angle of kinetic friction $\theta_k = \arctan(0.2) = 11.31°$.

From Equation (9.7), the slope is given in terms of the pitch by

$$\alpha = \arctan\left(\frac{P}{2\pi r}\right) = \arctan\left[\frac{5}{2\pi(15)}\right] = 3.04°.$$

The couple is

$$M = (0.015 \text{ m})(668 \text{ N}) \tan(11.31° + 3.04°) = 2.56 \text{ N-m}.$$

Problem 9.84 The vise exerts 80-lb forces on A. The threaded shafts are subjected only to axial loads by the jaws of the vise. The pitch of their threads is $p = 1/8$ in., the mean radius of the threads is $r = 1$ in., and the coefficient of static friction between the threads and the mating grooves is 0.2. Suppose that you want to loosen the vise by turning one of the shafts. Determine the couple you must apply (a) to shaft B; (b) to shaft C.

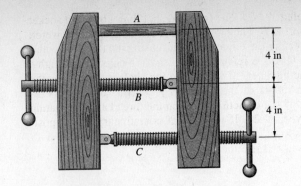

Solution: Isolate the left jaw. The sum of the moments about C:

$$\sum M_C = -4B + 8(80) = 0,$$

from which $B = 160$ lb (T). The sum of the forces:

$$\sum F_x = -80 + B - C = 0,$$

from which $C = 80$ lb (C). The pitch angle is

$$\alpha = \tan^{-1}\left(\frac{1}{16\pi}\right) = 1.14°.$$

The static friction angle is $\theta_s = \tan^{-1}(0.2) = 11.31°$. The moments required to loosen the vise are

$$M_B = \left(\frac{1}{12}\right)(160)\tan(11.31° - 1.14°) = 2.39 \text{ ft lb},$$

and $M_C = rC\tan(\theta_s - \alpha) = 1.2$ ft-lb.

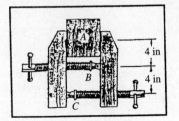

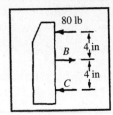

Problem 9.85 Suppose that you want to tighten the vise in Problem 9.84 by turning one of the shafts. Determine the couple you must apply (a) to shaft B; (c) to shaft C.

Solution: Use the solution to Problem 9.84. (a) The moment on shaft B required to tighten the vise is $M_B = rB\tan(\theta_s + \alpha)$. Note that $r = \frac{1}{12}$, $B = 160$ lb,

$$\alpha = \tan^{-1}\left(\frac{1}{16\pi}\right) = 1.14°$$

and $\theta_s = \tan^{-1}(0.2) = 11.31°$,

then $M_B = 2.94$ ft lb (b) For shaft C, $M_C = rC\tan(\theta_s + \alpha)$, where $C = 80$ lb, $M_C = 1.47$ ft-lb.

Problem 9.86 The threaded shaft has a ball and socket support at B. The 400-lb load A can be raised or lowered by rotating the threaded shaft, causing the threaded collar at C to move relative to the shaft. Neglect the weights of the members. The pitch of the shaft is $p = \frac{1}{4}$ in., the mean radius of the thread is $r = 1$ in., and the coefficient of static friction between the thread and the mating groove is 0.24. If the system is stationary in the position shown, what couple is necessary to start the shaft rotating to raise the load?

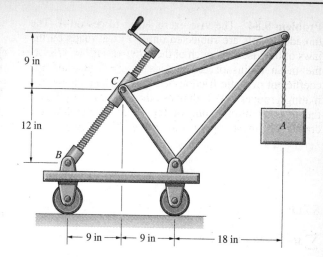

Solution: Denote the lower right pin support by D. The length of the connecting member CD is $L_{CD} = \sqrt{9^2 + 12^2} = 15$ in. The angle between the threaded shaft and member CD is

$$\beta = 2\tan^{-1}\left(\frac{9}{12}\right) = 73.74°.$$

The sum of the moments about D is

$$\sum M_D = L_{CD}F\cos(90 - \beta) - 18W = 0,$$

from which $F = 500$ lb. The pitch angle is

$$\alpha = \tan^{-1}\left(\frac{p}{2\pi r}\right) = 2.28°.$$

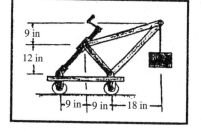

The angle of static friction is $\theta_s = \tan^{-1}(0.24) = 13.5°$. The moment needed to start the threaded collar in motion is

$$M = rF\tan(\theta_s + \alpha) = \left(\frac{1}{12}\right)(500)\tan(13.5° + 2.28°)$$

$$= 11.77 \text{ ft-lb}$$

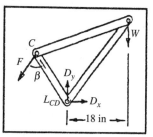

Problem 9.87 In Problem 9.86, if the system is stationary in the position shown, what couple is necessary to start the shaft rotating to lower the load?

Solution: Use the results of the solution to Problem 9.86. The moment is $M = rF\tan(\theta_s - \alpha)$, where

$$r = \left(\frac{1}{12}\right) \text{ ft,}$$

$$F = 500 \text{ lb,}$$

$$\theta_s = 13.5°,$$

and $\alpha = 2.28°$,

from which $M = 8.26$ ft lb

Problem 9.88 The car jack is operated by turning the threaded shaft at A. The threaded shaft fits into a mating groove in the collar at B, causing the collar to move relative to the shaft as the shaft turns. As a result, points B and D move closer together or farther apart, causing point C (where the jack is in contact with the car) to move up or down. The pitch of the threaded shaft is $p = 5$ mm, the mean radius of the thread is $r = 10$ mm, and the coefficient of kinetic friction between the thread and the mating groove is 0.15. What couple is necessary to turn the shaft at a constant rate and raise the jack when it is in the position shown if $F = 6.5$ kN?

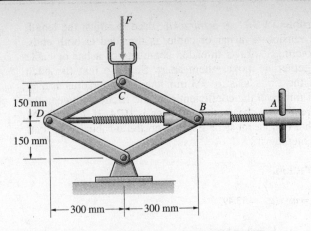

Solution: Isolate members BC and BD. Assume that half the car load is carried by these members. The equilibrium conditions for member BC are:

$$\sum F_x = C_x - B_x = 0,$$

$$\sum M_B = 0.3\left(\frac{F}{2}\right) - 0.15C_x = 0.$$

These equations are solved for

$$\frac{F}{2} = \frac{6.5}{2} = 3.25 \text{ kN}$$

to obtain $B_x = 6.5$ kN, which is the force on the collar to be balanced by the rotating threaded shaft. The pitch angle is

$$\alpha = \tan^{-1}\left(\frac{5}{2\pi 10}\right) = 4.55°.$$

The angle of kinetic friction is

$$\theta_s = \tan^{-1}(0.15) = 8.53°.$$

The moment required to rotate the shaft at a constant rate is

$$M = (0.01)(6.5)\tan(8.53° + 4.55°) = 0.0151 \text{ kN}$$

$$m = 15.1 \text{ N m}$$

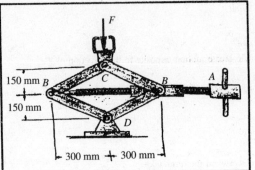

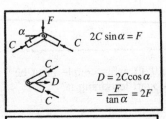

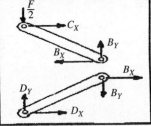

Problem 9.89 In Problem 9.88, what couple is necessary to turn the threaded shaft at a constant rate and lower the jack when it is in the position shown if the force $F = 6.5$ kN?

Solution: Use the results of the solution of Problem 9.88. The moment required to lower the jack at a constant rate is $M = rB\tan(\theta_k - \alpha)$, where $r = 0.01$ m, $B = 6500$ N, $\theta_k = 8.53°$, $\alpha = 4.55°$, from which $M = 4.52$ N-m

Problem 9.90 A *turnbuckle*, used to adjust the length or tension of a bar or cable, is threaded at both ends. Rotating it draws threaded segments of a bar or cable together or moves them apart. Suppose that the pitch of the threads is $p = 3$ mm their mean radius is $r = 25$ mm, and the coefficient of static friction between the threads and the mating grooves is 0.24. If $T = 800$ N, what couple must be exerted on the turnbuckle to start tightening it?

Solution:

$\theta_s = a \tan(\mu_s) = 13.49°$

$\alpha = a \tan\left(\dfrac{p}{2\pi r}\right) = 1.09°$

$M = rT \tan(\theta_s + \alpha)$

since M tends to create motion opposite to the direction of T.

$M = (0.025)(800 \text{ N}) \tan(14.59°)$

$M = 5.21$ N-m

for each screw.

There are two screws in the turnbuckle.

$\therefore M = 10.42$ N-m

Problem 9.91 In Problem 9.90, what couple must be exerted on the turnbuckle to start loosening it?

Solution:

$\theta_s = a \tan(\mu_s) = 13.49°$

$\alpha = a \tan\left(\dfrac{p}{2\pi r}\right) = 1.09°$

$M = rT \tan(\theta_s - \alpha)$

$r = 0.025$ m,

$T = 800$ N

$M = 4.40$ N-m

for one screw. The turnbuckle has two screws.

$\therefore M_{\text{TOTAL}} = 8.80$ N-m

Problem 9.92 Member *BE* of the frame has a turn-buckle. (See Problem 9.90.) The threads have pitch $p = 1$ mm, their mean radius is $r = 6$ mm, and the coefficient of static friction between the threads and the mating grooves is 0.2. What couple must be exerted on the turnbuckle to start loosening it?

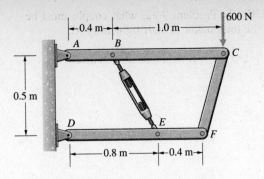

Solution: This problem has two ports. First, we find the tension in the two force member *BE*. Then we analyze the turnbuckle.

$$\tan\theta = \frac{0.5}{0.4}$$

$$\theta = 51.3°$$

$$\tan\phi = \frac{0.5}{0.2}$$

$$\phi = 68.2°$$

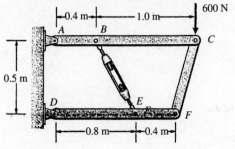

$$\sum F_x: \quad A_x + T_{BE}\cos\theta + F_{CF}\cos\phi = 0 \qquad (1)$$

$$\sum F_y: \quad A_y - T_{BE}\sin\theta + F_{CF}\sin\phi - 600 = 0 \qquad (2)$$

$$\sum M_A: \quad -0.4T_{BE}\sin\theta + 1.4F_{CF}\sin\phi - 1.4(600) = 0 \quad (3)$$

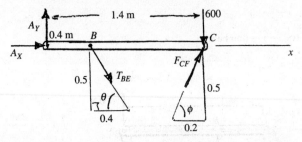

$$\sum F_x: \quad D_x - T_{BE}\cos\theta - F_{CF}\cos\phi = 0 \qquad (4)$$

$$\sum F_y: \quad D_y + T_{BE}\sin\theta - F_{CF}\sin\phi = 0 \qquad (5)$$

$$\sum M_D: \quad 0.8T_{BE}\sin\theta - 1.2F_{CF}\sin\phi = 0 \qquad (6)$$

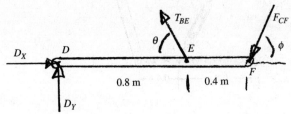

Unknowns: A_x, A_y, D_x, D_y, T_{BE}, F_{CF} (6 eqns, 6 unknowns)

Solving,

$$T_{BE} = 2017 \text{ N}$$

Now to analyze the turnbuckle

$$\tan\theta_s = \mu_s = 0.2$$

$$\theta_s = 11.31°$$

$$\tan\alpha = \frac{p}{2\pi r} = \frac{1}{2\pi(6)}$$

$$\alpha = 1.52°$$

For one screw, to loosen

$$M = rT_{BE}\tan(\theta_s - \alpha)$$

$$M = 2.09 \text{ N}$$

For two screws (turnbuckle)

$$M_{TOTAL} = 4.18 \text{ N-m}$$

Problem 9.93 In Problem 9.92, what couple must be
exerted on the turnbuckle to start tightening it?

Solution: In Problem 9.92, the tension in the turnbuckle was

$T_{BE} = 2017$ N

$r = 0.006$ m

$p = 0.001$ mm

$\tan \theta_s = \mu_s = 0.2$

$\theta_s = 11.31°$

$\tan \alpha = \dfrac{p}{2\pi r}$

$\alpha = 1.52°$

For one screw, to tighten,

$M = rT_{BE} \tan(\theta_s + \alpha)$

$M = 2.756$ N-m

For two screws (turnbuckle)

$M = 5.51$ N-m

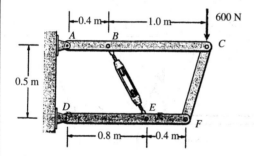

Problem 9.94 Members CD and DG of the truss have turnbuckles. (See Problem 9.90.) The pitch of the threads is $p = 4$ mm, their mean radius is $r = 10$ mm, and the coefficient of static friction between the threads and the mating grooves is 0.18. What couple must be exerted on the turnbuckle of member CD to start loosening it?

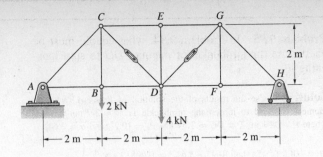

Solution: *The complete structure as a free body:* The equilibrium conditions:

$$\sum M_A = -2(2) - 4(4) + 8H = 0,$$

from which $H = \dfrac{20}{8} = 2.5$ kN.

$$\sum F_y = A_y + H - 2 - 4 = 0,$$

from which $A_Y = 3.5$ kN.

$$\sum F_x = A_x = 0.$$

The method of joints: The interior angles GHF, DFG, BDC, and BAC are each $\beta = 45°$.

Joint H: (1) $0 = -GH \cos \beta - FH$,

(2) $0 = GH \sin \beta + H$.

Joint F: (3) $0 = FH - DF$,

(4) $GF = 0$.

Joint G: (5) $0 = GH \cos \beta - EG - DG \cos \beta$,

(6) $0 = -GH \sin \beta - DG \sin \beta$.

Joint E: (7) $0 = EG - CE$,

(8) $0 = DE$.

Joint D: (9) $0 = DG \cos \beta - CD \cos \beta + DF - DB$,

(10) $0 = DG \sin \beta + CD \sin \beta + DE - 4$.

Joint C: (11) $0 = CD \cos \beta - AC \cos \beta + CE$,

(12) $0 = -CD \sin \beta - AC \sin \beta - BC$.

Joint B : (13) $0 = BD - AB$,

(14) $0 = BC - 2$.

Joint A: (15) $0 = AB + A_x + AC \cos \beta$,

(16) $0 = A_y + AC \sin \beta$.

These equations are solved: The results in detail:

$GH = -3.54$ kN,

$FH = 2.5$ kN,

$DF = 2.5$ kN,

$GF = 0$,

$EG = -5$ kN,

$DG = 3.54$ kN,

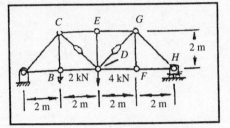

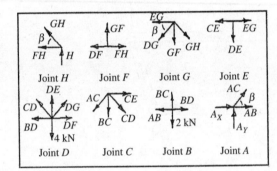

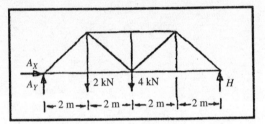

$DE = 0$,

$CD = 2.12$ kN,

$AC = -4.95$ kN,

$BC = 2$ kN,

$BD = 3.5$ kN,

$AB = 3.5$ kN.

The members of interest here are $CD = 2.12$ kN and $DG = 3.54$ kN. The pitch angle is

$$\alpha = \tan^{-1} \left(\frac{4}{(2\pi)(10)} \right) = 3.64°.$$

The static friction angle is $\theta_s = \tan^{-1}(0.18) = 10.20°$. The moment required to loosen the turnbuckle is

$$M = 2(0.01)(2.12) \tan(10.2° - 3.64°) = 0.00488 \text{ kN}$$

$$m = 4.88 \text{ N m}$$

Problem 9.95 In Problem 9.94, what couple must be exerted on the turnbuckle of member DG to start loosening it?

Solution: Use the results of the solution of Problem 9.94. The moment required to loosen the turnbuckle is $M = 2rT \tan(\theta_s - \alpha)$, where $r = 0.01$ m, $T = DG = 3.54$ kN, $\theta_s = 10.2°$, and $\alpha = 3.64°$

$$M = 2(0.01)(3.54) \tan(10.2° - 3.64°) = 0.00813 \text{ kN}$$

$$m = 8.13 \text{ N m}$$

Problem 9.96 The load $W = 800$ N can be raised or lowered by rotating the threaded shaft. The distances are $b = 75$ mm and $h = 200$ mm. The pinned bars are each 300 mm in length. The pitch of the threaded shaft is $p = 5$ mm, the mean radius of the thread is $r = 15$ mm, and the coefficient of kinetic friction between the thread and the mating groove is 0.2. When the system is in the position shown, what couple must be exerted to turn the threaded shaft at a constant rate, raise the load?

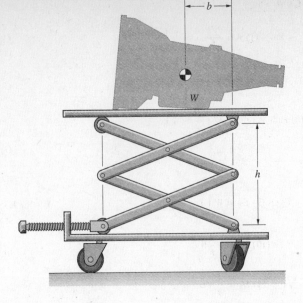

Solution: The vertical distances HE, BE, AD, DG are 100 mm. The included angle ABC is

$$\beta = \sin^{-1}\left(\frac{50 \text{ mm}}{150 \text{ mm}}\right) = 19.47°.$$

The distance $L = 300 \cos \beta$ mm. Isolate the members and write the equilibrium equations, beginning at the top: *Isolate the frame AB which supports the load W.* The equilibrium conditions are

(1) $\sum M_B = -AL + Wb = 0,$

(2) $\sum F_y = A - W + B_y = 0,$

$\sum F_x = B_x = 0$

Isolate BD: (3) $\sum F_y = -B_y - C_y + D_y = 0,$

(4) $\sum F_x = -C_x + D_x = 0,$

(5) $\sum M_D = \left(\frac{h}{4}\right)C_x - \left(\frac{L}{2}\right)C_y - LB = 0$

Isolate DH: (6) $\sum F_y = -D_y - F_y + H_y = 0,$

(7) $\sum F_x = -D_x - F_x + H_x = 0,$

(8) $\sum M_H = \left(\frac{h}{4}\right)F_x + \left(\frac{L}{2}\right)F_y + LD_y$

$+ \left(\frac{h}{2}\right)D_x = 0$

Isolate AE (9) $\sum F_y = -A + C_y + E_y = 0,$

(10) $\sum F_x = C_x + E_x = 0,$

(11) $\sum M_E = -\left(\frac{h}{4}\right)(C_x) - \left(\frac{L}{2}\right)C_y + LA = 0.$

Isolate EG (12) $\sum F_y = -E_y + F_y + G_y = 0,$

(13) $\sum F_x = -E_x + F_x + G_x = 0,$

(14) $\sum M_G = -\frac{h}{4}F_x + \left(\frac{L}{2}\right)F_y - LE_y$

$+ \left(\frac{h}{2}\right)E_x = 0.$

These 14 equations in 14 unknowns are to be solved to determine the reaction G_x, which is the force that the threaded shaft must overcome to raise the load at a constant rate. An analytic solution is obtained as follows:

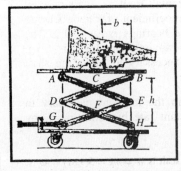

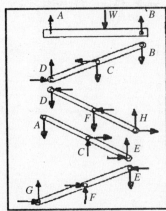

9.96 *Contd.*

From (1) $A = \dfrac{Wb}{L}$.

From (2) $B = W\left(1 - \dfrac{b}{L}\right)$.

From (8) and (11) $C_y = W\left(\dfrac{2b}{L} - 1\right)$,

$C_x = \dfrac{2WL}{h}$.

From (9) $E_y = W\left(1 - \dfrac{b}{L}\right)$.

From (10) $E_x = -\dfrac{2}{h}WL$.

From (4) $D_x = \dfrac{2}{h}WL$

From (3) $D_y = \dfrac{Wb}{L}$.

From (8) and (14) $F_y = W\left(1 - \dfrac{2b}{L}\right)$,

$F_x = \dfrac{6WL}{h}$.

From (12) $G_y = \dfrac{Wb}{L}$

Check: This value of G_y is expected from the overall equilibrium conditions. *check.* From (13)

$$G_x = \dfrac{4WL}{h}.$$

Substitute:

$$G_x = \dfrac{1200W}{h}\cos\beta N.$$

Note that

$$\cos\beta = \sqrt{1 - \left(\dfrac{h}{600}\right)^2},$$

from which

$$G_x = 2W\dfrac{\sqrt{600^2 - h^2}}{h}.$$

The pitch angle is

$$\alpha = \tan^{-1}\left(\dfrac{5}{2\pi(15)}\right) = 3.037°.$$

The angle of kinetic friction is

$$\theta_k = \tan^{-1}(0.2) = 11.31°.$$

The moment required to raise the load at a constant rate:

$$M = rG_x\tan(\theta_k + \alpha) = 0.003836G_x = 17.36 \text{ N m}.$$

Problem 9.97 The horizontal shaft is supported by two journal bearings. The coefficient of kinetic friction between the shaft and the bearings is $\mu_k = 0.2$. The radius of the shaft is 20 mm, and its mass is 5 kg. Determine the couple M necessary to rotate the shaft at a constant rate.

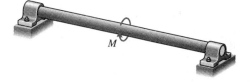

Strategy: You can obtain the moment necessary to rotate the shaft at a constant rate by replacing θ_s by θ_k in Eq. (9.12).

Solution: The weight of the shaft is $W = mg = 5(9.81) = 49$ N, divided between two bearings. The angle of kinetic friction is $\theta_k = \tan^{-1}(0.2) = 11.31°$. The moment per bearing is

$$M = \left(\dfrac{W}{2}\right)(0.02)\sin\theta_k = 0.096 \text{ N m}.$$

The total moment is $M_t = 0.192$ N m

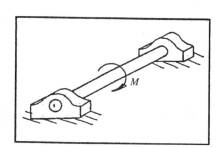

Problem 9.98 The horizontal shaft is supported by two journal bearings. The coefficient of static friction between the shaft and the bearings is $\mu_s = 0.3$. The radius of the shaft is 20 mm, and its mass is 5 kg. Determine the largest mass m that can be suspended as shown without causing the stationary shaft to slip in the bearings.

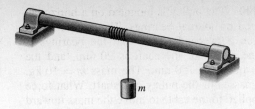

Solution: The weight of the shaft is $W = mg = 5(9.81) = 49$ N. This weight is divided between two bearings. The angle of static friction is $\theta_s = \tan^{-1}(0.3) = 16.7°$. The load per bearing is

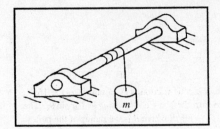

$$F = \frac{W + W_m}{2},$$

and the moment required to start rotation is

$$M_m = (W + W_m)r \sin \theta_s$$

where W_m is the suspended weight,

$$W_m = \frac{M_m}{r}.$$

From which

$$W_m r = (W + W_m)r \sin \theta_s,$$

from which

$$m = \frac{W}{g}\left(\frac{\sin \theta_s}{1 - \sin \theta_s}\right) = 2.02 \text{ kg}.$$

Problem 9.99 Suppose that in Problem 9.98 the mass $m = 8$ kg and the coefficient of kinetic friction between the shaft and bearings is $\mu_k = 0.26$. What couple must be applied to the shaft to raise the mass at a constant rate?

Solution: From the solution to Problem 9.98 the moment required is

$$M_{\text{applied}} = (W + W_m)r \sin \theta_k,$$

where $W_m = mg$ is the weight of the suspended mass. The moment required to raise the suspended mass is $M_m = W_m r$. The total moment is the sum of the moment required to turn the shaft and the moment required to raise the mass:

$$M_{\text{total}} = (W + mg)r \sin \theta_k + W_m r$$

$$= (49 + 78.5)(0.02)\sin(14.6°) + 1.57 = 2.21 \text{ N m}$$

Problem 9.100 The pulley is mounted on a horizontal shaft supported by journal bearings. The coefficient of kinetic friction between the shaft and the bearings is $\mu_k = 0.3$. The radius of the shaft is 20 mm, and the radius of the pulley is 150 mm. The mass $m = 10$ kg. Neglect the masses of the pulley and shaft. What force T must be applied to the cable to move the mass upward at a constant rate?

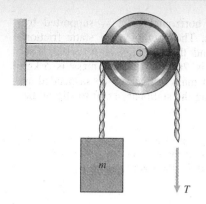

Solution: The angle of kinetic friction is $\theta_k = \tan^{-1}(\mu_k) = 16.7°$. The moment required to turn the shaft is $M = (mg + T)r \sin \theta_k$. The applied moment is $M = (T - mg)R$ where R is the radius of the pulley. Equating and reducing:

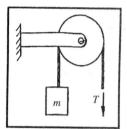

$$T = mg \left(\frac{1 + \dfrac{r}{R} \sin \theta_k}{1 - \dfrac{r}{R} \sin \theta_k} \right) = (98.1) \left(\frac{1.0383}{0.9617} \right) = 105.92 \text{ N}$$

Problem 9.101 In Problem 9.100, what force T must be applied to the cable to lower the mass at a constant rate?

Solution: Form the solution to Problem 9.100, $\theta_k = \tan^{-1}(\mu_k) = 16.7°$, and $M = (mg + T)r \sin \theta_k$. The applied moment is $M = (mg - T)R$. Substitute and reduce:

$$T = mg \left(\frac{1 - \dfrac{r}{R} \sin \theta_k}{1 + \dfrac{r}{R} \sin \theta_k} \right) = (98.1) \left(\frac{0.9617}{1.0383} \right) = 90.86 \text{ N}$$

Problem 9.102 The pulley of 8-in. radius is mounted on a shaft of 1-in. radius. The shaft is supported by two journal bearings. The coefficient of static friction between the bearings and the shaft is $\mu_s = 0.15$. Neglect the weights of the pulley and shaft. The 50-Ib block A rests on the floor. If sand is slowly added to the bucket B, what do the bucket and sand weigh when the shaft slips in the bearings?

Solution: (See Problem 9.100). The angle of static friction is $\theta_s = \tan^{-1}(\mu_s) = 8.53°$. The moment required to start rotation for both bearings is $M = r(B + W) \sin \theta_s$. The applied moment is $M = (B - W)R$, where R is the radius of the pulley. Substitute and reduce:

$$B = W \left(\frac{1 + \dfrac{r}{R} \sin \theta_s}{1 - \dfrac{r}{R} \sin \theta_s} \right) = (50) \left(\frac{1.0185}{0.9815} \right) = 51.9 \text{ lb}$$

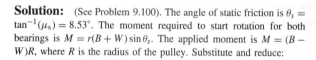

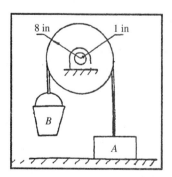

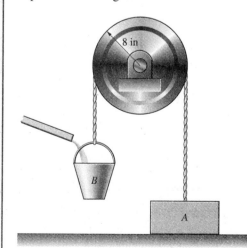

Problem 9.103 The pulley of 50-mm radius is mounted on a shaft of 10-mm radius. The shaft is supported by two journal bearings. The mass of the block A is 8 kg. Neglect the weights of the pulley and shaft. If a force $T = 84$ N is necessary to raise the block A at a constant rate, what is the coefficient of kinetic friction between the shaft and the bearings?

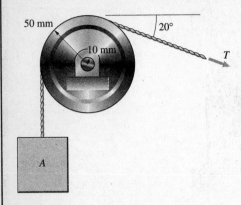

Solution: The weight is $W = mg = 78.5$ N. The force on the pulley is

$$F = \sqrt{(W + T \sin \alpha)^2 + (T \cos \alpha)^2},$$

where $\alpha = 20°$.

$$F = \sqrt{107.2^2 + 78.9^2} = 133.13 \text{ N}.$$

The moment required to raise the mass at constant rate for both bearings is $M = rF \sin \theta_k = 1.33 \sin \theta_k$. The applied moment is $M = (T - W)R = 0.276$ N m. Substitute and reduce:

$$\sin \theta_k = \frac{(T - W)R}{rF} = \frac{0.276}{1.33} = 0.2073,$$

from which

$$\theta_k = 11.96°$$

and $\mu_k = \tan(11.96°) = 0.2119$

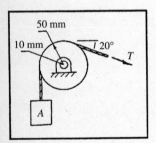

Problem 9.104 The mass of the suspended object is 4 kg. The pulley has a 100-mm radius and is rigidly attached to a horizontal shaft supported by journal bearings. The radius of the horizontal shaft is 10 mm and the coefficient of kinetic friction between the shaft and the bearings is 0.26. What tension must the person exert on the rope to raise the load at a constant rate?

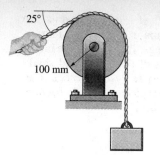

Solution:

$R = 0.1$ m

$\mu_k = 0.26$

Shaft radius 0.01 m

$\mu_k(\text{shaft}) = 0.26$

$\tan\theta_k = \mu_k$

$\theta_k = 14.57°$

$M_s = rF\sin\theta_k$

$m = 4$ kg

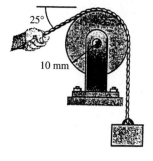

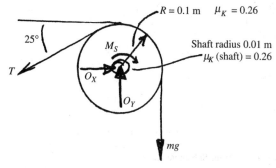

To Find F, we must find the forces acting on the shaft.

$\sum F_x: \quad O_x - T\cos 25° = 0 \qquad$ **(1)**

$\sum F_y: \quad O_y - T\sin 25° - mg = 0 \quad$ **(2)**

$\qquad F = \sqrt{O_x^2 + O_y^2} \qquad\qquad$ **(3)**

$\sum M_o: \quad RT - Rmg - M_s = 0 \qquad$ **(4)**

$\qquad M_s = rF\sin\theta_k \qquad\qquad$ **(5)**

Unknowns: O_x, O_y, T, M_s, F

Solving, we get

$T = 40.9$ N

Also,

$F = 67.6$ N,

$M_s = 0.170$ N-m

$O_x = 37.1$ N,

$O_y = 56.5$ N

Problem 9.105   In Problem 9.104, what tension must the person exert to lower the load at a constant rate?

Solution: This problem is very much like Problem 9.104—only the direction of M_s is changed. The analysis is the same except equation (4), which becomes

$$RT - Rmg + M_s = 0 \quad \textbf{(4)}$$

We again have 5 eqns. in 5 unknowns. Solving,

$T = 37.6$ N

Also

$F = 64.8$ N,

$M_s = 0.163$ N-m

$O_x = 34.1$ N,

$O_y = 55.1$ N

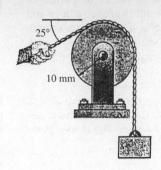

Problem 9.106   The radius of the pulley is 200 mm, and it is mounted on a shaft of 20-mm radius. The coefficient of static friction between the pulley and shaft is $\mu_s = 0.18$. If $F_A = 200$ N, what is the largest force F_B that can be applied without causing the pulley to turn? Neglect the weight of the pulley.

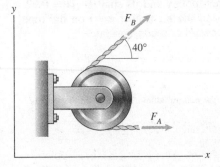

Solution: The magnitude of the force on the shaft supporting the pulley is

$$F = \sqrt{(F_A + F_B \cos 40°)^2 + (F_B \sin 40°)^2}. \quad \textbf{(1)}$$

The couple exerted on the pulley by the rope is $M = (0.2 \text{ m})(F_B - F_A)$. (2) From Equation (9.12), the largest couple which will not cause the shaft to slip is $M = rF \sin\theta_s$, where $r = 0.02$ m and $\theta_s = \arctan(0.18) = 10.2°$. Substituting Equations (1) and (2) into Equation (3), we obtain

$$(0.2)(F_B - 200)$$

$$= (0.02) \sin(10.2°)\sqrt{(200 + F_B \cos 40°)^2 + (F_B \sin 40°)^2}.$$

Solving this equation, we obtain $F_B = 206.8$ N.

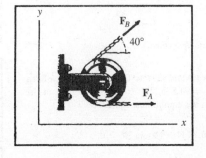

Problem 9.107   The mass of the pulley in Problem 9.106 is 4 kg. The force $F_A = 200$ N. Including the effect of the weight of the pulley, determine the largest force F_B that can be applied without causing the pulley to turn, and compare your answer to that of Problem 9.106.

Solution: The solution is identical to the solution of Problem 9.106 with Equation (1) replaced by

$$F = \sqrt{(F_A + F_B \cos 40°)^2 + [F_B \sin 40°]^2}.$$

The result is $F_B = 206.6$ N.

Problem 9.108 The two pulleys have a radius of 4 in. and are mounted on shafts of 1-in. radius supported by journal bearings. Neglect the weights of the pulleys and shafts. The tension in the spring is 40 lb. The coefficient of kinetic friction between the shafts and the bearings is $\mu_k = 0.3$. What couple M is required to turn the left pulley at a constant rate?

Solution: The angle of kinetic friction is $\theta_k = \tan^{-1}(0.3) = 16.7°$. The load on the bearings is $F = 40$ lb. The moment required to turn both pulleys at constant rate is $M = 2rF \sin \theta_k$. This is equal to the applied moment,

$$M_{\text{applied}} = 2rF \sin \theta_k = (2)\left(\frac{1}{12}\right) 40 \sin(16.7°) = 1.92 \text{ ft lb}$$

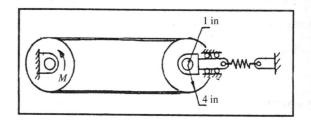

Problem 9.109 The weights of the two boxes are $W_1 = 100$ lb and $W_2 = 50$ lb. The coefficient of kinetic friction between the left box and the inclined surface is $\mu_k = 0.14$. Each pulley has a 6-in. radius and is mounted on a shaft of $\frac{1}{2}$-in. radius. The coefficient of kinetic friction between each pulley and its shaft is $\mu_k = 0.12$. Determine the tension the man must exert on the rope to pull the boxes upward at a constant rate.

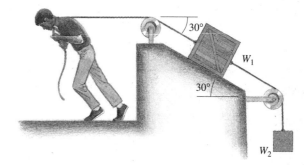

Solution: Consider the bottom pulley: The force on the shaft is

$$F = \sqrt{(T_A \cos 30°)^2 + (T_A \sin 30° - 50)^2}.$$

(1) The couple exerted on the pulley is $M = (6 \text{ in})(T_A - 50)$.
(2) The angle of kinetic friction is $\theta_s = \arctan(0.12) = 6.84°$ M and F are related by

$$m = rF \sin \theta_s = \left(\frac{1}{2} \text{ in}\right) F \sin 6.84°.$$

(3) Substituting Equations (1) and (2) into Equation (3) and solving for T_A, we obtain $T_A = 50.5$ lb. The free body diagram of the box is as shown. From the equilibrium equations

$$\sum F_x = T_A - T_B + 0.14 N + 100 \sin 30° = 0,$$

$$\sum F_y = N - 100 \cos 30° = 0$$

we obtain $T_B = 112.6$ N. Now consider the top pulley: The force on the shaft is

$$F = \sqrt{(T_B \cos 30° - T)^2 + (-T_B \sin 30°)^2}.$$

The couple exerted on the pulley is $M = (6 \text{ in})(T - T_B)$. M and F are related by

$$M = rF \sin \theta_s = \left(\frac{1}{2} \text{ in.}\right) F \sin 6.84°.$$

Substituting Equations (4) and (5) into Equation (6) and solving for T we obtain $T = 113.2$ N.

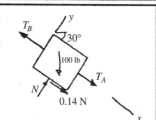

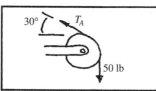

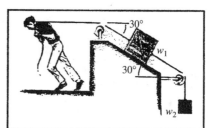

Problem 9.110 Each pulley has a radius of 100 mm and a mass of 2 kg. Both are mounted on shafts of 5-mm radius supported by journal bearings. The coefficient of kinetic friction between the shafts and the bearings is $\mu_k = 0.18$. The mass of A is 14 kg. What force T is required to raise A at a constant rate?

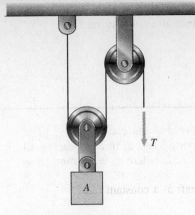

Solution: The angle of kinetic friction is $\theta_k = \tan^{-1}(0.18) = 10.2°$. The weight of A is $W_A = 14\,g = 137.34$ N. The weight of each pulley is $W_P = 2\,g = 19.62$ N. Denote the tension in the left cable by P and the tension in the middle cable by Q.

Consider the left Pulley: The force on the pulley is $W = W_A + W_P = 156.96$ N. The moment required to turn the pulley on its bearing is $M = rW \sin\theta_k$. The applied moment is $M_{applied} = (Q - P)R$, from which $(Q - P)R = rW \sin\theta_k$. The sum of the tensions in the cables: $P + Q = W$, from which

$$Q = \frac{W}{2}\left(1 + \left(\frac{r}{R}\right)\sin\theta_k\right) = 79.18 \text{ N}.$$

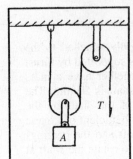

Consider the right Pulley: The force on the pulley is $F = Q + T + W_P$. The moment required to turn the pulley on its bearing is $M = r(Q + T + W_P)\sin\theta_k$.

The applied moment is $M_{applied} = (T - Q)R$, from which $(T - Q)R = r(T + Q + W_P)\sin\theta_k$. Reduce algebraically:

$$T = \left(\frac{Q\left(1 + \left(\frac{r}{R}\right)\sin\theta_k\right) + W_P\left(\frac{r}{R}\right)\sin\theta_k}{1 - \left(\frac{r}{R}\right)\sin\theta_k}\right) = 80.77 \text{ N}$$

Problem 9.111 The circular flat-ended shaft is pressed into the thrust bearing by an axial load of 100 N. Neglect the weight of the shaft. The coefficients of friction between the end of the shaft and the bearing are $\mu_s = 0.20$ and $\mu_k = 0.15$. What is the largest couple M that can be applied to the stationary shaft without causing it to rotate in the bearing?

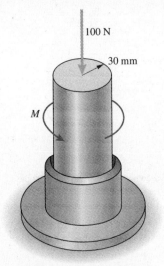

Solution: The bearing meets the conditions for Eq. (9.14). For impending rotation, the moment is

$$M = \frac{2}{3}\mu_s Fr = \left(\frac{2}{3}\right)(0.2)(100)(0.03) = 0.4 \text{ N m}$$

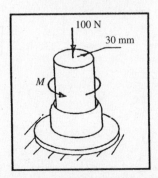

Problem 9.112 In Problem 9.111, what couple M is required to rotate the shaft at a constant rate?

Solution: The bearing meets the conditions for Eq. (10.17). The moment required to sustain a constant rate of rotation is

$$M = \left(\frac{2}{3}\right)\mu_k F r = \left(\frac{2}{3}\right)(0.15)(100)(0.03) = 0.3 \text{ N m}$$

Problem 9.113 Suppose that the end of the shaft in Problem 9.111 is supported by a thrust bearing of the type shown in Fig. 9.22, where $r_o = 30$ mm, $r_i = 10$ mm, $\alpha = 30°$, and $\mu_k = 0.15$. What couple M is required to rotate the shaft at a constant rate?

Solution: The bearing meets the conditions for Eq (9.13). The moment required to sustain a constant rate of rotation is

$$M = \left(\frac{2\mu_k F}{3\cos\alpha}\right)\left(\frac{r_o^3 - r_i^3}{r_o^2 - r_i^2}\right) = 0.3753 \text{ N m}$$

Problem 9.114 The disk D is rigidly attached to the vertical shaft. The shaft has flat ends supported by thrust bearings. The disk and the shaft together have a mass of 220 kg and the diameter of the shaft is 50 mm. The vertical force exerted on the end of the shaft by the upper thrust bearing is 440 N. The coefficient of kinetic friction between the ends of the shaft and the bearings is 0.25. What couple M is required to rotate the shaft at a constant rate?

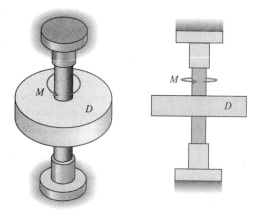

Solution: There are two thrust bearings, one at the top and one at the bottom

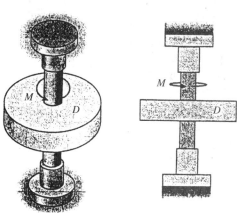

$F_U = 440$ N

$m = 220$ kg

$\sum F_y:$

$F_L - F_U - mg = 0$

$F_L = 2598.2$ N.

The couple necessary to turn D at a constant rate is the sum of the couples for the two bearings.

$M_U = \frac{2}{3}\mu_k F_U r$

$M_L = \frac{2}{3}\mu_k F_L r$

$r = 0.025$ m

$\mu_k = 0.25$

Solving,

$M_U = 1.833$ N-m

$M_L = 10.826$

$M_{TOTAL} = 12.7$ N-m

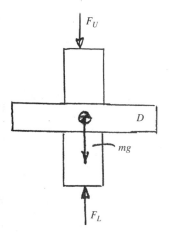

Problem 9.115 Suppose that the ends of the shaft in Problem 9.114 are supported by thrust bearings of the type shown in Fig. 9.22, where $r_o = 25$ mm, $r_i = 6$ mm, $\alpha = 45°$, and $\mu_k = 0.25$. What couple M is required to rotate the shaft at a constant rate?

Solution: There are two thrust bearings, one at the top and one at the bottom.

$F_U = 440$ N

$m = 220$ kg

$\sum F_y:$

$F_L - F_U - mg = 0$

$F_L = 2598.2$ N.

The couple necessary to turn D at a constant rate is the sum of the couples for the two bearings.

For the bearings used

$$m = \frac{2\mu_k F}{3\cos\alpha}\frac{(r_o^3 - r_i^3)}{(r_o^2 - r_i^2)}$$

$\alpha = 45°, \quad r_o = 0.025$ m

$\mu_k = 0.25, \quad r_i = 0.006$ m

Thus,

$$M_U = \frac{2\mu_k F_U}{3\cos\alpha}\frac{(r_o^3 - r_i^3)}{(r_o^2 - r_i^2)} = 2.7 \text{ N-m}$$

$$M_L = \frac{2\mu_k F_L}{3\cos\alpha}\frac{(r_o^3 - r_i^3)}{(r_o^2 - r_i^2)} = 16.0 \text{ N-m}$$

$M_{\text{TOTAL}} = M_U + M_L = 18.7$ N-m

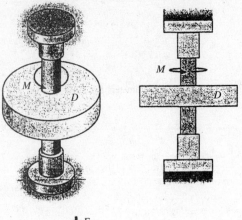

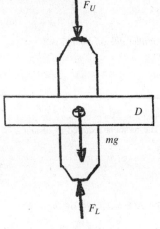

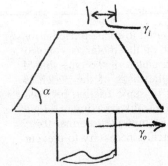

Problem 9.116 The shaft is supported by thrust bearings that subject it to an axial load of 800 N. The coefficients of kinetic friction between the shaft and the left and right bearings are 0.20 and 0.26, respectively. What couple is required to rotate the shaft at a constant rate?

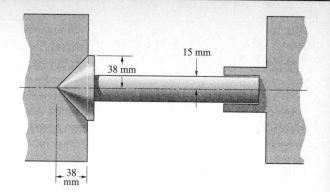

Solution: *The left bearing:* The parameters are

$r_o = 38$ mm,

$r_i = 0$,

$\alpha = 45°$,

$\mu_k = 0.2$,

and $F = 800$ N.

The moment required to sustain a constant rate of rotation is

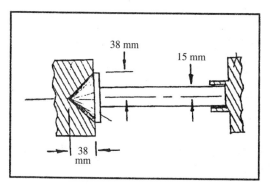

$$M_{\text{left}} = \frac{2\mu_k F}{3 \cos \alpha} \left(\frac{r_o^3 - r_i^3}{r_o^2 - r_i^2} \right) = 5.73 \text{ N m}.$$

The right bearing: This is a flat-end bearing. The parameters are $\mu_k = 0.26$, $r = 15$ mm, and $F = 800$ N. The moment required to sustain a constant rate of rotation is

$$M_{\text{right}} = \frac{2\mu_k F r}{3} = 2.08 \text{ N m}.$$

The sum of the moments: $M = 5.73 + 2.08 = 7.81$ N m

Problem 9.117 A motor is used to rotate a paddle for mixing chemicals. The shaft of the motor is coupled to the paddle using a friction clutch of the type shown in Fig. 9.25. The radius of the disks of the clutch is 120 mm, and the coefficient of static friction between the disks is 0.6. If the motor transmits a maximum torque of 15 N-m to the paddle, what minimum normal force between the plates of the clutch is necessary to prevent slipping?

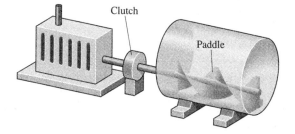

Solution: The moment necessary to prevent slipping is

$$M = \frac{2\mu_s F r}{3} = \frac{2(0.6)(0.12)F}{3} = 15 \text{ N m}.$$

Solve: $F = 312.5$ N

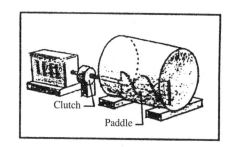

Problem 9.118 The thrust bearing is supported by contact of the collar C with a fixed plate. The area of contact is an annulus with an inside diameter $D_1 = 40$ mm and an outside diameter $D_2 = 120$ mm. The coefficient of kinetic friction between the collar and the plate is $\mu_k = 0.3$. The force $F = 400$ N. What couple M is required to rotate the shaft at a constant rate?

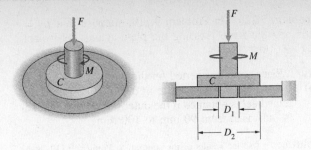

Solution: This is a thrust bearing with parameters

$\mu_k = 0.3$,

$\alpha = 0$,

$r_o = 60$ mm,

$r_i = 20$ mm,

and $F = 400$ N.

The moment required to sustain rotation at a constant rate is

$$M = \frac{2\mu_k F}{3} \left(\frac{r_o^3 - r_i^3}{r_o^2 - r_i^2} \right) = 5.2 \text{ N m}$$

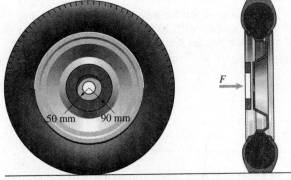

Problem 9.119 An experimental automobile brake design works by pressing the red annular plate against the rotating wheel. If $\mu_k = 0.6$, what force F pressing the plate against the wheel is necessary to exert a couple of 200 N-m on the wheel?

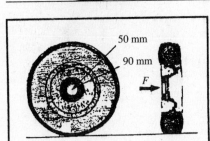

Solution: This is a thrust bearing with parameters

$\mu_k = 0.6$,

$\alpha = 0$,

$r_o = 90$ mm,

$r_i = 50$ mm,

and $M = 200$ N m.

The moment is

$$M = \frac{2\mu_k F}{3} \left(\frac{r_o^3 - r_i^3}{r_o^2 - r_i^2} \right).$$

Solve:

$$F = \frac{3M}{2\mu_k} \left(\frac{r_o^2 - r_i^2}{r_o^3 - r_i^3} \right) = 4635.8 \text{ N-m}$$

Problem 9.120 In Problem 9.119, suppose that $\mu_k = 0.65$ and the force pressing the plate against the wheel is $F = 2$ kN.

(a)   What couple is exerted on the wheel?
(b)   What percentage increase in the couple exerted on the wheel is obtained if the outer radius of the brake is increased from 90 mm to 100 mm?

Solution: Use the results of the solution to Problem 9.119, with parameters $\mu_k = 0.65$, $F = 2$ kN.

(a)   The moment is

$$M = \frac{2\mu_k F}{3}\left(\frac{r_o^3 - r_i^3}{r_o^2 - r_i^2}\right) = 0.0935 \text{ kN-m} = 93.5 \text{ N-m}$$

(b)   The new moment is

$$M = \frac{2\mu_k F}{3}\left(\frac{r_o^3 - r_i^3}{r_o^2 - r_i^2}\right) = 0.1011 \text{ kN-m} = 101.1 \text{ N-m}.$$

The percentage increase is

$$\Delta M\% = \left(\frac{101.1 - 93.5}{93.5}\right)100 = 8.17\%$$

Problem 9.121 The coefficient of static friction between the plates of the car's clutch is 0.8. If the plates are pressed together with a force $F = 2.60$ kN, what is the maximum torque the clutch will support without slipping?

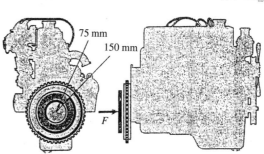

Solution:

$$M = \frac{2\mu_s F}{3\cos\alpha}\frac{(r_o^3 - r_i^3)}{(r_o^2 - r_i^2)}$$

where $\alpha = 90°$, $(\cos\alpha \equiv 1)$

$F = 2600$ N,

$r_o = 0.15$ m

$r_i = 0.075$ m

Solving for M,

$M = 243$ N-m

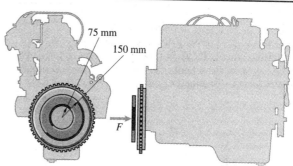

Problem 9.122 The "Morse taper" is used to support the workpiece on a machinist's lathe. The taper is driven into the spindle and is held in place by friction. If the spindle exerts a uniform pressure $p = 15$ psi on the taper and $\mu_s = 0.2$, what couple must be exerted about the axis of the taper to loosen it?

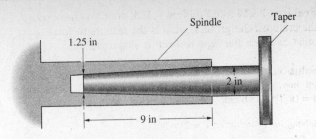

Solution: The outer radius of the taper is $r_o = 1$ in., and the inner radius is $r_i = 0.6.5$ in. The angle of the taper is

$$\alpha = 90 - \tan^{-1}\left(\frac{r_o - r_i}{L}\right) = 90 - \tan^{-1}\left(\frac{1 - 0.625}{9}\right) = 87.6^\circ.$$

The active area of contact of the taper is the area of a truncated cone:

$$A = \frac{\pi(r_o^2 - r_i^2)}{\cos\alpha} = 45.99 \text{ in}^2.$$

Check: This expression can be verified using the Pappus-Guldinus Theorem (see Example 7.15) where

$$y = \frac{r_o + r_i}{2},$$

and $L = \dfrac{r_o - r_i}{\cos\alpha}.$

check. The normal force on the taper is $N = pA = 689.8$ lb, and the axial force on the taper is $F = N\cos\alpha = 28.72$ lb. The taper is equivalent to a thrust bearing with the parameters $\mu_s = 0.2$, $\alpha = 87.6^\circ$, $r_o = 1$ in, $r_i = 0.625$ in, and $F = 28.72$ lb. The moment required to initiate slip is

$$M = \frac{2\mu_s F}{3\cos\alpha}\left(\frac{r_o^3 - r_i^3}{r_o^2 - r_i^2}\right) = 114.1 \text{ in lb} = 9.51 \text{ ft-lb}$$

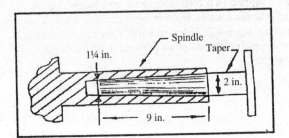

Problem 9.123 Suppose that you want to lift a 50-lb crate off the ground by using a rope looped over a tree limb as shown. The coefficient of static friction between the rope and the limb is 0.4, and the rope is wound 120° around the limb. What force must you exert to lift the crate?

Strategy: The tension necessary to cause impending slip of the rope on the limb is given by Eq. (9.17), with $T_1 = 50$ lb, $\mu_s = 0.4$, and $\beta = (\pi/180)(120)$ rad.

Solution: This meets the conditions for Eq. (9.17). The angle in radians is

$$\beta = (120^\circ)\left(\frac{\pi}{180}\right) = 2.094 \text{ radians.}$$

The force required is $T = 50e^{\mu_s\beta} = 115.6$ lb

Problem 9.124 In Problem 9.123, once you have lifted the crate off the ground, what is the minimum force you must exert on the rope to keep it suspended?

Solution: If T is decreased until slip of the rope toward the left impends, Equation (9.17) is $50 = Te^{\mu_s \beta}$ where $\mu_s = 0.4$ and $\beta = (\pi/180)(120)$ rad.

Solving for T, we obtain $T = 21.6$ lb.

Problem 9.125 *Winches* are used on sailboats to help support the forces exerted by the sails on the ropes (*sheets*) holding them in position. The winch shown is a post that will rotate in the clockwise direction (seen from above), but will not rotate in the counterclockwise direction. The sail exerts a tension $T_S = 800$ N on the sheet, which is wrapped two complete turns around the winch. The coefficient of static friction between the sheet and the winch is $\mu_s = 0.2$. What tension T_C must the crew member exert on the sheet to prevent it from slipping on the winch?

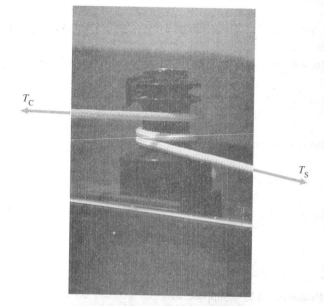

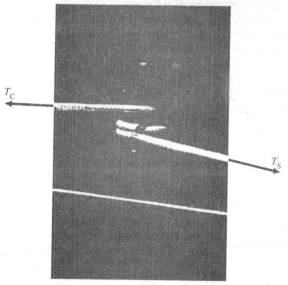

Solution:

$$T_s = T_c e^{\mu_s \beta}$$

$$T_s = 800 \text{ N} \quad \mu_s = 0.2$$

$$\beta = 4\pi$$

Solving,

$$T_c = 64.8 \text{ N}$$

Problem 9.126 The coefficient of kinetic friction between the sheet and the winch in Problem 9.125 is $\mu_k = 0.16$. If the crew member wants to let the sheet slip at a constant rate, releasing the sail, what initial tension T_C must he exert on the sheet as it begins slipping?

Solution:

$$T_s = T_c e^{\mu_k \beta}$$

$T_s = 800 \text{ N}, \mu_k = 0.16$

$\beta = 4\pi$

Solving

$T_c = 107.1 \text{ N}$

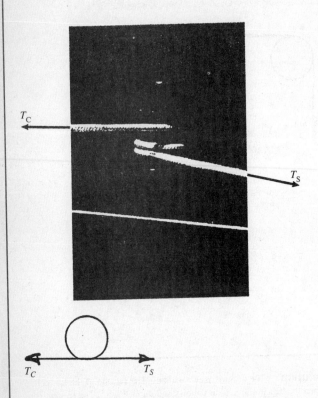

Problem 9.127 The mass of the block A is 18 kg. The rope is wrapped one and one-fourth turns around the fixed wooden post. The coefficients of friction between the rope and post are $\mu_s = 0.15$ and $\mu_k = 0.12$. What force would the person have to exert to raise the block at a constant rate?

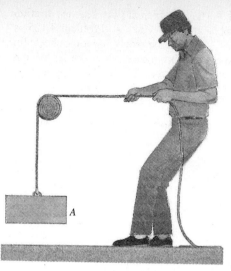

Solution:

$\beta = 2.5\pi$

$\mu_k = 0.12$

$m = 18$ kg.

$T = (mg)e^{\mu_k \beta}$

Solving,

$T = 453$ N

Problem 9.128 The weight of the block A is W. The disk is supported by a smooth bearing. The coefficient of kinetic friction between the disk and the belt is μ_k. What couple M is necessary to turn the disk at a constant rate?

Solution: The angle is $\beta = \pi$ radians. The tension in the left belt when the belt is slipping on the disk is $T_{\text{left}} = We^{\mu_k \beta}$. The tension in the right belt is $T_{\text{right}} = W$. The moment applied to the disk is

$$M = R(T_{\text{left}} - T_{\text{right}}) = R(We^{\mu_k \beta} - W) = RW(e^{\mu_k \pi} - 1).$$

This is the moment that is required to rotate the disk at a constant rate.

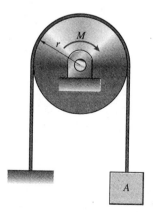

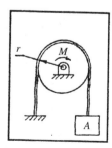

Problem 9.129 The couple required to turn the wheel of the exercise bicycle is adjusted by changing the weight W. The coefficient of kinetic friction between the wheel and the belt is μ_k. Assume the wheel turns clockwise.

(a) Show that the couple M required to turn the wheel is $M = WR(1 - e^{-3.4\mu_k})$.

(b) If $W = 40$ lb and $\mu_k = 0.2$, what force will the scale S indicate when the bicycle is in use?

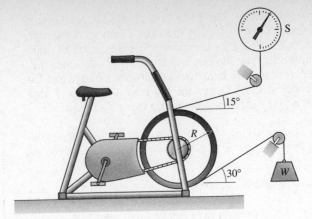

Solution: Let β be the angle in radians of the belt contact with wheel. The tension in the top belt when the belt slips is $T_{upper} = We^{-\mu_k\beta}$. The tension in the lower belt is $T_{lower} = W$. The moment applied to the wheel is

$$M = R(T_{lower} - T_{upper}) = RW(1 - e^{-\mu_k\beta}).$$

This is the moment required to turn the wheel at a constant rate. The angle β in radians is

$$\beta = \pi + (30 - 15)\left(\frac{\pi}{180}\right) = 3.40 \text{ radians},$$

from which $M = RW(1 - e^{-3.4\mu_k})$. (b) The upper belt tension is

$$T_{upper} = 40e^{-3.4(0.2)} = 20.26 \text{ lb}.$$

This is also the reading of the scale S.

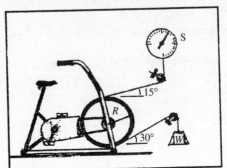

Problem 9.130 The box B weighs 50 lb. The coefficient of friction between the cable and the fixed round supports are $\mu_s = 0.4$ and $\mu_k = 0.3$.

(a) What is the minimum force F required to support the box?

(b) What force F is required to move the box upward at a constant rate?

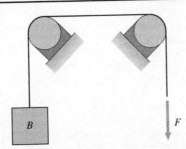

Solution: The angle of contact between the cable and each round support is $\beta = \dfrac{\pi}{2}$ radians.

(a) Denote the tension in the horizontal part of the cable by H. The tension in H is $H = We^{-\mu_s\beta}$. The force F is

$$F = He^{-\mu_s\beta} = We^{-2\mu_s\beta},$$

from which $F = 14.23$ lb is the force necessary to hold the box stationary.

(b) As the box is being raised,

$$H = We^{\mu_k\beta},$$

and $F = He^{\mu_k\beta} = We^{2\mu_k\beta}$,

from which $F = 128.32$ lb

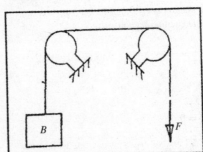

Problem 9.131 The 20-kg box A is held in equilibrium on the inclined surface by the force T acting on the rope wrapped over the fixed cylinder. The coefficient of static friction between the box and the inclined surface is 0.1. The coefficient of static friction between the rope and the cylinder is 0.05. Determine the largest value of T that will not cause the box to slip up the inclined surface.

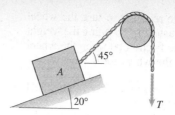

Solution: Assuming that slip of the box up the surface impends. The free body diagrams of the box and rope around the cylinder are as shown.

From the equilibrium equations

$$\sum F_x = T_A \cos 45° - N \sin 20° - 0.1\,N \cos 20° = 0,$$

$$\sum F_y = T_A \sin 45° + N \cos 20° - 0.1\,N \sin 20° - (20)(9.81) = 0$$

we obtain $T_A = 90.2$ N. Equation (9.17) is $T = T_A e^{\mu_s \beta}$ where $\mu_s = 0.05$ and $\beta = (\pi/180)(135)$ rad. Solving for T we obtain $T = 101$ N.

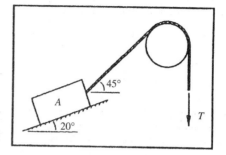

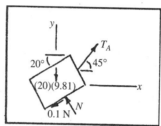

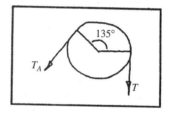

Problem 9.132 In Problem 9.131, determine the smallest value of T necessary to hold the box in equilibrium on the inclined surface.

Solution: In this case, we assume that slip of the box down the surface impends. This requires reversing the direction of the friction force in the free body diagram of Problem 9.131. The friction now acts up the surface and the friction on the drum is reversed. See the free body diagrams. From the equilibrium equations,

$$\sum F_X = T_A \cos(45°) - N \sin(20°) + 0.1\,N \cos(20°) = 0,$$

and $\sum F_Y = T_A \sin(45°) + N \cos(20°) + 0.1\,N \sin(20°)$

$$- (20)(9.81) = 0.$$

Solving, we obtain $T_A = 56.3$ N. We can now use this to find the force T that must be applied to the rope to keep the box from slipping down the plane. Eq. (9.17) is $T_A = T e^{\mu_s \beta}$, where $\mu_s = 0.05$ and $\beta = (\pi/180)(135)$ rad. Solving for T, we obtain $T = 50.1$ N.

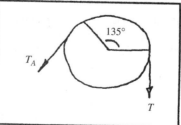

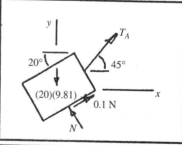

Problem 9.133 The mass of the block A is 14 kg. The coefficient of kinetic friction between the rope and the cylinder is 0.2. If the cylinder is rotated at a constant rate, first in the counterclockwise direction and then in the clockwise direction, the difference in the height of block A is 0.3 m. What is the spring constant k?

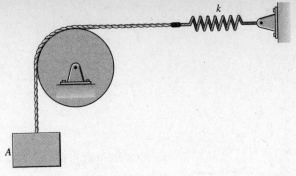

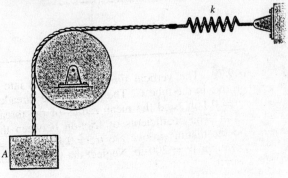

Solution:

$T_1 = T_2 e^{\mu_k \beta}$

Case 1: Clockwise Rotation

$\mu_k = 0.2$

$m = 14$ kg

$\beta = \pi/2$

$mg = T_{s1} e^{(0.2)(\pi/2)}$

$T_{s1} = 100.31$ N

Case 2: Counterclockwise Rotation

$T_{s2} = mg e^{(0.2)(\pi/2)}$

$T_{s2} = 188.03$ N

we know

$\qquad T_{s1} = k\delta_1$

$\qquad T_{s2} = k\delta_2$

$\quad T_{s2} - T_{s1} = k(\delta_2 - \delta_1)$

and $\delta_2 - \delta_1 = 0.3$ m

$k = (T_{s2} - T_{s1})/(\delta_2 - \delta_1)$

$k = 292$ N/m

Case 1: Clockwise Rotation

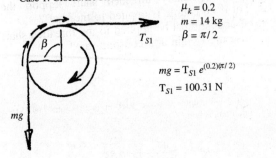

$\mu_k = 0.2$
$m = 14$ kg
$\beta = \pi/2$

$mg = T_{S1} e^{(0.2)(\pi/2)}$
$T_{S1} = 100.31$ N

Case 2: Counterclockwise Rotation

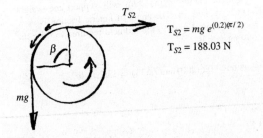

$T_{S2} = mg\, e^{(0.2)(\pi/2)}$
$T_{S2} = 188.03$ N

Problem 9.134 If the force F in Example 9.10 is increased to 400 N, what are the largest values of the couples M_A and M_B for which the belt will not slip?

Solution: From Example 9.10, $b = 500$ mm, $\mu_s = 0.8$, $R_a = 200$ mm, $R_b = 100$ mm. The angle of contact for pulley A is $\beta_a = \pi + 2\alpha$. The angle of contact for pulley B is $\beta_b = \pi - 2\alpha$, where

$$\alpha = \sin^{-1}\left(\frac{R_a - R_b}{b}\right) = \sin^{-1}\left(\frac{0.1}{0.5}\right) = 0.2014 \text{ radians.}$$

The belt contact is less for pulley B, so it is most likely to slip first. The couples are in opposition so that the tension in the upper belt is greater than the tension in the lower belt: For belt B:

$$T_{\text{upper}} = T_{\text{lower}} e^{\mu_s \beta_b} = 8.945 T_{\text{lower}}.$$

The force is

$$F = (T_{\text{upper}} + T_{\text{lower}}) \cos\alpha,$$

from which

$$T_{\text{lower}} = \frac{F}{(1 + e^{\mu_s \beta_b}) \cos\alpha} = 41.05 \text{ N,}$$

and $T_{\text{upper}} = 8.945 T_{\text{lower}} = 367.19$ N.

The couples are

$$M_b = R_b(T_{\text{upper}} - T_{\text{lower}}) = 32.61 \text{ N-m.}$$

$$M_a = R_a(T_{\text{upper}} - T_{\text{lower}}) = 65.23 \text{ N-m}$$

Problem 9.135 If the belt in Example 9.10 is a V-belt with angle $\gamma = 45°$, what are the largest values of the couples M_A and M_B for which the belt will not slip?

Solution: From Example 9.10, $b = 500$ mm, $\mu_s = 0.8$,

$$R_a = 200 \text{ mm,}$$

$$R_b = 100 \text{ mm,}$$

and $F = 200$ N.

Use the results of Problem 9.134: The contact angle for belt B is $\beta_b = \pi - 2\alpha = 2.7389$ radians, where $\alpha = 0.2014$ radians. For brevity, denote

$$\Psi = \frac{\mu_s \beta_b}{\sin\dfrac{\gamma}{2}} = 5.7256.$$

The tensions are related by

$$T_{\text{upper}} = T_{\text{lower}} e^{\Psi} = 306.62 T_{\text{lower}}.$$

The force

$$F = 200 = (T_{\text{upper}} + T_{\text{lower}}) \cos\alpha,$$

from which

$$T_{\text{lower}} = \frac{F}{(1 + 306.62) \cos\alpha} = 0.664 \text{ N,}$$

and $T_{\text{upper}} = 203.5$ N.

The couples are

$$M_a = R_a(T_{\text{upper}} - T_{\text{lower}}) = 40.56 \text{ N-m,}$$

$$M_b = R_b(T_{\text{upper}} - T_{\text{lower}}) = 20.28 \text{ N-m}$$

Problem 9.136 The spring exerts a 320-N force on the left pulley. The coefficient of static friction between the flat belt and the pulleys is $\mu_s = 0.5$. The right pulley cannot rotate. What is the largest couple M that can be exerted on the left pulley without causing the belt to slip?

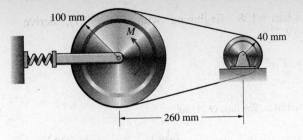

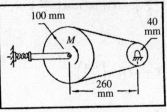

Solution: The angle of the belt relative to the horizontal is

$$\alpha = \sin^{-1}\left(\frac{100 - 40}{260}\right) = 0.2329 \text{ radians}.$$

For the right pulley the angle of contact is $\beta_{right} = \pi - 2\alpha = 2.676$ radians. The sum of the horizontal components of the tensions equals the force exerted by the spring:

$$F = (T_{upper} + T_{lower})\cos\alpha = 320 \text{ N}.$$

Since the angle of contact is less on the right pulley, it should slip there first. At impending slip, the tensions are related by

$$T_{upper} = T_{lower}e^{\mu_s\beta_{right}} = 3.811 T_{lower}.$$

Substitute and solve:

$$T_{lower}(1 + e^{0.5(2.676)}) = \frac{320}{\cos\alpha},$$

from which

$$T_{lower} = 68.34 \text{ N},$$

and $T_{upper} = 260.48$ N.

The moment applied to the wheel on the right is

$$M_{applied} = R(T_{upper} - T_{lower}) = 0.1(192.16) = 19.22 \text{ N-m}$$

Problem 9.137 Suppose that the belt in Problem 9.136 is a V-belt with angle $\gamma = 30°$. What is the largest couple M that can be exerted on the left pulley without causing the belt to slip?

Solution: Use the results of the solution to Problem 9.136, as applicable: The angle of contact with the right pulley is $\beta_{right} = 2.676$ radians. The sum of the horizontal components of the tensions equals the force exerted by the spring:

$$F = (T_{upper} + T_{lower})\cos\alpha = 320 \text{ N}.$$

Since the angle of contact is less on the right pulley, it will slip there. At impending slip, the tensions are related by $T_{upper} = T_{lower}e^{\Psi}$, where for brevity

$$\Psi = \frac{\mu_s\beta_{right}}{\sin\left(\frac{\gamma}{2}\right)} = 5.169$$

has been substituted. Substitute and solve:

$$T_{lower}(1 + e^{\Psi}) = \frac{320}{\cos\alpha},$$

from which

$$T_{lower} = 1.86 \text{ N},$$

and $T_{upper} = 327.01$ N.

The moment applied to the wheel on the right is

$$M_{applied} = R(T_{upper} - T_{lower}) = 0.1(325.16) = 32.52 \text{ N-m}$$

Problem 9.138 Beginning with Eqs. (9.21), derive Eq. (9.22):

$$T_2 = T_1 e^{\mu_s \beta / \sin(\gamma/2)}.$$

Solution: The Eqs. (9.21) are:

$$\sum F_{\text{tangential}} = 2\mu_s \Delta N + T \cos\left(\frac{\Delta\alpha}{2}\right) - (T + \Delta T) \cos\left(\frac{\Delta\alpha}{2}\right)$$

$$= 0$$

$$\sum F_{\text{normal}} = 2\Delta N \sin\left(\frac{\gamma}{2}\right) - (T + \Delta T) \sin\left(\frac{\Delta\alpha}{2}\right)$$

$$- T \sin\left(\frac{\Delta\alpha}{2}\right) = 0.$$

These can be written as two simultaneous equations in two unknowns:

$$a_{11} \Delta N + a_{12} \Delta T = 0,$$

$$a_{21} \Delta N + a_{22} \Delta T = 2T \sin(\eta),$$

where for brevity

$$\eta = \frac{\Delta\alpha}{2}.$$

These have the solution

$$\Delta T = \frac{2T \sin(\eta) a_{11}}{\det},$$

where $\det = a_{11} a_{22} - a_{12} a_{21}$ is the determinant of the coefficients. Reducing term by term: $a_{11} = 2\mu_s$, and

$$\det = -2(\mu_s \sin(\eta) - \sin\left(\frac{\gamma}{2}\right) \cos(\eta)).$$

The angle $\Delta\alpha$ is small, so $\eta \ll 1$, and from an expansion in a Taylor's series about $\eta = 0$,

$$\sin(\eta) = \eta - \frac{\eta^3}{3!} + \cdots, \cos(\eta) = 1 - \frac{\eta^2}{2} + \cdots.$$

For small η, $\eta \ll 1$, only the first terms in the expansion apply, so that $a_{11} \sin\eta = 2\mu_s \eta$, and

$$\det = -2\left(\mu_s \eta - \sin\left(\frac{\gamma}{2}\right)\right).$$

The solution:

$$\Delta T = \frac{-\mu_s T(\Delta\alpha)}{\left(\mu_s \left(\frac{\Delta\alpha}{2}\right) - \sin\frac{\gamma}{2}\right)}.$$

Divide both sides by $\Delta\alpha$ and take the limit:

$$\lim_{\Delta\alpha \to 0} \left(\frac{\Delta T}{\Delta\alpha}\right) = \frac{dT}{d\alpha} = \lim_{\Delta\alpha \to 0} \left(\frac{\mu_s T}{\left(\mu_s \Delta\alpha - \sin\frac{\gamma}{2}\right)}\right)$$

$$= \frac{\mu T}{\sin\frac{\gamma}{2}},$$

from which

$$\frac{dT}{d\alpha} = \frac{\mu_s T}{\sin\frac{\gamma}{2}}.$$

This first order differential equation can be solved by the standard separation of variables procedure:

$$\int_{T_1}^{T_2} \frac{dT}{T} = \int_{\alpha_1}^{\alpha_2} \frac{\mu_s}{\sin\frac{\gamma}{2}} d\alpha,$$

from which

$$\log_e(T_2) - \log_e(T_1) = \frac{\mu_s}{\sin\frac{\gamma}{2}} (\alpha_2 - \alpha_1).$$

Define $\beta = \alpha_2 - \alpha_1$, and simplify:

$$\log_e\left(\frac{T_2}{T_1}\right) = \left(\frac{\mu_s \beta}{\sin\frac{\gamma}{2}}\right),$$

or alternatively

$$T_2 = T_1 e^{\frac{\mu_s \beta}{\sin\frac{\gamma}{2}}}$$

Problem 9.139 The mass of the block A is 20 kg, and the coefficient of static friction between the block and the floor is $\mu_s = 0.3$. The spring constant $k = 1$ kN/m, and the spring is unstretched. How far can the slider B be moved to the right without causing the block to slip?

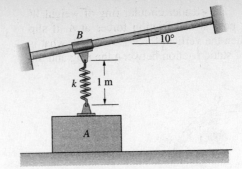

Solution: Let A_o be the original position with unstretched spring, and let B be the new position. The distance to the right is d. The angle $\alpha = 10°$. The new length of the spring is

$$L = \sqrt{(1 + d \tan \alpha)^2 + d^2}.$$

The spring force is $kL - 1$. The angle θ is given by

$$\theta = \sin^{-1}\left(\frac{d}{L}\right),$$

and the horizontal component of the force in the block is

$$F = (kL - 1)\sin\theta = k(L - 1)\left(\frac{d}{L}\right) = k\frac{d(L - 1)}{L}.$$

The normal force exerted by the floor on the block is $N = W - k(L - 1)\cos\theta$. The equilibrium condition at impending slip is $F - \mu_s N = 0$, from which

$$k\frac{d(L - 1)}{L} - \mu_s(W - k(L - 1)\cos\theta) = 0.$$

Graph the equation

$$f(d) = k\frac{d(L - 1)}{L} - \mu_s(W - k(L - 1)\cos\theta),$$

where

$$L = \sqrt{(1 + d \tan \alpha)^2 + d^2},$$

and $\theta = \sin^{-1}\left(\frac{d}{L}\right),$

and determine the zero crossing point. The zero crossing point corresponds to $d = 0.317$ m, which is the horizontal distance to the right. The distance along the sliding bar is

$$D = \frac{d}{\cos 10°} = 0.322 \text{ m}$$

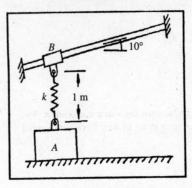

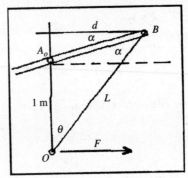

Problem 9.140 The slender circular ring of weight W is supported by normal and friction forces at A. If slip is impending when the vertical force $F = 0.4W$, what is the coefficient of static friction between the ring and the support?

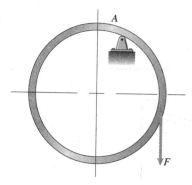

Solution: Let θ be the angle between the x-axis and point A. The normal force is normal to the ring, and the friction force is tangential to the ring. The sum of forces:

$$\sum F_x = N \cos \theta - \mu_s N \sin \theta = 0,$$

$$\sum F_y = N \sin \theta + \mu_s N \cos \theta - W - F = 0.$$

The sum of the moments about the center of the ring:

$$\sum M_c = +R \mu_s N - RF = 0.$$

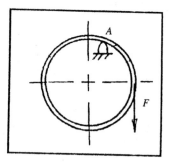

Substitute $F = 0.4W$ and reduce each equation to obtain the three equations:

$$\mu_s = \cot \theta,$$

$$N = \frac{1.4W}{\sin \theta + \mu_s \cos \theta},$$

and $\mu_s N = 0.4W$.

Combine the three conditions and reduce algebraically to obtain

$$\cos \theta = \left(\frac{0.4}{1.4} \right) = 0.2857,$$

from which $\theta = 73.4°$,

and $\mu_s = \cot 73.4° = 0.298$.

Problem 9.141 Suppose that the vertical force on the ring in Problem 9.140 is $F = KW$ and slip is impending. Draw a graph of K as a function of the coefficient of static friction between the ring and the support for $0 \le \mu_s \le 1$.

Solution: Use the solution to Problem 9.140. The normal force is normal to the ring, and the friction force is tangential to the ring. The equilibrium conditions are: The sum of forces:

$$\sum F_x = N \cos \theta - \mu_s N \sin \theta = 0,$$

$$\sum F_y = N \sin \theta + \mu_s N \cos \theta - W - F = 0.$$

The sum of the moments about the center of the ring:

$$\sum M_c = +R \mu_s N - RF = 0,$$

where θ is the angle between the y-axis and point A. Substitute the condition $F = KW$ and reduce to obtain the three intermediate equations: $\mu_s = \cot \theta$,

$$N = \frac{(1 + K)W}{\sin \theta + \mu_s \cos \theta},$$

and $\dfrac{\mu_s(1 + K)}{\sin \theta + \mu_s \cos \theta} = K$.

Combine and reduce to obtain:

$$\cos \theta = \frac{K}{1 + K},$$

or $K = \dfrac{\cos \theta}{1 - \cos \theta}$.

Since $0 \le \mu_s \le 1$, then from $\mu_s = \cot \theta$, and $45° \le \theta \le 90°$ it is permissible to use the relation

$$\sin \theta = \sqrt{1 - \cos^2 \theta}$$

with a positive sign. Thus

$$\mu_s = \cot \theta = \frac{\cos \theta}{\sqrt{1 - \cos^2 \theta}},$$

$$\cos \theta = \frac{\mu_s}{\sqrt{1 + \mu_s^2}},$$

and $K = \dfrac{\mu_s}{\sqrt{1 + \mu_s^2} - \mu_s}$.

This is graphed over the range $0 \le \mu_s \le 1$. The limits on K are

$$0 \le K \le \frac{1}{\sqrt{2} - 1} \cong 2.414.$$

Check.

$$\lim K_{\mu_s \to 0} = \left[\frac{\mu_s}{\sqrt{1 + \mu_s^2} - \mu_s} \right]_{\mu_s \to 0} \to 0.$$

$$\lim K_{\mu_s \to 1} = \left[\frac{\mu_s}{\sqrt{1 + \mu_s^2} - \mu_s} \right]_{\mu_s \to 1} \to \frac{1}{\sqrt{2} - 1} = 2.4142.$$

check.

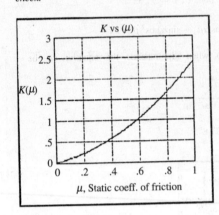

K vs (μ)

$K(\mu)$

μ, Static coeff. of friction

Problem 9.142 The mass of the 3-m bar is 20 kg, and the coefficient of static friction between the ends of the bar and the circular surface is $\mu_s = 0.3$. What is the largest value of the angle α for which the bar will not slip?

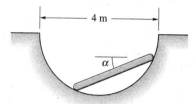

Solution: From the solution to Problem 9.51, the equilibrium equations can be used to obtain the equation

$$\sin \alpha (1 - \cos^2 \beta)\mu_s^2 + \cos \alpha \mu_s - \sin \alpha \cos^2 \beta = 0$$

where $\beta = \arcsin(1.5/2)$, when slip impends. this equation can be written

$$\tan \alpha = \frac{\mu_s}{\cos^2 \beta - \mu_s^2(1 - \cos^2 \beta)}.$$

Solving, we obtain $\alpha = 37.8°$.

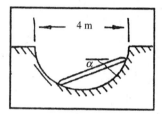

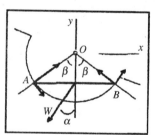

Problem 9.143 The load $W = 800$ N can be raised or lowered by rotating the threaded shaft. The distance $b = 75$ mm, and the pinned bars are each 300 mm in length. The pitch of the threaded shaft is $p = 5$ mm, the mean radius of the thread is $r = 15$ mm, and the coefficient of kinetic friction between the thread and the mating groove is 0.2. Draw a graph of the moment that must be exerted to turn the threaded shaft at a constant rate, raising the load, as a function of the height h from $h = 100$ mm to $h = 400$ mm.

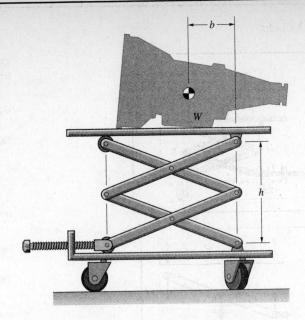

Solution: Assume that the threaded shaft is to be turned at a constant rate. Use the solution to Problem 9.96, as applicable. The vertical distances HE, BE, AD, DG are

$$y = \frac{h}{2} \text{ mm}.$$

The included angle BAC is

$$\beta = \sin^{-1}\left(\frac{h}{600}\right).$$

The distance AB is $L = 300\cos\beta$ mm. Isolate the members and write the equilibrium equations, beginning at the top: *Isolate the frame AB which supports the load W.* The equilibrium conditions are

(1) $\sum M_B = -AL + Wb = 0,$

(2) $\sum F_y = A - W + B_y = 0,$

$\sum F_x = B_x = 0$

Isolate BD : (3) $\sum F_y = -B_y - C_y + D_y = 0,$

(4) $\sum F_x = -C_x + D_x = 0,$

(5) $\sum M_D = \left(\frac{h}{4}\right)C_x - \left(\frac{L}{2}\right)C_y - LB = 0$

Isolate DH: (6) $\sum F_y = -D_y - F_y + H_y = 0,$

(7) $\sum F_x = -D_x - F_x + H_x = 0,$

(8) $\sum M_H = \left(\frac{h}{4}\right)F_x + \left(\frac{L}{2}\right)F_y + LD_y$

$\qquad\qquad + \left(\frac{h}{2}\right)D_x = 0$

Isolate AE (9) $\sum F_y = -A + C_y + E_y = 0,$

(10) $\sum F_x = C_x + E_x = 0,$

(11) $\sum M_E = -\left(\frac{h}{4}\right)(C_x) - \left(\frac{L}{2}\right)C_y + LA = 0.$

Isolate EG (12) $\sum F_y = -E_y + F_y + G_y = 0,$

(13) $\sum F_x = -E_x + F_x + G_x = 0,$

(14) $\sum M_G = -\frac{h}{4}F_x + \left(\frac{L}{2}\right)F_y - LE_y + \left(\frac{h}{2}\right)E_x$

$\qquad\qquad = 0.$

These 14 equations in 14 unknowns are to be solved to determine the reaction G_x, which is the force that the threaded shaft must overcome to raise the load at a constant rate. An analytic solution is obtained as follows:

From (1) $A = \dfrac{Wb}{L}.$

From (2) $B = W\left(1 - \dfrac{b}{L}\right).$

From (8) and (11) $C_y = W\left(\dfrac{2b}{L} - 1\right),$

$$C_x = \frac{2WL}{h}.$$

From (9) $E_y = W\left(1 - \dfrac{b}{L}\right).$

From (10) $E_x = -\dfrac{2}{h}WL.$

866

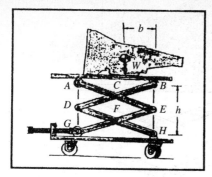

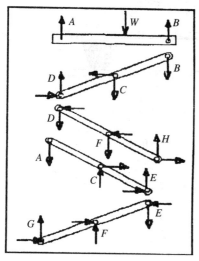

Check: This value of G_y is expected from the equilibrium conditions for the complete structure. *check.* Substitute to obtain

$$G_x = \frac{1200W}{h} \cos \beta.$$

Note that

$$\cos \beta = \sqrt{1 - \left(\frac{h}{600}\right)^2},$$

from which

$$G_x = 2W \frac{\sqrt{600^2 - h^2}}{h}.$$

The pitch angle is

$$\alpha = \tan^{-1}\left(\frac{5}{2\pi(15)}\right) = 3.037°.$$

The angle of kinetic friction is

$$\theta_k = \tan^{-1}(0.2) = 11.31°.$$

The moment required to raise the load at a constant rate:

$$M = rG_x \tan(\theta_k + \alpha) = 0.003836 G_x.$$

The graph of the moment that must be exerted on the threaded shaft to raise the 800 N load is shown as a function of the height h over the range $100 \le h \le 400$ (mm).

From (4) $D_x = \dfrac{2}{h}WL$

From (3) $D_y = \dfrac{Wb}{L}.$

From (8) and (14) $F_y = W\left(1 - \dfrac{2b}{L}\right),$

$$F_x = \frac{6WL}{h}.$$

From (13) $G_x = \dfrac{4WL}{h}.$

From (12) $G_y = \dfrac{Wb}{L}$

Problem 9.144 The 10-lb metal disk A is at the center of the inclined surface. The coefficient of static friction between the disk and the surface is 0.3. What is the largest tension in the string AB that will not cause the disk to slip?

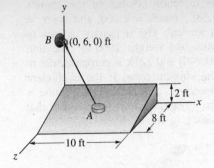

Solution: The coordinates of the disk A are (5, 1, 4) ft, so the position vector of point B relative to A is

$$\mathbf{r}_{AB} = (0-5)\mathbf{i} + (6-1)\mathbf{j} + (0-4)\mathbf{k} \text{ ft.}$$

We can express the force exerted on the disk by the string as

$$\mathbf{T} = T\frac{\mathbf{r}_{AB}}{|\mathbf{r}_{AB}|} = T(-0.615\mathbf{i} + 0.615\mathbf{j} - 0.492\mathbf{k}).$$

The sum of the of the forces exerted on the disk by the string and the weight of the disk is

$$\mathbf{T} - 10\mathbf{j} = 0.615T\mathbf{i} + (0.615T - 10)\mathbf{j} - 0.492T\mathbf{k}.$$

The components of this force normal and parallel to the surface are balanced by the normal force and friction force, respectively. To determine these components, we need a unit vector $\mathbf{e}$ perpendicular to the surface: The angle $t_a = \arctan(2/8) = 14.0°$, so

$$\mathbf{e} = \cos\beta\mathbf{j} + \sin\beta\mathbf{k} = 0.970\mathbf{j} + 0.243\mathbf{k}.$$

The normal force N is equal to the magnitude of the component of $\mathbf{T} - 10\mathbf{j}$ perpendicular to the surface:

$$N = |\mathbf{e} \cdot (\mathbf{T} - 10\mathbf{j})|$$

(1) Since

$$N^2 + f^2 = |\mathbf{T} - 10\mathbf{j}|^2,$$

(2) the friction force is

$$f = \sqrt{|\mathbf{T} - 10\mathbf{j}|^2 - N^2}.$$

As the tension T increases, f will increase until $f = \mu_s N$ when slip impends. If we choose a value of T we can determine N from Equation (1) and f from Equation (2). By drawing a graph of the ratio f/N as a function of T we can determine the value of T for which $f/N = \mu_s = 0.3$. The resulting graph is shown: From the graph we estimate that $f/N = 0.3$ at $T = 3.8$ lb. By examining computed results near $f/N = 0.3$, we determine that the largest tension is $T = 3.84$ lb

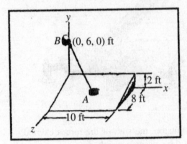

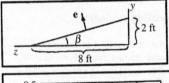

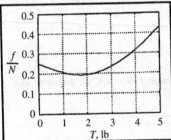

Problem 9.145 The direction cosines of the crane's cable are $\cos\theta_x = 0.588$, $\cos\theta_y = 0.766$, and $\cos\theta_z = 0.260$. The y axis is vertical. The stationary caisson to which the cable is attached weighs 2000 lb. The unit vector $\mathbf{e} = 0.260\mathbf{i} + 0.940\mathbf{j} + 0.221\mathbf{k}$ is perpendicular to the ground where the caisson rests. If the coefficient of static friction between the caisson and the ground is $\mu_s = 0.4$, what is the largest tension in the cable that will not cause the caisson to slip?

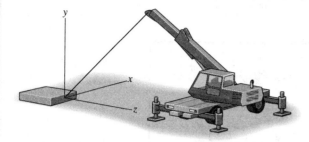

Solution: If T is the cable tension, the sum of the forces exerted on the caisson by the cable and the caisson's weight is

$$\mathbf{T} - 2000\mathbf{j} = 0.588T\mathbf{i} + (0.766T - 2000)\mathbf{j} + 0.260T\mathbf{k}.$$

The components of this force normal and parallel to the ground are balanced by the normal force N and friction force f respectively. The normal force is $N = |(\mathbf{T} - 2000\mathbf{j} \cdot \mathbf{e})|$, (1) and since $f^2 + N^2 = |\mathbf{T} - 2000\mathbf{j}|^2$, the friction force is $f = \sqrt{|\mathbf{T} - 2000\mathbf{j}|^2 - N^2}$ (2). If we choose a value of T we can determine N from Equation (1) and f from equation (2) By drawing a graph of f/N as a function of T, we can determine the value of T for which $f/N = \mu_s = 0.4$. The graph is shown: From the graph we estimate that $f/N = 0.4$ at $T = 180$ lb. By examining computed results near $f/N = 0.4$, we determine that the largest tension is $T = 186$ lb.

Problem 9.146 The thrust bearing is supported by contact of the collar C with a fixed plate. The area of contact is an annulus with inside diameter D_1 and outside diameter D_2. Suppose that because of thermal constraints, you want the area of contact to be 0.02 m². The coefficient of kinetic friction between the collar and the plate is $\mu_k = 0.3$. The force $F = 600$ N, and the couple M required to rotate the shaft at a constant rate is 10 N-m. What are the diameters D_1, and D_2?

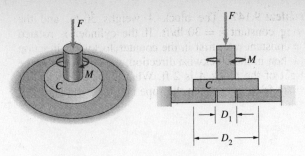

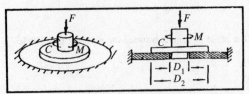

Solution: . The moment required to sustain rotation at a constant rate is

$$M = \frac{2\mu_k F}{3}\left(\frac{r_o^3 - r_i^3}{r_o^2 - r_i^2}\right).$$

Note that the total area is $A_T = \pi(r_o^2 - r_i^2)$, from which

$$M = \frac{\pi\mu_k F}{12 A_T}(D_2^3 - D_1^3).$$

Solve, and note that

$$D_2^2 = \frac{4A_T}{\pi} + D_1^2,$$

from which

$$\left(\frac{4A_T}{\pi} + D_1^2\right)^{3/2} - D_1^3 = \frac{12 A_T M}{\pi\mu_k F}.$$

From which

$$(D_1^2 + 0.02546)^{3/2} - D_1^3 - 0.00424 = 0.$$

The value of D_1 is determined by graphing the function

$$f(D_1) = (D_1^2 + 0.02546)^{3/2} - D_1^3 - 0.00424$$

to determine the zero crossings. The zero crossing occurs at $D_1 = 29.169 = 29.2$ mm, from which the outside diameter is

$$D_2 = \sqrt{\frac{4A_T}{\pi} + D_1^2} = 162.2 \text{ mm}$$

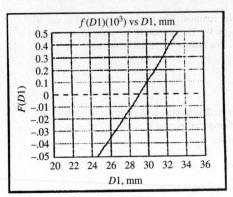

$f(D1)(10^3)$ vs $D1$, mm

870

Problem 9.147 The block A weighs 30 lb, and the spring constant $k = 30$ lb/ft. If the cylinder is rotated at a constant rate, first in the counterclockwise direction and then in the clockwise direction, the difference in the height of the block A is 2 ft. What is the coefficient of kinetic friction between the rope and the cylinder?

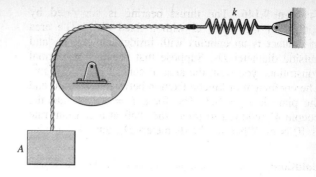

Solution: The angle of contact between the rope and the cylinder is

$$\beta = \frac{\pi}{2} \text{ radians.}$$

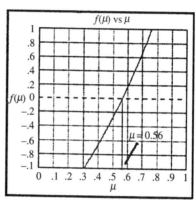

For counterclockwise rotation: The tension in the belt to the left of the cylinder is $T_{\text{left}} = W$. The tension in the horizontal part is $H = T_{\text{left}}e^{\mu_k\beta} = We^{\mu_k\beta}$. The elongation of the spring is

$$s_1 = \frac{H}{k} = \frac{We^{\mu_k\beta}}{k}.$$

For clockwise rotation: The tension in the belt to the left is $T_{\text{left}} = W$. The tension in the horizontal part is $H = T_{\text{left}}e^{-\mu_k\beta} = We^{-\mu_k\beta}$. The elongation of the spring is

$$s_2 = \frac{H}{k} = \frac{We^{-\mu_k\beta}}{k}.$$

The difference in elongations is

$$s_1 - s_2 = \frac{W}{k}(e^{\mu_k\beta} - e^{-\mu_k\beta}) = 2 \text{ ft.}$$

Graph the function

$$f(\mu_k) = \frac{W}{k}(e^{\mu_k\beta} - e^{-\mu_k\beta}) - 2$$

against μ_k to find the zero crossings. The crossing occurs at $\mu_k = 0.56$, approximately. *Check:* An analytic solution is obtained using the well known relation:

$$\frac{W}{k}(e^{\mu_k\beta} - e^{-\mu_k\beta}) = \frac{2W}{k}\sin h(\mu_k\beta) = 2 \text{ ft,}$$

from which

$$\mu_k = \frac{\sinh^{-1}\left(\dfrac{W}{k}\right)}{\beta} = \frac{2\sinh^{-1}(1)}{\pi} = 0.561$$

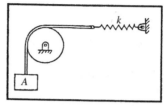

Problem 9.148 The coefficient of static friction between the 1-kg slider and the vertical bar is $\mu_s = 0.6$. The constant of the spring is $k = 20$ N/m, and its unstretched length is 1 m. Determine the range of values of y at which the slider will remain stationary on the bar.

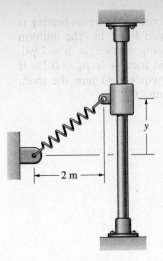

Solution: The weight of the slider is $W = 9.81$ N. The spring length is $L = \sqrt{y^2 + 4}$. The elongation of the spring is $\Delta L = \sqrt{y^2 + 4} - 1$. The force exerted by the spring is $F = k\Delta L$. The angle formed by the spring is

$$\beta = \tan^{-1}\left(\frac{y}{2}\right).$$

The normal force on the slider is $N = F\cos\beta$. The friction force parallel to the bar is $f = \mu_s N$. The friction force opposes slip, so that it is up when β is positive, and down when β is negative. Thus the sum of the forces parallel to the bar is

$$\sum F_y = -W - F\sin\beta + \mu_s N \,\mathrm{sgn}(\beta) = 0,$$

where $\mathrm{sgn}(\beta)$ is the standard signature function (called signum) with unit value and the sign of β.

Substitute and reduce:

$$f(y) = -\frac{W}{k} - (\sqrt{y^2 + 4} - 1)(\sin\beta - \mu_s\,\mathrm{sgn}(\beta)\cos\beta) = 0.$$

The function $f(y)$, where

$$\beta = \tan^{-1}\left(\frac{y}{2}\right),$$

is graphed as a function of y to determine the zero crossings. Tabulated values show zero crossings at $y = -1.9625 = -1.963$ m and $y = 0.225$ m, hence the range of values for which the slider will be stationary is $-1.963 < y < 0.225$ (m)

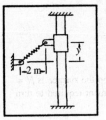

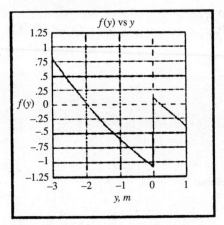

Problem 9.149 The axial force on the thrust bearing is $F = 200$ lb, and the dimension $b = 6$ in. The uniform pressure exerted by the mating surface is $p = 7$ psi, and the coefficient of kinetic friction is $\mu_k = 0.28$. If a couple $M = 360$ in-lb is required to turn the shaft, what are the dimensions D_o and D_i?

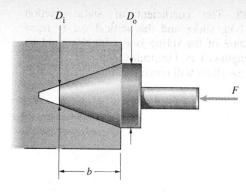

Solution: The angle of the taper is

$$\alpha = 90 - \tan^{-1}\left(\frac{D_o - D_i}{2b}\right).$$

The active area of contact is

$$A = \frac{\pi(D_o^2 - D_i^2)}{4\cos\alpha},$$

the area of a truncated cone. The normal force on the surface is $N = pA$, and the axial force is $F = N\cos\alpha$. The moment required to turn the shaft is

$$M = \frac{\mu_k F}{3\cos\alpha}\left(\frac{D_o^3 - D_i^3}{D_o^2 - D_i^2}\right).$$

Substitute the axial force:

$$M = \frac{\pi\mu_k p}{12\cos\alpha}(D_o^3 - D_i^3),$$

from which

$$D_o^3 - D_i^3 = \frac{12M\cos\alpha}{\pi\mu_k p}.$$

Eliminate D_o by the relation:

$$D_o^2 = \frac{4F}{\pi p} + D_i^2,$$

to obtain

$$f(D_i) = (D_i^2 + \frac{4F}{\pi p})^{3/2} - D_i^3 - \frac{12M\cos\alpha}{\pi\mu_k p} = 0.$$

Substitute values to obtain

$$f(D_i) = (D_i^2 + 36.378)^{3/2} - D_i^3 - 701.58\cos\alpha = 0,$$

where

$$\alpha = 90 - \tan^{-1}\left(\frac{\sqrt{D_i^2 + 36.378} - D_i}{12}\right).$$

The function $f(D_i)$ is graphed to determine the zero crossings. Tabulated values show a zero crossing at $D_i = 1.834$ in. The outer diameter is obtained from

$$D_o = \left(\frac{4F}{\pi p} + D_i^2\right)^{1/2} = 6.31 \text{ in}$$

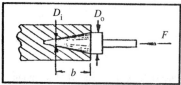

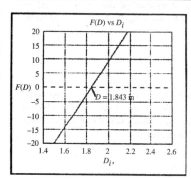

F(D) vs D_i

Problem 9.150 The weight of the box is $W = 30$ lb, and the force F is perpendicular to the inclined surface. The coefficient of static friction between the box and the inclined surface is $\mu_s = 0.2$.

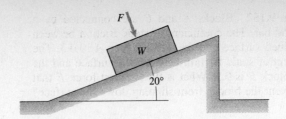

(a) If $F = 30$ lb, what is the magnitude of the friction force exerted on the stationary box?

(b) If $F = 10$ lb, show that the box cannot remain at rest on the inclined surface.

Solution: The maximum friction force is defined to be $f = \mu_s N$, where N is the normal force.

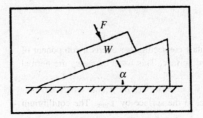

(a) The box is stationary, hence the friction force is equal to the force acting to move the box down the plane:

$$\sum F_P = f - W_P = 0,$$

from which $f = W_P = W \sin \alpha = 10.26$ lb

(b) The component of force parallel to the surface is $W_P = W \sin \alpha = 10.26$ lb acting to move the box down the plane. The friction force is $f = \mu_s(10 + 30 \cos \alpha) = 7.638$ lb, acting to hold the box in place. Since $W_P > f$, the box will move.

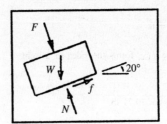

Problem 9.151 In Problem 9.150, what is the smallest force F necessary to hold the box stationary on the inclined surface?

Solution: At impending slip, the sum of the forces parallel to the surface is

$$\sum F_P = f - W_P = 0,$$

from which $f = W_P$. The friction force is $f = \mu_s(F + W \cos \alpha)$, and $W_P = W \sin \alpha$. Equate and solve:

$$F = W\left(\frac{\sin \alpha}{\mu_s} - \cos \alpha\right) = 30\left(\frac{\sin 20°}{0.2} - \cos 20°\right) = 23.1 \text{ lb}$$

Problem 9.152 Blocks A and B are connected by a horizontal bar. The coefficient of static friction between the inclined surface and the 400-lb block A is 0.3. The coefficient of static friction between the surface and the 300-lb block B is 0.5. What is the smallest force F that will prevent the blocks from slipping down the surface?

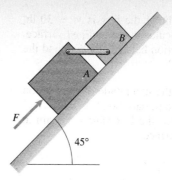

$45°$

Solution: The (horizontal) connecting bar exerts a component of force normal to the inclined surface. This force increases the normal force exerted on B by the inclined plane, and reduces the normal force exerted on A by the inclined plane. Isolate B. Denote the component of the linkage force parallel to the surface by f_{link}. The equilibrium conditions on B are

$$\sum F = -f_{\text{link}} + B\sin\alpha - \mu_{sB}N_B = 0,$$

where $N_B = B\cos\alpha + f_{\text{link}}$, (where f_{link} forms the sides of a right triangle), from which

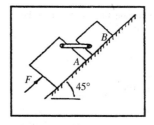

$$f_{\text{link}} = \frac{B}{(1+\mu_{sB})}(\sin\alpha - \mu_{sB}\cos\alpha) = 70.71 \text{ lb.}$$

Isolate A. The equilibrium conditions are

$$\sum F = f_{\text{link}} - F + A\sin\alpha - \mu_{sA}N_A = 0,$$

where $N_A = A\cos\alpha - f_{\text{link}}$, from which

$$F - f_{\text{link}} = A(\sin\alpha - \mu_{sA}\cos\alpha) + \mu_{sA}f_{\text{link}} = 219.2 \text{ lb.}$$

The total force required to keep the blocks from slipping is

$$F = 70.71 + 219.2 = 289.91 \text{ lb}$$

Problem 9.153 What force F is necessary to cause the blocks in Problem 9.152 to start sliding up the plane?

Solution: The friction forces oppose impending motion up the plane. Use the results of the solution to Problem 9.152 with the friction forces reversed. *Isolate B.* The linkage force is

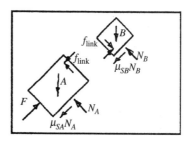

$$f_{\text{link}} = \frac{B}{(1-\mu_{sB})}(\sin\alpha + \mu_{sB}\cos\alpha) = 636.4 \text{ lb.}$$

Isolate A. The resultant force on A is

$$F - f_{\text{link}} = A(\sin\alpha + \mu_{sA}\cos\alpha) - \mu_{sA}f_{\text{link}} = 176.78 \text{ lb.}$$

The resultant force required to cause the blocks to start to move up the plane is $F = 636.4 + 176.8 = 813.2 \text{ lb}$

Problem 9.154 The masses of crates A and B are 25 kg and 30 kg, respectively. The coefficient of static friction between the contacting surfaces is $\mu_s = 0.34$. What is the largest value of α for which the crates will remain in equilibrium?

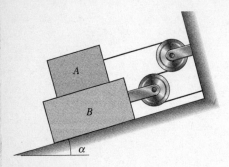

Solution: Choose a coordinate system with the x-axis parallel to the inclined surface. Denote the tension in the cables by T. Suppose that at impending slip the lower box tends to move up the plane and the upper box tends to move down the plane. Thus, for the lower box:

$$\sum F_x = -W_B \sin\alpha - \mu_s(W_A + W_B)\cos\alpha - \mu_s W_A \cos\alpha + 2T$$

$$= 0.$$

For the upper box,

$$\sum F_x = +\mu_s W_A \cos\alpha - W_A \sin\alpha + T = 0.$$

Eliminate T from the two equations, and reduce:

$$(W_B - 2W_A)\sin\alpha + \mu_s(4W_A + W_B)\cos\alpha = 0,$$

from which

$$\alpha = \tan^{-1}\left(\frac{\mu_s(4W_A + W_B)}{(2W_A - W_B)}\right) = \tan^{-1}\left(\frac{0.34(1275.3)}{196.2}\right) = 65.65°$$

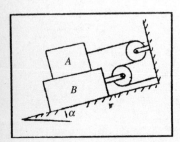

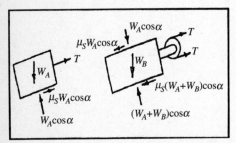

Problem 9.155 The side of a soil embankment has a 45° slope (Fig. a). If the coefficient of static friction of soil on soil is $\mu_s = 0.6$, will the embankment be stable or will it collapse? If it will collapse, what is the smallest slope that can be stable?

Strategy: Draw a free-body diagram by isolating part of the embankment as shown in Fig. b.

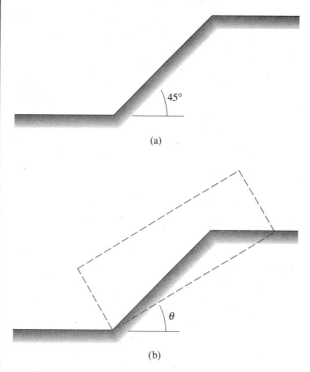

(a)

(b)

Solution: The strategy is to analyze the free body diagram formed by isolating part of the embankment, as shown.

The sum of the force parallel to the slope are:

$$\sum F_x = -W \sin\theta + \mu_s W \cos\theta = 0,$$

from which the required value of the coefficient of static friction is: $\mu_s = \tan\theta = \tan 45° = 1$. Since the coefficient of static friction of soil on soil is less than the required value, the embankment will collapse. The smallest slope that will be stable is $\alpha = \tan^{-1}(0.6) = 30.96 = 31°$ This problem is very similar to the problem of the box on an incline.

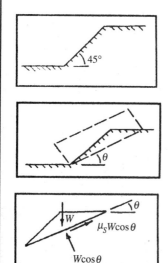

Problem 9.156 The mass of the van is 2250 kg, and the coefficient of static friction between its tires and the road is 0.6. If its front wheels are locked and its rear wheels can turn freely, what is the largest value of α for which it can remain in equilibrium?

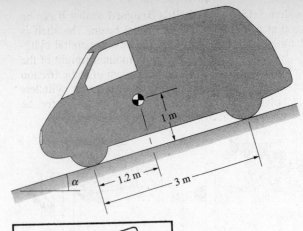

Solution: Choose a coordinate system with the x-axis parallel to the incline. The weight of the van is $W = mg = 22072.5$ N. The moment about the point of contact of the rear wheels is

$$\sum M_R = (3 - 1.2)W\cos\alpha + 1W\sin\alpha - 3\,N = 0,$$

from which the normal force at the front wheels is

$$N = \frac{W(1.8\cos\alpha + \sin\alpha)}{3}.$$

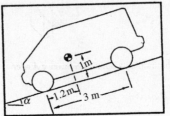

The sum of the forces parallel to the inclined surface is

$$\sum F_x = +\mu_s N - W\sin\alpha = 0.$$

Combine and reduce:

$$\mu_s\left(\frac{1.8}{3}\right)\cos\alpha + \left(\frac{\mu_s}{3} - 1\right)\sin\alpha = 0,$$

from which

$$\alpha = \tan^{-1}\left(\frac{1.8\mu_s}{3 - \mu_s}\right) = \tan^{-1}(0.45) = 24.2°$$

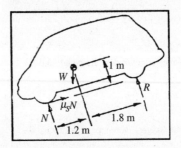

Problem 9.157 In Problem 9.156, what is the largest value of α for which the van can remain in equilibrium if it points up the slope?

Solution: The sum of the moments about the point of contact of the rear wheels is

$$\sum M_R = -1.8W\cos\alpha + 1W\sin\alpha + 3\,N = 0.$$

The normal force is

$$N = \frac{W(1.8\cos\alpha - \sin\alpha)}{3}.$$

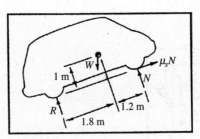

The sum of forces parallel to the incline is

$$\sum F_x = +\mu_s N - W\sin\alpha = 0.$$

Combine and reduce:

$$\frac{1.8\mu_s}{3}\cos\alpha - \left(\frac{\mu_s}{3} + 1\right)\sin\alpha = 0,$$

from which

$$\alpha = \tan^{-1}\left(\frac{1.8\mu_s}{\mu_s + 3}\right) = 16.7°$$

Problem 9.158 The shelf is designed so that it can be placed at any height on the vertical beam. The shelf is supported by friction between the two horizontal cylinders and the vertical beam. The combined weight of the shelf and camera is W. If the coefficient of static friction between the vertical beam and the horizontal cylinders is μ_s, what is the minimum distance b necessary for the shelf to stay in place?

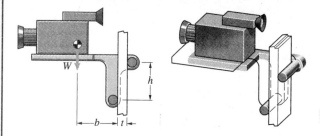

Solution: Take the sum of the moments about the lower cylinder

$$\sum M_{LC} = +bW - hF_{NU} + t\mu_s F_{NU} = 0.$$

The sum of the forces

$$\sum F_y = F_{NU} - F_{NL} = 0,$$

from which the normal forces at the two cylinders are equal, and

$$F_N = \frac{bW}{(h - \mu_s t)}.$$

The force causing slippage is the weight, which is balanced by the friction force:

$$0 = -W + 2\mu_s F_N = -W + \frac{2\mu_s bW}{(h - t\mu_s)} = 0,$$

from which

$$b = \frac{h - t\mu_s}{2\mu_s} = \left(\frac{1}{2}\right)\left(\frac{h}{\mu_s} - t\right).$$

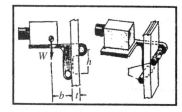

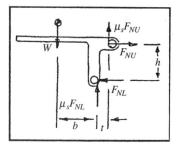

Problem 9.159 The 20-lb homogenous object is supported at A and B. The distance $h = 4$ in., friction can be neglected at B, and the coefficient of static friction at A is 0.4. Determine the largest force F that can be exerted without causing the object to slip.

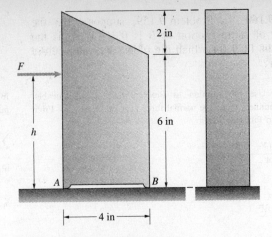

Solution: Choose a coordinate system with origin at A and the x-axis parallel to the floor. Divide the object into a "rectangular" volume and a "triangular" (wedge) volume. The volume of the lower rectangular portion is $V_1 = 4(6)(1) = 24$ in^3. The centroidal coordinates are $x_1 = 2$ in, $y_1 = 3$ in. The wedge has a volume

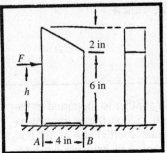

$$V_2 = \left(\frac{1}{2}\right)(4)(2)(1) = 4 \text{ in}^3,$$

and the centroid is at

$$x_2 = (4/3) \text{ in},$$

$$y_2 = 6 + \frac{2}{3} \text{ in}.$$

The center of mass is located at

$$x = \frac{2(24) + (4/3)4}{28} = 1.90 \text{ in}.$$

The moment about B is

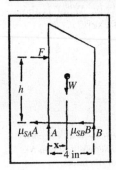

$$\sum M_B = -hF + W(4 - x) - 4A = 0,$$

from which the normal force at A is

$$A = \frac{-hF + (4 - x)W}{4}.$$

The sum of the forces parallel to x is

$$\sum F_x = -\mu_s A + F = 0,$$

from which

$$F\left(1 + \frac{\mu_s h}{4}\right) - \frac{\mu_s(4 - x)W}{4} = 0,$$

and $F = \dfrac{\mu_s(4 - x)W}{(4 + \mu_s h)} = 2.993 = 2.99$ lb

Problem 9.160 In Problem 9.159, suppose that the coefficient of static friction at B is 0.36. What is the largest value of h for which the object will slip before it tips over?

Solution: Use the solution to Problem 9.159, as applicable. Tipping is imminent when the normal force at A becomes zero. From the solution to Problem 9.159,

$$A = \frac{-hF + (4 - \mathbf{x})W}{4},$$

from which

$$h_{\text{tip}} = \frac{(4 - \mathbf{x})W}{F}.$$

The sum of the forces parallel to the y axis is

$$\sum F_y = A + B - W = 0,$$

from which the normal force at $B = W - A$. The sum of the forces parallel to the x-axis

$$\sum F_x = -\mu_{sA}A - \mu_{sB}B + F = 0,$$

from which, for $A = 0$, $F = \mu_{sB}W$. Combine and reduce to obtain

$$h_{\text{tip}} = \frac{(4 - \mathbf{x})}{\mu_{sB}} = 5.82 \text{ in}$$

Problem 9.161 The 180-lb climber is supported in the "chimney" by the normal and friction forces exerted on his shoes and back. The static coefficients of friction between his shoes and the wall and between his back and the wall are 0.8 and 0.6, respectively. What is the minimum normal force his shoes must exert?

Solution: Choose a coordinate system with the x-axis horizontal and y-axis vertical. Let N_s be the normal force exerted by shoes, N_b the normal force exerted by his back. The sum of the forces:

$$\sum F_x = N_s \cos 4° - N_b \cos 3° - \mu_{ss}N_s \sin 4° + \mu_{sB}N_b \sin 3° = 0,$$

$$\sum F_y = N_s \sin 4° + N_b \sin 3° + \mu_{ss}N_s \cos 4° + \mu_{sB}N_b \cos° - W$$

$$= 0.$$

Reduce to two simultaneous equations in two unknowns:

$$a_{11}N_s + a_{12}N_b = 0,$$

and $a_{21}N_s + a_{22}N_b = W,$

where

$$a_{11} = \cos 4° - \mu_{ss} \sin 4° = 0.9418,$$

$$a_{12} = -\cos 3° + \mu_{sB} \sin 3° = -0.9672,$$

$$a_{21} = \sin 4° + \mu_{ss} \cos 4° = 0.8678,$$

and $a_{22} = \sin 3° + \mu_{sB} \cos 3° = 0.6515.$

The equations have the solutions

$$N_s = -\frac{a_{12}W}{\det},$$

and $N_b = \frac{a_{11}W}{\det},$

where

$$\det = a_{11}a_{22} - a_{12}a_{21} = 1.4529$$

is the determinant of the coefficients. The result: $\boxed{N_s = 119.83 \text{ lb}}$

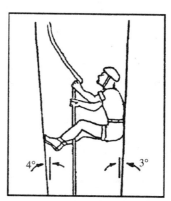

Problem 9.162 The sides of the 200-lb door fit loosely into grooves in the walls. Cables at A and B raise the door at a constant rate. The coefficient of kinetic friction between the door and the grooves is $\mu_k = 0.3$. What force must the cable A exert to continue raising the door at a constant rate if the cable at B breaks?

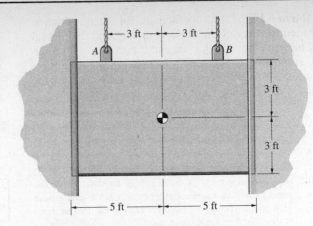

Solution: Since the door fits loosely in the grooves, assume that the moment due to the unbalance when cable B breaks causes the door to contact the upper right and lower left corners. Thus the normal force on the sides occur at these corners. The friction forces at the corners oppose movement. The sum of the moments about the lower left corner is

$$\sum M_L = 2A - 5W + 6\ N_R - 10\mu_k N_R = 0.$$

The sum of the forces:

$$\sum F_x = N_L - N_R = 0,$$

from which $N_L = N_R$, and

$$\sum F_y = A - W - \mu_k N_R - \mu_k N_L = 0.$$

Combine to obtain the two simultaneous equations:

$$2A + (6 - 10\mu_k)N_R = 5W,$$

and $A - 2\mu_k N_R = W.$

These have the solution:

$$A = -\frac{(2\mu_k)(5W)}{\det} - \frac{(6 - 10\mu_k)W}{\det},$$

where $\det = 6(\mu_k - 1)$ is the determinant of the coefficients. Reducing:

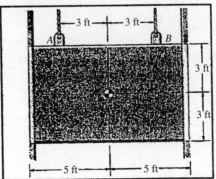

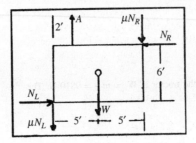

$$\boxed{A = \frac{(-10\mu_k - (6 - 10\mu_k))W}{-6(1 - \mu_k)} = \frac{W}{1 - \mu_k} = 285.71\ \text{lb}}$$

Problem 9.163 The coefficients of static friction between the tires of the 1000-kg tractor and the ground and between the 450-kg crate and the ground are 0.8 and 0.3, respectively. Starting from rest, what torque must the tractor's engine exert on the rear wheels to cause the crate to move? (The front wheels can turn freely.)

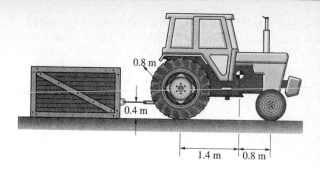

0.8 m

0.4 m

1.4 m   0.8 m

Solution: The weight of the crate is $W = mg = 4414.5$ N. The force required to produce imminent slip of the crate on level ground is $F_c = \mu_s W = 0.3(4414.5) = 1324.5$ N. This is the friction force exerted by the ground on the tires,

$$\sum F_x = -F_c + f_{\text{tires}} = 0.$$

The friction force is related to the torque about the axle (both wheels) by

$$\sum M_{\text{axle}} = T - 0.8 f_{\text{tires}} = 0,$$

from which $\boxed{T = 0.8 F_c = 1059.5 \text{ N m}}$

0.8 m

0.4 m   1.4 m 0.8 m

Problem 9.164 In Problem 9.163, what is the most massive crate the tractor can cause to move from rest if its engine can exert sufficient torque? What torque is necessary?

Solution: The weight of the tractor is $W_t = m_t g = 9810$ N. The sum of the moments about the front wheels is

$$\sum M_F = +0.8 W_t + 0.4 \mu_{sc} W_c - 2.2 N = 0,$$

where N is the normal force on the rear wheels. The sum of the forces at imminent tire slip is

$$\sum F_x = -\mu_{sc} W_c + \mu_{st} N = 0,$$

from which

$$N = \left(\frac{\mu_{sc}}{\mu_{st}}\right) W_c.$$

Substitute into the first equation and reduce:

$$W_c = \frac{0.8 \mu_{st} W_t}{(2.2 \mu_{sc} - 0.4 \mu_{sc}\mu_{st})} = 11131.9 \text{ N},$$

from which the mass of the crate is

$$\boxed{m_c = \frac{W_c}{g} = 1134.75 = 1134.8 \text{ kg}}.$$

The friction force on the tires is $f_{\text{tires}} = \mu_{sc} W_c = 3339.6$ N, from which the torque on the axle (both wheels) is

$$\boxed{T = 0.8 f_{\text{tires}} = 2671.7 \text{ N m}}$$

Problem 9.165 The mass of the vehicle is 900 kg, it has rear-wheel drive, and the coefficient of static friction between its tires and the surface is 0.65. The coefficient of static friction between the crate and the surface is 0.4. If the vehicle attempts to pull the crate up the incline, what is the largest value of the mass of the crate for which it will slip up the incline before the vehicle's tires slip?

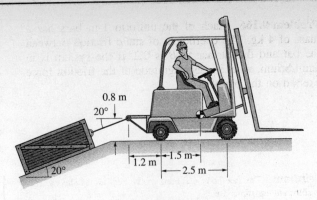

Solution: The normal force between the crate and the incline is $N_c = W_c \cos\theta$, where $\theta = 20°$. The drawbar force parallel to the incline is $F_d = -W_c \sin\theta - \mu_{sc} N_c$. For brevity write $\psi = \sin\theta + \mu_{sc}\cos\theta$. The horizontal component of the drawbar force at the tractor is $F_{dh} = F_d \cos\theta = -W_c\psi\cos\theta$. The vertical component of the drawbar force at the tractor is $F_{dv} = F_d \sin\theta = -W_c\psi\sin\theta$. The weight of the tractor is $W_t = 900\,g = 8829$ N. The sum of the moments about the front wheels is

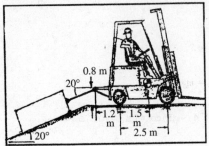

$$\sum M_F = 1W_t - 0.8F_{dh} - 3.7F_{dv} - 2.5\,N = 0,$$

from which

$$0 = W_t + (0.8\cos\theta + 3.7\sin\theta)W_c\psi - 2.5\,N = 0.$$

The sum of the force parallel to the ground is

$$\sum F_x = F_{dh} + \mu_{st}N = 0,$$

from which

$$N = \frac{W_c\psi\cos\theta}{\mu_{st}}.$$

Substitute and reduce:

$$W_c = \frac{\mu_{st}W_t}{((2.5 - 0.8\mu_{st})\cos\theta - 3.7\mu_{st}\sin\theta)(\sin\theta + \mu_{sc}\cos\theta)}$$

$$= 7701.1\ \text{N}.$$

The mass of the crate is

$$\boxed{m_c = \frac{W_c}{g} = 785\ \text{kg}}$$

Problem 9.166 Each of the uniform 1-m bars has a mass of 4 kg. The coefficient of static friction between the bar and the surface at B is 0.2. If the system is in equilibrium, what is the magnitude of the friction force exerted on the bar at B?

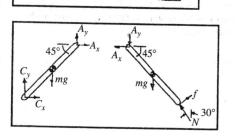

Solution: The free body diagrams of the bars are as shown. The equilibrium equations are

Left bar:

$$\sum F_x = C_x + A_x = 0,$$

$$\sum F_y = C_y + A_y - mg = 0,$$

$$\sum M_{(\text{leftend})} = (1)\cos 45° A_y - (1)\cos 45° A_x - (0.5)\cos 45° mg$$

$$= 0,$$

Right bar:

$$\sum F_x = -A_x + f\cos 30° - N\sin 30° = 0,$$

$$\sum F_y = -A_y - mg + f\sin 30° + N\cos 30° = 0,$$

$$\sum M_{(\text{rightend})} = (1)\cos 45° A_x + (1)\cos 45° A_y + (0.5)\cos 45° mg$$

$$= 0,$$

Solving, we obtain $N = 43.8$ N and $f = 2.63$ N.

Problem 9.167 In Problem 9.166, what is the minimum coefficient of static friction between the bar and the surface at B necessary for the system to be in equilibrium?

Solution: From the solution of Problem 9.166, the normal and friction forces are $N = 43.8$ N and $f = 2.63$ N. Slip impends when $f = \mu_s N$ so, $\mu_s = \dfrac{2.63}{43.8} = 0.06.$

Problem 9.168 The collars A and B each have a mass of 2 kg. If friction between collar B and the bar can be neglected, what minimum coefficient of static friction between collar A and the bar is necessary for the collars to remain in equilibrium in the position shown?

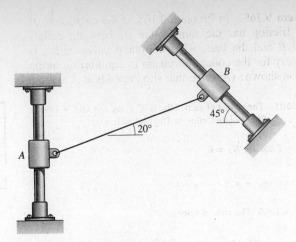

Solution: The weight of each collar is $W = mg = 19.62$ N. Denote $\theta = 45°$, $\alpha = 20°$. The unit vector parallel to the bar holding B is

$$\mathbf{e}_B = -\mathbf{i}\sin\theta + \mathbf{j}\cos\theta.$$

The weight of B is $\mathbf{W} = -\mathbf{j}|\mathbf{W}|$. The components of the weight of B parallel to the bar is

$$W_{PB} = (\mathbf{e}_B \cdot \mathbf{W})\mathbf{e}_B = -|\mathbf{W}|\cos\theta\mathbf{e}_B.$$

This force must be balanced by a component of the force in the connecting wire for B to remain stationary. The components of the tension in the wire are

$$\mathbf{T} = |\mathbf{T}|(\mathbf{i}\cos(180° + \alpha) + \mathbf{j}\sin(180° + \alpha))$$

$$= |\mathbf{T}|(-\mathbf{i}\cos\alpha - \mathbf{j}\sin\alpha),$$

from which the component of $\mathbf{T}$ parallel to the bar supporting B is

$$\mathbf{T}_{PB} = (\mathbf{e}_B \cdot \mathbf{T})\mathbf{e}_B = |\mathbf{T}|\sin(\theta - \alpha)\mathbf{e}_B.$$

The sum of forces along $\mathbf{e}_B$:

$$|\mathbf{T}|\sin(\theta - \alpha)\sin\theta - |\mathbf{W}|\cos\theta\sin\theta = 0,$$

from which:

$$\frac{|\mathbf{W}|}{|\mathbf{T}|} = \frac{\sin(\theta - \alpha)}{\cos\theta}.$$

The unit vector parallel to the bar supporting A is $\mathbf{e}_A = \mathbf{j}$. The component of $\mathbf{T}$ parallel to the bar supporting A is $|\mathbf{T}_{PA}| = -\mathbf{j} \cdot \mathbf{T} = |\mathbf{T}|\sin\alpha$, and the force exerted by $\mathbf{T}$ on the slider A perpendicular to the bar is $|\mathbf{N}_A| = -\mathbf{i} \cdot |\mathbf{T}| = |\mathbf{T}|\cos\alpha$, where the negative sign is used because the tension at A is in opposition to the tension at B (tension is reversed).

The sum of forces parallel to the bar is

$$\sum F_A = +\mu_s|\mathbf{N}_A| - |\mathbf{W}| + |\mathbf{T}_{PA}| = 0,$$

from which

$$\mu_s|\mathbf{T}|\cos\alpha - |\mathbf{W}| + |\mathbf{T}|\sin\alpha = 0,$$

and $\mu_s = \dfrac{|\mathbf{W}|}{|\mathbf{T}|}\left(\dfrac{1}{\cos\alpha}\right) - \tan\alpha.$

Substitute and reduce:

$$\boxed{\mu_s = \left(\frac{\sin(\theta - \alpha)}{\cos\alpha\cos\theta}\right) - \tan\alpha = 0.272}$$

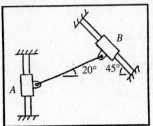

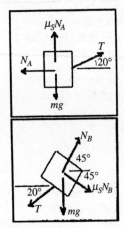

Problem 9.169 In Problem 9.168, if the coefficient of static friction has the same value μ_s between collars A and B and the bars, what minimum value of μ_s, is necessary for the collars to remain in equilibrium in the position shown? (Assume that slip impends at A and B.)

Solution: The weight of each collar is $W = mg = 19.62$ N. Denote $\theta = 45°$, $\alpha = 20°$. *Isolate Collar A*. The sum of forces:

$$\sum F_x = T\cos\alpha - N_A = 0,$$

$$\sum F_y = T\sin\alpha + \mu_s N_A - mg = 0.$$

Isolate Collar B: The sum of forces:

$$\sum F_x = N_B \cos\theta + \mu_s N_B \cos\theta - T\cos\alpha = 0.$$

$$\sum F_y = N_B \sin\theta - \mu_s N_B \sin\theta - T\sin\alpha = 0.$$

These are four equations in four unknowns. Solve: $T = 45.4$ N, $N_A = 42.6$ N, $N_B = 55$ N, and $\boxed{\mu_s = 0.0963}$. This is the minimum coefficient of friction required to maintain equilibrium.

Problem 9.170 The clamp presses two pieces of wood together. The pitch of the threads is $p = 2$ mm, the mean radius of the thread is $r = 8$ mm, and the coefficient of kinetic friction between the thread and the mating groove is 0.24. What couple must be exerted on the thread shaft to press the pieces of wood together with a force of 200 N?

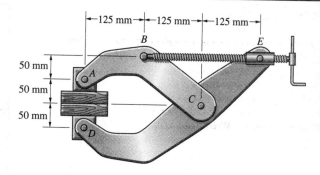

Solution: The free-body diagram of the upper arm of the clamp is shown.

From the equilibrium equation

$$\sum M_{\text{(ptc)}} = -(0.25)(200) - 0.1BE = 0,$$

we find that $BE = -500$ N. The compressive load in BE is 500 N.

The slope of the thread is

$$\alpha = \arctan\left(\frac{P}{2\pi r}\right)$$

$$= \arctan\left[\frac{0.002}{2\pi(0.008)}\right]$$

$$= 2.279°.$$

The angle of friction is

$$\theta_k = \arctan(0.24) = 13.496°.$$

From Eq. (9.9) with $\theta_s = \theta_k$, the required couple is

$$M = rF\tan(\theta_k + \alpha)$$

$$= (0.008)(500)\tan(13.496° + 2.279°)$$

$$= 1.13 \text{ N-m}.$$

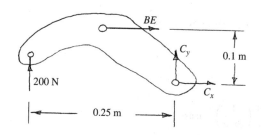

Problem 9.171 In Problem 9.170, the coefficient of static friction between the thread and the mating groove is 0.28. After the threaded shaft is rotated sufficiently to press the pieces of wood together with a force of 200 N, what couple must be exerted on the shaft to loosen it?

Solution: First, find the forces in the parts of the clamp. Then analyze the threaded shaft. *BE* is a two force member

$$\sum F_x: \quad BE + C_x = 0 \qquad \text{(1)}$$

$$\sum F_y: \quad 200 + C_y = 0 \qquad \text{(2)}$$

$$\sum M_A: \quad -0.05BE + 0.05C_x + 0.25C_y = 0 \quad \text{(3)}$$

Solving, we get

$BE = -500$ N   (compression)

$C_x = 500$ N

$C_y = -200$ N

We don't have to solve for additional forces because we used the fact that member *BE* was a two force member.

From Problem 9.170, $P = 2$ mm, $r = 8$ mm. We have $\mu_s = 0.28$. We want to loosen the clamp (Turn the clamp such that the motion is in the direction of the axial force.

To do this,

$$M = rF \tan(\theta_s - \alpha)$$

where

$$\tan \theta_s = \mu_s = 0.28$$

$$\theta_s = 15.64°$$

$$\tan \alpha = P/2\pi r = \frac{2}{2\pi(8)}$$

$$\alpha = 2.28°$$

$$F = |BE| = 500 \text{ N}$$

Solving

$$M = 0.950 \text{ N-m}$$

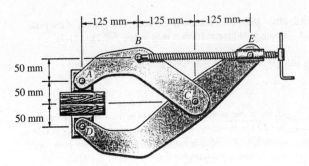

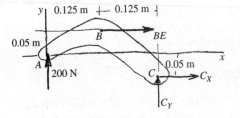

Problem 9.172 The axles of the tram are supported by journal bearing. The radius of the wheels is 75 mm, the radius of the axles is 15 mm, and the coefficient of kinetic friction between the axles and the bearings is $\mu_k = 0.14$. The mass of the tram and its load is 160 kg. If the weight of the tram and its load is evenly divided between the axles, what force P is necessary to push the tram at a constant speed?

Solution: Assume that there are two bearings per axle. The weight of the tram is $W = mg = 1569.6$ N. This load is divided between four bearings:

$$F = \frac{W}{4} = 392.4 \text{ N}.$$

The angle of kinetic friction is $\theta_k = \tan^{-1}(\mu_k) = 7.97°$. The moment required to turn each bearing at a constant rate is $M = Fr \sin \theta_k = 0.8161$ N m, and the force per wheel is

$$P_w = \frac{M}{R} = \frac{0.8161}{0.075} = 10.88 \text{ N}.$$

The total force required to push the tram is $\boxed{P = 4P_w = 43.5 \text{ N}}$

Problem 9.173 The two pulleys have a radius of 6 in. and are mounted on shafts of 1-in. radius supported by journal bearings. Neglect the weights of the pulleys and shafts. The coefficient of kinetic friction between the shafts and the bearings is $\mu_k = 0.2$. If a force $T = 200$ lb is required to raise the man at a constant rate, what is his weight?

Solution: Denote the tension in the horizontal portion of the cable by H. The angle of kinetic friction is $\theta_k = \tan^{-1}(0.2) = 11.31°$

Consider the right Pulley: The force on the right pulley is

$$F = \sqrt{T^2 + H^2}.$$

The magnitude of the moment required to turn the shaft in the bearing is $M_{\text{right}} = r\sqrt{T^2 + H^2}\sin\theta_k$. The applied moment is $M_{\text{applied}} = (T - H)R$, from which $(T - H)R = r\sqrt{T^2 + H^2}\sin\theta_k$. Square both sides and reduce to obtain the quadratic:

$$H^2 - 2TH\left(\frac{1}{1 - \left(\dfrac{r}{R}\right)^2 \sin^2\theta_k}\right) + T^2 = 0,$$

or $H^2 - 2(200.214)H + 40000 = 0.$

This has the solutions: $H = 200.214 \pm \sqrt{200.214^2 - 40000} = 209.46$, 190.95. The lesser root corresponds to the horizontal tension, $H = 190.97 = 191$ lb.

Consider the left Pulley: The force on the pulley is $F_{\text{left}} = \sqrt{W^2 + H^2}$. The applied moment is $M_{\text{applied}} = -(H - W)R$, from which $(H - W)R = r\sqrt{W^2 + H^2}\sin\theta_k$. Square both sides and reduce to the quadratic:

$$W^2 - 2\left(\frac{H}{1 - \left(\dfrac{r}{R}\right)^2 \sin^2\theta_k}\right)W + H^2 = 0,$$

or $W^2 - 2(191.1)W + 36431.9 = 0.$

This has the solutions: $W_{1,2} = 191.166 \pm \sqrt{191.166^2 - 36431.9} = 199.9$ lb, 182.25 lb. By an analogous argument to that used in Problem 10.92, the lesser root corresponds to the weight of the man, $W_{\text{raised}} = 182.3$ lb

Problem 9.174 If the man in Problem 9.173 weighs 160 lb, what force T is necessary to lower him at a constant rate?

Solution: Use the solution to Problem 9.173, with $W = 160$ lb. *Begin with the left pulley*: the quadratic relation between the weight and the horizontal tension is

$$H^2 - 2\left(\frac{W}{1-\left(\frac{r}{R}\right)^2\sin^2\theta_k}\right)H + W^2 = 0,$$

   or $H^2 - 2(160.171)H + 25600 = 0$.

This has the solutions:

$$H_{1,2} = 160.171 \pm \sqrt{160.171^2 - 25600} = 167.57 \text{ lb}, 152.77 \text{ lb}.$$

The lesser root corresponds to the horizontal tension: $H = 152.77$ lb

Consider the right pulley: The quadratic relation between the tension and the horizontal tension is

$$T^2 - 2\left(\frac{H}{1-\left(\frac{r}{R}\right)^2\sin^2\theta_k}\right)T + H^2 = 0,$$

   or $T^2 - 2(152.93)T + 23338.4 = 0$.

This has the solutions:

$$T_{1,2} = 152.93 \pm \sqrt{152.93^2 - 23338.4} = 160 \text{ lb}, 145.87 \text{ lb}.$$

By previous arguments, the lesser root corresponds to the tension when the man is being lowered at a constant rate, $T_{\text{lower}} = 145.9$ lb.

Problem 9.175 If the two cylinders are held fixed, what is the range of W for which the two weights will remain stationary?

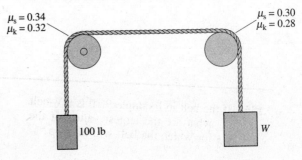

Solution: Denote the tension in the horizontal part of the rope by H. The angle of contact with each cylinder is

$$\beta = \frac{\pi}{2}.$$

Begin on the left with the known weight. Suppose that the known weight is on the verge (imminent slip) of being lowered. The tension is $T_L = 100$ lb. The tension in the horizontal portion of the rope is $H = T_L e^{-0.34\beta} = 58.62$ lb. The tension in the right part of the rope is $T_R = He^{-0.30\beta} = 36.59$ lb. This is the minimum weight for which the system will remain stationary. Suppose that the weight on the left is on the verge of being raised. The horizontal tension is $H = T_L e^{0.34\beta} = 170.59$ lb. The tension on the right is $T_R = He^{0.30\beta} = 273.3$ lb. This is the maximum weight for which the system will remain stationary.

Thus $\boxed{36.59 \leq W \leq 273.3 \text{ (lb)}}$

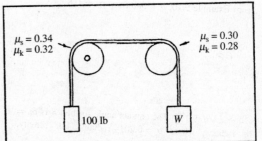

Problem 9.176 In Problem 9.175, if the system is initially stationary and the left cylinder is slowly rotated, determine the largest weight W that can be (a) raised; (b) lowered.

Solution: Assume that the rope does not slip on the slowly rotating cylinder, but is always at the point of imminent slip. The tension in the horizontal part as the cylinder is rotated is $H = T_L e^{0.34\beta} = 170.6$ lb, where the static coefficient of friction is used, since the rope does not slip. The tension in the right portion of the rope is $T_R = He^{-0.28\beta} = 109.88 = 110$ lb, where the kinetic coefficient of friction is used, since the rope slips at a steady rate. Thus (a) $\boxed{W = 110 \text{ lb}}$. (b) If the weight W is slowly being lowered, the tension in the horizontal portion is also $H = T_L e^{0.34\beta} = 170.6$ lb, and the tension in the right portion of the rope is $T_R = He^{0.28\beta} = 264.8$ lb, from which $\boxed{W = 264.8 \text{ lb}}$

Problem 10.1 Determine the reactions at the beam's built-in support. Then determine the internal forces and moment at A (a) by drawing the free-body diagram of the part of the beam to the left of A; (b) by drawing the free-body diagram of the part of the beam to the right of A.

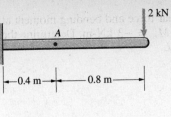

Solution: From the equilibrium equations

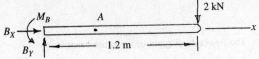

$$\sum F_x = B_x = 0,$$

$$\sum F_y = B_y - 2 = 0,$$

$$\sum M_{(pt.\ B)} = M_B - (2)(1.2) = 0,$$

we obtain $B_x = 0$, $B_y = 2$ kN, $M_B = 2.4$ kN-m.

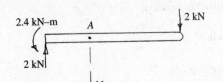

(a) $\sum F_x = P_A = 0,$

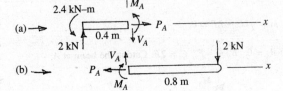

$$\sum F_y = 2 - V_A = 0,$$

$$\sum M_{(pt.\ A)} = M_A + 2.4 - (2)(0.4) = 0.$$

Solving, $P_A = 0$, $V_A = 2$ kN, $M_A = -1.6$ kN-m.

(b) $\sum F_x = -P_A = 0,$

$$\sum F_y = V_A - 2 = 0,$$

$$\sum M_{(pt.\ A)} = -M_A - (2)(0.8) = 0.$$

Solving, $P_A = 0$, $V_A = 2$ kN, $M_A = -1.6$ kN-m.

Problem 10.2 Determine the internal forces and moment at A.

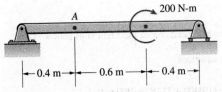

Solution: From the equilibrium equations

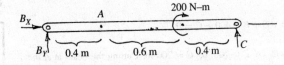

$$\sum F_x = B_x = 0,$$

$$\sum F_y = B_y + C = 0,$$

$$\sum M_{(pt.\ B)} = 1.4C - 200 = 0,$$

we obtain $B_x = 0$, $B_y = -142.9$ N, $C = 142.9$ N.

Cutting the beam at A, from the free-body diagram shown we obtain the equilibrium equations

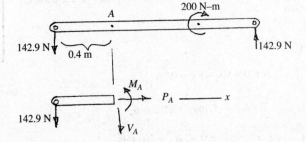

$$\sum F_x = P_A = 0,$$

$$\sum F_y = -142.9 - V_A = 0,$$

$$\sum M_{(rightend)} = M_A + (0.4)(142.9) = 0.$$

Solving, $P_A = 0$, $V_A = -142.9$ N, $M_A = -57.1$ N-m.

Problem 10.3 The shear force and bending moment at A are $V_A = -6$ kN and $M_A = -3$ kN-m. Determine the force F and dimension L.

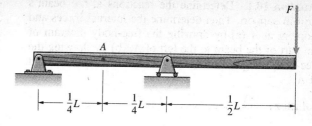

Solution: The free-body diagram of the entire beam is

Solving the equilibrium equations

$$\sum F_x = B_x = 0,$$

$$\sum F_y = B_y + C - F = 0,$$

$$\sum M_{(pt.\ B)} = \tfrac{1}{2}LC - LF = 0,$$

we obtain $B_x = 0$, $B_y = -F$, $C = 2F$. Cutting the beam at A,

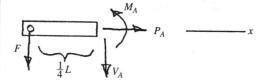

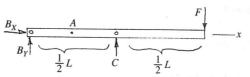

we obtain the equations

$$\sum F_y = -F - V_A = 0,$$

$$\sum M_{(rightend)} = M_A + \tfrac{1}{4}LF = 0.$$

Setting $V_A = -6$ kN and $M_A = -3$ kN-m and solving, we obtain

$$F = 6 \text{ kN}$$

and $L = 2$ m.

Problem 10.4 Determine the internal forces and moment at A.

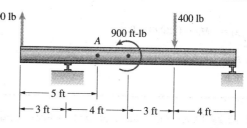

Solution: The free body diagram of the beam is as shown.

From the equilibrium equations

$$\sum M_{(leftend)} = 3B - (10)400 + (14)C + 900 = 0$$

$$\sum F_y = 100 + B - 400 + C = 0$$

the reactions are $B = 100$ lb, $C = 200$ lb. Cutting the beam at A the free body diagram of the part to the left is: From the equilibrium equations

$$\sum F_x = P_A = 0,$$

$$\sum F_y = 0 = 100 + 100 - V_A = 0,$$

$$\sum M_{(rightend)} = M_A - (5)100 - (2)100 = 0,$$

we obtain $P_A = 0$, $V_A = 200$ lb, $M_A = 700$ ft-lb.

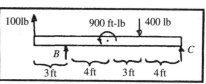

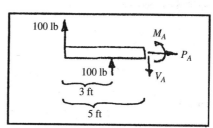

Problem 10.5 Determine the internal forces and moment at A.

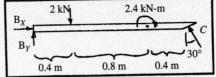

Solution: The free body diagram of the beam is as shown. From the equilibrium equations

$$\sum F_x = B_x - C \sin 30° = 0,$$

$$\sum F_y = B_y - 2 + C \cos 30° = 0,$$

$$\sum M_{\text{(leftend)}} = -(0.4)2 + (1.6)C \cos 30° - 2.4 = 0,$$

the reactions are $B_x = 1.15$ kN, $B_y = 0$, $C = 2.31$ kN. Cutting the beam at A the free body diagram of the part to the left is: From the equilibrium equations

$$\sum F_x = 1.15 + P_A = 0,$$

and $\sum F_y = -2 - V_A = 0$

$$\sum M_{\text{(rightend)}} = -(0.4)2 + M_A = 0,$$

we obtain $P_A = -1.15$ kN, $V_A = -2$ kN, $M_A = 0.8$ kN-m.

Problem 10.6 Determine the internal forces and moment at A for each loading.

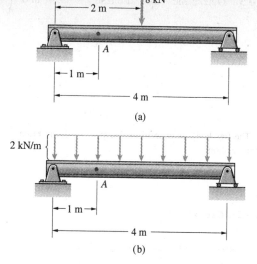

(a)

(b)

Solution: (a) Denote the reaction at the pinned left end by R, and the reaction at the roller support by B. The reaction at B:

$$\sum M = -2(8) + B(4) = 0,$$

from which $B = 4$ kN. The reaction at R:

$$\sum F_y = R_y - 8 + B = 0,$$

from which $R_y = 4$ kN.

$$\sum F_x = R_x = 0.$$

Make a cut at A: Isolate the left hand part. The sum of moments:

$$\sum M = M_A - 4(1) = 0,$$

from which $M_A = 4$ kN m $\quad V_A = 4$ kN $\quad P_A = 0$

(b) Determine the reaction at B: The sum of the moments about R:

$$\sum M_R = -\int_0^4 2x\,dx + 4B = 0,$$

from which

$$B = \left(\frac{1}{4}\right)\left[2\frac{x^2}{2}\right]_0^4 = \frac{16}{4} = 4 \text{ kN}.$$

The reaction at R:

$$\sum F_y = R_y - \int_0^4 2\,dx + B = 0,$$

from which

$$R_y = 8 - 4 = 4 \text{ kN},$$

$$\sum F_x = R_x = 0.$$

Make a cut at A: Isolate the left hand part. The sum of moments:

$$\sum M = M_A - (1)R_y + \int_0^1 2x\,dx = 0,$$

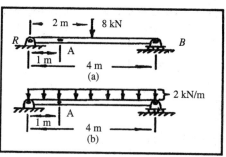

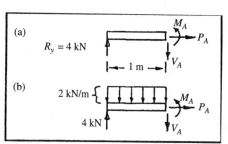

from which $M_A = R_y - 1 = 3$ kN m.

$$V_A = R_y - \int_0^1 2\,dx = 4 - 2 = 2 \text{ kN}$$

$$P_A = 0.$$

Problem 10.7 Model the ladder rung as a simply supported (pin supported) beam and assume that the 750-N load exerted by the person's shoe is uniformly distributed. Determine the internal forces and moment at A.

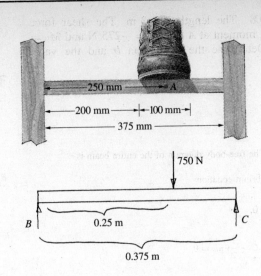

Solution:

$$\sum F_y = B + C - 750 = 0,$$

$$\sum M_{(pt.\ B)} = 0.375C - (0.25)(750) = 0.$$

Solving, $B = 250$ N, $C = 500$ N.

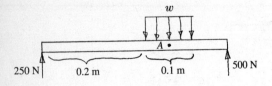

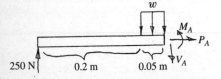

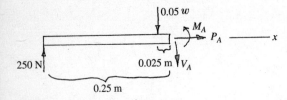

The distributed load is

$w = (750\ \text{N})/(0.1\ \text{m}) = 7500\ \text{N/m}$.

From the equilibrium equations

$$\sum F_x = P_A = 0,$$

$$\sum F_y = 250 - V_A - 0.05(7500) = 0,$$

$$\sum M_{(rightend)} = M_A - (250)(0.25)$$

$$+ (0.05)(7500)(0.025) = 0,$$

we obtain $P_A = 0$, $V_A = -125$ N, $M_A = 53.1$ N-m.

Problem 10.8 The length $L = 3$ m. The shear force and bending moment at A are $V_A = -275$ N and $M_A = 260$ N-m. Determine the dimension b and the value of w_0.

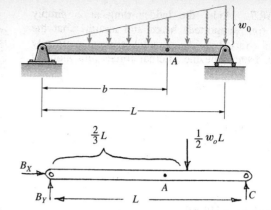

Solution: The free-body diagram of the entire beam is

From the equilibrium equations

$$\sum F_x = B_x = 0,$$

$$\sum F_y = B_y + C - \frac{1}{2}w_0 L = 0,$$

$$\sum M_{(\text{pt. } B)} = LC - \left(\frac{2}{3}L\right)\left(\frac{1}{2}w_0 L\right) = 0,$$

we obtain $B_x = 0$, $B_y = \frac{1}{6}w_0 L$, $C = \frac{1}{3}w_0 L$. Cutting the beam at A,

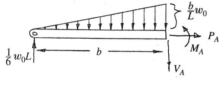

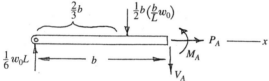

we obtain the equations

$$\sum F_y = \frac{1}{6}w_0 L - \frac{1}{2}b\left(\frac{b}{L}w_0\right) - V_A = 0,$$

$$\sum M_{(\text{rightend})} = M_A + \left(\frac{1}{3}b\right)\left(\frac{1}{2}\frac{b^2}{L}w_0\right) - b\left(\frac{1}{6}w_0 L\right) = 0.$$

Setting $L = 3$ m, $V_A = -275$ N, $M_A = 260$ N-m and solving yields $b = 2.40$ m, $w_0 = 600$ N/m.

Problem 10.9 If $x = 3$ m, what are the internal forces and moment at A?

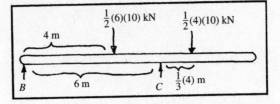

10 kN/m

x

6 m 4 m

Solution: Representing the distributed load as 2 forces, the free body diagram of the entire beam is as shown. From the equilibrium equations

$$\sum F_y = B + C - \frac{1}{2}(6)(10) - \frac{1}{2}(4)(10) = 0,$$

$$\sum M_{(pt.\ B)} = 6C - 4\left[\frac{1}{2}(6)(10)\right] - \left(6 + \frac{4}{3}\right)\left[\frac{1}{2}(4)(10)\right] = 0,$$

the reactions are $B = 5.56$ kN, $C = 44.4$ kN. Cutting the beam at A the free body diagram of the part to the left is as shown. Representing the distributed load by a force, and writing the equilibrium equations

$$\sum F_x = P_A = 0,$$

$$\sum F_y = 5.56 - \frac{1}{2}(3)\left[\frac{3}{6}(10)\right] - V_A = 0,$$

and $\sum M_{(pt.\ B)} = M_A - 3V_A - (2)\frac{1}{2}(3)\left[\frac{3}{6}(10)\right] = 0,$

we obtain $P_A = 0$, $V_A = -1.94$ kN, $M_A = 9.17$ kN-m.

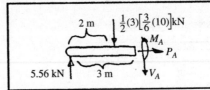

$\frac{1}{2}(6)(10)$ kN $\frac{1}{2}(4)(10)$ kN

4 m

B 6 m C $\frac{1}{3}(4)$ m

$\frac{3}{6}(10)$ kN/m

5.56 kN 3 m M_A P_A V_A

2 m $\frac{1}{2}(3)\left[\frac{3}{6}(10)\right]$ kN

M_A P_A

5.56 kN 3 m V_A

Problem 10.10 If $x = 8$ m in Problem 10.9, what are the internal forces and moment at A?

Solution: Cutting the beam at A the free body diagram of the part of the beam to the right is as shown. Representing the distributed load by a force, the equilibrium equations are

$$\sum F_x = -P_A = 0$$

$$\sum F_y = V_A - \frac{1}{2}(2)\left[\frac{2}{4}(10)\right] = 0,$$

$$\sum M_{(pt.\ A)} = -M_A - \left[\frac{1}{3}(2)\right]\frac{1}{2}(2)\left[\frac{2}{4}(10)\right] = 0$$

we obtain $P_A = 0$, $V_A = 5$ kN, $M_A = -3.33$ kN-m.

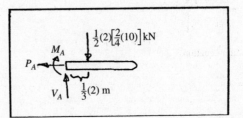

$\frac{2}{4}(10)$ kN/M

P_A M_A 2 m V_A

$\frac{1}{2}(2)\left[\frac{2}{4}(10)\right]$ kN

M_A P_A V_A $\frac{1}{3}(2)$ m

Problem 10.11 Determine the internal forces and moment at *B* for the loadings (a) and (b).

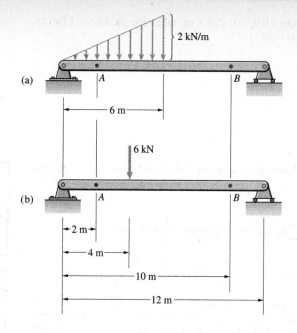

(a)

2 kN/m

|A

|B

6 m

6 kN

(b)

|A

|B

2 m

4 m

10 m

12 m

Solution: In both cases, the free-body diagram of the entire beam is

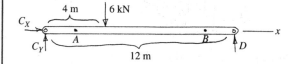

C_X

4 m

6 kN

C_Y

A

B

D

x

12 m

From the equilibrium equations

$$\sum F_x = C_x = 0,$$

$$\sum F_y = C_y + D - 6 = 0,$$

$$\sum M_{(pt. \ C)} = 12 \ D - (4)(6) = 0,$$

we obtain $C_x = 0$, $C_y = 4$ kN, $D = 2$ kN.

In both cases, the free-body diagram of the part of the beam to the right of *B* is

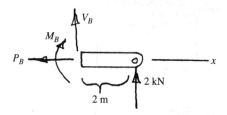

V_B

M_B

P_B

x

2 kN

2 m

From the equilibrium equations

$$\sum F_x = -P_B = 0,$$

$$\sum F_y = V_B + 2 = 0,$$

$$\sum M_{(leftend)} = -M_B + (2)(2) = 0,$$

we obtain $P_B = 0$, $V_B = -2$ kN, $M_B = 4$ kN-m in cases (a) and (b).

Problem 10.12 For the loading (a) and (b) shown in Problem 10.11, determine the internal forces and moment at A.

Solution: The reactions at the supports are determined in the solution to Problem 10.11.

In case (a), the free-body diagram of the part of the beam to the left of A is

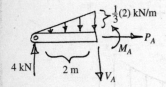

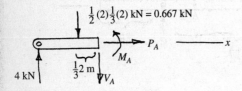

From the equilibrium equations

$$\sum F_x = P_A = 0,$$

$$\sum F_y = 4 - 0.667 - V_A = 0,$$

$$\sum M_{(rightend)} = M_A - (4)(2) + (0.667)\left(\frac{2}{3}\right) = 0$$

we obtain $P_A = 0$, $V_A = 3.33$ kN, $M_A = 7.56$ kN-m.

In case (b), the free-body diagram of the part of the beam to the left of A is

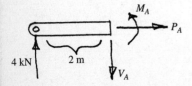

we see that $P_A = 0$, $V_A = 4$ kN, $M_A = (2)(4) = 8$ kN-m.

Problem 10.13 The distributed load is $w = 10x^2$ lb/ft. Determine the internal forces and moment at A.

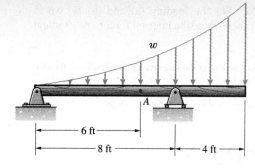

Solution: From the equilibrium equations

$$\sum F_x = B_x = 0,$$

$$\sum F_y = B_y + C - \int_0^{12} 10x^2\,dx = 0,$$

$$\sum M_{\text{(pt. B)}} = 8C - \int_0^{12} x10x^2\,dx = 0,$$

we obtain $B_x = 0$, $B_y = -720$ lb, $C = 6480$ lb.

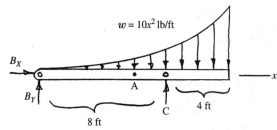

Cutting the beam at A, from the equilibrium equations

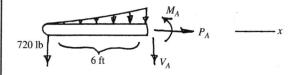

$$\sum F_y = -720 - V_A - \int_0^6 10x^2\,dx = 0,$$

$$\sum M_{\text{(leftend)}} = -6V_A + M_A - \int_0^6 x10x^2\,dx = 0,$$

we obtain $V_A = -1440$ lb, $M_A = -5400$ ft-lb.

Problem 10.14 Determine the internal forces and moment at A.

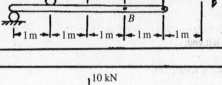

Solution: *The complete structure as a free body*: The sum of the moments about the right end:

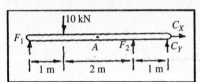

$$\sum M = 3(10) - 5R = 0,$$

from which $R = \dfrac{30}{5} = 6$ kN. The sum of forces in the y-Direction:

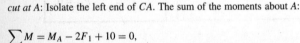

$$\sum F_y = R_y + C_y - 10 = 0,$$

from which $C_y = 4$ kN. *The element CA as a free body*: The sum of the moments about C:

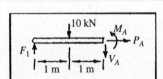

$$\sum M_C = -4F_1 + 10(3) - F_2 = 0.$$

The sum of the forces:

$$\sum F_y = C_y + F_2 - 10 + F_1 = 0.$$

Solve the simultaneous equations: $F_1 = 8$ kN, $F_2 = -2$ kN. *Make a cut at A*: Isolate the left end of CA. The sum of the moments about A:

$$\sum M = M_A - 2F_1 + 10 = 0,$$

from which

$$M_A = -10 + 16 = 6 \text{ kN m}$$

$$V_A = 8 - 10 = -2 \text{ kN},$$

$$P_A = 0$$

Problem 10.15 Determine the internal forces and moment at point B in Problem 10.14.

Solution: Use the solutions to Problem 10.14. *Make a cut at point B*: Isolate the left part. The sum of the moments about B:

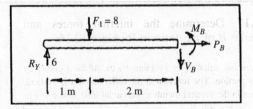

$$\sum M_B = M_B + 2F_1 - 3R_y = 0,$$

from which

$$M_B = -16 + 18 = 2 \text{ kN m}$$

$$V_B = R_y - F_1 = 6 - 8 = -2 \text{ kN}$$

$$P_B = 0$$

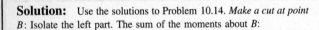

Problem 10.16 Determine the internal forces and moment at A.

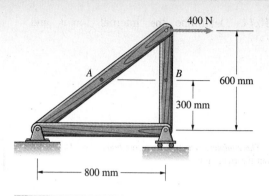

Solution: *The complete structure as a free body*: The sum of the moments about the left end:

$$\sum M_R = -600(400) + 800C_y = 0,$$

from which $C_y = 300$ N. The sum of the forces:

$$\sum F_y = R_y + 300 = 0,$$

from which $R_y = -300$ N.

$$\sum F_x = R_x + 400 = 0,$$

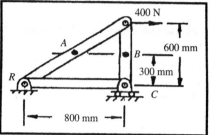

from which $R_x = -400$ N. *Make a cut at A*: Isolate the part to the left of A: The resultant force reaction at R is

$$R = \sqrt{400^2 + 300^2} = 500 \text{ N}$$

at an angle of

$$\theta = 180 + \tan^{-1}\frac{3}{4} = 216.9°.$$

The angle element RA relative to the horizontal is

$$\alpha = \tan^{-1}\left(\frac{3}{4}\right) = 36.9°.$$

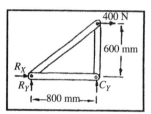
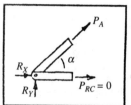

Thus the angle of RA is equal and 180 deg opposite to the reaction at R. Since the roller support prevents the horizontal member of the structure from exerting an x- component of load, the member RA bears the full reaction as an axial load. Thus $M^A = 0$ $V_A = 0$ and $P_A = 500$ N.

Problem 10.17 Determine the internal forces and moment at point B of the truss in Problem 10.16.

Solution: Use the solution to Problem 10.16. *Make a cut at B*: Isolate the lower portion. The reaction at the roller support is vertical, hence the reaction in the vertical member is an axial load, hence $M_B = 0$, $V_B = 0$, and $P_B = -300$ N.

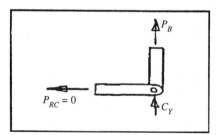

Problem 10.18 The axial force at A is $P_A = -12$ kN. What are the shear force and bending moment at A?

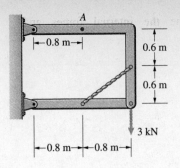

Solution: This problem has no unique solution.

Problem 10.19 The mass $m = 120$ kg. Determine the internal forces and moment at A.

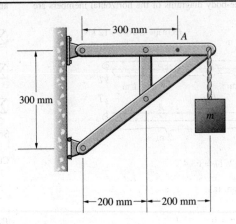

Solution: The free-body diagrams of the members are

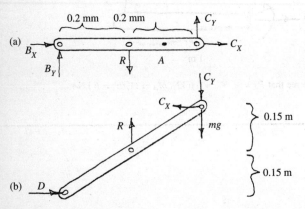

Cutting member (a) at A, we see that

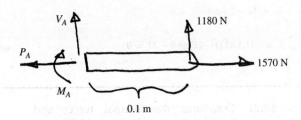

$P_A = 1570$ N,

$V_A = -1180$ N,

$M_A = (0.1)(1180) = 118$ N-m.

From free-body diagram (a),

$$\sum F_x = B_x + C_x = 0,$$

$$\sum F_y = B_y - R + C_y = 0,$$

$$\sum M_{(pt. \ B)} = -0.2\,R + 0.4\,C_y = 0,$$

and from free-body diagram (b),

$$\sum F_x = D - C_x = 0,$$

$$\sum F_y = R - C_y - mg = 0,$$

$$\sum M_{(pt. \ D)} = 0.2\,R + 0.3\,C_x$$

$$- 0.4\,C_y - 0.4\,mg = 0.$$

Setting $m = 120$ kg and $g = 9.81$ m/s^2 and solving, we find that $C_x = 1570$ N, $C_y = 1180$ N.

Problem 10.20 Determine the internal forces and moment at A.

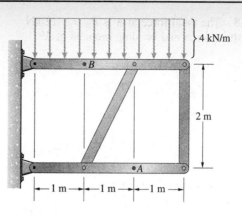

4 kN/m

2 m

|— 1 m —|— 1 m —|— 1 m —|

Solution: The free-body diagrams of the horizontal members are

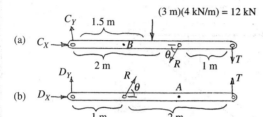

(a)

C_Y 1.5 m
C_X
$\cdot B$
2 m
$(3 \text{ m})(4 \text{ kN/m}) = 12 \text{ kN}$
θ
R
1 m
T

(b)

D_Y
D_X
R
θ
A
T
1 m   2 m

The angle $\theta = \arctan(2/1) = 63.4°$.

From free-body diagram (a),

$$\sum F_x = C_x - R\cos\theta = 0,$$

$$\sum F_y = C_y - 12 - R\sin\theta - T = 0,$$

$$\sum M_{(\text{pt. } C)} = -(1.5)(12) - 2R\sin\theta - 3T = 0,$$

and from free-body diagram (b),

$$\sum F_x = D_x + R\cos\theta = 0,$$

$$\sum F_y = D_y + R\sin\theta + T = 0,$$

$$\sum M_{(\text{pt. } D)} = (1)R\sin\theta + 3T = 0.$$

Solving, we obtain $C_x = -9$ kN, $C_y = 0$, and $T = 6$ kN.

Cutting member (b) at A,

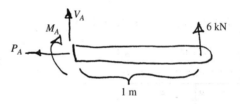

V_A
M_A
P_A
6 kN
1 m

we see that $P_A = 0$, $V_A = -6$ kN, $M_A = (1)(6) = 6$ kN-m.

Problem 10.21 Determine the internal forces and moment at point B of the frame in Problem 10.20.

Solution: See the solution of Problem 10.20. Cutting member (a) at B and including the distributed load acting on the part of the member to the left of B,

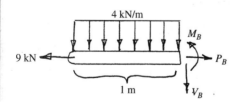

4 kN/m
M_B
9 kN
P_B
1 m
V_B

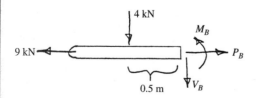

4 kN
M_B
9 kN
P_B
0.5 m
V_B

we see that $P_B = 9$ kN, $V_B = -4$ kN, $M_B = -(0.5)(4) = -2$ kN-m.

Problem 10.22 (a) Determine the internal forces and moment as functions of x.

(b) Draw the shear force and bending moment diagrams.

Strategy: Cut the beam at an arbitrary position x and draw the free body diagrams of the part on the left.

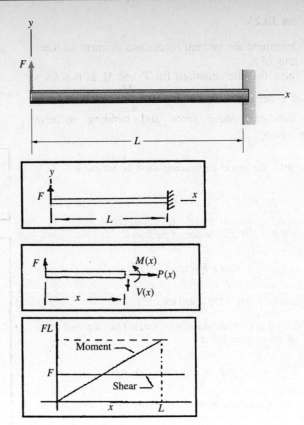

Solution: *Make a cut at point x units from the left end.* By definition, the shear is the sum of the forces to the left: $V_x = F$. The free body diagram of the left part: $M(x) - Fx = 0$, from which $M(x) = Fx$ which is a straight line with slope F ft lb/ft. The axial forces are zero $P(x) = 0$

Problem 10.23

(a) Determine the internal forces and moment as functions of x.

(b) Show that the equations for V and M as functions of x satisfy the equation $V = \dfrac{dM}{dx}$.

(c) Draw the shear force and bending moment diagrams.

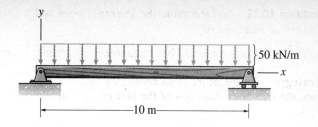

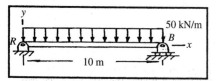

Solution: The sum of the moments about the left end is

$$\sum M = -\int_0^{10} 50x\, dx + 10B = 0,$$

from which $B = 250$ kN. The sum of the forces:

$$\sum F_y = R_y - \int_0^{10} 50\, dx + B = 0,$$

from which $R_Y = 500 - 250 = 250$ kN

(a) Make a cut at x. By definition, for a simple beam the shear is the sum of the forces to the left of x.

$$V(x) = \sum F = +R_y - \int_0^x 50\, dx = 250 - 50x \text{ (kN)},$$

which is straight line with intercept 250 kN and slope -50 kN/m. The free body diagram for the moment

$$\sum M = M(x) - R_y x + \int_0^x 50x\, dx = 0,$$

from which $M(x) = 250x - 25x^2$ kN m.

The axial force is zero, $P(x) = 0$. Note that

$$\frac{dM}{dx} = \frac{d(250x - 25x^2)}{dx} = 250 - 50x = V(x).$$

(c) The graphs are shown.

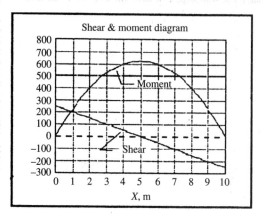

Problem 10.24

(a) Determine the internal forces and moment as functions of x.

(b) Show that the equations for V and M as functions of x satisfy the equation $V = \dfrac{dM}{dx}$.

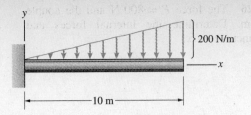

Solution: The free-body diagram of the entire beam is

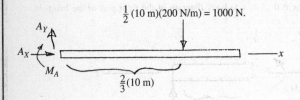

$$\frac{1}{2}(10\text{ m})(200\text{ N/m}) = 1000\text{ N}.$$

$$\frac{2}{3}(10\text{ m})$$

Applying the equilibrium equations, we obtain $A_x = 0$, $A_y = 1000$ N,

$$M_A = -\frac{2}{3}(10{,}000)\text{ N-m}$$

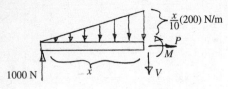

$$\frac{x}{10}(200)\text{ N/m}$$

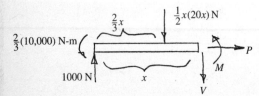

$$\frac{1}{2}x(20x)\text{ N}$$

$$\frac{2}{3}(10{,}000)\text{ N-m}$$

(a) We cut the beam at an arbitrary position x:

From the equilibrium equations

$$\sum F_y = 1000 - 10x^2 - V = 0,$$

$$\sum M_{(\text{rightend})} = M - 1000x + \left(\frac{1}{3}x\right)(10x^2)$$

$$+ \frac{2}{3}(10{,}000) = 0,$$

we obtain

$$V = 1000 - 10x^2 \text{ N},$$

$$M = 1000x - \frac{10}{3}x^3 - \frac{2}{3}(10{,}000)\text{ N-m}.$$

(b) $\dfrac{dM}{dx} = 1000 - 10x^2 = V.$

Problem 10.25 Draw the shear force and bending moment diagrams for the beam in Problem 10.24.

Solution:

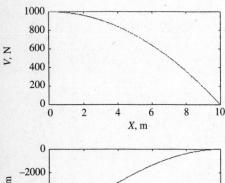

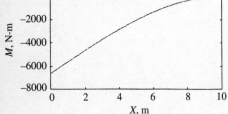

Problem 10.26 The force $F = 800$ N and the couple $C = 3600$ N-m. Determine the internal forces and moment as functions of x.

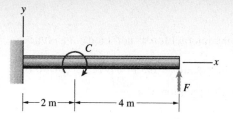

Solution: From the free-body diagram of the entire beam,

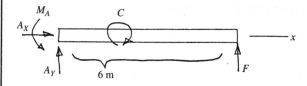

we obtain

$A_x = 0,$

$A_y = -F = -800$ N,

$M_A = C - 6F = 3600 - 6(800) = -1200$ N-m.

$0 < x < 2$ m. The free-body diagram is

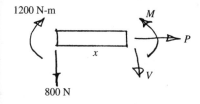

We see that $V = -800$ N, $M = 1200 - 800x$ N-m.

$2 < x < 6$ m. The free-body diagram of the right part of the beam is

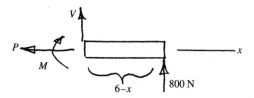

We see that $V = -800$ N, $M = 800(6 - x)$ N-m.

Problem 10.27 Draw the shear and bending moment diagrams for the beam in Problem 10.26.

Solution:

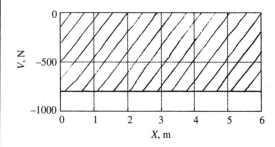

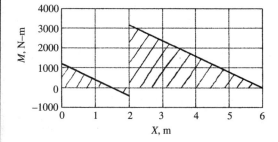

Problem 10.28

(a) Determine the internal forces and moment as functions of x.

(b) Determine the shear force and bending moment diagrams.

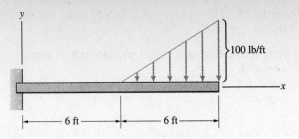

Solution: *The reactions at the left end*: The area under the load distribution is

$$F = \left(\tfrac{1}{2}\right)(6)(100) = 300 \text{ lb.}$$

The centroidal distance is

$$\mathbf{d} = 6 + \left(\tfrac{2}{3}\right)6 = 10 \text{ ft.}$$

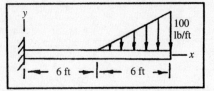

The sum of the moments about the left end:

$$\sum M = M^A - \mathbf{d}F = 0,$$

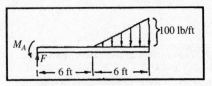

from which $M^A = 10(300) = 3000$ ft lb. *The shear and moment as a function of* x: Divide the beam into two intervals: $0 \le x \le 6$, and $6 < x \le 12$. *Interval 1*: The shear as a function of x: $V_1(x) = F = 300$ lb. The moment: $M_1(x) = Fx - M^A$, from which $M_1(x) = 300x - 3000$ ft lb. *Interval 2*: The load curve is a straight line, with intercept -100 lb/ft, and slope $\dfrac{100}{6}$. The shear diagram over this interval is

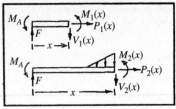

$$V_2(x) = F - \int_6^x \left(-100 + \frac{100}{6}x\right) dx$$

$$= F - 100\left[-x + \frac{1}{12}x^2\right]_6^x = 100\left(x - \frac{x^2}{12}\right)$$

Check: The load curve is continuous at $x = 6$, hence the shear diagram must be continuous at $x = 6$, (since the integral of a continuous function is also continuous) hence

$$V_1(6) = V_2(6)$$

$$V_1(6) = F = 300 = V_2(6)$$

$$= 100(6) - 100\left(\frac{36}{12}\right) = 300$$

check. The force due to the distributed load in the interval $6 \le x \le 12$ is

$$F_2(x) = \int_6^x w\, dx.$$

Integrate and reduce:

$$F_2(x) = 300 - 100x + \frac{25}{3}x^2.$$

The centroid distance from x is

$$\mathbf{d}_2 = \frac{(x-6)}{3}.$$

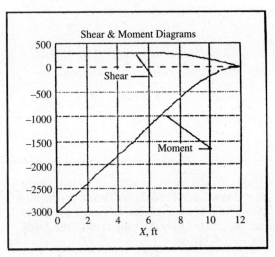

The moment about x is $M_2(x) = Fx - M^A - \mathbf{d}_2 F_2$. Substitute and reduce:

$$M_2(x) = -2400 + 50x^2 - \left(\frac{25}{9}\right)x^3 \text{ ft lb.}$$

Check: The moment must be zero at $x = 12$. *check*. *Check*: The moment must be continuous at $x = 6$, $M_1(6) = M_2(6)$, from which $M_1(6) = -1200$, and $M_2(6) = -1200$ *check*. The axial forces are zero, $P(x) = 0$

(b) The graph was drawn with **TK Solver Plus.**

910

Problem 10.29 The loads $F = 200$ N and $C = 800$ Nm.

(a) Determine the internal forces and moment as functions of x.
(b) Draw the shear force and bending moment diagrams.

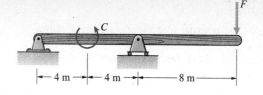

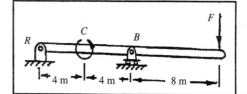

Solution: *The reactions at the supports:* The sum of the moments about the left end:

$$\sum M = C + 8B - 16F = 0,$$

from which

$$B = \left(\tfrac{1}{8}\right)(-C + 16F) = \left(\tfrac{1}{8}\right)(-800 + 16(200)) = 300 \text{ N}.$$

The sum of the forces: $\sum F_y = R_y + B - F = 0,$

from which $R_y = -100$ N. *The intervals as free bodies:* Divide the interval into three parts: $0 \leq x \leq 4$, $4 < x \leq 8$, and $8 < x \leq 16$. *Interval 1:* The shear is $V_1(x) = R_y = -100$ N. The moment is $M_1(x) = +R_yx = -100x$ N m. *Interval 2:* The shear is $V_2(x) = R_y = -100$ N. The sum of the moments is

$$\sum M^x = M_2(x) + C - R_yx = 0,$$

from which, $M_2(x) = -100x - 800$ Nm. *Interval 3:* The shear is $V_3(x) = R_Y + B = -100 + 300 = 200$ N. The sum of the moments is

$$\sum M^x = M_3(x) + C - R_yx - B(x - 8) = 0,$$

from which

$$M_3(x) = -800 - 100x + 300x - 2400 = 200x - 3200 \text{ N m}.$$

The axial forces are zero, $P(x) = 0$ in all intervals.

(b) The diagrams are shown.

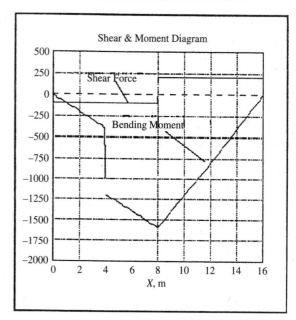

Problem 10.30 The beam in Problem 10.29 will safely support shear forces and bending moments of magnitudes 2 kN and 6.5 kN-m, respectively. On the basis of this criterion, can it safely be subjected to the loads $F = 1$ kN, $C = 1.6$ kN-m?

Solution: From the solution to Problem 10.29, the shear and the moments in the intervals are *Interval 1:* $V_1 = R_y$, $M_1(x) = R_yx$, *Interval 2:* $V_2(x) = R_y$, $M_2(x) = R_yx + C$, *Interval 3:* $V_3(x) = R_y + B$, $M_3(x) = (R_y + B)x + C - 8B$. The reactions are

$$B = \left(\tfrac{1}{8}\right)(16F - C),$$

and $R_y = F - B$.

The maximum shears in each interval have the magnitude rank:

$$|V_1(x)| = |V_2(x)| \leq |V_3(x)|,$$

so that the largest shear for a force $F = 1$ kN is $V_3(x) = R_y + B = F - B + B = F = 1$ kN, which can be safely supported. The maximum moment magnitudes in each interval have the rank: $|M_1(x)| \leq |M_2(x)| \leq |M_3(x)|$. The maximum moment magnitude occurs in the third interval:

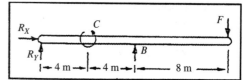

$$M_3(x) = (R_y + B)x + C - 8B = Fx + C - (16F - C)$$

$$= Fx - 16F + 2C.$$

The maximum magnitude occurs at $x = 8$, $|M_3(8)| = 8F = 8$ kN m and it exceeds the safe limit by 2.5 kN m. *NO*

Problem 10.31 Model the ladder rung as a simply supported (pin-supported) beam and assume that the 750-N load exerted by the person's shoe is uniformly distributed. Draw the shear force and bending moment diagrams.

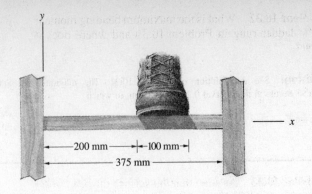

Solution: See the solution of Problem 10.7. The free-body diagram of the rung is

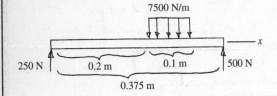

$0 < x < 0.2$ m

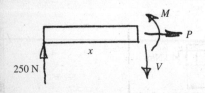

$V = 250$ N, $M = 250x$ N-m.

$0.2 < x < 0.3$ m

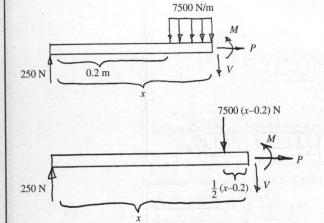

$V = 250 - 7500(x - 0.2)$ N,

$M = 250x - \frac{1}{2}7500(x - 0.2)^2$ N-m.

$0.3 < x < 0.375$ m

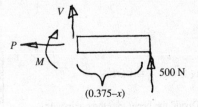

$V = -500$ N, $M = 500(0.375 - x)$ N-m.

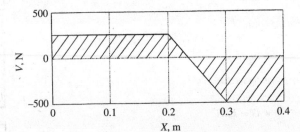

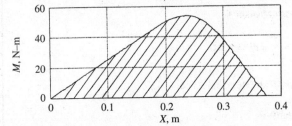

Problem 10.32 What is the maximum bending moment in the ladder rung in Problem 10.31 and where does it occur?

Solution: See the solution of Problem 10.31. The maximum moment occurs in the interval $0.2 < x < 0.3$ m, in which

$$M = 250x - 3750(x - 0.2)^2 \text{ N-m}.$$

Setting $\dfrac{dM}{dx} = 250 - 7500(x - 0.2) = 0,$

we find that the maximum moment occurs at $x = 0.233$ m. Substituting this value into the expression for M gives $M = 54.2$ N-m.

Problem 10.33 Assume that the surface the beam rests on exerts a uniformly distributed load. Draw the shear force and bending moment diagrams.

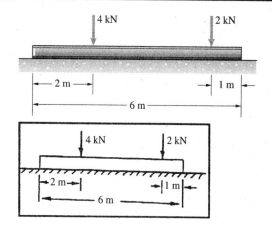

Solution: The load density is $w = \dfrac{6}{6} = 1$ kN/m.

The intervals as free bodies: Divide the beam into three intervals:

$0 \le x < 2$ (m),

$2 \le x < 5$ (m),

and $5 \le x \le 6$ (m).

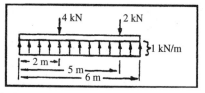

Interval 1: The shear force is

$$V_1(x) = \int_0^x w \, dx = x \text{ kN}.$$

The force to the left is

$$F_1(x) = \int_0^x w \, dx = x \text{ kN}.$$

The centroid distance from x is $\mathbf{d}_1 = \dfrac{x}{2}$.

The moment is

$$M_1(x) = F_1(x)\mathbf{d}_1 = \dfrac{x^2}{2} \text{ kN m}.$$

Interval 2: The shear force is

$$V_2(x) = V_1(x) - 4 = x - 4 \text{ kN}.$$

The moment is

$$M_2(x) = M_1(x) - 4(x - 2) = \dfrac{x^2}{2} - 4x + 8 \text{ kN m}.$$

Interval 3: The shear force is

$$V_3(x) = x - 4 - 2 = x - 6 \text{ kN}.$$

The bending moment is

$$M_3(x) = M_2(x) - 2(x - 5) = \dfrac{x^2}{2} - 6x + 18 \text{ kN}.$$

The shear and moment diagrams are shown.

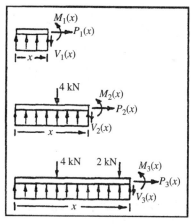

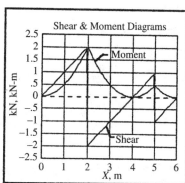

Problem 10.34 The homogeneous beams AB and CD weigh 600 lb and 500 lb, respectively. Draw the shear force and bending moment diagrams for beam CD.

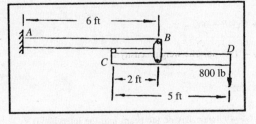

Solution: *The element CD as a free body*. The sum of the moments about point C:

$$\sum M_C = -500(2.5) + 2B - 5(800) = 0,$$

from which $B = 2625$ lb. The sum of the forces:

$$\sum F_y = C + B - 800 - 500 = 0,$$

from which $C = 800 + 500 - 2625 = -1325$ lb. The weight density

$$w = \frac{500}{5} = 100 \text{ lb/ft}.$$

The intervals as free bodies: Divide CD into two intervals: $0 \le x < 2$ (ft), and $2 \le x < 5$ (ft). *Interval 1*: The shear force

$$V_1(x) = C - \int_0^x w\,dx = -1325 - 100x \text{ lb}.$$

The distributed force is

$$F_1^{CD} = \int_0^x w\,dx = 100x.$$

The centroidal distance from x is $\mathbf{d}_1^{CD} = \frac{x}{2}$. The bending moment:

$$M_1^{CD}(x) = Cx - 50x^2 = -1325x - 50x^2 \text{ lb ft}.$$

Interval 2: The shear force:

$$V_2(x) = C - \int_0^X w\,dx + B = 1300 - 100x \text{ lb}.$$

The moment $M_2^{CD}(x) = M_1^{CD} + B(x - 2)$, from which

$$M_2(x) = -1325x - 50x^2 + 2625x - 5250$$

$$= 1300x - 50x^2 - 5250$$

Check: The moment is continuous at $x = 2$.

$$M_1^{CD}(2) = -1325(2) - 50(2^2) = -2850 \text{ lb ft}.$$

$$M_2^{CD} = 1300(2) - 50(2^2) - 5250 = -2850 \text{ lb ft}.$$

check.

Check: The moment is zero at $x = 5$.

$$M_2^{CD}(5) = 1300(5) - 50(5^2) - 5250 = 0.$$

check.

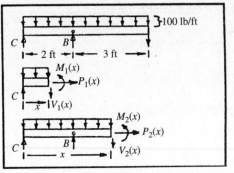

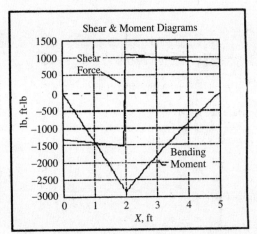

914

Problem 10.35 Draw the shear force and bending moment diagrams for beam AB in Problem 10.34.

Solution: Use the solution to Problem 10.34. The reactions at C and B are $C = 1325$ lb and $B = -2625$ lb. *The member AB as a free body*: The sum of the moments about A is

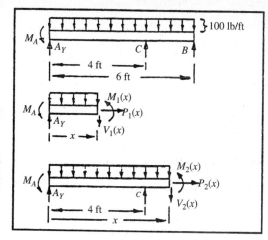

$$\sum M_A = M_A + 4C + 6B - 600(3) = 0,$$

from which $M_A = 12250$ ft lb.

$$\sum F_Y = A_y + C + B - 600 = 0,$$

from which $A_y = 1900$ lb. The weight density is

$$w = \frac{600}{6} = 100 \text{ ft/lb}.$$

The intervals as free bodies: Divide the beam into the intervals: $0 \leq x < 4$ (ft) and $4 \leq x < 6$ (ft). *Interval 1*: The shear force:

$$V_1^{AB}(x) = A_y - \int_0^x w\,dx = 1900 - 100x \text{ lb}.$$

The distributed force is

$$F_1^{AB} = \int_0^x w\,dx = 100x.$$

The centroid distance from x is

$$\mathbf{d}_1^{AB} = \frac{x}{2}.$$

The moment is

$$M_1^{AB}(x) = -M_A + A_yx - F_1^{AB}(x)\mathbf{d}_1^{AB},$$

from which $M_1^{AB}(x) = -12250 + 1900x - 50x^2$ ft lb.

Interval 2: The shear force is

$$V_2^{AB}(x) = V_1^{AB}(x) + C = 3225 - 100x \text{ lb}.$$

The moment is

$$M_2^{AB}(x) = M_1^{AB}(x) + C(x - 4),$$

$$M_2^{AB}(x) = -17550 + 3225x - 50x^2 \text{ ft lb}.$$

Check: The moment is continuous at $x = 4$.

$$M_1^{AB}(4) = -12250 + 1900(4) - 50(4^2) = -5450 \text{ lb ft}.$$

$$M_2^{AB}(4) = -17550 + 3225(4) - 50(4^2) = -5450 \text{ lb ft}.$$

check.

Check: The moment is zero at $x = 6$.

$$M_2^{AB}(6) = -17550 + 3225(6) - 50(6^2) = 0.$$

check.

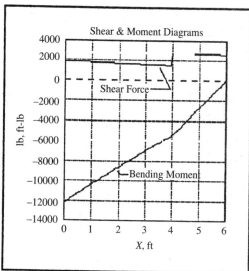

Problem 10.36   Determine the shear force as a function of x.

Solution: The free-body diagram of the entire beam is

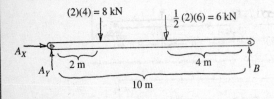

Applying the equilibrium equations yields $A_x = 0$, $A_y = 8.8$ kN, $B = 5.2$ kN.

$0 < x < 4$ m

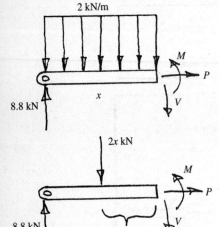

We see that $V = 8.8 - 2x$ kN.

$4 < x < 10$ m

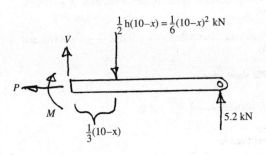

Using similar triangles,

$$\frac{h}{10 - x} = \frac{2 \text{ kN/m}}{6},$$

so $h = \dfrac{1}{3}(10 - x)$ kN/m,

and the free-body diagram is

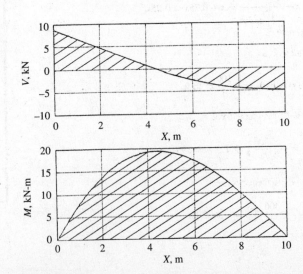

The shear force is $V = \dfrac{1}{6}(10 - x)^2 - 5.2$ kN.

Problem 10.37   Draw the shear force and bending moment diagrams for the beam in Problem 10.36.

Solution: See the solution of Problem 10.36. $0 < x < 4$ m. The shear force is $V = 8.8 - 2x$ kN, and from the free-body diagram in the solution of Problem 10.36,

$$M = 8.8x - \left(\frac{1}{2}x\right)(2x)$$

$$= 8.8x - x^2 \text{ kN-m}.$$

$4 < x < 10$ m. The shear force is $V = \dfrac{1}{6}(10 - x)^2 - 5.2$ kN, and from the free-body diagram in the solution of Problem 10.36,

$$M = 5.2(10 - x) - \frac{1}{6}(10 - x)^2 \frac{1}{3}(10 - x)$$

$$= 5.2(10 - x) - \frac{1}{18}(10 - x)^3 \text{ kN-m}.$$

Problem 10.38 The load $F = 4650$ lb. Draw the shear force and bending moment diagrams.

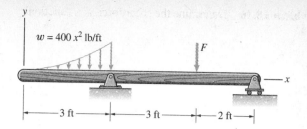

Solution: *The structure as a free body:* Denote the left support reaction by A and the right support reaction by B. The equivalent force exerted by the load is

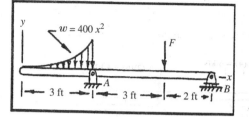

$$F_L = -\int_0^3 (400x^2)\, dx = -\left(\frac{400}{3}\right)[x^3]_0^3 = -3600 \text{ lb.}$$

The equivalent moment about the left end is

$$M_L = -\int_0^3 (400x^2)x\, dx = -100[x^4]_0^3 = -8100 \text{ ft lb.}$$

The sum of the moments about the left end:

$$\sum M = -M + 3A - 6(4650) + 8B = 0.$$

The sum of the forces:

$$\sum F_y = A_y - 3600 - 4650 + B = 0.$$

Solve these two simultaneous equations for the reactions: $A = 6000$ lb, and $B = 2250$ lb.

Divide the beam into 3 intervals: $0 \le x < 3$ (ft), $3 \le x < 6$ (ft), and $6 \le x < 8$ (ft).

Interval 1: The shear force is

$$V_1(x) = -\int_0^x 400x^2 dx = -\left(\frac{400}{3}\right)x^3 \text{ lb.}$$

The distributed force is

$$F_1(x) = \int_0^x w\, dx = \left(\frac{400}{3}\right)x^3 \text{ lb.}$$

The centroid distance from x is

$$\mathbf{d}_1 = x - \frac{\int_0^x wx\, dx}{\int_0^x w\, dx} = x - 0.75x = 0.25x.$$

The moment is

$$M_1(x) = -F_1\mathbf{d}_1 = -\frac{100}{3}x^4 \text{ lb ft.}$$

Interval 2: The shear force is

$$V_2(x) = -\left(\frac{400}{3}\right)(3^3) + A = 2400 \text{ lb.}$$

The total distributed force is

$$F_1(3) = -\frac{400}{3}(3^3) = -3600 \text{ lb.}$$

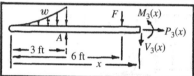

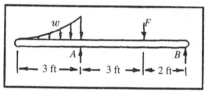

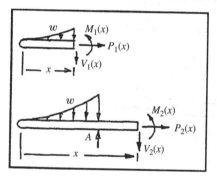

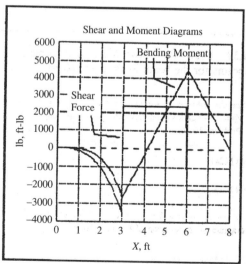

Shear and Moment Diagrams

10.38 *Contd.*

The centroid distance from x is

$$\mathbf{d}_2 = x - (0.75)(3) = x - 2.25.$$

The bending moment is

$$M_2(x) = F_1(3)\mathbf{d}_2 + A(x-3) = 2400x - 9900 \text{ lb ft.}$$

Interval 3: The shear force is

$$V_3(x) = V_2(x) - F = 2400 - 4650 = -2250 \text{ lb.}$$

The bending moment is

$$M_3(x) = M_2(x) - F(x-6) = -2250x + 18000 \text{ ft lb.}$$

Check: The moments are continuous at $x=3$ and $x=6$.

$$M_1(3) = -\frac{100}{3}(3^4) = -2700 \text{ lb ft.}$$

$$M_2(3) = 2400(3) - 9900 = -2700 \text{ lb ft. } check.$$

$$M_2(6) = 2400(6) - 9900 = 4500 \text{ lb ft.}$$

$$M_3(6) = -2250(6) - 18000 = 4500 \text{ lb ft. } check.$$

Check: The moment is zero at $x=8$.

$$M_3(8) = -2250(8) + 18000 = 0 \text{ } check.$$

Problem 10.39 If the load $F = 2150$ lb in Problem 10.38, what are the maximum and minimum shear forces and bending moments, and at what values of x do they occur?

Solution: Use the solutions and the solution procedures used in Problem 10.38. *The structure as a free body*: From the solution to Problem 10.38, the equivalent force due to the distributed load is $F_L = -3600$ lb. The moment about the left end due to the distributed load is $M = -8100$ ft lb. Denote the left support reaction by A, and the right support reaction by B. The sum of the moments about the left end is

$$\sum M = -8100 + 3A - 6(2150) + 8B = 0.$$

The sum of the forces

$$\sum F_Y = -3600 + A - 2150 + B = 0.$$

Solve these simultaneous equations to obtain $A = 5000$ lb, and $B = 750$ lb. Divide the beam into 3 intervals: $0 \le x < 3$ (ft), $3 \le x < 6$ (ft), and $6 \le x < 8$ (ft).

Interval 1: The shear force is

$$V_1(x) = -\left(\frac{400}{3}\right)x^3 \text{ lb.}$$

The moment is $M_1(x) = -\left(\frac{100}{3}\right)x^4.$

Interval 2: The shear force is

$$V_2(x) = -3600 + A = 1400 \text{ lb.}$$

The moment is $M_2(x) = -F_1(3)\mathbf{d}_2 + A(x-3),$

where from Problem 10.38 $F_1(3) = 3600$ lb and $\mathbf{d}_2 = x - 2.25$. Substitute and reduce: $M_2(x) = 1400x - 6900$ ft lb. *Interval 3*: The shear force is $V_3(x) = V_2(x) - F = -750$ lb. The moment is

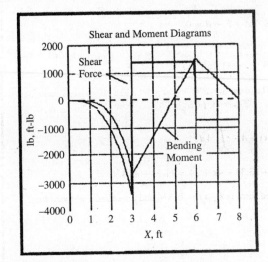

Shear and Moment Diagrams

$$M_3(x) = M_2(x) - F(x-6) = -750x + 6000 \text{ lb ft.}$$

From inspection of the shear force and moment diagrams, the minimum value of the shear force occurs at $x = 3$ ft, $V_{Min} = -3600$ lb, and the maximum occurs in the second interval, $3 \le x < 6$ (ft), $V_{MAX} = V_2(x) = 1400$ lb. The minimum value of the bending moment occurs at $x = 3$ ft,

$$M_{Min} = M_2(3) = 1400(3) - 6900 = -2700 \text{ ft lb.}$$

The maximum value of the moment occurs at $x = 6$ ft,

$$M_{Max} = 1400(6) - 6900 = 1500 \text{ ft lb.}$$

Problem 10.40 Draw the shear force and bending moment diagrams.

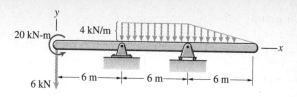

Solution: *The structure as a free body:* Denote the reaction at the left support by A and the reaction at the right support by B. The equivalent force due to the load distribution is the area:

$$F = 4(6) + \left(\frac{1}{2}\right)4(6) = 36 \text{ kN}.$$

The moment about the left end of the distribution is the sum of products of the force and the centroidal distances

$$M = 4(6)(3) + \left(\frac{1}{2}\right)4(6)\left(6 + \frac{6}{3}\right) = 168 \text{ kN m}.$$

The sum of the moments about the left support is

$$\sum M_A = 20 + 6(6) - M + 6B = 0,$$

from which $B = 18.67$ kN. The sum of the forces:

$$\sum F_Y = -6 + A - F + B = 0,$$

from which $A = 23.33$ kN. Divide the beam into three intervals: $0 \leq x < 6$ (m), $6 \leq x < 12$ (m), and $12 \leq x < 18$ (m).

Interval 1: The shear force is $V_1(x) = -6$. The bending moment is $M_1(x) = -6x - 20$ kN m. *Interval 2*: The shear force is

$$V_2(x) = V_1(x) + A - \int_6^x 4\,dx$$

$$= -6 + 23.33 - 4x + 24 = 41.33 - 4x \text{ kN}.$$

The distributed force is $F_2(x) = 4x$ kN, and the centroid distance from x is

$$\mathbf{d}_2 = \frac{x-6}{2}.$$

The bending moment is

$$M_2(x) = M_1(x) - F_2(x)\mathbf{d}_2 + A(x - 6).$$

Substitute and reduce:

$$M_2(x) = 41.33x - 2x^2 - 232 \text{ kN m}$$

Interval 3: The shear force is

$$V_3(x) = V_2(12) + B - \int_{12}^x \left(-\frac{2}{3}x + 12\right) dx.$$

$$V_3(x) = \left(\frac{1}{3}\right)x^2 - 12x + 108 \text{ kN}.$$

The distributed force in the 3rd interval is

$$F_3(x) = \int_{12}^x w_3\,dx.$$

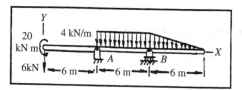

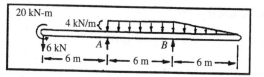

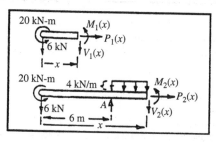

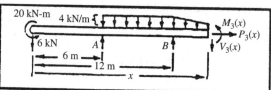

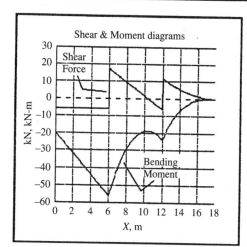

10.40 *Contd.*

The centroid distance from x is

$$\mathbf{d}_3 = x - \frac{\int_{12}^x w_3 x\, dx}{\int_{12}^x w_3\, dx},$$

from which

$$F_3(x)\mathbf{d}_3 = xF_3(x) - \int_{12}^x w_3 x\, dx$$

is the moment. The total moment is

$$M_3(x) = V_2(12)(x - 12) + F_3(x)\mathbf{d}_3 + B(x - 12).$$

The load density:

$$w_3(x) = -\frac{2}{3}x + 12 \text{ kN}.$$

Substitute and reduce:

$$M_3(x) = \left(\frac{1}{9}\right)x^3 - 6x^2 + 108x - 648 \text{ kN m}.$$

Check: The moments are continuous at $x = 6$ and $x = 12$.

$$M_1(6) = -6(6) - 20 = -56 \text{ kN m}.$$

$$M_2(6) = 41.33(6) - 2(6^2) - 232 = -56 \text{ kN m } check.$$

$$M_2(12) = 41.33(12) - 2(12^2) - 232 = -24 \text{ kN m},$$

$$M_3(12) = \left(\frac{1}{9}\right)(12^3) - 6(12^2) + 108(12) - 648 = -24.$$

check.
Check: The moment vanishes at $x = 18$.

$$M_3(18) = \left(\frac{1}{9}\right)(18^3) - 6(18^2) + 108(18) - 648 = 0. \; check.$$

The shear force and moment diagram are shown for the complete beam.

Problem 10.41 Determine V and M as functions of x.

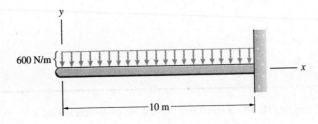

Solution: We determine V by integrating the equation

$$\frac{dV}{dx} = -w = -600 \text{ N/m}.$$

$$\int_0^V dV = \int_0^x -600\, dx,$$

$$V = -600x \text{ N}.$$

Then we determine M by integrating

$$\frac{dM}{dx} = V = -600x \text{ N}.$$

$$\int_0^M dM = \int_0^x -600x\, dx$$

$$M = -300x^2 \text{ N-m}.$$

Problem 10.42 The length $L = 6$ m and $w_0 = 1200$ N/m.

(a) Determine V and M as functions of x.
(b) Draw a free-body diagram and use the equilibrium equations to determine the reactions at the built-in support. Use the results of part (a) to check your answers.

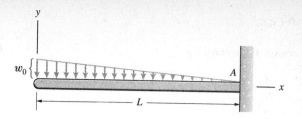

Solution: The distributed load is a linear function of x,

$$w = a + bx.$$

At $x = 0$, $w = w_o = 1200$ N/m, and at $x = L = 6$ m, $w = 0$. With these conditions we find that $a = 1200$ and $b = -200$:

$$w = 1200 - 200x \text{ N/m}.$$

(a)
$$\frac{dV}{dx} = -w = 200x - 1200 \text{ N/m}.$$

$$\int_0^V dV = \int_0^x (200x - 1200)\, dx,$$

$$V = 100x^2 - 1200x \text{ N}.$$

$$\frac{dM}{dx} = V = 100x^2 - 1200x \text{ N}.$$

$$\int_0^M dM = \int_0^x (100x^2 - 1200x)\, dx$$

$$M = \frac{100}{3}x^3 - 600x^2 \text{ N-m}.$$

(b) The free-body diagram of the entire beam is

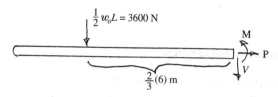

from which we obtain $V = -3600$ N, $M = -(4)(3600) = -14,400$ N-m. These values are obtained by setting $x = 6$ m in the expressions in part (a).

Problem 10.43 Determine V and M as functions of x.

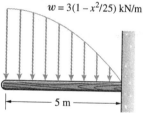

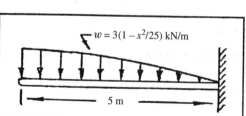

Solution: The shear force is

$$V(x) = -\int 3\left(1 - \frac{x^2}{25}\right) dx + C_1 = -3\left(x - \frac{x^3}{75}\right) + C_1.$$

At $x = 0$, $V(0) = 0$, hence $C_1 = 0$, and

$$V(x) = -3\left(x - \frac{x^3}{75}\right) \text{ kN}.$$

The moment is

$$M(x) = \int V(x)\, dx + C_2 = -3\left(\frac{x^2}{2} - \frac{x^4}{300}\right) + C_2.$$

At $x = 0$, $M(0) = 0$, hence $C_2 = 0$, and

$$M(x) = -3\left(\frac{x^2}{2} - \frac{x^4}{300}\right) \text{ kN m}$$

Problem 10.44 Determine V and M as functions of x.

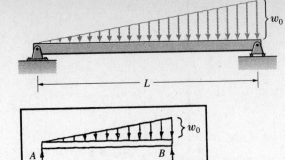

Solution: Denote the left support reaction by A and the right support reaction by B. The load curve is a straight line with intercept zero and slope $\dfrac{w_o}{L}$. The area under the curve is $F = \left(\frac{1}{2}\right) w_o L$. The moment about the left support is

$$\sum M_A = -\int_0^L \left(\frac{w_o}{L}\right) x^2 \, dx + BL = 0,$$

from which

$$B = \left(\frac{1}{L}\right)\left(\frac{w_o L^2}{3}\right) = \frac{w_o L}{3}.$$

The sum of the forces

$$\sum F_y = A - \left(\frac{1}{2}\right) w_o L + \frac{w_o L}{3} = 0,$$

from which

$$A = \frac{w_o L}{6}.$$

The shear force is

$$V(x) = \frac{w_o L}{6} - \int \left(\frac{w_o}{L}\right) x \, dx$$

$$= \frac{w_o L}{6} - \frac{w_o x^2}{2L} = \frac{w_o}{2}\left(\frac{L}{3} - \frac{x^2}{L}\right).$$

The moment is

$$M(x) = \int V(x)\,dx + C_1 = \frac{w_o x}{6}\left(L - \frac{x^2}{L}\right) + C_1.$$

At $x = 0$, $M(0) = 0$, hence $C_1 = 0$,

and $M(x) = \dfrac{w_o x}{6}\left(L - \dfrac{x^2}{L}\right)$

Problem 10.45 Determine V and M as functions of x.

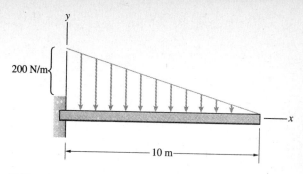

Solution: Representing the distributed load by a force, the free body diagram of the entire beam is: The reactions are $A_x = 0$ $A_y = 1000$ N

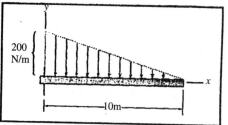

$$M_A = \left(\frac{10}{3}\right)\left[\frac{1}{2}(10)(200)\right] = 3333 \text{ N} = M$$

expressing the distributed load as a linear function $w = ax + b$ and using the conditions that $w = 200$ N/m at $x = 0$ and $w = 0$ at $x = 10$ m we find that $w = -20x + 200$ N/m

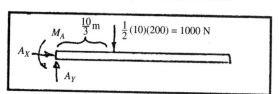

From equation (10.2),

$$\frac{dV}{dx} = -w = 20x - 200,$$

$$\int_{1000}^{V} dV = \int_{0}^{x} (20x - 200)\, dx = V - 1000$$

$$= \left[20\frac{x^2}{2} - 200x\right]_0^x = 10x^2 - 200x,$$

$$V = 10x^2 - 200x + 1000 \text{ N}$$

From equation (10.3),

$$\frac{dM}{dx} = V = 10x^2 - 200x + 1000,$$

$$\int_{-3333}^{M} dM = \int_{0}^{x} (10x^2 - 200x + 1000)\, dx$$

$$M + 3333 = \left[10\frac{x^3}{3} - 200\frac{x^2}{2} + 1000x\right]_0^x,$$

$$\text{or } M = \frac{10}{3}x^3 - 100x^2 + 1000x - 3333 \text{ N-m.}$$

Problem 10.46 Determine V and M as functions of x for $0 < x < 1$ m.

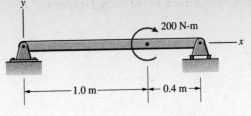

200 N-m

1.0 m — 0.4 m

Solution: From the equilibrium equations

$$\sum F_x = A_x = 0,$$

$$\sum F_y = A_y + B = 0,$$

$$\sum M_{(pt.\ A)} = 1.4B - 200 = 0,$$

we obtain $A_x = 0$, $A_y = -143$ N, $B = 143$ N.

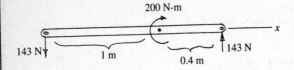

200 N-m

143 N ⊥   1 m   143 N

0.4 m

The reaction at $x = 0$ causes a 143-N drop in V. From $x = 0$ to $x = 1$ m, $dV/dx = -w = 0$, so

$$V = -143 \text{ N}, \quad 0 < x < 1 \text{ m}.$$

Then $\dfrac{dM}{dx} = V = -143$ N,

$$\int_0^M dm = \int_0^x -143\,dx,$$

$$M = -143x \text{ N-m}, 0 < x < 1 \text{ m}$$

Problem 10.47 For the beam in Problem 10.46, determine V and M as functions of x for $1 < x < 1.4$ m.

Solution: See the solution of Problem 10.46. At $x = 1$ m, $V = -143$ N. From $x = 1$ m to $x = 1.4$ m, $dV/dx = -w = 0$, so

$$V = -143 \text{ N}, \quad 1 < x < 1.4 \text{ m}.$$

At $x = 1$ m, $M = -143(1) = -143$ N-m. The clockwise couple causes a 200 N-m increase to $M = -143 + 200 = 57$ N-m. Therefore

$$\frac{dm}{dx} = V = -143 \text{ N-m},$$

$$\int_{57}^M dM = \int_1^x -143\,dx,$$

$$M = 57 - 143(x - 1)$$

$$= 200 - 143x \text{ N-m}.$$

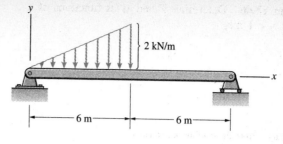

Solution: From the equilibrium equations

$$\sum F_x = A_x = 0,$$

$$\sum F_y = A_y + B - 6 = 0,$$

$$\sum M_{(\text{pt. } A)} = 12B - \frac{2}{3}(6)(6) = 0,$$

we obtain $A_x = 0$, $A_y = 4$ kN, $B = 2$ kN.

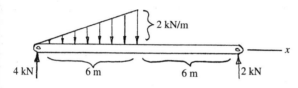

$0 < x < 6$ m

$$\frac{dV}{dx} = -w = -\left(\frac{x}{6}\right)2 = -\frac{1}{3}x \text{ kN/m}.$$

At $x = 0$, $V = 4$ kN. Integrating,

$$\int_4^V dV = \int_0^x -\frac{1}{3}x \, dx,$$

$$V = 4 - \frac{1}{6}x^2 \text{ kN}.$$

$$\frac{dM}{dx} = V = 4 - \frac{1}{6}x^2 \text{ kN}.$$

$$\int_0^M dM = \int_0^x \left(4 - \frac{1}{6}x^2\right) dx$$

$$M = 4x - \frac{1}{18}x^3 \text{ kN-m}.$$

6 m $< x < 12$ m

At $x = 6$ m, $V = 4 - \frac{1}{6}(6)^2 = -2$ kN and $M = 4(6) - \frac{1}{18}(6)^3 = 12$ kN-m.

$$\frac{dV}{dx} = -w = 0,$$

$$\int_{-2}^V dV = 0,$$

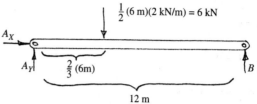

$$V = -2 \text{ kN}.$$

$$\frac{dM}{dx} = V = -2 \text{ kN},$$

$$\int_{12}^M dM = \int_6^x -2 \, dx,$$

$$M = 12 - 2(x - 6)$$

$$= -2(x - 12) \text{ kN-m}.$$

Problem 10.49 Determine V and M as functions of x for the beam AB.

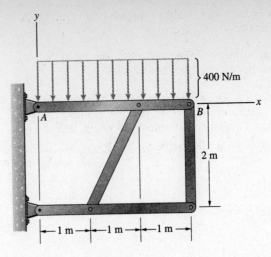

Solution: Solving the frame problem (see the solution of Problem 10.20), the reactions on beam AB are

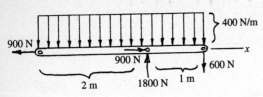

$\dfrac{dM}{dx} = V = 1800 - 400x \text{ N},$

$\displaystyle\int_{-800}^{M} dM = \int_{2}^{x} (1800 - 400x)\,dx,$

$M = -3600 + 1800x - 200x^2 \text{ N-m}.$

$0 < x < 2 \text{ m}$

$\dfrac{dV}{dx} = -w = -400 \text{ N/m},$

$\displaystyle\int_{0}^{V} dV = \int_{0}^{x} -400\,dx,$

$V = -400x \text{ N}.$

$\dfrac{dM}{dx} = V = -400x,$

$\displaystyle\int_{0}^{M} dM = \int_{0}^{x} -400x\,dx,$

$M = -200x^2 \text{ N-m}.$

$2 < x < 3 \text{ m}$ At $x = 2$ m,

$V = -400(2) = -800 \text{ N}.$

The reaction causes an 1800-N increase to

$V = -800 + 1800 = 1000 \text{ N}.$

At $x = 2$ m, $M = -200(2)^2 = -800$ N-m.

$\dfrac{dV}{dx} = -w = -400 \text{ N/m},$

$\displaystyle\int_{1000}^{V} dV = \int_{2}^{x} -400\,dx$

$V = 1000 - 400(x - 2)$

$= 1800 - 400x \text{ N}.$

Problem 10.50 The cable supports a uniformly distributed load $w = 1$ kN/m.

(a) What is the maximum tension in the cable?
(b) What is the length of the cable?

Strategy: You know the coordinates of the attachment points of the cable relative to its lowest point, so you can use Eq. (10.10) to determine the coefficient a and then use $a = \dfrac{w}{T_0}$ to determine the tension at the lowest point.

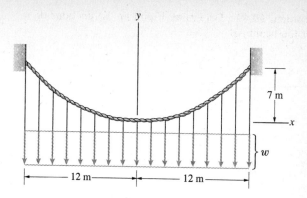

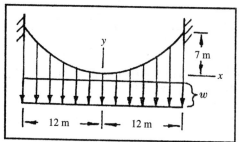

Solution: (a) The equation of the parabola is $y = \frac{1}{2}ax^2$, from which

$$a = 2\left(\frac{7}{12^2}\right) = 0.09722.$$

The tension at the lowest point is

$$T_0 = \frac{w}{a} = \frac{1}{0.09722} = 10.286 \text{ kN}.$$

The maximum tension is

$$T_{MAX} = T_0\sqrt{1 + a^2x^2},$$

which for $x = 12$, $T_{MAX} = 15.8$ kN. The length of the right half of the cable is

$$s = (1/2)\left(x\sqrt{1 + a^2x^2} + \left(\frac{1}{a}\right)\ln(ax + \sqrt{1 + a^2x^2})\right),$$

from which, for $x = 12$, $s = 14.33$ m, and the total length of the cable is $L = 2s = 28.66$ m

---

Problem 10.51 The cable in Problem 10.50 will safely support a tension of 40 kN. On the basis of this criterion, what is the largest value of the distributed load w?

Solution: From Equation (10.11), the tension as a function of x is

$$T = T_0\sqrt{1 + a^2x^2}.$$

The maximum tension occurs at $x = 12$ m, so we set

$$T = 40,000 \text{ N} = T_0\sqrt{1 + a^2(12)^2}.$$

T_0 is related to w by $a = w/T_0$,

$$40,000 = \frac{w}{a}\sqrt{1 + 144a^2} \quad \text{(1)}$$

We can determine a by setting $x = 12$ m and $y = 7$ m in equation (10.10):

$$y = \frac{1}{2}ax^2, \quad 7 = \frac{1}{2}a(12)^2.$$

Solving $a = 0.0972$ m^{-1}. Substituting this value into Equation (1) and solving for w we obtain $w = 2530$ N/m.

Problem 10.52 A cable is used to suspend a pipeline above a river. The towers supporting the cable are 36 m apart. The lowest point of the cable is 1.4 m below the tops of the towers. The mass of the suspended pipe is 2700 kg.

(a) What is the maximum tension in the cable?
(b) What is the suspending cable's length?

Solution: The distributed load is

$$w = \frac{(2700 \text{ kg})(9.81 \text{ m/s}^2)}{36 \text{ m}} = 736 \text{ N/m}.$$

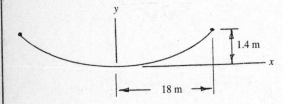

(a) Setting $x = 18$ m, $y = 1.4$ m in Eq. (10.10),

$$1.4 = \tfrac{1}{2}a(18)^2,$$

we obtain

$$a = \frac{w}{T_0} = 0.00864 \text{ m}^{-1}.$$

Therefore the tension at $x = 0$ is

$$T_0 = \frac{w}{a} = \frac{736}{0.00864} = 85,100 \text{ N}.$$

From Eq. (10.11), the maximum tension is

$$T = T_0\sqrt{1 + a^2(18)^2} = 86,200 \text{ N}.$$

(b) Setting $x = 18$ m in Eq. (10.12), the length of the cable is

$$2s = 18\sqrt{1 + a^2(18)^2} + \frac{1}{a}\ln(18a + \sqrt{1 + a^2(18)^2})$$

$$= 36.14 \text{ m}.$$

Problem 10.53 In Problem 10.52, let the lowest point of the cable be a distance h below the tops of the towers supporting the cable.

(a) If the cable will safely support a tension of 70 kN, what is the minimum safe value of h?
(b) If h has the value determined in part (a), what is the suspending cable's length?

Solution: See the solution of Problem 10.52.

(a) The distributed load is $w = 736$ N/m. Therefore

$$w = 736 = aT_0, \quad (1)$$

And setting $x = 18$ m and $T = 70,000$ N in Eq. (10.11),

$$70,000 = T_0\sqrt{1 + (18)^2a^2}. \quad (2)$$

From Eqs. (1) and (2) we obtain $a = 0.0107$ m^{-1}, $T_0 = 68,700$ N. From Eq. (10.10),

$$h = \tfrac{1}{2}(0.0107)(18)^2$$

$$= 1.734 \text{ m}.$$

(b) From Eq. (10.12), the length of the cable is

$$2s = 18\sqrt{1 + a^2(18)^2} + \frac{1}{a}\ln(18a + \sqrt{1 + a^2(18)^2})$$

$$= 36.22 \text{ m}.$$

Problem 10.54 The cable supports a uniformly distributed load $w = 750$ N/m. The lowest point of the cable is 0.18 m below the attachment points C and D. Determine the axial loads in the truss members AC and BC.

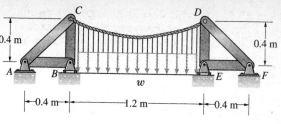

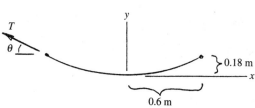

Solution:

$y = \frac{1}{2}ax^2$:

$0.18 = \frac{1}{2}a(0.6)^2.$

From this equation we obtain $a = 1$ m^{-1}.

Therefore

$T_0 = \dfrac{w}{a} = 750$ N

and $T = T_0\sqrt{1 + a^2(0.6)^2} = 875$ N.

From the equation

$\tan\theta = ax = (1)(0.6),$

we obtain $\theta = 30.96°$.

The free-body diagram of joint C is shown.

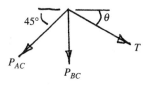

From the equations

$\sum F_x = T\cos\theta - P_{AC}\cos 45° = 0,$

$\sum F_y = -T\sin\theta - P_{BC}$

$\qquad - P_{AC}\sin 45° = 0,$

we obtain

$P_{AC} = 1061$ N,

$P_{BC} = -1200$ N.

Problem 10.55 The cable supports a railway bridge between two tunnels. The distributed load is $w = 1$ MN/m, and $h = 40$ m.

(a) What is the maximum tension in the cable?
(b) What is the length of the cable?

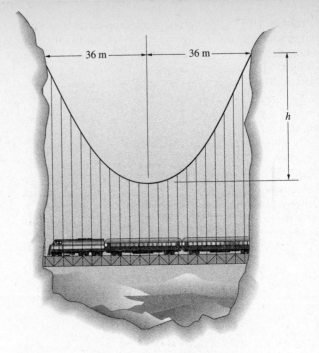

Solution: The parameter

$$a = 2\frac{y}{x^2} = 2\frac{40}{36^2} = 0.06173.$$

The tension at the lowest point:

$$T_0 = \frac{w}{a} = \frac{1 \times 10^6}{a} = 16200 \text{ kN.}$$

The maximum tension: $T_{MAX} = T_0\sqrt{1 + a^2x^2}$, which, for $x = 36$ m, $T_{MAX} = 39477$ kN. The cable length is

$$s(x) = \left(x\sqrt{1 + a^2x^2} + \frac{1}{a} \ln \left(ax + \sqrt{1 + a^2x^2} \right) \right),$$

which, for $x = 36$ m, $L = 112.66$ m.

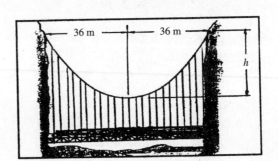

Problem 10.56 The cable in Problem 10.55 will safely support a tension of 40 MN. What is the shortest cable that can be used, and what is the corresponding value of h?

Solution: The tension at the lowest point is

$$T_0 = \frac{w}{a}.$$

The maximum tension is

$$T_{MAX} = T_0\sqrt{1 + a^2x^2}.$$

Square both sides, substitute and reduce algebraically: $T_o^2 = T_{MAX}^2 - w^2x^2$. The terms on the right are known: $T_{MAX}^2 = 40^2(10^6)$, and $w^2x^2 = 36^2(10^6)$. Solve for the parameter a,

$$a^2 = \frac{10^6}{(40^2 - 36^2)(10^6)} = 3.29 \times 10^{-3},$$

from which $a = 0.0574$. The height is

$$h = \left(\tfrac{1}{2}\right) ax^2 = \left(\tfrac{1}{2}\right)(0.0574)(36^2) = 37.165 \text{ m.}$$

The length is

$$s(x) = \left(x\sqrt{1 + a^2x^2} + \frac{1}{a} \ln \left(ax + \sqrt{1 + a^2x^2} \right) \right),$$

which, for $x = 36$ m, $L = 108.26$ m

Problem 10.57 An oceanographic research ship tows an instrument package from a cable. Hydrodynamic drag subjects the cable to a uniformly distributed force $w = 2$ lb/ft. The tensions in the cable at 1 and 2 are 800 lb and 1300 lb, respectively. Determine the distance h.

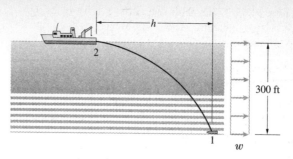

Solution: If one assumes that the cable is tangent to the vertical at the point 1, so that the 800 lb is the tension at the lowest point, the data is inconsistent; therefore the point 1 must be at a distance x_1 from the lowest point. There are three unknowns in the problem: the distance x_1, the tension at the lowest point T_0, and the parameter a. The three equations that define these unknowns are:

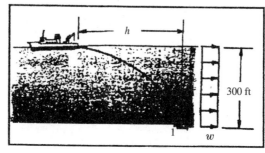

(1) $\quad 800 = T_0\sqrt{1 + a^2 x_1^2}$,

(2) $\quad T_0 = \dfrac{w}{a} = \dfrac{2}{a}$,

(3) $\quad 1300 = T_0\sqrt{1 + a^2(x_1 + 300)^2}$.

These are reduced to two equations in two unknowns:

(1) $\quad 800 = \left(\dfrac{2}{a}\right)\sqrt{1 + a^2 x_1^2}$,

(2) $\quad 1300 = \left(\dfrac{2}{a}\right)\sqrt{1 + a^2(x_1 + 300)^2}$ and solved by iteration using

TK Solver Plus. The result: $a = 3.596 \times 10^{-3}$, $x_1 = 287.5$ ft. Using these values, the distance is

$$h = \left(\tfrac{1}{2}\right)a(x_1 + 300)^2 - \left(\tfrac{1}{2}\right)a x_1^2 = 471.94 \text{ ft}$$

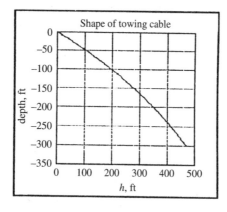

Problem 10.58 Draw a graph of the shape of the cable in Problem 10.57.

Solution: The following equations are graphed:

(1) IF $d > x_1$ then $w = h - \left(\tfrac{1}{2}\right)ad^2 + \left(\tfrac{1}{2}\right)a x_1^2$,

(2) $z = 300 + x_1 - d$, where $h = 471.9$ ft, $a = 3.59573 \times 10^{-3}$, $x_1 = 287.5$ ft. The value w is plotted on the abscissa, and z is plotted on the ordinate. The result is a graph of the depth of the cable against the horizontal extension.

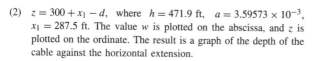

Problem 10.59 The mass of the rope per unit length is 0.10 kg/m. The tension at its lowest point is 4.6 N.

(a) What is the maximum tension in the rope?
(b) What is the rope's length?

Strategy: Use the given information to evaluate the coefficient $a = w/T_0$. Because the rope is loaded only by its own weight, the tension is given as a function of x by Eq. (10.21) and the length of the rope in the horizontal interval from its lowest point to x is given by Eq. (10.22).

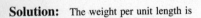

Solution: The weight per unit length is

$w = (0.1 \text{ kg/m})(9.81 \text{ m/s}^2) = 0.981 \text{ N/m}.$

(a) $a = \dfrac{w}{T_0} = \dfrac{0.981}{4.6} = 0.213 \text{ m}^{-1}.$

From Eq. (10.21), the maximum tension is

$T = T_0 \cosh(ax)$

$\quad = 4.6 \cosh[(0.213)(6)]$

$\quad = 8.91 \text{ N}.$

(b) From Eq. (10.22), the length is

$2s = \dfrac{2 \sinh[(0.213)(6)]}{0.213}$

$\quad = 15.55 \text{ m}.$

Problem 10.60 The stationary balloon's tether is horizontal at point O where it is attached to the truck. The mass per unit length of the tether is 0.45 kg/m. The tether exerts a 50-N horizontal force on the truck. The horizontal distance from point O to point A where the tether is attached to the balloon is 20 m. What is the height of point A relative to point O?

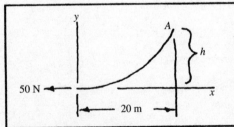

Solution:

$a = \dfrac{w}{T_0} = \dfrac{(9.81)(0.45)}{50} = 0.0883 \text{ m}^{-1}.$

From equation (10.20),

$y = \dfrac{1}{a}[\cosh(ax) - 1]$

$h = \dfrac{1}{0.0883}\{\cosh[(0.0883)(20)] - 1\} = 22.8 \text{ m}.$

Problem 10.61 In Problem 10.60, determine the magnitudes of the horizontal and vertical components of the force exerted on the balloon at A by the tether.

Solution: From the solution to Problems 10.60, $a = 0.0883$ m^{-1}. The value of the tension at $x = 20$ m is

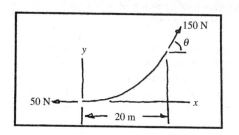

$$T = T_0 \cosh(ax) = 50 \cosh[(0.0883)(20)] = 150 \text{ N}.$$

The slope at $x = 20$ m (Equation 10.19) is

$$\sigma = \tan\theta = \sinh(ax) = \sinh[(0.0883)(20)] = 2.84,$$

so $\theta = \arctan 2.84 = 70.6°$. The horizontal and vertical components are

$$T_x = (150)\cos\theta = 50 \text{ N}$$

$$T_y = (150)\sin\theta = 142 \text{ N}.$$

Problem 10.62 The mass per unit length of lines AB and BC is 2 kg/m. The tension at the lowest point of cable AB is 1.8 kN. The two lines exert equal horizontal forces at B.

(a) Determine the sags h_1 and h_2.
(b) Determine the maximum tensions in the two lines.

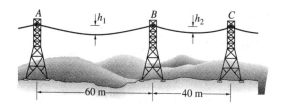

Solution: The lines meet the condition for a catenary. (a) *The line AB.* The weight density is

$$w = 2(9.81) = 19.62 \text{ N/m}.$$

The parameter

$$a_1 = \frac{w}{T_{AB}} = \frac{19.62}{1800} = 0.0109.$$

The sag is

$$h_1 = \left(\frac{1}{a_1}\right)(\cosh(30a_1) - 1) = 4.949 \text{ m}.$$

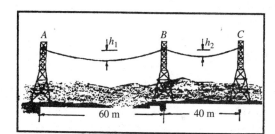

The line BC. The horizontal component of the tension at B is $T_{AB} = 1.8$ kN. Thus the tension at the lowest point in BC is 1.8 kN, and the parameter a for line BC is equal to a_1. The sag is

$$h_2 = \left(\frac{1}{a_1}\right)(\cosh(20a_1) - 1) = 2.189 \text{ m}.$$

(b) *The line AB.* The maximum tension is

$$T_{\text{MAX}}^{AB} = T_{AB} \cosh(30a_1) = 1897.1 \text{ N}.$$

The line BC. The maximum tension is

$$T_{\text{MAX}}^{BC} = T_{AB} \cosh(20a_1) = 1842.9 \text{ N}.$$

Problem 10.63 The rope is loaded by 2-kg masses suspended at 1-m intervals along its length. The mass of the rope itself is negligible. The tension in the rope at its lowest point is 100 N. Determine h and the maximum tension in the rope.

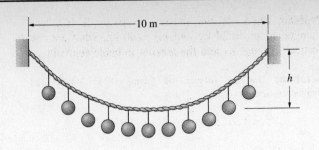

Strategy: Obtain an approximate answer by modeling the discrete loads on the rope as a load uniformly distributed along its length.

Solution: The equivalent distributed load is

$$w = \frac{(2 \text{ kg})(9.81 \text{ m/s}^2)}{1 \text{ m}} = 19.62 \text{ N/m}.$$

Therefore $a = \dfrac{w}{T_0} = \dfrac{19.62}{100} = 0.196 \text{ m}^{-1}.$

From Eq. (10.20),

$$h = \frac{1}{a}\{\cosh[a(5)] - 1\} = 2.66 \text{ m}.$$

From Eq. (10.21), the maximum tension is

$$T = T_0 \cosh ax = (100)\cosh[a(5)] = 152 \text{ N}.$$

Problem 10.64 In Example 10.9, what are the tensions in cable segments 1 and 3?

Solution: See the solution of Example 10.9. Cutting cable segment 1, we obtain the free-body diagram

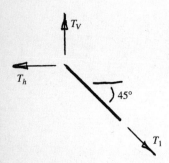

From the equation

$$\sum F_x = -T_h + T_1 \cos 45° = 0,$$

we obtain $T_1 = \dfrac{T_h}{\cos 45°} = \dfrac{131}{\cos 45°} = 185 \text{ N}.$

Cutting cable segment 3, we obtain the free-body diagram

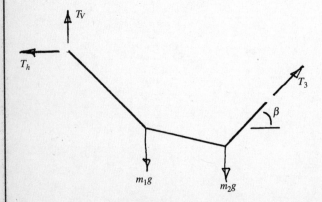

The angle β is

$$\beta = \arctan\left(\frac{h_2}{1}\right) = \arctan(1.25) = 51.3°.$$

From the equation

$$\sum F_x = -T_h + T_3 \cos \beta = 0,$$

we obtain

$$T_3 = \frac{T_h}{\cos \beta} = \frac{131}{\cos 51.3°} = 209 \text{ N}.$$

Problem 10.65 If the masses in Example 10.9 are changed to $m_1 = 24$ kg and $m_2 = 40$ kg, what are the vertical distance h_2 and the tension in cable segment 3?

Solution: See the solution of Example 10.9. Solving the equilibrium equations

$$T_h - T_v = 0,$$

$$h_2 T_h - 2T_v + m_1 g = 0,$$

$$-3T_v + 2m_1 g + m_2 g = 0$$

with $m_1 = 24$ kg

and $m_2 = 40$ kg,

we obtain

$$T_h = T_v = 288 \text{ N}$$

and $h_2 = 1.18$ m.

Cutting cable segment 3, we obtain the free-body diagram

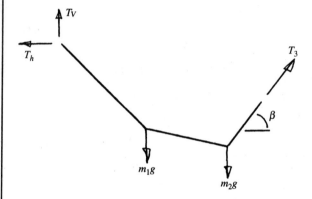

The angle β is

$$\beta = \arctan\left(\frac{h_2}{1}\right) = \arctan(1.18) = 49.8°.$$

From the equation

$$\sum F_x = -T_h + T_3 \cos\beta = 0,$$

we obtain

$$T_3 = \frac{T_h}{\cos\beta} = \frac{288}{\cos 49.8°} = 445 \text{ N}.$$

Problem 10.66 Two weights, $W_1 = W_2 = 50$ lb, are suspended from a cable. The vertical distance $h_1 = 4$ ft.

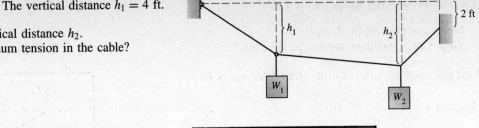

(a) Determine the vertical distance h_2.
(b) What is the maximum tension in the cable?

Solution: The strategy is to make cuts along the string and sum the moments to the left of each cut. The three simultaneous equations are then solved for the unknowns. Make a cut at left attachment and to the right of W_1. Denote the components of the force exerted by the string by F_H and F_V, with sign indicating direction. The sum of the moments about the right end:

$$\sum M = -6F_V - h_1F_H = 0.$$

Make the cut to the right of W_2. The sum of the moments about the right end:

$$\sum M = -h_2F_H - 16F_V + 10W_1 = 0.$$

Make the cut at the right attachment point and sum the moments to the left:

$$\sum M = -19F_V - h_2F_H + 13W_1 + 3W_2 = 0.$$

Solve:

$$h_2 = 4 \text{ ft},$$

$$F_V = 50 \text{ lb},$$

and $F_H = -75$ lb.

From the sum of the forces for the complete string the tension in the right support string is equal to the tension in the string. Thus the maximum tension is

$$T = \sqrt{F_V^2 + F_H^2} = 90.14 \text{ lb}.$$

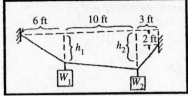

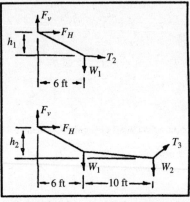

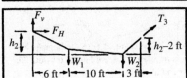

Problem 10.67 In Problem 10.66, $W_1 = 50$ lb, $W_2 = 100$ lb, and the vertical distance $h_1 = 4$ ft.

(a) Determine the vertical distance h_2.
(b) What is the maximum tension in the cable?

Solution: (a) Cut the cable at the left and just to the right of w_1:

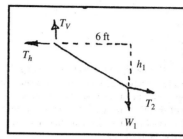

$$\sum M_{\text{(rightend)}} = h_1 T_h - 6T_v = 0 \quad \textbf{(1)}$$

Cut the cable at the left and just to the right of w_2:

$$\sum M_{\text{(rightend)}} = h_2 T_h - 16T_v + 10w_1 = 0 \quad \textbf{(2)}.$$

Cut the cable at the left and right:

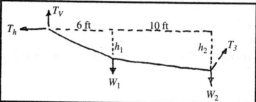

$$\sum M_{\text{(rightend)}} = 2T_h - 19T_v + 13w_1 + 3w_2 = 0. \quad \textbf{(3)}$$

Knowing

$W_1 = 50$ lb.

$W_2 = 100$ lb

and $h_1 = 4$ ft,

equations (1), (2) and (3) can be solved for T_h T_v and h_2, obtaining

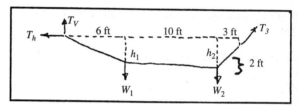

$T_h = 89.1$ lb,

$T_v = 59.4$ lb,

$h_2 = 5.05$ ft.

(b) The maximum tension occurs in the segment with the largest slope relative to the horizontal. In this problem T_3 is the largest tension. The angle between T_3 and the horizontal: is

$$\theta = \arctan\left(\frac{h_2 - 2}{3}\right) = 45.5°.$$

Summing horizontal forces on the third free body diagram, we obtain $-T_h + T_3 \cos\theta = 0$, so

$$T_3 = \frac{T_h}{\cos\theta} = \frac{89.1}{\cos 45.5°} = 127 \text{ lb}.$$

Problem 10.68 Three identical masses $m = 10$ kg are suspended from the cable. Determine the vertical distance h_1 and h_3 and draw a sketch of the configuration of the cable.

Solution: Cutting to the right of the left mass

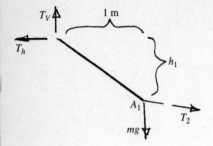

The configuration of the cable is

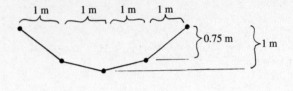

we obtain

$$\sum M_{(\text{pt}A_1)} = h_1 T_h - (1)T_n = 0. \quad (1)$$

Cutting to the right of the middle mass,

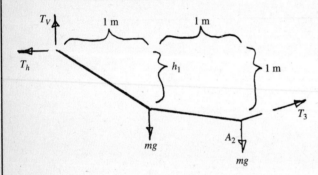

we obtain

$$\sum M_{(\text{pt}A_2)} = (1)T_h - (2)T_n + (1)mg = 0. \quad (2)$$

Cutting to the right of the right mass, we obtain

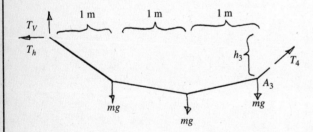

$$\sum M_{(\text{pt}A_3)} = h_3 T_h - (3)T_n + (2)mg + (1)mg = 0. \quad (3)$$

Because of symmetry, $h_3 = h_1$, so we can solve Eqs. (1)–(3), obtaining

$T_h = 196$ N,

$T_n = 147$ N,

and $h_1 = h_3 = 0.75$ m.

Problem 10.69 In Problem 10.68, what are the tensions in cable segments 1 and 2?

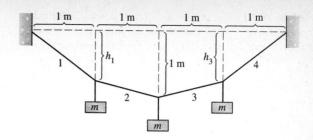

Solution: See the solution of Problem 10.68. Cutting cable segment 1, we obtain

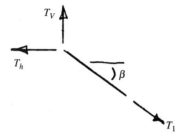

The angle β is

$$\beta = \arctan\left(\frac{h_1}{1}\right) = \arctan(0.75) = 36.9°.$$

From the equation

$$\sum F_x = -T_h + T_1 \cos \beta = 0,$$

we obtain

$$T_1 = \frac{T_h}{\cos \beta} = \frac{196}{\cos 36.9°} = 245 \text{ N}.$$

Cutting cable segment 2, we obtain

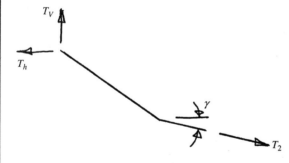

The angle γ is

$$\gamma = \arctan\left(\frac{1 - h_1}{1}\right) = \arctan(0.25) = 14.0°.$$

From the equation

$$\sum F_x = -T_h + T_2 \cos \gamma = 0,$$

we obtain

$$T_2 = \frac{T_h}{\cos \gamma} = \frac{196}{\cos 14.0°} = 202 \text{ N}.$$

Problem 10.70 Three masses are suspended from the cable, where $m = 30$ kg, and the vertical distance $h_1 = 400$ mm. Determine the vertical distance h_2 and h_3.

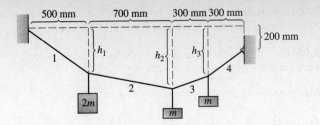

Solution: Cutting to the right of the left mass,

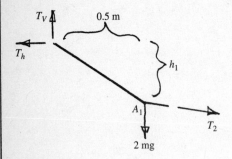

we obtain

$$\sum M_{(ptA_1)} = h_1 T_h - (0.5)T_n = 0. \quad (1)$$

Cutting to the right of the middle mass,

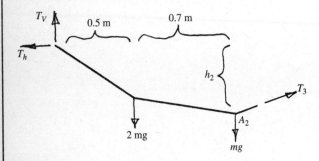

we obtain

$$\sum m_{(ptA_2)} = h_2 T_h - (1.2)T_n + (0.7)2\, mg = 0. \quad (2)$$

Cutting to the right of the right mass, we obtain

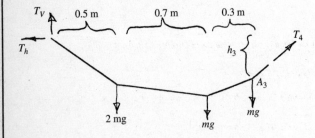

$$\sum M_{(ptA_3)} = h_3 T_h - (1.5)T_n + (1)2\, mg + (0.3)\, mg = 0. \quad (3)$$

Finally, cutting at the right attachment point,

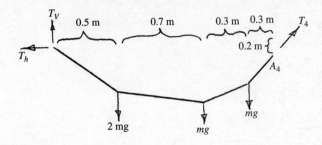

we obtain

$$\sum M_{(ptA_4)} = (0.2)T_h - (1.8)T_n + (1.3)2\, mg$$

$$+ (0.6)\, mg + (0.3)\, mg = 0. \quad (4)$$

Solving Equations (1)–(4), we obtain $T_h = 831$ N, $T_n = 665$ N, $h_2 = 464$ mm, $h_3 = 385$ mm.

Problem 10.71 In Problem 10.70, what is the maximum tension in the cable, and where does it occur?

Solution: The tension is greatest in the segment with the greatest slope, which is either segment 1 or segment 4.

Slope of segment 1 (see the solution of Problem 10.71):

$$\frac{h_1}{500} = \frac{400}{500} = 0.8.$$

Slope of segment 4:

$$\frac{h_3 - 200}{300} = \frac{385 - 200}{300} = 0.62.$$

Cutting segment 1, we obtain

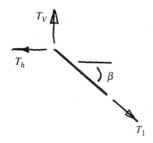

The angle β is

$$\beta = \arctan\left(\frac{h_1}{500}\right) = \arctan\left(\frac{400}{500}\right) = 38.7°.$$

From the equation

$$\sum F_x = -T_h + T_1 \cos\beta = 0,$$

we obtain

$$T_1 = \frac{T_h}{\cos\beta} = \frac{831}{\cos 38.7°} = 1060 \text{ N}.$$

Problem 10.72 The cable in the system shown in Problem 10.70 will safely support a tension of 15 kN. If the vertical distance $h_1 = 200$ mm, what is the largest safe value of m?

Solution: See the solution of Problem 10.71. The greatest tension occurs in segment 1 and the angle β is

$$\beta = \arctan\left(\frac{h_1}{500}\right) = \arctan\left(\frac{200}{500}\right) = 21.8°.$$

Setting

$$T_1 = 15,000 = \frac{T_h}{\cos\beta},$$

we obtain $T_h = 13,900$ N.

From Eq. (1) of the solution of Problem 10.70,

$$0.2T_h - 0.5T_n = 0,$$

we obtain $T_n = 5570$ N. Then from Eq. (4),

$$0.2T_h - 1.8T_n + 3.5\,mg = 0,$$

we obtain $m = 211$ kg.

Problem 10.73 The beam's length is $L = 10$ m and the distributed load is

$$w = 20x\left(1 - \frac{x^3}{L^3}\right).$$

What is the maximum bending moment in the beam, and where does it occur?

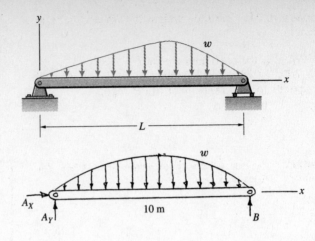

Solution: From the equilibrium equations

$$\sum F_y = A_y + B - \int_0^{10} 20x\left(1 - \frac{x^3}{L^3}\right)dx = 0,$$

$$\sum M_{(\text{ptA})} = 10B - \int_0^{10} 20x^2\left(1 - \frac{x^3}{L^3}\right)dx = 0,$$

we obtain $A_y = 267$ N, $B = 333$ N.

$$\frac{dV}{dx} = -w = -20x\left(1 - \frac{x^3}{L^3}\right),$$

$$\int_{267}^{V} dV = \int_0^x -20x\left(1 - \frac{x^3}{L^3}\right)dx,$$

$$V = 267 - 10x^2 + \frac{4x^5}{L^3}.$$

$$\frac{dM}{dx} = V = 267 - 10x^2 + \frac{4x^5}{L^3},$$

$$\int_0^M dM = \int_0^x \left(267 - 10x^2 + \frac{4}{L^3}x^5\right)dx,$$

$$M = 267x - \frac{10}{3}x^3 + \frac{2}{3L^3}x^6.$$

The bending moment is a maximum where $dM/dx = V = 0$:

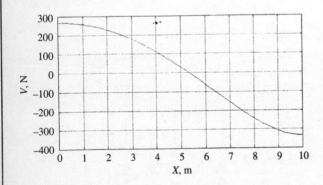

$V = 0$ at $x = 5.33$ m, where $M = 932$ N-m.

Problem 10.74 The rope weighs 1 N/m and is 16 m in length.

(a) What is the maximum tension?
(b) What is the vertical distance from the attachment points to the lowest point of the rope?

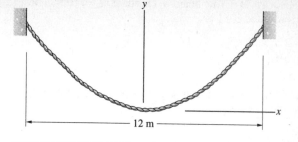

Solution: The rope satisfies the condition for a catenary. The parameter a is found from

$$s = \left(\frac{\sinh(ax)}{a}\right),$$

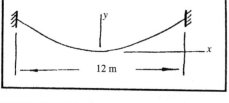

from which $f(a) = 8a - \sinh(6a) = 0$. A graph of the function $f(a)$ over the range $0.1 < a \le 0.3$ shows a zero crossing for a value of $a = 0.2252$ approximately. The tension at the lowest point is

$$T_0 = \frac{w}{a} = 4.44 \text{ N}.$$

(a) The maximum tension is $T_{\text{MAX}} = T_0 \cosh(6a) = 9.15$ N
(b) The sag is $h = \left(\frac{1}{a}\right)(\cosh(6a) - 1) = 4.709$ m

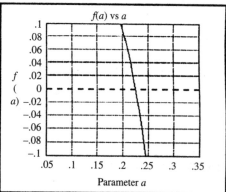

f(a) vs a

Problem 10.75 A chain weighs 20 lb and is 20 ft long. It is suspended from two points of equal height that are 10 ft apart.

(a) Determine the maximum tension in the chain.
(b) Draw a sketch of the shape of the chain.

Solution: The chain satisfies the condition for a catenary. The weight density is

$$w = \frac{20}{20} = 1 \text{ lb/ft}.$$

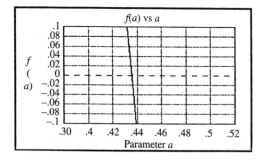

f(a) vs a

The parameter a is found from a graph of the function $f(a) = 10a - \sinh(5a) = 0$ over the range $0.4 < a \le 0.5$. The zero crossing occurs for $a = 0.4355$, approximately. The tension at the lowest point is

$$T_0 = \frac{w}{a} = 2.97 \text{ lb}.$$

The maximum tension is

$$T = T_0 \cosh(5a) = 10.26 \text{ lb}$$

Problem 10.76 An engineer wants to suspend high-voltage power lines between poles 200 m apart. Each line has a mass of 2 kg/m.

(a) If the engineer wants to subject the lines to a tension greater than 10 kN, what should be the maximum allowable sag between poles? That is, what is the largest allowable vertical distance between the attachment points and the lowest point of the line?

(b) What is the length of each line?

Solution: The lines meet the conditions for a catenary. The maximum tension is

$$T = T_0 \cosh(ax) = \frac{w}{a} \cosh(100a).$$

The parameter a is found by plotting the function

$$f(a) = 10000 - 19.62 \left(\frac{\cosh(100a)}{a} \right) = 0$$

over the range $0 < a \le 0.04$. The zero crossings occur at values $a = 0.002$ and $a = 0.036$, approximately, so that there are two possible solutions. The maximum sag is

$$y = \left(\frac{1}{a} \right) (\cosh(100a) - 1).$$

For $a = 0.002$ the sag is $y_1 = 10.04$ m. For $a = 0.036$, $y_2 = 481.93$ m. (a) The second value is not a practical value, obviously, and the maximum allowable sag is $h = 10.04$ m. (b) The length of the line is

$$L = 2 \left(\frac{\sinh(100a)}{a} \right) = 201.34 \text{ m}$$

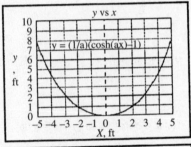

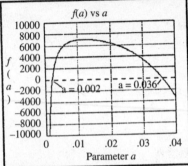

Problem 10.77 The mass per unit length of lines AB and BC is 2 kg/m. The length of line AB is 62 m. The two lines have equal horizontal forces at B.

(a) Determine the sags h_1 and h_2.
(b) Determine the maximum tensions in the two lines.

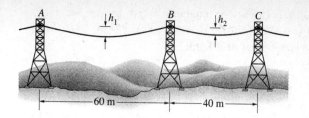

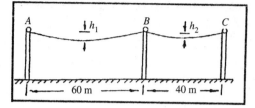

Solution: The lines meet the conditions for a catenary. The weight density is $w = 2(9.81) = 19.62$ N/m

Line AB: The length of line AB is

$$s = \frac{\sinh(30a)}{a}.$$

The parameter a is found by graphing the function

$$f(a) = 31 - \frac{\sinh(30a)}{a} = 0.$$

The zero crossing occurs at a value $a = 0.0148$, approximately. The tension at the lowest point is

$$T_0 = \frac{w}{a} = \frac{19.62}{0.0148} = 1322.68.$$

The sag is

$$h_1 = \left(\frac{1}{a}\right)(\cosh(30a) - 1) = 6.786 \text{ m}.$$

The maximum tension is

$$T_{MAX}^{AB} = T_0 \cosh(30a) = 1455.8 \text{ N}$$

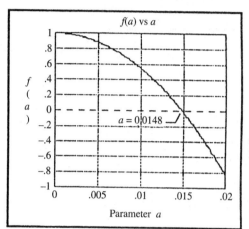

Line BC: The horizontal component of the force is the same for both lines, T_0. The weight density is the same for both lines, hence the parameter a is the same for lines. The sag is $h_2 = (1/a)(\cosh(20a) - 1) = 2.99$ m. The max tension is $T_{MAX}^{BC} = T_o \cosh(20a) = 1381.3$ N

Problem 10.78 The mass per unit length of the lines AB and BC in Problem 10.77 is 2 kg/m. The sag $h_1 = 4.5$ m, but the length of line AB is unknown. The two lines exert equal horizontal forces at B.

(a) Determine the sag h_2.
(b) Determine the maximum tensions in the two lines.

Solution: The weight density is $w = 2g = 19.62$ N/m. The sag

$$h_1 = \left(\frac{1}{a}\right)(\cosh(ax) - 1).$$

Solve

$$f(a) = 4.5 - \frac{\cosh(30a) - 1}{a} = 0$$

by iteration, to obtain $a = 0.009926$. The tension at the lowest point is

$$T_0 = \frac{w}{a} = 1976.5 \text{ N}.$$

This is also the tension at the lowest point in BC, and

(a) $h_2 = \dfrac{\cosh(20a) - 1}{a} = 1.992$ m.

(b) The maximum tensions are

$$T_{AB} = T_0 \cosh(30a) = 2064.8 \text{ N},$$

$$T_{BC} = T_0 \cosh(20a) = 2015.6 \text{ N}$$

Problem 10.79 Two 30-ft cables A and B are suspended from points of equal height that are 20 ft apart. Cable A is subjected to a 200-lb load uniformly distributed horizontally. Cable B is subjected to a 200-lb load distributed uniformly along its length. What are the maximum tensions in the two cables?

Solution: The shape of cable A is described by a parabola; the shape of cable B is described by a catenary. *Cable A:* The weight density is

$$w_A = \frac{200}{20} = 10 \text{ lb/ft.}$$

The parameter a is found by plotting the function

$$f(a) = 30 - 10\sqrt{1 + a^2(10)^2} - \left(\frac{1}{a}\right)\ln(10a$$

$$+ \sqrt{1 + a^2(10)^2}) = 0.$$

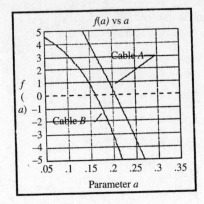

The zero crossing occurs at $a = 0.2055$, approximately. The tension at the lowest point is

$$T_{0A} = \frac{w_A}{a} = 48.65 \text{ lb.}$$

The maximum tension is

$$T_A = T_{0A}\sqrt{1 + 100a^2} = 111.21 \text{ lb}$$

Cable B: The weight density is

$$w_B = \frac{200}{30} = 6.6667 \text{ lb/ft.}$$

The parameter a is found by plotting the function

$$f(a) = 15 - \frac{\sinh(10a)}{a} = 0.$$

The zero crossing occurs at $a = 0.1622$. The tension at the lowest point is

$$T_{0B} = \frac{w_B}{a} = 41.098 \text{ lb.}$$

The maximum is

$$T_B = T_{0B}\cosh(10a) = 108.1 \text{ lb}$$

Problem 10.80 Draw a graph of the two cables in Problem 10.79, comparing their shapes.

Solution: The functions

$$y_A = \left(\frac{1}{2}\right)ax^2$$

and $y_B = \left(\frac{1}{a}\right)(\cosh(ax) - 1)$

are graphed over the range $-10 \le x \le +10$. The lower graph is the shape of Cable B.

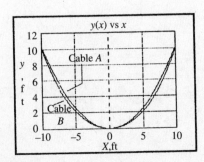

Problem 10.81 The masses $m_1 = 10$ kg and $m_2 = 20$ kg. The total length of the three segments of rope is 5 m.

(a) What are h_1 and h_2?
(b) What is the maximum tension in the rope?

Strategy: If you choose a value of h_1, you can determine h_2 and then L. By obtaining a graph of L as a function of h_1, you can determine the value of h_1 that corresponds to $L = 5$ m.

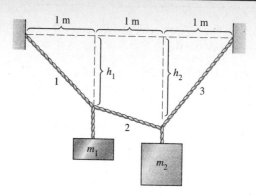

Solution: Cutting to the right of m_1,

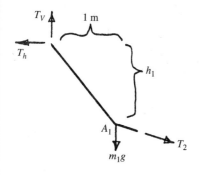

we obtain $\sum M_{(ptA_1)} = h_1 T_h - (1)T_v = 0.$ **(1)**

Cutting to the right of m_2,

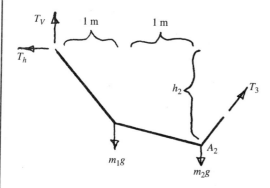

we obtain $\sum M_{(ptA_2)} = h_2 T_h - (2)T_n + (1)m_1 g = 0.$ **(2)**

Cutting at the right attachment point, we obtain

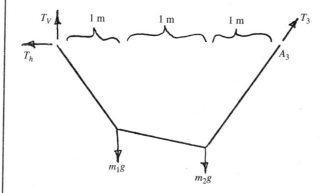

$$\sum M_{(ptA_3)} = -(3)T_v + (2)m_1 g + (1)m_2 g = 0. \quad \textbf{(3)}$$

(a) Choosing a value of h_1, Eqs. (1)–(3) can be solved for T_h, T_v and h_2. The length of the segments are

$$L_1 = \sqrt{1 + h_1^2},$$

$$L_2 = \sqrt{1 + (h_2 - h_1)^2},$$

$$L_3 = \sqrt{1 + h_2^2}.$$

We plot $L = L_1 + L_2 + L_3$ as a function of h_1:

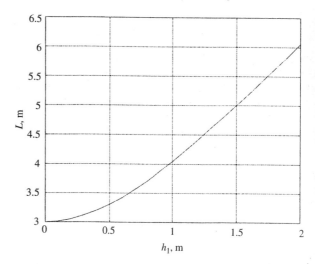

By examining results near $h_1 = 1.5$ m, we find that $L = 5$ m when $h_1 = 1.502$ m. From Eqs. (1)–(3) we obtain

$$h_2 = 1.878 \text{ m},$$

$$T_h = 87.1 \text{ N},$$

$$T_v = 130.8 \text{ N}.$$

10.81 Contd.

(b) Segment 3 has the greatest slope. From the free-body diagram obtained by cutting to the right of m_2,

$$\sum F_x = -T_h + T_3 \cos \beta = 0,$$

where

$$\beta = \arctan\left(\frac{h_2}{1}\right) = \arctan(1.878) = 62.0°.$$

Therefore

$$T_3 = \frac{T_h}{\cos \beta} = \frac{87.1}{\cos 62.0°} = 185 \text{ N}.$$

Problem 10.82 A deep submersible research vehicle operates at a depth of 1000 m. The average mass density of the water is $\rho = 1025$ kg/m³. Atmospheric pressure is $p_{\text{atm}} = 1 \times 10^5$ Pa. Determine the pressure on the vehicle's surface (a) in pascals (Pa); (b) in pounds per square inch (psi).

Solution:

(a) From Eq. (10.26),

$$P = P_0 + \gamma x$$

$$= 1 \times 10^5 + (1025)(9.81)(1000)$$

$$= 1.016 \times 10^7 \text{ Pa (N/m}^2).$$

(b) $P = 1.016 \times 10^7 \text{ N/m}^2 \times \left(\frac{1 \text{ lb}}{4.448 \text{ N}}\right)$

$$\times \left(\frac{1 \text{ m}}{39.37 \text{ in.}}\right)^2 = 1470 \text{ psi}.$$

Problem 10.83 An engineer planning a water system for a new community estimates that at maximum expected usage, the pressure drop between the central system and the farthest planned fire hydrant will be 25 psi. Fire fighting personnel indicate that a gage pressure of 40 psi at the fire hydrant is required. The weight density of the water is $\gamma = 62.4$ lb/ft³. How tall would a water tower at the central system have to be to provide the needed pressure?

Solution: The total pressure will be $65\left(\frac{\text{lb}}{\text{in}^2}\right)$. A tower of height h will produce a pressure of $P = \gamma h$, where the units are to be consistent. The tower height is $h = \left(\frac{P}{\gamma}\right)$.

Let the tower height be in feet:

$$h \text{ ft} = \left(\frac{1}{62.4}\right)\left(\frac{\text{ft}^3}{\text{lb}}\right)(65)\left(\frac{\text{lb}}{\text{in}^2}\right)\left(\frac{12 \text{ in}}{1 \text{ ft}}\right)^2 = 150 \text{ ft}$$

Problem 10.84 A cube of material is suspended below the surface of a liquid of weight density γ. By calculating the forces exerted on the faces of the cube by pressure, show that their sum is an upward force of magnitude γb^3.

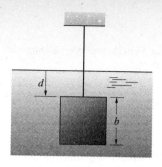

Solution: Neglect the pressures on the supporting wire. The force on the top surface is $F_{TOP} = \gamma d b^2$. The force on the sides is

$$F_S = \gamma \left(d + \frac{b}{2}\right) b^2,$$

where $\left(d + \frac{b}{2}\right)$

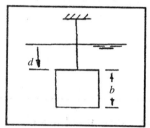

is the distance of the centroid of the area from the surface. The force on the bottom surface is $F_{BOTTOM} = \gamma(d + b)b^2$. The forces on the sides cancel by symmetry. The difference between the downward force on the top surface and the upward force on the bottom surface is the resultant:

$$R = \gamma(d + b)b^2 - \gamma d b^2 = \gamma b^3.$$

Problem 10.85 The area shown subjected to a *uniform* pressure $p_{atm} = 1 \times 10^5$ Pa.

(a) What is the total force exerted on the area by the pressure?

(b) What is the moment about the y-axis due to the pressure?

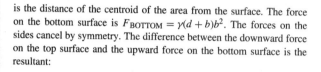

Solution: The element of area is $dA = dx\,dy$. (a) The element of force is $dF = p\,dA$. Integrating:

$$F = \int_A p\,dA = (10^5) \int_0^1 dx \int_0^{x^2} dy = (10^5) \int_0^1 x^2\,dx$$

$$= \left(\frac{10^5}{3}\right) N = 3.33 \times 10^4 \text{ N}$$

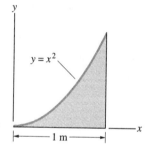

(b) The element of moment about the y-axis is $dM = px\,dA$. Integrating:

$$M_{y-\text{axis}} = \int_A px\,dA = p \int_0^1 x\,dx \int_0^{x^2} dy = p \int_0^1 x^3\,dx,$$

$$M_{y-\text{axis}} = \left(\frac{10^5}{4}\right) = 2.5 \times 10^4 \text{ N m}$$

Problem 10.86 Determine the coordinates of the center of pressure in Problem 10.85.

Solution: The center of pressure

$$x = \frac{\int_A px\, dA}{p\int_A dA} = \frac{2.5 \times 10^4}{3.33 \times 10^4} = 0.75 \text{ m}.$$

$$y = \frac{\int_A py\, dA}{\int_A p\, dA} = \frac{p\int dx \int_0^{x^2} y\, dy}{3.33 \times 10^4} = \frac{\frac{p}{2}\int_0^1 x^4\, dx}{3.33 \times 10^4},$$

$$y = \frac{\frac{p}{10}}{3.333 \times 10^4} = 0.3 \text{ m}$$

Problem 10.87 The area shown is subjected to a *uniform* pressure $p_{atm} = 14.7$ psi.

(a) What is the total force exerted on the area by the pressure?
(b) What is the moment about the y axis due to the pressure on the area?

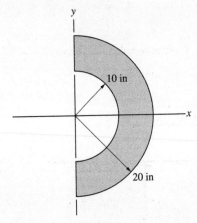

Solution: (a) The total force is

$$F = \int_A P_{atm}\, dA = P_{atm}\int_A dA = P_{atm}A$$

$$= 14.7\frac{\text{lb}}{\text{in}^2}\left[\frac{1}{2}\pi(20)^2 - \frac{1}{2}\pi(10)^2\right]\text{in}^2 = 6930 \text{ lb}.$$

(b) We can represent the pressure by an equivalent force F acting at the center of pressure. Since the pressure is uniform, the center of pressure is at the centroid of the plane area. From Appendix b, the x coordinate of the centroid is

$$x = \frac{\left[\frac{4(20)}{3\pi}\right]\left[\frac{1}{2}\pi(20)^2\right] - \left[\frac{4(10)}{3\pi}\right]\left[\frac{1}{2}\pi(10)^2\right]}{\frac{1}{2}\pi(20)^2 - \frac{1}{2}\pi(10)^2} = 9.90 \text{ in}.$$

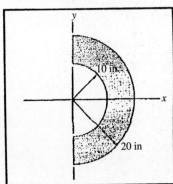

The moment about the y axis is

$$xF = (9.90)(6930) = 68,600 \text{ in-lb}.$$

Problem 10.88 Determine the coordinates of the center of pressure in Problem 10.87.

Solution: See the solution of part (b) of Problem 10.87. The location of the center of pressure is $x_p = 9.90$ in, $y_p = 0$.

Problem 10.89 The top of the rectangular plate is 2 m below the surface of a lake. Atmospheric pressure $p_{atm} = 1 \times 10^5$ Pa and the mass density of water is $\rho = 1000$ kg/m^3.

(a) What is the maximum pressure exerted on the plate by the water?

(b) Determine the force exerted on a face of the plate by the pressure of the water.

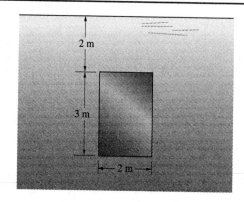

Solution:

(a) The maximum pressure occurs at the bottom of the plate:

$$P = P_0 + \gamma x$$

$$= 1 \times 10^5 + (1000)(9.81)(5)$$

$$= 1.49 \times 10^5 \text{ Pa.}$$

(b)

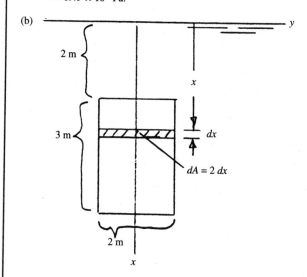

The force is

$$F = \int_A P \, dA$$

$$= \int_2^5 (P_0 + \gamma x) 2 \, dx$$

$$= \int_2^5 [1 \times 10^5 + (1000)(9.81)x] 2 \, dx$$

$$= 806{,}000 \text{ N.}$$

Problem 10.90 In Problem 10.89, how far below the top of the plate is the center of pressure located?

Solution: See the solution of Problem 10.89. The moment due to the pressure about the y axis is

$$M = \int_A x p \, dA$$

$$= \int_2^5 x(P_0 + \gamma x)2 \, dx$$

$$= \int_2^5 [1 \times 10^5 x + (1000)(9.81)x^2]2 \, dx$$

$$= 2{,}865{,}000 \text{ N-m}.$$

The x-coordinate of the center of pressure is

$$x_P = \frac{M}{F} = \frac{2{,}865{,}000}{806{,}000} = 3.55 \text{ m}.$$

The distance below the top of the plate is $x_P - 2 \text{ m} = 1.55 \text{ m}.$

Problem 10.91 The width of the dam (the dimension into the page) is 100 m. The mass density of the water is $\rho = 1000 \text{ kg/m}^3$. Determine the force exerted on the dam by the gage pressure of the water (a) by integration; (b) by calculating the "volume" of the pressure distribution.

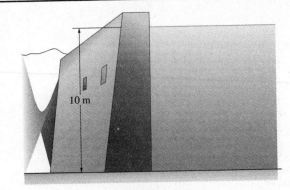

Solution: For gage pressure, we neglect the pressure of the atmosphere. (a) The weight density of the water is

$$\gamma = 1000(9.81) = 9810 \text{ N/m}^3.$$

The force on the dam is

$$F = \int_A p \, dA = 100\gamma \int_0^{10} x \, dx = 5000\gamma = 49.05 \times 10^6 \text{ N}$$

(b) The pressure distribution is a triangle, with base 10γ and altitude 10 m. The length dimension of this "solid" is 100 m. The volume of this triangular "solid" is

$$V = \left(\tfrac{1}{2}\right) 100(10)(9810) = 49.05 \times 10^6 \text{ N}$$

Problem 10.92 In Problem 10.91, how far down from the surface of the water is the center of pressure due to the gage pressure of the water on the dam?

Solution: The center of pressure is the centroid of the pressure distribution, which is a triangle of altitude 10 m and base 10γ. The centroid of a triangle is $\left(\tfrac{1}{3}\right)$ of the altitude, or, from the surface,

$$\mathbf{d} = \left(\tfrac{2}{3}\right) 10 = 6.67 \text{ m}$$

Problem 10.93 The width of the gate (the dimension into the page) is 3 m. Atmospheric pressure $p_{atm} = 1 \times 10^5$ Pa and the mass density of the water is $\rho = 1000$ kg/m^3. Determine the horizontal force and couple exerted on the gate by its built-in support A.

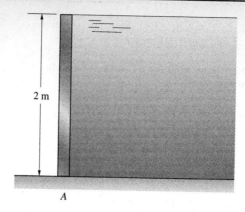

2 m

A

Solution: The gage pressure at the bottom of the gate is

$$P_g = \gamma x = (1000)(9.81)(2),$$

so the "volume" of the pressure distribution is

$$F = \tfrac{1}{2}(2)P_g(3)$$

$$= \tfrac{1}{2}(2)(1000)(9.81)(2)(3)$$

$$= 58,860 \text{ N}.$$

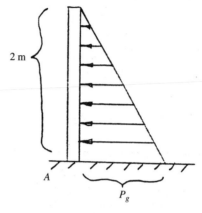

2 m

A

P_g

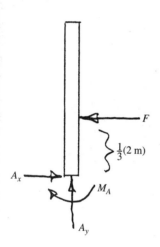

F

$\tfrac{1}{3}(2 \text{ m})$

A_x

M_A

A_y

we see that

$$A_x = F = 58.9 \text{ kN},$$

$$M_A = \tfrac{1}{3}(2)F = 39.2 \text{ kN-m}.$$

Problem 10.94 The homogenous gate weighs 100 lb, and its width (the dimension into the page) is 3 ft. The weight density of the water is $\gamma = 62.4$ lb/ft³, and the atmospheric pressure is $p_{atm} = 2120$ lb/ft². Determine the reactions at A and B.

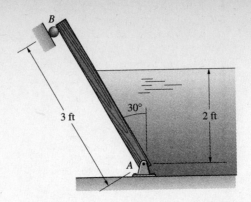

Solution: The atmospheric pressure acts on both sides of the gate, so it is ignored. The strategy is use the "volume" of the pressure distribution to compute the force acting on the face of the gate. The pressure distribution is a triangle with base 2γ. The pressure acts over an area

$$\left(\frac{6}{\cos(30)}\right) = 6.92 \text{ ft}^2.$$

Thus the "volume" is $F = \left(\frac{1}{2}\right)(62.4)(2)(6.92) = 432.32$ lb. This force acts normally to the surface of the gate, or at an angle of $\theta = 210°$ relative to the positive x-axis. The centroid of the pressure is

$$\mathbf{d} = \left(\frac{2}{3}\right)\left(\frac{1}{\cos 30°}\right) = 0.7698 \text{ ft}$$

along the inner face of the gate from A. The sum of the moments about A is

$$\sum M_A = \mathbf{d}F + W(1.5)\sin 30° - 3B = 0,$$

from which $B = 135.933$ lb, normal to the inner face of the gate. The sum of the forces normal to the gate surface is

$$\sum F_N = +A_N - F + B - W\sin 30° = 0,$$

from which $A_N = 346.4$ lb at an angle $\alpha = 30°$ relative to the positive x axis. The sum of the forces acting parallel to the gate surface is

$$\sum F_P = A_P - W\cos(30°) = 0,$$

from which $A_P = 86.6$ lb at an angle of 120°. Thus the components of the reaction at A are $A_x = -346.3\cos(210°) + 86.6\cos(120°) = 256.7$ lb, to the right, and $A_y = -346.3\sin(210°) + 86.6\sin(120°) = 248.2$ lb upward.

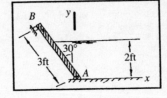

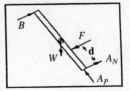

Problem 10.95 The width of the gate (the dimension into the page) is 2 m and there is water of depth $d = 1$ m on one side. Atmospheric pressure $p_{atm} = 1 \times 10^5$ Pa and the mass density of the water is $\rho = 1000$ kg/m^3. Determine the horizontal forces exerted on the gate at A and B.

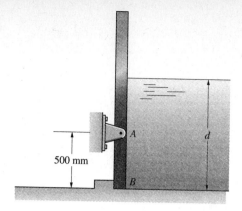

500 mm

Solution: The "volume" of the gage pressure distribution is

$$F = \tfrac{1}{2}\rho g d (2)$$

$$= \delta p d^2$$

$$= (1000)(9.81)(1)^2$$

$$= 9810 \text{ N}.$$

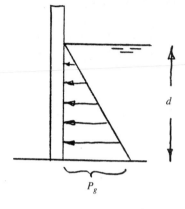

P_g

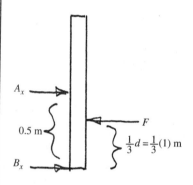

A_x

0.5 m

F

$\tfrac{1}{3}d = \tfrac{1}{3}(1)$ m

B_x

Applying the equilibrium equations, we find that

$$A_x = \tfrac{2}{3}F = 6540 \text{ N},$$

$$B_x = \tfrac{1}{3}F = 3270 \text{ N}.$$

Problem 10.96 The gate in Problem 10.95 is designed to rotate and release the water when the depth d exceeds a certain value. What is that depth?

Solution: See the solution of Problem 10.95. The gate rotates when

$$\tfrac{1}{3}d > \tfrac{1}{2} \text{ m},$$

$$d > \tfrac{3}{2} \text{ m}.$$

Problem 10.97 The dam has water of depth 4 ft on one side. The width of the dam (the dimension into the page) is 8 ft. The weight density of the water is $\gamma = 62.4$ lb/ft³, and the atmospheric pressure $p_{atm} = 2120$ lb/ft². If you neglect the weight of the dam, what are the reactions at A and B?

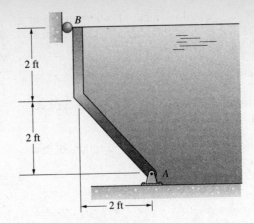

Solution: To simplify the analysis of the pressure forces, we will draw a free body diagram of the dam and the volume of water shown: The left side and top of the free body diagram are subjected to atmospheric pressure, and the right side is subjected to the sum of atmospheric pressure and the gage pressure of the water, so we only need to consider the gage pressure. Let us represent the pressure force on the right side by an equivalent force: We can determine F by calculating the "volume" of the pressure distribution:

$$F = \tfrac{1}{2} p (4 \text{ ft})(8 \text{ ft}) = \tfrac{1}{2} \gamma (4)(4)(8) = 3990 \text{ lb}$$

the complete free body diagram is: The two weights are

$$w_1 = \gamma (2 \text{ ft})(2 \text{ ft})(8 \text{ ft}) = 2000 \text{ lb}$$

$$w_2 = \tfrac{1}{2} \gamma (2 \text{ ft})(2 \text{ ft})(8 \text{ ft}) = 988 \text{ lb.}$$

From the equilibrium equations

$$\sum F_x = A_x + B - F = 0$$

$$\sum F_y = A_y - w_1 - w_2 = 0$$

$$\sum M_{(pt.A)} = -4B + \left(\frac{4}{3}\right) F + (1) W_1 + \frac{1}{3} W_2 = 0,$$

we obtain $A_x = 2000$ lb, $A_y = 3000$ lb, $B = 2000$ lb.

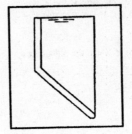

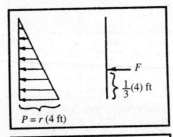

$P = r \,(4 \text{ ft})$

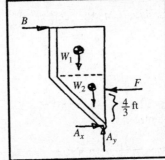

Problem 10.98 A spherical tank of 400-mm inner radius is full of water ($\rho = 1000$ kg/m³). The pressure of the water at the top of the tank is 4×10^5 Pa.

(a) What is the pressure of the water at the bottom of the tank?
(b) What is the total force exerted on the inner surface of the tank by the pressure of the water?

Strategy: For (b), draw a free-body diagram of the sphere of water in the tank.

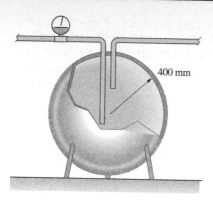

400 mm

Solution: The weight density is $\gamma = \rho g = 9810$ N/m³. ((a) The pressure distribution is $P(x) = p_0 + \gamma x$.) The pressure at the bottom of the tank is $P(0.8) = p_0 + \gamma\,(0.5) = 4 \times 10^5 + (9810)(0.8) = 4.0785 \times 10^5$ Pa.

(b) From the free body diagram of the sphere of water, the unbalanced force is the weight of water, acting downward:

$$W = \left(\frac{4}{3}\right)\pi R^3 \gamma = 2629.9 \text{ N}$$

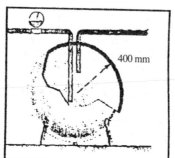

400 mm

Problem 10.99 Consider a plane, vertical area A below the surface of a liquid. Let p_0 be the pressure at the surface.

(a) Show that the force exerted on the area is $F = \mathbf{p}A$, where $\mathbf{p} = p_0 + \gamma\mathbf{x}$ is the pressure of the liquid at the centroid of the area.
(b) Show that the x coordinate of the center of pressure is

$$x_P = \mathbf{x} + \frac{\gamma I_{y'}}{\mathbf{p}A},$$

where $I_{y'}$ is the moment of interia of the area about the y' axis through its centroid.

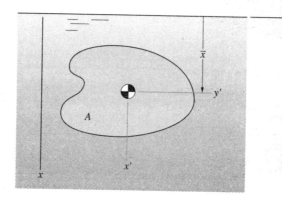

Solution: (a) The definition of the centroid of the area is

$$\mathbf{x}A = \int_A x\,dA.$$

The force on the plate is

$$F = \int_A p\,dA = p_0\int_A dA + \gamma\int_A x\,dA = p_0 A + \gamma\mathbf{x}A.$$

But by definition, the pressure at the centroid of the area is $\mathbf{p} = p_0 + \gamma\mathbf{x}$, hence $F = \mathbf{p}A$.

(b) The moment about the y axis is

$$M_{y-\text{axis}} = \int_A px\,dA = p_0\int_A x\,dA + \gamma\int_A x^2\,dA.$$

The moment of inertia is defined:

$$I_y A = \int_A x^2\,dA,$$

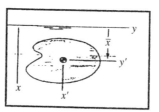

from which the moment is $M_{y-\text{axis}} = p_0\mathbf{x}A + \gamma I_y$. But the moment is also given by $M_{y-\text{axis}} = Fx_P$, where F is the force on the plate and x_P is the distance to the center of pressure. Thus $\mathbf{p}Ax_P = p_0\mathbf{x}A + \gamma I_y$,

from which $x_P = \left(\dfrac{p_0}{\mathbf{p}}\right)\mathbf{x} + \dfrac{\gamma I_y}{\mathbf{p}A}$.

From the parallel axis theorem, $I_y = \mathbf{x}^2 A + I_{y'}$. Substitute and reduce:

$$x_P = \frac{(p_0 + \gamma\mathbf{x})\mathbf{x}}{\mathbf{p}} + \frac{\gamma I_{y'}}{\mathbf{p}A} = \mathbf{x} + \frac{\gamma I_{y'}}{\mathbf{p}A},$$

which demonstrates the required result.

Problem 10.100 A circular plate of 1-m radius is below the surface of a stationary pool of water. Atmospheric pressure is $p_{atm} = 10^5$ Pa, and the mass density of the water is $\rho = 1000$ kg/m^3. Determine (a) the force exerted on the face of the plate by the pressure of the water; (b) the x coordinate of the center of pressure. (See Problem 10.99.)

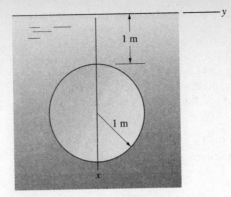

Solution: (a) From Problem 10.99, the pressure on the face of the plate is $F = \mathbf{p}A$, where $\mathbf{p}$ is the pressure at the centroid of the area.

$$F = (p_0 + \gamma 2)(\pi 1^2) = 375.8 \text{ kN}.$$

(b) From Problem 10.99,

$$x_P = \mathbf{x} + \frac{\gamma I_{y'}}{\mathbf{p}A} = 2 + \frac{9810\left(\dfrac{\pi 1^4}{4}\right)}{F} = 2.0205 \text{ m}$$

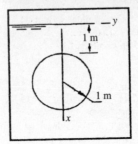

Problem 10.101 A tank consists of a cylinder with hemispherical ends. It is filled with water ($\rho = 1000$ kg/m^3). The pressure of the water at the top of the tank is 140 kPa. Determine the magnitude of the force exerted by the pressure of the water on one of the hemispherical end of the tank.

Strategy: Draw a free-body diagram of the water to the right of the dashed line in the figure. See Example 10.13.

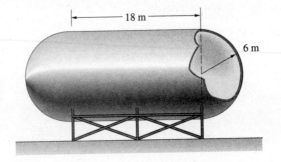

Solution: The free-body diagram is

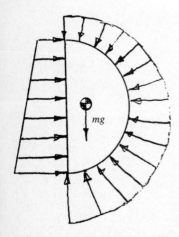

The force exerted by the pressure distribution on the curved surface (equal and opposite to the force exerted on the tank's hemispherical end) can be determined from the fact that the free-body diagram is in equilibrium.

The magnitude of the vertical component is

$$mg = (1000)\frac{1}{2}\left(\frac{4}{3}\pi R^3\right)(9.81) = 4.44 \times 10^6 \text{ N}.$$

To determine the horizontal component, see Problem 10.99. The pressure at the centroid is

$$\mathbf{p} = 140,000 + (1000)(9.81)(6) = 199,000 \text{ Pa},$$

so the horizontal component is

$$\mathbf{p}A = (199,000)\pi(6)^2 = 22.5 \times 10^6 \text{ N}.$$

The magnitude of the force is

$$\sqrt{(mg)^2 + (\mathbf{p}A)^2} = 22.9 \text{ MN}.$$

Problem 10.102   An object of volume V and weight W is suspended below the surface of the stationary liquid of weight density γ (Fig. a). Show that the tension in the cord is $W - V\gamma$. In other words, show that the pressure distribution on the surface of the object exerts an upward force equal to the product of the object's volume and the weight density of the water. The result is due to Archimedes (287–212 B.C.)

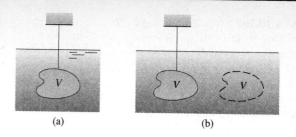

(a)   (b)

Strategy: Draw the free-body diagram of a volume of liquid that has the same shape and position as the object (Fig. b).

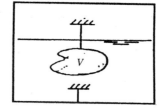

Solution: The result follows from the free body diagram of the space occupied by the object and the development of the force exerted by the pressure in terms of the volume of the object. Let A be the area bounding the volume V. The force exerted on a surface A is

$$\mathbf{F} = -\int_A \mathbf{n}\, p\, dA,$$

where $\mathbf{n}$ is a unit vector normal to the elemental surface dA, positive outward from the surface, and the negative sign comes from the equilibrium condition that the reaction force acts oppositely to the unit vector. Choose an $x,\ y,\ z$ coordinate system such that the elemental forces are

$$\mathbf{n}\, p\, dA = \mathbf{i}\, p\, dy\, dz + \mathbf{j}\, p\, dx\, dz + \mathbf{k}\, p\, dx\, dy.$$

The force becomes

$$\mathbf{F} = -\int_A \mathbf{i}\, p\, dy\, dz - \int_A \mathbf{j}\, p\, dx\, dz - \int_A \mathbf{k}\, p\, dx\, dy.$$

But these integrals can also be written as

$$\mathbf{F} = -\mathbf{i}\int_V \frac{\partial p}{\partial x} dx\, dy\, dz - \mathbf{j}\int_V \frac{\partial p}{\partial y} dx\, dy\, dz - \mathbf{k}\int_V \frac{\partial p}{\partial z} dx\, dy\, dz.$$

This set of integrals can be collapsed into

$$\mathbf{F} = -\int_A \mathbf{n}\, p\, dA = -\int_V \nabla p\, dV,$$

where the volume V is bounded by the surface A, ∇p is a shorthand notation for

$$\nabla p = \mathbf{i}\frac{\partial p}{\partial x} + \mathbf{j}\frac{\partial p}{\partial y} + \mathbf{k}\frac{\partial p}{\partial z},$$

and $dV = dx\, dy\, dz$. The pressure $p = p_0 + \gamma x$, from which $\nabla p = \mathbf{i}\gamma$, and the integral becomes

$$\mathbf{F} = -\int_A \mathbf{n}\, p\, dA = -\mathbf{i}\gamma \int_V dV = -\mathbf{i}\gamma V.$$

The weight of the object acts in the positive x direction, so the resultant force is $\mathbf{F}_R = \mathbf{i}(W - \gamma V)$

Problem 10.103 Determine the internal forces and moment at B (a) if $x = 250$ mm; (b) if $x = 750$ mm.

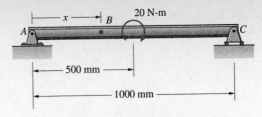

Solution: (a) The sum of the moments about A

$$\sum M_A = -20 + 1C = 0,$$

from which $C = 20$ N. The sum of forces

$$\sum F_y = A_y + C = 0,$$

from which $A_y = -C = -20$ N.

$$\sum F_x = A_x = 0$$

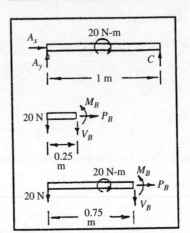

(a) *Make a cut at B. Isolate the left hand part. The sum of moments*

$$\sum M = M_B + 0.25(20) = 0,$$

from which

$M_B = -5$ N m.

$V_B = -20$ N,

$P_B = 0.$

(b) *Make a cut at B: Isolate the left hand part. The sum of moments:*

$$\sum M = M_B - 20 + 0.75(20) = 0,$$

from which

$M_B = 5$ N-m.

$V_B = -20$ N,

$P_B = 0.$

Problem 10.104 Determine the internal forces and moment (a) at B; (b) at C.

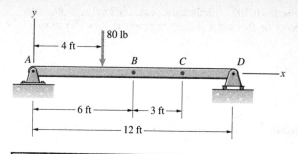

Solution: The sum of the moments about A is

$$\sum M_A = -4(80) + 12D = 0,$$

from which $D = \dfrac{80}{3}$ lb. The sum of forces:

$$\sum F_y = A_y - 80 + D = 0,$$

from which $A_y = \dfrac{160}{3} = 53.33$ lb.

$$\sum F_x = A_x = 0$$

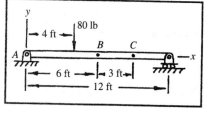

(a) *Make a cut at B. Isolate the left hand part. The sum of moments*

$$\sum M = M_B + 2(80) - 6(53.33) = 0,$$

from which

$$M_B = 160 \text{ ft lb.}$$

$$V_B = 53.33 - 80 = -26.7 \text{ lb.}$$

$$P_B = 0$$

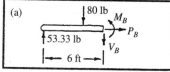

(b) *Make a cut at C: The sum of moments*

$$\sum M = M_C + 80(5) - 9(53.33) = 0,$$

from which

$$M_C = 80 \text{ ft lb.}$$

$$V_C = -80 + 53.33 = -26.7 \text{ lb.}$$

$$P_C = 0$$

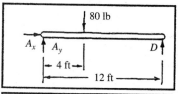

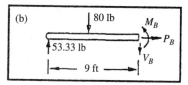

Problem 10.105 (a) Determine the maximum bending moment in the beam and the value of x where it occurs. (b) Show that the equations for V and M as functions of x satisfy the equation $V = dM/dx$.

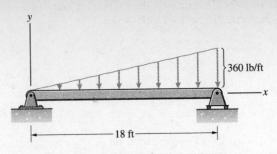

Solution: The distributed load is a straight line function of x, with zero intercept and slope

$$\frac{360}{18} = 20 \text{ lb/ft}^2,$$

from which $w(x) = 20x$ lb/ft. The total moment about the left end due to the loading is

$$M = \int_0^{18} w(x)x\,dx = \frac{20}{3}[x^3]_0^{18} = 38880 \text{ ft lb}.$$

The reaction at the right end is

$$\sum M = -38880 + 18B = 0,$$

from which $B = 2160$ lb. The reaction at the left end is

$$\sum F_y = R_y - \int_0^{18} 20x\,dx + B = 0,$$

from which

$$R_y = [10x^2]_0^{18} - 2160 = 1080 \text{ lb}.$$

(a) The shear as a function of x is

$$V(x) = \sum F = R_y - \int_0^x 20x\,dx = 1080 - 10x^2 \text{ lb}.$$

The moment as a function of x is

$$M(x) = R_y x - \int_0^x 10x^2\,dx = 1080x - \left(\frac{10}{3}\right)x^3 \text{ ft lb}.$$

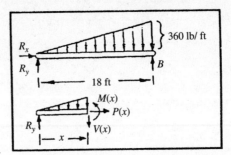

The maximum moment occurs where $\dfrac{dM}{dx} = 0 = 1080 - 10x^2 = 0$, or at $x = \sqrt{\dfrac{1080}{10}} = 10.39$ ft.

The maximum moment is $M_{\text{MAX}} = 1080(10.39) - \dfrac{10}{3}(10.39)^3$
$= 7482.5$ ft lb

(b) The shear is

$$\frac{dM}{dx} = \frac{d(1080x - \left(\frac{10}{3}\right)x^3)}{dx} = 1080 - 10x^2 \text{ lb}.$$

Problem 10.106 Draw the shear and bending moment diagrams for the beam in Problem 10.105.

Solution: The shear and moment diagrams were graphed using **TK Solver 2**. The graph is shown.

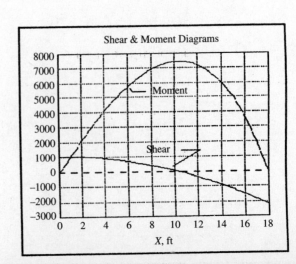

Problem 10.107 Determine the shear force and bending moment diagram's for the beam.

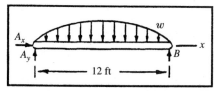

$w = 10(12x - x^2)$ lb/ft

12 ft

Solution: Denote the reactions at the left and right ends by A and B, respectively. The total force due to the load is

$$F = \int_0^{12} 10(12x - x^2)\, dx = 10\left[6x^2 - \frac{x^3}{3}\right]_0^{12} = 2880 \text{ lb.}$$

The moment about the left end due to the load is

$$M_{\text{LOAD}} = \int_0^{12} 10(12x - x^2)x\, dx = 10\left[4x^3 - \frac{x^4}{4}\right]_0^{12}.$$

$$M_{\text{LOAD}} = 17280 \text{ ft lb.}$$

The sum of the moments about the left end:

$$\sum M_A = -M + 12B = 0,$$

from which $B = 1440$ lb. The sum of the forces:

$$\sum F_y = A_y + B - F = 0,$$

from which $A_y = 1440$ lb. Beginning from the left end, the shear is

$$V(x) = -\int_0^X 10(12x - x^2) + 1440$$

$$V(x) = -10\left(6x^2 - \frac{x^3}{3}\right) + 1440.$$

The moment is

$$M = \int V(x)\, dx + C = -10\left(2x^3 - \frac{x^4}{12}\right) + 1440x + C.$$

The moment is zero at $x = 0$, hence the constant $C = 0$, and the moment is

$$M = -10\left(2x^3 - \frac{x^4}{12}\right) + 1440x$$

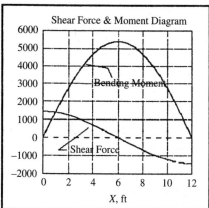

Shear Force & Moment Diagram

Bending Moment

Shear Force

X, ft

963

Problem 10.108 Draw the shear force and bending moment diagrams for beam ABC.

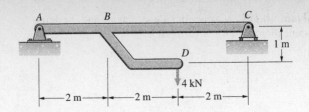

Solution: *The structure as a free body.* The sum of the moments about A:

$$\sum M_A = -4(4) + 6C = 0,$$

from which $C = \dfrac{16}{6} = \dfrac{8}{3}$ kN. The sum of the forces

$$\sum F_y = A_y - 4 + C = 0,$$

from which $A_y = 4 - \dfrac{8}{3} = \dfrac{4}{3}$ kN.

The intervals as free bodies: Divide the beam into two intervals, $0 \le x < 2$, and $2 \le x < 6$.

Interval 1: The shear is

$$V_1(x) = A_y = \dfrac{4}{3} \text{ kN.}$$

The moment is

$$M_1(x) = A_y x = \dfrac{4}{3} x \text{ kN m.}$$

Interval 2: The shear is

$$V_2(x) = A_y - 4 = \dfrac{4}{3} - 4 = -\dfrac{8}{3} \text{ kN.}$$

The moment at B is $B = -2(4) = -8$ kN m. The internal moment is

$$M_2(x) = A_y x + B - 4(x - 2) \text{ kN m,}$$

$$M_2(x) = -\dfrac{8}{3} x + 16 \text{ kN m}$$

The diagrams are shown. The discontinuity in the moment at $x = 2$ is due to the moment exerted at B by the force at D. This moment acts like a couple, in that its magnitude is independent of the distance x along the beam ABC.

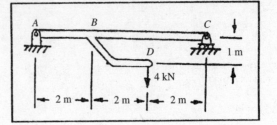

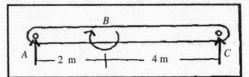

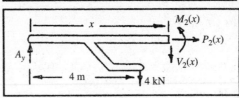

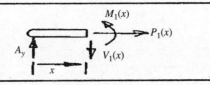

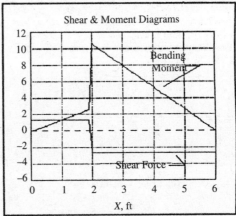

Shear & Moment Diagrams

964

Problem 10.109 Draw the shear force and bending moment diagrams for beam ABC.

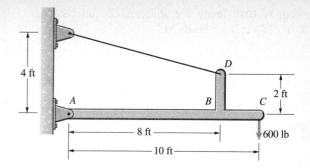

Solution: *The structure as a free body:* The angle of the cable at D relative to the horizontal is

$$\theta = \tan^{-1}\left(\tfrac{1}{4}\right) = 14°.$$

Denote the tension in the cable by T. The sum of the moments about A is

$$\sum M_A = 2T\cos\theta + 8T\sin\theta - 10(600) = 0,$$

from which $T = 1546.2$ lb. The sum of the forces:

$$\sum F_y = A_y - 600 + T\sin\theta = 0,$$

from which $A_y = 225$ lb. *The intervals as free bodies:* Divide the beam into two intervals: $0 \leq x < 8$, and $8 \leq x \leq 10$. *Interval 1:* The shear force is $V_1(x) = A_y$. The internal bending moment is $M_1(x) = A_y x = 225x$. *Interval 2:* The shear force is $V_2(x) = A_y + T\sin\theta = 600$ lb. The sum of the moments is

$$\sum M^x(x) = M_2(x) - A_y x - (T\sin\theta)(x-8) + 2T\cos\theta = 0,$$

from which $M_2(x) = 600x - 6000$ ft lb.

The diagrams are shown. The discontinuity in the moment at $x = 8$ is due to the moment exerted on the beam by the horizontal component of the cable tension at D. This horizontal component of tension exerts a moment that is independent of the distance x along the beam ABC. In this sense, it behaves like a couple.

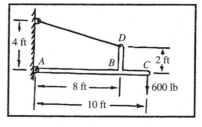

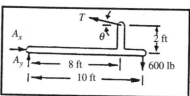

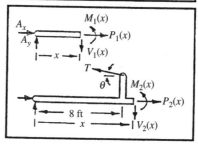

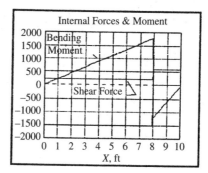

Internal Forces & Moment

Bending Moment

Shear Force

X, ft

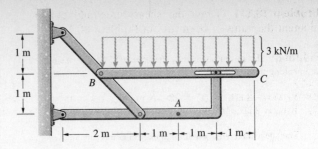

Solution: Denote the reactions at the slide support of BC by D, and the reactions at the upper and lower pin supports by E and G respectively, and the reaction at the pin connection on the beam GB by H. The total force due to the load is

$$F = \int_0^4 3\,dx = 12 \text{ kN}.$$

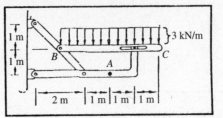

The moment about the left end of BC is

$$M = \int_0^4 3x\,dx = 24 \text{ kN m}.$$

The sum of the moments about the point B is

$$\sum M_B = -M + 3D = 0,$$

from which $D = 8$ kN. The sum of the forces:

$$\sum F_y = B - F + D = 0,$$

from which $B = 4$ kN is the vertical reaction at B. The centroid distance of the load from the left end of BC is

$$d = \frac{M}{F} = \frac{24}{12} = 2 \text{ m}.$$

The sum of the moments about the upper pin support is

$$\sum M = -(1+2)F + 2G_x = 0,$$

from which $G_x = 18$ kN. With these known quantities, the following equations can be written: (See figure to right for assumed positive directions.)

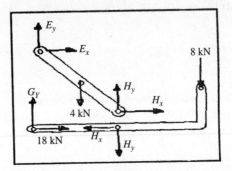

Sum of moments about H for lower member yields $G_y = -8$ kN. The sum of the forces for the lower member yields:

$$H_y = -16 \text{ kN}$$

and $H_x = 18$ kN.

Divide the lower member into two parts

$$0 \le x < 2 \text{ (m)}$$

and $2 \le x < 3$ (m).

Part 1: The shear is $V_1(x) = -8$ kN. The moment is

$$M_1(x) = \int V_1(x)\,dx + C_1 = -8x + C_1.$$

The moment at $x = 0$, $M_1(0) = 0$, from which $C_1 = 0$, and $M_1(x) = -8x$. *Part 2:* The shear is $V_2(x) = V_1(x) + 16 = 8$ kN. The moment is

$$M_2(x) = \int V_2(x)\,dx + C_2 = 8x + C_2.$$

The moment is continuous at $x = 2$, $M_1(2) = M_2(2)$, from which $C_2 = -32$, and the moment is $M_2(x) = 8x - 32$ kN m. Thus at point A, $x = 3$, the internal forces and bending moment are

$$V_2(3) = 8 \text{ kN},$$

$$P(3) = 0,$$

$$M_2(3) = 24 - 32 = -8 \text{ kN m}$$

Problem 10.111   Draw the shear force and bending moment diagrams of beam BC in Problem 10.110.

Solution: From the solution to Problem 10.110, the shear force and bending moment are:

(1) $V_1(x) = -8$ kN, $M_1(x) = -8x$ kN m, $(0 \leq x < 2$ m),
(2) $V_2(x) = 8$ kN, $M_2(x) = 8x - 32$ kN m, $(2 \leq x < 4$ m)

The shear force and bending moment diagrams are shown.

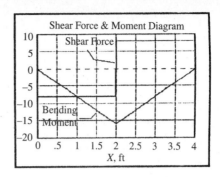

Problem 10.112   Determine the internal forces and moments at B (a) if $x = 250$ mm; (b) if $x = 750$ mm.

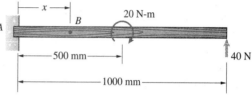

Solution: *The complete beam:* The sum of the moments about A is

$$\sum M_A = M_A - 20 + 1(40) = 0,$$

from which $M_A = -20$ N m. The sum of the forces:

$$\sum F_y = A_y + 40 = 0,$$

from which $A_y = -40$ N.

$$\sum F_x = A_x = 0$$

The internal forces at $x = 250$ mm. The shear is $V_1(x) = -40$ N. The moment is

$$M_1(x) = \int V_1(x)\, dx + C_1 = -40x + C_1$$

At $x = 0$, $M_1(0) = -M_A = 20$ N m, from which $C_1 = 20$ kN. Thus the moment is $M(0.25) = -40(0.25) + 20 = 10$ Nm. *The internal forces at* $x = 750$ mm. Divide the beam into two segments:

$$0 \leq x < 0.5 \text{ (m)},$$

and $0.5 \leq x < 0.75$ (m).

The shear in the second segment is $V_2(x) = -40$ N. The moment is

$$M_2(x) = \int V_2(x)\, dx + C_2 = -40x + C_2.$$

A known discontinuity exists in the moment at $x = 0.5$ m, $M_1(0.5) - M_2(0.5) = -20$ N m, from which $C_2 = 40$ and the moment is $M_2(x) = -40x + 40$ Nm. At $x = 0.75$, $M_2(0.75) = -40(0.75) + 40 = 10$ N m. The axial forces $P(x) = 0$ everywhere.

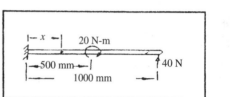

Problem 10.113 Draw the shear force and bending moment diagrams for the beam in Problem 10.112.

Solution: From the solution to Problem 10.112, the shear and bending moment are

$$V_1(x) = -40 \text{ N},$$

$$M_1(x) = -40x + 20 \text{ Nm } (0 \le x < 0.5 \text{ m}),$$

and $V_2(x) = -40 \text{ N},$

$$M_2(x) = -40x + 40 \text{ Nm}, \quad (0.5 \le x < 1 \text{ m})$$

The shear force and bending moment diagrams are shown.

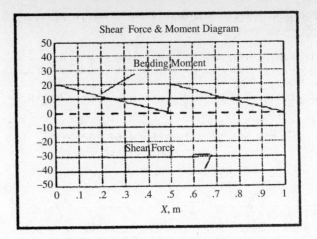

Problem 10.114 The homogenous beam weighs 1000 lb. What are the internal forces and bending moments at its midpoint?

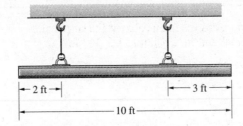

Solution: Denote the support reactions by A and B. The load distribution is $w = 1000/10 = 100$ lb/ft. The moment about the left end due to the load of the beam is

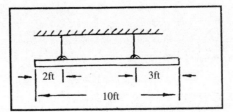

$$M_L = \int_0^{10} wx \, dx = 100 \left[\frac{x^2}{2} \right]_0^{10} = 5000 \text{ ft lb}.$$

The sum of the moments about the left end is

$$\sum M = -M_L + 2A + 7B = 0$$

The sum of the forces:

$$\sum F_y = A + B - 1000 = 0.$$

Solve the two simultaneous equations to obtain: $A = 400$ lb, $B = 600$ lb.

$$\sum F_x = 0.$$

Divide the left half of the beam into two parts: $0 \le x < 2$ (ft) and $2 \le x < 5$ (ft).

Part 1: The shear is $V_1(x) = -100x$. The moment is

$$M_1(x) = \int V_1(x) \, dx + C_1 = -50x^2 + C_1.$$

At $x = 0$, $M_1(0) = 0$, thus $C_1 = 0$, and the moment is $M_1(x) = -50x^2$.

Part 2: The shear is $V_2(x) = V_1(x) + 400$ lb. The moment is

$$M_2(x) = \int V_2(x) \, dx + C_2 = -50x^2 + 400x + C_2.$$

The moment is continuous at $x = 2$, $M_1(2) = M_2(2)$, from which $C_2 = -800$, and the moment is $M_2(x) = -50x^2 + 400x - 800$. At the midpoint, $x = 5$ ft, the shear is $V_2(5) = -100(5) + 400 = -100$ lb and the moment is $M_2(5) = -50(25) + 400(5) - 800 = -50$ ft lb. The axial force is zero, $P(5) = 0$

Problem 10.115 Draw the shear force and bending moment diagrams for the beam in Problem 10.114.

Solution: From the solution for Problem 10.114, the shear force and bending moment are:

(1) $V_1(x) = -100x$ lb, $M_1(x) = -50x^2$ ft lb, $(0 \le x < 2$ ft$)$.
(2) $V_2(x) = -100x + 400$ lb, $M_2(x) = -50x^2 + 400x - 800$ ft lb, $(2 \le x < 7$ ft$)$.
(3) $V_3(x) - 100x + 1000$ lb, $M_3(x) = -50x^2 + 1000x - 5000$ ft lb, $(7 \le x < 10$ ft$)$.

The shear force and bending moment diagrams are shown.

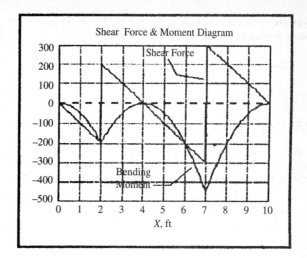

Problem 10.116 At A the main cable of the suspension bridge is horizontal and its tension is 1×10^8 lb.

(a) Determine the distributed load acting on the cable.
(b) What is the tension at B?

Solution: (a) The parameter

$$a = 2\frac{y}{x^2} = 2\frac{300}{900} = 7.4074 \times 10^{-4}.$$

The distributed load is

$$w = T_0 a = (1 \times 10^8)(7.4 \times 10^{-4}) = 7.4074 \times 10^4 \text{ lb/ft}$$

(b) The tension at B is

$$T_B = T_0 \sqrt{1 + a^2(900)^2} = 1.2 \times 10^8 \text{ lb}$$

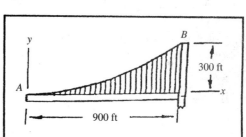

Problem 10.117 The power line has a mass of 1.4 kg/m. If the line will safely support a tension of 5 kN, determine whether it will safely support an ice accumulation of 4 kg/m.

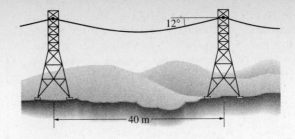

Solution: The power line meets the conditions for a catenary. The weight density with an ice load is

$$\gamma = (1.4 + 4)(9.81) = 52.974 \text{ N/m}.$$

The angle at the attachment point is related to the length and the parameter a by $sa = \tan\theta$. But $sa = \sinh(ax)$, and x is known. Thus the parameter can be found from

$$a = \frac{\sinh^{-1}(\tan\theta)}{x} = \frac{\sinh^{-1}(0.2126)}{20} = 0.01055.$$

The tension at the lowest point is

$$T_0 = \frac{w}{a} = 5021.53 = 5.02 \text{ kN}.$$

The maximum tension is

$$T = T_0 \cosh(ax) = 5133.7 = 5.133 \text{ kN}.$$

Thus the line will not sustain the load.

Problem 10.118 The water depth at the center of the elliptical aquarium window is 20 ft. Determine the magnitude of the net force exerted on the window by the pressure of the seawater ($\gamma = 64 \text{ lb/ft}^3$) and the atmospheric pressure of the air on the opposite side. (See Problem 10.99.)

Solution: The force on the plate is

$$F = \int_A p \, dA.$$

The pressure is $p = p_0 + \gamma x - p_0 = \gamma x$, where the atmospheric pressure cancels, since it appears on both sides. The force:

$$F = \gamma \int_A x \, dA = \gamma \bar{x} A,$$

hence the force on the window is $F = 1280A$ lb. The area of the ellipse is $A = \pi ab = 21\pi$, and the force is $F = 84445$ lb

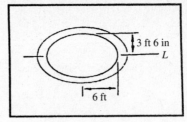

Problem 10.119 In Problem 10.118, determine the magnitude of the net moment exerted on the window about the horizontal axis L by the pressure of the seawater ($\gamma = 64$ lb/ft^3) and the atmospheric pressure of the air on the opposite side. (See Problem 10.99.)

Solution: The moment is

$$M = \int px\,dA = \gamma \int x^2\,dA = \gamma I_y.$$

The area moment of inertia for an ellipse is

$$I_y = \frac{\pi a b^3}{4} = 202 \text{ ft}^4,$$

and the moment is $M = \gamma I_y = 12930.8$ ft lb.

Problem 10.120 The gate has water of 2-m depth on one side. The width of the gate (the dimension into the paper) is 4 m, and its mass is 160 kg. The mass density of the water is $\rho = 1000$ kg/m^3 and atmospheric pressure is $p_{atm} = 10^5$ Pa. Determine the reactions on the gate at A and B. (The support B exerts only a horizontal reaction on the gate.)

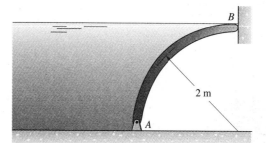

Solution: Consider the free-body diagram shown. The weight of the gate is

$$W = (160)(9.81) = 1570 \text{ N},$$

and $x_2 = R - \dfrac{2R}{\pi} = 0.727$ m.

The pressure force

$$F = \tfrac{1}{2}(\gamma R)R(4)$$

$$= \tfrac{1}{2}(1000)(9.81)(2)^2(4)$$

$$= 78{,}480 \text{ N},$$

and $y = \tfrac{1}{3}R = 0.667$ m.

The area below the gate is

$$A_b = \tfrac{1}{4}\pi R^2 = 3.142 \text{ m}^2,$$

and the centroid of A_b is at

$$x_b = R - \frac{4R}{3\pi} = 1.151 \text{ m}.$$

The area above the gate is

$$A_a = R^2 - A_b = 0.858 \text{ m}^2.$$

The centroid of $A_a \cup A_b$ is at $x = R/2$, so

$$\frac{R}{2} = \frac{x_1 A_a + x_b A_b}{A_a + A_b},$$

from which we obtain $x_1 = 0.447$ m.

The weight of the water is $Q = \gamma A_a(4) = 33{,}700$ N.

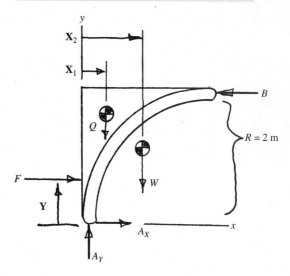

From the equilibrium equations

$$\sum F_x = F + A_x - B = 0,$$

$$\sum F_y = A_y - W - Q = 0,$$

$$\sum M_{(ptA)} = RB - yF - x_1 Q - x_2 W = 0,$$

we obtain

$$A_x = -44.2 \text{ kN},$$

$$A_y = 35.3 \text{ kN},$$

$$B = 34.3 \text{ kN}.$$

Problem 10.121 The dam has water of depth 4 ft on one side. The width of the dam (the dimension into the page) is 8 ft. The weight density of the water is $\gamma = 62.4$ lb/ft^3, and atmospheric pressure is $p_{atm} = 2120$ lb/ft^2. If you neglect the weight of the dam, what are the reactions at A and B?

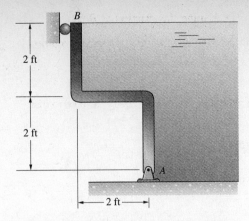

Solution: The atmospheric pressure acts on both faces of the dam, so it is ignored. The strategy is to use the "volume" of the pressure distribution to the determine the reactions. The pressure distribution is a triangle of base 4γ and altitude 4 ft. The force on the vertical faces of the dam is

$$F_1 = \left(\tfrac{1}{2}\right)(4)(4)(\gamma)8 = 3993.6 \text{ lb.}$$

The moment about A due to the force on the vertical faces is

$$M_1 = \left(\tfrac{4}{3}\right)F_1 = 5324.8 \text{ ft lb.}$$

The force on the horizontal face of the dam is

$$F_2 = (2)(\gamma)(2)(8) = 1996.8 \text{ lb.}$$

The moment about A due to the force on the horizontal face is $M_2 = 1F_2 = 1996.8$ ft lb. The sum of the moments about A: $\sum M_A = M_1 + M_2 - 4B = 0$, from which $B = 1830.4$ lb. The sum of the forces: $\sum F_x = A_x - F_1 + B = 0$, from which $A_x = 2163.3$ lb to the right. $\sum F_y = A_y - F_2 = 0$, from which $A_y = 1996.8$ lb upward.

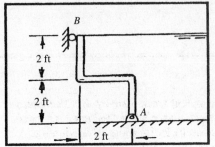

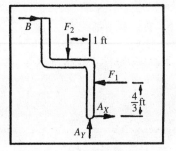

Problem 11.1   Determine the reaction at B.

Strategy: Subject the beam to a virtual rotation about A.

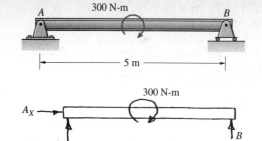

300 N-m

Solution: The virtual work done as the result of a virtual rotation $\delta\theta$ about A is

$$\delta U = -300\delta\theta + B(5\delta\theta) = 0,$$

so $B = \dfrac{300}{5} = 60$ N.

Problem 11.2

(a) Determine the virtual work done by the 2-kN force and the 2.4 kN-m couple when the beam is rotated through a counterclockwise angle $\delta\theta$ about point A.

(b) Use the result of (a) to determine the reaction at B.

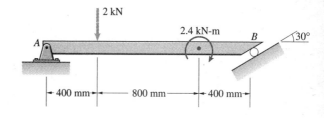

Solution:

(a) The virtual work done by the 2-kN force and the 2.4 kN-m couple is

$$\delta U = -2(0.4\delta\theta) - 2.4\delta\theta.$$

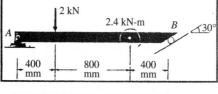

(b) The virtual work done by the reaction B is

$$\delta U = B\cos 30°(1.6\delta\theta),$$

so

$$-2(0.4\delta\theta) - 2.4\delta\theta + B\cos 30°(1.6\delta\theta) = 0.$$

Solving, $B = 2.31$ kN.

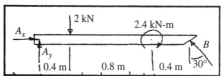

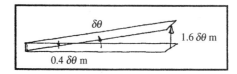

Problem 11.3   Determine the tension in the cable.

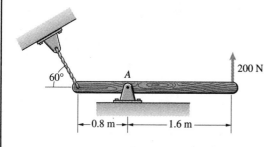

Solution: When the beam rotates through a counterclockwise angle $\delta\theta$, the virtual work is

$$\delta U = 200(1.6\delta\theta) - T\sin 60°(0.8\delta\theta) = 0,$$

so

$$T = \frac{(200)(1.6)}{0.8\sin 60°} = 462 \text{ N}.$$

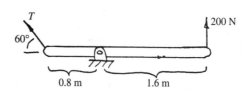

Problem 11.4 The L-shaped bar is in equilibrium. Determine F.

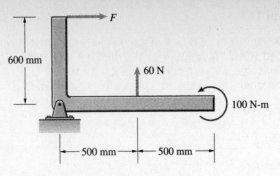

Solution: Perform a virtual rotation about the pinned support:

$$\delta U = (100\delta\theta + 0.5(60)\delta\theta - 0.6F\delta\theta) = 0,$$

from which $(100 + 60(0.5) - 0.6F)\delta\theta = 0$,

$$\text{or } F = \frac{100 + 0.5(60)}{0.6} = 216.7 \text{ N}$$

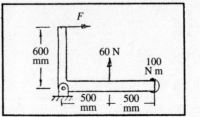

Problem 11.5 The dimension $L = 2$ m and $w_0 = 400$ N/m.

(a) Determine the virtual work done by the distributed load when the beam is rotated through a counterclockwise angle $\delta\theta$ about point A.

(b) Use the result of part (a) to determine the reaction at B.

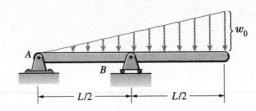

Strategy: To do part (a), remember that the force exerted by the distributed load on an element of the beam of length dx is $w\,dx$. You can calculate the virtual work done by the force $w\,dx$ and then integrate to obtain the virtual work done by the entire distributed load.

Solution:

(a) The distributed load is $w = \dfrac{w_o}{L}x$. The work done during a counterclockwise rotation $\delta\theta$ is

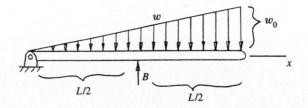

$$-\int_0^L (x\delta\theta)(w\,dx) = -\int_0^L x\frac{w_o}{L}x\,dx\delta\theta$$

$$= -\frac{w_o}{L}\left[\frac{x^3}{3}\right]_0^L \delta\theta$$

$$= -\frac{w_o L^2}{3}\delta\theta$$

$$= -\frac{(400)(2)^2}{3}\delta\theta$$

$$= -533\delta\theta \text{ N-m}.$$

(b) The total virtual work is $\delta U = (1)\delta\theta B - 533\delta\theta = 0$, so $B = 533$ N.

Problem 11.6

(a) Determine the virtual work done by the distributed load when the beam is rotated through a counter-clockwise angle $\delta\theta$ about point A.

(b) Determine the reactions at the built-in support A.

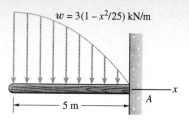

Solution:

(a) The moment arm about A is $5 - x$, so the virtual work is

$$\int_0^L (5 - x)\delta\theta w \, dx = \int_0^5 (5 - x)[3000(1 - x^2/25)] \, dx \delta\theta$$

$$= 31,250\delta\theta \text{ N-m}.$$

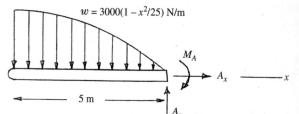

(b) $w = 3000(1 - x^2/25)$ N/m

Virtual translation δx:

$$\delta U = A_x \delta x = 0 \Rightarrow A_x = 0$$

Virtual translation δy:

The downward force due to the distributed load is

$$\int_0^L w \, dx = \int_0^5 3000(1 - x^2/25) \, dx = 10,000 \text{ N}.$$

$$\delta U \quad = A_y \delta y - 10,000 \delta y = 0$$

$$\Rightarrow A_y \quad = 10,000 \text{ N}.$$

Virtual rotation $\delta\theta$ about A:

$$\delta U \quad = -M_A \delta\theta + 31,250\delta\theta = 0$$

$$\Rightarrow M_A = 31,250 \text{ N-m}.$$

Problem 11.7
The mechanism is in equilibrium. Determine the force R in terms of F.

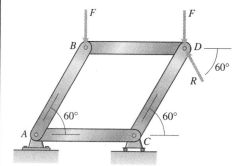

Solution: For brevity, define $\alpha = 60°$. Suppose that a virtual rotation of elements AB and CD occur: the virtual work is

$$\delta U = -L\cos\alpha F\delta\theta - (L + L\cos\alpha)F\delta\theta$$

$$+ R(L + L\cos\alpha)\sin\alpha\delta\theta + RL\sin\alpha\cos\alpha\delta\theta = 0,$$

from which

$$(-(1 + 2\cos\alpha)F + R\sin\alpha(1 + 2\cos\alpha))\delta\theta = 0,$$

or

$$R = \frac{F}{\sin\alpha} = 1.155F$$

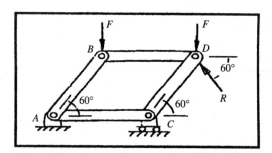

975

Problem 11.8 Determine the reaction at the roller support.

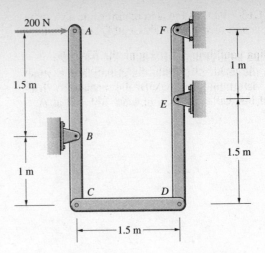

Solution: Assume that B and E remain fixed, and give bar ABC a clockwise virtual rotation $\delta\theta$:

Notice that (1) $\delta\theta = (1.5)\delta\beta$.

$\delta U = 200(1.5)(\delta\theta) - F(1)(\delta\beta) = 0$,

so

$$F = \frac{200(1.5)(\delta\theta)}{\delta\beta}$$

$$= 200(1.5)(1.5)$$

$$= 450 \text{ N}.$$

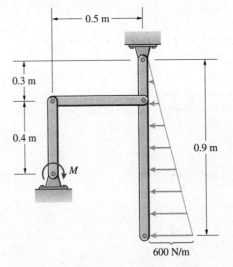

(1) $\delta\theta$ (1.5) $\delta\beta$

Problem 11.9 Determine the couple M necessary for the mechanism to be in equilibrium.

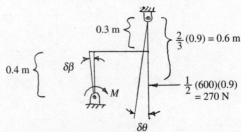

Solution: Notice that $(0.3)\delta\theta = (0.4)\delta\beta$.

$\delta U = 270(0.6\delta\theta) - M\delta\beta = 0$,

so

$$M = \frac{(270)(0.6)\delta\theta}{\delta\beta}$$

$$= \frac{(270)(0.6)(0.4)}{(0.3)}$$

$$= 216 \text{ N-m}.$$

Problem 11.10 The system is in equilibrium. The total mass of the suspended load and assembly A is 120 kg.

(a) By using equilibrium, determine the force F.
(b) Using the result of (a) and the principle of virtual work, determine the distance the suspended load rises if the cable is pulled upward 300 mm at B.

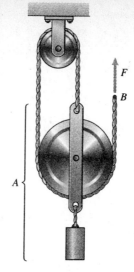

Solution: The weight of assembly and load is $W = 1177.2$ N.

(a) The sum of the forces is

$$\sum F_Y = F - W + 2R = 0,$$

where R is the tension in the cable. The tension in the cable is F if the pulleys have no bearing losses. Thus

$$F = \frac{W}{3} = 392.4 \text{ N}.$$

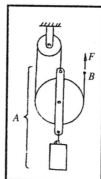

(b) Do a virtual translation of the assembly A in the vertical direction. The work done is $\delta U = -W\delta y + F\delta x = 0$, from which the ratio

$$\frac{\delta x}{\delta y} = \frac{W}{F}.$$

The ratio of translations of the assembly A and the point B is

$$\frac{300}{y_A} = \frac{W}{F} = 3,$$

using the result of Part (a) for F. The assembly A rises

$$y_A = \frac{300}{3} = 100 \text{ mm}$$

when point B is moved upward 300 mm.

Problem 11.11 Determine the force P necessary for the mechanism to be in equilibrium.

Solution: Denote axial forces in the left horizontal member by R_1 and the right horizontal member by R_2. Do a virtual rotation of the leftmost vertical member about the pin support:

$$\delta U = (400F - 800R_1)\delta\theta = 0,$$

from which

$$R_1 = \frac{F}{2}.$$

Do a virtual rotation of the middle vertical member about the pin support:

$$\delta U = (-200R_1 - M + 1000R_2)\delta\theta = 0,$$

from which

$$R_2 = \frac{M + 200R_1}{1000} = \frac{M + 100F}{1000}.$$

Do a virtual rotation of the right vertical member about the pin support:

$$\delta U = (+400P - 600R_2)\delta\theta = 0,$$

from which

$$P = \frac{3}{2}R_2 = \left(\frac{3}{2}\right)\frac{M + 100F}{1000} = \frac{3M}{2000} + \frac{3F}{20}.$$

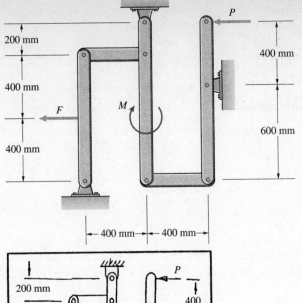

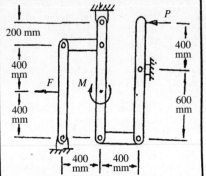

Problem 11.12 The system is in equilibrium, the weights of the bars are negligible, and the angle $\alpha = 20°$. Determine the magnitude of the friction force exerted on the bar at A.

Solution: The free body diagram is as shown. From the geometry, the horizontal position of the pt where F is applied is $x = L\sin\alpha$. Taking the differential of this expression,

$$\delta x = L\cos\alpha\,\delta\alpha.$$

The horizontal position of A is $x_A = 2L\sin\alpha$, so

$$\delta x_A = 2L\cos\alpha\,\delta\alpha.$$

If α is increased by $\delta\alpha$, the virtual work is

$$\delta u = F\delta x - f\,\delta x_A$$

$$= FL\cos\alpha\,\delta\alpha - f2L\cos\alpha\,\delta\alpha = 0,$$

$$f = \tfrac{1}{2}F.$$

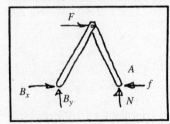

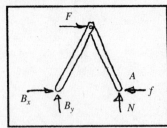

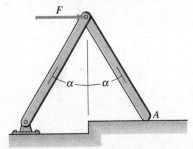

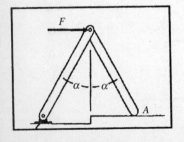

Problem 11.13 Determine the magnitude of the force exerted on the wall by the block at A.

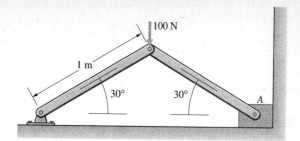

Solution:

$$x^2 + y^2 = 1$$

$$2x\,dx + 2y\,dy = 0.$$

δy is a *decrease* in y, so

$$\delta x = dx,$$

$$\delta y = -dy,$$

and $\delta y = \dfrac{x}{y}$

$$\delta x = \frac{1}{\tan 30°}\delta x.$$

$$\delta U = 100\delta y - F(2\delta x),$$

so

$$F = \frac{100\delta y}{2\delta x}$$

$$= \frac{100}{2\tan 30°}$$

$$= 86.6 \text{ N}.$$

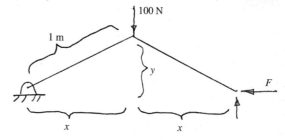

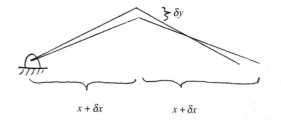

Problem 11.14 Show that δx is related to $\delta\alpha$ by

$$\delta x = \frac{L_1 x \sin\alpha}{x - L_1 \cos\alpha}\delta\alpha.$$

Strategy: Write the law of cosines in terms of α and take the derivative of the resulting equation with respect to α. (See Example 11.2)

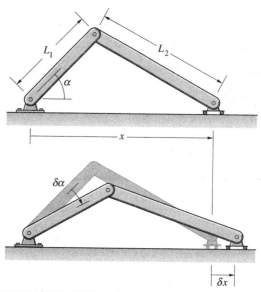

Solution: Denote the horizontal distance from the pin support to the roller support by x. The law of cosines:

$$L_2^2 = x^2 + L_1^2 - 2xL_1 \cos\alpha,$$

from which

$$x^2 - 2xL_1 \cos\alpha + (L_1^2 - L_2^2) = 0.$$

Take the variation with respect to x and, α,

$$dx(2x - 2L_1 \cos\alpha) + 2xL_1 \sin\alpha\,d\alpha = 0,$$

from which

$$dx = -\frac{L_1 x \sin\alpha}{x - L_1 \cos\alpha}d\alpha.$$

The negative sign for the differential indicates that as α increases, x decreases, as expected. However, the virtual rotation $\delta\alpha$ is a decrease in α, (See Example 11.1) so that the virtual rotation has the opposite sign to the variation,

$$\delta x = \frac{L_1 x \sin\alpha}{x - L_1 \cos\alpha}\delta\alpha$$

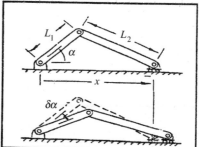

Problem 11.15 The linkage is in equilibrium. What is the force F?

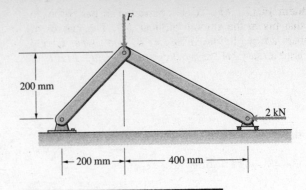

Solution: Use the result of the solution to Problem 11.14. Perform a virtual rotation about the pin support of the left member. The virtual work is $\delta U = 200F\delta\alpha - 2\delta x = 0$, from which

$$F = \frac{1}{100}\frac{\delta x}{\delta\alpha}.$$

Use the result obtained in Problem 11.14,

$$F = \frac{1}{100}\left(\frac{xL_1\sin\alpha}{x - L_1\cos\alpha}\right).$$

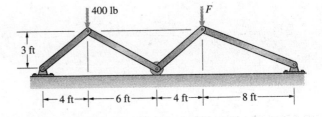

From the dimensions given: $L_1 = \sqrt{200^2 + 200^2} = \sqrt{2}(200)$ mm, and $x = 600$ mm and the interior angle is $\alpha = 45°$. From which $F = 3$ kN

Problem 11.16 The linkage is in equilibrium. What is the force F?

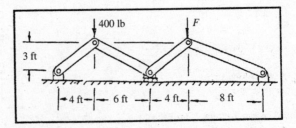

Solution: Denote the horizontal reaction at the roller support by R_H. Perform a virtual rotation about the left pinned support: $\delta U = 400(4)\delta\alpha - R_H\delta x$, from which

$$R_H = 1600\frac{\delta\alpha}{\delta x}.$$

Use the result of the solution to Problem 11.14,

$$R_H = 1600\left(\frac{x - L_1\cos\alpha}{xL_1\sin\alpha}\right).$$

From the dimensions given, $L_1 = \sqrt{3^2 + 4^2} = 5$ ft, $x = 10$ ft, and the interior angle is

$$\alpha = \tan^{-1}\left(\frac{3}{4}\right) = 36.9°,$$

from which $R_H = 320$ lb. Perform a virtual rotation about the right pin support: $\delta U = +8F\delta\theta - R_H\delta x = 0$, from which

$$F = \frac{R_H}{8}\frac{\delta x}{\delta\theta}.$$

Use the result from Problem 11.14:

$$F = \frac{R_H}{8}\left(\frac{xL_1\sin\theta}{x - L_1\cos\theta}\right).$$

From the dimensions given,

$$L_1 = \sqrt{8^2 + 3^2} = 8.54 \text{ ft},$$

$$x = 12 \text{ ft},$$

and $\theta = \tan^{-1}\left(\frac{3}{8}\right) = 20.56°.$

From which the force is $F = 360$ lb

Problem 11.17 Bar AC is connected to bar BD by a pin that fits in the smooth vertical slot. The masses of the bars are negligible. If $M_A = 30$ N-m, what couple M_B is necessary for the system to be in equilibrium?

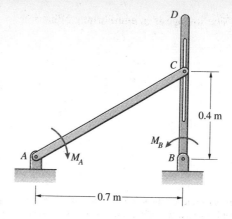

Solution:

$$x^2 + y^2 = L^2 = (0.7)^2 + (0.4)^2.$$

$$2x\,dx + 2y\,dy = 0.$$

The δy shown is a *decrease* in y, so

$$\delta x = dx,$$

$$\delta y = -dy$$

and $\delta y = \dfrac{x}{y}\delta x = \dfrac{0.7}{0.4}\delta x.$

$$\delta\beta = \frac{\delta x}{y} = \frac{1}{0.4}\delta x. \qquad (1)$$

$$\delta\theta = \frac{\sqrt{\delta x^2 + \delta y^2}}{L} = \frac{1}{L}\sqrt{1 + \left(\frac{\delta y}{\delta x}\right)^2}\,\delta x$$

$$= \frac{1}{\sqrt{(0.7)^2 + (0.4)^2}}\sqrt{1 + \left(\frac{0.7}{0.4}\right)^2}\,\delta x. \qquad (2)$$

The virtual work is

$$\delta U = M_A\delta\theta - M_B\delta\beta = 0.$$

Substituting Eqs. (1) and (2), we obtain

$$(M_A - M_B)\delta x = 0,$$

so $M_A = M_B = 30$ N-m.

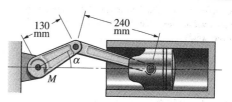

Problem 11.18 The angle $\alpha = 20°$, and the force exerted on the stationary piston by pressure is 4 kN toward the left. What couple M is necessary to keep the system in equilibrium?

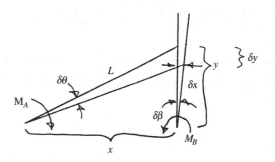

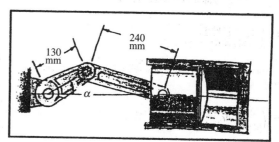

Solution: Perform a virtual rotation of the crank: $\delta U = M\delta\alpha + F\delta x = 0$, from which

$$M = F\frac{\delta x}{\delta\alpha}.$$

Use the results of the solution to Problem 11.14,

$$M = F\left(\frac{xL_1\sin\alpha}{x - L_1\cos\alpha}\right).$$

From the dimensions given, $L_1 = 130$ mm, and from the cosine law, $240^2 = x^2 + 130^2 - 2(x)(130)\cos\alpha$, from which $x^2 - 2(122.16)x - 40700 = 0$, which has the solutions $x = 358$, -113.7 mm. Since a negative x has no meaning here, $x = 358$ mm. Substituting and reducing:

$$M = 269.97 = 270 \text{ kN}$$

$mm = 270$ N m

Problem 11.19 The structure is subjected to a 400-N load and is held in place by a horizontal cable. Determine the tension in the cable.

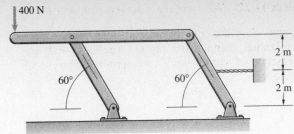

Solution: Perform a virtual rotation about the pin supports. The load can only move vertically, since the structure is a parallelogram. In virtual motion, the point of attachment of the cable will move horizontally. The virtual work is $\delta U = F\delta y - T\delta x = 0$, from which

$$T = F\frac{\delta y}{\delta x}.$$

Note that for a virtual rotation,

$$\frac{\delta y}{\delta \alpha} = L\cos\alpha,$$

and $\dfrac{\delta x}{\delta \alpha} = \dfrac{L}{2}\sin\alpha$,

where L is the length of a pin supported member. Thus

$$\frac{\delta y}{\delta x} = \frac{2}{\tan\alpha},$$

and

$$T = F\left(\frac{2}{\tan\alpha}\right) = 400\left(\frac{2}{1.732}\right) = 461.88 = 462 \text{ N}$$

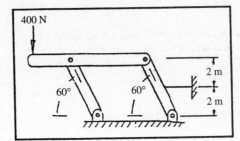

Problem 11.20 If the car jack is subjected to a force $F = 6.5$ kN, what is the tension in the threaded shaft between B and D?

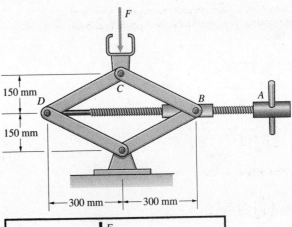

Solution: Denote the tension in BD by T. Perform a virtual closing of the distance BD. The virtual work is

$$\delta U = -F\delta y + T\delta x = 0,$$

from which

$$T = F\frac{\delta y}{\delta x}.$$

Half of the interior angle CDB is

$$\alpha = \tan^{-1}\left(\frac{150}{300}\right) = 26.56°.$$

The vertical motion is $\delta y = L\cos\alpha\delta\alpha$, where L is the length of member DC. The horizontal motion is $\delta x = L\sin\alpha\delta\alpha$, from which

$$\frac{\delta y}{\delta x} = \frac{1}{\tan\alpha}.$$

The tension is

$$T = \frac{F}{\tan\alpha} = \frac{6.5}{0.5} = 13 \text{ kN}$$

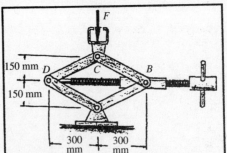

Problem 11.21 What are the reactions at A and B?

Strategy: Use the equilibrium equations to determine the horizontal components of the reactions, and use the principle of virtual work to determine the vertical components.

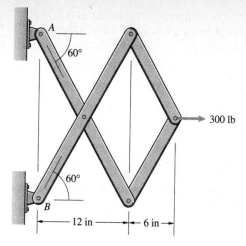

300 lb

12 in — 6 in

Solution: Denote the angle $\alpha = 60°$ and the distance AC by L. The sum of the moments about A is

$$\sum M_A = \left(\frac{12}{2\tan\alpha}\right)(300) + \left(\frac{12}{\tan\alpha}\right)B_x = 0,$$

from which $B_x = -150$ lb. The sum of the forces:

$$\sum F_x = A_x + B_x + 300 = 0,$$

from which $A_x = -B_x - 300 = -150$ lb. The sum of the forces in the vertical direction is

$$\sum F_y = A_y + B_y = 0,$$

from which $A_y = -B_y$. Denote the distance between A and B by y and the distance from the wall to the point of application of the force as x. Then

$$x = \left(\frac{3}{2}\right)\sqrt{L^2 - y^2}.$$

Take the variation of both sides,

$$\delta x = \left(\frac{3}{2}\right)\frac{-y\delta y}{\sqrt{L^2 - y^2}} = \left(\frac{1}{8}\right)(-y\delta y),$$

$y = 12\tan\alpha$, from which

$$\frac{\delta x}{\delta y} = -\left(\frac{1}{8}\right)(12\tan\alpha).$$

Perform a virtual elongation of the mechanism in the x-direction. The virtual work is

$$\delta U = 300\delta x - A_y\frac{\delta y}{2} + B_y\frac{\delta y}{2} = 0,$$

from which

$$\left(\frac{1}{2}\right)(A_y - B_y) = 300\frac{\delta x}{\delta y} = A_y.$$

The vertical reaction is

$$A_y = \left(\frac{3}{2}\right)300\tan\alpha = 779.4 \text{ lb},$$

and $B_y = -A_y = -779.4$ lb

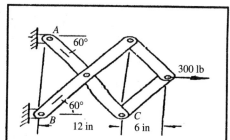

Problem 11.22 This device raises a load W by extending the hydraulic actuator DE. The bars AD and BC are each 2 m long, and the distances $b = 1.4$ m and $h = 0.8$ m. If $W = 4$ kN, what force must the actuator exert to hold the load in equilibrium?

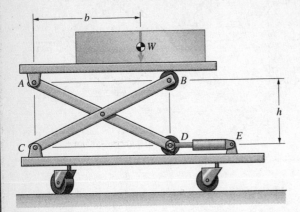

Solution: Perform a virtual vertical displacement of the load. Denote the distance CD by x. The virtual work is $\delta U = -W\delta h + D\delta x = 0$, from which

$$D = W\frac{\delta h}{\delta x}.$$

The distances are related: $h = \sqrt{L^2 - x^2}$, where L is the length of bar BC, from which

$$\frac{\delta h}{\delta x} = -\frac{x}{\sqrt{L^2 - x^2}} = -\frac{x}{h}.$$

Thus

$$D = -W\frac{x}{h} = -W\frac{\sqrt{L^2 - h^2}}{h}.$$

Substitute numerical values:

$$D = -4\frac{\sqrt{4 - 0.8^2}}{0.8} = -9.165 = -9.17 \text{ kN,}$$

where the negative sign implies that the force is directed parallel to the negative x-axis.

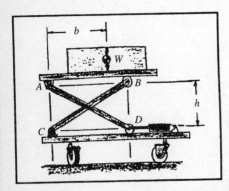

Problem 11.23 Determine the force P necessary for the mechanism to be in equilibrium.

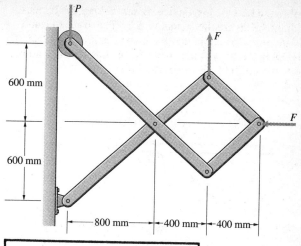

Solution: The height of pt. C is

$$y_c = 2L_{AB}\sin\theta.$$

From

$$\frac{dy_c}{d\theta} = 2L_{AB}\cos\theta,$$

we obtain

$$\delta y_c = 2L_{AB}\cos\theta\delta\theta.$$

The height of pt. D is

$$y_D = L_{AD}\sin\theta.$$

From

$$\frac{dy_D}{d\theta} = L_{AD}\cos\theta,$$

we obtain

$$\delta y_D = L_{AD}\cos\theta\delta\theta.$$

The horizontal position of pt E is

$$x_E = (L_{AB} + 2L_{BD})\cos\theta.$$

From

$$\frac{dx_E}{d\theta} = -(L_{AB} + 2L_{BD})\sin\theta,$$

we see that

$$\delta x_E = -(L_{AB} + 2L_{BD})\sin\theta\delta\theta.$$

The virtual work resulting from a virtual rotation $\delta\theta$ is

$$\delta U = -P\delta y_c + F\delta y_D - F\delta x_E$$

$$= -P(2L_{AB}\cos\theta\delta\theta)$$

$$\quad + F(L_{AD}\cos\theta\delta\theta)$$

$$\quad + F(L_{AB} + 2L_{BD})\sin\theta\delta\theta = 0.$$

Solving,

$$P = \frac{[L_{AD}\cos\theta + (L_{AB} + 2L_{BD})\sin\theta]F}{2L_{AB}\cos\theta}.$$

Substituting the lengths and $\theta = \arctan(600/800)$, we obtain

$$P = 1.5\,F.$$

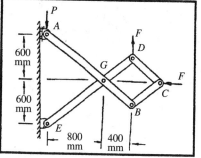

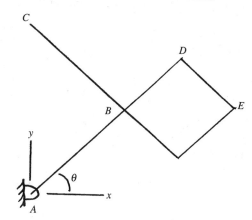

985

Problem 11.24 The collar A weighs 100 lb, and friction is negligible. Determine the tension in cable AB.

Strategy: Let s be the distance along the bar from C to the collar, and let $\mathbf{e}_{CD}$ be a unit vector that points from C toward D. To apply the principle of virtual work, let the collar undergo a virtual displacement $\delta s\mathbf{e}_{CD}$.

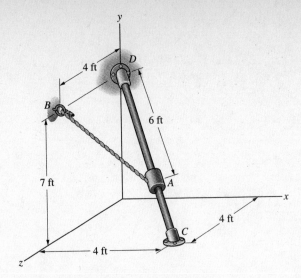

Solution: The position vector from C to D is

$$\mathbf{r}_{CD} = -4\mathbf{i} + 7\mathbf{j} - 4\mathbf{k} \text{ (ft)},$$

so

$$\mathbf{e}_{CD} = \frac{\mathbf{r}_{CD}}{|\mathbf{r}_{CD}|} = -\frac{4}{9}\mathbf{i} + \frac{7}{9}\mathbf{j} - \frac{4}{9}\mathbf{k}.$$

To obtain the coordinates of pt. A, w add the vector from the origin to pt. C and the vector from C to A:

$$4\mathbf{i} + 4\mathbf{k} + (L_{CD} - 6)\mathbf{e}_{CD} = 2.67\mathbf{i} + 2.33\mathbf{j} + 2.67\mathbf{k} \text{ (ft)}.$$

The position vector from A to B is therefore

$$\mathbf{r}_{AB} = -2.67\mathbf{i} + (7 - 2.33)\mathbf{j} + (4 - 2.67)\mathbf{k} \text{ (ft)}$$

and we can write the force $\mathbf{T}$ exerted on the collar by the cable as

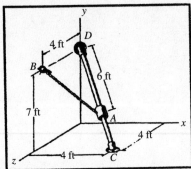

$$\mathbf{T} = T\frac{\mathbf{r}_{AB}}{|\mathbf{r}_{AB}|} = T(-0.482\mathbf{i} + 0.843\mathbf{j} + 0.241\mathbf{k}).$$

Letting the collar undergo a virtual displacement $\delta s\mathbf{e}_{CD}$, the virtual work is (see free-body diagram)

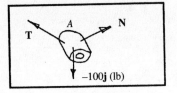

$$\delta U = \delta s\mathbf{e}_{CD} \cdot (\mathbf{T} + \mathbf{N} - 100\mathbf{j}) = 0.$$

But $\mathbf{e}_{CD} \cdot \mathbf{N} = 0$ because $\mathbf{e}_{CD}$ and $\mathbf{N}$ are perpendicular. So we obtain

$$\mathbf{e}_{CD} \cdot (\mathbf{T} - 100\mathbf{j}) = \left(-\frac{4}{9}\right)(-0.482T)$$

$$+ \left(\frac{7}{9}\right)(0.843T - 100) + \left(-\frac{4}{9}\right)(0.241T) = 0.$$

Solving, we obtain $T = 102$ lb.

Problem 11.25 The potential energy of a conservative system is given by $V = 2x^3 + 3x^2 - 12x$.

(a) For what values of x is the system in equilibrium?
(b) Determine whether the equilibrium positions you found in (a) are stable or unstable.

Solution:

(a) The system is in equilibrium when

$$\frac{dV}{dx} = 6x^2 + 6x - 12 = 0.$$

This is a quadratic equation in x: it is put into canonical form by dividing by 6, $x^2 + 2bx + c = 0$, from which

$$b = \tfrac{1}{2}$$

and $c = -2$. The solutions are

$$x = -b \pm \sqrt{b^2 - c} = 1, \quad = -2.$$

(b) The stable and unstable positions are determined by the sign of the second derivative:

$$\frac{d^2V}{d^2x} = 12x + 6.$$

For $x = 1$, $\left[\dfrac{d^2V}{d^2x}\right]_{x=1} = 18 > 0,$

and the equilibrium is stable at $x = 1$. For

$x = -2$, $\left[\dfrac{d^2V}{d^2x}\right]_{x=-2} = -18 < 0,$

and the equilibrium is unstable at $x = -2$.

Problem 11.26 The potential energy of a conservative system is given by $V = 2q^3 - 21q^2 + 72q$.

(a) For what values of q is the system in equilibrium?
(b) Determine whether the equilibrium positions you found in (a) are stable or unstable.

Solution:

(a) The equilibrium positions are given by

$$\frac{dV}{dx} = 6q^2 - 42q + 72 = 0.$$

In canonical form: $q^2 + 2bq + c = 0$, where

$$b = -\tfrac{7}{2},$$

and $c = 12$.

The solutions: $q = -b \pm \sqrt{b^2 - c} = 4, = 3$
(b) The second derivative is

$$\frac{d^2V}{dq^2} = 12q - 42.$$

For $q = 4$,

$$\left[\frac{d^2V}{dq^2}\right]_{q=4} = 6 > 0,$$

and *the equilibrium is stable*. For $q = 3$,

$$\left[\frac{d^2V}{dq^2}\right]_{q=3} = -6 < 0,$$

and the *equilibrium is unstable*.

Problem 11.27 The mass $m = 2$ kg and the spring constant $k = 100$ N/m. The spring is unstretched when $x = 0$.

(a) Determine the value of x for which the mass is in equilibrium.
(b) In the equilibrium position stable or unstable?

Solution:

(a) The potential energy is

$$V = \tfrac{1}{2}kx^2 - mgx.$$

Setting

$$\frac{dV}{dx} = kx - mg = 0,$$

we obtain

$$x = \frac{mg}{k} = \frac{(2)(9.81)}{100} = 0.196 \text{ m}.$$

(b) $\dfrac{d^2V}{dx^2} = k > 0$, so the equilibrium position is stable.

Problem 11.28 The *nonlinear* spring exerts a force $-kx + \varepsilon x^3$ on the mass, where k and ε are constants. Determine the potential energy V associated with the force exerted on the mass by the spring.

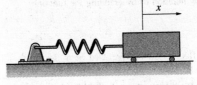

Solution: The potential energy of the spring is

$$V(x) = -\int (-kx + \varepsilon x^3)\,dx + C = \frac{1}{2}kx^2 - \frac{\varepsilon x^4}{4} + C.$$

Choose $x = 0$ as the datum point, $V(0) = 0$, hence $C = 0$, and the potential energy associated with the force is

$$V(x) = \frac{1}{2}kx^2 - \frac{\varepsilon x^4}{4}$$

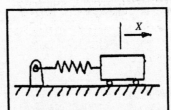

Problem 11.29 The 1-kg mass is suspended from the nonlinear spring described in Problem 11.28. The constants $k = 10$ and $\varepsilon = 1$, where x is in meters.

(a) Show that the mass is in equilibrium when $x = 1.12$ m and when $x = 2.45$ m.

(b) Determine whether the equilibrium positions are stable or unstable.

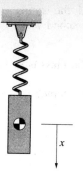

Solution: In Problem 11.28 the potential energy of the spring is shown to be

$$V(x) = \frac{1}{2}kx^2 - \frac{\varepsilon x^4}{4}.$$

The potential energy of the mass is

$$V(x) = -\int W\,dx = -Wx,$$

where the datum is $x = 0$. The total potential energy is

$$V_{\text{total}}(x) = -Wx + \frac{1}{2}kx^2 - \frac{\varepsilon x^4}{4}.$$

The equilibrium points are determined from

$$\frac{dV}{dx} = -W + kx - \varepsilon x^3 = 0.$$

This cubic may be solved by iteration or by graphing the function

$$f(x) = -W + kx - \varepsilon x^3$$

to find the zero crossings. Both methods were used here: the graph was used to get approximate values, and these values were then refined by iteration (using **TK Solver Plus**). The results: $x = 1.12$ m, and $x = 2.45$ m. (b) The second derivative of the potential energy at $x = 1.12$ m is

$$\left[\frac{d^2V}{dx^2}\right]_{x=1.12} = [10 - 3x^2]_{x=1.12} = 6.2 > 0,$$

and *the system is stable.* For $x = 2.45$ m,

$$\left[\frac{d^2V}{dx^2}\right]_{x=2.45} = [10 - 3x^2]_{x=2.45} = -7.98 < 0,$$

and *the system is unstable.*

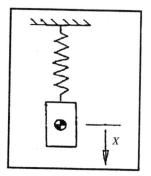

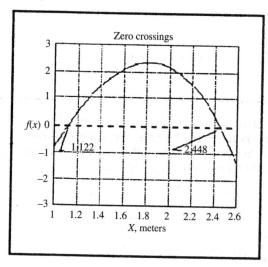

Problem 11.30 The two straight segments of the bar are each of weight W and length L. Determine whether the equilibrium position shown is stable if (a) $0 < \alpha_0 < 90°$; (b) $90° < \alpha_0 < 180°$.

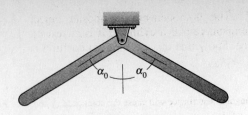

Solution: From a heuristic argument, if the bars hang straight down ($\alpha_0 = 0$) they are equivalent to one bar suspended at one end, and they should be stable in this position. If the bars are straight out ($\alpha_0 = 90°$) they are equivalent to a bar suspended at its midpoint, and as a balanced bar they should be neutrally stable. If the bars are positioned upward ($90° < \alpha_0 < 180°$), the bars will be unbalanced everywhere, and the system will be unstable in every position. This heuristic reasoning suggests the strategy to treat the composite bar as if it were a mass point suspended (supported) at the pin support. The mass point will be located at the center of weight of the composite. It will behave like a pendulum under the action of gravity.

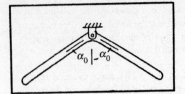

Choose a coordinate system with origin at the pin support with the x-axis positive downward. Denote the right and left bars by the subscripts R and L. The center of weight of each bar has the coordinates:

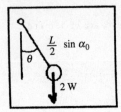

$$\mathbf{x}_R = \frac{L}{2} \cos \alpha_0,$$

$$\mathbf{y}_R = \frac{L}{2} \sin \alpha_0;$$

$$\mathbf{x}_L = \frac{L}{2} \cos \alpha_0,$$

$$\mathbf{y}_L = -\frac{L}{2} \sin \alpha_0.$$

The coordinates of the center of weight of the composite is

$$\mathbf{x} = \frac{W\mathbf{x}_R + W\mathbf{x}_L}{2W} = \frac{L}{2} \cos \alpha_0,$$

and $\mathbf{y} = \dfrac{W\mathbf{y}_R + W\mathbf{y}_L}{2W} = 0.$

Suppose that a small angular displacement θ occurs. The potential energy of the equivalent system under this displacement is

$$V = -(2W) \left(\frac{L}{2} \cos \alpha_0 \right) \cos \theta = -WL \cos \alpha_0 \cos \theta.$$

The equilibrium points are determined by

$$\frac{dV}{d\theta} = WL \cos \alpha_0 \sin \theta = 0,$$

from which $\theta = 0$, and $\theta = \pi$. The stability of the equilibrium points is determined from

$$\left[\frac{d^2 V}{d\theta^2} \right]_{\theta=0} = [WL \cos \alpha_0 \cos \theta]_{\theta=0} = WL \cos \alpha_0.$$

The stability depends upon the value of α_0: (a) in the interval $0 < \alpha_0 < 90°$, $WL \cos \alpha_0 > 0$, and *the system is stable.* (b) At the point $\alpha_0 = 0$, $WL > 0$, and *the system is stable.* (c) In the interval $90° < \alpha_0 < 180°$, $WL \cos \alpha_0 < 0$, and *the system is unstable.* If the *mechanical constraints permit the system to reach the equilibrium point at $\theta = \pi$, the results above are reversed: (a) is unstable, (b) is unstable, and (c) is stable.*

Problem 11.31 The homogeneous composite object consists of a hemisphere and a cylinder. It is at rest on the plane surface. Show that this equilibrium position is stable only if $L < R/\sqrt{2}$.

Solution: An angular disturbance will cause the composite system to rock about the radial center of the hemisphere. The change in potential energy, if it occurs, must be a change in the height of the composite mass caused by motion about the radial center. This suggests the pendulum analogy: a point mass at the composite mass center, suspended (supported) from the radial center.

Choose a coordinate system with the y-axis along the axis of the cylinder, positive upward, the x-axis parallel to the floor, and the origin at the point of contact with the floor.

The center of mass of the cylinder is located on the axis of the cylinder at

$$y = \frac{L}{2} + R.$$

The center of mass of the hemisphere is located at

$$y = \frac{5R}{8}.$$

The mass of the cylinder is $m_{cyl} = \rho \pi R^2 L$, where ρ is the mass density in kg/m^3. The mass of the hemisphere is

$$\tfrac{2}{3}\pi \rho R^3.$$

The location of the mass centroid of the composite is

$$y = \frac{\pi \rho R^2 L \left(\frac{L}{2} + R\right) + \frac{2}{3}\pi \rho R^3 \left(\frac{5R}{8}\right)}{\pi \rho R^2 L + \left(\frac{2}{3}\right)\pi \rho R^3} = \frac{L\left(\frac{L}{2} + R\right) + \frac{5}{12}R^2}{L + \frac{2}{3}R}.$$

Suppose that the system is subjected to a small angular rotation about the point of contact with the floor. The length of the equivalent pendulum is $R - y$. The potential energy due to this rotation is $V = -(R - y)W \cos \theta$. The point of equilibrium is

$$\frac{dV}{d\theta} = (R - y)W \sin \theta = 0,$$

from which $\theta = 0$ is a point of equilibrium. The stability is determined by

$$\left[\frac{d^2 V}{d\theta^2}\right]_{\theta=0} = \left[(R - y)W \cos \theta\right]_{\theta=0} = (R - y)W.$$

Note that R and y are both positive numbers, from which, if $R > y$, the system is stable; if $R < y$, the system is unstable. Reduce algebraically:

$$R - y = R - \frac{\left(L\left(\frac{L}{2} + R\right) + \frac{5}{12}R^2\right)}{L + \frac{2}{3}R}$$

$$= \frac{RL + \frac{2}{3}R^2 - \frac{L^2}{2} - RL - \frac{5}{12}R^2}{L + \frac{2}{3}R} = \frac{\frac{3}{12}R^2 - \frac{L^2}{2}}{L + \frac{2}{3}R}.$$

Retain only the numerator, since the denominator must be positive always: The condition for stability is

$$\frac{3}{12}R^2 > \frac{L^2}{2}.$$

Take the positive square root:

$$R > \sqrt{2}L,$$

or $L < \dfrac{R}{\sqrt{2}}.$

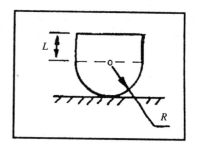

Problem 11.32 The homogenous composite object consists of a hemisphere and a cone. It is at rest on the plane surface. Show that this equilibrium position is stable only if $h < \sqrt{3}\,R$.

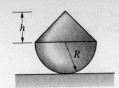
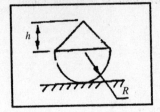

Solution: .Use the same strategy used to solve Problem 11.31: a point mass at the composite mass center, suspended (supported) at the radial center. Choose a coordinate system with the y-axis along the axis of the cone, positive upward, the x-axis parallel to the floor, and the origin at the point of contact with the floor. The mass of the cone is

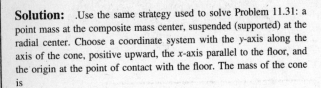

$$m_{cyl} = \tfrac{1}{3}\rho\pi R^2 h,$$

where ρ is the mass density. The center of mass of the cone is

$$y = \frac{h}{4} + R.$$

The mass of the hemisphere is

$$\tfrac{2}{3}\pi\rho R^3.$$

The center of mass of the hemisphere is located at $y = \dfrac{5R}{8}$.

The location of the mass centroid of the composite is

$$y = \frac{\pi\rho R^2 \dfrac{h}{3}\left(\dfrac{h}{4}+R\right) + \dfrac{2}{3}\pi\rho R^3\left(\dfrac{5R}{8}\right)}{\pi\rho R^2 \dfrac{h}{3} + \left(\dfrac{2}{3}\right)\pi\rho R^3} = \frac{\dfrac{h}{3}\left(\dfrac{h}{4}+R\right) + \dfrac{5}{12}R^2}{\dfrac{h}{3}+\dfrac{2}{3}R}.$$

For a small angular rotation θ the length of the equivalent pendulum is $R - \mathbf{y}$. The potential energy due to this rotation is $V = -(R - \mathbf{y})W\cos\theta$. The point of equilibrium is

$$\frac{dV}{d\theta} = (R - \mathbf{y})W\sin\theta = 0,$$

from which $\theta = 0$ is a point of equilibrium. The stability is determined by

$$\left[\frac{d^2 V}{d\theta^2}\right]_{\theta=0} = [(R - \mathbf{y})W\cos\theta]_{\theta=0} = (R - \mathbf{y})W,$$

from which, if $R > \mathbf{y}$, the system is stable; if $R < \mathbf{y}$, the system is unstable. Reduce:

$$R - \mathbf{y} = \frac{\dfrac{Rh}{3} + \dfrac{2}{3}R^2 - \dfrac{h^2}{12} - \dfrac{Rh}{3} - \dfrac{5}{12}R^2}{\dfrac{h}{3}+\dfrac{2}{3}R} = \frac{\dfrac{R^2}{4} - \dfrac{h^2}{12}}{\dfrac{h}{3}+\dfrac{2R}{3}},$$

from which, (since the denominator is always positive) if

$$\frac{R^2}{4} - \frac{h^2}{12} > 0,$$

the system is stable. Thus

$$R^2 > \frac{h^2}{3},$$

or, taking the positive square root: $\sqrt{3}R > h$

Problem 11.33 The homogenous bar has weight W, and the spring is unstretched when the bar is vertical ($\alpha = 0$).

(a) Use potential energy to show that the bar is in equilibrium when $\alpha = 0$.

(b) Show that the equilibrium position $\alpha = 0$ is stable only if $2kL > W$.

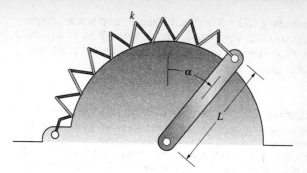

Solution:

(a) The potential energy of the spring is

$$V_{spring} = \int ks\,ds = \frac{1}{2}ks^2,$$

where the datum is $\alpha = 0$. Noting $s = L\alpha$, then

$$V_{spring} = \frac{k}{2}L^2\alpha^2.$$

The height of the center of the bar relative to the pinned end is

$$\frac{L}{2}\cos\alpha;$$

using the pinned end as the datum:

$$V_{bar} = \frac{WL}{2}\cos\alpha,$$

from which

$$V_{tot} = \frac{k}{2}L^2\alpha^2 + \frac{WL}{2}\cos\alpha.$$

The equilibrium point is

$$\frac{dV_{tot}}{d\alpha} = kL^2\alpha - \frac{WL}{2}\sin\alpha = 0,$$

from which

$$\frac{2kL}{W}\alpha - \sin\alpha = 0.$$

This is a transcendental equation in α, with at least one solution $\alpha = 0$.

(b) Stability is determined by

$$\left[\frac{d^2V_{tot}}{d\alpha^2}\right]_{\alpha=0} = \left[\frac{2kL}{W} - \cos\alpha\right]_{\alpha=0} = \frac{2kL}{W} - 1,$$

from which if

$$\frac{2kL}{W} - 1 > 0,$$

the system is stable. Thus the condition for stability at $\alpha = 0$ is
$2kL > W$

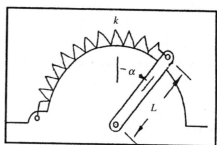

Problem 11.34 Suppose that the bar in Problem 11.33 is in equilibrium when $\alpha = 20°$.

(a) Show that the spring constant $k = 0.490 \dfrac{W}{L}$.

(b) Determine whether the equilibrium position is stable.

Solution: Use the results of the solution to Problem 11.33. The equilibrium condition is

$$\frac{2kL}{W}\alpha - \sin\alpha = 0,$$

from which, for $\alpha \neq 0$, divide by:

$$\frac{2kL}{W} = \frac{\sin\alpha}{\alpha},$$

or $k = \left(\dfrac{W}{L}\right)\dfrac{\sin\alpha}{2\alpha} = 0.490\left(\dfrac{W}{L}\right)$

(where α is in radians.) (b) The condition for stability is

$$\left[\frac{2kL}{W} - \cos\alpha\right]_{\alpha=20°} > 0,$$

from which $2(0.4899) - 0.9397 > 0$, which is satisfied. *The system is stable. Check:* From a heuristic argument, two sets of equilibrium conditions apply: If the spring force is weaker than the gravity force in the neighborhood of $\alpha = 0$, the bar should rotate under the action of gravity until this tendency is balanced by the increased spring force, at which point by analogy with the mass-spring system (see Problem 11.29) the system should be in stable equilibrium. If, however, the spring force is greater that the gravity force in the neighborhood of $\alpha = 0$, the system should remain close to $\alpha = 0$, which will be a position of stable equilibrium. This heuristic argument is supported as follows: (1) The equilibrium condition

$$\frac{2kL}{W}\alpha - \sin\alpha = 0,$$

for $\alpha \neq 0$, is satisfied if

$$\frac{2kL}{W} = \frac{\sin\alpha}{\alpha},$$

($0 < \alpha < 90°$), which is the first set of equilibrium conditions. The condition for stability is

$$\frac{\sin\alpha}{\alpha} - \cos\alpha > 0,$$

which is satisfied for all $0 < \alpha < 90°$, and the system is stable for $\alpha > 0$. Taking the limit as α goes to zero, the equilibrium position at $\alpha = 0$ is neutrally stable if

$$\frac{2kL}{W} = \frac{\sin\alpha}{\alpha}.$$

(2) If $2kL > W$, a second set of conditions apply: the $\alpha = 0$ position is stable (see Problem 11.33), and *this is the only equilibrium position* since

$$\frac{2kL}{W}\alpha - \sin\alpha = 0$$

has no solution except $\alpha = 0$ for

$$\frac{2kL}{W} > 1.$$

check.

Problem 11.35 The bar AB has mass m and length L. The spring is unstretched when the bar is vertical ($\alpha = 0$). The light collar C slides on the smooth vertical bar so that the spring remains horizontal. Show that the equilibrium position $\alpha = 0$ is stable only if $2kL > mg$.

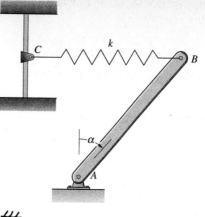

Solution: The potential energy is

$$V = \frac{1}{2}k(L\sin\alpha)^2 + mg\frac{L}{2}\cos\alpha,$$

so $\dfrac{dV}{d\alpha} = kL^2\sin\alpha\cos\alpha - mg\frac{L}{2}\sin\alpha$ **(1)**

and $\dfrac{d^2V}{d\alpha^2} = kL^2(\cos^2\alpha - \sin^2\alpha) - mg\frac{L}{2}\cos\alpha$

$$= kL^2(2\cos^2\alpha - 1) - mg\frac{L}{2}\cos\alpha. \quad \textbf{(2)}$$

Notice that $dV/d\alpha = 0$ at $\alpha = 0$. Substituting $\alpha = 0$ into Eq. (2) yields

$$\frac{d^2V}{d\alpha^2} = kL^2 - mg\frac{L}{2}.$$

Therefore

$$\frac{d^2V}{d\alpha^2} > 0$$

only if $2kL > mg$.

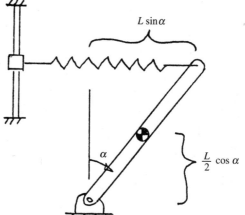

Problem 11.36 The bar AB in Problem 11.35 has mass $m = 4$ kg, length 2 m, and the spring constant is $k = 12$ N/m.

(a) Determine the value of α in the range $0 < \alpha < 90°$ for which the bar is in equilibrium.
(b) Is the equilibrium position determined in part (a) stable?

Solution:

(a) From Eq. (1) at the solution of Problem 11.35,

$$\frac{dV}{d\alpha} = \left(kL^2\cos\alpha - mg\frac{L}{2}\right)\sin\alpha.$$

Setting

$$kL^2\cos\alpha - mg\frac{L}{2} = 0,$$

we obtain

$$\alpha = \arccos\left(\frac{mg}{2kL}\right)$$

$$= \arccos\left[\frac{(4)(9.81)}{2(12)(2)}\right]$$

$$= 35.2°.$$

(b) From Eq. (2) of the solution of Problem 11.35,

$$\frac{d^2V}{d\alpha^2} = kL^2(2\cos^2\alpha - 1) - mg\frac{L}{2}\cos\alpha.$$

Substituting $\alpha = 35.2°$,

$$\frac{d^2V}{d\alpha^2} = (12)(2)^2(2\cos^2 35.2° - 1)$$

$$- (4)(9.81)(1)\cos 35.2°$$

$$= -15.9 \text{ N-m}.$$

This equilibrium position is unstable.

Problem 11.37 The bar AB has weight W and length L. The spring is unstretched when the bar is vertical ($\alpha = 0$). The light collar C slides on the smooth horizontal bar so that the spring remains vertical. Show that the equilibrium position $\alpha = 0$ is unstable.

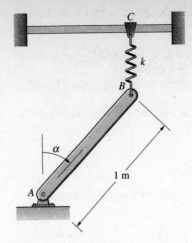

Solution: The potential energy of the spring is

$$V_{\text{spring}} = \int ks\,ds = \tfrac{1}{2}ks^2,$$

where the datum is $\alpha = 0$. Noting $s = L(1 - \cos\alpha)$, then

$$V_{\text{spring}} = \frac{k}{2}L^2(1 - \cos\alpha)^2.$$

The height of the center of the bar above the pin joint is

$$\frac{L}{2}\cos\alpha.$$

With the pin joint as the datum, the potential energy of the bar is

$$V_{\text{bar}} = \frac{WL}{2}\cos\alpha,$$

from which $V_{\text{tot}} = \dfrac{k}{2}L^2(1 - \cos\alpha)^2 + \dfrac{WL}{2}\cos\alpha.$

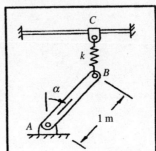

The equilibrium point is

$$\frac{dV_{\text{tot}}}{d\alpha} = kL^2(1 - \cos\alpha)\sin\alpha - \frac{WL}{2}\sin\alpha = 0,$$

from which

$$\left(\frac{2kL}{W}(1 - \cos\alpha) - 1\right)\sin\alpha = 0,$$

which has at least one solution: $\alpha = 0$. Stability is determined by

$$\left[\frac{d^2V}{d\alpha^2}\right]_{\alpha=0} = \left[\left(\frac{2kL}{W}\sin^2\alpha\right)\right.$$

$$\left. + \left(\frac{2kL}{W}(1 - \cos\alpha) - 1\right)\cos\alpha\right]_{\alpha=0} = -1.$$

Since $\left[\dfrac{d^2V}{d\alpha^2}\right]_{\alpha=0} = -1 < 0,$

the *system is unstable at the equilibrium position* $\alpha = 0$.

Problem 11.38 The bar AB described in Problem 11.37 has a mass of 2 kg, and the spring constant is $k = 80$ N/m.

(a) Determine the value of α in the range $0 < \alpha < 90°$ for which the bar is in equilibrium.
(b) Is the equilibrium position determined in (a) stable?

Solution: Use the solution to Problem 11.37. The condition for equilibrium is

$$\left(\frac{2kL}{W}(1 - \cos\alpha) - 1 \right) \sin\alpha = 0,$$

from which the non-zero position of equilibrium is determined by

$$\left(\frac{2kL}{W}(1 - \cos\alpha) - 1 \right) = 0.$$

Substitute numerical values to obtain

$$\frac{2kL}{W} = 8.1549.$$

The zero crossing of a graph of

$$f(\alpha) = \left(\frac{2kL}{W} \right)(1 - \cos\alpha) - 1$$

was determined approximately over the interval $0 < \alpha < 90°$, and this crossing value was then refined by iteration (using **TK Solver Plus**).

The equilibrium point occurs at: $\alpha = 28.67 = 28.7°$. The condition for stability is

$$\left[\frac{d^2V}{d\alpha^2} \right]_{\alpha = \alpha_i} = \left[\left(\frac{2kL}{W} \sin^2\alpha \right) \right.$$

$$\left. + \left(\frac{2kL}{W}(1 - \cos\alpha) - 1 \right) \cos\alpha \right]_{\alpha = \alpha_i}.$$

For $\alpha = 28.7°$,

$$\left[\frac{d^2V}{d\alpha^2} \right]_{\alpha = 28.7} = 1.88 > 0,$$

so *the system is stable at this equilibrium point*

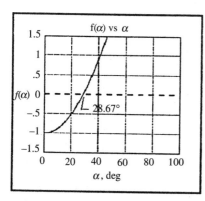

Problem 11.39 Each homogenous bar is of mass m and length L. The spring is unstretched when $\alpha = 0$. If $mg = kL$, determine the value of α in the range $0 < \alpha < 90°$ for which the system is in equilibrium.

Solution: The potential energy of the spring is

$$V = \tfrac{1}{2}ks^2.$$

Noting that

$$s = 2L(1 - \cos\alpha),$$

$$V = 2kL^2(1 - \cos\alpha)^2.$$

The potential energy of the bars is

$$V_{\text{bars}} = \frac{WL}{2}\cos\alpha + WL\cos\alpha + \frac{WL}{2}\cos\alpha = 2WL\cos\alpha,$$

where the datum point is the lower pin joint. The total energy is

$$V = 2kL^2(1 - \cos\alpha)^2 + 2WL\cos\alpha.$$

The equilibrium condition is

$$\frac{dV}{d\alpha} = \left(\frac{2kL}{W}(1 - \cos\alpha) - 1\right)\sin\alpha = 0.$$

The non zero position of equilibrium is, when $W = kL$, $2(1 - \cos\alpha) - 1 = 0$. Reduce:

$$1 - \cos\alpha = \tfrac{1}{2},$$

from which

$$\cos\alpha = \tfrac{1}{2},$$

$$\alpha = \cos^{-1}(\tfrac{1}{2}) = 60°$$

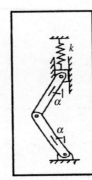

Problem 11.40 Determine whether the equilibrium position found in Problem 11.39 is stable or unstable.

Solution: Use the solution to Problem 11.39. The condition for an equilibrium point is

$$\frac{dV}{d\alpha} = \left(\frac{2kL}{W}(1 - \cos\alpha) - 1\right)\sin\alpha = 0.$$

The condition for stability is

$$\left[\frac{d^2V}{d\alpha^2}\right]_{\alpha=60°} = \left[\frac{2kL}{W}(\sin^2\alpha - \cos^2\alpha)\right.$$

$$\left. + \left(\frac{2kL}{W} - 1\right)\cos\alpha\right]_{\alpha=60°} = 1.5 > 0,$$

so the position is stable.

Problem 11.41 The string is unstretched when $\alpha = 90°$. If $mg = bk/2$, determine the value of α in the range $0 < \alpha < 90°$ for which the system is in equilibrium.

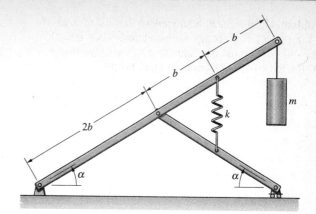

Solution: Neglect the weight of the bars. The potential energy of the mass m is $V_{\text{mass}} = mg(4b\sin\alpha)$. The potential energy of the spring

$$V_{\text{spring}} = \tfrac{1}{2}k(\Delta s)^2.$$

The uncompressed length of the spring is $2b$. The compressed length is $(3b\sin\alpha - b\sin\alpha) = 2b\sin\alpha$, from which

$$\Delta s = 2b - (3b\sin\alpha - b\sin\alpha) = 2b(1 - \sin\alpha),$$

from which $V_{\text{spring}} = 2kb^2(1 - \sin\alpha)^2$.

The total potential energy:

$$V_{\text{tot}} = (4\,mgb\sin\alpha + 2kb^2(1 - \sin\alpha)^2).$$

The equilibrium condition is:

$$\frac{dV}{d\alpha} = 4\,mgb\cos\alpha - 4kb^2\cos\alpha(1 - \sin\alpha) = 0,$$

from which

$$\left[\frac{dV}{d\alpha}\right]_{mg=\frac{bk}{2}} = \left(\sin\alpha - \frac{1}{2}\right)\cos\alpha = 0.$$

Equilibrium occurs at $\cos\alpha = 0$, $\alpha = 90°$ and

$$\sin\alpha = \tfrac{1}{2},$$

$$\alpha = 30°$$

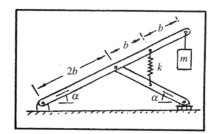

Problem 11.42 Determine whether the equilibrium position found in Problem 11.41 is stable or unstable.

Solution: From the solution to Problem 11.41 the derivative of the potential energy is

$$\frac{dV}{d\alpha} = 4\,mgb\cos\alpha - 4\,kb^2\cos\alpha(1 - \sin\alpha),$$

from which

$$\left[\frac{d^2V}{d\alpha^2}\right] = -4\,mgb\sin\alpha + 4\,kb^2\sin\alpha(1 - \sin\alpha) + 4\,kb^2\cos^2\alpha.$$

The condition for stability is:

$$\left[\frac{d^2V}{d\alpha^2}\right]_{\alpha=30°} = 3\,kb^2 > 0,$$

so *the equilibrium position is stable.*

Problem 11.43 The bar weighs 15 lb. The spring is unstretched when $\alpha = 0$. The bar is in equilibrium when $\alpha = 30°$. Determine the spring constant k.

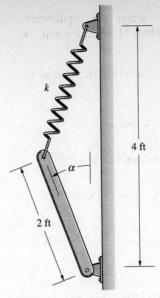

Solution: From the cosine law, the length of the spring is

$$d^2 = 2^2 + 4^2 - 16\cos\alpha,$$

from which $d = 2\sqrt{5 - 4\cos\alpha}$.

The spring extension is

$$\Delta = d - 2 = 2(\sqrt{5 - 4\cos\alpha} - 1).$$

The potential energy of the spring is

$$V = \frac{k\Delta^2}{2}.$$

The potential energy of the bar is $V_{\text{bar}} = W\cos\alpha$. The total potential energy is

$$V_{\text{tot}} = \frac{k\Delta^2}{2} + W\cos\alpha.$$

Noting

$$\frac{d\Delta}{d\alpha} = \frac{4\sin\alpha}{\sqrt{5 - 4\cos\alpha}},$$

the equilibrium condition is

$$\frac{dV}{d\alpha} = \frac{k(8\sin\alpha)(\sqrt{5 - 4\cos\alpha} - 1)}{\sqrt{5 - 4\cos\alpha}} - W\sin\alpha = 0.$$

Solve for the spring constant:

$$k = \frac{W\sqrt{5 - 4\cos\alpha}}{8(\sqrt{5 - 4\cos\alpha} - 1)}.$$

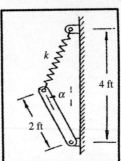

Substitute values:

$$\sqrt{5 - 4\cos\alpha} = 1.2393,$$

$$k = \frac{15(1.2393)}{8(0.2393)}$$

$$= 9.71 \text{ lb/ft}$$

Problem 11.44 Determine whether the equilibrium positions of the bar in Problem 11.43 are stable or unstable.

Solution: Use the solution to Problem 11.43. The condition for equilibrium is

$$\frac{dV}{d\alpha} = \frac{k(8\sin\alpha)(\sqrt{5 - 4\cos\alpha} - 1)}{\sqrt{5 - 4\cos\alpha}} - W\sin\alpha = 0.$$

For brevity write $L = \sqrt{5 - 4\cos\alpha}$. The derivative is

$$\frac{dV}{d\alpha} = \left(\frac{8k(L-1)}{L} - W\right)\sin\alpha = \left(8k - W - \frac{8k}{L}\right)\sin\alpha,$$

from which the second derivative is

$$\frac{d^2V}{d\alpha^2} = \frac{16k}{L^3}\sin^2\alpha + \left(8k - W - \frac{8k}{L}\right)\cos\alpha.$$

The condition for stability is determined from

$$\left[\frac{d^2V}{d\alpha^2}\right]_{\alpha=\alpha_i}.$$

For $\alpha = 0$,

$$\left[\frac{d^2V}{d\alpha^2}\right]_{\alpha=0} = -W = -15 < 0,$$

so that the equilibrium position is unstable. For $\alpha = 30°$,

$$\left[\frac{d^2V}{d\alpha^2}\right]_{\alpha=30°} = 20.4 > 0,$$

so that the equilibrium point is stable.

Problem 11.45 Each bar is of weight W, and the spring is unstretched when $\alpha = 90°$.

(a) Show that the system is in equilibrium when $\alpha = \arcsin(W/4kL)$.

(b) Is the equilibrium position described in (a) stable?

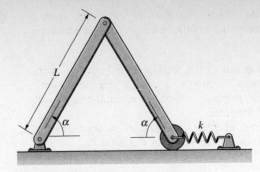

Solution: The potential energy of the spring is

$$V = \tfrac{1}{2}ks^2.$$

Noting

$$s = 2L\cos\alpha,$$

$$V = 2kL^2\cos^2\alpha.$$

The potential energy of the bars is $V_{\text{bars}} = WL\sin\alpha$, where the datum is the lower pin joints. The total potential energy is $V_{\text{tot}} = 2kL^2\cos^2\alpha + WL\sin\alpha$. The condition for equilibrium is

$$\frac{dV}{d\alpha} = \left(1 - \frac{4kL}{W}\sin\alpha\right)\cos\alpha = 0.$$

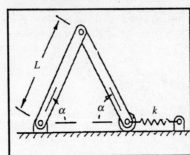

This has the solutions

$$\alpha = \cos^{-1}(0) = 90°,$$

and $\alpha = \sin^{-1}\left(\dfrac{W}{4kL}\right).$

(b) The second derivative is

$$\frac{d^2V}{d\alpha^2}$$

$$= \left(\frac{4kL}{W}\right)(\sin^2\alpha - \cos^2\alpha) - \sin\alpha$$

$$= \left(\frac{4kL}{W}\right)(2\sin^2\alpha - 1) - \sin\alpha.$$

The condition for stability:

$$\left[\frac{d^2V}{d\alpha^2}\right]_{\alpha=\sin^{-1}\left(\frac{W}{4kL}\right)}$$

$$= \frac{1}{\sin\alpha}(2\sin^2\alpha - 1) - \sin\alpha$$

$$= \frac{\sin^2\alpha - 1}{\sin\alpha} < 0,$$

since in the interval

$$0 < \alpha < 90°,$$

$$0 < \sin\alpha < 1.$$

The equilibrium is unstable for this position.

Problem 11.46 The 1-kg mass is suspended from a *nonlinear* spring that exerts a force $-10x + x^3$, where x is in meters.

(a) Draw a graph of the total potential energy of the system as a function of x from $x = 0$ to $x = 4$ m.
(b) Use your graph to estimate the equilibrium positions of the mass.
(c) Determine whether the equilibrium positions you obtained in (b) are stable or unstable.

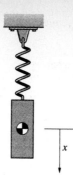

Solution: As the mass moves downward, the potential energy of the weight decreases, and the potential energy in the spring increases. The potential energy of the spring is

$$V_{\text{spring}} = -\int (-10x + x^3)\, dx = 5x^2 - \frac{x^4}{4} + C.$$

Choose the datum point $x = 0$, hence $C = 0$. The potential energy of the mass is

$$V_{\text{mass}} = -mgx = -9.81x.$$

The total energy is

$$V_{\text{tot}} = 5x^2 - \frac{x^4}{4} - 9.81x.$$

The graph is shown. The equilibrium positions occur at local minima and maxima in the graph: at $x = 1.12$ m and $x = 2.45$ m. The *local minimum* at $x = 1.12$ m means that this position is a *stable equilibrium*, and the *local maximum* at $x = 2.45$ m means that this position is an *unstable equilibrium*.

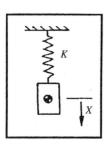

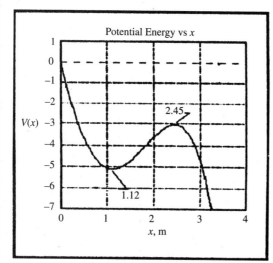

Problem 11.47 Suppose that the homogenous bar in Problem 11.33 weighs 20 lb and has length $L = 2$ ft, and that $k = 4$ lb/ft.

(a) Determine the values of α in the range $0 < \alpha < 90°$ for which the bar is in equilibrium.

(b) Is the equilibrium position found in (a) stable?

Solution: Use the results of the solution to Problem 11.33. The equilibrium condition is

$$\frac{2kL}{W}\alpha - \sin\alpha = 0,$$

from which $\dfrac{2kL}{W} = \dfrac{\sin\alpha}{\alpha} = \dfrac{2(4)(2)}{20} = 0.8.$

The ratio

$$f(\alpha) = \frac{\sin\alpha}{\alpha}$$

(where α is in radians) is graphed against the α in degrees to get an approximate value of the angle which satisfies this condition, and then this value was refined by iteration (using **TK Solver 2**) to obtain $\alpha = 64.8°$ (b) The condition for stability is

$$\frac{2kL}{W} - \cos\alpha > 0,$$

from which $0.8 - 0.4258 > 0$, which is satisfied. *The system is stable.* (See the solution to Problem 11.34, in which it is shown that this system is stable at every equilibrium point in the interval $0 < \alpha < 90°$, and neutrally stable at $\alpha = 0$ when $\dfrac{2kL}{W} = \dfrac{\sin\alpha}{\alpha}$.)

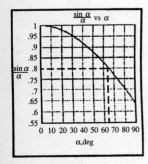

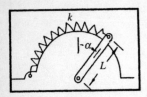

1004

Problem 11.48 The bar in Problem 11.43 weighs 15 lb, and the spring is unstretched when $\alpha = 0$. The spring constant is $k = 6$ lb/ft.

(a) Determine the value of α in the range $0 < \alpha < 90°$ for which the bar is in equilibrium.

(b) Is the equilibrium position found in (a) stable?

Solution: From the cosine law, the length of the spring is

$$d^2 = 2^2 + 4^2 - 16 \cos\alpha,$$

from which $d = 2\sqrt{5 - 4\cos\alpha}$.

The spring extension is

$$\Delta = d - 2 = 2(\sqrt{5 - 4\cos\alpha} - 1).$$

The potential energy of the spring is

$$V = \frac{k\Delta^2}{2}.$$

The potential energy of the bar is

$$V_{\text{bar}} = W \cos\alpha.$$

The total potential energy is

$$V_{\text{tot}} = \frac{k\Delta^2}{2} + W \cos\alpha.$$

The equilibrium condition is

$$\frac{dV}{d\alpha} = k\Delta \frac{d\Delta}{d\alpha} - W \sin\alpha$$

$$= \left(\frac{8k(\sqrt{5 - 4\cos\alpha} - 1)}{\sqrt{5 - 4\cos\alpha}} - W \right) \sin\alpha$$

$$= 0.$$

The non zero value of α that satisfies the equilibrium condition is $(8k - W)\sqrt{5 - 4\cos\alpha} - 8k = 0$.

A graph of the function

$$f(\alpha) = \left(1 - \frac{W}{8k} \right) \sqrt{5 - 4\cos\alpha} - 1$$

was used to get an estimate of the zero crossing point value of α, and this estimate was then refined by iteration to obtain $\alpha = 43.86 = 43.9°$.

(b) The stability of the equilibrium point may be determined from a graph of the potential energy in the neighborhood surrounding the equilibrium point. The graph of

$$V_{\text{tot}} = \frac{k\Delta^2}{2} + W \cos\alpha,$$

where $\Delta^2 = 4(\sqrt{5 - 4\cos\alpha} - 1)^2$, against the angle α is shown. From the local minimum at $\alpha = 43.9°$, *the equilibrium is stable*.

Check: From the solution to Problem 11.44, the second derivative is

$$\frac{d^2V}{d\alpha^2} = \frac{16k}{L^3} \sin^2\alpha$$

$$+ \left(8k - W - \frac{8k}{L} \right) \cos\alpha,$$

where $L = \sqrt{5 - 4\cos\alpha}$. Stability of equilibrium is determined by

$$\left[\frac{d^2V}{d\alpha^2} \right]_{\alpha=43.9°} = 14.99 > 0,$$

so the *equilibrium is stable. check.*

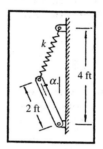

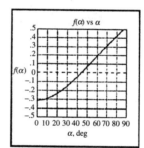

1005

Problem 11.49 The homogenous bar has length L and mass $4m$.

(a) Determine the value of α in the range $0 < \alpha < 90°$ for which the bar is in equilibrium.

(b) Is the equilibrium position found in (a) stable?

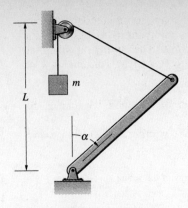

Solution: The length of the cable between the bar and the pulley is

$$d = \sqrt{L^2 + L^2 - 2L^2\cos\alpha} = \sqrt{2}L\sqrt{1 - \cos\alpha}.$$

Let the total length of the cable be L_{tot}. The potential energy of the mass m is $V_m = -mgx$ where

$$x = L_{tot} - \sqrt{2}L\sqrt{1 - \cos\alpha},$$

where it is assumed that the weight is always "above the ground" at any allowed value of α. The potential energy of the bar is

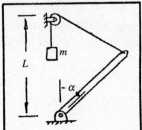

$$V_{bar} = 4\,mg\left(\frac{L}{2}\right)\cos\alpha.$$

The total energy is

$$V_{tot} = -mgL_{tot} + mg\sqrt{2}L\sqrt{1 - \cos\alpha} + 2\,mgL\cos\alpha.$$

The condition for equilibrium is

$$\frac{dV}{d\alpha} = \left(\frac{1}{\sqrt{2}\sqrt{1 - \cos\alpha}} - 2\right)\sin\alpha = 0.$$

The equilibrium points are determined by $\sin\alpha = 0$ and

$$\frac{1}{\sqrt{2}\sqrt{1 - \cos\alpha}} - 2 = 0,$$

from which

$$\alpha = 0$$

and $\alpha = \cos^{-1}\left(\dfrac{7}{8}\right) = 28.96 = 29°$.

The stability of equilibrium is determined by

$$\frac{d^2V}{d\alpha^2} = -\frac{\sin^2\alpha}{2D^3} + \left(\frac{1}{D} - 2\sqrt{2}\right)\cos\alpha,$$

where for brevity $D = \sqrt{1 - \cos\alpha}$. For $\alpha = 29°$,

$$\left[\frac{d^2V}{d\alpha^2}\right]_{\alpha=29°} = -2.65 < 0,$$

so *the equilibrium point is unstable.*

Problem 11.50 The 2-m long, 10-kg homogenous bar is pinned at A and at its midpoint B to light collars that slide on a smooth bar. The spring attached at A is unstretched when $\alpha = 0$, and its constant is $k = 1.2$ kN/m.

(a) Determine the value of α when the bar is in equilibrium.
(b) Determine whether the equilibrium position found in (a) is stable.

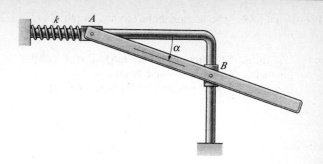

Solution: The potential energy of the spring is

$$V_{\text{spring}} = \tfrac{1}{2}k(1 - \cos\alpha)^2.$$

The potential energy of the bar is $V_{\text{bar}} = -mg\sin\alpha$. The total potential energy is

$$V_{\text{tot}} = \tfrac{1}{2}k(1 - \cos\alpha)^2 - mg\sin\alpha.$$

The equilibrium condition is

$$\frac{dV}{d\alpha} = -\left(\frac{mg}{k} + \sin\alpha\right)\cos\alpha + \sin\alpha = 0.$$

The function

$$f(\alpha) = -\left(\frac{mg}{k} + \sin\alpha\right)\cos\alpha + \sin\alpha$$

is graphed over the interval to estimate the value of α at the zero crossing, and this value is refined by iteration to obtain $\alpha = 30.53°$.

(b) The graph of the potential energy

$$V_{\text{tot}} = \tfrac{1}{2}k(1 - \cos\alpha)^2 - mg\sin\alpha$$

as a function of α shows a local minimum at about $\alpha = 30.5°$, so *the equilibrium position is stable. Check:* The second derivative is

$$\frac{d^2V}{d\alpha^2} = \left(\frac{mg}{k} + \sin\alpha\right)\sin\alpha - \cos^2\alpha + \cos\alpha.$$

The condition for stability is

$$\left[\frac{d^2V}{d\alpha^2}\right]_{a=30.5°} = 0.42 > 0,$$

so *the equilibrium position is stable. check.*

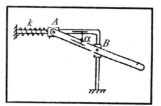

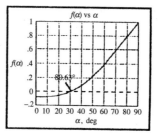

f(α) vs α

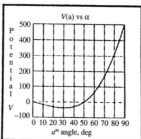

V(a) vs α

Problem 11.51

(a) Determine the couple exerted on the beam at A.
(b) Determine the vertical force exerted on the beam at A.

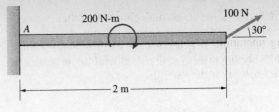

Solution:

(a) Perform a virtual rotation about A:

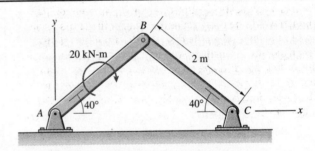

$$\delta U = M_A \delta\theta - 200\delta\theta + 2(100)\sin 30°\delta\theta = 0,$$

from which

$$(M_A - 200 + 2(100)\sin 30°)\delta\theta = 0,$$

from which

$$M_A = 200 - 2(50) = 100 \text{ N m}.$$

(b) Perform a virtual translation of the bar in the y-direction:

$$\delta U = A_y\delta y + 100(\sin 30°)\delta y = 0,$$

from which

$$(A_y + 50)\delta y = 0,$$

or $A_y = -50$ N

Problem 11.52 The structure is subjected to a 20 kN-m couple. Determine the horizontal reaction at C.

Solution: The interior angle at B is $100°$. Denote the axial force in BC by R_{BC}. Do a virtual rotation of member AB about A:

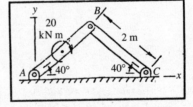

$$\delta U = (-20 + 2R_{BC}\sin 100°)\delta\theta = 0,$$

from which

$$R_{BC} = \frac{20}{2\cos 10°} = 10.15 \text{ kN}.$$

The horizontal component of the axial force is

$$R_x = R_{BC}\cos 40° = 7.778 = -7.8 \text{ kN}$$

(directed parallel to the negative x-axis.)

Problem 11.53 The "rack and pinion" mechanism is used to exert a vertical force on a sample at A for a stamping operation. If a force $F = 30$ lb is exerted on the handle, use the principle of virtual work to determine the force exerted on the sample.

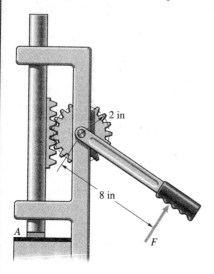

Solution: Perform a virtual rotation of the handle. The virtual work is $\delta U = 8F\delta\theta + A\delta x = 0$, from which

$$A = -8F\frac{\delta\theta}{\delta x}.$$

The angular rotation is related to the vertical translation by $2\delta\theta = -\delta x$, from which

$$\frac{\delta\theta}{\delta x} = -\frac{1}{2},$$

and $A = 4F = 120$ lb

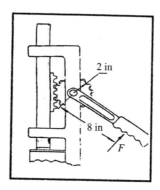

Problem 11.54 If you were assigned to calculate the force exerted on the bolt by the pliers when the grips are subjected to forces F as shown in Fig. a, you could carefully measure the dimensions, draw free-body diagrams, and use the equilibrium equations. But another approach would be to measure the change in the distance between the jaws when the distance between the handles is changed by a small amount. If your measurements indicate that the distance d in Fig. b decreases by 1 mm when D is decreased 8 mm, what is the approximate value of the force exerted on the bolt by each jaw when the forces F are applied?

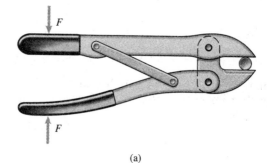

(a)

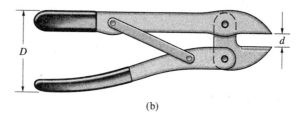

(b)

Solution: Let L be the distance between the points of application of the forces F and the point of application of the gripping force at the jaw. The ratio of the motions indicates that the "effective" axis of rotation of a jaw is located $\frac{8}{9}L$ from the point of application of F. Perform a virtual rotation about this axis:

$$\delta U = \left(\frac{8}{9}\right)LF\delta\theta - \left(\frac{1}{9}\right)Lf\delta\theta = 0,$$

from which $(8F - f)\delta\theta = 0$, or $f = 8F$. This result is approximate because some work is done by the mechanism as the handle is closed. In addition, the closure of the handles produces a translation of one handle relative to the other in the direction required to close the jaws, and this translation does work since it is associated with moment about the effective axis; hence not all of the virtual work due to a virtual rotation is included in the above expression.

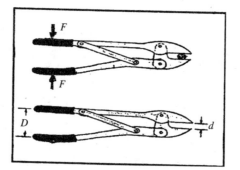

Problem 11.55 The system is in equilibrium. The total weight of the suspended load and assembly A is 300 lb.

(a) By using equilibrium, determine the force F.
(b) Using the result of (a) and the principle of virtual work, determine the distance the suspended load rises if the cable is pulled downward 1 ft at B.

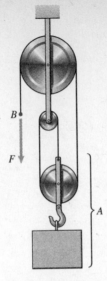

Solution:

(a) Isolate the assembly A. The sum of the forces:

$$\sum F_y = -W - 3F = 0,$$

where F is the tension in the cable, from which

$$F = \frac{W}{3} = 100 \text{ lb.}$$

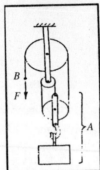

(b) Perform a virtual translation of the assembly A in the vertical direction. The virtual work: $\delta U = -W\delta y + F\delta x = 0$, from which

$$\frac{\delta x}{\delta y} = \frac{W}{F} = 3.$$

The ratio of translations of the assembly A and the point B is $\frac{1}{y_A} = 3$, from which $y_A = \frac{1}{3}$ ft

---

Problem 11.56 The system is in equilibrium.

(a) By drawing free-body diagrams and using equilibrium equations, determine the couple M.
(b) Using the result of (a) and the principle of virtual work, determine the angle through which pulley B rotates if pulley A rotates through an angle α.

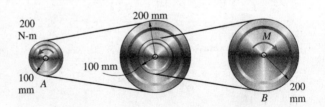

Solution: The pulleys are frictionless and the belts do not slip. Denote the left pulley by A and the right pulley by B. Denote the upper and lower tensions in the belts at pulley A by T_3, T_4, at B by T_1, T_2.

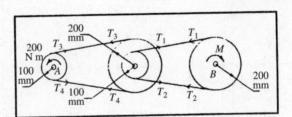

(a) For pulley A: (1) $(T_3 - T_4)(0.1) = 200$ N m, For pulley B (2) $M = (T_1 - T_2)(0.2)$. For the center pulley, (3) $(T_1 - T_2)(0.1) = (T_3 - T_4)(0.2)$. Combine and solve: $M = (4)(200) = 800$ N m

(b) Perform a virtual rotation of the pulley A. The virtual work of the system is $\delta U = M_1\delta\alpha - M\delta\theta = 0$, from which

$$\frac{\delta\theta}{\delta\alpha} = \frac{M_1}{M} = \frac{200}{800} = \frac{1}{4},$$

from which $\theta = \frac{\alpha}{4}$

Problem 11.57 The mechanism is in equilibrium. Neglect friction between the horizontal bar and the collar. Determine M in terms of F, α, and L.

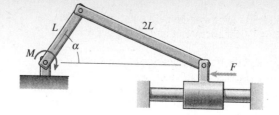

Solution: Perform a virtual rotation about the left pin support. $\delta U = M\delta\alpha - F\delta x = 0$, from which

$$M = F\frac{\delta x}{\delta\alpha}.$$

Using the results of the solution to Problem 11.14,

$$M = F\left(\frac{xL\sin\alpha}{x - L\cos\alpha}\right).$$

From the dimensions given and the cosine law, $4L^2 = x^2 + L^2 - 2Lx\cos\alpha$, from which $x^2 - 2xL\cos\alpha - 3L^2 = 0$, which has the solution

$$x = L\cos\alpha \pm \sqrt{L^2\cos^2\alpha + 3L^2} = L(\cos\alpha \pm \sqrt{\cos^2\alpha + 3}).$$

Since a negative value of x has no meaning here,

$$x = L(\cos\alpha + \sqrt{\cos^2\alpha + 3}).$$

Substitute into the expression for the moment, and reduce:

$$M = FL\sin\alpha\left(1 + \frac{\cos\alpha}{\sqrt{\cos^2\alpha + 3}}\right).$$

From the identity, $\cos^2\alpha = 1 - \sin^2\alpha$, an alternate form of the solution is

$$M = FL\sin\alpha\left(1 + \frac{\cos\alpha}{\sqrt{4 - \sin^2\alpha}}\right).$$

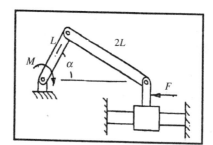

Problem 11.58 In an injection casting machine, a couple M applied to arm AB exerts a force on the injection piston at C. Given that the horizontal component of the force exerted at C is 4 kN, use the principle of virtual work to determine M.

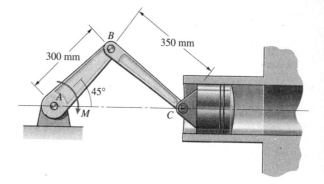

Solution: Perform a virtual rotation of the crank. The virtual work is

$$\delta U = M\delta\theta + F\delta x = 0,$$

from which

$$M = -F\frac{\delta x}{\delta\theta}.$$

Denote the interior angle ACB by β, and the interior angle ABC by α. From the sine law,

$$\frac{0.35}{\sin 45°} = \frac{0.3}{\sin\beta},$$

from which

$$\beta = \sin^{-1}\left(\frac{0.3}{0.35}\sin 45°\right) = 37.3°,$$

and $\alpha = 180° - 45° - 37.3° = 97.69°$.

The distance AC is

$$\frac{x}{\sin\alpha} = \frac{0.35}{\sin 45°},$$

from which $x = 0.490$ m. From the solution to Problem 11.14,

$$\frac{\delta x}{\delta\theta} = \frac{0.3(0.49)\sin 45°}{0.49 - 0.3\cos 45°} = 0.374.$$

The moment is $M = -0.374F = -0.374(4) = -1.5$ kN m

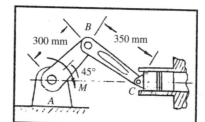

Problem 11.59 Show that if bar AB is subjected to a clockwise virtual rotation $\delta\alpha$, bar CD undergoes a counterclockwise virtual rotation $(b/a)\delta\alpha$.

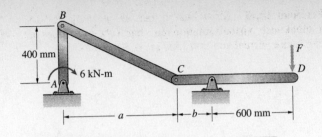

Solution: The coordinates of pts B and C are

$B_x = 400 \sin\alpha,$

$B_y = 400 \cos\alpha,$

$C_x = (a+b) - b\cos\beta,$

$C_y = -b\sin\beta.$

We know that

$(C_x - B_x)^2 + (C_y - B_y)^2 = \text{constant}.$

The derivative of this equation with respect to α is

$$2(C_x - B_x)\left(\frac{dC_x}{d\alpha} - \frac{dB_x}{d\alpha}\right) + 2(C_y - B_y)\left(\frac{dC_y}{d\alpha} - \frac{dB_y}{d\alpha}\right)$$

$$= 2(a + b - b\cos\beta - 400\sin\alpha)\left(b\sin\beta\frac{d\beta}{d\alpha} - 400\cos\alpha\right)$$

$$+ 2(-b\sin\beta - 400\cos\alpha)\left(-b\cos\beta\frac{d\beta}{d\alpha} + 400\sin\alpha\right) = 0.$$

At $\alpha = 0$, $\beta = 0$, this equation is

$$2a(-400) + 2(-400)\left(-b\frac{d\beta}{d\alpha}\right) = 0,$$

from which we obtain

$$\delta\beta = \frac{a}{b}\delta\alpha.$$

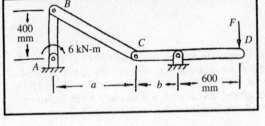

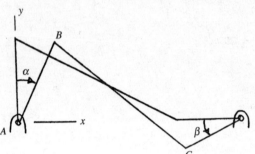

Problem 11.60 The system in Problem 11.59 is in equilibrium, $a = 800$ mm, and $b = 400$ mm. Use the principle of virtual work to determine the force F.

Solution: See the solution of Problem 11.59. When bar AB undergoes a clockwise virtual rotation $\delta\alpha$, the virtual work is

$$\delta U = 6\delta\alpha - F(0.6\delta\beta)$$

$$= 6\delta\alpha - F\left(0.6\frac{a}{b}\delta\alpha\right) = 0,$$

so

$$F = \frac{6b}{0.6a} = 5 \text{ kN}.$$

Problem 11.61 Show that if bar AB is subjected to a clockwise virtual rotation $\delta\alpha$, bar CD undergoes a clockwise virtual rotation $[ad/(ac + bc - bd)]\delta\alpha$.

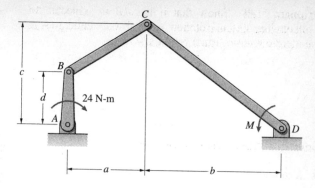

Solution: Denote the interior acute angle formed by BC with the horizontal by β, the obtuse interior angle at C by γ, and the interior acute angle at D by ψ. Perform a virtual translation δX parallel to the bar BC. (Note: This is often a useful step where cranks- and connecting-rod-like mechanisms are involved.) Then

$$\delta X \cos\beta = d\,\delta\alpha,$$

and $\delta X \sin\gamma = \mathbf{CD}\delta\theta,$

from which

$$\frac{\delta\theta}{\delta\alpha} = \frac{d\cos\beta}{\mathbf{CD}\sin\gamma}.$$

Noting that

$$\sin\gamma = \sin(90° - \beta + 90° - \psi)$$

$$= \sin(\beta + \psi) = \sin\beta\cos\psi + \sin\psi\cos\beta,$$

and $\cos\beta = \dfrac{a}{\mathbf{BC}},$

$$\sin\psi = \frac{c}{\mathbf{CD}},$$

$$\sin\beta = \frac{c-d}{\mathbf{BC}},$$

$$\cos\psi = \frac{b}{\mathbf{CD}}.$$

Substitute:

$$\frac{\delta\theta}{\delta\alpha} = \frac{d\left(\dfrac{a}{\mathbf{BC}}\right)}{\mathbf{CD}\left(\dfrac{a}{\mathbf{BC}} \times \dfrac{c}{\mathbf{CD}} + \dfrac{b}{\mathbf{CD}} \times \dfrac{(c-d)}{\mathbf{BC}}\right)} = \frac{ad}{ac + bc - bd}$$

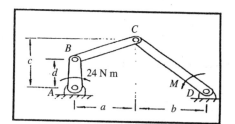

Problem 11.62 The system in Problem 11.61 is in equilibrium, $a = 300$ mm, $b = 350$ mm, $c = 350$ mm, and $d = 200$ mm. Use the principle of virtual work to determine the couple M.

Solution: Perform a virtual rotation of the crank at A. The virtual work is

$$\delta U = -M_1\delta\alpha + M\delta\theta = 0,$$

from which $\dfrac{\delta\theta}{\delta\alpha} = \dfrac{M_1}{M}.$

From the solution Problem 11.61,

$$\frac{\delta\theta}{\delta\alpha} = \frac{ad}{ac + bc - bd},$$

from which

$$M = \frac{M_1(ac + bc - bd)}{ad} = (24)2.625 = 63 \text{ N m}$$

1013

Problem 11.63 The mass of the bar is 10 kg, and it is 1 m in length. Neglect the masses of the two collars. The spring is unstretched when the bar is vertical ($\alpha = 0$), and the spring constant is $k = 100$ N/m. Determine the values of α at which the bar is in equilibrium.

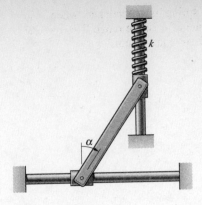

Solution: The potential energy of the spring is

$$V = \tfrac{1}{2}ks^2.$$

Noting that $s = L(1 - \cos\alpha)$, then

$$V = \tfrac{1}{2}kL^2(1 - \cos\alpha)^2.$$

The potential energy of the bar is

$$V_{\text{bar}} = \frac{WL}{2}\cos\alpha,$$

where the datum point is the lower pin joint. From which

$$V_{\text{tot}} = \frac{kL^2}{2}(1 - \cos\alpha)^2 + \frac{WL}{2}\cos\alpha.$$

The condition for equilibrium is

$$\frac{dV}{d\alpha} = \left(\frac{2kL}{W}(1 - \cos\alpha) - 1\right)\sin\alpha = 0.$$

The equilibrium points are $\alpha = 0$, and the value of α determined by

$$\frac{2kL}{W}(1 - \cos\alpha) - 1 = 0,$$

from which

$$\cos\alpha = 1 - \frac{W}{2kL}.$$

Substitute numerical values:

$$\cos\alpha = 0.5095,$$

or $\alpha = \cos^{-1}(0.5095) = 59.369 = 59.4°$.

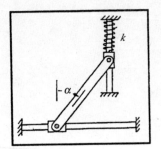

Problem 11.64 Determine whether the equilibrium positions of the bar in Problem 11.63 are stable or unstable.

Solution: Use the solution to Problem 11.63. The equilibrium condition is

$$\frac{dV}{d\alpha} = \left(\frac{2kL}{W}(1 - \cos\alpha) - 1\right)\sin\alpha = 0.$$

The stability condition is determined by

$$\left[\frac{d^2V}{d\alpha^2}\right]_{\alpha=\alpha_i} = \left[\left(\frac{2kL}{W}\right)(\sin^2\alpha - \cos^2\alpha)\right.$$

$$\left. + \left(\frac{2kL}{W} - 1\right)\cos\alpha\right]_{\alpha=\alpha_i}.$$

For $\alpha = 0$,

$$\left[\frac{d^2V}{d\alpha^2}\right]_{\alpha=0} = -1 < 0,$$

so the equilibrium point is unstable. For $\alpha = 59.4°$,

$$\left[\frac{d^2V}{d\alpha^2}\right]_{\alpha=59.4°} = 1.51 > 0,$$

so the equilibrium point is stable.

Problem 11.65 The spring is unstretched when $\alpha = 90°$. Determine the value of α in the range $0 < \alpha < 90°$ for which the system is in equilibrium.

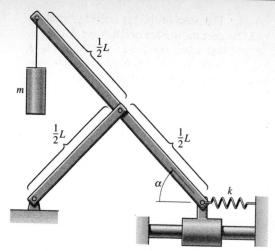

Solution: Choose a coordinate system such that the equilibrium position of the spring occurs at $x = 0$ and at $y = L$. The potential energy is

$$V = mgy + \frac{kx^2}{2}.$$

Noting that

$$y = L\sin\alpha$$

and $x = L\cos\alpha$,

then

$$V = mgL\sin\alpha + \frac{kL^2}{2}\cos^2\alpha.$$

The equilibrium condition is

$$\frac{dV}{d\alpha} = 0 = (mg - kL\sin\alpha)\cos\alpha = 0.$$

This has two solutions:

$$\cos\alpha = 0,$$

and $\sin\alpha = \dfrac{mg}{kL}$.

In the interval $0 < \alpha < 90°$, only one solution exists,

$$\alpha = \sin^{-1}\left(\frac{mg}{kL}\right)$$

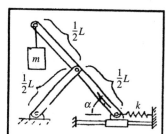

Problem 11.66 Determine whether the equilibrium position found in Problem 11.65 is stable or unstable.

Solution: Use the solution to Problem 11.65. The stability condition is

$$\frac{d^2V}{d\alpha^2} = -mg\sin\alpha + kL(\sin^2\alpha - \cos^2\alpha) = kL(\sin^2\alpha - 1) < 0.$$

The system is unstable.

Problem 11.67 The hydraulic cylinder C exerts a horizontal force at A, raising the weight W. Determine the magnitude of the force the hydraulic cylinder must exert to support the weight in terms of W and α.

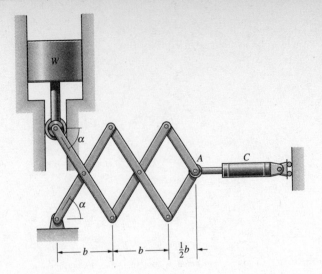

Solution: The distance $x = 2.5b$, so $\delta x = 2.5\delta b$.

Notice that $y^2 + b^2 = $ constant. Taking the derivative of this equation with respect to y,

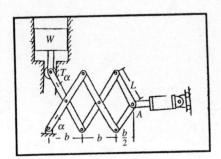

$$2y + 2b\frac{db}{dy} = 0,$$

we obtain

$$\delta y = -\frac{b}{y}\delta b.$$

The virtual work is

$$\delta U = -W\delta y - F\delta x$$

$$= -W\left(-\frac{b}{y}\delta b\right) - F(2.5\delta b) = 0,$$

so

$$F = \frac{b}{2.5y}W = \frac{W}{2.5\tan\alpha}.$$

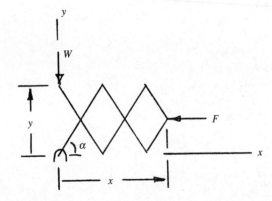